COLLEGE PHYSICS:
A STRATEGIC APPROACH

Volume I
Second Custom Edition for Oregon State University

Taken from:
College Physics: A Strategic Approach, Second Edition
by Randall D. Knight, Brian Jones, and Stuart Field

Instructor's Solutions Manual by Randall D. Knight, Brian Jones, Stuart Field, Larry K. Smith, Pawan
Kahol, and Marllin Simon for *College Physics: A Strategic Approach,* Second Edition
by Randall D. Knight, Brian Jones, and Stuart Field

Learning Solutions

New York   Boston   San Francisco
London   Toronto   Sydney   Tokyo   Singapore   Madrid
Mexico City   Munich   Paris   Cape Town   Hong Kong   Montreal

Cover Art: Courtesy of PhotoDisc/Getty Images

Taken from:

College Physics: A Strategic Approach, Second Edition
by Randall D. Knight, Brian Jones, and Stuart Field
Copyright © 2010, 2007 by Pearson Education, Inc.
Published by Addison-Wesley
Boston, Massachusetts 02116

Instructor's Solutions Manual by Randall D. Knight, Brian Jones, Stuart Field, Larry K. Smith, Pawan Kahol, and
Marllin Simon for *College Physics: A Strategic Approach,* Second Edition
by Randall D. Knight, Brian Jones, and Stuart Field
Copyright © 2010 by Pearson Education, Inc.
Published by Addison-Wesley

This special edition published in cooperation with Pearson Learning Solutions.

Pearson Learning Solutions, 501 Boylston Street, Suite 900, Boston, MA 02116
A Pearson Education Company
www.pearsoned.com

Printed in the United States of America

5 6 7 8 9 10 V092 15 14 13 12

000200010270589902

AD

ISBN 10: 0-558-87733-8
ISBN 13: 978-0-558-87733-0

Contents

COLLEGE PHYSICS:
A STRATEGIC APPROACH

PART

I

Force and Motion

The cheetah is the fastest land animal, able to run at speeds exceeding 60 miles per hour. Nonetheless, the rabbit has an advantage in this chase. It can *change* its motion more quickly and will likely escape. How can you tell, by looking at the picture, that the cheetah is changing its motion?

Why Things Change

Each of the seven parts of this book opens with an overview that gives you a look ahead, a glimpse of where your journey will take you in the next few chapters. It's easy to lose sight of the big picture while you're busy negotiating the terrain of each chapter. In Part I, the big picture is, in a word, *change*.

Simple observations of the world around you show that most things change. Some changes, such as aging, are biological. Others, such as sugar dissolving in your coffee, are chemical. We will look at changes that involve *motion* of one form or another—running and jumping, throwing balls, lifting weights.

There are two big questions we must tackle to study how things change by moving:

- **How do we describe motion?** How should we measure or characterize the motion if we want to analyze it mathematically?
- **How do we explain motion?** Why do objects have the particular motion they do? Why, when you toss a ball upward, does it go up and then come back down rather than keep going up? What are the "laws of nature" that allow us to predict an object's motion?

Two key concepts that will help answer these questions are *force* (the "cause") and *acceleration* (the "effect"). Our basic tools will be three laws of motion elucidated by Isaac Newton. Newton's laws relate force to acceleration, and we will use them to explain and explore a wide range of problems. As we learn to solve problems dealing with motion, we will learn basic techniques that we can apply in all the parts of this book.

Simplifying Models

Reality is extremely complicated. We would never be able to develop a science if we had to keep track of every detail of every situation. Suppose we analyze the tossing of a ball. Is it necessary to analyze the way the atoms in the ball are connected? Do we need to analyze what you ate for breakfast and the biochemistry of how that was translated into muscle power? These are interesting questions, of course. But if our task is to understand the motion of the ball, we need to simplify!

We can do a perfectly fine analysis if we treat the ball as a round solid and your hand as another solid that exerts a force on the ball. This is a *model* of the situation. A model is a simplified description of reality—much as a model airplane is a simplified version of a real airplane—that is used to reduce the complexity of a problem to the point where it can be analyzed and understood.

Model building is a major part of the strategy that we will develop for solving problems in all parts of the book. We will introduce different models in different parts. We will pay close attention to where simplifying assumptions are being made, and why. Learning *how* to simplify a situation is the essence of successful modeling—and successful problem solving.

1 Representing Motion

As this skier moves in a graceful arc through the air, the direction of his motion, and the distance between each of his positions and the next, are constantly changing. What language should we use to describe this motion?

LOOKING AHEAD ▶

The goals of Chapter 1 are to introduce the fundamental concepts of motion and to review the related basic mathematical principles.

The Chapter Preview

Each chapter will start with an overview of the material to come. You should read these chapter previews carefully to get a sense of the content and structure of the chapter.

Arrows will show the connections and flow between different topics in the preview.

A chapter preview is a visual presentation that outlines the big ideas and the organization of the chapter to come.

The chapter previews not only let you know what is coming, but also help you make connections with material you have already seen.

Looking Back ◀◀
We'll tell you what material from previous chapters is especially important to review to best understand the new material.

Describing Motion

Pictures like the one above or the one at right give us valuable clues about motion.

This picture shows successive images of a frog jumping. The images of the frog are getting farther apart, so the frog must be speeding up.

You will learn to make much simpler pictures to describe the key features of motion.

$t = 0\,s \quad 1\,s \quad 2\,s \quad 3\,s \quad 4\,s \quad 5\,s \quad 6\,s\,7\,s\,8\,s$
● ● ● ● ● ● ●●

Car starts braking here

This diagram tells us everything we need to know about the motion of a car.

Numbers and Units

For a full description of motion, we need to assign numbers to physical quantities such as speed.

This speedometer gives speed in both miles per hour and kilometers per hour. You will learn how to use and convert units and how to describe large and small numbers.

Vectors

Numbers alone aren't enough, sometimes the direction is important too. We'll use **vectors** to represent such quantities.

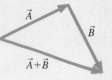

When you push a swing, the direction of the force makes a difference.

$\vec{A}$ $\vec{B}$ $\vec{A} + \vec{B}$

You will see how to do simple math with vectors.

1.1 Motion: A First Look

The concept of motion is a theme that will appear in one form or another throughout this entire book. You have a well-developed intuition about motion, based on your experiences, but you'll see that some of the most important aspects of motion can be rather subtle. We need to develop some tools to help us explain and understand motion, so rather than jumping immediately into a lot of mathematics and calculations, this first chapter focuses on visualizing motion and becoming familiar with the concepts needed to describe a moving object.

One key difference between physics and other sciences is how we set up and solve problems. We'll often use a two-step process to solve motion problems. The first step is to develop a simplified *representation* of the motion so that key elements stand out. For example, the photo of the skier at the start of the chapter allows us to observe his position at many successive times. It is precisely by considering this sort of picture of motion that we will begin our study of this topic. The second step is to analyze the motion with the language of mathematics. The process of putting numbers on nature is often the most challenging aspect of the problems you will solve. In this chapter, we will explore the steps in this process as we introduce the basic concepts of motion.

Types of Motion

As a starting point, let's define **motion** as the change of an object's position or orientation with time. Examples of motion are easy to list. Bicycles, baseballs, cars, airplanes, and rockets are all objects that move. The path along which an object moves, which might be a straight line or might be curved, is called the object's **trajectory.**

FIGURE 1.1 shows four basic types of motion that we will study in this book. In this chapter, we will start with the first type of motion in the figure, motion along a straight line. In later chapters, we will learn about circular motion, which is the motion of an object along a circular path; projectile motion, the motion of an object through the air; and rotational motion, the spinning of an object about an axis.

FIGURE 1.1 Four basic types of motion.

Straight-line motion

Circular motion

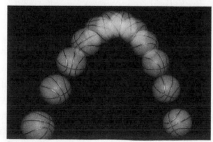
Projectile motion

Rotational motion

FIGURE 1.2 Several frames from the video of a car.

FIGURE 1.3 A motion diagram of the car shows all the frames simultaneously.

The same amount of time elapses between each image and the next.

Making a Motion Diagram

An easy way to study motion is to record a video of a moving object with a stationary camera. A video camera takes images at a fixed rate, typically 30 images every second. Each separate image is called a *frame*. As an example, FIGURE 1.2 shows several frames from a video of a car going past. Not surprisingly, the car is in a different position in each frame.

NOTE ▶ It's important to keep the camera in a *fixed position* as the object moves by. Don't "pan" it to track the moving object. ◀

Suppose we now edit the video by layering the frames on top of each other and then look at the final result. We end up with the picture in FIGURE 1.3. This composite image, showing an object's positions at several *equally spaced instants of time*, is called a **motion diagram.** As simple as motion diagrams seem, they will turn out to be powerful tools for analyzing motion.

Now let's take our camera out into the world and make some motion diagrams. The following table illustrates how a motion diagram shows important features of different kinds of motion.

Examples of motion diagrams

The ball is in the same position in all four frames.

An object that occupies only a *single position* in a motion diagram is *at rest.*

A stationary ball on the ground.

Images that are *equally spaced* indicate an object moving with *constant speed.*

A skateboarder rolling down the sidewalk.

An *increasing distance* between the images shows that the object is *speeding up.*

A sprinter starting the 100-meter dash.

A *decreasing distance* between the images shows that the object is *slowing down.*

A car stopping for a red light.

A more complex motion diagram shows changes in speed and direction.

A basketball free throw.

We have defined several concepts (at rest, constant speed, speeding up, and slowing down) in terms of how the moving object appears in a motion diagram. These are called **operational definitions,** meaning that the concepts are defined in terms of a particular procedure or operation performed by the investigator. For example, we could answer the question Is the airplane speeding up? by checking whether or not the images in the plane's motion diagram are getting farther apart. Many of the concepts in physics will be introduced as operational definitions. This reminds us that physics is an experimental science.

STOP TO THINK 1.1 Which car is going faster, A or B? Assume there are equal intervals of time between the frames of both videos.

Car A   Car B

NOTE ▶ Each chapter in this textbook has several *Stop to Think* questions. These questions are designed to see if you've understood the basic ideas that have just been presented. The answers are given at the end of the chapter, but you should make a serious effort to think about these questions before turning to the answers. If you answer correctly and are sure of your answer rather than just guessing, you can proceed to the next section with confidence. But if you answer incorrectly, it would be wise to reread the preceding sections carefully before proceeding onward. ◀

The Particle Model

For many objects, the motion of the object *as a whole* is not influenced by the details of the object's size and shape. To describe the object's motion, all we really need to keep track of is the motion of a single point: You could imagine looking at the motion of a dot painted on the side of the object.

In fact, for the purposes of analyzing the motion, we can often consider the object *as if* it were just a single point, without size or shape. We can also treat the object *as if* all of its mass were concentrated into this single point. An object that can be represented as a mass at a single point in space is called a **particle.**

If we treat an object as a particle, we can represent the object in each frame of a motion diagram as a simple dot. FIGURE 1.4 shows how much simpler motion diagrams appear when the object is represented as a particle. Note that the dots have been numbered 0, 1, 2, … to tell the sequence in which the frames were exposed. These diagrams still convey a complete understanding of the object's motion.

Treating an object as a particle is, of course, a simplification of reality. Such a simplification is called a **model.** Models allow us to focus on the important aspects of a phenomenon by excluding those aspects that play only a minor role. The **particle model** of motion is a simplification in which we treat a moving object as if all of its mass were concentrated at a single point. Using the particle model may allow us to see connections that are very important but that are obscured or lost by examining all the parts of an extended, real object. Consider the motion of the two objects shown in FIGURE 1.5. These two very different objects have exactly the same motion diagram. As we will see, all objects falling under the influence of gravity move in exactly the same manner if no other forces act. The simplification of the particle model has revealed something about the physics that underlies both of these situations.

Not all motions can be reduced to the motion of a single point, as we'll see. But for now, the particle model will be a useful tool in understanding motion.

FIGURE 1.4 Simplifying a motion diagram using the particle model.

(a) Motion diagram of a car stopping

(b) Same motion diagram using the particle model

The same amount of time elapses between each frame and the next.

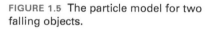

Numbers show the order in which the frames were taken.

A single dot is used to represent the object.

FIGURE 1.5 The particle model for two falling objects.

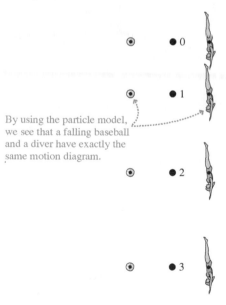

By using the particle model, we see that a falling baseball and a diver have exactly the same motion diagram.

STOP TO THINK 1.2 Three motion diagrams are shown. Which is a dust particle settling to the floor at constant speed, which is a ball dropped from the roof of a building, and which is a descending rocket slowing to make a soft landing on Mars?

A.	B.	C.
0 ●	0 ●	0 ●
1 ●		
2 ●	1 ●	
		1 ●
3 ●	2 ●	
		2 ●
4 ●	3 ●	
		3 ●
	4 ●	4 ●
5 ●	5 ●	5 ●

1.2 Position and Time: Putting Numbers on Nature

To develop our understanding of motion further, we need to be able to make quantitative measurements: We need to use numbers. As we analyze a motion diagram, it is useful to know where the object is (its *position*) and when the object was at that position (the *time*). We'll start by considering the motion of an object that can move only along a straight line. Examples of this **one-dimensional** or "1-D" motion are a bicyclist moving along the road, a train moving on a long straight track, and an elevator moving up and down a shaft.

Position and Coordinate Systems

FIGURE 1.6 Describing your position.

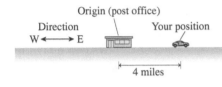

Sometimes measurements have a natural origin. This snow depth gauge has its origin set at road level.

Suppose you are driving along a long, straight country road, as in FIGURE 1.6, and your friend calls and asks where you are. You might reply that you are 4 miles east of the post office, and your friend would then know just where you were. Your location at a particular instant in time (when your friend phoned) is called your **position.** Notice that to know your position along the road, your friend needed three pieces of information. First, you had to give her a reference point (the post office) from which all distances are to be measured. We call this fixed reference point the **origin.** Second, she needed to know how far you were from that reference point or origin—in this case, 4 miles. Finally, she needed to know which side of the origin you were on: You could be 4 miles to the west of it or 4 miles to the east.

We will need these same three pieces of information in order to specify any object's position along a line. We first choose our origin, from which we measure the position of the object. The position of the origin is arbitrary, and we are free to place it where we like. Usually, however, there are certain points (such as the well-known post office) that are more convenient choices than others.

In order to specify how far our object is from the origin, we lay down an imaginary axis along the line of the object's motion. Like a ruler, this axis is marked off in equally spaced divisions of distance, perhaps in inches, meters, or miles, depending on the problem at hand. We place the zero mark of this ruler at the origin, allowing us to locate the position of our object by reading the ruler mark where the object is.

Finally, we need to be able to specify which side of the origin our object is on. To do this, we imagine the axis extending from one side of the origin with increasing positive markings; on the other side, the axis is marked with increasing *negative* numbers. By reporting the position as either a positive or a negative number, we know on what side of the origin the object is.

These elements—an origin and an axis marked in both the positive and negative directions—can be used to unambiguously locate the position of an object. We call this a **coordinate system.** We will use coordinate systems throughout this book, and we will soon develop coordinate systems that can be used to describe the positions of objects moving in more complex ways than just along a line. FIGURE 1.7 shows a coordinate system that can be used to locate various objects along the country road discussed earlier.

FIGURE 1.7 The coordinate system used to describe objects along a country road.

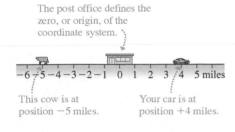

Although our coordinate system works well for describing the positions of objects located along the axis, our notation is somewhat cumbersome. We need to keep saying things like "the car is at position +4 miles." A better notation, and one that will become particularly important when we study motion in two dimensions, is to use a symbol such as x or y to represent the position along the axis. Then we can say "the cow is at $x = -5$ miles." The symbol that represents a position along an axis is called a **coordinate.** The introduction of symbols to represent positions (and, later, velocities and accelerations) also allows us to work with these quantities mathematically.

FIGURE 1.8 below shows how we would set up a coordinate system for a sprinter running a 50-meter race (we use the standard symbol "m" for meters). For horizontal motion like this we usually use the coordinate *x* to represent the position.

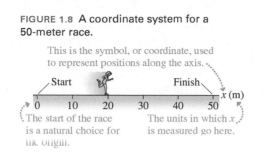

FIGURE 1.8 A coordinate system for a 50-meter race.

This is the symbol, or coordinate, used to represent positions along the axis.

The start of the race is a natural choice for the origin.

The units in which *x* is measured go here.

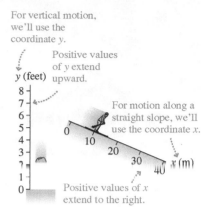

FIGURE 1.9 Examples of one-dimensional motion.

For vertical motion, we'll use the coordinate *y*.

Positive values of *y* extend upward.

For motion along a straight slope, we'll use the coordinate *x*.

Positive values of *x* extend to the right.

Motion along a straight line need not be horizontal. As shown in FIGURE 1.9, a rock falling vertically downward and a skier skiing down a straight slope are also examples of straight-line or one-dimensional motion.

Time

The pictures in Figure 1.9 show the position of an object at just one instant of time. But a full motion diagram represents how an object moves as time progresses. So far, we have labeled the dots in a motion diagram by the numbers 0, 1, 2, . . . to indicate the order in which the frames were exposed. But to fully describe the motion, we need to indicate the *time,* as read off a clock or a stopwatch, at which each frame of a video was made. This is important, as we can see from the motion diagram of a stopping car in FIGURE 1.10. If the frames were taken 1 second apart, this motion diagram shows a leisurely stop; if 1/10 of a second apart, it represents a screeching halt.

For a complete motion diagram, we thus need to label each frame with its corresponding time (symbol *t*) as read off a clock. But when should we start the clock? Which frame should be labeled *t* = 0? This choice is much like choosing the origin *x* = 0 of a coordinate system: You can pick any arbitrary point in the motion and label it "*t* = 0 seconds." This is simply the instant you decide to start your clock or stopwatch, so it is the origin of your time coordinate. A video frame labeled "*t* = 4 seconds" means it was taken 4 seconds after you started your clock. We typically choose *t* = 0 to represent the "beginning" of a problem, but the object may have been moving before then.

To illustrate, FIGURE 1.11 shows the motion diagram for a car moving at a constant speed and then braking to a halt. Two possible choices for the frame labeled *t* = 0 seconds are shown; our choice depends on what part of the motion we're interested in. Each successive position of the car is then labeled with the clock reading in seconds (abbreviated by the symbol "s").

FIGURE 1.10 Is this a leisurely stop or a screeching halt?

FIGURE 1.11 The motion diagram of a car that travels at constant speed and then brakes to a halt.

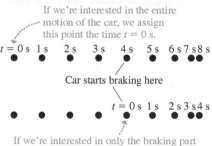

If we're interested in the entire motion of the car, we assign this point the time *t* = 0 s.

Car starts braking here

If we're interested in only the braking part of the motion, we assign *t* = 0 s here.

Changes in Position and Displacement

Now that we've seen how to measure position and time, let's return to the problem of motion. To describe motion we'll need to measure the *changes* in position that occur with time. Consider the following:

Sam is standing 50 feet (ft) east of the corner of 12th Street and Vine. He then walks to a second point 150 ft east of Vine. What is Sam's change of position?

FIGURE 1.12 shows Sam's motion on a map. We've placed a coordinate system on the map, using the coordinate *x*. We are free to place the origin of our coordinate system wherever we wish, so we have placed it at the intersection. Sam's initial position is then at $x_i = 50$ ft. The positive value for x_i tells us that Sam is east of the origin.

FIGURE 1.12 Sam undergoes a displacement Δx from position x_i to position x_f.

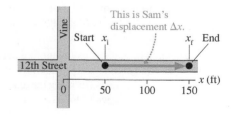

The size and the direction of the displacement both matter. Roy Riegels (pursued above by teammate Benny Lom) found this out in dramatic fashion in the 1928 Rose Bowl when he recovered a fumble and ran 69 yards—toward his own team's end zone. An impressive distance, but in the wrong direction!

FIGURE 1.13 A displacement is a signed quantity. Here Δx is a negative number.

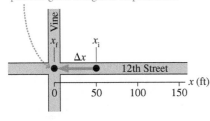

FIGURE 1.14 The motion diagram of a bicycle moving to the right at a constant speed.

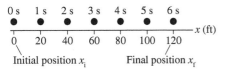

NOTE ▶ We will label special values of x or y with subscripts. The value at the start of a problem is usually labeled with a subscript "i," for *initial,* and the value at the end is labeled with a subscript "f," for *final.* For cases having several special values, we will usually use subscripts "1," "2," and so on. ◀

Sam's final position is $x_f = 150$ ft, indicating that he is 150 ft east of the origin. You can see that Sam has changed position, and a *change* of position is called a **displacement**. His displacement is the distance labeled Δx in Figure 1.12. The Greek letter delta (Δ) is used in math and science to indicate the *change* in a quantity. Thus Δx indicates a change in the position x.

NOTE ▶ Δx is a *single* symbol. You cannot cancel out or remove the Δ in algebraic operations. ◀

To get from the 50 ft mark to the 150 ft mark, Sam clearly had to walk 100 ft, so the change in his position—his displacement—is 100 ft. We can think about displacement in a more general way, however. **Displacement is the *difference* between a final position x_f and an initial position x_i.** Thus we can write

$$\Delta x = x_f - x_i = 150 \text{ ft} - 50 \text{ ft} = 100 \text{ ft}$$

NOTE ▶ A general principle, used throughout this book, is that the change in any quantity is the final value of the quantity minus its initial value. ◀

Displacement is a *signed quantity;* that is, it can be either positive or negative. If, as shown in FIGURE 1.13, Sam's final position x_f had been at the origin instead of the 150 ft mark, his displacement would have been

$$\Delta x = x_f - x_i = 0 \text{ ft} - 50 \text{ ft} = -50 \text{ ft}$$

The negative sign tells us that he moved to the *left* along the x-axis, or 50 ft *west.*

Change in Time

A displacement is a change in position. In order to quantify motion, we'll need to also consider changes in *time,* which we call **time intervals.** We've seen how we can label each frame of a motion diagram with a specific time, as determined by our stopwatch. FIGURE 1.14 shows the motion diagram of a bicycle moving at a constant speed, with the times of the measured points indicated.

The displacement between the initial position x_i and the final position x_f is

$$\Delta x = x_f - x_i = 120 \text{ ft} - 0 \text{ ft} = 120 \text{ ft}$$

Similarly, we define the time interval between these two points to be

$$\Delta t = t_f - t_i = 6 \text{ s} - 0 \text{ s} = 6 \text{ s}$$

A time interval Δt measures the elapsed time as an object moves from an initial position x_i at time t_i to a final position x_f at time t_f. Note that, unlike Δx, Δt is always positive because t_f is always greater than t_i.

EXAMPLE 1.1 **How long a ride?**

Carol is enjoying a bicycle ride on a country road that runs east-west past a water tower. Define a coordinate system so that increasing x means moving east. At noon, Carol is 3 miles (mi) east of the water tower. A half-hour later, she is 2 mi west of the water tower. What is her displacement during that half-hour?

PREPARE Although it may seem like overkill for such a simple problem, you should start by making a drawing, like the one in FIGURE 1.15, with the x-axis along the road. Distances are measured with respect to the water tower, so it is a natural origin for the

FIGURE 1.15 A drawing of Carol's motion.

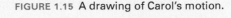
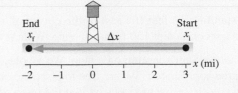

coordinate system. Once the coordinate system is established, we can show Carol's initial and final positions and her displacement between the two.

SOLVE We've specified values for Carol's initial and final positions in our drawing. We can thus compute her displacement:

$$\Delta x = x_f - x_i = (-2 \text{ mi}) - (3 \text{ mi}) = -5 \text{ mi}$$

ASSESS Once we've completed the solution to the problem, we need to go back to see if it makes sense. Carol is moving to the west, so we expect her displacement to be negative—and it is. We can see from our drawing in Figure 1.15 that she has moved 5 miles from her starting position, so our answer seems reasonable.

NOTE ▶ All of the numerical examples in the book are worked out with the same three-step process: Prepare, Solve, Assess. It's tempting to cut corners, especially for the simple problems in these early chapters, but you should take the time to do all of these steps now, to practice your problem-solving technique. We'll have more to say about our general problem-solving strategy in Chapter 2. ◀

STOP TO THINK 1.3 Sarah starts at a positive position along the x-axis. She then undergoes a negative displacement. Her final position

A. Is positive.   B. Is negative.   C. Could be either positive or negative.

1.3 Velocity

We all have an intuitive sense of whether something is moving very fast or just cruising slowly along. To make this intuitive idea more precise, let's start by examining the motion diagrams of some objects moving along a straight line at a *constant* speed, objects that are neither speeding up nor slowing down. This motion at a constant speed is called **uniform motion.** As we saw for the skateboarder in Section 1.1, for an object in uniform motion, successive frames of the motion diagram are *equally spaced*. We know now that this means that the object's displacement Δx is the same between successive frames.

To see how an object's displacement between successive frames is related to its speed, consider the motion diagrams of a bicycle and a car, traveling along the same street as shown in FIGURE 1.16. Clearly the car is moving faster than the bicycle: In any 1-second time interval, the car undergoes a displacement $\Delta x = 40$ ft, while the bicycle's displacement is only 20 ft.

The distances traveled in 1 second by the bicycle and the car are a measure of their speeds. The greater the distance traveled by an object in a given time interval, the greater its speed. This idea leads us to define the speed of an object as

$$\text{speed} = \frac{\text{distance traveled in a given time interval}}{\text{time interval}} \quad (1.1)$$

Speed of a moving object

FIGURE 1.16 Motion diagrams for a car and a bicycle.

During each second, the car moves twice as far as the bicycle. Hence the car is moving at a greater speed.

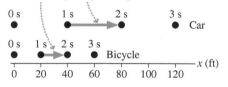

For the bicycle, this equation gives

$$\text{speed} = \frac{20 \text{ ft}}{1 \text{ s}} = 20 \frac{\text{ft}}{\text{s}}$$

while for the car we have

$$\text{speed} = \frac{40 \text{ ft}}{1 \text{ s}} = 40 \frac{\text{ft}}{\text{s}}$$

The speed of the car is twice that of the bicycle, which seems reasonable.

NOTE ▶ The division gives units that are a fraction: ft/s. This is read as "feet per second," just like the more familiar "miles per hour." ◀

FIGURE 1.17 Two bicycles traveling at the same speed, but with different velocities.

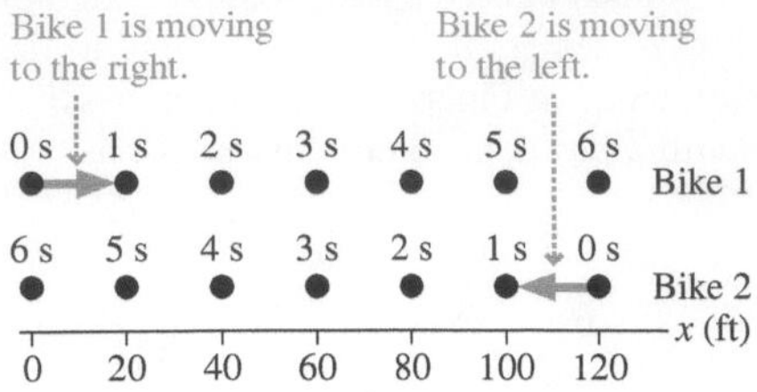

Bike 1 is moving to the right.   Bike 2 is moving to the left.

To fully characterize the motion of an object, it is important to specify not only the object's speed but also the *direction* in which it is moving. For example, FIGURE 1.17 shows the motion diagrams of two bicycles traveling at the same speed of 20 ft/s. The two bicycles have the same speed, but something about their motion is different—the *direction* of their motion.

The problem is that the "distance traveled" in Equation 1.1 doesn't capture any information about the direction of travel. But we've seen that the *displacement* of an object does contain this information. We can then introduce a new quantity, the **velocity,** as

$$\text{velocity} = \frac{\text{displacement}}{\text{time interval}} = \frac{\Delta x}{\Delta t} \qquad (1.2)$$

Velocity of a moving object

The velocity of bicycle 1 in Figure 1.17, computed using the 1 second time interval between the $t = 2$ s and $t = 3$ s positions, is

$$v = \frac{\Delta x}{\Delta t} = \frac{x_3 - x_2}{3\,\text{s} - 2\,\text{s}} = \frac{60\,\text{ft} - 40\,\text{ft}}{1\,\text{s}} = +20\,\frac{\text{ft}}{\text{s}}$$

while the velocity for bicycle 2, during the same time interval, is

$$v = \frac{\Delta x}{\Delta t} = \frac{x_3 - x_2}{3\,\text{s} - 2\,\text{s}} = \frac{60\,\text{ft} - 80\,\text{ft}}{1\,\text{s}} = -20\,\frac{\text{ft}}{\text{s}}$$

NOTE ▶ We have used x_2 for the position at time $t = 2$ seconds and x_3 for the position at time $t = 3$ seconds. The subscripts serve the same role as before—identifying particular positions—but in this case the positions are identified by the time at which each position is reached. ◄

The two velocities have opposite signs because the bicycles are traveling in opposite directions. **Speed measures only how fast an object moves, but velocity tells us both an object's speed** *and its direction.* A positive velocity indicates motion to the right or, for vertical motion, upward. Similarly, an object moving to the left, or down, has a negative velocity.

NOTE ▶ Learning to distinguish between speed, which is always a positive number, and velocity, which can be either positive or negative, is one of the most important tasks in the analysis of motion. ◄

The velocity as defined by Equation 1.2 is actually what is called the *average* velocity. On average, over each 1 s interval bicycle 1 moves 20 ft, but we don't know if it was moving at exactly the same speed at every moment during this time interval. In Chapter 2, we'll develop the idea of *instantaneous* velocity, the velocity of an object at a particular instant in time. Since our goal in this chapter is to *visualize* motion with motion diagrams, we'll somewhat blur the distinction between average and instantaneous quantities, refining these definitions in Chapter 2, where our goal will be to develop the mathematics of motion.

EXAMPLE 1.2   Finding the speed of a seabird

Albatrosses are seabirds that spend most of their lives flying over the ocean looking for food. With a stiff tailwind, an albatross can fly at high speeds. Satellite data on one particularly speedy albatross showed it 60 miles east of its roost at 3:00 PM and then, at 3:20 PM, 86 miles east of its roost. What was its velocity?

PREPARE The statement of the problem provides us with a natural coordinate system: We can measure distances with respect to the roost, with distances to the east as positive. With this coordinate system, the motion of the albatross appears as in FIGURE 1.18. The motion takes place between 3:00 and 3:20, a time interval of 20 minutes, or 0.33 hour.

FIGURE 1.18 The motion of an albatross at sea.

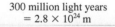

SOLVE We know the initial and final positions, and we know the time interval, so we can calculate the velocity:

$$v = \frac{\Delta x}{\Delta t} = \frac{x_f - x_i}{0.33 \text{ h}} = \frac{26 \text{ mi}}{0.33 \text{ h}} = 79 \text{ mph}$$

ASSESS The velocity is positive, which makes sense because Figure 1.18 shows that the motion is to the right. A speed of 79 mph is certainly fast, but the problem said it was a "particularly speedy" albatross, so our answer seems reasonable. (Indeed, albatrosses have been observed to fly at such speeds in the very fast winds of the Southern Ocean. This problem is based on real observations, as will be our general practice in this book.)

The "Per" in Meters Per Second

The units for speed and velocity are a unit of distance (feet, meters, miles) divided by a unit of time (seconds, hours). Thus we could measure velocity in units of m/s or mph, pronounced "meters *per* second" and "miles *per* hour." The word "per" will often arise in physics when we consider the ratio of two quantities. What do we mean, exactly, by "per"?

If a car moves with a speed of 23 m/s, we mean that it travels 23 meters *for each* 1 second of elapsed time. The word "per" thus associates the number of units in the numerator (23 m) with *one* unit of the denominator (1 s). We'll see many other examples of this idea as the book progresses. You may already know a bit about *density;* you can look up the density of gold and you'll find that it is 19.3 g/cm^3 ("grams *per* cubic centimeter"). This means that there are 19.3 grams of gold *for each* 1 cubic centimeter of the metal. Thinking about the word "per" in this way will help you better understand physical quantities whose units are the ratio of two other units.

1.4 A Sense of Scale: Significant Figures, Scientific Notation, and Units

Physics attempts to explain the natural world, from the very small to the exceedingly large. And in order to understand our world, we need to be able to *measure* quantities both minuscule and enormous. A properly reported measurement has three elements. First, we can measure our quantity with only a certain precision. To make this precision clear, we need to make sure that we report our measurement with the correct number of *significant figures*.

Second, writing down the really big and small numbers that often come up in physics can be awkward. To avoid writing all those zeros, scientists use *scientific notation* to express numbers both big and small.

Finally, we need to choose an agreed-upon set of *units* for the quantity. For speed, common units include meters per second and miles per hour. For mass, the kilogram is the most commonly used unit. Every physical quantity that we can measure has an associated set of units.

300 million light years
= 2.8×10^{24} m

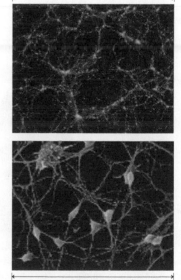

120 μm = 1.2×10^{-4} m

From galaxies to cells ... BIO In science, we need to express numbers both very large and very small. The top image is a computer simulation of the structure of the universe. Bright areas represent regions of clustered galaxies. The bottom image is cortical nerve cells. Nerve cells relay signals to each other through a complex web of dendrites. These images, though similar in appearance, differ in scale by a factor of about 2×10^{28}!

FIGURE 1.19 The precision of a measurement depends on the instrument used to make it.

These calipers have a precision of 0.01 mm.

Walter Davis's best long jump on this day was reported as 8.24 m. This implies that the actual length of the jump was between 8.235 m and 8.245 m, a spread of only 0.01 m, which is 1 cm. Does this claimed accuracy seem reasonable?

TRY IT YOURSELF

How tall are you really? If you measure your height in the morning, just after you wake up, and then in the evening, after a full day of activity, you'll find that your evening height is *shorter* by as much as 3/4 inch. Your height decreases over the course of the day as gravity compresses and reshapes your spine. If you give your height as 66 3/16 in, you are claiming more significant figures than are truly warranted; the 3/16 in isn't really reliably known because your height can vary by more than this. Expressing your height to the nearest inch is plenty!

Measurements and Significant Figures

When we measure any quantity, such as the length of a bone or the weight of a specimen, we can do so with only a certain *precision*. The digital calipers in FIGURE 1.19 can make a measurement to within ±0.01 mm, so they have a precision of 0.01 mm. If you made the measurement with a ruler, you probably couldn't do better than about ±1 mm, so the precision of the ruler is about 1 mm. The precision of a measurement can also be affected by the skill or judgment of the person performing the measurement. A stopwatch might have a precision of 0.001 s, but, due to your reaction time, your measurement of the time of a sprinter would be much less precise.

It is important that your measurement be reported in a way that reflects its actual precision. Suppose you use a ruler to measure the length of a particular specimen of a newly discovered species of frog. You judge that you can make this measurement with a precision of about 1 mm, or 0.1 cm. In this case, the frog's length should be reported as, say, 6.2 cm. We interpret this to mean that the actual value falls between 6.15 cm and 6.25 cm and thus rounds to 6.2 cm. Reporting the frog's length as simply 6 cm is saying less than you know; you are withholding information. On the other hand, to report the number as 6.213 cm is wrong. Any person reviewing your work would interpret the number 6.213 cm as meaning that the actual length falls between 6.2125 cm and 6.2135 cm, thus rounding to 6.213 cm. In this case, you are claiming to have knowledge and information that you do not really possess.

The way to state your knowledge precisely is through the proper use of **significant figures.** You can think of a significant figure as a digit that is reliably known. A measurement such as 6.2 cm has *two* significant figures, the 6 and the 2. The next decimal place—the hundredths—is not reliably known and is thus not a significant figure. Similarly, a time measurement of 34.62 s has four significant figures, implying that the 2 in the hundredths place is reliably known.

When we perform a calculation such as adding or multiplying two or more measured numbers, we can't claim more accuracy for the result than was present in the initial measurements. Nine out of ten numbers used in a calculation might be known with a precision of 0.01%, but if the tenth number is poorly known, with a precision of only 10%, then the result of the calculation cannot possibly be more precise than 10%.

Determining the proper number of significant figures is straightforward, but there are a few definite rules to follow. We will often spell out such technical details in what we call a "Tactics Box." A Tactics Box is designed to teach you particular skills and techniques. Each Tactics Box will use the ✐ icon to designate exercises in the *Student Workbook* that you can use to practice these skills.

TACTICS BOX 1.1 Using significant figures (MP)™

❶ When you multiply or divide several numbers, or when you take roots, the number of significant figures in the answer should match the number of significant figures of the *least* precisely known number used in the calculation:

Three significant figures

$$3.73 \times 5.7 = 21$$

Two significant figures

Answer should have the *lower* of the two, or two significant figures.

Continued

❷ When you add or subtract several numbers, the number of decimal places in the answer should match the *smallest* number of decimal places of any number used in the calculation:

18.54 — Two decimal places
+106.6 — One decimal place
125.1 — Answer should have the *lower* of the two, or one decimal place.

❸ **Exact numbers** have no uncertainty and, when used in calculations, do not change the number of significant figures of measured numbers. Examples of exact numbers are π and the number 2 in the relation $d = 2r$ between a circle's diameter and radius.

There is one notable exception to these rules:

■ It is acceptable to keep one or two extra digits during *intermediate* steps of a calculation. The goal here is to minimize round-off errors in the calculation. But the *final* answer must be reported with the proper number of significant figures.

Exercise 15 ✐

EXAMPLE 1.3 **Measuring the velocity of a car**

To measure the velocity of a car, clocks A and B are set up at two points along the road, as shown in **FIGURE 1.20**. Clock A is precise to 0.01 s, while B is precise to only 0.1 s. The distance between these two clocks is carefully measured to be 124.5 m. The two clocks are automatically started when the car passes a trigger in the road; each clock stops automatically when the car passes that clock. After the car has passed both clocks, clock A is found to read $t_A = 1.22$ s, and clock B to read $t_B = 4.5$ s. The time from the less-precise clock B is correctly reported with fewer significant figures than that from A. What is the velocity of the car, and how should it be reported with the correct number of significant figures?

FIGURE 1.20 Measuring the velocity of a car.

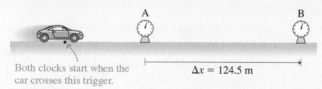

Both clocks start when the car crosses this trigger.

$\Delta x = 124.5$ m

PREPARE To calculate the velocity, we need the displacement Δx and the time interval Δt as the car moves between the two clocks. The displacement is given as $\Delta x = 124.5$ m; we can calculate the time interval as the difference between the two measured times.

SOLVE The time interval is:

This number has one decimal place.

This number has two decimal places.

$$\Delta t = t_B - t_A = (4.5 \text{ s}) - (1.22 \text{ s}) = 3.3 \text{ s}$$

By rule 2 of Tactics Box 1.1, the result should have *one* decimal place.

We can now calculate the velocity with the displacement and the time interval:

The displacement has four significant figures.

$$v = \frac{\Delta x}{\Delta t} = \frac{124.5 \text{ m}}{3.3 \text{ s}} = 38 \text{ m/s}$$

The time interval has two significant figures.

By rule 1 of Tactics Box 1.1, the result should have *two* significant figures.

ASSESS Our final value has two significant figures. Suppose you had been hired to measure the speed of a car this way, and you reported 37.72 m/s. It would be reasonable for someone looking at your result to assume that the measurements you used to arrive at this value were correct to four significant figures and thus that you had measured time to the nearest 0.001 second. Our correct result of 38 m/s has all of the accuracy that you can claim, but no more!

Scientific Notation

It's easy to write down measurements of ordinary-sized objects: Your height might be 1.72 meters, the weight of an apple 0.34 pound. But the radius of a hydrogen atom is 0.000000000053 m, and the distance to the moon is 384000000 m. Keeping track of all those zeros is quite cumbersome.

Beyond requiring you to deal with all the zeros, writing quantities this way makes it unclear how many significant figures are involved. In the distance to the moon given above, how many of those digits are significant? Three? Four? All nine?

Writing numbers using scientific notation avoids both these problems. A value in scientific notation is a number with one digit to the left of the decimal point and zero or more to the right of it, multiplied by a power of ten. This solves the problem of all the zeros and makes the number of significant figures immediately apparent. In scientific notation, writing the distance to the sun as 1.50×10^{11} m implies that three digits are significant; writing it as 1.5×10^{11} m implies that only two digits are.

Even for smaller values, scientific notation can clarify the number of significant figures. Suppose a distance is reported as 1200 m. How many significant figures does this measurement have? It's ambiguous, but using scientific notation can remove any ambiguity. If this distance is known to within 1 m, we can write it as 1.200×10^3 m, showing that all four digits are significant; if it is accurate to only 100 m or so, we can report it as 1.2×10^3 m, indicating two significant figures.

Tactics Box 1.2 shows how to convert a number to scientific notation, and how to correctly indicate the number of significant figures.

TACTICS BOX 1.2   Using scientific notation   (MP)™

To convert a number into scientific notation:

❶ For a number greater than 10, move the decimal point to the left until only one digit remains to the left of the decimal point. The remaining number is then multiplied by 10 to a power; this power is given by the number of spaces the decimal point was moved. Here we convert the diameter of the earth to scientific notation:

We move the decimal point until there is only   Since we moved the decimal point
one digit to its left, counting the number of steps.   6 steps, the power of ten is 6.

$$6\,370\,000 \text{ m} = 6.37 \times 10^6 \text{ m}$$

The number of digits here equals the number of significant figures.

❷ For a number less than 1, move the decimal point to the right until it passes the first digit that isn't a zero. The remaining number is then multiplied by 10 to a negative power; the power is given by the number of spaces the decimal point was moved. For the diameter of a red blood cell we have:

We move the decimal point until it passes the first   Since we moved the decimal point
digit that is not a zero, counting the number of steps.   6 steps, the power of ten is −6.

$$0.000\,007\,5 \text{ m} = 7.5 \times 10^{-6} \text{ m}$$

The number of digits here equals the number of significant figures.

Exercise 16 🖉

Proper use of significant figures is part of the "culture" of science. We will frequently emphasize these "cultural issues" because you must learn to speak the same language as the natives if you wish to communicate effectively! Most students know the rules of significant figures, having learned them in high school, but many fail to apply them. It is important that you understand the reasons for significant figures and that you get in the habit of using them properly.

Units

As we have seen, in order to measure a quantity we need to give it a numerical value. But a measurement is more than just a number—it requires a *unit* to be given. You can't go to the deli and ask for "three quarters of cheese." You need to use a unit—here, one of weight, such as pounds—in addition to the number.

In your daily life, you probably use the English system of units, in which distances are measured in inches, feet, and miles. These units are well adapted for daily life, but they are rarely used in scientific work. Given that science is an international discipline, it is also important to have a system of units that is recognized around the world. For these reasons, scientists use a system of units called *le Système Internationale d'Unités,* commonly referred to as **SI units.** SI units were originally developed by the French in the late 1700s as a way of standardizing and regularizing numbers for commerce and science. We often refer to these as *metric units* because the meter is the basic standard of length.

The three basic SI quantities, shown in Table 1.1, are time, length (or distance), and mass. Other quantities needed to understand motion can be expressed as combinations of these basic units. For example, speed and velocity are expressed in meters per second or m/s. This combination is a ratio of the length unit (the meter) to the time unit (the second).

Using Prefixes

We will have many occasions to use lengths, times, and masses that are either much less or much greater than the standards of 1 meter, 1 second, and 1 kilogram. We will do so by using *prefixes* to denote various powers of ten. For instance, the prefix "kilo" (abbreviation k) denotes 10^3, or a factor of 1000. Thus 1 km equals 1000 m, 1 MW equals 10^6 watts, and 1 μV equals 10^{-6} V. Table 1.2 lists the common prefixes that will be used frequently throughout this book. A more extensive list of prefixes is shown inside the cover of the book.

Although prefixes make it easier to talk about quantities, the proper SI units are meters, seconds, and kilograms. Quantities given with prefixed units must be converted to base SI units before any calculations are done. Thus 23.0 cm must be converted to 0.230 m before starting calculations. The exception is the kilogram, which is already the base SI unit.

Unit Conversions

Although SI units are our standard, we cannot entirely forget that the United States still uses English units. Even after repeated exposure to metric units in classes, most of us "think" in English units. Thus it remains important to be able to convert back and forth between SI units and English units. Table 1.3 shows some frequently used conversions that will come in handy.

One effective method of performing unit conversions begins by noticing that since, for example, 1 mi = 1.609 km, the ratio of these two distances—*including their units*—is equal to 1, so that

$$\frac{1 \text{ mi}}{1.609 \text{ km}} = \frac{1.609 \text{ km}}{1 \text{ mi}} = 1$$

A ratio of values equal to 1 is called a **conversion factor.** The following Tactics Box shows how to make a unit conversion.

The importance of units In 1999, the $125 million Mars Climate Orbiter burned up in the Martian atmosphere instead of entering a safe orbit from which it could perform observations. The problem was faulty units! An engineering team had provided critical data on spacecraft performance in English units, but the navigation team assumed these data were in metric units. As a consequence, the navigation team had the spacecraft fly too close to the planet, and it burned up in the atmosphere.

TABLE 1.1 Common SI units

Quantity	Unit	Abbreviation
time	second	s
length	meter	m
mass	kilogram	kg

TABLE 1.2 Common prefixes

Prefix	Abbreviation	Power of 10
mega-	M	10^6
kilo-	k	10^3
centi-	c	10^{-2}
milli-	m	10^{-3}
micro-	μ	10^{-6}
nano-	n	10^{-9}

TABLE 1.3 Useful unit conversions

1 inch (in) = 2.54 cm
1 foot (ft) = 0.305 m
1 mile (mi) = 1.609 km
1 mile per hour (mph) = 0.447 m/s
1 m = 39.37 in
1 km = 0.621 mi
1 m/s = 2.24 mph

TACTICS
BOX 1.3 **Making a unit conversion**

❶ Start with the quantity you wish to convert.

❷ Multiply by the appropriate conversion factor. Because this conversion factor is equal to 1, multiplying by it does not change the value of the quantity—only its units.

❺ Remember to convert your final answer to the correct number of significant figures!

$$60 \text{ mi} = 60 \text{ mi} \times \frac{1.609 \text{ km}}{1 \text{ mi}} = 96.54 \text{ km} = 97 \text{ km}$$

❸ You can cancel the original unit (here, miles) because it appears in both the numerator and the denominator.

❹ Calculate the answer; it is in the desired units. Remember, 60 mi and 96.54 km are the same distance; they are simply in different units.

Exercise 17

Note that we've rounded the answer to 97 kilometers because the distance we're converting, 60 miles, has only two significant figures.

More complicated conversions can be done with several successive multiplications of conversion factors, as we see in the next example.

EXAMPLE 1.4 **Can a bicycle go that fast?**

In Section 1.3, we calculated the speed of a bicycle to be 20 ft/s. Is this a reasonable speed for a bicycle?

PREPARE In order to determine whether or not this speed is reasonable, we will convert it to more familiar units. For speed, the unit you are most familiar with is likely miles per hour.

SOLVE We first collect the necessary unit conversions:

$$1 \text{ mi} = 5280 \text{ ft} \qquad 1 \text{ hour (1 h)} = 60 \text{ min} \qquad 1 \text{ min} = 60 \text{ s}$$

We then multiply our original value by successive factors of 1 in order to convert the units:

We want to cancel feet here in the numerator . . .

. . . so we multiply by $1 = \dfrac{1 \text{ mi}}{5280 \text{ ft}}$

to get the feet in the denominator.

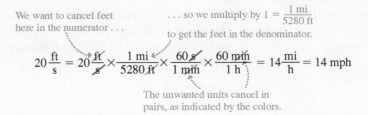

$$20 \frac{\text{ft}}{\text{s}} = 20 \frac{\text{ft}}{\text{s}} \times \frac{1 \text{ mi}}{5280 \text{ ft}} \times \frac{60 \text{ s}}{1 \text{ min}} \times \frac{60 \text{ min}}{1 \text{ h}} = 14 \frac{\text{mi}}{\text{h}} = 14 \text{ mph}$$

The unwanted units cancel in pairs, as indicated by the colors.

ASSESS Our final result of 14 miles per hour (14 mph) is a very reasonable speed for a bicycle, which gives us confidence in our answer. If we had calculated a speed of 140 miles per hour, we would have suspected that we had made an error because this is quite a bit faster than the average bicyclist can travel!

How many jellybeans are in the jar? Some reasoning about the size of one bean and the size of the jar can give you a one-significant-figure estimate.

Estimation

When scientists and engineers first approach a problem, they may do a quick measurement or calculation to establish the rough physical scale involved. This will help establish the procedures that should be used to make a more accurate measurement—or the estimate may well be all that is needed.

Suppose you see a rock fall off a cliff and would like to know how fast it was going when it hit the ground. By doing a mental comparison with the speeds of familiar objects, such as cars and bicycles, you might judge that the rock was traveling at about 20 mph. This is a one-significant-figure estimate. With some luck, you can probably distinguish 20 mph from either 10 mph or 30 mph, but you certainly cannot distinguish 20 mph from 21 mph just from a visual appearance. A one-significant-figure estimate or calculation, such as this estimate of speed, is called an **order-of-magnitude estimate.** An order-of-magnitude estimate is indicated by the symbol $\sim$, which indicates even less precision than the "approximately equal" symbol $\approx$. You would report your estimate of the speed of the falling rock as $v \sim 20$ mph.

A useful skill is to make reliable order-of-magnitude estimates on the basis of known information, simple reasoning, and common sense. This is a skill that is acquired by practice. Tables 1.4 and 1.5 have information that will be useful for doing estimates.

TABLE 1.4 Some approximate lengths

	Length (m)
Circumference of the earth	4×10^7
Distance from New York to Los Angeles	5×10^6
Distance you can drive in 1 hour	1×10^5
Altitude of jet planes	1×10^4
Distance across a college campus	1000
Length of a football field	100
Length of a classroom	10
Length of your arm	1
Width of a textbook	0.1
Length of your little fingernail	0.01
Diameter of a pencil lead	1×10^{-3}
Thickness of a sheet of paper	1×10^{-4}
Diameter of a dust particle	1×10^{-5}

EXAMPLE 1.5   **How fast do you walk?**

Estimate how fast you walk, in meters per second.

PREPARE In order to compute speed, we need a distance and a time. If you walked a mile to campus, how long would this take? You'd probably say 30 minutes or so—half an hour. Let's use this rough number in our estimate.

SOLVE Given this estimate, we compute speed as

$$\text{speed} = \frac{\text{distance}}{\text{time}} \sim \frac{1 \text{ mile}}{1/2 \text{ hour}} = 2 \frac{\text{mi}}{\text{h}}$$

But we want the speed in meters per second. Since our calculation is only an estimate, we use an approximate form of the conversion factor from Table 1.3:

$$1 \frac{\text{mi}}{\text{h}} \approx 0.5 \frac{\text{m}}{\text{s}}$$

This gives an approximate walking speed of 1 m/s.

ASSESS Is this a reasonable value? Let's do another estimate. Your stride is probably about 1 yard long—about 1 meter. And you take about one step per second; next time you are walking, you can count and see. So a walking speed of 1 meter per second sounds pretty reasonable.

TABLE 1.5 Some approximate masses

	Mass (kg)
Large airliner	1×10^5
Small car	1000
Large human	100
Medium-size dog	10
Science textbook	1
Apple	0.1
Pencil	0.01
Raisin	1×10^{-3}
Fly	1×10^{-4}

This sort of estimation is very valuable. We will see many cases in which we need to know an approximate value for a quantity before we start a problem or after we finish a problem, in order to assess our results.

STOP TO THINK 1.4 Rank in order, from the most to the fewest, the number of significant figures in the following numbers. For example, if B has more than C, C has the same number as A, and A has more than D, give your answer as B > C = A > D.

A. 0.43   B. 0.0052   C. 0.430   D. 4.321×10^{-10}

1.5 Vectors and Motion: A First Look

Many physical quantities, such as time, temperature, and weight, can be described completely by a number with a unit. For example, the mass of an object might be 6 kg and its temperature 30° C. When a physical quantity is described by a single number (with a unit), we call it a **scalar quantity.** A scalar can be positive, negative, or zero.

Vectors and scalars

Scalars

Time, temperature and weight are all *scalar* quantities. To specify your weight, the temperature outside, or the current time, you only need a single number.

Vectors

The velocity of the race car is a *vector*. To fully specify a velocity, we need to give its magnitude (e.g., 120 mph) *and* its direction (e.g., west).

The force with which the boy pushes on his friend is another example of a vector. To completely specify this force, we must know not only how hard he pushes (the magnitude) but also in which direction.

The boat's displacement is the straight-line connection from its initial to its final position.

Many other quantities, however, have a directional quality and cannot be described by a single number. To describe the motion of a car, for example, you must specify not only how fast it is moving, but also the *direction* in which it is moving. A **vector quantity** is a quantity that has both a *size* (How far? or How fast?) and a *direction* (Which way?). The size or length of a vector is called its **magnitude.** The magnitude of a vector can be positive or zero, but it cannot be negative.

Some examples of vector and scalar quantities are shown on the left.

We graphically represent a vector as an *arrow*, as illustrated for the velocity and force vectors. The arrow is drawn to point in the direction of the vector quantity, and the *length* of the arrow is proportional to the magnitude of the vector quantity.

When we want to represent a vector quantity with a *symbol,* we need somehow to indicate that the symbol is for a vector rather than for a scalar. We do this by drawing an arrow over the letter that represents the quantity. Thus $\vec{r}$ and $\vec{A}$ are symbols for vectors, whereas r and A, without the arrows, are symbols for scalars. In handwritten work you *must* draw arrows over all symbols that represent vectors. This may seem strange until you get used to it, but it is very important because we will often use both r and $\vec{r}$, or both A and $\vec{A}$, in the same problem, and they mean different things!

NOTE ▶ The arrow over the symbol always points to the right, regardless of which direction the actual vector points. Thus we write $\vec{r}$ or $\vec{A}$, never $\overleftarrow{r}$ or $\overleftarrow{A}$, ◀

Displacement Vectors

For motion along a line, we found in Section 1.2 that the displacement is a quantity that specifies not only how *far* an object moves but also the *direction*—to the left or to the right—that the object moves. Since displacement is a quantity that has both a magnitude (How far?) and a direction, it can be represented by a vector, the **displacement vector.** FIGURE 1.21 shows the displacement vector for Sam's trip that we discussed earlier. We've simply drawn an arrow—the vector—from his initial to his final position and assigned it the symbol $\vec{d}_S$. Because $\vec{d}_S$ has both a magnitude and a direction, it is convenient to write Sam's displacement as $\vec{d}_S = (100$ ft, east$)$. The first value in the parentheses is the magnitude of the vector (i.e., the size of the displacement), and the second value specifies its direction.

FIGURE 1.21 Two displacement vectors.

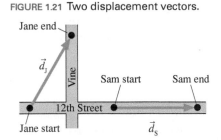

Also shown in Figure 1.21 is the displacement vector $\vec{d}_J$ for Jane, who started on 12th Street and ended up on Vine. As with Sam, we draw her displacement vector as an arrow from her initial to her final position. In this case, $\vec{d}_J = 100$ ft, 30° east of north).

Jane's trip illustrates an important point about displacement vectors. Jane started her trip on 12th Street and ended up on Vine, leading to the displacement vector shown. But to get from her initial to her final position, she needn't have walked along the straight-line path denoted by $\vec{d}_J$. If she walked east along 12th Street to the intersection and then headed north on Vine, her displacement would still be the vector shown. **An object's displacement vector is drawn from the object's initial position to its final position, regardless of the actual path followed between these two points.**

Vector Addition

Let's consider one more trip for the peripatetic Sam. In FIGURE 1.22, he starts at the intersection and walks east 50 ft; then he walks 100 ft to the northeast through a vacant lot. His displacement vectors for the two legs of his trip are labeled $\vec{d}_1$ and $\vec{d}_2$ in the figure.

Sam's trip consists of two legs that can be represented by the two vectors $\vec{d}_1$ and $\vec{d}_2$, but we can represent his trip as a whole, from his initial starting position to his overall final position, with the *net* displacement vector labeled $\vec{d}_{net}$. Sam's net displacement is in a sense the *sum* of the two displacements that made it up, so we can write

$$\vec{d}_{net} = \vec{d}_1 + \vec{d}_2$$

Sam's net displacement thus requires the *addition* of two vectors, but vector addition obeys different rules from the addition of two scalar quantities. The directions of the two vectors, as well as their magnitudes, must be taken into account. Sam's trip suggests that we can add vectors together by putting the "tail" of one vector at the tip of the other. This idea, which is reasonable for displacement vectors, in fact is how *any* two vectors are added. Tactics Box 1.4 shows how to add two vectors $\vec{A}$ and $\vec{B}$.

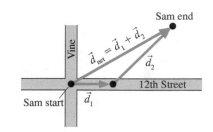

FIGURE 1.22 Sam undergoes two displacements.

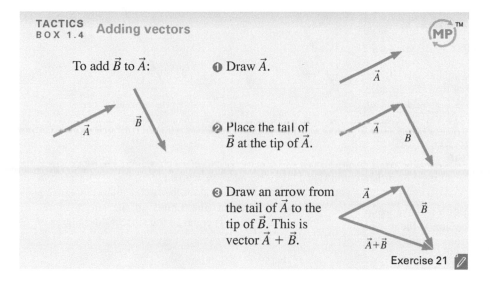

TACTICS BOX 1.4 **Adding vectors**

To add $\vec{B}$ to $\vec{A}$:

$\vec{A}$ $\vec{B}$

❶ Draw $\vec{A}$.

❷ Place the tail of $\vec{B}$ at the tip of $\vec{A}$.

❸ Draw an arrow from the tail of $\vec{A}$ to the tip of $\vec{B}$. This is vector $\vec{A} + \vec{B}$.

Exercise 21

Vectors and Trigonometry

When we need to add displacements or other vectors in more than one dimension, we'll end up computing lengths and angles of triangles. This is the job of trigonometry. Trigonometry will be our primary mathematical tool for vector addition; let's review the basic ideas.

Suppose we have a right triangle with hypotenuse H, angle θ, side opposite the angle O, and side adjacent to the angle A, as shown in FIGURE 1.23. The sine, cosine, and tangent (which we write as "sin," "cos," and "tan") of angle θ are defined as ratios of the sides of the triangle:

$$\sin\theta = \frac{O}{H} \qquad \cos\theta = \frac{A}{H} \qquad \tan\theta = \frac{O}{A} \qquad (1.3)$$

If you know the angle θ and the length of one side, you can use the sine, cosine, or tangent to find the lengths of the other sides. For example, if you know θ and the length A of the adjacent side, you can find the hypotenuse H by rearranging the middle Equation 1.3 to give $H = A/\cos\theta$.

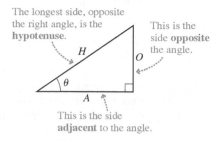

FIGURE 1.23 A right triangle.

The longest side, opposite the right angle, is the **hypotenuse**.

This is the side **opposite** the angle.

This is the side **adjacent** to the angle.

Conversely, if you know two sides of the triangle, you can find the angle θ by using inverse trigonometric functions:

$$\theta = \sin^{-1}\left(\frac{O}{H}\right) \qquad \theta = \cos^{-1}\left(\frac{A}{H}\right) \qquad \theta = \tan^{-1}\left(\frac{O}{A}\right) \qquad (1.4)$$

We will make regular use of these relationships in the following chapters.

EXAMPLE 1.6 How far north and east?

Suppose Alex is navigating using a compass. She starts walking at an angle 60° north of east and walks a total of 100 m. How far north is she from her starting point? How far east?

PREPARE A sketch of Alex's motion is shown in FIGURE 1.24a. We've shown north and east as they would be on a map, and we've noted Alex's displacement as a vector, giving its magnitude and direction. FIGURE 1.24b shows a triangle with this displacement as the hypotenuse. Alex's distance north of her starting point and her distance east of her starting point are the sides of this triangle.

SOLVE The sine and cosine functions are ratios of sides of right triangles, as we saw above. With the 60° angle as noted, the distance north of the starting point is the opposite side of the triangle; the distance east is the adjacent side. Thus:

distance north of start = (100 m) sin (60°) = 87 m

distance east of start = (100 m) cos (60°) = 50 m

ASSESS Both of the distances we calculated are less than 100 m, as they must be, and the distance east is less than the distance north, as our diagram in Figure 1.24b shows it should be. Our

answers seem reasonable. In finding the solution to this problem, we "broke down" the displacement into two different distances, one north and one east. This hints at the idea of the *components* of a vector, something we'll explore in the next chapter.

FIGURE 1.24 An analysis of Alex's motion.

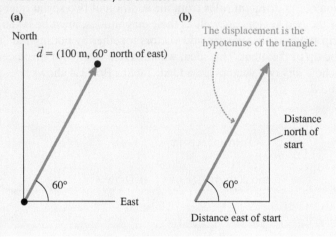

(a)

North

$\vec{d} = (100 \text{ m}, 60° \text{ north of east})$

60°

East

(b)

The displacement is the hypotenuse of the triangle.

Distance north of start

60°

Distance east of start

EXAMPLE 1.7 How far away is Anna?

Anna walks 90 m due east and then 50 m due north. What is her displacement from her starting point?

PREPARE Let's start with the sketch in FIGURE 1.25a. We set up a coordinate system with Anna's original position as the origin, and then we drew her two subsequent motions as the two displacement vectors $\vec{d}_1$ and $\vec{d}_2$.

FIGURE 1.25 Analyzing Anna's motion.

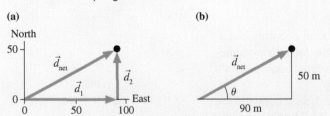

(a)

North

50

$\vec{d}_{net}$

$\vec{d}_2$

$\vec{d}_1$

0

0   50   100

East

(b)

$\vec{d}_{net}$

θ

90 m

50 m

SOLVE We drew the two vector displacements with the tail of one vector starting at the head of the previous one—exactly what is needed to form a vector sum. The vector $\vec{d}_{net}$ in Figure 1.25a is the vector sum of the successive displacements and thus represents Anna's net displacement from the origin.

Anna's distance from the origin is the length of this vector $\vec{d}_{net}$. FIGURE 1.25b shows that this vector is the hypotenuse of a right triangle with sides 50 m (because Anna walked 50 m

north) and 90 m (because she walked 90 m east). We can compute the magnitude of this vector, her net displacement, using the Pythagorean theorem (the square of the length of the hypotenuse of a triangle is equal to the sum of the squares of the lengths of the sides):

$$d_{net}^2 = (50 \text{ m})^2 + (90 \text{ m})^2$$

$$d_{net} = \sqrt{(50 \text{ m})^2 + (90 \text{ m})^2} = 103 \text{ m} \approx 100 \text{ m}$$

We have rounded off to the appropriate number of significant figures, giving us 100 m for the magnitude of the displacement vector. How about the direction? Figure 1.25b identifies the angle that gives the angle north of east of Anna's displacement. In the right triangle, 50 m is the opposite side and 90 m is the adjacent side, so the angle is given by

$$\theta = \tan^{-1}\left(\frac{50 \text{ m}}{90 \text{ m}}\right) = \tan^{-1}\left(\frac{5}{9}\right) = 29°$$

Putting it all together, we get a net displacement of

$$\vec{d}_{net} = (100 \text{ m}, 29° \text{ north of east})$$

ASSESS We can use our drawing to assess our result. If the two sides of the triangle are 50 m and 90 m, a length of 100 m for the hypotenuse seems about right. The angle is certainly less than 45°, but not too much less, so 29° seems reasonable.

Velocity Vectors

We've seen that a basic quantity describing the motion of an object is its velocity. Velocity is a vector quantity because its specification involves not only how fast an object is moving (its speed) but also the direction in which the object is moving. We thus represent the velocity of an object by a **velocity vector** $\vec{v}$ that points in the direction of the object's motion, and whose magnitude is the object's speed.

FIGURE 1.26a shows the motion diagram of a car accelerating from rest. We've drawn vectors showing the car's displacement between successive positions of the motion diagram. How can we draw the velocity vectors on this diagram? First, note that the direction of the displacement vector is the direction of motion between successive points in the motion diagram. But the velocity of an object also points in the direction of motion, so an object's velocity vector points in the same direction as its displacement vector. Second, we've already noted that the magnitude of the velocity vector—How fast?—is the object's speed. Because higher speeds imply greater displacements in the same time interval, you can see that the length of the velocity vector should be proportional to the length of the displacement vector between successive points on a motion diagram. Consequently, the vectors connecting each dot of a motion diagram to the next, which we previously labeled as displacement vectors, could equally well be identified as velocity vectors. This is shown in FIGURE 1.26b. **From now on, we'll show and label velocity vectors on motion diagrams rather than displacement vectors.**

NOTE ▶ The velocity vectors shown in Figure 1.26b are actually *average* velocity vectors. Because the velocity is steadily increasing, it's a bit less than this average at the start of each time interval, and a bit more at the end. In Chapter 2 we'll refine these ideas as we develop the idea of instantaneous velocity. ◀

FIGURE 1.26 The motion diagram for a car starting from rest.

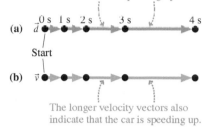

The displacement vectors are lengthening. This means the car is speeding up.

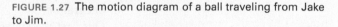

The longer velocity vectors also indicate that the car is speeding up.

EXAMPLE 1.8	Drawing a ball's motion diagram

Jake hits a ball at a 60° angle from the horizontal. It is caught by Jim. Draw a motion diagram of the ball that shows velocity vectors rather than displacement vectors.

PREPARE This example is typical of how many problems in science and engineering are worded. The problem does not give a clear statement of where the motion begins or ends. Are we interested in the motion of the ball only during the time it is in the air between Jake and Jim? What about the motion *as* Jake hits it (ball rapidly speeding up) or *as* Jim catches it (ball rapidly slowing down)? Should we include Jim dropping the ball after he catches it? The point is that *you* will often be called on to make a *reasonable interpretation* of a problem statement. In this problem, the details of hitting and catching the ball are complex. The motion of the ball through the air is easier to describe, and it's a motion you might expect to learn about in a physics class. So our *interpretation* is that the motion diagram should start as the ball leaves Jake's bat (ball already moving) and should end the instant it touches Jim's hand (ball still moving). We will model the ball as a particle.

SOLVE With this interpretation in mind, FIGURE 1.27 shows the motion diagram of the ball. Notice how, in contrast to the car of Figure 1.26, the ball is already moving as the motion diagram movie begins. As before, the velocity vectors are shown by

connecting the dots with arrows. You can see that the velocity vectors get shorter (ball slowing down), get longer (ball speeding up), and change direction. Each $\vec{v}$ is different, so this is *not* constant-velocity motion.

FIGURE 1.27 The motion diagram of a ball traveling from Jake to Jim.

ASSESS We haven't learned enough to make a detailed analysis of the motion of the ball, but it's still worthwhile to do a quick assessment. Does our diagram make sense? Think about the velocity of the ball—we show it moving upward at the start and downward at the end. This does match what happens when you toss a ball back and forth, so our answer seems reasonable.

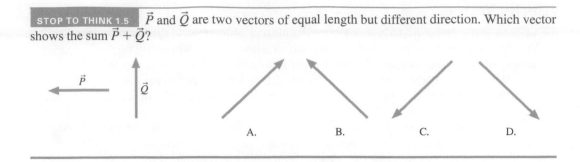

STOP TO THINK 1.5 $\vec{P}$ and $\vec{Q}$ are two vectors of equal length but different direction. Which vector shows the sum $\vec{P} + \vec{Q}$?

A.   B.   C.   D.

1.6 Where Do We Go from Here?

This first chapter has been an introduction to some of the fundamental ideas about motion and some of the basic techniques that you will use in the rest of the course. You have seen some examples of how to make *models* of a physical situation, thereby focusing in on the essential elements of the situation. You have learned some practical ideas, such as how to convert quantities from one kind of units to another. The rest of this book—and the rest of your course—will extend these themes. You will learn how to model many kinds of physical systems, and learn the technical skills needed to set up and solve problems using these models.

In each chapter of this book, you'll learn both new principles and more tools and techniques. We are starting with motion, but, by the end of the book, you'll have learned about more abstract concepts such as magnetic fields and the structure of the nucleus of the atom. As you proceed, you'll find that each new chapter depends on those that preceded it. The principles and the problem-solving strategies you learned in this chapter will still be needed in Chapter 30.

We'll give you some assistance integrating new ideas with the material of previous chapters. When you start a chapter, the **chapter preview** will let you know which topics are especially important to review. And the last element in each chapter will be an **integrated example** that brings together the principles and techniques you have just learned with those you learned previously. The integrated nature of these examples will also be a helpful reminder that the problems of the real world are similarly complex, and solving such problems requires you to do just this kind of integration.

Our first integrated example is reasonably straightforward because there's not much to integrate yet. The examples in future chapters will be much richer.

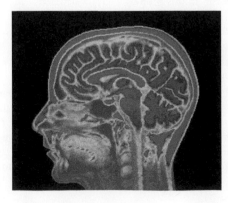

◄ Chapter 28 ends with an integrated example that explores the basic physics of magnetic resonance imaging (MRI), explaining how the interaction of magnetic fields with the nuclei of atoms in the body can be used to create an image of the body's interior.

INTEGRATED EXAMPLE 1.9   **A goose gets its bearings**

Migrating geese determine direction using many different tools: by noting local landmarks, by following rivers and roads, and by using the position of the sun in the sky. When the weather is overcast so that they can't use the sun's position to get their bearings, geese may start their day's flight in the wrong direction. FIGURE 1.28 shows the path of a Canada goose that flew in a straight line for some time before making a corrective right-angle turn. One hour after beginning, the goose made a rest stop on a lake due east of its original position.

FIGURE 1.28 Trajectory of a misdirected goose.

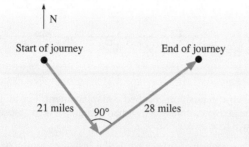

a. How much extra distance did the goose travel due to its initial error in flight direction? That is, how much farther did it fly than if it had simply flown directly to its final position on the lake?
b. What was the flight speed of the goose?
c. A typical flight speed for a migrating goose is 80 km/h. Given this, does your result seem reasonable?

PREPARE Figure 1.28 shows the trajectory of the goose, but it's worthwhile to redraw Figure 1.28 and note the displacement from the start to the end of the journey, the shortest distance the goose could have flown. (The examples in the chapter to this point have used professionally rendered drawings, but these are much more careful and detailed than you are likely to make. FIGURE 1.29 shows a drawing that is more typical of what you might actually do when working problems yourself.) Drawing and labeling the displacement between the starting and ending points in Figure 1.29 show that it is the hypotenuse of a right triangle, so we can use our rules for triangles as we look for a solution.

FIGURE 1.29 A typical student sketch shows the motion and the displacement of the goose.

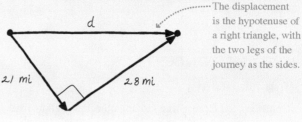

The displacement is the hypotenuse of a right triangle, with the two legs of the journey as the sides.

SOLVE

a. The minimum distance the goose *could* have flown, if it flew straight to the lake, is the hypotenuse of a triangle with sides 21 mi and 28 mi. This straight-line distance is

$$d = \sqrt{(21 \text{ mi})^2 + (28 \text{ mi})^2} = 35 \text{ mi}$$

The actual distance the goose flew is the sum of the distances traveled for the two legs of the journey:

$$\text{distance traveled} = 21 \text{ mi} + 28 \text{ mi} = 49 \text{ mi}$$

The extra distance flown is the difference between the actual distance flown and the straight-line distance—namely, 14 miles.

b. To compute the flight speed, we need to consider the distance that the bird actually flew. The flight speed is the total distance flown divided by the total time of the flight:

$$v = \frac{49 \text{ mi}}{1.0 \text{ h}} = 49 \text{ mi/h}$$

c. To compare our calculated speed with a typical flight speed, we must convert our solution to km/h, rounding off to the correct number of significant digits:

$$49 \frac{\text{mi}}{\text{h}} \times \frac{1.61 \text{ km}}{1.00 \text{ mi}} = 79 \frac{\text{km}}{\text{h}}$$

A calculator will return many more digits, but the original data had only two significant figures, so we report the final result to this accuracy.

ASSESS In this case, an assessment was built into the solution of the problem. The calculated flight speed matches the expected value for a goose, which gives us confidence that our answer is correct. As a further check, our calculated net displacement of 35 mi seems about right for the hypotenuse of the triangle in Figure 1.29.

SUMMARY

The goals of Chapter 1 have been to introduce the fundamental concepts of motion and to review the related basic mathematical principles.

IMPORTANT CONCEPTS

Motion Diagrams

The **particle model** represents a moving object as if all its mass were concentrated at a single point. Using this model, we can represent motion with a **motion diagram,** where dots indicate the object's positions at successive times. In a motion diagram, the time interval between successive dots is always the same.

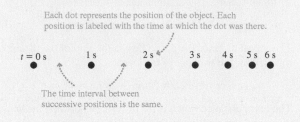

Each dot represents the position of the object. Each position is labeled with the time at which the dot was there.

$t = 0\,s$ 1 s   2 s   3 s   4 s   5 s   6 s

The time interval between successive positions is the same.

Scalars and Vectors

Scalar quantities have only a magnitude and can be represented by a single number. Temperature, time, and mass are scalars.

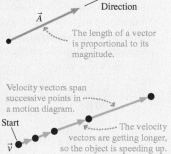

Direction

$\vec{A}$

The length of a vector is proportional to its magnitude.

A **vector** is a quantity described by both a magnitude and a direction. Velocity and displacement are vectors.

Velocity vectors can be drawn on a motion diagram by connecting successive points with a vector.

Velocity vectors span successive points in a motion diagram.

Start

$\vec{v}$

The velocity vectors are getting longer, so the object is speeding up.

Describing Motion

Position locates an object with respect to a chosen coordinate system. It is described by a **coordinate.**

The *coordinate* is the variable used to describe the position.

x (mi)
$-6\ -5\ -4\ -3\ -2\ -1\quad 0\quad 1\quad 2\quad 3\quad 4\quad 5$

This cow is at $x = -5$ miles.   This car is at $x = +4$ miles.

A change in position is called a **displacement.** For motion along a line, a displacement is a signed quantity. The displacement from x_i to x_f is $\Delta x = x_f - x_i$.

Time is measured from a particular instant to which we assign $t = 0$. A **time interval** is the elapsed time between two specific instants t_i and t_f. It is given by $\Delta t = t_f - t_i$.

Velocity is the ratio of the displacement of an object to the time interval during which this displacement occurs:

$$v = \frac{\Delta x}{\Delta t}$$

Units

Every measurement of a quantity must include a **unit**.

The standard system of units used in science is the **SI system**. Common SI units include:

- Length: meters (m)
- Time: seconds (s)
- Mass: kilograms (kg)

APPLICATIONS

Working with Numbers

In **scientific notation,** a number is expressed as a decimal number between 1 and 10 multiplied by a power of ten. In scientific notation, the diameter of the earth is 1.27×10^7 m.

A **prefix** can be used before a unit to indicate a multiple of 10 or 1/10. Thus we can write the diameter of the earth as 12,700 km, where the k in km denotes 1000.

We can perform a **unit conversion** to convert the diameter of the earth to a different unit, such as miles. We do so by multiplying by a conversion factor equal to 1, such as 1 = 1 mi/1.61 km.

Significant figures are reliably known digits. The number of significant figures for:

- **Multiplication, division, and powers** is set by the value with the fewest significant figures.
- **Addition and subtraction** is set by the value with the smallest number of decimal places.

An **order-of-magnitude estimate** is an estimate that has an accuracy of about one significant figure. Such estimates are usually made using rough numbers from everyday experience.

For homework assigned on MasteringPhysics, go to www.masteringphysics.com

Problem difficulty is labeled as | (straightforward) to ||||| (challenging).

Problems labeled BIO are of biological or medical interest.

QUESTIONS

Conceptual Questions

1. a. Write a paragraph describing the *particle model*. What is it, and why is it important?
   b. Give two examples of situations, different from those described in the text, for which the particle model is appropriate.
   c. Give an example of a situation, different from those described in the text, for which it would be inappropriate.

2. A softball player slides into second base. Use the particle model to draw a motion diagram of the player from the time he begins to slide until he reaches the base. Number the dots in order, starting with zero.

3. A car travels to the left at a steady speed for a few seconds, then brakes for a stop sign. Use the particle model to draw a motion diagram of the car for the entire motion described here. Number the dots in order, starting with zero.

4. A ball is dropped from the roof of a tall building and students in a physics class are asked to sketch a motion diagram for this situation. A student submits the diagram shown in Figure Q1.4. Is the diagram correct? Explain.

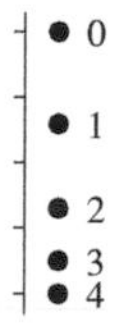

   • 0
   • 1
   • 2
   • 3
   • 4

   FIGURE Q1.4

5. Write a sentence or two describing the difference between position and displacement. Give one example of each.

6. Give an example of a trip you might take in your car for which the distance traveled as measured on your car's odometer is not equal to the displacement between your initial and final positions.

7. Write a sentence or two describing the difference between speed and velocity. Give one example of each.

8. The motion of a skateboard along a horizontal axis is observed for 5 s. The initial position of the skateboard is negative with respect to a chosen origin, and its velocity throughout the 5 s is also negative. At the end of the observation time, is the skateboard closer to or farther from the origin than initially? Explain.

9. Can the velocity of an object be positive during a time interval in which its position is always negative? Can its velocity be positive during a time interval in which its displacement is negative?

10. Two friends watch a jogger complete a 400 m lap around the track in 100 s. One of the friends states, "The jogger's velocity was 4 m/s during this lap." The second friend objects, saying, "No, the jogger's speed was 4 m/s." Who is correct? Justify your answer.

11. A softball player hits the ball and starts running toward first base. Draw a motion diagram, using the particle model, showing her velocity vectors during the first few seconds of her run.

12. A child is sledding on a smooth, level patch of snow. She encounters a rocky patch and slows to a stop. Draw a motion diagram, using the particle model, showing her velocity vectors.

13. A skydiver jumps out of an airplane. Her speed steadily increases until she deploys her parachute, at which point her speed quickly decreases. She subsequently falls to earth at a constant rate, stopping when she lands on the ground. Draw a motion diagram, using the particle model, that shows her position at successive times and includes velocity vectors.

14. Your roommate drops a tennis ball from a third-story balcony. It hits the sidewalk and bounces as high as the second story. Draw a motion diagram, using the particle model, showing the ball's velocity vectors from the time it is released until it reaches the maximum height on its bounce.

15. A car is driving north at a steady speed. It makes a gradual 90° left turn without losing speed, then continues driving to the west. Draw a motion diagram, using the particle model, showing the car's velocity vectors as seen from a helicopter hovering over the highway.

16. A toy car rolls down a ramp, then across a smooth, horizontal floor. Draw a motion diagram, using the particle model, showing the car's velocity vectors.

17. Estimate the average speed with which you go from home to campus (or another trip you commonly make) via whatever mode of transportation you use most commonly. Give your answer in both mph and m/s. Describe how you arrived at this estimate.

18. Estimate the number of times you sneezed during the past year. Describe how you arrived at this estimate.

19. Density is the ratio of an object's mass to its volume. Would you expect density to be a vector or a scalar quantity? Explain.

Multiple-Choice Questions

20. | A student walks 1.0 mi west and then 1.0 mi north. Afterward, how far is she from her starting point?
    A. 1.0 mi   B. 1.4 mi
    C. 1.6 mi   D. 2.0 mi

21. | Which of the following motions is described by the motion diagram of Figure Q1.21?
    A. An ice skater gliding across the ice.
    B. An airplane braking to a stop after landing.
    C. A car pulling away from a stop sign.
    D. A pool ball bouncing off a cushion and reversing direction.

   FIGURE Q1.21
   0 1   2   3   4   5
   •• •   •   •   •   •

22. | A bird flies 3.0 km due west and then 2.0 km due north. What is the magnitude of the bird's displacement?
    A. 2.0 km   B. 3.0 km
    C. 3.6 km   D. 5.0 km

23. ‖ A bird flies 3.0 km due west and then 2.0 km due north. Another bird flies 2.0 km due west and 3.0 km due north. What is the angle between the net displacement vectors for the two birds?
    A. 23°   B. 34°   C. 56°   D. 90°
24. ‖ A woman walks briskly at 2.00 m/s. How much time will it take her to walk one mile?
    A. 8.30 min   B. 13.4 min   C. 21.7 min   D. 30.0 min
25. ‖ Compute 3.24 m + 0.532 m to the correct number of significant figures.
    A. 3.7 m   B. 3.77 m   C. 3.772 m   D. 3.7720 m
26. ‖ A rectangle has length 3.24 m and height 0.532 m. To the correct number of significant figures, what is its area?
    A. 1.72 m^2 B. 1.723 m^2
    C. 1.7236 m^2 D. 1.72368 m^2

27. ‖ The earth formed 4.57×10^9 years ago. What is this time in seconds?
    A. 1.67×10^{12} s   B. 4.01×10^{13} s
    C. 2.40×10^{15} s   D. 1.44×10^{17} s
28. ‖ An object's average density ρ is defined as the ratio of its mass to its volume: $\rho = M/V$. The earth's mass is 5.94×10^{24} kg, and its volume is 1.08×10^{12} km^3. What is the earth's average density?
    A. 5.50×10^3 kg/m^3 B. 5.50×10^6 kg/m^3
    C. 5.50×10^9 kg/m^3 D. 5.50×10^{12} kg/m^3

PROBLEMS

Section 1.1 Motion: A First Look

1. ‖ You've made a video of a car as it skids to a halt to avoid hitting an object in the road. Use the images from the video to draw a motion diagram of the car from the time the skid begins until the car is stopped.
2. ‖ A man rides a bike along a straight road for 5 min, then has a flat tire. He stops for 5 min to repair the flat, but then realizes he cannot fix it. He continues his journey by walking the rest of the way, which takes him another 10 min. Use the particle model to draw a motion diagram of the man for the entire motion described here. Number the dots in order, starting with zero.
3. ‖ A jogger running east at a steady pace suddenly develops a cramp. He is lucky: A westbound bus is sitting at a bus stop just ahead. He gets on the bus and enjoys a quick ride home. Use the particle model to draw a motion diagram of the jogger for the entire motion described here. Number the dots in order, starting with zero.

Section 1.2 Position and Time: Putting Numbers on Nature

4. ‖ Figure P1.4 shows Sue between her home and the cinema. What is Sue's position x if
    a. Her home is the origin?
    b. The cinema is the origin?

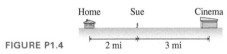

FIGURE P1.4   2 mi   3 mi

5. ‖ Keira starts at position $x = 23$ m along a coordinate axis. She then undergoes a displacement of -45 m. What is her final position?
6. ‖ A car travels along a straight east-west road. A coordinate system is established on the road, with x increasing to the east. The car ends up 14 mi west of the intersection with Mulberry Road. If its displacement was -23 mi, how far from and on which side of Mulberry Road did it start?
7. ‖ Foraging bees often move in straight lines away from and toward their hives. Suppose a bee starts at its hive and flies 500 m due east, then flies 400 m west, then 700 m east. How far is the bee from the hive?

Section 1.3 Velocity

8. ‖ A security guard walks 110 m in one trip around the perimeter of the building. It takes him 240 s to make this trip. What is his speed?
9. ‖ List the following items in order of decreasing speed, from greatest to least: (i) A wind-up toy car that moves 0.15 m in 2.5 s. (ii) A soccer ball that rolls 2.3 m in 0.55 s. (iii) A bicycle that travels 0.60 m in 0.075 s. (iv) A cat that runs 8.0 m in 2.0 s.
10. ‖ Figure P1.10 shows the motion diagram for a horse galloping in one direction along a straight path. Not every dot is labeled, but the dots are at equally spaced instants of time. What is the horse's velocity
    a. During the first ten seconds of its gallop?
    b. During the interval from 30 s to 40 s?
    c. During the interval from 50 s to 70 s?

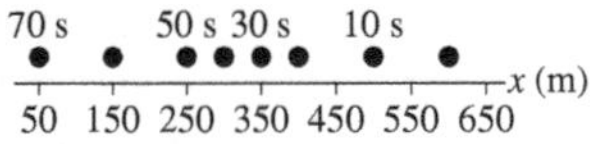

70 s   50 s 30 s   10 s
● ● ●●●● ● ● ●—x (m)
50 150 250 350 450 550 650

FIGURE P1.10

11. ‖ It takes Harry 35 s to walk from $x = -12$ m to $x = -47$ m. What is his velocity?
12. ‖ A dog trots from $x = -12$ m to $x = 3$ m in 10 s. What is its velocity?
13. ‖ A ball rolling along a straight line with velocity 0.35 m/s goes from $x = 2.1$ m to $x = 7.3$ m. How much time does this take?

Section 1.4 A Sense of Scale: Significant Figures, Scientific Notation, and Units

14. ‖ Convert the following to SI units:
    a. 9.12 μs   b. 3.42 km
    c. 44 cm/ms   d. 80 km/hour
15. ‖ Convert the following to SI units:
    a. 8.0 in   b. 66 ft/s   c. 60 mph
16. ‖ Convert the following to SI units:
    a. 1.0 hour   b. 1.0 day   c. 1.0 year
17. ‖ List the following three speeds in order, from smallest to largest: 1 mm per μs, 1 km per ks, 1 cm per ms.

18. | How many significant figures does each of the following numbers have?
    a. 6.21   b. 62.1   c. 0.620   d. 0.062
19. | How many significant figures does each of the following numbers have?
    a. 0.621   b. 0.006200
    c. 1.0621   d. 6.21×10^3
20. | Compute the following numbers to 3 significant figures.
    a. 33.3×25.4 b. $33.3 - 25.4$
    c. $\sqrt{33.3}$ d. $333.3 \div 25.4$
21. |||| The Empire State Building has a height of 1250 ft. Express this height in meters, giving your result in scientific notation with three significant figures.
22. | Estimate (don't measure!) the length of a typical car. Give your answer in both feet and meters. Briefly describe how you arrived at this estimate.
23. ||| Blades of grass grow from the bottom, so, as growth occurs,
    BIO the top of the blade moves upward. During the summer, when your lawn is growing quickly, estimate this speed in m/s. Explain how you made this estimate, and express your result in scientific notation.
24. || Estimate the average speed with which the hair on your head
    BIO grows. Give your answer in both m/s and μm/h. Briefly describe how you arrived at this estimate.
25. || Estimate the average speed at which your fingernails grow, in
    BIO both m/s and μm/h. Briefly describe how you arrived at this estimate.

Section 1.5 Vectors and Motion: A First Look

26. | Carol and Robin share a house. To get to work, Carol walks north 2.0 km while Robin drives west 7.5 km. How far apart are their workplaces?
27. | Joe and Max shake hands and say goodbye. Joe walks east 0.55 km to a coffee shop, and Max flags a cab and rides north 3.25 km to a bookstore. How far apart are their destinations?
28. || A city has streets laid out in a square grid, with each block 135 m long. If you drive north for three blocks, then west for two blocks, how far are you from your starting point?
29. || A butterfly flies from the top of a tree in the center of a garden to rest on top of a red flower at the garden's edge. The tree is 8.0 m taller than the flower, and the garden is 12 m wide. Determine the magnitude of the butterfly's displacement.
30. ||| A garden has a circular path of radius 50 m. John starts at the easternmost point on this path, then walks counterclockwise around the path until he is at its southernmost point. What is John's displacement? Use the (magnitude, direction) notation for your answer.
31. || Migrating geese tend to travel in straight-line paths at approx-
    BIO imately constant speed. A goose flies 32 km south, then turns to fly 20 km west. How far is the goose from its original position?
32. |||| A ball on a porch rolls 60 cm to the porch's edge, drops 40 cm, continues rolling on the grass, and eventually stops 80 cm from the porch's edge. What is the magnitude of the ball's net displacement, in centimeters?
33. || A kicker punts a football from the very center of the field to the sideline 43 yards downfield. What is the net displacement of the ball? (A football field is 53 yards wide.)

General Problems

Problems 34 through 40 are motion problems similar to those you will learn to solve in Chapter 2. For now, simply *interpret* the problem by drawing a motion diagram showing the object's position and its velocity vectors. **Do *not* solve these problems** or do any mathematics.

34. || In a typical greyhound race, a dog accelerates to a speed of
    BIO 20 m/s over a distance of 30 m. It then maintains this speed. What would be a greyhound's time in the 100 m dash?
35. || Billy drops a watermelon from the top of a three-story building, 10 m above the sidewalk. How fast is the watermelon going when it hits?
36. || Sam is recklessly driving 60 mph in a 30 mph speed zone when he suddenly sees the police. He steps on the brakes and slows to 30 mph in three seconds, looking nonchalant as he passes the officer. How far does he travel while braking?
37. || A speed skater moving across frictionless ice at 8.0 m/s hits a 5.0-m-wide patch of rough ice. She slows steadily, then continues on at 6.0 m/s. What is her acceleration on the rough ice?
38. || The giant eland, an African antelope, is an exceptional
    BIO jumper, able to leap 1.5 m off the ground. To jump this high, with what speed must the eland leave the ground?
39. || A ball rolls along a smooth horizontal floor at 10 m/s, then starts up a 20° ramp. How high does it go before rolling back down?
40. || A motorist is traveling at 20 m/s. He is 60 m from a stop light when he sees it turn yellow. His reaction time, before stepping on the brake, is 0.50 s. What steady deceleration while braking will bring him to a stop right at the light?

Problems 41 through 46 show a motion diagram. For each of these problems, write a one or two sentence "story" about a *real object* that has this motion diagram. Your stories should talk about people or objects by name and say what they are doing. Problems 34 through 40 are examples of motion short stories.

41. |

FIGURE P1.41

42. |

FIGURE P1.42

43. |

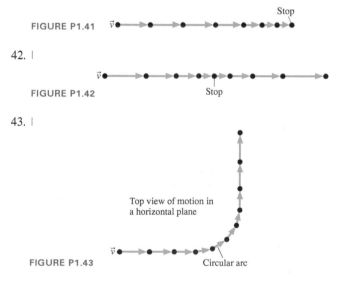

Top view of motion in a horizontal plane

FIGURE P1.43   Circular arc

44.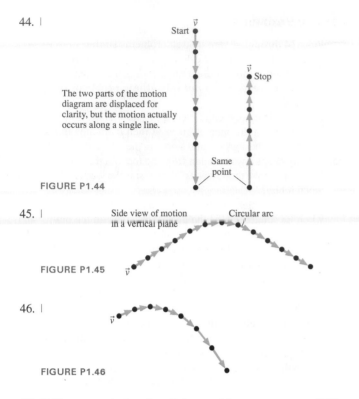

FIGURE P1.44

45.

FIGURE P1.45

46.

FIGURE P1.46

47. ||||| How many inches does light travel in one nanosecond? The speed of light is 3.0×10^8 m/s.

48. | Joseph watches the roadside mile markers during a long car trip on an interstate highway. He notices that at 10:45 A.M. they are passing a marker labeled 101, and at 11:00 A.M. the car reaches marker 119. What is the car's speed, in mph?

49. || Alberta is going to have dinner at her grandmother's house, but she is running a bit behind schedule. As she gets onto the highway, she knows that she must exit the highway within 45 min if she is not going to arrive late. Her exit is 32 mi away. What is the slowest speed at which she could drive and still arrive in time? Express your answer in miles per hour.

50. || The end of Hubbard Glacier in Alaska advances by an average of 105 feet per year. What is the speed of advance of the glacier in m/s?

51. | The earth completes a circular orbit around the sun in one year. The orbit has a radius of 93,000,000 miles. What is the speed of the earth around the sun in m/s? Report your result using scientific notation.

52. ||| Shannon decides to check the accuracy of her speedometer. She adjusts her speed to read exactly 70 mph on her speedometer and holds this steady, measuring the time between successive mile markers separated by exactly 1.00 mile. If she measures a time of 54 s, is her speedometer accurate? If not, is the speed it shows too high or too low?

53. || Motor neurons in mammals transmit signals from the brain to
BIO skeletal muscles at approximately 25 m/s. Estimate how much time in ms (10^{-3} s) it will take for a signal to get from your brain to your hand.

54. ||| Satellite data taken several times per hour on a particular
BIO albatross showed travel of 1200 km over a time of 1.4 days.
   a. Given these data, what was the bird's average speed in mph?
   b. Data on the bird's position were recorded only intermittently. Explain how this means that the bird's actual average speed was higher than what you calculated in part a.

55. | Your brain communicates with your body using *nerve*
BIO *impulses,* electrical signals propagated along axons. Axons come in two varieties: insulated axons with a sheath made of myelin, and uninsulated axons with no such sheath. Myelinated (sheathed) axons conduct nerve impulses much faster than unmyelinated (unsheathed) axons. The impulse speed depends on the diameter of the axons and the sheath, but a typical myelinated axon transmits nerve impulses at a speed of about 25 m/s, much faster than the typical 2.0 m/s for an unmyelinated axon. Figure P1.55 shows three equal-length nerve fibers consisting of eight axons in a row. Nerve impulses enter at the left side simultaneously and travel to the right.
   a. Draw motion diagrams for the nerve impulses traveling along fibers A, B, and C.
   b. Which nerve impulse arrives at the right side first?
   c. Which will be last?

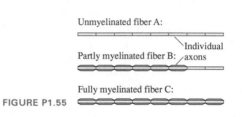

FIGURE P1.55

56. || The bacterium *Escherichia coli* (or *E. coli*) is a single-celled
BIO organism that lives in the gut of healthy humans and animals. Its body shape can be modeled as a 2-μm-long cylinder with a 1 μm diameter, and it has a mass of 1×10^{-12} g. Its chromosome consists of a single double-stranded chain of DNA 700 times longer than its body length. The bacterium moves at a constant speed of 20 μm/s, though not always in the same direction. Answer the following questions about *E. coli* using SI units (unless specifically requested otherwise) and correct significant figures.
   a. What is its length?
   b. Diameter?
   c. Mass?
   d. What is the length of its DNA, in millimeters?
   e. If the organism were to move along a straight path, how many meters would it travel in one day?

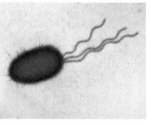

57. || The bacterium *Escherichia*
BIO *coli* (or *E. coli*) is a single-celled organism that lives in the gut of healthy humans and animals. When grown in a uniform medium rich in salts and amino acids, it swims along zig-zag paths at a constant speed. Figure P1.57 shows the positions of an *E. coli* as it moves from point A to point

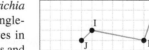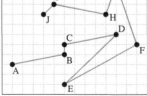

FIGURE P1.57

J. Each segment of the motion can be identified by two letters, such as segment BC. During which segments, if any, does the bacterium have the same
   a. Displacement?   b. Speed?   c. Velocity?

58. ‖ In 2003, the population of the United States was 291 million people. The per-capita income was $31,459. What was the total income of everyone in the United States? Express your answer in scientific notation, with the correct number of significant figures.

59. ‖ The sun is 30° above the horizon. It makes a 52-m-long shadow of a tall tree. How high is the tree?

60. ‖ A large passenger aircraft accelerates down the runway for a distance of 3000 m before leaving the ground. It then climbs at a steady 3.0° angle. After the plane has traveled 3000 m along this new trajectory, (a) how high is it, and (b) how far horizontally is it, from its initial position?

61. ‖ Starting from its nest, an eagle flies at constant speed for 3.0 min due east, then 4.0 min due north. From there the eagle flies directly to its nest at the same speed. How long is the eagle in the air?

62. ‖ John walks 1.00 km north, then turns right and walks 1.00 km east. His speed is 1.50 m/s during the entire stroll.
    a. What is the magnitude of his displacement, from beginning to end?
    b. If Jane starts at the same time and place as John, but walks in a straight line to the endpoint of John's stroll, at what speed should she walk to arrive at the endpoint just when John does?

Passage Problems

Growth Speed

The images of trees in Figure P1.63 come from a catalog advertising fast-growing trees. If we mark the position of the top of the tree in the successive years, as shown in the graph in the figure, we obtain a motion diagram much like ones we have seen for other kinds of motion. The motion isn't steady, of course. In some months the tree grows rapidly; in other months, quite slowly. We can see, though, that the average speed of growth is fairly constant for the first few years.

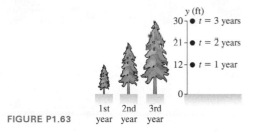

FIGURE P1.63

63. | What is the tree's speed of growth, in feet per year, from $t = 1$ yr to $t = 3$ yr?
    A. 12 ft/yr   B. 9 ft/yr   C. 6 ft/yr   D. 3 ft/yr

64. | What is this speed in m/s?
    A. 9×10^{-8} m/s   B. 3×10^{-9} m/s
    C. 5×10^{-6} m/s   D. 2×10^{-6} m/s

65. | At the end of year 3, a rope is tied to the very top of the tree to steady it. This rope is staked into the ground 15 feet away from the tree. What angle does the rope make with the ground?
    A. 63°   B. 60°   C. 30°   D. 27°

STOP TO THINK ANSWERS

Stop to Think 1.1: B. The images of B are farther apart, so B travels a greater distance than does A during the same intervals of time.

Stop to Think 1.2: A. Dropped ball. **B.** Dust particle. **C.** Descending rocket.

Stop to Think 1.3: C. Depending on her initial positive position and how far she moves in the negative direction, she could end up on either side of the origin.

Stop to Think 1.4: D > C > B = A.

Stop to Think 1.5: B. The vector sum is found by placing the tail of one vector at the head of the other.

2 Motion in One Dimension

A horse can run at 35 mph, much faster than a human. And yet, surprisingly, a man can win a race against a horse if the length of the course is right. When, and how, can a man outrun a horse?

LOOKING AHEAD ▶

The goal of Chapter 2 is to describe and analyze linear motion.

Describing Motion

We began discussing motion in Chapter 1. In Chapter 2, you'll learn more ways to represent motion. You will also learn general strategies for solving problems.

From time t_1 to t_2, the car continues at a constant speed. From time t_2 to t_3, the car is braking, and the velocity decreases.

Motion diagrams and graphs are key parts of the problem-solving strategies that we will develop in this chapter.

> **Looking Back** ◀◀
> 1.5 Velocity vectors and motion diagrams

Analyzing Motion

Once you know how to describe motion, you'll be ready to do some analysis.

The main engines of a Saturn V fire for $2\frac{1}{2}$ minutes. How high will the rocket be and how fast will it be going when the engines shut off?

Position

Position is defined in terms of a coordinate system and units of our choosing.

A game of football is really about motion in one dimension with a well-defined coordinate system.

> **Looking Back** ◀◀
> 1.2 Position and displacement

Constant Velocity

One important case we will consider is motion in a straight line at a constant velocity— uniform motion.

Each minute, the ship moves the same distance in the same direction.

Velocity

Velocity is the rate of change of position.

A small change in position during an interval of time means a small velocity; a larger change means a larger velocity.

> **Looking Back** ◀◀
> 1.3 Velocity

Constant Acceleration

Another special case is motion with constant acceleration.

We think of acceleration as "speeding up," but braking to a stop involves a change in velocity—an acceleration—as well.

Acceleration

Acceleration is the rate of change of velocity.

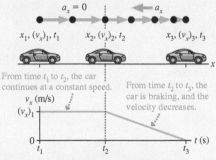

A cheetah is capable of a rapid change in velocity—that is a large acceleration. We'll see how to solve problems of changing velocity by using the concept of acceleration.

Free Fall

Free fall is a special case of constant acceleration.

Once the coin leaves your hand, it's in free fall, and its motion is similar to that of a falling ball or a jumping gazelle.

2.1 Describing Motion

The modern name for the mathematical description of motion, without regard to causes, is **kinematics.** The term comes from the Greek word *kinema,* meaning "movement." You know this word through its English variation *cinema*—motion pictures! This chapter will focus on the kinematics of motion in one dimension, motion along a straight line.

Representing Position

As we saw in Chapter 1, kinematic variables such as position and velocity are measured with respect to a coordinate system, an axis that *you* impose on a system. We will use an *x*-axis to analyze both horizontal motion and motion on a ramp; a *y*-axis will be used for vertical motion. We will adopt the convention that the positive end of an *x*-axis is to the right and the positive end of a *y*-axis is up. This convention is illustrated in FIGURE 2.1.

Now, let's look at a practical problem of the sort that we first saw in Chapter 1. FIGURE 2.2 is a motion diagram, made at 1 frame per minute, of a straightforward situation: A student walking to school. She is moving horizontally, so we use the variable *x* to describe her motion. We have set the origin of the coordinate system, $x = 0$, at her starting position, and we measure her position in meters. We have included velocity vectors connecting successive positions on the motion diagram, as we saw we could do in Chapter 1. The motion diagram shows that she leaves home at a time we choose to call $t = 0$ min, and then makes steady progress for a while. Beginning at $t = 3$ min there is a period in which the distance traveled during each time interval becomes shorter—perhaps she slowed down to speak with a friend. Then, at $t = 6$ min, the distances traveled within each interval are longer—perhaps, realizing she is running late, she begins walking more quickly.

FIGURE 2.1 Sign conventions for position.

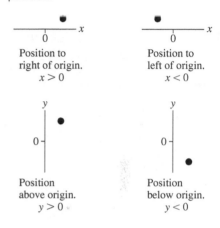

Position to right of origin. $x > 0$

Position to left of origin. $x < 0$

Position above origin. $y > 0$

Position below origin. $y < 0$

FIGURE 2.2 The motion diagram of a student walking to school and a coordinate axis for making measurements.

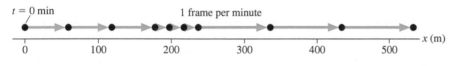

$t = 0$ min   1 frame per minute

Every dot in the motion diagram of Figure 2.2 represents the student's position at a particular time. For example, the student is at position $x = 120$ m at $t = 2$ min. Table 2.1 lists her position for every point in the motion diagram.

The motion diagram of Figure 2.2 is one way to represent the student's motion. Presenting the data as in Table 2.1 is a second way to represent this motion. A third way to represent the motion is to make a graph. FIGURE 2.3 is a graph of the positions of the student at different times; we say it is a graph of *x* versus *t* for the student. We have merely taken the data from the table and plotted these particular points on the graph.

NOTE ▶ A graph of "*a* versus *b*" means that *a* is graphed on the vertical axis and *b* on the horizontal axis. ◀

We can flesh out the graph of Figure 2.3, though. Common sense tells us that the student was *somewhere specific* at all times: There was never a time when she failed to have a well-defined position, nor could she occupy two positions at one time. (As reasonable as this belief appears to be, we'll see that it's not entirely accurate when we get to quantum physics!) We also can assume that, from the start to the end of her motion, the student moved *continuously* through all intervening points of space, so

TABLE 2.1 Measured positions of a student walking to school

Time t (min)	Position x (m)	Time t (min)	Position x (m)
0	0	5	220
1	60	6	240
2	120	7	340
3	180	8	440
4	200	9	540

FIGURE 2.3 A graph of the student's motion.

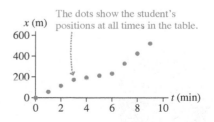

The dots show the student's positions at all times in the table.

FIGURE 2.4 Extending the graph of Figure 2.3 to a position-versus-time graph.

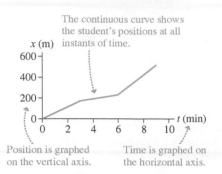

FIGURE 2.4 Extending the graph of Figure 2.3 to a position-versus-time graph.

The continuous curve shows the student's positions at all instants of time.

Position is graphed on the vertical axis.

Time is graphed on the horizontal axis.

we can represent her motion as a continuous curve that passes through the measured points, as shown in FIGURE 2.4. Such a continuous curve that shows an object's position as a function of time is called a **position-versus-time graph** or, sometimes, just a *position graph*.

NOTE ▶ A graph is *not* a "picture" of the motion. The student is walking along a straight line, but the graph itself is not a straight line. Further, we've graphed her position on the vertical axis even though her motion is horizontal. A graph is an *abstract representation* of motion. We will place significant emphasis on the process of interpreting graphs, and many of the exercises and problems will give you a chance to practice these skills. ◀

CONCEPTUAL EXAMPLE 2.1   Interpreting a car's position-versus-time graph

The graph in FIGURE 2.5 represents the motion of a car along a straight road. Describe (in words) the motion of the car.

FIGURE 2.5 Position-versus-time graph for the car.

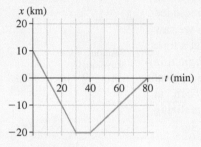

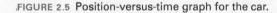

FIGURE 2.6 Looking at the position-versus-time graph in detail.

1. At $t = 0$ min, the car is 10 km to the right of the origin.

2. The value of x decreases for 30 min, indicating that the car is moving to the left.

5. The car reaches the origin at $t = 80$ min.

3. The car stops for 10 min at a position 20 km to the left of the origin.

4. The car starts moving back to the right at $t = 40$ min.

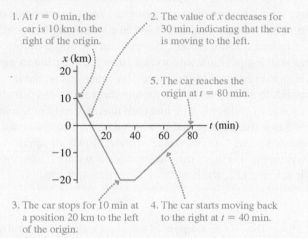

REASON The vertical axis in Figure 2.5 is labeled "x (km)"; position is measured in kilometers. Our convention for motion along the x-axis given in Figure 2.1 tells us that x increases as the car moves to the right and x decreases as the car moves to the left. The graph thus shows that the car travels to the left for 30 minutes, stops for 10 minutes, then travels to the right for 40 minutes. It ends up 10 km to the left of where it began. FIGURE 2.6 gives a full explanation of the reasoning.

ASSESS The car travels to the left for 30 minutes and to the right for 40 minutes. Nonetheless, it ends up to the left of where it started. This means that the car was moving faster when it was moving to the left than when it was moving to the right. We can deduce this fact from the graph as well, as we will see in the next section.

Representing Velocity

FIGURE 2.7 Sign conventions for velocity.

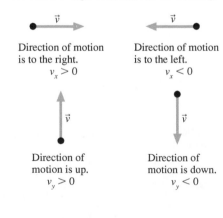

Direction of motion is to the right.
$v_x > 0$

Direction of motion is to the left.
$v_x < 0$

Direction of motion is up.
$v_y > 0$

Direction of motion is down.
$v_y < 0$

Velocity is a vector; it has both a magnitude and a direction. When we draw a velocity vector on a diagram, we use an arrow labeled with the symbol $\vec{v}$ to represent the magnitude and the direction. For motion in one dimension, vectors are restricted to point only "forward" or "backward" for horizontal motion (or "up" or "down" for vertical motion). This restriction lets us simplify our notation for vectors in one dimension. When we solve problems for motion along an x-axis, we will represent velocity with the symbol v_x. v_x will be positive or negative, corresponding to motion to the right or the left, as shown in FIGURE 2.7. For motion along a y-axis, we will use the symbol v_y to represent the velocity; the sign conventions are also illustrated in Figure 2.7. We will use the symbol v, with no subscript, to represent the speed of an object. **Speed is the *magnitude* of the velocity vector** and is always positive.

For motion along a line, the definition of velocity from Chapter 1 can be written as

$$v_x = \frac{\Delta x}{\Delta t} \tag{2.1}$$

This agrees with the sign conventions in Figure 2.7. If Δx is positive, x is increasing, the object is moving to the right, and Equation 2.1 gives a positive value for velocity. If Δx is negative, x is decreasing, the object is moving to the left, and Equation 2.1 gives a negative value for velocity.

Equation 2.1 is the first of many kinematic equations we'll see in this chapter. We'll often specify equations in terms of the coordinate x, but if the motion is vertical, in which case we use the coordinate y, the equations can be easily adapted. For example, Equation 2.1 for motion along a vertical axis becomes

$$v_y = \frac{\Delta y}{\Delta t} \tag{2.2}$$

From Position to Velocity

Let's take another look at the motion diagram of the student walking to school. As we see in FIGURE 2.8, where we have repeated the motion diagram of Figure 2.2, her motion has three clearly defined phases. In each phase her speed is constant (because the velocity vectors have the same length) but the speed varies from phase to phase.

FIGURE 2.8 Revisiting the motion diagram of the student walking to school.

Her motion has three different phases; similarly, the position-versus-time graph redrawn in FIGURE 2.9a has three clearly defined segments with three different slopes. Looking at the different segments of the graph, we can see that there's a relationship between her speed and the slope of the graph: **A faster speed corresponds to a steeper slope.**

FIGURE 2.9 Revisiting the graph of the motion of the student walking to school.

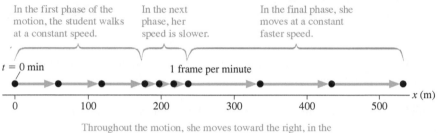

The correspondence is actually deeper than this. Let's look at the slope of the third segment of the position-versus-time graph, as shown in FIGURE 2.9b. The slope of a graph is defined as the ratio of the "rise," the vertical change, to the "run," the horizontal change. For the segment of the graph shown, the slope is:

$$\text{slope of graph} = \frac{\text{rise}}{\text{run}} = \frac{\Delta x}{\Delta t}$$

This ratio has a physical meaning—it's the velocity, exactly as we defined it in Equation 2.1. We've shown this correspondence for one particular graph, but it is a

Time lines BIO This section of the trunk of a pine tree shows the light bands of spring growth and the dark bands of summer and fall growth in successive years. If you focus on the spacing of successive dark bands, you can think of this picture as a motion diagram for the tree, representing its growth in diameter. The years of rapid growth (large distance between dark bands) during wet years and slow growth (small distance between dark bands) during years of drought are readily apparent.

general principle: **The slope of an object's position-versus-time graph is the object's velocity at that point in the motion.** This principle also holds for negative slopes, which correspond to negative velocities. We can associate the slope of a position-versus-time graph, a *geometrical* quantity, with velocity, a *physical* quantity. This is an important aspect of interpreting position-versus-time graphs, as outlined in Tactics Box 2.1.

TACTICS BOX 2.1 Interpreting position-versus-time graphs

Information about motion can be obtained from position-versus-time graphs as follows:

❶ Determine an object's *position* at time t by reading the graph at that instant of time.

❷ Determine the object's *velocity* at time t by finding the slope of the position graph at that point. Steeper slopes correspond to faster speeds.

❸ Determine the *direction of motion* by noting the sign of the slope. Positive slopes correspond to positive velocities and, hence, to motion to the right (or up). Negative slopes correspond to negative velocities and, hence, to motion to the left (or down).

Exercises 2,3 🖉

NOTE ▶ The slope is a ratio of intervals, $\Delta x/\Delta t$, not a ratio of coordinates; that is, the slope is *not* simply x/t. ◀

NOTE ▶ We are distinguishing between the actual slope and the *physically meaningful* slope. If you were to use a ruler to measure the rise and the run of the graph, you could compute the actual slope of the line as drawn on the page. That is not the slope we are referring to when we equate the velocity with the slope of the line. Instead, we find the *physically meaningful* slope by measuring the rise and run using the scales along the axes. The "rise" Δx is some number of meters; the "run" Δt is some number of seconds. The physically meaningful rise and run include units, and the ratio of these units gives the units of the slope. ◀

We can now use the approach of Tactics Box 2.1 to analyze the student's position-versus-time graph that we saw in Figure 2.4. We can determine her velocity during the first phase of her motion by measuring the slope of the line:

FIGURE 2.10 Deducing the velocity-versus-time graph from the position-versus-time graph.

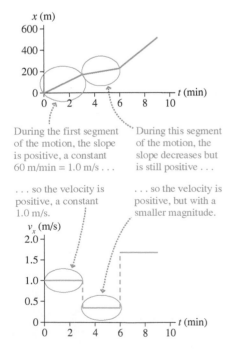

During the first segment of the motion, the slope is positive, a constant 60 m/min = 1.0 m/s . . .

During this segment of the motion, the slope decreases but is still positive . . .

. . . so the velocity is positive, a constant 1.0 m/s.

. . . so the velocity is positive, but with a smaller magnitude.

$$v_x = \text{slope} = \frac{\Delta x}{\Delta t} = \frac{180 \text{ m}}{3 \text{ min}} = 60 \frac{\text{m}}{\text{min}} \times \frac{1 \text{ min}}{60 \text{ s}} = 1.0 \text{ m/s}$$

In completing this calculation, we've converted to more usual units for speed, m/s. During this phase of the motion, her velocity is constant, so a graph of velocity versus time appears as a horizontal line at 1.0 m/s, as shown in FIGURE 2.10. We can do similar calculations to show that her velocity during the second phase of her motion (i.e., the slope of the position graph) is +0.33 m/s, and then increases to +1.7 m/s during the final phase. We combine all of this information to create the **velocity-versus-time graph** shown in Figure 2.10.

An inspection of the velocity-versus-time graph shows that it matches our understanding of the student's motion: There are three phases of the motion, each with constant speed. In each phase, the velocity is positive because she is always moving to the right. The second phase is slow (low velocity) and the third phase fast (high velocity.) All of this can be clearly seen on the velocity-versus-time graph, which is yet another way to represent her motion.

NOTE ▶ The velocity-versus-time graph in Figure 2.10 includes vertical segments in which the velocity changes instantaneously. Such rapid changes are an idealization; it actually takes a small amount of time to change velocity. ◀

EXAMPLE 2.2   **Analyzing a car's position graph**

FIGURE 2.11 gives the position-versus-time graph of a car.

a. Draw the car's velocity-versus-time graph.
b. Describe the car's motion in words.

FIGURE 2.11 The position-versus-time graph of a car.

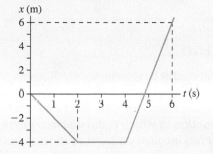

PREPARE Figure 2.11 is a graphical representation of the motion. The car's position-versus-time graph is a sequence of three straight lines. Each of these straight lines represents uniform motion at a constant velocity. We can determine the car's velocity during each interval of time by measuring the slope of the line.

SOLVE

a. From $t = 0$ s to $t = 2$ s ($\Delta t = 2$ s) the car's displacement is $\Delta x = -4$ m $- 0$ m $= -4$ m. The velocity during this interval is

$$v_x = \frac{\Delta x}{\Delta t} = \frac{-4 \text{ m}}{2 \text{ s}} = -2 \text{ m/s}$$

The car's position does not change from $t = 2$ s to $t = 4$ s ($\Delta x = 0$ m), so $v_x = 0$ m/s. Finally, the displacement

between $t = 4$ s and $t = 6$ s ($\Delta t = 2$ s) is $\Delta x = 10$ m. Thus the velocity during this interval is

$$v_x = \frac{10 \text{ m}}{2 \text{ s}} = 5 \text{ m/s}$$

These velocities are represented graphically in FIGURE 2.12.

FIGURE 2.12 The velocity-versus-time graph for the car.

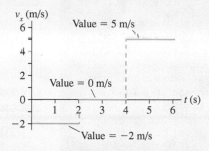

b. The velocity-versus-time graph of Figure 2.12 shows the motion in a way that we can describe in a straightforward manner: The car backs up for 2 s at 2 m/s, sits at rest for 2 s, then drives forward at 5 m/s for 2 s.

ASSESS Notice that the velocity graph and the position graph look completely different. They should! The value of the velocity graph at any instant of time equals the *slope* of the position graph. Since the position graph is made up of segments of constant slope, the velocity graph should be made up of segments of constant *value*, as it is. This gives us confidence that the graph we have drawn is correct.

From Velocity to Position

We've now seen how to move between different representations of uniform motion. There's one last issue to address: If you have a graph of velocity versus time, how can you determine the position graph?

Suppose you leave a lecture hall and begin walking toward your next class, which is down the hall to the west. You then realize that you left your textbook (which you always bring to class with you!) at your seat. You turn around and run back to the lecture hall to retrieve it. A velocity-versus-time graph for this motion appears as the top graph in FIGURE 2.13. There are two clear phases to the motion: walking away from class (velocity +1.0 m/s) and running back (velocity −3.0 m/s.) How can we deduce your position-versus-time graph?

As before, we can analyze the graph segment by segment. This process is shown in Figure 2.13, in which the upper velocity-versus-time graph is used to deduce the lower position-versus-time graph. For each of the two segments of the motion, the sign of the velocity tells us whether the slope of the graph is positive or negative; the magnitude of the velocity tells how steep the slope is. The final result makes sense; it shows 15 seconds of slowly increasing position (walking away) and then 5 seconds of rapidly decreasing position (running back.) And you end up back where you started.

There's one important detail that we didn't talk about in the preceding paragraph: How did we know that the position graph started at $x = 0$ m? The velocity graph tells us the *slope* of the position graph, but it doesn't tell us where the position graph should start. Although you're free to select any point you choose as the origin of the coordinate system, here it seems reasonable to set $x = 0$ m at your starting point in the lecture hall; as you walk away, your position increases.

FIGURE 2.13 Deducing a position graph from a velocity-versus-time graph.

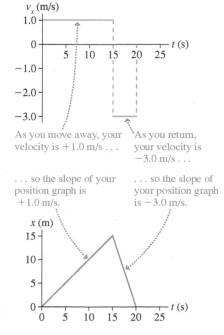

As you move away, your velocity is +1.0 m/s . . .

As you return, your velocity is −3.0 m/s . . .

. . . so the slope of your position graph is +1.0 m/s.

. . . so the slope of your position graph is −3.0 m/s.

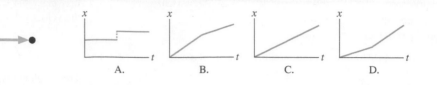

STOP TO THINK 2.1 Which position-versus-time graph best describes the motion diagram at left?

A.   B.   C.   D.

A ship on a constant heading at a steady speed is a practical example of uniform motion.

FIGURE 2.14 Motion diagram and position-versus-time graph for uniform motion.

Uniform motion

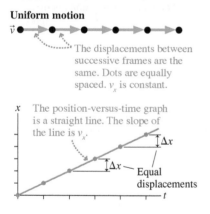

The displacements between successive frames are the same. Dots are equally spaced. v_x is constant.

The position-versus-time graph is a straight line. The slope of the line is v_x.

Δx

Δx — Equal displacements

FIGURE 2.15 Position-versus-time graph for an object in uniform motion.

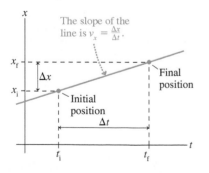

The slope of the line is $v_x = \frac{\Delta x}{\Delta t}$.

x_f

Δx Final position

x_i

Initial position

Δt

t_i t_f

2.2 Uniform Motion

If you drive your car on a straight road at a perfectly steady 60 miles per hour (mph), you will cover 60 mi during the first hour, another 60 mi during the second hour, yet another 60 mi during the third hour, and so on. This is an example of what we call *uniform motion*. **Straight-line motion in which equal displacements occur during any successive equal-time intervals is called uniform motion** or constant-velocity motion.

NOTE ▶ The qualifier "any" is important. If during each hour you drive 120 mph for 30 min and stop for 30 min, you will cover 60 mi during each successive 1 hour interval. But you will *not* have equal displacements during successive 30 min intervals, so this motion is not uniform. Your constant 60 mph driving is uniform motion because you will find equal displacements no matter how you choose your successive time intervals. ◀

FIGURE 2.14 shows a motion diagram and a graph for an object in uniform motion. Notice that the position-versus-time graph for uniform motion is a straight line. This follows from the requirement that all values of Δx corresponding to the same value of Δt be equal. In fact, an alternative definition of uniform motion is: **An object's motion is uniform if and only if its position-versus-time graph is a straight line.**

Equations of Uniform Motion

An object is in uniform motion along the x-axis with the linear position-versus-time graph shown in FIGURE 2.15. Recall from Chapter 1 that we denote the object's initial position as x_i at time t_i. The term "initial" refers to the starting point of our analysis or the starting point in a problem. The object may or may not have been in motion prior to t_i. We use the term "final" for the ending point of our analysis or the ending point of a problem, and denote the object's final position x_f at the time t_f. As we've seen, the object's velocity v_x along the x-axis can be determined by finding the slope of the graph:

$$v_x = \frac{\text{rise}}{\text{run}} = \frac{\Delta x}{\Delta t} = \frac{x_f - x_i}{t_f - t_i} \tag{2.3}$$

Equation 2.3 can be rearranged to give

$$x_f = x_i + v_x \, \Delta t \tag{2.4}$$

Position equation for an object in uniform motion (v_x is constant)

where $\Delta t = t_f - t_i$ is the interval of time in which the object moves from position x_i to position x_f. Equation 2.4 applies to any time interval Δt during which the velocity is constant. We can also write this in terms of the object's displacement, $\Delta x = x_f - x_i$:

$$\Delta x = v_x \, \Delta t \tag{2.5}$$

The velocity of an object in uniform motion tells us the amount by which its position changes during each second. An object with a velocity of 20 m/s *changes* its position by 20 m during every second of motion: by 20 m during the first second of its motion, by another 20 m during the next second, and so on. We say that position is changing at the *rate* of 20 m/s. If the object starts at $x_i = 10$ m, it will be at $x = 30$ m after 1 s of motion and at $x = 50$ m after 2 s of motion. Thinking of velocity like this will help you develop an intuitive understanding of the connection between velocity and position.

Physics may seem densely populated with equations, but most equations follow a few basic forms. The mathematical form of Equation 2.5 is a type that we will see again: The displacement Δx is *proportional* to the time interval Δt.

NOTE ▶ The important features of a proportional relationship are described below. In this text, the first time we use a particular mathematical form we will provide such an overview. In future chapters, when we see other examples of this type of relationship, we will refer back to this overview. ◄

✏️ Proportional relationships

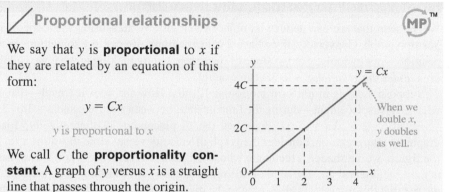

We say that y is **proportional** to x if they are related by an equation of this form:

$$y = Cx$$

y is proportional to x

We call C the **proportionality constant**. A graph of y versus x is a straight line that passes through the origin.

SCALING If x has the initial value x_1, then y has the initial value $y_1 = Cx_1$. Changing x from x_1 to x_2 changes y from y_1 to y_2. The ratio of y_2 to y_1 is

$$\frac{y_2}{y_1} = \frac{Cx_2}{Cx_1} = \frac{x_2}{x_1}$$

The ratio of y_2 to y_1 is exactly the same as the ratio of x_2 to x_1. If y is proportional to x, which is often written $y \propto x$, then x and y change by the same factor.

- If you double x, you double y.
- If you decrease x by a factor of 3, you decrease y by a factor of 3.

If two variables have a proportional relationship, we can draw important conclusions from ratios without knowing the value of the proportionality constant C. We can often solve problems in a very straightforward manner by looking at such ratios. This is an important skill called *ratio reasoning*.

Exercise 11 ✏️

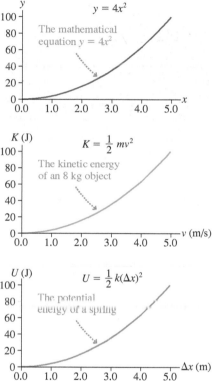

Mathematical Forms These three figures show graphs of a mathematical equation, the kinetic energy of a moving object versus its speed, and the potential energy of a spring versus the displacement of the end of the spring. All three graphs have the same overall appearance. The three expressions differ in their variables, but all three equations have the same **mathematical form**. There are only a handful of different mathematical forms that we'll use in this text. As we meet each form for the first time, we will give an overview. When you see it again, we'll insert an icon that refers back to the overview so that you can remind yourself of the key details.

EXAMPLE 2.3   **If a train leaves Cleveland at 2:00 . . .**

A train is moving due west at a constant speed. A passenger notes that it takes 10 minutes to travel 12 km. How long will it take the train to travel 60 km?

PREPARE For an object in uniform motion, Equation 2.5 shows that the distance traveled Δx is proportional to the time interval Δt, so this is a good problem to solve using ratio reasoning.

SOLVE We are comparing two cases: the time to travel 12 km and the time to travel 60 km. Because Δx is proportional to Δt, the ratio of the times will be equal to the ratio of the distances. The ratio of the distances is

$$\frac{\Delta x_2}{\Delta x_1} = \frac{60 \text{ km}}{12 \text{ km}} = 5$$

Continued

This is equal to the ratio of the times:

$$\frac{\Delta t_2}{\Delta t_1} = 5$$

$$\Delta t_2 = \text{ time to travel } 60 \text{ km} = 5\Delta t_1 = 5 \times (10 \text{ min}) = 50 \text{ min}$$

It takes 10 minutes to travel 12 km; it will take 50 minutes—5 times as long—to travel 60 km.

ASSESS For an object in steady motion, it makes sense that 5 times the distance requires 5 times the time. We can see that using ratio reasoning is a straightforward way to solve this problem. We don't need to know the proportionality constant (in this case, the velocity); we just used ratios of distances and times.

From Velocity to Position, One More Time

We've seen that we can deduce an object's velocity by measuring the slope of its position graph. Conversely, if we have a velocity graph, we can say something about position—not by looking at the slope of the graph, but by looking at what we call the *area under the graph*. Let's look at an example.

Suppose a car is in uniform motion at 12 m/s. How far does it travel—that is, what is its displacement—during the time interval between $t = 1.0$ s and $t = 3.0$ s?

Equation 2.5, $\Delta x = v_x \Delta t$, describes the displacement mathematically; for a graphical interpretation, consider the graph of velocity versus time in FIGURE 2.16. In the figure, we've shaded a rectangle whose height is the velocity v_x and whose base is the time interval Δt. The area of this rectangle is $v_x \Delta t$. Looking at Equation 2.5, we see that this quantity is also equal to the displacement of the car. The area of this rectangle is the area between the axis and the line representing the velocity; we call it the "area under the graph." We see that the **displacement Δx is equal to the area under the velocity graph during interval Δt.**

Whether we use Equation 2.5 or the area under the graph to compute the displacement, we get the same result:

$$\Delta x = v_x \Delta t = (12 \text{ m/s})(2.0 \text{ s}) = 24 \text{ m}$$

Although we've shown that the displacement is the area under the graph only for uniform motion, where the velocity is constant, we'll soon see that this result applies to any one-dimensional motion.

FIGURE 2.16 Displacement is the area under a velocity-versus-time graph.

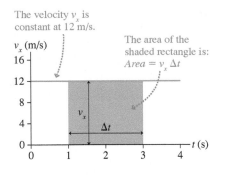

The velocity v_x is constant at 12 m/s.

The area of the shaded rectangle is: $Area = v_x \Delta t$

NOTE ▶ Wait a minute! The displacement $\Delta x = x_f - x_i$ is a length. How can a length equal an area? Recall that earlier, when we found that the velocity is the slope of the position graph, we made a distinction between the *actual* slope and the *physically meaningful* slope? The same distinction applies here. The velocity graph does indeed bound a certain area on the page. That is the actual area, but it is *not* the area to which we are referring. Once again, we need to measure the quantities we are using, v_x and Δt, by referring to the scales on the axes. Δt is some number of seconds, while v_x is some number of meters per second. When these are multiplied together, the *physically meaningful* area has units of meters, appropriate for a displacement. ◀

STOP TO THINK 2.2   Four objects move with the velocity-versus-time graphs shown. Which object has the largest displacement between $t = 0$ s and $t = 2$ s?

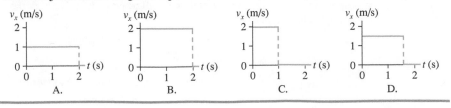

2.3 Instantaneous Velocity

The objects we've studied so far have moved with a constant, unchanging velocity or, like the car in Example 2.1, changed abruptly from one constant velocity to another. This is not very realistic. Real moving objects speed up and slow down, *changing* their velocity. As an extreme example, think about a drag racer. In a typical race, the car begins at rest but, 1 second later, is moving at over 25 miles per hour!

For one-dimensional motion, an object changing its velocity is either speeding up or slowing down. When you drive your car, as you speed up or slow down—changing your velocity—a glance at your speedometer tells you how fast you're going *at that instant*. An object's velocity—a speed *and* a direction—at a specific *instant* of time *t* is called the object's **instantaneous velocity**.

But what does it mean to have a velocity "at an instant"? An instantaneous velocity of magnitude 60 mph means that the rate at which your car's position is changing—at that exact instant—is such that it would travel a distance of 60 miles in 1 hour *if* it continued at that rate without change. Said another way, if *just for an instant* your car matches the velocity of another car driving at a steady 60 mph, then your instantaneous velocity is 60 mph. **From now on, the word "velocity" will always mean instantaneous velocity.**

For uniform motion, we found that an object's position-versus-time graph is a straight line and the object's velocity is the slope of that line. In contrast, FIGURE 2.17 shows that the position-versus-time graph for a drag racer is a *curved* line. The displacement Δx during equal intervals of time gets greater as the car speeds up. Even so, we can use the slope of the position graph to measure the car's velocity. We can say that

instantaneous velocity v_x at time t = slope of position graph at time t (2.6)

But how do we determine the slope of a curved line at a particular point? The following table gives the necessary details.

A drag racer moves with rapidly changing velocity.

FIGURE 2.17 Position-versus-time graph for a drag racer.

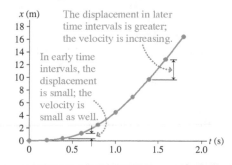

Finding the instantaneous velocity

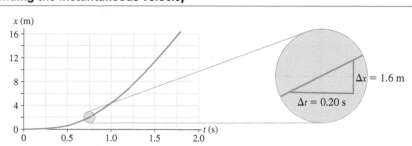 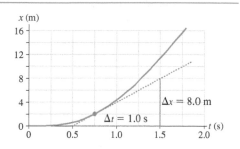

If the velocity changes, the position graph is a curved line. But we can still compute a slope by considering a small segment of the graph. Let's look at the motion in a very small time interval right around $t = 0.75$ s. This is highlighted with a circle, and we show a close-up in the next graph, at right.

Now that we have magnified a small part of the position graph, we see that the graph in this small part appears to have a constant slope. It is always possible to make the graph appear as a straight line by choosing a small enough time interval. We can find the slope of the line by calculating the rise over run, just as before:

$$v_x = \frac{1.6 \text{ m}}{0.20 \text{ s}} = 8.0 \text{ m/s}$$

This is the slope of the graph at $t = 0.75$ s and thus the velocity at this instant of time.

Graphically, the slope of the curve at a particular point is the same as the slope of a straight line drawn *tangent* to the curve at that point. **The slope of the tangent line is the instantaneous velocity at that instant of time.**

Calculating rise over run for the tangent line, we get

$$v_x = \frac{8.0 \text{ m}}{1.0 \text{ s}} = 8.0 \text{ m/s}$$

This is the same value we obtained from considering the close-up view.

Analyzing an elevator's position graph

FIGURE 2.18 shows the position-versus-time graph of an elevator.

a. Sketch an approximate velocity-versus-time graph.
b. At which point or points is the elevator moving the fastest?
c. Is the elevator ever at rest? If so, at which point or points?

FIGURE 2.18 The position-versus-time graph for an elevator.

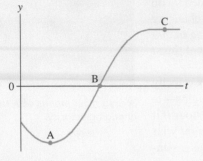

FIGURE 2.19 Finding a velocity graph from a position graph.

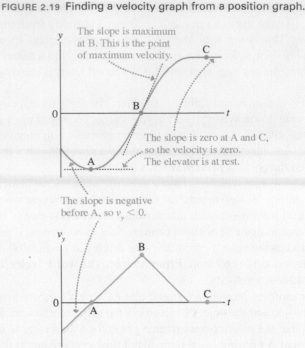

The slope is maximum at B. This is the point of maximum velocity.

The slope is zero at A and C, so the velocity is zero. The elevator is at rest.

The slope is negative before A, so $v_y < 0$.

REASON a. Notice that the position graph shows y versus t, rather than x versus t, indicating that the motion is vertical rather than horizontal. Our analysis of one-dimensional motion has made no assumptions about the direction of motion, so it applies equally well to both horizontal and vertical motion. As we just found, the velocity at a particular instant of time is the slope of a tangent line to the position-versus-time graph at that time. We can move point-by-point along the position-versus-time graph, noting the slope of the tangent at each point. This will give us the velocity at that point.

Initially, to the left of point A, the slope is negative and thus the velocity is negative (i.e., the elevator is moving downward). But the slope decreases as the curve flattens out, and by the time the graph gets to point A, the slope is zero. The slope then increases to a maximum value at point B, decreases back to zero a little before point C, and remains at zero thereafter. This reasoning process is outlined in FIGURE 2.19a, and FIGURE 2.19b shows the approximate velocity-versus-time graph that results.

The other questions were answered during the construction of the graph:

b. The elevator moves the fastest at point B where the slope of the position graph is the steepest.

c. A particle at rest has $v_y = 0$. Graphically, this occurs at points where the tangent line to the position-versus-time graph is horizontal and thus has zero slope. Figure 2.19 shows that the slope is zero at points A and C. At point A, the velocity is only instantaneously zero as the particle reverses direction from downward motion (negative velocity) to upward motion (positive velocity). At point C, the elevator has actually stopped and remains at rest.

ASSESS The best way to check our work is to look at different segments of the motion and see if the velocity and position graphs match. Until point A, y is decreasing. The elevator is going down, so the velocity should be negative, which our graph shows. Between points A and C, y is increasing, so the velocity should be positive, which is also a feature of our graph. The steepest slope is at point B, so this should be the high point of our velocity graph, as it is.

For uniform motion we showed that the displacement Δx is the area under the velocity-versus-time graph during time interval Δt. We can generalize this idea to the case of an object whose velocity varies. FIGURE 2.20a on the next page is the velocity-versus-time graph for an object whose velocity changes with time. Suppose we know the object's position to be x_i at an initial time t_i. Our goal is to find its position x_f at a later time t_f.

Because we know how to handle constant velocities, let's *approximate* the velocity function of Figure 2.20a as a series of constant-velocity steps of width Δt as shown in FIGURE 2.21b. The velocity during each step is constant (uniform motion), so we can calculate the displacement during each step as the area of the rectangle under the curve. The total displacement of the object between t_i and t_f can be found as the sum of all the individual displacements during each of the constant-velocity steps. We can see in Figure 2.20b that the total displacement is approximately equal to the area under the graph, even in the case where the velocity varies. Although the approximation shown in the figure is rather rough, with only nine steps, we can imagine that it could be made as accurate as desired by having more and more ever-narrower steps.

FIGURE 2.20 Approximating a velocity-versus-time graph with a series of constant-velocity steps.

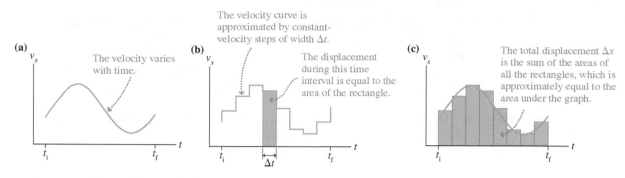

Consequently, an object's displacement is related to its velocity by

$$x_f - x_i = \Delta x = \text{area under the velocity graph } v_x \text{ between } t_i \text{ and } t_f \quad (2.7)$$

EXAMPLE 2.5   **The displacement during a rapid start**

FIGURE 2.21 shows the velocity-versus-time graph of a car pulling away from a stop. How far does the car move during the first 3.0 s?

PREPARE   Figure 2.21 is a graphical representation of the motion. The question How far? indicates that we need to find a displacement Δx rather than a position x. According to Equation 2.7, the car's displacement $\Delta x = x_f - x_i$ between $t = 0$ s and $t = 3$ s is the area under the curve from $t = 0$ s to $t = 3$ s.

FIGURE 2.21   Velocity-versus-time graph for the car of Example 2.5.

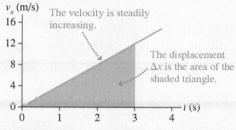

SOLVE   The curve in this case is an angled line, so the area is that of a triangle:

$$\Delta x = \text{area of triangle between } t = 0 \text{ s and } t = 3 \text{ s}$$

$$= \tfrac{1}{2} \times \text{base} \times \text{height} = \tfrac{1}{2} \times 3 \text{ s} \times 12 \text{ m/s} = 18 \text{ m}$$

The car moves 18 m during the first 3 seconds as its velocity changes from 0 to 12 m/s.

ASSESS   The physically meaningful area is a product of s and m/s, so Δx has the proper units of m. Let's check the numbers to see if they make physical sense. The final velocity, 12 m/s, is about 25 mph. Pulling away from a stop, you might expect to reach this speed in about 3 s—at least if you have a reasonably sporty vehicle! If the car had moved at a constant 12 m/s (the final velocity) during these 3 s, the distance would be 36 m. The actual distance traveled during the 3 s is 18 m—half of 36 m. This makes sense, as the velocity was 0 m/s at the start of the problem and increased steadily to 12 m/s.

STOP TO THINK 2.3   Which velocity-versus-time graph goes with the position-versus-time graph on the left?

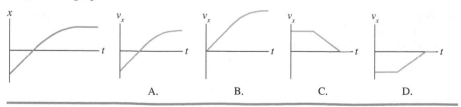

2.4 Acceleration

The goal of this chapter is to describe motion. We've seen that velocity describes the rate at which an object changes position. We need one more motion concept to complete the description, one that will describe an object whose velocity is changing.

As an example, let's look at a frequently quoted measurement of car performance, the time it takes the car to go from 0 to 60 mph. Table 2.2 shows this time for two different cars.

Let's look at motion diagrams for the Porsche and the Volkswagen in FIGURE 2.22. We can see two important facts about the motion. First, the lengths of the velocity vectors are increasing, showing that the speeds are increasing. Second, the velocity vectors for the Porsche are increasing in length more rapidly than those of the VW. The quantity we seek is one that measures how rapidly an object's velocity vectors change in length.

TABLE 2.2 Performance data for vehicles

Vehicle	Time to go from 0 to 60 mph
1997 Porsche 911 Turbo S	3.6 s
1973 Volkswagen Super Beetle Convertible	24 s

FIGURE 2.22 Motion diagrams for the Porsche and Volkswagen.

When we wanted to measure changes in position, the ratio $\Delta x / \Delta t$ was useful. This ratio, which we defined as the velocity, is the *rate of change of position*. Similarly, we can measure how rapidly an object's velocity changes with the ratio $\Delta v_x / \Delta t$. Given our experience with velocity, we can say a couple of things about this new ratio:

- The ratio $\Delta v_x / \Delta t$ is the *rate of change of velocity*.
- The ratio $\Delta v_x / \Delta t$ is the *slope of a velocity-versus-time graph*.

We will define this ratio as the **acceleration,** for which we use the symbol a_x:

$$a_x = \frac{\Delta v_x}{\Delta t} \tag{2.8}$$

Definition of acceleration as the rate of change of velocity

Similarly, $a_y = \Delta v_y / \Delta t$ for vertical motion.

As an example, let's calculate the acceleration for the Porsche and the Volkswagen. For both, the initial velocity $(v_x)_i$ is zero and the final velocity $(v_x)_f$ is 60 mph. Thus the *change* in velocity is $\Delta v_x = 60$ mph. In m/s, our SI unit of velocity, $\Delta v_x = 27$ m/s.

Now we can use Equation 2.8 to compute acceleration. Let's start with the Porsche, which speeds up to 27 m/s in $\Delta t = 3.6$ s:

$$a_{\text{Porsche }x} = \frac{\Delta v_x}{\Delta t} = \frac{27 \text{ m/s}}{3.6 \text{ s}} = 7.5 \frac{\text{m/s}}{\text{s}}$$

Here's the meaning of this final figure: Every second, the Porsche's velocity changes by 7.5 m/s. In the first second of motion, the Porsche's velocity increases by 7.5 m/s; in the next second, it increases by another 7.5 m/s, and so on. After 1 second, the velocity is 7.5 m/s; after 2 seconds, it is 15 m/s. This increase continues as long as the Porsche has this acceleration. We thus interpret the units as 7.5 meters per second, per second—7.5 (m/s)/s.

The Volkswagen's acceleration is

$$a_{\text{VW }x} = \frac{\Delta v_x}{\Delta t} = \frac{27 \text{ m/s}}{24 \text{ s}} = 1.1 \frac{\text{m/s}}{\text{s}}$$

Cushion kinematics When a car hits an obstacle head-on, the damage to the car and its occupants can be reduced by making the acceleration as small as possible. As we can see from Equation 2.8, acceleration can be reduced by making the *time* for a change in velocity as long as possible. This is the purpose of the yellow crash cushion barrels you may have seen in work zones on highways—to lengthen the time of a collision with a barrier.

In each second, the Volkswagen changes its speed by 1.1 m/s. This is only 1/7 the acceleration of the Porsche! The reasons the Porsche is capable of greater acceleration has to do with what *causes* the motion. We will explore the reasons for acceleration in Chapter 4. For now, we will simply note that the Porsche is capable of much greater acceleration, something you would have suspected.

NOTE ▶ It is customary to abbreviate the acceleration units (m/s)/s as m/s². For example, we'll write that the Volkswagen has an acceleration of 1.1 m/s². When you use this notation, keep in mind the *meaning* of the notation as "(meters per second) per second." ◀

TABLE 2.3 Velocity data for the Volkswagen and the Porsche

Time (s)	Velocity of VW (m/s)	Velocity of Porsche (m/s)
0	0	0
1	1.1	7.5
2	2.2	15.0
3	3.3	22.5
4	4.4	30.0

Representing Acceleration

Let's use the values we have computed for acceleration to make a table of velocities for the Porsche and the Volkswagen we considered earlier. Table 2.3 uses the idea that the VW's velocity increases by 1.1 m/s every second while the Porsche's velocity increases by 7.5 m/s every second. The data in Table 2.3 are the basis for the velocity-versus-time graphs in FIGURE 2.23. As you can see, an object undergoing constant acceleration has a straight-line velocity graph.

The slope of either of these lines—the rise over run—is $\Delta v_x / \Delta t$. Comparing this with Equation 2.8, we see that the equation for the slope is the same as that for the acceleration. That is, **an object's acceleration is the slope of its velocity-versus-time graph:**

$$\text{acceleration } a_x \text{ at time } t = \text{slope of velocity graph at time } t \qquad (2.9)$$

The VW has a smaller acceleration, so its velocity graph has a smaller slope.

FIGURE 2.23 Velocity-versus-time graphs for the two cars.

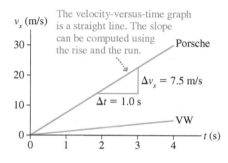

CONCEPTUAL EXAMPLE 2.6	Analyzing a car's velocity graph

FIGURE 2.24a is a graph of velocity versus time for a car. Sketch a graph of the car's acceleration versus time.

REASON The graph can be divided into three sections:

- An initial segment, in which the velocity increases at a steady rate.
- A middle segment, in which the velocity is constant.
- A final segment, in which the velocity decreases at a steady rate.

In each section, the acceleration is the slope of the velocity-versus-time graph. Thus the initial segment has constant, positive acceleration, the middle segment has zero acceleration, and the

final segment has constant, *negative* acceleration. The acceleration graph appears in FIGURE 2.24b.

ASSESS This process is analogous to finding a velocity graph from the slope of a position graph. The middle segment having zero acceleration does *not* mean that the velocity is zero. The velocity is constant, which means it is *not changing* and thus the car is not accelerating. The car does accelerate during the initial and final segments. The magnitude of the acceleration is a measure of how quickly the velocity is changing. How about the sign? This is an issue we will address in the next section.

FIGURE 2.24 Finding an acceleration graph from a velocity graph.

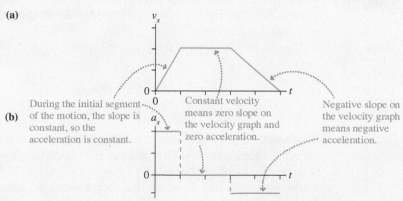

FIGURE 2.25 Determining the sign of the acceleration.

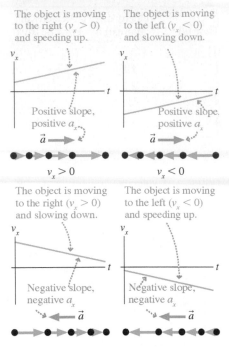

The Sign of the Acceleration

It's a natural tendency to think that a positive value of a_x or a_y describes an object that is speeding up while a negative value describes an object that is slowing down (decelerating). Unfortunately, this simple interpretation *does not work*.

Because an object can move right or left (or, equivalently, up and down) while either speeding up or slowing down, there are four situations to consider. FIGURE 2.25 shows a motion diagram and a velocity graph for each of these situations. As we've seen, an object's acceleration is the slope of its velocity graph, so a positive slope implies a positive acceleration and a negative slope implies a negative acceleration.

Acceleration, like velocity, is really a vector quantity, a concept that we will explore more fully in Chapter 3. Figure 2.25 shows the acceleration vectors for the four situations. The acceleration vector points in the same direction as the velocity vector $\vec{v}$ for an object that is speeding up and opposite to $\vec{v}$ for an object that is slowing down.

An object that speeds up as it moves to the right (positive v_x) has a positive acceleration, but an object that speeds up as it moves to the left (negative v_x) has a negative acceleration. Whether or not an object that is slowing down has a negative acceleration depends on whether the object is moving to the right or to the left. This is admittedly a bit more complex than thinking that negative acceleration always means slowing down, but our definition of acceleration as the slope of the velocity graph forces us to pay careful attention to the sign of the acceleration.

> **STOP TO THINK 2.4** A particle moves with the velocity-versus-time graph shown here. At which labeled point is the magnitude of the acceleration the greatest?

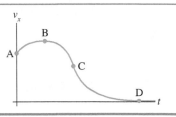

FIGURE 2.26 The red dots show the positions of the top of the Saturn V rocket at equally spaced intervals of time during liftoff.

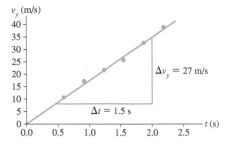

2.5 Motion with Constant Acceleration

For uniform motion—motion with constant velocity—we found in Equation 2.3 a simple relationship between position and time. It's no surprise that there are also simple relationships that connect the various kinematic variables in constant-acceleration motion. We will start with a concrete example, the launch of a Saturn V rocket like the one that carried the Apollo astronauts to the moon in the 1960s and 1970s. FIGURE 2.26 shows one frame from a video of a rocket lifting off the launch pad. The red dots show the positions of the top of the rocket at equally spaced intervals of time in earlier frames of the video. This is a motion diagram for the rocket, and we can see that the velocity is increasing. The graph of velocity versus time in FIGURE 2.27 shows that the velocity is increasing at a fairly constant rate. We can approximate the rocket's motion as constant acceleration.

We can use the slope of the graph in Figure 2.27 to determine the acceleration of the rocket:

$$a_y = \frac{\Delta v_y}{\Delta t} = \frac{27 \text{ m/s}}{1.5 \text{ s}} = 18 \text{ m/s}^2$$

This acceleration is more than double the acceleration of the Porsche, and it goes on for quite a long time—the first phase of the launch lasts over 2 minutes! How fast is the rocket moving at the end of this acceleration, and how far has it traveled? To answer questions like these, we first need to work out some basic kinematic formulas for motion with constant acceleration.

FIGURE 2.27 A graph of the rocket's velocity versus time.

▶ **Solar sailing** A rocket achieves a high speed by having a very high acceleration. A different approach is represented by a solar sail. A spacecraft with a solar sail accelerates due to the pressure of sunlight from the sun on a large, mirrored surface. The acceleration is minuscule, but it can continue for a long, long time. After an acceleration period of a few *years,* the spacecraft will reach a respectable speed!

Constant-Acceleration Equations

Consider an object whose acceleration a_x remains constant during the time interval $\Delta t = t_f - t_i$. At the beginning of this interval, the object has initial velocity $(v_x)_i$ and initial position x_i. Note that t_i is often zero, but it need not be. FIGURE 2.28a shows the acceleration-versus-time graph. It is a horizontal line between t_i and t_f, indicating a *constant* acceleration.

The object's velocity is changing because the object is accelerating. We can use the acceleration to find $(v_x)_f$ at a later time t_f. We defined acceleration as

$$a_x = \frac{\Delta v_x}{\Delta t} = \frac{(v_x)_f - (v_x)_i}{\Delta t} \tag{2.10}$$

which is rearranged to give

$$(v_x)_f = (v_x)_i + a_x \Delta t \tag{2.11}$$

Velocity equation for an object with constant acceleration

NOTE ▶ We have expressed this equation for motion along the *x*-axis, but it is a general result that will apply to any axis. ◀

The velocity-versus-time graph for this constant-acceleration motion, shown in FIGURE 2.28b, is a straight line with value $(v_x)_i$ at time t_i and with slope a_x.

We would also like to know the object's position x_f at time t_f. As you learned earlier, the displacement Δx during a time interval Δt is the area under the velocity-versus-time graph. The shaded area in Figure 2.28b can be subdivided into a rectangle of area $(v_x)_i \Delta t$ and a triangle of area $\frac{1}{2}(a_x \Delta t)(\Delta t) = \frac{1}{2}a_x(\Delta t)^2$. Adding these gives

$$x_f = x_i + (v_x)_i \Delta t + \tfrac{1}{2}a_x(\Delta t)^2 \tag{2.12}$$

Position equation for an object with constant acceleration

where $\Delta t = t_f - t_i$ is the elapsed time. The fact that the time interval Δt appears in the equation as $(\Delta t)^2$ causes the position-versus-time graph for constant-acceleration motion to have a parabolic shape. For the rocket launch of Figure 2.26, a graph of the position of the top of the rocket versus time appears as in FIGURE 2.29.

Equations 2.11 and 2.12 are two of the basic kinematic equations for motion with constant acceleration. They allow us to predict an object's position and velocity at a future instant of time. We need one more equation to complete our set, a direct relationship between displacement and velocity. To derive this relationship, we first use Equation 2.11 to write $\Delta t = ((v_x)_f - (v_x)_i)/a_x$. We can substitute this into Equation 2.12 to obtain

$$(v_x)_f^2 = (v_x)_i^2 + 2a_x \Delta x \tag{2.13}$$

Relating velocity and displacement for constant-acceleration motion

In Equation 2.13 $\Delta x = x_f - x_i$ is the *displacement* (not the distance!). Notice that Equation 2.13 does not require knowing the time interval Δt. This is an important equation in problems where you're not given information about times. Equations 2.11, 2.12, and 2.13 are the key equations for motion with constant acceleration. These results are summarized in Table 2.4.

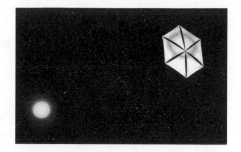

FIGURE 2.28 **Acceleration and velocity graphs for motion with constant acceleration.**

(a) Acceleration

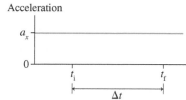

The displacement Δx is the area under this curve: the sum of the area of a triangle . . .

(b) Velocity . . . and a rectangle.

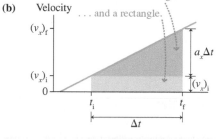

FIGURE 2.29 **Position-versus-time graph for the Saturn V rocket launch.**

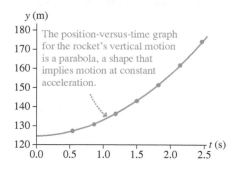

The position-versus-time graph for the rocket's vertical motion is a parabola, a shape that implies motion at constant acceleration.

TABLE 2.4 Kinematic equations for motion with constant acceleration

$$(v_x)_f = (v_x)_i + a_x \Delta t$$
$$x_f = x_i + (v_x)_i \Delta t + \tfrac{1}{2}a_x(\Delta t)^2$$
$$(v_x)_f^2 = (v_x)_i^2 + 2a_x \Delta x$$

EXAMPLE 2.7 **Coming to a stop**

As you drive in your car at 15 m/s (just a bit under 35 mph), you see a child's ball roll into the street ahead of you. You hit the brakes and stop as quickly as you can. In this case, you come to rest in 1.5 s. How far does your car travel as you brake to a stop?

PREPARE The problem statement gives us a description of motion in words. To help us visualize the situation, FIGURE 2.30 illustrates the key features of the motion with a motion diagram and a

FIGURE 2.30 Motion diagram and velocity graph for a car coming to a stop.

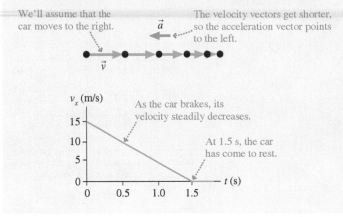

We'll assume that the car moves to the right.

The velocity vectors get shorter, so the acceleration vector points to the left.

$\vec{a}$

$\vec{v}$

v_x (m/s)

As the car brakes, its velocity steadily decreases.

At 1.5 s, the car has come to rest.

15

10

5

0

0   0.5   1.0   1.5 t (s)

velocity graph. The graph is based on the car slowing from 15 m/s to 0 m/s in 1.5 s.

SOLVE We've assumed that your car is moving to the right, so its initial velocity is $(v_x)_i = +15$ m/s. After you come to rest, your final velocity is $(v_x)_f = 0$ m/s. The acceleration is given by Equation 2.10:

$$a_x = \frac{\Delta v_x}{\Delta t} = \frac{(v_x)_f - (v_x)_i}{\Delta t} = \frac{0 \text{ m/s} - 15 \text{ m/s}}{1.5 \text{ s}} = -10 \text{ m/s}^2$$

An acceleration of –10 m/s² (really –10 m/s per second) means the car slows by 10 m/s every second.

Now that we know the acceleration, we can compute the distance that the car moves as it comes to rest using Equation 2.12:

$$x_f - x_i = (v_x)_i \Delta t + \tfrac{1}{2} a_x (\Delta t)^2$$
$$= (15 \text{ m/s})(1.5 \text{ s}) + \tfrac{1}{2}(-10 \text{ m/s}^2)(1.5 \text{ s})^2 = 11 \text{ m}$$

ASSESS 11 m is a little over 35 feet. That's a reasonable distance for a quick stop while traveling at about 35 mph. The purpose of the Assess step is not to prove that your solution is correct but to use common sense to recognize answers that are clearly wrong. Had you made a calculation error and ended up with an answer of 1.1 m—less than 4 feet—a moment's reflection should indicate that this couldn't possibly be correct.

1.1–1.3   Activ ONLINE Physics

Graphs will be an important component of our problem solutions, so we want to consider the types of graphs we are likely to encounter in more detail. FIGURE 2.31 is a graphical comparison of motion with constant velocity (uniform motion) and motion with constant acceleration. Notice that uniform motion is really a special case of constant-acceleration motion in which the acceleration happens to be zero.

FIGURE 2.31 Motion with constant velocity and constant acceleration. These graphs assume $x_i = 0$, $(v_x)_i > 0$, and (for constant acceleration) $a_x > 0$.

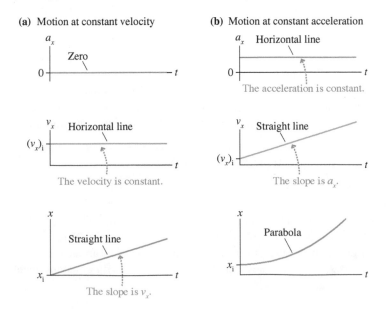

(a) Motion at constant velocity

(b) Motion at constant acceleration

For motion at constant acceleration, a graph of position versus time is a *parabola*. This is a new mathematical form, one that we will see again. If $(v_x)_i = 0$, the second equation in Table 2.4 is simply

$$\Delta x = \tfrac{1}{2}a_x(\Delta t)^2 \tag{2.14}$$

Δx depends on the *square* of Δt; we call this a *quadratic relationship*.

Quadratic relationships (MP)™

Two quantities are said to have a **quadratic relationship** if y is proportional to the square of x. We write the mathematical relationship as

$$y = Ax^2$$

y is proportional to x^2

The graph of a quadratic relationship is a parabola.

SCALING If x has the initial value x_1, then y has the initial value $y_1 = A(x_1)^2$. Changing x from x_1 to x_2 changes y from y_1 to y_2. The ratio of y_2 to y_1 is

$$\frac{y_2}{y_1} = \frac{A(x_2)^2}{A(x_1)^2} = \left(\frac{x_2}{x_1}\right)^2$$

The ratio of y_2 to y_1 is the square of the ratio of x_2 to x_1. If y is a quadratic function of x, a change in x by some factor changes y by the square of that factor:

- If you increase x by a factor of 2, you increase y by a factor of $2^2 = 4$.
- If you decrease x by a factor of 3, you decrease y by a factor of $3^2 = 9$.

Generally, we can say that:
   Changing x by a factor of c changes y by a factor of c^2.

Exercise 19 ✎

Graph labels: $y = Ax^2$; Doubling x causes y to change by a factor of 4.

Getting up to speed BIO A bird must have a minimum speed to fly. Generally, the larger the bird, the faster the takeoff speed. Small birds can get moving fast enough to fly with a vigorous jump, but larger birds may need a running start. This swan must accelerate for a long distance in order to achieve the high speed it needs to fly, so it makes a frenzied dash across the frozen surface of a pond. Swans require a long, clear stretch of water or land to become airborne. Airplanes require an even faster takeoff speed and thus an even longer runway, as we will see.

EXAMPLE 2.8 | **Displacement of a drag racer**

A drag racer, starting from rest, travels 6.0 m in 1.0 s. Suppose the car continues this acceleration for an additional 4.0 s. How far from the starting line will the car be?

PREPARE We assume that the acceleration is constant, so the displacement will follow Equation 2.14. This is a *quadratic relationship,* so the displacement will scale as the square of the time.

SOLVE After 1.0 s, the car has traveled 6.0 m; after another 4.0 s, a total of 5.0 s will have elapsed. The time has increased by a factor of 5, so the displacement will increase by a factor of 5^2, or 25. The total displacement is

$$\Delta x = 25(6.0 \text{ m}) = 150 \text{ m}$$

ASSESS This is a big distance in a short time, but drag racing is a fast sport, so our answer makes sense.

STOP TO THINK 2.5 A cyclist is at rest at a traffic light. When the light turns green, he begins accelerating at 1.2 m/s^2. How many seconds after the light turns green does he reach his cruising speed of 6.0 m/s?

   A. 1.0 s   B. 2.0 s   C. 3.0 s   D. 4.0 s   E. 5.0 s

Dinner at a distance BIO A chameleon's tongue is a powerful tool for catching prey. Certain species can extend the tongue to a distance of over 1 ft in less than 0.1 s! A study of the kinematics of the motion of the chameleon tongue, using techniques like those in this chapter, reveals that the tongue has a period of rapid acceleration followed by a period of constant velocity. This knowledge is a very valuable clue in the analysis of the evolutionary relationships between chameleons and other animals.

Building a complex structure requires careful planning. The architect's visualization and drawings have to be complete before the detailed procedures of construction get under way. The same is true for solving problems in physics.

2.6 Solving One-Dimensional Motion Problems

The big challenge when solving a physics problem is to translate the words into symbols that can be manipulated, calculated, and graphed. This translation from words to symbols is the heart of problem solving in physics. Ambiguous words and phrases must be clarified, the imprecise must be made precise, and you must arrive at an understanding of exactly what the question is asking.

In this section we will explore some general problem-solving strategies that we will use throughout the text, applying them to problems of motion along a line.

A Problem-Solving Strategy

The first step in solving a seemingly complicated problem is to break it down into a series of smaller steps. In worked examples in the text, we use a problem-solving strategy that consists of three steps: *prepare, solve,* and *assess*. Each of these steps has important elements that you should follow when you solve problems on your own.

(MP)™ **Problem-Solving Strategy**

PREPARE The Prepare step of a solution is where you identify important elements of the problem and collect information you will need to solve it. It's tempting to jump right to the Solve step, but a skilled problem solver will spend the most time on this step, the preparation. Preparation includes:

- **Drawing a picture.** In many cases, this is the most important part of a problem. The picture lets you model the problem and identify the important elements. As you add information to your picture, the outline of the solution will take shape. For the problems in this chapter, a picture could be a motion diagram or a graph—or perhaps both.
- **Collecting necessary information.** The problem's statement may give you some values of variables. Other important information may be implied or must be looked up in a table. Gather everything you need to solve the problem and compile it in a list.
- **Doing preliminary calculations.** There are a few calculations, such as unit conversions, that are best done in advance of the main part of the solution.

SOLVE The Solve step of a solution is where you actually do the mathematics or reasoning necessary to arrive at the answer needed. This is the part of the problem-solving strategy that you likely think of when you think of "solving problems." But don't make the mistake of starting here! The Prepare step will help you be certain you understand the problem before you start putting numbers in equations.

ASSESS The Assess step of your solution is very important. When you have an answer, you should check to see whether it makes sense. Ask yourself:

- **Does my solution answer the question that was asked?** Make sure you have addressed all parts of the question and clearly written down your solutions.
- **Does my answer have the correct units and number of significant figures?**
- **Does the value I computed make physical sense?** In this book all calculations use physically reasonable numbers. You will not be given a problem to solve in which the final velocity of a bicycle is 100 miles per hour! If your answer seems unreasonable, go back and check your work.
- **Can I estimate what the answer should be to check my solution?**
- **Does my final solution make sense in the context of the material I am learning?**

The Pictorial Representation

Many physics problems, including 1-D motion problems, often have several variables and other pieces of information to keep track of. The best way to tackle such problems is to draw a picture, as we noted when we introduced a general problem-solving strategy. But what kind of picture should you draw?

In this section, we will begin to draw **pictorial representations** as an aid to solving problems. A pictorial representation shows all of the important details that we need to keep track of and will be very important in solving motion problems.

TACTICS BOX 2.2 Drawing a pictorial representation (MP)™

❶ **Sketch the situation.** Not just any sketch: Show the object at the *beginning* of the motion, at the *end*, and at any point where the character of the motion changes. Very simple drawings are adequate.
❷ **Establish a coordinate system.** Select your axes and origin to match the motion.
❸ **Define symbols.** Use the sketch to define symbols representing quantities such as position, velocity, acceleration, and time. *Every* variable used later in the mathematical solution should be defined on the sketch.

We will generally combine the pictorial representation with a **list of values,** which will include:

■ *Known information.* Make a table of the quantities whose values you can determine from the problem statement or that you can find quickly with simple geometry or unit conversions.
■ *Desired unknowns.* What quantity or quantities will allow you to answer the question?

Exercise 21 ✐

EXAMPLE 2.9 Drawing a pictorial representation

Complete a pictorial representation and a list of values for the following problem: A rocket sled accelerates at 50 m/s^2 for 5 s. What are the total distance traveled and the final velocity?

PREPARE FIGURE 2.32a shows a pictorial representation as drawn by an artist in the style of the figures in this book. This is

FIGURE 2.32 Constructing a pictorial representation and a list of values.

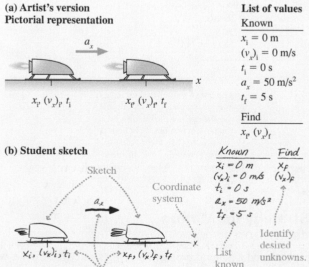

(a) Artist's version
Pictorial representation

a_x

$x_i, (v_x)_i, t_i$ $x_f, (v_x)_f, t_f$ x

List of values

Known
$x_i = 0 \text{ m}$
$(v_x)_i = 0 \text{ m/s}$
$t_i = 0 \text{ s}$
$a_x = 50 \text{ m/s}^2$
$t_f = 5 \text{ s}$

Find
$x_f, (v_x)_f$

(b) Student sketch

Sketch
Coordinate system
a_x

$x_i, (v_x)_i, t_i$ $x_f, (v_x)_f, t_f$

Define symbols.

Known   Find
$x_i = 0 \text{ m}$ x_f
$(v_x)_i = 0 \text{ m/s}$ $(v_x)_f$
$t_i = 0 \text{ s}$
$a_x = 50 \text{ m/s}^2$
$t_f = 5 \text{ s}$

List known information.   Identify desired unknowns.

certainly neater and more artistic than the sketches you will make when solving problems yourself! FIGURE 2.32b shows a sketch like one you might actually do. It's less formal, but it contains all of the important information you need to solve the problem.

NOTE ▶ Throughout this book we will illustrate select examples with actual hand-drawn figures so that you have them to refer to as you work on your own pictures for homework and practice. ◀

Let's look at how these pictures were constructed. The motion has a clear beginning and end; these are the points sketched. A coordinate system has been chosen with the origin at the starting point. The quantities x, v_x, and t are needed at both points, so these have been defined on the sketch and distinguished by subscripts. The acceleration is associated with an interval between these points. Values for two of these quantities are given in the problem statement. Others, such as $x_i = 0 \text{ m}$ and $t_i = 0 \text{ s}$, are inferred from our choice of coordinate system. The value $(v_x)_i = 0 \text{ m/s}$ is part of our *interpretation* of the problem. Finally, we identify x_f and $(v_x)_f$ as the quantities that will answer the question. We now understand quite a bit about the problem and would be ready to start a quantitative analysis.

ASSESS We didn't *solve* the problem; that was not our purpose. Constructing a pictorial representation and a list of values is part of a systematic approach to interpreting a problem and getting ready for a mathematical solution.

The Visual Overview

The pictorial representation and the list of values are a very good complement to the motion diagram and other ways of looking at a problem that we have seen. As we translate a problem into a form we can solve, we will combine these elements into what we will term a **visual overview.** The visual overview will consist of some or all of the following elements:

- A *motion diagram.* A good strategy for solving a motion problem is to start by drawing a motion diagram.
- A *pictorial representation,* as defined above.
- A *graphical representation.* For motion problems, it is often quite useful to include a graph of position and/or velocity.
- A *list of values.* This list should sum up all of the important values in the problem.

Future chapters will add other elements to this visual overview of the physics.

EXAMPLE 2.10 **Kinematics of a rocket launch**

A Saturn V rocket is launched straight up with a constant acceleration of 18 m/s². After 150 s, how fast is the rocket moving and how far has it traveled?

PREPARE FIGURE 2.33 shows a visual overview of the rocket launch that includes a motion diagram, a pictorial representation, and a list of values. The visual overview shows the whole problem in a nutshell. The motion diagram illustrates the motion of the rocket. The pictorial representation (produced according to Tactics Box 2.2) shows axes, identifies the important points of the motion, and defines variables. Finally, we have included a list of values that gives the known and unknown quantities. In the visual overview we have taken the statement of the problem in words and made it much more precise; it contains everything you need to know about the problem.

SOLVE Our first task is to find the final velocity. Our list of values includes the initial velocity, the acceleration, and the time interval, so we can use the first kinematic equation of Table 2.4 to find the final velocity:

$$(v_y)_f = (v_y)_i + a_y\,\Delta t = 0 \text{ m/s} + (18\text{ m/s}^2)(150\text{ s})$$
$$= 2700 \text{ m/s}$$

The distance traveled is found using the second equation in Table 2.4:

$$y_f = y_i + (v_y)_i\,\Delta t + \tfrac{1}{2}a_y(\Delta t)^2$$
$$= 0 \text{ m} + (0 \text{ m/s})(150\text{ s}) + \tfrac{1}{2}(18 \text{ m/s}^2)(150\text{ s})^2$$
$$= 2.0 \times 10^5 \text{ m} = 200 \text{ km}$$

ASSESS The acceleration is very large, and it goes on for a long time, so the large final velocity and large distance traveled seem reasonable.

FIGURE 2.33 Visual overview of the rocket launch.

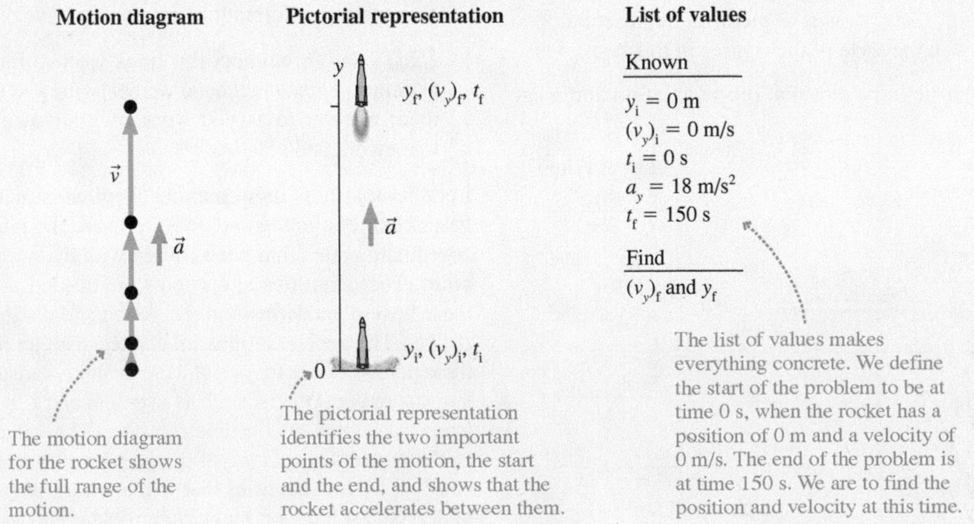

Motion diagram **Pictorial representation** **List of values**

$y_f, (v_y)_f, t_f$

$\vec{a}$

$y_i, (v_y)_i, t_i$

Known

$y_i = 0 \text{ m}$
$(v_y)_i = 0 \text{ m/s}$
$t_i = 0 \text{ s}$
$a_y = 18 \text{ m/s}^2$
$t_f = 150 \text{ s}$

Find

$(v_y)_f \text{ and } y_f$

The motion diagram for the rocket shows the full range of the motion.

The pictorial representation identifies the two important points of the motion, the start and the end, and shows that the rocket accelerates between them.

The list of values makes everything concrete. We define the start of the problem to be at time 0 s, when the rocket has a position of 0 m and a velocity of 0 m/s. The end of the problem is at time 150 s. We are to find the position and velocity at this time.

Problem-Solving Strategy for Motion with Constant Acceleration

1.4–1.6, 1.8, 1.9, 1.11–1.14

Activ**Physics** ONLINE

Earlier in this section, we introduced a general problem-solving strategy. Now we will adapt this general strategy to solving problems of motion with constant acceleration. We will introduce such specific problem-solving strategies in future chapters as well.

Motion with constant acceleration (MP)™

PREPARE Draw a visual overview of the problem. This should include a motion diagram, a pictorial representation, and a list of values; a graphical representation may be useful for certain problems.

SOLVE The mathematical solution is based on the three equations in Table 2.4.

- Though the equations are phrased in terms of the variable x, it's customary to use y for motion in the vertical direction.
- Use the equation that best matches what you know and what you need to find. For example, if you know acceleration and time and are looking for a change in velocity, the first equation is the best one to use.
- Uniform motion with constant velocity has $a = 0$.

ASSESS Is your result believable? Does it have proper units? Does it make sense?

Exercise 25 ✎

EXAMPLE 2.11 Calculating the minimum length of a runway

A fully loaded Boeing 747 with all engines at full thrust accelerates at 2.6 m/s^2. Its minimum takeoff speed is 70 m/s. How much time will the plane take to reach its takeoff speed? What minimum length of runway does the plane require for takeoff?

PREPARE The visual overview of FIGURE 2.34 summarizes the important details of the problem. We set x_i and t_i equal to zero at the starting point of the motion, when the plane is at rest and the acceleration begins. The final point of the motion is when the plane achieves the necessary takeoff speed of 70 m/s. The plane is accelerating to the right, so we will compute the time for the plane to reach a velocity of 70 m/s and the position of the plane at this time, giving us the minimum length of the runway.

FIGURE 2.34 Visual overview for an accelerating plane.

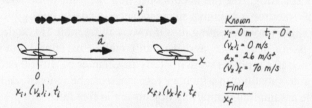

SOLVE First we solve for the time required for the plane to reach takeoff speed. We can use the first equation in Table 2.4 to compute this time:

$$(v_x)_f = (v_x)_i + a_x \, \Delta t$$

$$70 \text{ m/s} = 0 \text{ m/s} + (2.6 \text{ m/s}^2) \, \Delta t$$

$$\Delta t = \frac{70 \text{ m/s}}{2.6 \text{ m/s}^2} = 26.9 \text{ s}$$

We keep an extra significant figure here because we will use this result in the next step of the calculation.

Given the time that the plane takes to reach takeoff speed, we can compute the position of the plane when it reaches this speed using the second equation in Table 2.4:

$$x_f = x_i + (v_x)_i \, \Delta t + \tfrac{1}{2} a_x (\Delta t)^2$$

$$= 0 \text{ m} + (0 \text{ m/s})(26.9 \text{ s}) + \tfrac{1}{2}(2.6 \text{ m/s}^2)(26.9 \text{ s})^2$$

$$= 940 \text{ m}$$

Our final answers are thus that the plane will take 27 s to reach takeoff speed, with a minimum runway length of 940 m.

ASSESS Think about the last time you flew; 27 s seems like a reasonable time for a plane to accelerate on takeoff. Actual runway lengths at major airports are 3000 m or more, a few times greater than the minimum length, because they have to allow for emergency stops during an aborted takeoff. (If we had calculated a distance far greater than 3000 m, we would know we had done something wrong!)

EXAMPLE 2.12 Finding the braking distance

A car is traveling at a speed of 30 m/s, a typical highway speed, on wet pavement. The driver sees an obstacle ahead and decides to stop. From this instant, it takes him 0.75 s to begin applying the brakes. Once the brakes are applied, the car experiences an acceleration of -6.0 m/s^2. How far does the car travel from the instant the driver notices the obstacle until stopping?

PREPARE This problem is more involved than previous problems we have solved, so we will take more care with the visual overview in FIGURE 2.35. In addition to a motion diagram and a pictorial representation, we include a graphical representation. Notice that there are two different phases of the motion: a constant-velocity phase before braking begins, and a steady slowing

Continued

FIGURE 2.35 Visual overview for a car braking to a stop.

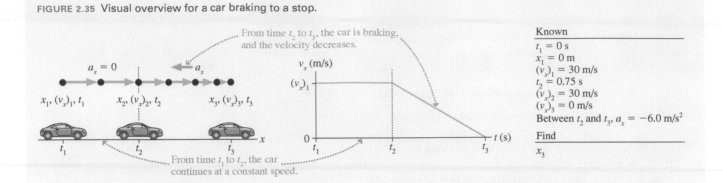

From time t_2 to t_3, the car is braking, and the velocity decreases.

From time t_1 to t_2, the car continues at a constant speed.

Known
$t_1 = 0$ s
$x_1 = 0$ m
$(v_x)_1 = 30$ m/s
$t_2 = 0.75$ s
$(v_x)_2 = 30$ m/s
$(v_x)_3 = 0$ m/s
Between t_2 and t_3, $a_x = -6.0$ m/s^2

Find
x_3

down once the brakes are applied. We will need to do two different calculations, one for each phase. Consequently, we've used numerical subscripts rather than a simple i and f.

SOLVE From t_1 to t_2 the velocity stays constant at 30 m/s. This is uniform motion, so the position at time t_2 is computed using Equation 2.4:

$$x_2 = x_1 + (v_x)_1(t_2 - t_1) = 0 \text{ m} + (30 \text{ m/s})(0.75 \text{ s})$$
$$= 22.5 \text{ m}$$

At t_2, the velocity begins to decrease at a steady -6.0 m/s^2 until the car comes to rest at t_3. This time interval can be computed using the first equation in Table 2.4, $(v_x)_3 = (v_x)_2 + a_x \Delta t$:

$$\Delta t = t_3 - t_2 = \frac{(v_x)_3 - (v_x)_2}{a_x} = \frac{0 \text{ m/s} - 30 \text{ m/s}}{-6.0 \text{ m/s}^2} = 5.0 \text{ s}$$

The position at time t_3 is computed using the second equation in Table 2.4; we take point 2 as the initial point and point 3 as the final point for this phase of the motion and use $\Delta t = t_3 - t_2$:

$$x_3 = x_2 + (v_x)_2 \Delta t + \tfrac{1}{2}a_x(\Delta t)^2$$
$$= 22.5 \text{ m} + (30 \text{ m/s})(5.0 \text{ s}) + \tfrac{1}{2}(-6.0 \text{ m/s}^2)(5.0 \text{ s})^2$$
$$= 98 \text{ m}$$

x_3 is the position of the car at the end of the problem—and so the car travels 98 m before coming to rest.

ASSESS The numbers for the reaction time and the acceleration on wet pavement are reasonable ones for an alert driver in a car with good tires. The final distance is quite large—it is more than the length of a football field.

1.7, 1.10

2.7 Free Fall

A particularly important example of constant acceleration is the motion of an object moving under the influence of gravity only, and no other forces. This motion is called **free fall**. Strictly speaking, free fall occurs only in a vacuum, where there is no air resistance. But if you drop a hammer, air resistance is nearly negligible, so we'll make only a very slight error in treating it *as if* it were in free fall. If you drop a feather, air resistance is *not* negligible, and we can't make this approximation. Motion with air resistance is a problem we will study in Chapter 5. Until then, we will restrict our attention to situations in which air resistance can be ignored, and we will make the reasonable assumption that falling objects are in free fall.

As part of his early studies of motion, Galileo did the first careful experiments on free fall and made the surprising observation that two objects of different weight dropped from the same height will, if air resistance can be neglected, hit the ground at the same time and with the same speed. In fact—as Galileo surmised, and as a famous demonstration on the moon showed—in a vacuum, where there is no air resistance, this holds true for *any* two objects.

Galileo's discovery about free fall means that **any two objects in free fall, regardless of their mass, have the same acceleration.** This is an especially important conclusion. FIGURE 2.36a shows the motion diagram of an object that was released from rest and falls freely. The motion diagram and graph would be identical for a falling baseball or a falling boulder! FIGURE 2.36b shows the object's velocity graph. As we can see, the velocity changes at a steady rate. The slope of the velocity-versus-time graph is the free-fall acceleration $a_{\text{free fall}}$.

Instead of dropping the object, suppose we throw it upward. What happens then? You know that the object will move up and that its speed will decrease as it rises.

"Looks like Mr. Galileo was correct..." was the comment made by Apollo 15 astronaut David Scott, who dropped a hammer and a feather on the moon. The objects were dropped from the same height at the same time and hit the ground simultaneously—something that would not happen in the atmosphere of the earth!

FIGURE 2.36 Motion of an object in free fall.

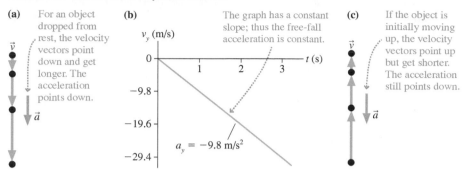

(a) For an object dropped from rest, the velocity vectors point down and get longer. The acceleration points down.

$\vec{v}$ $\vec{a}$

(b) The graph has a constant slope; thus the free-fall acceleration is constant.

v_y (m/s)

$a_y = -9.8$ m/s^2

(c) If the object is initially moving up, the velocity vectors point up but get shorter. The acceleration still points down.

$\vec{v}$ $\vec{a}$

This is illustrated in the motion diagram of FIGURE 2.36c, which shows a surprising result: Even though the object is moving up, its acceleration still points down. In fact, **the free-fall acceleration always points down,** no matter what direction an object is moving.

NOTE ▶ Despite the name, free fall is not restricted to objects that are literally falling. Any object moving under the influence of gravity only, and no other forces, is in free fall. This includes objects falling straight down, objects that have been tossed or shot straight up, objects in projectile motion (such as a passed football), and, as we will see, satellites in orbit. In this chapter we consider only objects that move up and down along a vertical line; projectile motion will be studied in Chapter 3. ◀

The free-all acceleration is always in the same direction, and on earth, it always has approximately the same magnitude. Careful measurements show that the value of the free-fall acceleration varies slightly at different places on the earth, but for the calculations in this book we will use the the following average value:

$$\vec{a}_{\text{free fall}} = (9.80 \text{ m/s}^2, \text{ vertically downward}) \qquad (2.15)$$

Standard value for the acceleration of an object in free fall

The magnitude of the **free-fall acceleration** has the special symbol g:

$$g = 9.80 \text{ m/s}^2$$

We will generally work with two significant figures and so will use $g = 9.8$ m/s^2. Several points about free fall are worthy of note:

- g, by definition, is *always* positive. **There will never be a problem that uses a negative value for g.**
- The velocity graph in Figure 2.36b has a negative slope. Even though a falling object speeds up, it has *negative* acceleration. Alternatively, notice that the acceleration vector $\vec{a}_{\text{free fall}}$ points down. Thus g is *not* the object's acceleration, simply the magnitude of the acceleration. The one-dimensional acceleration is

$$a_y = a_{\text{free fall}} = -g$$

It is a_y that is negative, not g.
- Because free fall is motion with constant acceleration, we can use the kinematic equations of Table 2.4 with the acceleration being due to gravity, $a_y = -g$.
- g is not called "gravity." Gravity is a force, not an acceleration. g is the *free-fall acceleration.*
- $g = 9.80$ m/s^2 only on earth. Other planets have different values of g. You will learn in Chapter 6 how to determine g for other planets.

Some of the children are moving up and some are moving down, but all are in free fall—and so are accelerating downward at 9.8 m/s^2.

TRY IT YOURSELF

A reaction time challenge Hold a \$1 (or larger!) bill by an upper corner. Have a friend prepare to grasp a lower corner, putting her fingers *near but not touching* the bill. Tell her to try to catch the bill when you drop it by simply closing her fingers without moving her hand downward—and that if she can catch it, she can keep it. Don't worry; the bill's free fall will keep your money safe. In the few tenths of a second that it takes your friend to react, free fall will take the bill beyond her grasp.

■ We will sometimes compute acceleration in units of g. An acceleration of 9.8 m/s^2 is an acceleration of $1g$; an acceleration of 19.6 m/s^2 is $2g$. Generally, we can compute

$$\text{acceleration (in units of } g) = \frac{\text{acceleration (in units of m/s}^2)}{9.8 \text{ m/s}^2} \qquad (2.16)$$

This allows us to express accelerations in units that have a definite physical reference.

EXAMPLE 2.13   **Analyzing a rock's fall**

A heavy rock is dropped from rest at the top of a cliff and falls 100 m before hitting the ground. How long does the rock take to fall to the ground, and what is its velocity when it hits?

PREPARE FIGURE 2.37 shows a visual overview with all necessary data. We have placed the origin at the ground, which makes $y_i = 100$ m.

FIGURE 2.37 Visual overview of a falling rock.

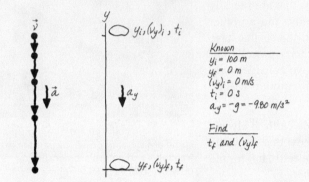

Known
$y_i = 100$ m
$y_f = 0$ m
$(v_y)_i = 0$ m/s
$t_i = 0$ s
$a_y = -g = -9.80$ m/s^2

Find
t_f and $(v_y)_f$

SOLVE Free fall is motion with the specific constant acceleration $a_y = -g$. The first question involves a relation between time and distance, a relation expressed by the second equation in Table 2.4. Using $(v_y)_i = 0$ m/s and $t_i = 0$ s, we find

$$y_f = y_i + (v_y)_i \, \Delta t + \tfrac{1}{2} a_y \, \Delta t^2 = y_i - \tfrac{1}{2} g \, \Delta t^2 = y_i - \tfrac{1}{2} g t_f^2$$

We can now solve for t_f:

$$t_f = \sqrt{\frac{2(y_i - y_f)}{g}} = \sqrt{\frac{2(100 \text{ m} - 0 \text{ m})}{9.80 \text{ m/s}^2}} = 4.52 \text{ s}$$

Now that we know the fall time, we can use the first kinematic equation to find $(v_y)_f$:

$$(v_y)_f = (v_y)_i - g \, \Delta t = -g t_f = -(9.80 \text{ m/s}^2)(4.52 \text{ s})$$

$$= -44.3 \text{ m/s}$$

ASSESS Are the answers reasonable? Well, 100 m is about 300 feet, which is about the height of a 30-floor building. How long does it take something to fall 30 floors? Four or five seconds seems pretty reasonable. How fast would it be going at the bottom? Using an approximate version of our conversion factor 1 m/s ≈ 2 mph, we find that 44.3 m/s ≈ 90 mph. That also seems like a pretty reasonable speed for something that has fallen 30 floors. Suppose we had made a mistake. If we misplaced a decimal point we could have calculated a speed of 443 m/s, or about 900 mph! This is clearly *not* reasonable. If we had misplaced the decimal point in the other direction, we would have calculated a speed of 4.3 m/s ≈ 9 mph. This is another unreasonable result, because this is slower than a typical bicycling speed.

CONCEPTUAL EXAMPLE 2.14   **Analyzing the motion of a ball tossed upward**

Draw a motion diagram and a velocity-versus-time graph for a ball tossed straight up in the air from the point that it leaves the hand until just before it is caught.

REASON You know what the motion of the ball looks like: The ball goes up, and then it comes back down again. This complicates the drawing of a motion diagram a bit, as the ball retraces its route as it falls. A literal motion diagram would show the upward motion and downward motion on top of each other, leading to confusion. We can avoid this difficulty by horizontally separating the upward motion and downward motion diagrams. This will not affect our conclusions because it does not change any of the vectors. The motion diagram and velocity-versus-time graph appear as in FIGURE 2.38 on the next page.

ASSESS The highest point in the ball's motion, where it reverses direction, is called a *turning point*. What are the velocity and the acceleration at this point? We can see from the motion diagram that the velocity vectors are pointing upward but getting shorter

as the ball approaches the top. As it starts to fall, the velocity vectors are pointing downward and getting longer. There must be a moment—just an instant as $\vec{v}$ switches from pointing up to pointing down—when the velocity is zero. Indeed, the ball's velocity *is* zero for an instant at the precise top of the motion! We can also see on the velocity graph that there is one instant of time when $v_y = 0$. This is the turning point.

But what about the acceleration at the top? Many people expect the acceleration to be zero at the highest point. But recall that the velocity at the top point is changing—from up to down. If the velocity is changing, there *must* be an acceleration. The slope of the velocity graph at the instant when $v_y = 0$—that is, at the highest point—is no different than at any other point in the motion. The ball is still in free fall with acceleration $a_y = -g$!

Another way to think about this is to note that zero acceleration would mean no change of velocity. When the ball reached zero velocity at the top, it would hang there and not fall if the acceleration were also zero!

FIGURE 2.38 Motion diagram and velocity graph of a ball tossed straight up in the air.

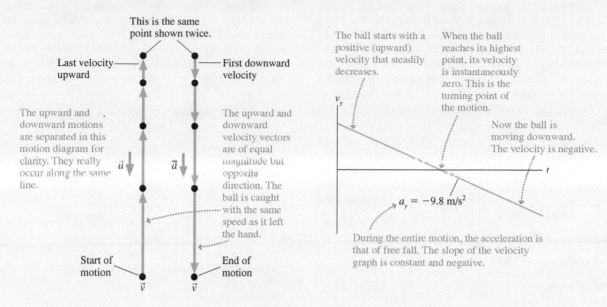

This is the same point shown twice.

Last velocity upward

First downward velocity

The upward and downward motions are separated in this motion diagram for clarity. They really occur along the same line.

The upward and downward velocity vectors are of equal magnitude but opposite direction. The ball is caught with the same speed as it left the hand.

Start of motion

End of motion

$\vec{v}$ $\vec{v}$

$\vec{a}$ $\vec{a}$

The ball starts with a positive (upward) velocity that steadily decreases.

When the ball reaches its highest point, its velocity is instantaneously zero. This is the turning point of the motion.

Now the ball is moving downward. The velocity is negative.

$a_y = -9.8 \text{ m/s}^2$

During the entire motion, the acceleration is that of free fall. The slope of the velocity graph is constant and negative.

EXAMPLE 2.15   **Finding the height of a leap**

A springbok is an antelope found in southern Africa that gets its name from its remarkable jumping ability. When a springbok is startled, it will leap straight up into the air—a maneuver called a "pronk." A springbok goes into a crouch to perform a pronk. It then extends its legs forcefully, accelerating at 35 m/s² for 0.70 m as its legs straighten. Legs fully extended, it leaves the ground and rises into the air.

a. At what speed does the springbok leave the ground?
b. How high does it go?

PREPARE We begin with the visual overview shown in FIGURE 2.39, where we've identified two different phases of the motion: the springbok pushing off the ground and the springbok rising into the air. We'll treat these as two separate problems that we solve in turn. We will "re-use" the variables y_i, y_f, $(v_y)_i$, and $(v_y)_f$ for the two phases of the motion.

For the first part of our solution, in Figure 2.39a we choose the origin of the y-axis at the position of the springbok deep in the crouch. The final position is the top extent of the push, at the instant the springbok leaves the ground. We want to find the velocity at this position because that's how fast the springbok is moving as it leaves the ground. Figure 2.39b essentially starts over—we have defined a new vertical axis with its origin at the ground, so the highest point of the springbok's motion is a

FIGURE 2.39 A visual overview of the springbok's leap.

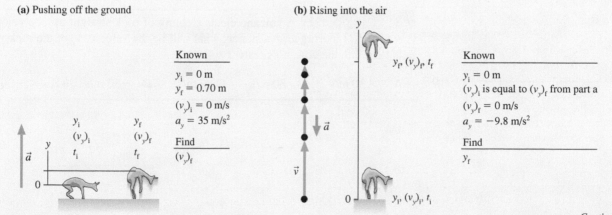

(a) Pushing off the ground

y_i
$(v_y)_i$
t_i

y_f
$(v_y)_f$
t_f

$\vec{a}$

0

Known
$y_i = 0 \text{ m}$
$y_f = 0.70 \text{ m}$
$(v_y)_i = 0 \text{ m/s}$
$a_y = 35 \text{ m/s}^2$

Find
$(v_y)_f$

(b) Rising into the air

$y_f, (v_y)_f, t_f$

$\vec{a}$

$\vec{v}$

$y_i, (v_y)_i, t_i$

0

Known
$y_i = 0 \text{ m}$
$(v_y)_i$ is equal to $(v_y)_f$ from part a
$(v_y)_f = 0 \text{ m/s}$
$a_y = -9.8 \text{ m/s}^2$

Find
y_f

Continued

distance above the ground. The table of values shows the key piece of information for this second part of the problem: The initial velocity for part b is the final velocity from part a.

After the springbok leaves the ground, this is a free-fall problem because the springbok is moving under the influence of gravity only. We want to know the height of the leap, so we are looking for the height at the top point of the motion. This is a turning point of the motion, with the instantaneous velocity equal to zero. Thus y_f, the height of the leap, is the springbok's position at the instant $(v_y)_f = 0$.

SOLVE a. For the first phase, pushing off the ground, we have information about displacement, initial velocity, and acceleration, but we don't know anything about the time interval. The third equation in Table 2.4 is perfect for this type of situation. We can rearrange it to solve for the velocity with which the springbok lifts off the ground:

$$(v_y)_f^2 = v_i^2 + 2a_y\Delta y = (0 \text{ m/s})^2 + 2(35 \text{ m/s}^2)(0.70 \text{ m}) = 49 \text{ m}^2/\text{s}^2$$

$$(v_y)_f = \sqrt{49 \text{ m}^2/\text{s}^2} = 7.0 \text{ m/s}$$

The springbok leaves the ground with a speed of 7.0 m/s.

b. Now we are ready for the second phase of the motion, the vertical motion after leaving the ground. The third equation in Table 2.4 is again appropriate because again we don't know the time. Because $y_i = 0$, the springbok's displacement is $\Delta y = y_f - y_i = y_f$, the height of the vertical leap. From part a, the initial velocity is $(v_y)_i = 7.0$ m/s, and the final velocity is $(v_y)_f = 0$. This is free-fall motion, with $a_y = -g$; thus

$$(v_y)_f^2 = 0 = (v_y)_i^2 - 2g\Delta y = (v_y)_i^2 - 2gy_f$$

which gives

$$(v_y)_i^2 = 2gy_f$$

Solving for y_f, we get a jump height of

$$y_f = \frac{(7.0 \text{ m/s})^2}{2(9.8 \text{ m/s}^2)} = 2.5 \text{ m}$$

ASSESS 2.5 m is a remarkable leap—a bit over 8 ft—but these animals are known for their jumping ability, so this seems reasonable.

FIGURE 2.40 Velocity-versus-time and position-versus-time graphs for a sprint between a man and a horse.

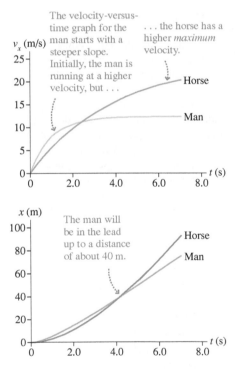

The caption accompanying the photo at the start of the chapter asked a question about animals and their athletic abilities: Who is the winner in a race between a horse and a man? The surprising answer is "It depends." Specifically, the winner depends on the length of the race.

Some animals are capable of high speed; others are capable of great acceleration. Horses can run much faster than humans, but, when starting from rest, humans are capable of much greater initial acceleration. FIGURE 2.40 shows velocity and position graphs for an elite male sprinter and a thoroughbred racehorse. The horse's maximum velocity is about twice that of the man, but the man's initial acceleration—the slope of the velocity graph at early times—is about twice that of the horse. As the second graph shows, a man could win a *very* short race. For a longer race, the horse's higher maximum velocity will put it in the lead; the men's world-record time for the mile is a bit under 4 min, but a horse can easily run this distance in less than 2 min.

For a race of many miles, another factor comes into play: energy. A very long race is less about velocity and acceleration than about endurance—the ability to continue expending energy for a long time. In such endurance trials, humans often win. We will explore such energy issues in Chapter 11.

STOP TO THINK 2.6   A volcano ejects a chunk of rock straight up at a velocity of $v_y = 30$ m/s. Ignoring air resistance, what will be the velocity v_y of the rock when it falls back into the volcano's crater?

A. > 30 m/s   B. 30 m/s   C. 0 m/s   D. -30 m/s   E. < -30 m/s

INTEGRATED EXAMPLE 2.16   **Speed versus endurance**

Cheetahs have the highest top speed of any land animal, but they usually fail in their attempts to catch their prey because their endurance is limited. They can maintain their maximum speed of 30 m/s for only about 15 s before they need to stop.

Thomson's gazelles, their preferred prey, have a lower top speed than cheetahs, but they can maintain this speed for a few minutes. When a cheetah goes after a gazelle, success or failure is a simple matter of kinematics: Is the cheetah's high speed enough to allow it to reach its prey before the cheetah runs out of steam? The following problem uses realistic data for such a chase.

A cheetah has spotted a gazelle. The cheetah leaps into action, reaching its top speed of 30 m/s in a few seconds. At this instant, the gazelle, 160 m from the running cheetah, notices the danger and heads directly away. The gazelle accelerates at 4.5 m/s² for 6.0 s, then continues running at a constant speed. After reaching its maximum speed, the cheetah can continue running for only 15 s. Does the cheetah catch the gazelle, or does the gazelle escape?

PREPARE The example asks, "Does the cheetah catch the gazelle?" Our most challenging task is to translate these words into a graphical and mathematical problem that we can solve using the techniques of the chapter.

There are two related problems: the motion of the cheetah and the motion of the gazelle, for which we'll use the subscripts "C" and "G". Let's take our starting time, $t_1 = 0$ s, as the instant that the gazelle notices the cheetah and begins to run. We'll take the position of the cheetah at this instant as the origin of our coordinate system, so $x_{1C} = 0$ m and $x_{1G} = 160$ m—the gazelle is 160 m away when it notices the cheetah. We've used this information to draw the visual overview in FIGURE 2.41, which includes motion diagrams and velocity graphs for the cheetah and the gazelle. The visual overview sums up everything we know about the problem.

With a clear picture of the situation, we can now rephrase the problem this way: Compute the position of the cheetah and the position of the gazelle at $t_3 = 15$ s, the time when the cheetah needs to break off the chase. If $x_{3G} \geq x_{3C}$, then the gazelle stays out in front and escapes. If $x_{3G} < x_{3C}$, the cheetah wins the race—and gets its dinner.

SOLVE The cheetah is in uniform motion for the entire duration of the problem, so we can use Equation 2.4 to solve for its position at $t_3 = 15$ s:

$$x_{3C} = x_{1C} + (v_x)_{1C}\Delta t = 0 \text{ m} + (30 \text{ m/s})(15 \text{ s}) = 450 \text{ m}$$

The gazelle's motion has two phases: one of constant acceleration and then one of constant velocity. We can solve for the position and the velocity at t_2, the end of the first phase, using the first two equations in Table 2.4. Let's find the velocity first:

$$(v_x)_{2G} = (v_x)_{1G} + (a_x)_G\Delta t = 0 \text{ m/s} + (4.5 \text{ m/s}^2)(6.0 \text{ s}) = 27 \text{ m/s}$$

The gazelle's position at t_2 is:

> Δt is the time for this phase of the motion, $t_2 - t_1 = 6.0$ s.

$$x_{2G} = x_{1G} + (v_x)_{1G}\,\Delta t + \tfrac{1}{2}(a_x)_G(\Delta t)^2$$
$$= 160 \text{ m} + 0 + \tfrac{1}{2}(4.5 \text{ m/s}^2)(6.0 \text{ s})^2 = 240 \text{ m}$$

> The gazelle has a head start; it begins at $x_{1G} = 160$ m.

From t_2 to t_3 the gazelle moves at a constant speed, so we can use the uniform motion equation, Equation 2.4, to find its final position:

> The gazelle begins this phase of the motion at $x_{2G} = 240$ m.
> Δt for this phase of the motion is $t_3 - t_2 = 9.0$ s.

$$x_{3G} = x_{2G} + (v_x)_{2G}\,\Delta t = 240 \text{ m} + (27 \text{ m/s})(9.0 \text{ s}) = 480 \text{ m}$$

x_{3C} is 450 m; x_{3G} is 480 m. The gazelle is 30 m ahead of the cheetah when the cheetah has to break off the chase, so the gazelle escapes.

ASSESS Does our solution make sense? Let's look at the final result. The numbers in the problem statement are realistic, so we expect our results to mirror real life. The speed for the gazelle is close to that of the cheetah, which seems reasonable for two animals known for their speed. And the result is the most common occurrence—the chase is close, but the gazelle gets away.

FIGURE 2.41 Visual overview for the cheetah and for the gazelle.

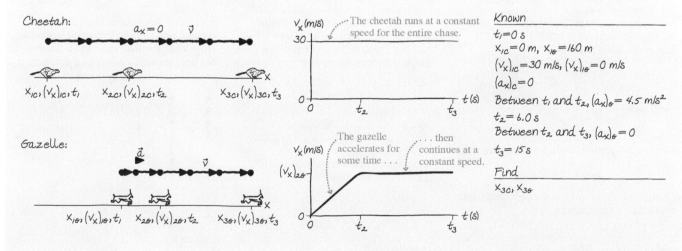

SUMMARY

The goal of Chapter 2 has been to describe and analyze linear motion.

GENERAL STRATEGIES

Problem-Solving Strategy

Our general problem-solving strategy has three parts:

PREPARE Set up the problem:

- Draw a picture.
- Collect necessary information.
- Do preliminary calculations.

SOLVE Do the necessary mathematics or reasoning.

ASSESS Check your answer to see if it is complete in all details and makes physical sense.

Visual Overview

A visual overview consists of several pieces that completely specify a problem. This may include any or all of the elements below:

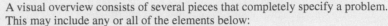

| Motion diagram | Pictorial representation | Graphical representation | List of values |

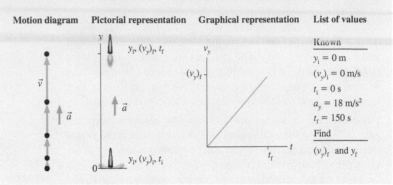

IMPORTANT CONCEPTS

Velocity is the rate of change of position:

$$v_x = \frac{\Delta x}{\Delta t}$$

Acceleration is the rate of change of velocity:

$$a_x = \frac{\Delta v_x}{\Delta t}$$

The units of acceleration are m/s^2.

An object is speeding up if v_x and a_x have the same sign, slowing down if they have opposite signs.

A position-versus-time graph plots position on the vertical axis against time on the horizontal axis.

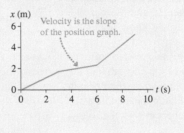

A velocity-versus-time graph plots velocity on the vertical axis against time on the horizontal axis.

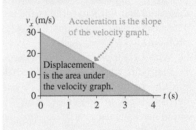

APPLICATIONS

Uniform motion

An object in uniform motion has a constant velocity. Its velocity graph is a horizontal line; its position graph is linear.

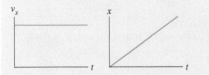

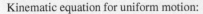

Kinematic equation for uniform motion:

$$x_f = x_i + v_x \, \Delta t$$

Uniform motion is a special case of constant-acceleration motion, with $a_x = 0$.

Motion with constant acceleration

An object with constant acceleration has a constantly changing velocity. Its velocity graph is linear; its position graph is a parabola.

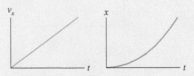

Kinematic equations for motion with constant acceleration:

$$(v_x)_f = (v_x)_i + a_x \, \Delta t$$

$$x_f = x_i + (v_x)_i \, \Delta t + \frac{1}{2} a_x (\Delta t)^2$$

$$(v_x)_f^2 = (v_x)_i^2 + 2a_x \, \Delta x$$

Free fall

Free fall is a special case of constant-acceleration motion; the acceleration has magnitude $g = 9.80 \, m/s^2$ and is always directed vertically downward whether an object is moving up or down.

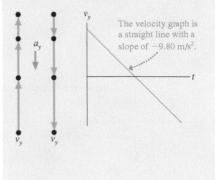

The velocity graph is a straight line with a slope of $-9.80 \, m/s^2$.

™ For homework assigned on MasteringPhysics, go to
www.masteringphysics.com

Problems labeled **INT** integrate significant material from earlier
chapters; **BIO** are of biological or medical interest.

Problem difficulty is labeled as | (straightforward) to ||||| (challenging).

QUESTIONS

Conceptual Questions

1. A person gets in an elevator on the ground floor and rides it to the top floor of a building. Sketch a velocity-versus-time graph for this motion.
2. a. Give an example of a vertical motion with a positive velocity and a negative acceleration.
   b. Give an example of a vertical motion with a negative velocity and a negative acceleration.
3. Sketch a velocity-versus-time graph for a rock that is thrown straight upward, from the instant it leaves the hand until the instant it hits the ground.
4. You are driving down the road at a constant speed. Another car going a bit faster catches up with you and passes you. Draw a position graph for both vehicles on the same set of axes, and note the point on the graph where the other vehicle passes you.
5. A car is traveling north. Can its acceleration vector ever point south? Explain.
6. Certain animals are capable of running at great speeds; other **BIO** animals are capable of tremendous accelerations. Speculate on which would be more beneficial to a predator—large maximum speed or large acceleration.
7. A ball is thrown straight up into the air. At each of the following instants, is the ball's acceleration a_y equal to g, $-g$, 0, $< g$, or $> g$?
   a. Just after leaving your hand?
   b. At the very top (maximum height)?
   c. Just before hitting the ground?
8. A rock is *thrown* (not dropped) straight down from a bridge into the river below.
   a. Immediately after being released, is the magnitude of the rock's acceleration greater than g, less than g, or equal to g? Explain.
   b. Immediately before hitting the water, is the magnitude of the the rock's acceleration greater than g, less than g, or equal to g? Explain.
9. Figure Q2.9 shows an object's position-versus-time graph. The letters A to E correspond to various segments of the motion in which the graph has constant slope.

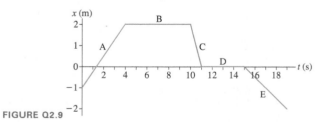

FIGURE Q2.9

   a. Write a realistic motion short story for an object that would have this position graph.
   b. In which segment(s) is the object at rest?

   c. In which segment(s) is the object moving to the right?
   d. Is the speed of the object during segment C greater than, equal to, or less than its speed during segment E? Explain.
10. Figure Q2.10 shows the position graph for an object moving along the horizontal axis.
   a. Write a realistic motion short story for an object that would have this position graph.
   b. Draw the corresponding velocity graph.

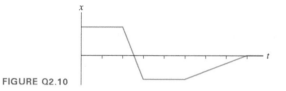

FIGURE Q2.10

11. Figure Q2.11 shows the position-versus-time graphs for two objects, A and B, that are moving along the same axis.
   a. At the instant $t = 1$ s, is the speed of A greater than, less than, or equal to the speed of B? Explain.
   b. Do objects A and B ever have the *same* speed? If so, at what time or times? Explain.

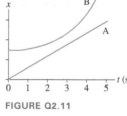

FIGURE Q2.11

12. Figure Q2.12 shows a position-versus-time graph. At which lettered point or points is the object
   a. Moving the fastest?
   b. Moving to the left?
   c. Speeding up?
   d. Slowing down?
   e. Turning around?

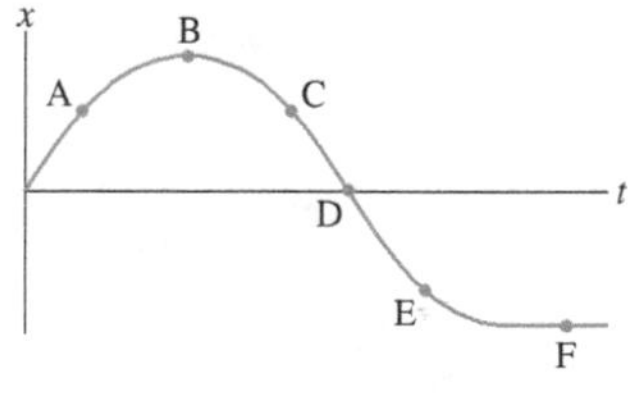

FIGURE Q2.12

13. Figure Q2.13 is the velocity-versus-time graph for an object moving along the x-axis.
   a. During which segment(s) is the velocity constant?
   b. During which segment(s) is the object speeding up?
   c. During which segment(s) is the object slowing down?
   d. During which segment(s) is the object standing still?
   e. During which segment(s) is the object moving to the right?

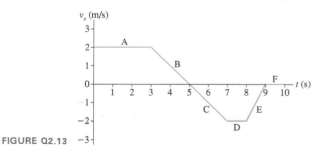

FIGURE Q2.13

14. A car traveling at velocity v takes distance d to stop after the brakes are applied. What is the stopping distance if the car is initially traveling at velocity $2v$? Assume that the acceleration due to the braking is the same in both cases.

Multiple-Choice Questions

15. | Figure Q2.15 shows the position graph of a car traveling on a straight road. At which labeled instant is the speed of the car greatest?

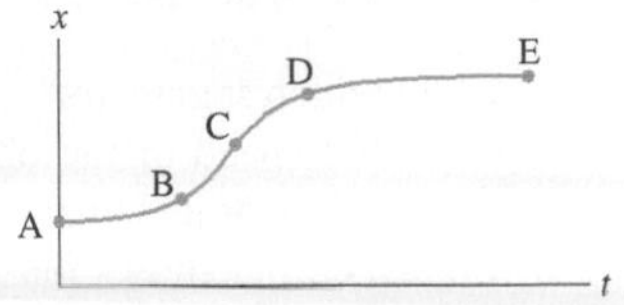

16. | Figure Q2.16 shows the position graph of a car traveling on a straight road. The velocity at instant 1 is _____ and the velocity at instant 2 is _____.
    A. positive, negative
    B. positive, positive
    C. negative, negative
    D. negative, zero
    E. positive, zero

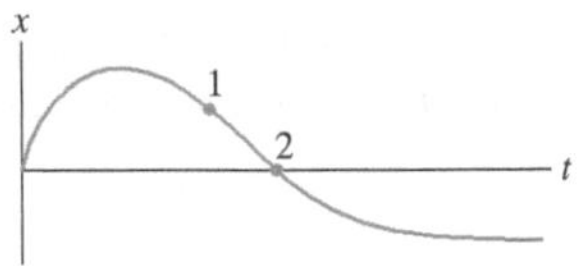

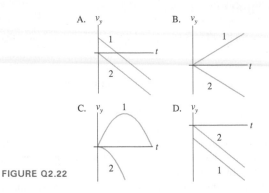

FIGURE Q2.15

FIGURE Q2.16

17. | Figure Q2.17 shows an object's position-versus-time graph. What is the velocity of the object at $t = 6$ s?
    A. 0.67 m/s
    B. 0.83 m/s
    C. 3.3 m/s
    D. 4.2 m/s
    E. 25 m/s

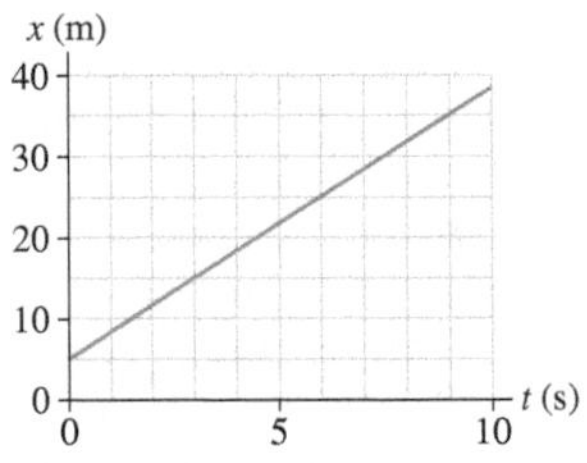

FIGURE Q2.17

18. | The following options describe the motion of four cars A–D. Which car has the largest acceleration?
    A. Goes from 0 m/s to 10 m/s in 5.0 s
    B. Goes from 0 m/s to 5.0 m/s in 2.0 s
    C. Goes from 0 m/s to 20 m/s in 7.0 s
    D. Goes from 0 m/s to 3.0 m/s in 1.0 s

19. | A car is traveling at $v_x = 20$ m/s. The driver applies the brakes, and the car slows with $a_x = -4.0$ m/s². What is the stopping distance?
    A. 5.0 m
    B. 25 m
    C. 40 m
    D. 50 m

20. ‖ Velocity-versus-time graphs for three drag racers are shown in Figure Q2.20. At $t = 5.0$ s, which car has traveled the furthest?
    A. Andy
    B. Betty
    C. Carl
    D. All have traveled the same distance

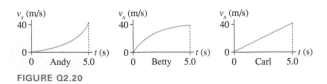

FIGURE Q2.20

21. | Which of the three drag racers in Question 20 had the greatest acceleration at $t = 0$ s?
    A. Andy
    B. Betty
    C. Carl
    D. All had the same acceleration

22. ‖ Ball 1 is thrown straight up in the air and, at the same instant, ball 2 is released from rest and allowed to fall. Which velocity graph in Figure Q2.22 best represents the motion of the two balls?

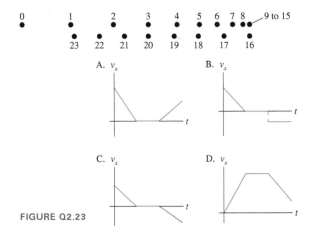

FIGURE Q2.22

23. ‖ Figure Q2.23 shows a motion diagram with the clock reading (in seconds) shown at each position. From $t = 9$ s to $t = 15$ s the object is at the same position. After that, it returns along the same track. The positions of the dots for $t \geq 16$ s are offset for clarity. Which graph best represents the object's *velocity?*

FIGURE Q2.23

24. ‖ A car can go from 0 to 60 mph in 7.0 s. Assuming that it could maintain the same acceleration at higher speeds, how long would it take the car to go from 0 to 120 mph?
    A. 10 s
    B. 14 s
    C. 21 s
    D. 28 s

25. ‖ A car can go from 0 to 60 mph in 12 s. A second car is capable of twice the acceleration of the first car. Assuming that it could maintain the same acceleration at higher speeds, how much time will this second car take to go from 0 to 120 mph?
    A. 12 s
    B. 9.0 s
    C. 6.0 s
    D. 3.0 s

PROBLEMS

Section 2.1 Describing Motion

1. ▌ Figure P2.1 shows a motion diagram of a car traveling down a street. The camera took one frame every second. A distance scale is provided.
   a. Measure the x-value of the car at each dot. Place your data in a table, similar to Table 2.1, showing each position and the instant of time at which it occurred.
   b. Make a graph of x versus t, using the data in your table. Because you have data only at certain instants of time, your graph should consist of dots that are not connected together.

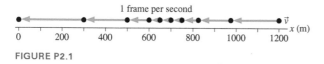

FIGURE P2.1

2. ▌ For each motion diagram in Figure P2.2, determine the sign (positive or negative) of the position and the velocity.

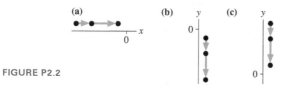

FIGURE P2.2

3. ▌ Write a short description of the motion of a real object for which Figure P2.3 would be a realistic position-versus-time graph.

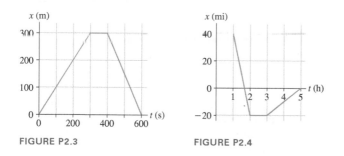

FIGURE P2.3   FIGURE P2.4

4. ▌ Write a short description of the motion of a real object for which Figure P2.4 would be a realistic position-versus-time graph.
5. ▌ The position graph of Figure P2.5 shows a dog slowly sneaking up on a squirrel, then putting on a burst of speed.
   a. For how many seconds does the dog move at the slower speed?
   b. Draw the dog's velocity-versus-time graph. Include a numerical scale on both axes.

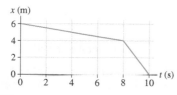

FIGURE P2.5

6. ▌ The position graph of Figure P2.6 represents the motion of a ball being rolled back and forth by two children.
   a. At what positions are the two children sitting?
   b. Draw the ball's velocity-versus-time graph. Include a numerical scale on both axes.

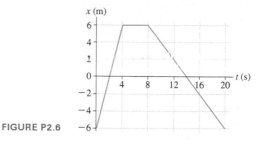

FIGURE P2.6

7. ▌ A rural mail carrier is driving slowly, putting mail in mailboxes near the road. He overshoots one mailbox, stops, shifts into reverse, and then backs up until he is at the right spot. The velocity graph of Figure P2.7 represents his motion.
   a. Draw the mail carrier's position-versus-time graph. Assume that $x = 0$ m at $t = 0$ s.
   b. What is the position of the mailbox?

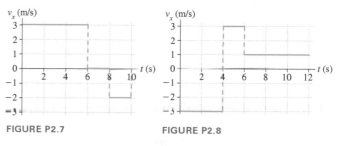

FIGURE P2.7   FIGURE P2.8

8. ▌ For the velocity-versus-time graph of Figure P2.8:
   a. Draw the corresponding position-versus-time graph. Assume that $x = 0$ m at $t = 0$ s.
   b. What is the object's position at $t = 12$ s?
   c. Describe a moving object that could have these graphs.
9. ▌ A bicyclist has the position-versus-time graph shown in Figure P2.9. What is the bicyclist's velocity at $t = 10$ s, at $t = 25$ s, and at $t = 35$ s?

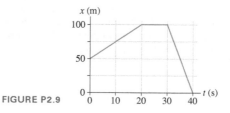

FIGURE P2.9

Section 2.2 Uniform Motion

10. ▌ In college softball, the distance from the pitcher's mound to the batter is 43 feet. If the ball leaves the bat at 100 mph, how much time elapses between the hit and the ball reaching the pitcher?

11. ‖ Alan leaves Los Angeles at 8:00 A.M. to drive to San Francisco, 400 mi away. He travels at a steady 50 mph. Beth leaves Los Angeles at 9:00 A.M. and drives a steady 60 mph.
    a. Who gets to San Francisco first?
    b. How long does the first to arrive have to wait for the second?

12. ‖ Richard is driving home to visit his parents. 125 mi of the trip are on the interstate highway where the speed limit is 65 mph. Normally Richard drives at the speed limit, but today he is running late and decides to take his chances by driving at 70 mph. How many minutes does he save?

13. ‖‖ In a 5.00 km race, one runner runs at a steady 12.0 km/h and another runs at 14.5 km/h. How long does the faster runner have to wait at the finish line to see the slower runner cross?

14. ‖‖‖ In an 8.00 km race, one runner runs at a steady 11.0 km/h and another runs at 14.0 km/h. How far from the finish line is the slower runner when the faster runner finishes the race?

15. ‖ A car moves with constant velocity along a straight road. Its position is $x_1 = 0$ m at $t_1 = 0$ s and is $x_2 = 30$ m at $t_2 = 3.0$ s. Answer the following by considering ratios, without computing the car's velocity.
    a. What is the car's position at $t = 1.5$ s?
    b. What will be its position at $t = 9.0$ s?

16. ‖ While running a marathon, a long-distance runner uses a stopwatch to time herself over a distance of 100 m. She finds that she runs this distance in 18 s. Answer the following by considering ratios, without computing her velocity.
    a. If she maintains her speed, how much time will it take her to run the next 400 m?
    b. How long will it take her to run a mile at this speed?

Section 2.3 Instantaneous Velocity

17. ‖ Figure P2.17 shows the position graph of a particle.
    a. Draw the particle's velocity graph for the interval 0 s $\leq t \leq 4$ s.
    b. Does this particle have a turning point or points? If so, at what time or times?

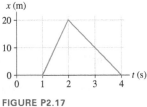

FIGURE P2.17

18. ‖ A somewhat idealized graph of the speed of the blood in the ascending aorta during one beat of the heart appears as in Figure P2.18.
    a. Approximately how far, in cm, does the blood move during one beat?
    b. Assume similar data for the motion of the blood in your aorta. Estimate how many beats of the heart it will it take the blood to get from your heart to your brain.

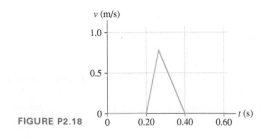

FIGURE P2.18

19. ‖‖ A car starts from $x_i = 10$ m at $t_i = 0$ s and moves with the velocity graph shown in Figure P2.19.
    a. What is the object's position at $t = 2$ s, 3 s, and 4 s?
    b. Does this car ever change direction? If so, at what time?

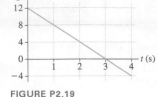

FIGURE P2.19

20. ‖ Figure P2.20 shows a graph of actual position-versus-time data for a particular type of drag racer known as a "funny car."
    a. Estimate the car's velocity at 2.0 s.
    b. Estimate the car's velocity at 4.0 s.

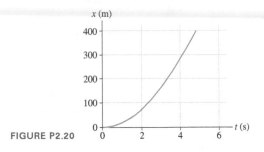

FIGURE P2.20

Section 2.4 Acceleration

21. ‖ Figure P2.21 shows the velocity graph of a bicycle. Draw the bicycle's acceleration graph for the interval 0 s $\leq t \leq 4$ s. Give both axes an appropriate numerical scale.

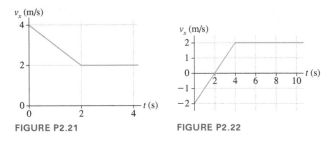

FIGURE P2.21   FIGURE P2.22

22. ‖‖‖ Figure P2.22 shows the velocity graph of a train that starts from the origin at $t = 0$ s.
    a. Draw position and acceleration graphs for the train.
    b. Find the acceleration of the train at $t = 3.0$ s.

23. ‖ For each motion diagram shown earlier in Figure P2.2, determine the sign (positive or negative) of the acceleration.

24. ‖ Figure P2.18 showed data for the speed of blood in the aorta. Determine the magnitude of the acceleration for both phases, speeding up and slowing down.

25. ‖ Figure P2.25 is a somewhat simplified velocity graph for Olympic sprinter Carl Lewis starting a 100 m dash. Estimate his acceleration during each of the intervals A, B, and C.

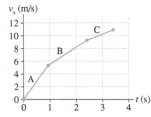

FIGURE P2.25

Section 2.5 Motion with Constant Acceleration

26. ‖ A Thomson's gazelle can reach a speed of 13 m/s in 3.0 s. A lion can reach a speed of 9.5 m/s in 1.0 s. A trout can reach a speed of 2.8 m/s in 0.12 s. Which animal has the largest acceleration?

27. ‖ When striking, the pike, a
BIO predatory fish, can accelerate
from rest to a speed of 4.0 m/s
in 0.11 s.
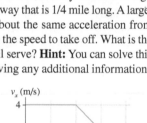
   a. What is the acceleration of
the pike during this strike?
   b. How far does the pike move
during this strike?

28. ‖ a. What constant acceleration, in SI units, must a car have to
go from zero to 60 mph in 10 s?
   b. What fraction of g is this?
   c. How far has the car traveled when it reaches 60 mph?
Give your answer both in SI units and in feet.

29. ‖ Light-rail passenger trains that provide transportation within
and between cities are capable of modest accelerations. The
magnitude of the maximum acceleration is typically 1.3 m/s²,
but the driver will usually maintain a constant acceleration that
is less than the maximum. A train travels through a congested
part of town at 5.0 m/s. Once free of this area, it speeds up to 12
m/s in 8.0 s. At the edge of town, the driver again accelerates,
with the same acceleration, for another 16 s to reach a higher
cruising speed. What is the final speed?

30. ‖ A speed skater moving across frictionless ice at 8.0 m/s hits a
5.0-m-wide patch of rough ice. She slows steadily, then continues on at 6.0 m/s. What is her acceleration on the rough ice?

31. ‖ A small propeller airplane can comfortably achieve a high
enough speed to take off on a runway that is 1/4 mile long. A large,
fully loaded passenger jet has about the same acceleration from
rest, but it needs to achieve twice the speed to take off. What is the
minimum runway length that will serve? **Hint:** You can solve this
problem using ratios without having any additional information.

32. ‖ Figure P2.32 shows a velocity-versus-time graph for a particle moving along the x-axis.
At $t = 0$ s, assume that $x = 0$ m.
   a. What are the particle's position, velocity, and acceleration at $t = 1.0$ s?
   b. What are the particle's position, velocity, and acceleration at $t = 3.0$ s?

v_x (m/s)

FIGURE P2.32

Section 2.6 Solving One-Dimensional Motion Problems

33. ‖ A driver has a reaction time of 0.50 s, and the maximum
deceleration of her car is 6.0 m/s². She is driving at 20 m/s
when suddenly she sees an obstacle in the road 50 m in front of
her. Can she stop the car in time to avoid a collision?

34. ‖ Chameleons catch insects with their tongues, which they can
BIO rapidly extend to great lengths. In a typical strike, the chameleon's
tongue accelerates at a remarkable 250 m/s² for 20 ms, then
travels at constant speed for another 30 ms. During this total
time of 50 ms, 1/20 of a second, how far does the tongue reach?

35. ‖ You're driving down the highway late one night at 20 m/s
when a deer steps onto the road 35 m in front of you. Your reaction time before stepping on the brakes is 0.50 s, and the maximum deceleration of your car is 10 m/s².
   a. How much distance is between you and the deer when you
come to a stop?
   b. What is the maximum speed you could have and still not hit
the deer?

36. ‖ A light-rail train going from one station to the next on a
straight section of track accelerates from rest at 1.1 m/s² for 20 s.
It then proceeds at constant speed for 1100 m before slowing
down at 2.2 m/s² until it stops at the station.
   a. What is the distance between the stations?
   b. How much time does it take the train to go between the
stations?

37. ‖ A simple model for a person running the 100 m dash is to
assume the sprinter runs with constant acceleration until
reaching top speed, then maintains that speed through the finish
line. If a sprinter reaches his top speed of 11.2 m/s in 2.14 s,
what will be his total time?

Section 2.7 Free Fall

38. ‖ Ball bearings can be made by letting spherical drops of
molten metal fall inside a tall tower—called a *shot tower*—and
solidify as they fall.
   a. If a bearing needs 4.0 s to solidify enough for impact, how
high must the tower be?
   b. What is the bearing's impact velocity?

39. ‖ In the chapter, we saw that a person's reaction time is gener-
BIO ally not quick enough to allow the person to catch a dollar bill
dropped between the fingers. If a typical reaction time in this
case is 0.25 s, how long would a bill need to be for a person to
have a good chance of catching it?

40. ‖ A ball is thrown vertically upward with a speed of 19.6 m/s.
   a. What are the ball's velocity and height after 1.00, 2.00, 3.00,
and 4.00 s?
   b. Draw the ball's velocity-versus-time graph. Give both axes
an appropriate numerical scale.

41. ‖ A student at the top of a building of height h throws ball A
straight upward with speed v_0 and throws ball B straight downward with the same initial speed.
   a. Compare the balls' accelerations, both direction and magnitude, immediately after they leave her hand. Is one acceleration larger than the other? Or are the magnitudes equal?
   b. Compare the final speeds of the balls as they reach the
ground. Is one larger than the other? Or are they equal?

42. ‖ Excellent human jumpers can leap straight up to a height of
110 cm off the ground. To reach this height, with what speed
would a person need to leave the ground?

43. ‖ A football is kicked straight up into the air; it hits the ground
5.2 s later.
   a. What was the greatest height reached by the ball? Assume it
is kicked from ground level.
   b. With what speed did it leave the kicker's foot?

44. ‖‖ In an action movie, the villain is rescued from the ocean by
grabbing onto the ladder hanging from a helicopter. He is so
intent on gripping the ladder that he lets go of his briefcase of
counterfeit money when he is 130 m above the water. If the
briefcase hits the water 6.0 s later, what was the speed at which
the helicopter was ascending?

45. ‖‖ A rock climber stands on top of a 50-m-high cliff overhang-
ing a pool of water. He throws two stones vertically downward
1.0 s apart and observes that they cause a single splash. The initial speed of the first stone was 2.0 m/s.
   a. How long after the release of the first stone does the second
stone hit the water?
   b. What was the initial speed of the second stone?
   c. What is the speed of each stone as they hit the water?

General Problems

46. ▌ Actual velocity data for a lion pursuing prey are shown in
BIO Figure P2.46. Estimate:
   a. The initial acceleration of the lion.
   b. The acceleration of the lion at 2 s and at 4 s.
   c. The distance traveled by the lion between 0 s and 8 s.

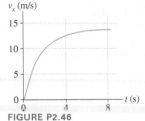

FIGURE P2.46

Problems 47 and 48 concern *nerve impulses*, electrical signals propagated along nerve fibers consisting of many *axons* (fiberlike extensions of nerve cells) connected end-to-end. Axons come in two varieties: insulated axons with a sheath made of myelin, and uninsulated axons with

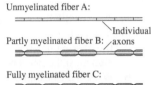

FIGURE P2.47

no such sheath. Myelinated (sheathed) axons conduct nerve impulses much faster than unmyelinated (unsheathed) axons. The impulse speed depends on the diameter of the axons and the sheath, but a typical myelinated axon transmits nerve impulses at a speed of about 25 m/s, much faster than the typical 2.0 m/s for an unmyelinated axon. Figure P2.47 shows small portions of three nerve fibers consisting of axons of equal size. Two-thirds of the axons in fiber B are myelinated.

47. ▌ Suppose nerve impulses simultaneously enter the left side of
BIO the nerve fibers sketched in Figure P2.47, then propagate to the right. Draw qualitatively accurate position and velocity graphs for the nerve impulses in all three cases. A nerve fiber is made up of many axons, but show the propagation of the impulses only over the six axons shown here.

48. ▌ Suppose that the nerve fibers in Figure P2.47 connect a fin-
BIO ger to your brain, a distance of 1.2 m.
   a. What are the travel times of a nerve impulse from finger to brain along fibers A and C?
   b. For fiber B, 2/3 of the length is composed of myelinated axons, 1/3 unmyelinated axons. Compute the travel time for a nerve impulse on this fiber.
   c. When you touch a hot stove with your finger, the sensation of pain must reach your brain as a nerve signal along a nerve fiber before your muscles can react. Which of the three fibers gives you the best protection against a burn? Are any of these fibers unsuitable for transmitting urgent sensory information?

49. ▌ A truck driver has a shipment of apples to deliver to a destination 440 miles away. The trip usually takes him 8 hours. Today he finds himself daydreaming and realizes 120 miles into his trip that he is running 15 minutes later than his usual pace at this point. At what speed must he drive for the remainder of the trip to complete the trip in the usual amount of time?

50. ▌ When you sneeze, the air in your lungs accelerates from rest
BIO to approximately 150 km/h in about 0.50 seconds.
   a. What is the acceleration of the air in m/s²?
   b. What is this acceleration, in units of g?

51. ▌ Figure P2.51 shows the motion diagram, made at two frames of film per second, of a ball rolling along a track. The track has a 3.0-m-long sticky section.

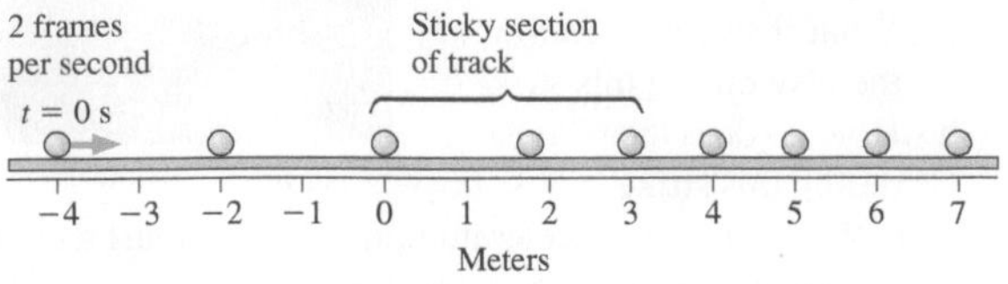

FIGURE P2.51

   a. Use the scale to determine the positions of the center of the ball. Place your data in a table, similar to Table 2.1, showing each position and the instant of time at which it occurred.
   b. Make a graph of x versus t for the ball. Because you have data only at certain instants of time, your graph should consist of dots that are not connected together.
   c. What is the *change* in the ball's position from $t = 0$ s to $t = 1.0$ s?
   d. What is the *change* in the ball's position from $t = 2.0$ s to $t = 4.0$ s?
   e. What is the ball's velocity before reaching the sticky section?
   f. What is the ball's velocity after passing the sticky section?
   g. Determine the ball's acceleration on the sticky section of the track.

52. ▌ Julie drives 100 mi to Grandmother's house. On the way to Grandmother's, Julie drives half the *distance* at 40 mph and half the distance at 60 mph. On her return trip, she drives half the *time* at 40 mph and half the time at 60 mph.
   a. How long does it take Julie to complete the trip to Grandmother's house?
   b. How long does the return trip take?

53. ▌ The takeoff speed for an Airbus A320 jetliner is 80 m/s. Velocity data measured during takeoff are as shown in the table.

t(s)	v_x(m/s)
0	0
10	23
20	46
30	69

   a. What is the takeoff speed in miles per hour?
   b. What is the jetliner's acceleration during takeoff?
   c. At what time do the wheels leave the ground?
   d. For safety reasons, in case of an aborted takeoff, the runway must be three times the takeoff distance. Can an A320 take off safely on a 2.5-mi-long runway?

54. ▌ Does a real automobile have constant acceleration? Measured data for a Porsche 944 Turbo at maximum acceleration are as shown in the table.

t(s)	v_x(mph)
0	0
2	28
4	46
6	60
8	70
10	78

   a. Convert the velocities to m/s, then make a graph of velocity versus time. Based on your graph, is the acceleration constant? Explain.
   b. Draw a smooth curve through the points on your graph, then use your graph to *estimate* the car's acceleration at 2.0 s and 8.0 s. Give your answer in SI units. **Hint:** Remember that acceleration is the slope of the velocity graph.

55. ‖ People hoping to travel to other worlds are faced with huge challenges. One of the biggest is the time required for a journey. The nearest star is 4.1×10^{16} m away. Suppose you had a spacecraft that could accelerate at $1.0g$ for half a year, then continue at a constant speed. (This is far beyond what can be achieved with any known technology.) How long would it take you to reach the nearest star to earth?

56. ‖ You are driving to the grocery store at 20 m/s. You are 110 m from an intersection when the traffic light turns red. Assume that your reaction time is 0.70 s and that your car brakes with constant acceleration.
    a. How far are you from the intersection when you begin to apply the brakes?
    b. What acceleration will bring you to rest right at the intersection?
    c. How long does it take you to stop?

57. | When you blink your eye, the upper lid goes from rest with your
BIO eye open to completely covering your eye in a time of 0.024 s.
    a. Estimate the distance that the top lid of your eye moves during a blink.
    b. What is the acceleration of your eyelid? Assume it to be constant.
    c. What is your upper eyelid's final speed as it hits the bottom eyelid?

58. ‖ A bush baby, an African
BIO primate, is capable of leaping vertically to the remarkable height of 2.3 m. To jump this high, the bush baby accelerates over a distance of 0.16 m while rapidly extending its legs. The acceleration during the jump is approximately constant. What is the acceleration in m/s^2 and in g's?

59. ‖ When jumping, a flea reaches a takeoff speed of 1.0 m/s over
BIO a distance of 0.50 mm.
    a. What is the flea's acceleration during the jump phase?
    b. How long does the acceleration phase last?
    c. If the flea jumps straight up, how high will it go? (Ignore air resistance for this problem; in reality, air resistance plays a large role, and the flea will not reach this height.)

60. ‖ Certain insects can achieve
BIO seemingly impossible accelerations while jumping. The click beetle accelerates at an astonishing $400g$ over a distance of 0.60 cm as it rapidly bends its thorax, making the "click" that gives it its name.
    a. Assuming the beetle jumps straight up, at what speed does it leave the ground?
    b. How much time is required for the beetle to reach this speed?
    c. Ignoring air resistance, how high would it go?

61. ‖‖ Divers compete by diving into a 3.0-m-deep pool from a platform 10 m above the water. What is the magnitude of the minimum acceleration in the water needed to keep a diver from hitting the bottom of the pool? Assume the acceleration is constant.

62. ‖‖ A student standing on the ground throws a ball straight up. The ball leaves the student's hand with a speed of 15 m/s when the hand is 2.0 m above the ground. How long is the ball in the air before it hits the ground? (The student moves her hand out of the way.)

63. ‖‖ A rock is tossed straight up with a speed of 20 m/s. When it returns, it falls into a hole 10 m deep.
    a. What is the rock's velocity as it hits the bottom of the hole?
    b. How long is the rock in the air, from the instant it is released until it hits the bottom of the hole?

64. ‖‖‖ A 200 kg weather rocket is loaded with 100 kg of fuel and fired straight up. It accelerates upward at 30.0 m/s^2 for 30.0 s, then runs out of fuel. Ignore any air resistance effects.
    a. What is the rocket's maximum altitude?
    b. How long is the rocket in the air?
    c. Draw a velocity-versus-time graph for the rocket from liftoff until it hits the ground.

65. ‖‖‖ A juggler throws a ball straight up into the air with a speed of 10 m/s. With what speed would she need to throw a second ball half a second later, starting from the same position as the first, in order to hit the first ball at the top of its trajectory?

66. ‖‖‖ A hotel elevator ascends 200 m with a maximum speed of 5.0 m/s. Its acceleration and deceleration both have a magnitude of 1.0 m/s^2.
    a. How far does the elevator move while accelerating to full speed from rest?
    b. How long does it take to make the complete trip from bottom to top?

67. ‖‖‖ A car starts from rest at a stop sign. It accelerates at 2.0 m/s^2 for 6.0 seconds, coasts for 2.0 s, and then slows down at a rate of 1.5 m/s^2 for the next stop sign. How far apart are the stop signs?

68. ‖‖‖ A toy train is pushed forward and released at $x_i = 2.0$ m with a speed of 2.0 m/s. It rolls at a steady speed for 2.0 s, then one wheel begins to stick. The train comes to a stop 6.0 m from the point at which it was released. What is the train's acceleration after its wheel begins to stick?

69. ‖ Heather and Jerry are standing on a bridge 50 m above a river. Heather throws a rock straight down with a speed of 20 m/s. Jerry, at exactly the same instant of time, throws a rock straight up with the same speed. Ignore air resistance.
    a. How much time elapses between the first splash and the second splash?
    b. Which rock has the faster speed as it hits the water?

70. ‖‖‖ A motorist is driving at 20 m/s when she sees that a traffic light 200 m ahead has just turned red. She knows that this light stays red for 15 s, and she wants to reach the light just as it turns green again. It takes her 1.0 s to step on the brakes and begin slowing at a constant deceleration. What is her speed as she reaches the light at the instant it turns green?

71. ‖‖‖‖ A "rocket car" is launched along a long straight track at $t = 0$ s. It moves with constant acceleration $a_1 = 2.0$ m/s^2. At $t = 2.0$ s, a second car is launched along a parallel track, from the same starting point, with constant acceleration $a_2 = 8.0$ m/s^2.
    a. At what time does the second car catch up with the first one?
    b. How far have the cars traveled when the second passes the first?

72. ‖ A Porsche challenges a Honda to a 400 m race. Because the Porsche's acceleration of 3.5 m/s^2 is larger than the Honda's 3.0 m/s^2, the Honda gets a 50-m head start. Assume, somewhat unrealistically, that both cars can maintain these accelerations the entire distance. Who wins, and by how much time?

73. ||||| The minimum stopping distance for a car traveling at a speed of 30 m/s is 60 m, including the distance traveled during the driver's reaction time of 0.50 s.
    a. What is the minimum stopping distance for the same car traveling at a speed of 40 m/s?
    b. Draw a position-versus-time graph for the motion of the car in part a. Assume the car is at $x_i = 0$ m when the driver first sees the emergency situation ahead that calls for a rapid halt.

74. ||||| A rocket is launched straight up with constant acceleration. Four seconds after liftoff, a bolt falls off the side of the rocket. The bolt hits the ground 6.0 s later. What was the rocket's acceleration?

Passage Problems

Free Fall on Different Worlds

Objects in free fall on the earth have acceleration $a_y = -9.8$ m/s^2. On the moon, free-fall acceleration is approximately 1/6 of the acceleration on earth. This changes the scale of problems involving free fall. For instance, suppose you jump straight upward, leaving the ground with velocity v_i and then steadily slowing until reaching zero velocity at your highest point. Because your initial velocity is determined mostly by the strength of your leg muscles, we can assume your initial velocity would be the same on the moon. But considering the final equation in Table 2.4 we can see that, with a smaller free-fall acceleration, your maximum height would be greater. The following questions ask you to think about how certain athletic feats might be performed in this reduced-gravity environment.

75. | If an astronaut can jump straight up to a height of 0.50 m on earth, how high could he jump on the moon?
    A. 1.2 m   B. 3.0 m   C. 3.6 m   D. 18 m

76. | On the earth, an astronaut can safely jump to the ground from a height of 1.0 m; her velocity when reaching the ground is slow enough to not cause injury. From what height could the astronaut safely jump to the ground on the moon?
    A. 2.4 m   B. 6.0 m   C. 7.2 m   D. 36 m

77. | On the earth, an astronaut throws a ball straight upward; it stays in the air for a total time of 3.0 s before reaching the ground again. If a ball were to be thrown upward with the same initial speed on the moon, how much time would pass before it hit the ground?
    A. 7.3 s   B. 18 s   C. 44 s   D. 108 s

STOP TO THINK ANSWERS

Stop to Think 2.1: D. The motion consists of two constant-velocity phases; the second one has a greater velocity. The correct graph has two straight-line segments, with the second one having a steeper slope.

Stop to Think 2.2: B. The displacement is the area under a velocity-versus-time curve. In all four cases, the graph is a straight line, so the area under the curve is a rectangle. The area is the product of the length times the height, so the largest displacement belongs to the graph with the largest product of the length (the time interval, in s) times the height (the velocity, in m/s).

Stop to Think 2.3: C. Consider the slope of the position-versus-time graph; it starts out positive and constant, then decreases to zero. Thus the velocity graph must start with a constant positive value, then decrease to zero.

Stop to Think 2.4: C. Acceleration is the slope of the velocity-versus-time graph. The largest magnitude of the slope is at point C.

Stop to Think 2.5: E. An acceleration of 1.2 m/s^2 corresponds to an increase of 1.2 m/s every second. At this rate, the cruising speed of 6.0 m/s will be reached after 5.0 s.

Stop to Think 2.6: D. The final velocity will have the same *magnitude* as the initial velocity, but the velocity is negative because the rock will be moving downward.

3 Vectors and Motion in Two Dimensions

Once the leopard jumps, its trajectory is fixed by the initial speed and angle of the jump. How can we work out where the leopard will land?

LOOKING AHEAD ▶

The goals of Chapter 3 are to learn more about vectors and to use vectors as a tool to analyze motion in two dimensions.

Tools for Describing Motion

In the last chapter, we discussed motion along a line. In this chapter, we'll look at motion in which the direction changes. We'll need new tools.

Types of Motion

There are a few basic types of motion that we'll consider. In each case there is an acceleration due to a change in speed or direction—or both.

> **Looking Back ◀◀**
> 1.1–1.2 Basic motion concepts

Vectors

We use vectors to describe quantities, like velocity, for which both the magnitude and direction are important.

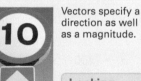

Vectors specify a direction as well as a magnitude.

> **Looking Back ◀◀**
> 1.5 Vectors

Motion on a Ramp

Gravity causes the motion, but it's not straight down—it's at an angle.

A speed skier is accelerating down a ramp. How fast is he moving at the end of his run?

> **Looking Back ◀◀**
> 2.5 Motion with constant acceleration

Vector Math

Our basic kinematic variables are vectors. Working with them means learning how to work with vectors.

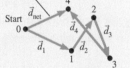

You'll learn how to add, subtract, and perform other mathematical operations on vectors.

Projectile Motion

Objects launched through the air follow a parabolic path. Water going over the falls, the leaping salmon, footballs, and jumping leopards all follow similar paths.

The salmon is moving horizontally and vertically—as do all objects undergoing projectile motion.

> **Looking Back ◀◀**
> 2.7 Free fall

Vector Components

We make measurements in a coordinate system. How do vectors fit in?

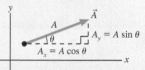

You'll learn how to find the components of vectors and how to add and subtract vectors using components.

Circular Motion

Motion in a circle at a constant speed involves acceleration, but not the constant acceleration you studied in Chapter 2.

The riders are moving at a constant speed but with an ever-changing direction. It is the changing direction that causes the acceleration and makes the ride fun.

3.1 Using Vectors

FIGURE 3.1 The velocity vector $\vec{v}$ has both a magnitude and a direction.

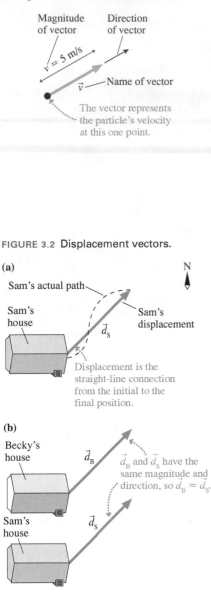

FIGURE 3.1 The velocity vector $\vec{v}$ has both a magnitude and a direction.

Magnitude of vector

Direction of vector

$v = 5$ m/s

$\vec{v}$ — Name of vector

The vector represents the particle's velocity at this one point.

FIGURE 3.2 Displacement vectors.

(a)

N

Sam's actual path

Sam's house

Sam's displacement

$\vec{d}_S$

Displacement is the straight-line connection from the initial to the final position.

(b)

Becky's house

$\vec{d}_B$

$\vec{d}_B$ and $\vec{d}_S$ have the same magnitude and direction, so $\vec{d}_B = \vec{d}_S$.

Sam's house

$\vec{d}_S$

In the previous chapter, we solved many problems in which an object moved in a straight-line path. In this chapter, we will look at particles that take curving paths—motion in two dimensions. Because the direction of motion will be so important, we need to develop an appropriate mathematical language to describe it—the language of vectors.

We introduced the concept of a vector in Chapter 1, and in the next few sections we will develop that concept into a useful and powerful tool. We will practice using vectors by analyzing a problem of motion in one dimension (that of motion on a ramp) and by studying the interesting notion of relative velocity. We will then be ready to analyze the two-dimensional motion of projectiles and of objects moving in a circle.

Recall from Chapter 1 that a vector is a quantity with both a size (magnitude) and a direction. FIGURE 3.1 shows how to represent a particle's velocity as a vector $\vec{v}$. The particle's speed at this point is 5 m/s *and* it is moving in the direction indicated by the arrow. The magnitude of a vector is represented by the letter without an arrow. In this case, the particle's speed—the magnitude of the velocity vector $\vec{v}$—is $v = 5$ m/s. The magnitude of a vector, a *scalar* quantity, cannot be a negative number.

> **NOTE** ▶ Although the vector arrow is drawn across the page, from its tail to its tip, this arrow does *not* indicate that the vector "stretches" across this distance. Instead, the arrow tells us the value of the vector quantity only at the one point where the tail of the vector is placed. ◀

We found in Chapter 1 that the displacement of an object is a vector drawn from its initial position to its position at some later time. Because displacement is an easy concept to think about, we can use it to introduce some of the properties of vectors. However, **all the properties we will discuss in this chapter (addition, subtraction, multiplication, components) apply to all types of vectors, not just to displacement.**

Suppose that Sam, our old friend from Chapter 1, starts from his front door, walks across the street, and ends up 200 ft to the northeast of where he started. Sam's displacement, which we will label $\vec{d}_S$, is shown in FIGURE 3.2a. The displacement vector is a straight-line connection from his initial to his final position, not necessarily his actual path. The dashed line indicates a possible route Sam might have taken, but his displacement is the vector $\vec{d}_S$.

To describe a vector we must specify both its magnitude and its direction. We can write Sam's displacement as

$$\vec{d}_S = (200 \text{ ft, northeast})$$

where the first number specifies the magnitude and the second item gives the direction. The magnitude of Sam's displacement is $d_S = 200$ ft, the distance between his initial and final points.

Sam's next-door neighbor Becky also walks 200 ft to the northeast, starting from her own front door. Becky's displacement $\vec{d}_B = (200 \text{ ft, northeast})$ has the same magnitude and direction as Sam's displacement $\vec{d}_S$. Because vectors are defined by their magnitude and direction, **two vectors are equal if they have the same magnitude and direction.** This is true regardless of the individual starting points of the vectors. Thus the two displacements in FIGURE 3.2b are equal to each other, and we can write $\vec{d}_B = \vec{d}_S$.

Vector Addition

As we saw in Chapter 1, we can combine successive displacements by vector addition. Let's review and extend this concept. FIGURE 3.3 shows the displacement of a hiker who starts at point P and ends at point S. She first hikes 4 miles to the east, then 3 miles to the north. The first leg of the hike is described by the displacement vector $\vec{A} = (4 \text{ mi, east})$. The second leg of the hike has displacement $\vec{B} = (3 \text{ mi, north})$. By definition, a vector from her initial position P to her final position S is also a displacement. This is vector $\vec{C}$ on the figure. $\vec{C}$ is the *net displacement* because it describes the net result of the hiker's having first displacement $\vec{A}$, then displacement $\vec{B}$.

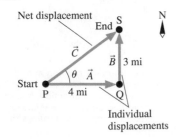

FIGURE 3.3 The net displacement $\vec{C}$ resulting from two displacements $\vec{A}$ and $\vec{B}$.

Net displacement

End

S

N

$\vec{C}$

$\vec{B}$ 3 mi

Start

P

θ $\vec{A}$

4 mi

Q

Individual displacements

The word "net" implies addition. The net displacement $\vec{C}$ is an initial displacement $\vec{A}$ *plus* a second displacement $\vec{B}$, or

$$\vec{C} = \vec{A} + \vec{B} \tag{3.1}$$

The sum of two vectors is called the **resultant vector.** Vector addition is commutative: $\vec{A} + \vec{B} = \vec{B} + \vec{A}$. You can add vectors in any order you wish.

Look back at Tactics Box 1.4 on page 19 to review the three-step procedure for adding two vectors. This tip-to-tail method for adding vectors, which is used to find $\vec{C} = \vec{A} + \vec{B}$ in Figure 3.3, is called *graphical addition.* Any two vectors of the same type—two velocity vectors or two force vectors—can be added in exactly the same way.

When two vectors are to be added, it is often convenient to draw them with their tails together, as shown in FIGURE 3.4a. To evaluate $\vec{D} + \vec{E}$, you could move vector $\vec{E}$ over to where its tail is on the tip of $\vec{D}$, then use the tip-to-tail rule of graphical addition. This gives vector $\vec{F} = \vec{D} + \vec{E}$ in FIGURE 3.4b. Alternatively, FIGURE 3.4c shows that the vector sum $\vec{D} + \vec{E}$ can be found as the diagonal of the parallelogram defined by $\vec{D}$ and $\vec{E}$. This method is called the *parallelogram rule* of vector addition.

FIGURE 3.4 Two vectors can be added using the tip-to-tail rule or the parallelogram rule.

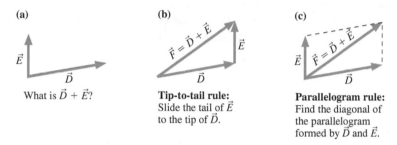

(a)

$\vec{E}$

$\vec{D}$

What is $\vec{D} + \vec{E}$?

(b)

$\vec{F} = \vec{D} + \vec{E}$

$\vec{E}$

$\vec{D}$

Tip-to-tail rule:
Slide the tail of $\vec{E}$
to the tip of $\vec{D}$.

(c)

$\vec{E}$ $\vec{F} = \vec{D} + \vec{E}$

$\vec{D}$

Parallelogram rule:
Find the diagonal of
the parallelogram
formed by $\vec{D}$ and $\vec{E}$.

Vector addition is easily extended to more than two vectors. FIGURE 3.5 shows the path of a hiker moving from initial position 0 to position 1, then position 2, then position 3, and finally arriving at position 4. These four segments are described by displacement vectors $\vec{d}_1$, $\vec{d}_2$, $\vec{d}_3$, and $\vec{d}_4$. The hiker's *net* displacement, an arrow from position 0 to position 4, is the vector $\vec{d}_{net}$. In this case,

$$\vec{d}_{net} = \vec{d}_1 + \vec{d}_2 + \vec{d}_3 + \vec{d}_4 \tag{3.2}$$

The vector sum is found by using the tip-to-tail method three times in succession.

Multiplication by a Scalar

The hiker in Figure 3.3 started with displacement $\vec{A}_1 = (4 \text{ mi, east})$. Suppose a second hiker walks twice as far to the east. The second hiker's displacement will then certainly be $\vec{A}_2 = (8 \text{ mi, east})$. The words "twice as" indicate a multiplication, so we can say

$$\vec{A}_2 = 2\vec{A}_1$$

Multiplying a vector by a positive scalar gives another vector of *different magnitude* but pointing in the *same direction.*

Let the vector $\vec{A}$ be specified as a magnitude A and a direction θ_A; that is, $\vec{A} = (A, \theta_A)$. Now let $\vec{B} = c\vec{A}$, where c is a positive scalar constant. Then

$$\vec{B} = c\vec{A} \text{ means that } (B, \theta_B) = (cA, \theta_A) \tag{3.3}$$

The vector is stretched or compressed by the factor c (i.e., vector $\vec{B}$ has magnitude $B = cA$), but $\vec{B}$ points in the same direction as $\vec{A}$. This is illustrated in FIGURE 3.6.

Suppose we multiply $\vec{A}$ by zero. Using Equation 3.3, we get

$$0 \cdot \vec{A} = \vec{0} = (0 \text{ m, direction undefined}) \tag{3.4}$$

The product is a vector having zero length or magnitude. This vector is known as the **zero vector,** denoted $\vec{0}$. The direction of the zero vector is irrelevant; you cannot describe the direction of an arrow of zero length!

FIGURE 3.5 The net displacement after four individual displacements.

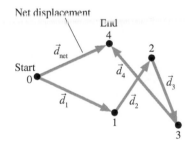

Net displacement

End
4

$\vec{d}_{net}$

Start
0

$\vec{d}_4$

2

$\vec{d}_3$

$\vec{d}_1$

$\vec{d}_2$

1

3

FIGURE 3.6 Multiplication of a vector by a positive scalar.

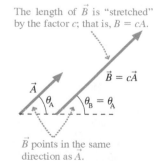

The length of $\vec{B}$ is "stretched"
by the factor c; that is, $B = cA$.

$\vec{A}$

$\vec{B} = c\vec{A}$

θ_A

$\theta_B = \theta_A$

$\vec{B}$ points in the same
direction as $\vec{A}$.

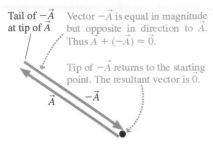

FIGURE 3.7 Vector $-\vec{A}$.

Tail of $-\vec{A}$ at tip of $\vec{A}$ — Vector $-\vec{A}$ is equal in magnitude but opposite in direction to $\vec{A}$. Thus $\vec{A} + (-\vec{A}) = \vec{0}$.

Tip of $-\vec{A}$ returns to the starting point. The resultant vector is $\vec{0}$.

$\vec{A}$ $-\vec{A}$

FIGURE 3.8 Vectors $\vec{A}$, $2\vec{A}$, and $-3\vec{A}$.

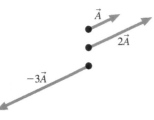

$\vec{A}$

$2\vec{A}$

$-3\vec{A}$

What happens if we multiply a vector by a negative number? Equation 3.3 does not apply if $c < 0$ because vector $\vec{B}$ cannot have a negative magnitude. Consider the vector $-\vec{A}$, which is equivalent to multiplying $\vec{A}$ by -1. Because

$$\vec{A} + (-\vec{A}) = \vec{0} \tag{3.5}$$

The vector $-\vec{A}$ must be such that, when it is added to $\vec{A}$, the resultant is the zero vector $\vec{0}$. In other words, the *tip* of $-\vec{A}$ must return to the *tail* of $\vec{A}$, as shown in FIGURE 3.7. This will be true only if $-\vec{A}$ is equal in magnitude to $\vec{A}$ but opposite in direction. Thus we can conclude that

$$-\vec{A} = (A, \text{direction opposite } \vec{A}) \tag{3.6}$$

Multiplying a vector by -1 reverses its direction without changing its length.

As an example, FIGURE 3.8 shows vectors $\vec{A}$, $2\vec{A}$, and $-3\vec{A}$. Multiplication by 2 doubles the length of the vector but does not change its direction. Multiplication by -3 stretches the length by a factor of 3 *and* reverses the direction.

Vector Subtraction

How might we *subtract* vector $\vec{B}$ from vector $\vec{A}$ to form the vector $\vec{A} - \vec{B}$? With numbers, subtraction is the same as the addition of a negative number. That is, $5 - 3$ is the same as $5 + (-3)$. Similarly, $\vec{A} - \vec{B} = \vec{A} + (-\vec{B})$. We can use the rules for vector addition and the fact that $-\vec{B}$ is a vector opposite in direction to $\vec{B}$ to form rules for vector subtraction.

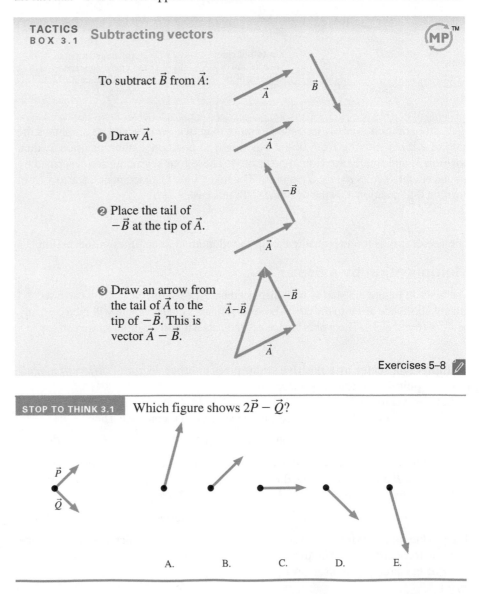

TACTICS BOX 3.1   **Subtracting vectors**   (MP)™

To subtract $\vec{B}$ from $\vec{A}$:

$\vec{A}$ $\vec{B}$

❶ Draw $\vec{A}$.

$\vec{A}$

❷ Place the tail of $-\vec{B}$ at the tip of $\vec{A}$.

$-\vec{B}$

$\vec{A}$

❸ Draw an arrow from the tail of $\vec{A}$ to the tip of $-\vec{B}$. This is vector $\vec{A} - \vec{B}$.

$\vec{A} - \vec{B}$ $-\vec{B}$

$\vec{A}$

Exercises 5–8

STOP TO THINK 3.1   Which figure shows $2\vec{P} - \vec{Q}$?

$\vec{P}$
$\vec{Q}$

A.   B.   C.   D.   E.

3.2 Using Vectors on Motion Diagrams

In Chapter 2, we defined velocity for one-dimensional motion as an object's displacement—the change in position—divided by the time interval in which the change occurs:

$$v_x = \frac{\Delta x}{\Delta t} = \frac{x_f - x_i}{\Delta t}$$

In two dimensions, an object's displacement is a vector. Suppose an object undergoes displacement $\vec{d}$ during the time interval Δt. Let's define an object's velocity *vector* to be

$$\vec{v} = \frac{\vec{d}}{\Delta t} = \left(\frac{d}{\Delta t}, \text{same direction as } \vec{d} \right) \qquad (3.7)$$

Definition of velocity in two or more dimensions

Notice that we've multiplied a vector by a scalar: The velocity vector is simply the displacement vector multiplied by the scalar $1/\Delta t$. Consequently, as we found in Chapter 1, **the velocity vector points in the direction of the displacement.** As a result, we can use the dot-to-dot vectors on a motion diagram to visualize the velocity.

NOTE ▶ Strictly speaking, the velocity defined in Equation 3.7 is the *average* velocity for the time interval Δt. This is adequate for using motion diagrams to visualize motion. As we did in Chapter 2, when we make Δt very small, we get an *instantaneous* velocity we can use in performing some calculations. ◀

EXAMPLE 3.1 **Finding the velocity of an airplane**

A small plane is 100 km due east of Denver. After 1 hour of flying at a constant speed in the same direction, it is 200 km due north of Denver. What is the plane's velocity?

PREPARE The initial and final positions of the plane are shown in FIGURE 3.9; the displacement $\vec{d}$ is the vector that points from the initial to the final position.

FIGURE 3.9 Displacement vector for an airplane.

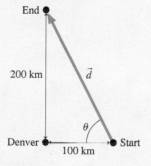

SOLVE The length of the displacement vector is the hypotenuse of a right triangle:

$$d = \sqrt{(100 \text{ km})^2 + (200 \text{ km})^2} = 224 \text{ km}$$

The direction of the displacement vector is described by the angle θ in Figure 3.9. From trigonometry, this angle is

$$\theta = \tan^{-1}\left(\frac{200 \text{ km}}{100 \text{ km}} \right) = \tan^{-1}(2.00) = 63.4°$$

Thus the plane's displacement vector is

$$\vec{d} = (224 \text{ km}, 63.4° \text{ north of west})$$

Because the plane undergoes this displacement during 1 hour, its velocity is

$$\vec{v} = \left(\frac{d}{\Delta t}, \text{same direction as } \vec{d} \right) = \left(\frac{224 \text{ km}}{1 \text{ h}}, 63.4° \text{ north of west} \right)$$
$$= (224 \text{ km/h}, 63.4° \text{ north of west})$$

ASSESS The plane's *speed* is the magnitude of the velocity, $v = 224$ km/h. This is approximately 140 mph, which is a reasonable speed for a small plane.

Lunging versus veering BIO The top photo shows a barracuda, a type of fish that catches prey with a rapid linear acceleration, a quick change in speed. The barracuda's body shape is optimized for such a straight-line strike. The butterfly fish in the bottom photo has a very different appearance. It can't rapidly change its speed, but its body shape lets it quickly change its direction. Once the barracuda gets up to speed, it can't change its direction very easily, so the butterfly fish can, by employing this other type of acceleration, avoid capture.

We defined an object's acceleration in one dimension as $a_x = \Delta v_x/\Delta t$. In two dimensions, we need to use a vector to describe acceleration. The vector definition of acceleration is a straightforward extension of the one-dimensional version:

$$\vec{a} = \frac{\vec{v}_f - \vec{v}_i}{t_f - t_i} = \frac{\Delta \vec{v}}{\Delta t} \qquad (3.8)$$

Definition of acceleration in two or more dimensions

There is an acceleration whenever there is a *change* in velocity. Because velocity is a vector, it can change in either or both of two possible ways:

1. The magnitude can change, indicating a change in speed.
2. The direction of motion can change.

In Chapter 2 we saw how to compute an acceleration vector for the first case, in which an object speeds up or slows down while moving in a straight line. In this chapter we will examine the second case, in which an object changes its direction of motion.

Suppose an object has an initial velocity $\vec{v}_i$ at time t_i and later, at time t_f, has velocity $\vec{v}_f$. The fact that the velocity *changes* tells us the object undergoes an acceleration during the time interval $\Delta t = t_f - t_i$. We see from Equation 3.8 that the acceleration points in the same direction as the vector $\Delta \vec{v}$. This vector is the change in the velocity $\Delta \vec{v} = \vec{v}_f - \vec{v}_i$, so to know which way the acceleration vector points, we have to perform the vector subtraction $\vec{v}_f - \vec{v}_i$. Tactics Box 3.1 showed how to perform vector subtraction. Tactics Box 3.2 shows how to use vector subtraction to find the acceleration vector.

TACTICS BOX 3.2 **Finding the acceleration vector**

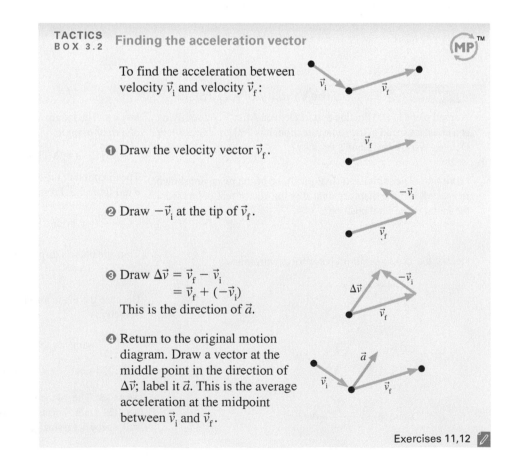

To find the acceleration between velocity $\vec{v}_i$ and velocity $\vec{v}_f$:

❶ Draw the velocity vector $\vec{v}_f$.

❷ Draw $-\vec{v}_i$ at the tip of $\vec{v}_f$.

❸ Draw $\Delta \vec{v} = \vec{v}_f - \vec{v}_i$
$= \vec{v}_f + (-\vec{v}_i)$
This is the direction of $\vec{a}$.

❹ Return to the original motion diagram. Draw a vector at the middle point in the direction of $\Delta \vec{v}$; label it $\vec{a}$. This is the average acceleration at the midpoint between $\vec{v}_i$ and $\vec{v}_f$.

Exercises 11,12

Now that we know how to determine acceleration vectors, we can make a complete motion diagram with dots showing the position of the object, average velocity vectors found by connecting the dots with arrows, and acceleration vectors found using Tactics Box 3.2. Note that there is *one* acceleration vector linking each *two* velocity vectors, and $\vec{a}$ is drawn at the dot between the two velocity vectors it links. Let's look at two examples, one with changing speed and one with changing direction.

EXAMPLE 3.2 | **Drawing the acceleration for a Mars descent**

A spacecraft slows as it safely descends to the surface of Mars. Draw a complete motion diagram for the last few seconds of the descent.

PREPARE FIGURE 3.10 shows two versions of a motion diagram: a professionally drawn version like you generally find in this text and a simpler version similar to what you might draw for a homework assignment. As the spacecraft slows in its descent, the dots get closer together and the velocity vectors get shorter.

SOLVE The inset in Figure 3.10 shows how Tactics Box 3.2 is used to determine the acceleration at one point. All the other acceleration vectors will be similar, because for each pair of velocity vectors the earlier one is longer than the later one.

ASSESS As the spacecraft slows, the acceleration vectors and velocity vectors point in opposite directions, consistent with what we learned about the sign of the acceleration in Chapter 2.

FIGURE 3.10 Motion diagram for a descending spacecraft.

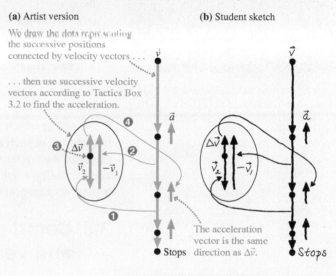

EXAMPLE 3.3 | **Drawing the acceleration for a Ferris wheel ride**

Anne rides a Ferris wheel at an amusement park. Draw a complete motion diagram for Anne's ride.

PREPARE FIGURE 3.11 shows 10 points of the motion during one complete revolution of the Ferris wheel. A person riding a Ferris wheel moves in a circle at a constant speed,

FIGURE 3.11 Motion diagram for Anne on a Ferris wheel.

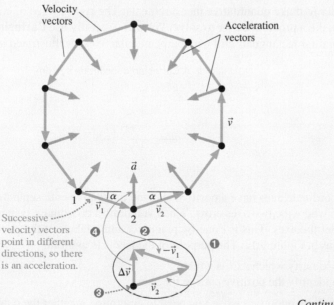

Continued

so we've shown equal distances between successive dots. As before, the velocity vectors are found by connecting each dot to the next. Note that the velocity vectors are *straight lines,* not curves.

We see that all the velocity vectors have the same length, but each has a different *direction,* and that means Anne is accelerating. This is not a "speeding up" or "slowing down" acceleration, but is, instead, a "change of direction" acceleration.

SOLVE   The inset to Figure 3.11 shows how to use the steps of Tactics Box 3.2 to find the acceleration at one particular position, at the bottom of the circle. Vector $\vec{v}_1$ is the velocity vector that leads into this dot, while $\vec{v}_2$ moves away from it. From the circular geometry of the main figure, the two angles marked α are equal. Thus we see that $\vec{v}_2$ and $-\vec{v}_1$ form an isosceles triangle and vector $\Delta\vec{v} = \vec{v}_2 - \vec{v}_1$ is exactly vertical, toward the center of the circle. If we did a similar calculation for each point of the motion, we'd find a similar result: In each case, the acceleration points toward the center of the circle.

ASSESS   The speed is constant but the direction is changing, so there is an acceleration, as we expect.

No matter which dot you select on the motion diagram of Figure 3.11, the velocities change in such a way that the acceleration vector $\vec{a}$ points directly toward the center of the circle. An acceleration vector that always points toward the center of a circle is called a *centripetal acceleration.* We will have much more to say about centripetal acceleration later in this chapter.

3.3 Coordinate Systems and Vector Components

In the past two sections, we have seen how to add and subtract vectors graphically, using these operations to deduce important details of motion. But the graphical combination of vectors is not an especially good way to find quantitative results. In this section we will introduce a *coordinate description* of vectors that will be the basis for doing vector calculations.

Coordinate Systems

As we saw in Chapter 1, the world does not come with a coordinate system attached to it. A coordinate system is an artificially imposed grid that you place on a problem in order to make quantitative measurements. The right choice of coordinate system will make a problem easier to solve. We will generally use **Cartesian coordinates,** the familiar rectangular grid with perpendicular axes, as illustrated in FIGURE 3.12.

Archaeologists establish a coordinate system so that they can precisely determine the positions of objects they excavate.

FIGURE 3.12   A Cartesian coordinate system.

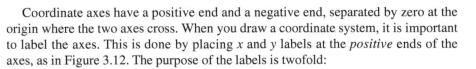

Coordinate axes have a positive end and a negative end, separated by zero at the origin where the two axes cross. When you draw a coordinate system, it is important to label the axes. This is done by placing x and y labels at the *positive* ends of the axes, as in Figure 3.12. The purpose of the labels is twofold:

- To identify which axis is which.
- To identify the positive ends of the axes.

This will be important when you need to determine whether the quantities in a problem should be assigned positive or negative values.

Component Vectors

FIGURE 3.13 shows a vector $\vec{A}$ and an *xy*-coordinate system that we've chosen. Once the directions of the axes are known, we can define two new vectors *parallel to the axes* that we call the **component vectors** of $\vec{A}$. Vector $\vec{A}_x$, called the *x-component vector,* is the projection of $\vec{A}$ along the *x*-axis. Vector $\vec{A}_y$, the *y-component vector,* is the projection of $\vec{A}$ along the *y*-axis. Notice that the component vectors are perpendicular to each other.

You can see, using the parallelogram rule, that $\vec{A}$ is the vector sum of the two component vectors:

$$\vec{A} = \vec{A}_x + \vec{A}_y \tag{3.9}$$

In essence, we have "broken" vector $\vec{A}$ into two perpendicular vectors that are parallel to the coordinate axes. We say that we have **decomposed** or **resolved** vector $\vec{A}$ into its component vectors.

> **NOTE** ▶ It is not necessary for the tail of $\vec{A}$ to be at the origin. All we need to know is the *orientation* of the coordinate system so that we can draw $\vec{A}_x$ and $\vec{A}_y$ parallel to the axes. ◀

Components

You learned in Chapter 2 to give the one-dimensional kinematic variable v_x a positive sign if the velocity vector $\vec{v}$ points toward the positive end of the *x*-axis and a negative sign if $\vec{v}$ points in the negative *x*-direction. The basis of this rule is that v_x is the *x-component* of $\vec{v}$. We need to extend this idea to vectors in general.

Suppose we have a vector $\vec{A}$ that has been decomposed into component vectors $\vec{A}_x$ and $\vec{A}_y$ parallel to the coordinate axes. We can describe each component vector with a single number (a scalar) called the **component**. The *x-component* and *y-component* of vector $\vec{A}$, denoted A_x and A_y, are determined as follows:

TACTICS BOX 3.3 Determining the components of a vector (MP)™

❶ The absolute value $|A_x|$ of the *x*-component A_x is the magnitude of the component vector $\vec{A}_x$.
❷ The *sign* of A_x is positive if $\vec{A}_x$ points in the positive *x*-direction, negative if $\vec{A}_x$ points in the negative *x*-direction.
❸ The *y*-component A_y is determined similarly.

Exercises 16–18 ✐

In other words, the component A_x tells us two things: how big $\vec{A}_x$ is and which end of the axis $\vec{A}_x$ points toward. FIGURE 3.14 shows three examples of determining the components of a vector.

> **NOTE** ▶ $\vec{A}_x$ and $\vec{A}_y$ are *component vectors*; they have a magnitude and a direction. A_x and A_y are simply *components*. The components A_x and A_y are scalars—just numbers (with units) that can be positive or negative. ◀

Much of physics is expressed in the language of vectors. We will frequently need to decompose a vector into its components or to "reassemble" a vector from its components, moving back and forth between the graphical and the component representations of a vector.

Let's start with the problem of decomposing a vector into its *x*- and *y*-components. FIGURE 3.15a on the next page shows a vector $\vec{A}$ at an angle θ above horizontal. It is *essential* to use a picture or diagram such as this to define the angle you are using to describe a vector's direction. $\vec{A}$ points to the right and up, so Tactics Box 3.3 tells us that the components A_x and A_y are both positive.

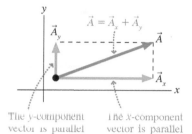

FIGURE 3.13 Component vectors $\vec{A}_x$ and $\vec{A}_y$ are drawn parallel to the coordinate axes such that $\vec{A} = \vec{A}_x + \vec{A}_y$.

The *y*-component vector is parallel to the *y*-axis.

The *x*-component vector is parallel to the *x*-axis.

FIGURE 3.14 Determining the components of a vector.

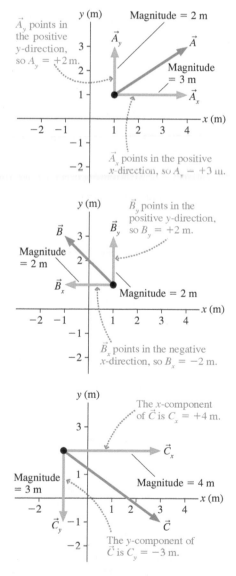

$\vec{A}_y$ points in the positive *y*-direction, so $A_y = +2$ m.

Magnitude = 2 m

Magnitude = 3 m

$\vec{A}_x$ points in the positive *x*-direction, so $A_x = +3$ m.

$\vec{B}_y$ points in the positive *y*-direction, so $B_y = +2$ m.

Magnitude = 2 m

Magnitude = 2 m

$\vec{B}_x$ points in the negative *x*-direction, so $B_x = -2$ m.

The *x*-component of $\vec{C}$ is $C_x = +4$ m.

Magnitude = 3 m

Magnitude = 4 m

The *y*-component of $\vec{C}$ is $C_y = -3$ m.

FIGURE 3.15 Breaking a vector into components.

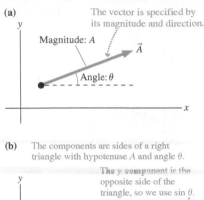

(a)

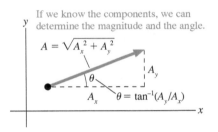

(b)

FIGURE 3.16 Specifying a vector from its components.

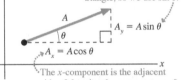

FIGURE 3.17 Relationships for a vector with a negative component.

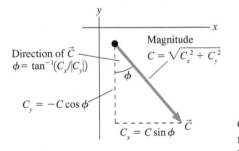

We can find the components using trigonometry, as illustrated in FIGURE 3.15b. For this case, we find that

$$A_x = A \cos \theta$$
$$A_y = A \sin \theta$$

(3.10)

where A is the magnitude, or length, of $\vec{A}$. These equations convert the length and angle description of vector $\vec{A}$ into the vector's components, but they are correct *only* if θ is measured from horizontal.

Alternatively, if we are given the components of a vector, we can determine the length and angle of the vector from the x- and y-components, as shown in FIGURE 3.16. Because A in Figure 3.16 is the hypotenuse of a right triangle, its length is given by the Pythagorean theorem:

$$A = \sqrt{A_x^2 + A_y^2}$$

(3.11)

Similarly, the tangent of angle θ is the ratio of the opposite side to the adjacent side, so

$$\theta = \tan^{-1}\left(\frac{A_y}{A_x}\right)$$

(3.12)

Equations 3.11 and 3.12 can be thought of as the "inverse" of Equations 3.10.

How do things change if the vector isn't pointing to the right and up—that is, if one of the components is negative? FIGURE 3.17 shows vector $\vec{C}$ pointing to the right and down. In this case, the component vector $\vec{C}_y$ is pointing *down,* in the negative y-direction, so the y-component C_y is a *negative* number. The angle ϕ is drawn measured from the y-axis, so the components of $\vec{C}$ are

$$C_x = C \sin \phi$$
$$C_y = -C \cos \phi$$

(3.13)

The roles of sine and cosine are reversed from those in Equations 3.10 because the angle ϕ is measured with respect to vertical, not horizontal.

> **NOTE** ▶ Whether the x- and y-components use the sine or cosine depends on how you define the vector's angle. As noted above, you *must* draw a diagram to define the angle that you use, and you must be sure to refer to the diagram when computing components. Don't use Equations 3.10 or 3.13 as general rules—they aren't! They appear as they do because of how we defined the angles. ◀

Next, let's look at the "inverse" problem for this case: determining the length and direction of the vector given the components. The signs of the components don't matter for determining the length; the Pythagorean theorem always works to find the length or magnitude of a vector because the squares eliminate any concerns over the signs. The length of the vector in Figure 3.17 is simply

$$C = \sqrt{C_x^2 + C_y^2}$$

(3.14)

When we determine the direction of the vector from its components, we must consider the signs of the components. Finding the angle of vector $\vec{C}$ in Figure 3.17 requires the length of C_y *without* the minus sign, so vector $\vec{C}$ has direction

$$\phi = \tan^{-1}\left(\frac{C_x}{|C_y|}\right)$$

(3.15)

Notice that the roles of x and y differ from those in Equation 3.12.

EXAMPLE 3.4   **Finding the components of an acceleration vector**

Find the x- and y-components of the acceleration vector $\vec{a}$ shown in FIGURE 3.18.

FIGURE 3.18 Acceleration vector $\vec{a}$ of Example 3.4.

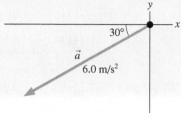

FIGURE 3.19 The components of the acceleration vector.

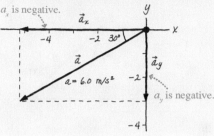

PREPARE It's important to *draw* the vectors. Making a sketch is crucial to setting up this problem. FIGURE 3.19 shows the original vector $\vec{a}$ decomposed into component vectors parallel to the axes.

SOLVE The acceleration vector $\vec{a} = (6.0 \text{ m/s}^2, 30°$ below the negative x-axis) points to the left (negative x-direction) and down (negative y-direction), so the components a_x and a_y are both negative:

$$a_x = -a\cos 30° = -(6.0 \text{ m/s}^2)\cos 30° = -5.2 \text{ m/s}^2$$
$$a_y = -a\sin 30° = -(6.0 \text{ m/s}^2)\sin 30° = -3.0 \text{ m/s}^2$$

ASSESS The magnitude of the y-component is less than that of the x-component, as seems to be the case in Figure 3.19, a good check on our work. The units of a_x and a_y are the same as the units of vector $\vec{a}$. Notice that we had to insert the minus signs manually by observing that the vector points down and to the left.

STOP TO THINK 3.2   What are the x- and y-components C_x and C_y of vector $\vec{C}$?

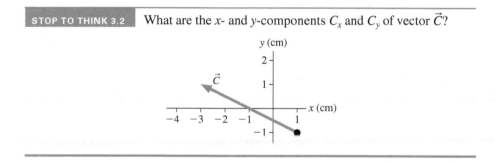

Working with Components

We've seen how to add vectors graphically, but there's an easier way: using components. To illustrate, let's look at the vector sum $\vec{C} = \vec{A} + \vec{B}$ for the vectors shown in FIGURE 3.20. You can see that the component vectors of $\vec{C}$ are the sums of the component vectors of $\vec{A}$ and $\vec{B}$. The same is true of the components: $C_x = A_x + B_x$ and $C_y = A_y + B_y$.

In general, if $\vec{D} = \vec{A} + \vec{B} + \vec{C} + \cdots$, then the x- and y-components of the resultant vector $\vec{D}$ are

$$D_x = A_x + B_x + C_x + \cdots$$
$$D_y = A_y + B_y + C_y + \cdots$$

(3.16)

This method of vector addition is called *algebraic addition*.

FIGURE 3.20 Using components to add vectors.

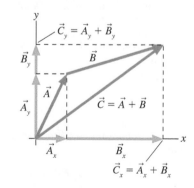

EXAMPLE 3.5   **Using algebraic addition to find a bird's displacement**

A bird flies 100 m due east from a tree, then 200 m northwest (that is, 45° north of west). What is the bird's net displacement?

PREPARE FIGURE 3.21a on the next page shows the displacement vectors $\vec{A} = (100 \text{ m, east})$ and $\vec{B} = (200 \text{ m, northwest})$ and also the net displacement $\vec{C}$. We draw vectors tip-to-tail if we are

going to add them graphically, but it's usually easier to draw them all from the origin if we are going to use algebraic addition. FIGURE 3.21b redraws the vectors with their tails together.

Continued

FIGURE 3.21 Finding the net displacement.

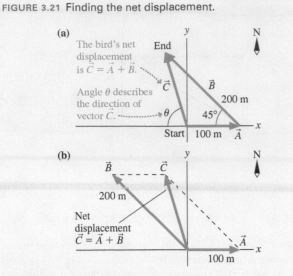

(a)

The bird's net displacement is $\vec{C} = \vec{A} + \vec{B}$.

Angle θ describes the direction of vector $\vec{C}$.

End

$\vec{C}$

$\vec{B}$

200 m

45°

Start | 100 m $\vec{A}$

N

(b)

$\vec{B}$

$\vec{C}$

200 m

Net displacement $\vec{C} = \vec{A} + \vec{B}$

$\vec{A}$

100 m

N

SOLVE To add the vectors algebraically we must know their components. From the figure these are seen to be

$$A_x = 100 \text{ m}$$

$$A_y = 0 \text{ m}$$

$$B_x = -(200 \text{ m})\cos 45° = -141 \text{ m}$$

$$B_y = (200 \text{ m})\sin 45° = 141 \text{ m}$$

We learned *from the figure* that $\vec{B}$ has a negative x-component. Adding $\vec{A}$ and $\vec{B}$ by components gives

$$C_x = A_x + B_x = 100 \text{ m} - 141 \text{ m} = -41 \text{ m}$$

$$C_y = A_y + B_y = 0 \text{ m} + 141 \text{ m} = 141 \text{ m}$$

The magnitude of the net displacement $\vec{C}$ is

$$C = \sqrt{C_x^2 + C_y^2} = \sqrt{(-41 \text{ m})^2 + (141 \text{ m})^2} = 147 \text{ m}$$

The angle θ, as defined in Figure 3.21, is

$$\theta = \tan^{-1}\left(\frac{C_y}{|C_x|}\right) = \tan^{-1}\left(\frac{141 \text{ m}}{41 \text{ m}}\right) = 74°$$

Thus the bird's net displacement is $\vec{C} = (147 \text{ m}, 74°$ north of west$)$.

ASSESS The final values of C_x and C_y match what we would expect from the sketch in Figure 3.21. The geometric addition was a valuable check on the answer we found by algebraic addition.

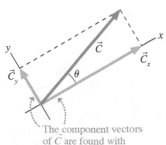

When you look at a trail map for a hike in a mountainous region, it will give the length of a trail *and* the elevation gain— an important variable! The elevation gain is simply d_y, the vertical component of the displacement for the hike.

FIGURE 3.22 A coordinate system with tilted axes.

$\vec{C}$

$\vec{C}_x$

$\vec{C}_y$

θ

The component vectors of $\vec{C}$ are found with respect to the tilted axes.

Vector subtraction and the multiplication of a vector by a scalar are also easily performed using components. To find $\vec{D} = \vec{P} - \vec{Q}$ we would compute

$$D_x = P_x - Q_x$$
$$D_y = P_y - Q_y \qquad (3.17)$$

Similarly, $\vec{T} = c\vec{S}$ is

$$T_x = cS_x$$
$$T_y = cS_y \qquad (3.18)$$

The next few chapters will make frequent use of *vector equations*. For example, you will learn that the equation to calculate the net force on a car skidding to a stop is

$$\vec{F} = \vec{n} + \vec{w} + \vec{f} \qquad (3.19)$$

Equation 3.19 is really just a shorthand way of writing the two simultaneous equations:

$$F_x = n_x + w_x + f_x$$
$$F_y = n_y + w_y + f_y \qquad (3.20)$$

In other words, a vector equation is interpreted as meaning: Equate the x-components on both sides of the equals sign, then equate the y-components. Vector notation allows us to write these two equations in a more compact form.

Tilted Axes

Although we are used to having the x-axis horizontal, there is no requirement that it has to be that way. In Chapter 1, we saw that for motion on a slope, it is often most convenient to put the x-axis along the slope. When we add the y-axis, this gives us a tilted coordinate system such as that shown in **FIGURE 3.22**.

Finding components with tilted axes is no harder than what we have done so far. Vector $\vec{C}$ in Figure 3.22 can be decomposed into component vectors $\vec{C}_x$ and $\vec{C}_y$, with $C_x = C\cos\theta$ and $C_y = C\sin\theta$.

STOP TO THINK 3.3   Angle ϕ that specifies the direction of $\vec{C}$ is computed as

A. $\tan^{-1}(C_x/C_y)$.
B. $\tan^{-1}(C_x/|C_y|)$.
C. $\tan^{-1}(|C_x|/|C_y|)$.
D. $\tan^{-1}(C_y/C_x)$.
E. $\tan^{-1}(C_y/|C_x|)$.
F. $\tan^{-1}(|C_y|/|C_x|)$.

3.4 Motion on a Ramp

In this section, we will examine the problem of motion on a ramp or incline. There are three reasons to look at this problem. First, it will provide good practice at using vectors to analyze motion. Second, it is a simple problem for which we can find an exact solution. Third, this seemingly abstract problem has real and important applications.

We begin with a constant-velocity example to give us some practice with vectors and components before moving on to the more general case of accelerated motion.

EXAMPLE 3.6   **Finding the height gained on a slope**

A car drives up a steep 10° slope at a constant speed of 15 m/s. After 10 s, how much height has the car gained?

PREPARE   FIGURE 3.23 is a visual overview, with x- and y-axes defined. The velocity vector $\vec{v}$ points up the slope. We are interested in the vertical motion of the car, so we decompose $\vec{v}$ into component vectors $\vec{v}_x$ and $\vec{v}_y$ as shown.

FIGURE 3.23 Visual overview of a car moving up a slope.

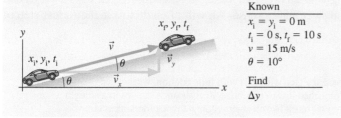

Known
$x_i = y_i = 0\ \text{m}$
$t_i = 0\ \text{s},\ t_f = 10\ \text{s}$
$v = 15\ \text{m/s}$
$\theta = 10°$

Find
Δy

SOLVE   The velocity component we need is v_y; this describes the vertical motion of the car. Using the rules for finding components outlined above, we find

$$v_y = v\sin\theta = (15\ \text{m/s})\sin(10°) = 2.6\ \text{m/s}$$

Because the velocity is constant, the car's vertical displacement (i.e., the height gained) during 10 s is

$$\Delta y = v_y\,\Delta t = (2.6\ \text{m/s})(10\ \text{s}) = 26\ \text{m}$$

ASSESS   The car is traveling at a pretty good clip—15 m/s is a bit faster than 30 mph—up a steep slope, so it should climb a respectable height in 10 s. 26 m, or about 80 ft, seems reasonable.

Accelerated Motion on a Ramp

FIGURE 3.24a on the next page shows a crate sliding down a frictionless (i.e., smooth) ramp tilted at angle θ. The crate accelerates due to the action of gravity, but it is *constrained* to accelerate parallel to the surface. What is the acceleration?

A motion diagram for the crate is drawn in FIGURE 3.24b. There is an acceleration because the velocity is changing, with both the acceleration and velocity vectors parallel to the ramp. We can take advantage of the properties of vectors to find the crate's acceleration. To do so, FIGURE 3.24c sets up a coordinate system with the x-axis along the ramp and the y-axis perpendicular. All motion will be along the x-axis.

FIGURE 3.24 Acceleration on an inclined plane.

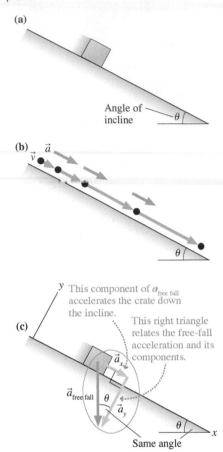

(a)

Angle of incline —— θ

(b)

θ

(c)

y This component of $a_{\text{free fall}}$ accelerates the crate down the incline.

This right triangle relates the free-fall acceleration and its components.

$\vec{a}_x$

$\vec{a}_{\text{free fall}}$ θ

$\vec{a}_y$

θ x

Same angle

If the incline suddenly vanished, the object would have a free-fall acceleration $\vec{a}_{\text{free fall}}$ straight down. As Figure 3.24c shows, this acceleration vector can be decomposed into two component vectors: a vector $\vec{a}_x$ that is *parallel* to the incline and a vector $\vec{a}_y$ that is *perpendicular* to the incline. The vector addition rules studied earlier in this chapter tell us that $\vec{a}_{\text{free fall}} = \vec{a}_x + \vec{a}_y$.

The motion diagram shows that the object's actual acceleration $\vec{a}_x$ is parallel to the incline. The surface of the incline somehow "blocks" the other component of the acceleration $\vec{a}_y$, through a process we will examine in Chapter 5, but $\vec{a}_x$ is unhindered. It is this component of $\vec{a}_{\text{free fall}}$, parallel to the incline, that accelerates the object.

We can use trigonometry to work out the magnitude of this acceleration. Figure 3.24c shows that the three vectors $\vec{a}_{\text{free fall}}$, $\vec{a}_y$, and $\vec{a}_x$ form a right triangle with angle θ as shown; this angle is the same as the angle of the incline. By definition, the magnitude of $\vec{a}_{\text{free fall}}$ is g. This vector is the hypotenuse of the right triangle. The vector we are interested in, $\vec{a}_x$, is opposite angle θ. Thus the value of the acceleration along a frictionless slope is

$$a_x = \pm g \sin \theta \qquad (3.21)$$

NOTE ▶ The correct sign depends on the direction in which the ramp is tilted. The acceleration in Figure 3.24 is $+g \sin \theta$, but upcoming examples will show situations in which the acceleration is $-g \sin \theta$. ◀

Let's look at Equation 3.21 to verify that it makes sense. A good way to do this is to consider some **limiting cases** in which the angle is at one end of its range. In these cases, the physics is clear and we can check our result. Let's look at two such possibilities:

1. Suppose the plane is perfectly horizontal, with $\theta = 0°$. If you place an object on a horizontal surface, you expect it to stay at rest with no acceleration. Equation 3.21 gives $a_x = 0$ when $\theta = 0°$, in agreement with our expectations.
2. Now suppose you tilt the plane until it becomes vertical, with $\theta = 90°$. You know what happens—the object will be in free fall, parallel to the vertical surface. Equation 3.21 gives $a_x = g$ when $\theta = 90°$, again in agreement with our expectations.

NOTE ▶ Checking your answer by looking at such limiting cases is a very good way to see if your answer makes sense. We will often do this in the Assess step of a solution. ◀

◀ **Extreme physics** A speed skier, on wide skis with little friction, wearing an aerodynamic helmet and crouched low to minimize air resistance, moves in a straight line down a steep slope—pretty much like an object sliding down a frictionless ramp. There is a maximum speed that a skier could possibly achieve at the end of the slope. Course designers set the starting point to keep this maximum speed within reasonable (for this sport!) limits.

EXAMPLE 3.7   **Maximum possible speed for a skier**

The Willamette Pass ski area in Oregon was the site of the 1993 U.S. National Speed Skiing Competition. The skiers started from rest and then accelerated down a stretch of the mountain with a reasonably constant slope, aiming for the highest possible speed at the end of this run. During this acceleration phase, the skiers traveled 360 m while dropping a vertical distance of 170 m. What is the fastest speed a skier could achieve at the end of this run? How much time would this fastest run take?

PREPARE We begin with the visual overview in FIGURE 3.25. The motion diagram shows the acceleration of the skier and the pictorial representation gives an overview of the problem including the dimensions of the slope. As before, we put the x-axis along the slope.

FIGURE 3.25 Visual overview of a skier accelerating down a slope.

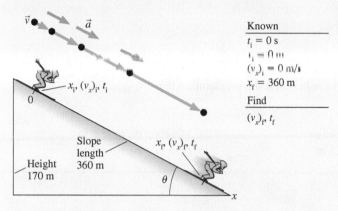

Known
$t_i = 0$ s
$x_i = 0$ m
$(v_x)_i = 0$ m/s
$x_f = 360$ m

Find
$(v_x)_f, t_f$

$x_i, (v_x)_i, t_i$

0

Slope length 360 m

$x_f, (v_x)_f, t_f$

Height 170 m

θ

x

SOLVE The fastest possible run would be one without any friction or air resistance, meaning the acceleration down the slope is given by Equation 3.21. The acceleration is in the positive x-direction, so we use the positive sign. What is the angle in Equation 3.21? Figure 3.25 shows that the 360-m-long slope is the hypotenuse of a triangle of height 170 m, so we use trigonometry to find

$$\sin\theta = \frac{170 \text{ m}}{360 \text{ m}}$$

which gives $\theta = \sin^{-1}(170/360) = 28°$. Equation 3.21 then gives

$$a_x = +g\sin\theta = (9.8 \text{ m/s}^2)(\sin 28°) = 4.6 \text{ m/s}^2$$

For linear motion with constant acceleration, we can use the third of the kinematic equations in Table 2.4: $(v_x)_f^2 = (v_x)_i^2 + 2a_x \Delta x$. The initial velocity $(v_x)_i$ is zero; thus:

This is the distance along the slope, the length of the run.

$$(v_x)_f = \sqrt{2a_x\Delta x} = \sqrt{2(4.6 \text{ m/s}^2)(360 \text{ m})} = 58 \text{ m/s}$$

This is the fastest that any skier could hope to be moving at the end of the run. Any friction or air resistance would decrease this speed. Because the acceleration is constant and the initial velocity $(v_x)_i$ is zero, the time of the fastest-possible run is

$$\Delta t = \frac{(v_x)_f}{a_x} = \frac{58 \text{ m/s}}{4.6 \text{ m/s}^2} = 13 \text{ s}$$

A speed skiing event is a quick affair!

ASSESS The final speed we calculated is 58 m/s, which is about 130 mph, reasonable because we expect a high speed for this sport. In the competition noted, the actual winning speed was 111 mph, not much slower than the result we calculated. Obviously, the efforts to minimize friction and air resistance are working!

Skis on snow have very little friction, but there are other ways to reduce the friction between surfaces. For instance, a roller coaster car rolls along a track on low-friction wheels. No drive force is applied to the cars after they are released at the top of the first hill: the speed changes due to gravity alone. The cars speed up as they go down hills and slow down as they climb.

EXAMPLE 3.8 **Speed of a roller coaster**

A classic wooden coaster has cars that go down a big first hill, gaining speed. The cars then ascend a second hill with a slope of 30°. If the cars are going 25 m/s at the bottom and it takes them 2.0 s to climb this hill, how fast are they going at the top?

PREPARE We start with the visual overview in FIGURE 3.26, which includes a motion diagram, a pictorial representation, and a list of values. We've done this with a sketch such as you might draw for your homework. Notice how the motion diagram of Figure 3.26 differs from that of the previous example: The velocity decreases as the car moves up the hill, so the acceleration vector is opposite the direction of the velocity vector. The motion is along the x-axis, as before, but the acceleration vector points in the negative x-direction, so the component a_x is negative. In the motion diagram, notice that we drew only a single acceleration vector—a reasonable shortcut because we know that the

acceleration is constant. One vector can represent the acceleration for the entire motion.

FIGURE 3.26 The coaster's speed decreases as it goes up the hill.

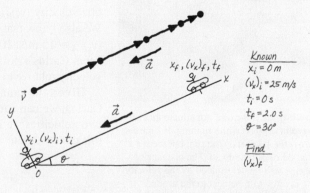

$x_f, (v_x)_f, t_f$

$x_i, (v_x)_i, t_i$

Known
$x_i = 0$ m
$(v_x)_i = 25$ m/s
$t_i = 0$ s
$t_f = 2.0$ s
$\theta = 30°$

Find
$(v_x)_f$

Continued

SOLVE To determine the final speed, we need to know the acceleration. We will assume that there is no friction or air resistance, so the magnitude of the roller coaster's acceleration is given by Equation 3.21 using the minus sign, as noted:

$$a_x = -g\sin\theta = -(9.8 \text{ m/s}^2)\sin 30° = -4.9 \text{ m/s}^2$$

The speed at the top of the hill can then be computed using our kinematic equation for velocity:

$$(v_x)_f = (v_x)_i + a_x \Delta t = 25 \text{ m/s} + (-4.9 \text{ m/s}^2)(2.0 \text{ s}) = 15 \text{ m/s}$$

ASSESS The speed is less at the top of the hill than at the bottom, as it should be, but the coaster is still moving at a pretty good clip at the top—almost 35 mph. This seems reasonable; a fast ride is a fun ride.

STOP TO THINK 3.4 A block of ice slides down a ramp. For which height and base length is the acceleration the greatest?

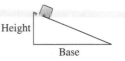
Height

Base

A. Height 4 m, base 12 m
B. Height 3 m, base 6 m
C. Height 2 m, base 5 m
D. Height 1 m, base 3 m

3.5 Relative Motion

You've now dealt many times with problems that say something like "A car travels at 30 m/s" or "A plane travels at 300 m/s." But, as we will see, we may need to be a bit more specific.

In FIGURE 3.27, Amy, Bill, and Carlos are watching a runner. According to Amy, the runner's velocity is $v_x = 5$ m/s. But to Bill, who's riding alongside, the runner is lifting his legs up and down but going neither forward nor backward relative to Bill. As far as Bill is concerned, the runner's velocity is $v_x = 0$ m/s. Carlos sees the runner receding in his rearview mirror, in the *negative* x-direction, getting 10 m farther away from him every second. According to Carlos, the runner's velocity is $v_x = -10$ m/s. Which is the runner's *true* velocity?

Velocity is not a concept that can be true or false. The runner's velocity *relative to Amy* is 5 m/s; that is, his velocity is 5 m/s in a coordinate system attached to Amy and in which Amy is at rest. The runner's velocity relative to Bill is 0 m/s, and the velocity relative to Carlos is −10 m/s. These are all valid descriptions of the runner's motion.

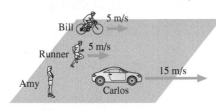

FIGURE 3.27 Amy, Bill, and Carlos each measure the velocity of the runner. The velocities are shown relative to Amy.

Relative Velocity

Suppose we know that the runner's velocity relative to Amy is 5 m/s; we will call this velocity $(v_x)_{RA}$. The second subscript "RA" means "**R**unner relative to **A**my." We also know that the velocity of Carlos relative to Amy is 15 m/s; we write this as $(v_x)_{CA} = 15$ m/s. It is equally valid to compute Amy's velocity relative to Carlos. From Carlos's point of view, Amy is moving to the left at 15 m/s; we write Amy's velocity relative to Carlos as $(v_x)_{AC} = -15$ m/s; note that $(v_x)_{AC} = -(v_x)_{CA}$.

Given the runner's velocity relative to Amy and Amy's velocity relative to Carlos, we can compute the runner's velocity relative to Carlos by combining the two velocities we know. The subscripts as we have defined them are our guide for this combination:

$$(v_x)_{RC} = (v_x)_{RA} + (v_x)_{AC} \tag{3.22}$$

The "A" appears on the right of the first expression and on the left of the second; when we combine these velocities, we "cancel" the A to get $(v_x)_{RC}$.

Throwing for the gold An athlete throwing the javelin does so while running. It's harder to throw the javelin on the run, but there's a very good reason to do so. The distance of the throw will be determined by the velocity of the javelin with respect to the ground—which is the sum of the velocity of the throw plus the velocity of the athlete. A faster run means a longer throw.

Generally, you can add two relative velocities in this manner, by "canceling" subscripts as in Equation 3.22. In Chapter 27, when we learn about relativity, we will have a more rigorous scheme for computing relative velocities, but this technique will serve our purposes at present.

EXAMPLE 3.9   **Speed of a seabird**

Researchers doing satellite tracking of albatrosses in the Southern Ocean observed a bird maintaining sustained flight speeds of 35 m/s—nearly 80 mph! This seems surprisingly fast until you realize that this particular bird was flying with the wind, which was moving at 23 m/s. What was the bird's airspeed—its speed relative to the air? This is a truer measure of its flight speed.

PREPARE FIGURE 3.28 shows the wind and the albatross moving to the right, so all velocities will be positive. We've shown the

FIGURE 3.28 Relative velocities for the albatross and the wind for Example 3.9.

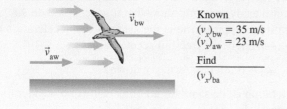

Known
$(v_x)_{bw} = 35$ m/s
$(v_x)_{aw} = 23$ m/s

Find
$(v_x)_{ba}$

velocity $(v_x)_{bw}$ of the bird with respect to the water, which is the measured flight speed, and the velocity $(v_x)_{aw}$ of the air with respect to the water, which is the known wind speed. We want to find the bird's airspeed—the speed of the bird with respect to the air.

SOLVE We need the subscript for the water to "cancel," so, according to Equation 3.22, we write

$$(v_x)_{ba} = (v_x)_{bw} + (v_x)_{wa}$$

The term $(v_x)_{wa}$, is the opposite of the second of our known values, so we use $(v_x)_{wa} = -(v_x)_{aw} = -23$ m/s to find

$$(v_x)_{ba} = (35 \text{ m/s}) + (-23 \text{ m/s}) = 12 \text{ m/s}$$

ASSESS 12 m/s—about 25 mph—is a reasonable airspeed for a bird. And it's slower than the observed flight speed, which makes sense because the bird is flying with the wind.

This technique for finding relative velocities also works for two-dimensional situations, as we see in the next example. Relative motion in two dimensions is another good exercise in working with vectors.

EXAMPLE 3.10   **Finding the ground speed of an airplane**

Cleveland is approximately 300 miles east of Chicago. A plane leaves Chicago flying due east at 500 mph. The pilot forgot to check the weather and doesn't know that the wind is blowing to the south at 100 mph. What is the plane's velocity relative to the ground?

PREPARE FIGURE 3.29 is a visual overview of the situation. We are given the speed of the **plane** relative to the **air** ($\vec{v}_{pa}$) and the

FIGURE 3.29 The wind causes a plane flying due east in the air to move to the southeast relative to the ground.

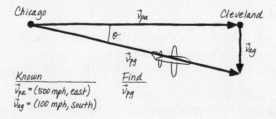

Known
$\vec{v}_{pa} = (500$ mph, east)
$\vec{v}_{ag} = (100$ mph, south)

Find
$\vec{v}_{pg}$

speed of the **air** relative to the **ground** ($\vec{v}_{ag}$); the speed of the **plane** relative to the ground will be the vector sum of these velocities:

$$\vec{v}_{pg} = \vec{v}_{pa} + \vec{v}_{ag}$$

This vector sum is shown in Figure 3.29.

SOLVE The plane's speed relative to the ground is the hypotenuse of the right triangle in Figure 3.29; thus:

$$v_{pg} = \sqrt{v_{pa}^2 + v_{ag}^2} = \sqrt{(500 \text{ mph})^2 + (100 \text{ mph})^2} = 510 \text{ mph}$$

The plane's direction can be specified by the angle θ measured from due east:

$$\theta = \tan^{-1}\left(\frac{100 \text{ mph}}{500 \text{ mph}}\right) = \tan^{-1}(0.20) = 11°$$

The velocity of the plane relative to the ground is thus

$$\vec{v}_{pg} = (510 \text{ mph}, 11° \text{ south of east})$$

ASSESS The good news is that the wind is making the plane move a bit faster relative to the ground; the bad news is that the wind is making the plane move in the wrong direction!

FIGURE 3.30 The motion of a tossed ball. The inset shows how to find the direction of $\Delta\vec{v}$, the change in velocity. This is the direction in which the acceleration $\vec{a}$ points.

(a)

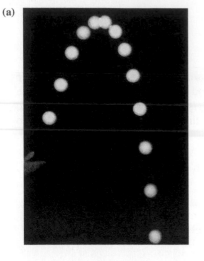

(b)

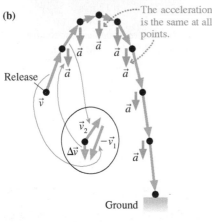

The acceleration is the same at all points.

Release

Ground

FIGURE 3.31 The launch and motion of a projectile.

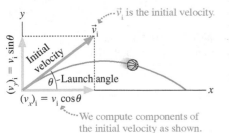

$\vec{v}_i$ is the initial velocity.

$(v_y)_i = v_i\sin\theta$

Initial velocity

θ—Launch angle

$(v_x)_i = v_i\cos\theta$

We compute components of the initial velocity as shown.

3.6 Motion in Two Dimensions: Projectile Motion

Balls flying through the air, long jumpers, and cars doing stunt jumps are all examples of the two-dimensional motion that we call *projectile motion*. Projectile motion is an extension to two dimensions of the free-fall motion we studied in Chapter 2. A **projectile is an object that moves in two dimensions under the influence of gravity and nothing else.** Although real objects are also influenced by air resistance, the effect of air resistance is small for reasonably dense objects moving at modest speeds, so we can ignore it for the cases we consider in this chapter. As long as we can neglect air resistance, any projectile will follow the same type of path: a trajectory with the mathematical form of a parabola. Because the form of the motion will always be the same, the strategies we develop to solve one projectile problem can be applied to others as well.

FIGURE 3.30a shows the parabolic arc of a ball tossed into the air; the camera has captured its position at equal intervals of time. In **FIGURE 3.30b** we show the motion diagram for this toss, with velocity vectors connecting the points. The acceleration vector points in the same direction as the change in velocity $\Delta\vec{v}$, which we can compute using the techniques of Tactics Box 3.2. You can see that the acceleration vector points straight down; a careful analysis would show that it has magnitude 9.80 m/s². Consequently, the acceleration of a projectile is the same as the acceleration of an object falling straight down—namely, the free-fall acceleration:

$$\vec{a}_{\text{free fall}} = (9.80 \text{ m/s}^2, \text{ straight down})$$

Because the free-fall acceleration is the same for all objects, it is no wonder that the shape of the trajectory—a parabola—is the same as well.

As the projectile moves, the free-fall acceleration will change the vertical component of the velocity, but there will be no change to the horizontal component of the velocity. Therefore, the vertical and horizontal components of the acceleration are

$$a_x = 0 \text{ m/s}^2$$
$$a_y = -g = -9.80 \text{ m/s}^2 \tag{3.23}$$

The vertical component of acceleration a_y for all projectile motion is just the familiar $-g$ of free fall, while the horizontal component a_x is zero.

Analyzing Projectile Motion

Suppose you toss a basketball down the court, as shown in **FIGURE 3.31**. To study this projectile motion, we've established a coordinate system with the x-axis horizontal and the y-axis vertical. The start of a projectile's motion is called the *launch,* and the angle θ of the initial velocity $\vec{v}_i$ above the horizontal (i.e., above the x-axis) is the **launch angle.** As you learned in Section 3.3, the initial velocity vector $\vec{v}_i$ can be expressed in terms of the x- and y-components $(v_x)_i$ and $(v_y)_i$. You can see from the figure that

$$(v_x)_i = v_i\cos\theta$$
$$(v_y)_i = v_i\sin\theta \tag{3.24}$$

where v_i is the initial speed.

NOTE ► The components $(v_x)_i$ and $(v_y)_i$ are not always positive. A projectile launched at an angle *below* the horizontal (such as a ball thrown downward from the roof of a building) has *negative* values for θ and $(v_y)_i$. However, the *speed* v_i is always positive. ◄

To see how the acceleration determines the subsequent motion, **FIGURE 3.32** shows a projectile launched at a speed of 22.0 m/s at an angle of 63° from the horizontal.

In Figure 3.32a, the initial velocity vector is broken into its horizontal and vertical components. In Figure 3.32b, the velocity vector and its component vectors are shown every subsequent 1.0 s. Because there is no horizontal acceleration ($a_x = 0$), the value of v_x never changes. In contrast, v_y decreases by 9.8 m/s every second. This is what it *means* to accelerate at $a_y = -9.8$ m/s² $= (-9.8$ m/s$)$ per second. Nothing *pushes* the projectile along the curve. Instead, the downward acceleration changes the velocity vector as shown, causing it to increase downward as the motion proceeds. At the end of the motion, when the ball is at the same height as it started, v_y is -19.6 m/s, the negative of its initial value. **The ball finishes its motion moving downward at the same speed as it started moving upward,** just as we saw in the case of one-dimensional free fall in Chapter 2.

You can see from Figure 3.32 that **projectile motion is made up of two independent motions: uniform motion at constant velocity in the horizontal direction and free-fall motion in the vertical direction.** In Chapter 2, we saw kinematic equations for constant-velocity and constant-acceleration motion. We can adapt these general equations to this current case: The horizontal motion is constant-velocity motion at $(v_x)_i$; the vertical motion is constant-acceleration motion with initial velocity $(v_y)_i$ and an acceleration of $a_y = -g$.

$$x_f = x_i + (v_x)_i \, \Delta t \qquad y_f = y_i + (v_y)_i \, \Delta t - \tfrac{1}{2}g(\Delta t)^2$$

$$(v_x)_f = (v_x)_i = \text{constant} \qquad (v_y)_f = (v_y)_i - g \, \Delta t$$

$$(3.25)$$

Equations of motion for the parabolic trajectory of a projectile

A close look at these equations reveals a surprising fact: **The horizontal and vertical components of projectile motion are independent of each other.** The initial horizontal velocity has *no* influence over the vertical motion, and vice versa. This independence of the horizontal and vertical motions is illustrated in FIGURE 3.33, which shows a strobe photograph of two balls, one shot horizontally and the other released from rest at the same instant. The *vertical* motions of the two balls are identical, and they hit the floor simultaneously. Neither ball has any initial motion in the vertical direction, so both fall distance h in the same amount of time.

Let's extend these ideas to consider a "classic" problem in physics:

A hungry hunter in the jungle wants to shoot down a coconut that is hanging from the branch of a tree. He aims the gun directly at the coconut, but as luck would have it the coconut falls from the branch at the exact instant the hunter pulls the trigger. Does the bullet hit the coconut?

FIGURE 3.34 shows a useful way to analyze this problem. Figure 3.34a shows the trajectory of a projectile. Without gravity, a projectile would follow a

FIGURE 3.32 The velocity and acceleration vectors of a projectile.

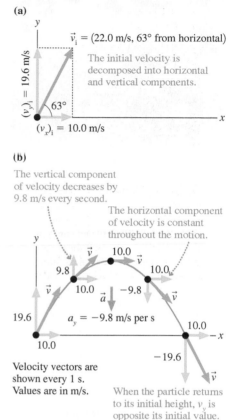

(a)

(b)

The vertical component of velocity decreases by 9.8 m/s every second.

The horizontal component of velocity is constant throughout the motion.

$a_y = -9.8$ m/s per s

Velocity vectors are shown every 1 s. Values are in m/s.

When the particle returns to its initial height, v_y is opposite its initial value.

FIGURE 3.33 A projectile launched horizontally falls in the same time as a projectile that is released from rest.

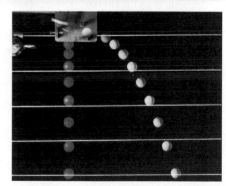

FIGURE 3.34 A projectile follows a parabolic trajectory because it "falls" a distance $\tfrac{1}{2}gt^2$ below a straight-line trajectory.

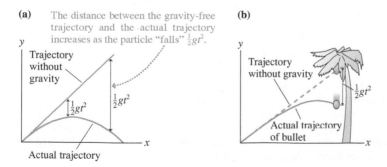

(a) The distance between the gravity-free trajectory and the actual trajectory increases as the particle "falls" $\tfrac{1}{2}gt^2$.

Trajectory without gravity

$\tfrac{1}{2}gt^2$

$\tfrac{1}{2}gt^2$

Actual trajectory

(b)

Trajectory without gravity

$\tfrac{1}{2}gt^2$

Actual trajectory of bullet

TRY IT YOURSELF

A game of catch in a moving vehicle
While riding in a car moving at a constant speed, toss a ball or a coin into the air. You can easily catch it! The ball and you continue to move forward at a constant speed during the ball's up-and-down vertical motion. The vertical motion is completely independent of, and unaffected by, the horizontal motion. From the point of a view of a person watching you drive by, the ball's motion would be a parabolic arc.

straight line. Because of gravity, the particle at time t has "fallen" a distance $\frac{1}{2}gt^2$ below this line. The separation grows as $\frac{1}{2}gt^2$, giving the trajectory its parabolic shape. Figure 3.34b applies this reasoning to the bullet and coconut. Although the bullet travels very fast, it follows a slightly curved trajectory, not a straight line. Had the coconut stayed on the tree, the bullet would have curved under its target because gravity causes it to fall a distance $\frac{1}{2}gt^2$ below the straight line. But $\frac{1}{2}gt^2$ is also the distance the coconut falls while the bullet is in flight. Thus, as Figure 3.34b shows, the bullet and the coconut fall the same distance and meet at the same point!

STOP TO THINK 3.5 A 100 g ball rolls off a table and lands 2 m from the base of the table. A 200 g ball rolls off the same table with the same speed. How far does it land from the base of the table?

A. <1 m.   B. 1 m.
C. Between 1 m and 2 m.   D. 2 m.
E. Between 2 m and 4 m.   F. 4 m.

3.7 Projectile Motion: Solving Problems

Now that we have a good idea of how projectile motion works, we can use that knowledge to solve some true two-dimensional motion problems.

EXAMPLE 3.11 **Planning a Hollywood stunt**

To get the shots of cars flying through the air in movies, it is sometimes necessary to drive a car off a cliff and film it. Suppose a stunt man drives a car off a 10-m-high cliff at a speed of 20 m/s. How far does the car land from the base of the cliff?

PREPARE We start with a visual overview of the situation in FIGURE 3.35. Note that we have chosen to put the origin of the coordinate system at the base of the cliff. We assume that the car is moving horizontally as it leaves the cliff. In this case, the x- and y-components of the initial velocity are

$$(v_x)_i = v_i = 20 \text{ m/s}$$
$$(v_y)_i = 0 \text{ m/s}$$

FIGURE 3.35 Visual overview for Example 3.11.

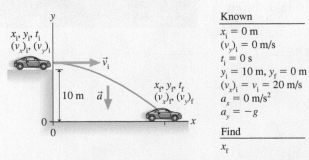

Known
$x_i = 0$ m
$(v_y)_i = 0$ m/s
$t_i = 0$ s
$y_i = 10$ m, $y_f = 0$ m
$(v_x)_i = v_i = 20$ m/s
$a_x = 0$ m/s^2
$a_y = -g$

Find
x_f

SOLVE Each point on the trajectory has x- and y-components of position, velocity, and acceleration but only *one* value of time. The time needed to move horizontally to the final position x_f is the *same* time needed to fall 10 m vertically. **Although the horizontal and vertical motions are independent, they are both**

related to the time t. This is a critical observation for solving projectile motion problems. We will call the time interval between the car leaving the cliff and landing on the ground Δt. In this problem, we'll analyze the vertical motion first. We can solve the vertical-motion equations for the time interval Δt. We'll then use that value of Δt in the equation for the horizontal motion.

The vertical motion is just free fall. The initial vertical velocity is zero; the car falls from $y_i = 10$ m to $y_f = 0$ m. We can analyze this motion using the vertical-position equation from Equations 3.25:

$$y_f = y_i + (v_y)_i \, \Delta t - \tfrac{1}{2}g(\Delta t)^2$$

$$0 \text{ m} = 10 \text{ m} + (0 \text{ m/s})(\Delta t) - \tfrac{1}{2}(9.8 \text{ m/s}^2)(\Delta t)^2$$

Rearranging the terms and then solving for Δt give

$$-10 \text{ m} = -\tfrac{1}{2}(9.8 \text{ m/s}^2)(\Delta t)^2$$

$$\Delta t = \sqrt{\frac{2(10 \text{ m})}{9.8 \text{ m/s}^2}} = 1.43 \text{ s}$$

Now that we have the time, we can use the horizontal-position equation from Equations 3.25 to find out where the car lands:

$$x_f = x_i + (v_x)_i \, \Delta t$$
$$x_f = 0 \text{ m} + (20 \text{ m/s})(1.43 \text{ s}) = 29 \text{ m}$$

ASSESS The cliff height is $h \approx 33$ ft and the initial horizontal velocity is $(v_x)_i \approx 40$ mph. At this speed, a car moves faster than 60 feet per second, so traveling $x_f = 29$ m ≈ 95 ft before hitting the ground seems quite reasonable.

The approach of Example 3.11 is a general one. We can condense the relevant details into a problem-solving strategy.

PROBLEM-SOLVING STRATEGY 3.1 **Projectile motion problems** (MP)™

PREPARE There are a number of steps that you should go through in setting up the solution to a projectile motion problem:

■ Make simplifying assumptions. Whether the projectile is a car or a basketball, the motion will be the same.
■ Draw a visual overview including a pictorial representation showing the beginning and ending points of the motion.
■ Establish a coordinate system with the x-axis horizontal and the y-axis vertical. In this case, you know that the horizontal acceleration will be zero and the vertical acceleration will be free fall: $a_x = 0$ and $a_y = -g$.
■ Define symbols and write down a list of known values. Identify what the problem is trying to find.

SOLVE There are two sets of kinematic equations for projectile motion, one for the horizontal component and one for the vertical:

Horizontal	Vertical
$x_f = x_i + (v_x)_i \, \Delta t$	$y_f = y_i + (v_y)_i \, \Delta t - \frac{1}{2}g(\Delta t)^2$
$(v_x)_f = (v_x)_i = \text{constant}$	$(v_y)_f = (v_y)_i - g \, \Delta t$

Δt **is the same for the horizontal and vertical components of the motion.** Find Δt by solving for the vertical or the horizontal component of the motion; then use that value to complete the solution for the other component.

ASSESS Check that your result has the correct units, is reasonable, and answers the question.

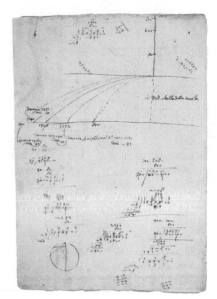

Galileo was the first person to make a serious study of projectile motion, deducing the independence of the horizontal and vertical components. This page from his notes shows his analysis of a projectile launched horizontally. In his day, this topic was cutting-edge science; now it is in Chapter 3 of a 30-chapter book!

Activ Physics ONLINE 3.1–3.7

EXAMPLE 3.12 **Checking the feasibility of a Hollywood stunt**

The main characters in the movie *Speed* are on a bus that has been booby-trapped to explode if its speed drops below 50 mph. But there is a problem ahead: A 50 ft section of a freeway overpass is missing. They decide to jump the bus over the gap. The road leading up to the break has an angle of about 5°. A view of the speedometer just before the jump shows that the bus is traveling at 67 mph. The movie bus makes the jump and survives. Is this realistic, or movie fiction?

PREPARE We begin by converting speed and distance to SI units. The initial speed is $v_i = 30$ m/s and the size of the gap is $L = 15$ m. Next, following the problem-solving strategy, we make a sketch, the visual overview shown in FIGURE 3.36, and a list of

FIGURE 3.36 Visual overview of the bus jumping the gap.

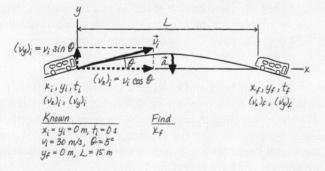

values. In choosing our axes, we've placed the origin at the point where the bus starts its jump. The initial velocity vector is tilted 5° above horizontal, so the components of the initial velocity are

$$(v_x)_i = v_i \cos\theta = (30 \text{ m/s})(\cos 5°) = 30 \text{ m/s}$$
$$(v_y)_i = v_i \sin\theta = (30 \text{ m/s})(\sin 5°) = 2.6 \text{ m/s}$$

How do we specify the "end" of the problem? By setting $y_f = 0$ m, we'll solve for the horizontal distance x_f at which the bus returns to its initial height. If x_f exceeds 50 ft, the bus successfully clears the gap. We have optimistically drawn our diagram as if the bus makes the jump, but . . .

SOLVE Problem-Solving Strategy 3.1 suggests using one component of the motion to solve for Δt. We will begin with the vertical motion. The kinematic equation for the vertical position is

$$y_f = y_i + (v_y)_i \, \Delta t - \frac{1}{2}g(\Delta t)^2$$

We know that $y_f = y_i = 0$ m. If we factor out Δt, the position equation becomes

$$0 = \Delta t\left((v_y)_i - \frac{1}{2}g \, \Delta t\right)$$

One solution to this equation is $\Delta t = 0$ s. This is a legitimate solution, but it corresponds to the instant when $y = 0$ at the beginning

Continued

of the trajectory. We want the second solution, for $y = 0$ at the end of the trajectory, which is when

$$0 = (v_y)_i - \tfrac{1}{2}g\,\Delta t = (2.6 \text{ m/s}) - \tfrac{1}{2}(9.8 \text{ m/s}^2)\,\Delta t$$

which gives

$$\Delta t = \frac{2 \times (2.6 \text{ m/s})}{9.8 \text{ m/s}^2} = 0.53 \text{ s}$$

During the 0.53 s that the bus is moving vertically it is also moving horizontally. The final horizontal position of the bus is $x_f = x_i + (v_x)_i\,\Delta t$, or

$$x_f = 0 \text{ m} + (30 \text{ m/s})(0.53 \text{ s}) = 16 \text{ m}$$

This is how far the bus has traveled horizontally when it returns to its original height. 16 m is a bit more than the width of the gap, so a bus coming off a 5° ramp at the noted speed would make it— just barely!

ASSESS We can do a quick check on our math by noting that the bus takes off and lands at the same height. This means, as we saw in Figure 3.32b, that the y-velocity at the landing should be the negative of its initial value. We can use the velocity equation for the vertical component of the motion to compute the final value and see that the final velocity value is as we predict:

$$(v_y)_f = (v_y)_i - g\,\Delta t$$
$$= (2.6 \text{ m/s}) - (9.8 \text{ m/s}^2)(0.53 \text{ s}) = -2.6 \text{ m/s}$$

During the filming of the movie, the filmmakers really did jump a bus over a gap in an overpass! The actual jump was a bit more complicated than our example because a real bus, being an extended object rather than a particle, will start rotating as the front end comes off the ramp. The actual stunt jump used an extra ramp to give a boost to the front end of the bus. Nonetheless, our example shows that the filmmakers did their homework and devised a situation in which the physics was correct.

The Range of a Projectile

When the quarterback throws a football down the field, how far will it go? What will be the **range** for this particular projectile motion, the horizontal distance traveled?

Example 3.12 was a range problem—for a given speed and a given angle, we wanted to know how far the bus would go. The speed and the angle are the two variables that determine the range. A higher speed means a greater range, of course. But how does angle figure in?

FIGURE 3.37 shows the trajectory that a projectile launched at 100 m/s will follow for different launch angles. At very small or very large angles, the range is quite small. If you throw a ball at a 75° angle, it will do a great deal of up-and-down motion, but it won't achieve much horizontal travel. If you throw a ball at a 15° angle, the ball won't be in the air long enough to go very far. These cases both have the same range, as Figure 3.37 shows.

If the angle is too small or too large, the range is shorter than it could be. The "just right" case that gives the maximum range when landing at the same elevation as the launch is a launch angle of 45°, as Figure 3.37 shows.

If that's true, why does a long jumper take off at an angle that is so much less than 45°, as shown in FIGURE 3.38? One reason is that he changes the position of his legs as he jumps—he doesn't really land at the same height as that from which he took off, which changes things a bit. But there's a more important reason. In Figure 3.37 we looked at the range of projectiles that were launched at the *same speed* to see that a 45° angle gave the longest range. But the biomechanics of running and jumping don't allow you to keep the same launch speed as you increase the angle of your jump. Any increase in your launch angle comes at the sacrifice of speed, so the situation of Figure 3.37 doesn't apply. The optimum angle for jumping is less than 45° because your faster jump speed outweighs the effect of a smaller jump angle.

For other projectiles, such as golf balls and baseballs, the optimal angle is less than 45° for a different reason: air resistance. Up to this point we've ignored air resistance, but for small objects traveling at high speeds, air resistance is critical. Aerodynamic forces come into play, causing the projectile's trajectory to deviate from a parabola. The maximum range for a golf ball comes at an angle much less than 45°, as you no doubt know if you have ever played golf.

FIGURE 3.37 Trajectories of a projectile for different launch angles, assuming air resistance can be neglected.

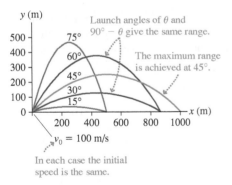

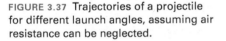

FIGURE 3.38 The trajectory of a long jumper.

▶ **Physics of fielding** BIO The batter hits a high fly ball, and the fielder makes a graceful arc to the exact spot where it lands, catching it on the run. He didn't estimate velocity and calculate the ball's trajectory, so how did he do it? The key is that the fielder is in constant motion. He monitors the relative motion of the ball as he runs and makes adjustments in his velocity to keep the ball at a constant angle with respect to him. By doing this, he'll be at the right spot when the ball lands. He doesn't know where the ball will land—just how to be there when it does!

3.8 Motion in Two Dimensions: Circular Motion

The 32 cars on the London Eye Ferris wheel move at a constant speed of about 0.5 m/s in a vertical circle of radius 65 m. The cars may move at a constant speed, but they do *not* move with constant velocity. Velocity is a vector that depends on both an object's speed *and* its direction of motion, and the direction of circular motion is constantly changing. This is the hallmark of **uniform circular motion**: constant speed, but continuously changing direction. We will introduce some basic ideas about circular motion in this section, then return to treat it in considerably more detail in Chapter 6. For now, we will consider only objects that move around a circular trajectory at constant speed.

Period, Frequency, and Speed

The time interval it takes an object to go around a circle one time, completing one revolution (abbreviated rev), is called the **period** of the motion. Period is represented by the symbol T.

Rather than specify the time for one revolution, we can specify circular motion by its **frequency,** the number of revolutions per second, for which we use the symbol f. An object with a period of one-half second completes 2 revolutions each second. Similarly, an object can make 10 revolutions in 1 s if its period is one-tenth of a second. This shows that frequency is the inverse of the period:

$$f = \frac{1}{T} \tag{3.26}$$

Although frequency is often expressed as "revolutions per second," *revolutions* are not true units but merely the counting of events. Thus the SI unit of frequency is simply inverse seconds, or s^{-1}. Frequency may also be given in revolutions per minute (rpm) or another time interval, but these usually need to be converted to s^{-1} before doing calculations.

FIGURE 3.39 shows an object moving at a constant speed in a circular path of radius R. We know the time for one revolution—one period T—and we know the distance traveled, so we can write an equation relating the period, the radius, and the speed:

$$v = \frac{2\pi R}{T} \tag{3.27}$$

Given Equation 3.26 relating frequency and period, we can also write this equation as

$$v = 2\pi f R \tag{3.28}$$

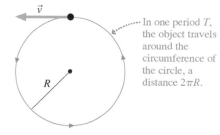

The London Eye Ferris wheel.

FIGURE 3.39 Relating frequency and speed.

In one period T, the object travels around the circumference of the circle, a distance $2\pi R$.

EXAMPLE 3.13 | **Spinning some tunes**

An audio CD has a diameter of 120 mm and spins at up to 540 rpm. When a CD is spinning at its maximum rate, how much time is required for one revolution? If a speck of dust rides on the outside edge of the disk, how fast is it moving?

PREPARE Before we get started, we need to do some unit conversions. The diameter of a CD is given as 120 mm, which is 0.12 m. The radius is 0.060 m. The frequency is given in rpm; we need to convert this to s^{-1}:

$$f = 540 \,\frac{\text{rev}}{\text{min}} \times \frac{1 \text{ min}}{60 \text{ s}} = 9.0 \,\frac{\text{rev}}{\text{s}} = 9.0 \text{ s}^{-1}$$

Continued

SOLVE The time for one revolution is the period; this is given by Equation 3.26:

$$T = \frac{1}{f} = \frac{1}{9.0 \text{ s}^{-1}} = 0.11 \text{ s}$$

The dust speck is moving in a circle of radius 0.12 m at a frequency of 9.0 s⁻¹. We can use Equation 3.28 to find the speed:

$$v = 2\pi f R = 2\pi(9.0 \text{ s}^{-1})(0.060 \text{ m}) = 3.4 \text{ m/s}$$

ASSESS If you've watched a CD spin, you know that it takes much less than a second to go around, so the value for the period seems reasonable. The speed we calculate for the dust speck is nearly 8 mph, but for a point on the edge of the CD to go around so many times in a second, it must be moving pretty fast.

Acceleration in Circular Motion

FIGURE 3.40 The velocity and acceleration vectors for circular motion.

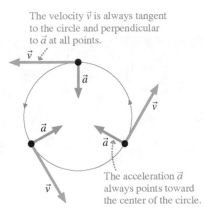

The velocity $\vec{v}$ is always tangent to the circle and perpendicular to $\vec{a}$ at all points.

The acceleration $\vec{a}$ always points toward the center of the circle.

It may seem strange to think that an object moving with constant speed can be accelerating, but that's exactly what an object in uniform circular motion is doing. It is accelerating because its velocity is changing as its direction of motion changes. What is the acceleration in this case? We saw in Example 3.3 that for circular motion at a constant speed, **the acceleration vector $\vec{a}$ points toward the center of the circle.** This is an idea that is worth reviewing. As you can see in FIGURE 3.40, the velocity is always tangent to the circle, so $\vec{v}$ and $\vec{a}$ are perpendicular to each other at all points on the circle.

An acceleration that always points directly toward the center of a circle is called a **centripetal acceleration.** The word "centripetal" comes from a Greek root meaning "center seeking."

NOTE ▶ Centripetal acceleration is not a new type of acceleration; all we are doing is *naming* an acceleration that corresponds to a particular type of motion. The magnitude of the centripetal acceleration is constant because each successive $\Delta\vec{v}$ in the motion diagram has the same length. ◀

To complete our description of circular motion, we need to find a quantitative relationship between the magnitude of the acceleration a and the speed v. Let's return to the case of the Ferris wheel. During a time Δt in which a car on the Ferris wheel moves around the circle from point 1 to point 2, the car moves through an angle θ and undergoes a displacement $\vec{d}$, as shown in FIGURE 3.41a. We've chosen a relatively large angle θ for our drawing so that angular relationships can be clearly seen, but for a small angle the displacement is essentially identical to the actual distance traveled, and we'll make this approximation.

FIGURE 3.41b shows how the velocity changes as the car moves, and FIGURE 3.41c shows the vector calculation of the change in velocity. The triangle we use to make this calculation is geometrically *similar* to the one that shows the displacement, as

FIGURE 3.41 Changing position and velocity for an object in circular motion.

(a)

As the car moves from point 1 to point 2, the displacement is $\vec{d}$.

(b)

The magnitude of the velocity is constant, but the direction changes.

(c)

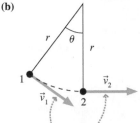

The change in velocity is a vector pointing toward the center of the circle.

$\Delta\vec{v} = \vec{v}_2 - \vec{v}_1$

This triangle is the same as in part a, but rotated.

These triangles are similar.

Figure 3.41c shows. This is a key piece of information: You'll remember from geometry that similar triangles have equal ratios of their sides, so we can write

$$\frac{\Delta v}{v} = \frac{d}{r} \tag{3.29}$$

where Δv is the magnitude of the velocity-change vector $\Delta \vec{v}$. We've used the unsubscripted speed v for the length of a side of the first triangle because it is the same for velocities $\vec{v}_1$ and $\vec{v}_2$.

Now we're ready to compute the acceleration. The displacement is just the speed v times the time interval Δt, so we can write

$$d = v\Delta t$$

We can substitute this for d in Equation 3.29 to obtain

$$\frac{\Delta v}{v} = \frac{v\Delta t}{r}$$

which we can rearrange like so:

$$\frac{\Delta v}{\Delta t} = \frac{v^2}{r}$$

We recognize the left-hand side of the equation as the acceleration, so this becomes

$$a = \frac{v^2}{r}$$

Combining this magnitude with the direction we noted above, we can write the centripetal acceleration as

$$\vec{a} = \left(\frac{v^2}{r}, \text{ toward center of circle} \right) \tag{3.30}$$

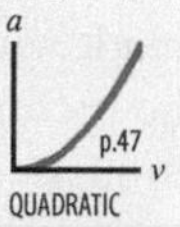

Centripetal acceleration of object moving in a circle of radius r at speed v

p.47

QUADRATIC

CONCEPTUAL EXAMPLE 3.14   **Acceleration on a swing**

A child is riding a playground swing. The swing rotates in a circle around a central point where the rope or chain for the swing is attached. The speed isn't changing at the lowest point of the motion, but the direction is—this is circular motion, with an acceleration directed upward, as shown in FIGURE 3.42. More acceleration will mean a more exciting ride. What change could the child make to increase the acceleration she experiences?

FIGURE 3.42 A child at the lowest point of motion on a swing.

REASON The acceleration the child experiences is the "changing direction" acceleration of circular motion, given by Equation 3.30. The acceleration depends on the speed and the radius of the circle. The radius of the circle is determined by the length of the chain or rope, so the only easy way to change the acceleration is to change the speed, which she could do by swinging higher. Because the acceleration is proportional to the square of the speed, doubling the speed means a fourfold increase in the acceleration.

ASSESS If you have ever ridden a swing, you know that the acceleration you experience is greater the faster you go—so our answer makes sense.

EXAMPLE 3.15   **Finding the acceleration of a Ferris wheel**

A typical carnival Ferris wheel has a radius of 9.0 m and rotates 6.0 times per minute. What magnitude acceleration do the riders experience?

PREPARE The cars on a Ferris wheel move in a circle at constant speed; the acceleration the riders experience is a centripetal acceleration.

SOLVE In order to use Equation 3.30 to compute an acceleration, we need to know the speed v of a rider on the Ferris wheel. The wheel rotates 6.0 times per minute; therefore, the time for one rotation (i.e., the period) is 10 s. We can use Equation 3.27 to find the speed:

$$v = \frac{2\pi R}{T} = \frac{(2\pi)(9.0 \text{ m})}{10 \text{ s}} = 5.7 \text{ m/s}$$

Knowing the speed, we can use Equation 3.30 to find the magnitude of the acceleration:

$$a = \frac{v^2}{r} = \frac{(5.7 \text{ m/s})^2}{9.0 \text{ m}} = 3.6 \text{ m/s}^2$$

ASSESS This is about 1/3 of the free-fall acceleration; the acceleration, in units of g, is $0.37g$. This is enough to notice, but not enough to be scary! Our answer seems reasonable.

What Comes Next: Forces

So far we have been studying motion without saying too much about what actually *causes* motion. Kinematics, the mathematical description of motion, is a good place to start because motion is very visible and very familiar. And in our study of motion we have introduced many of the basic tools, such as vectors, that we will use in the rest of the book.

But now it's time to look at what causes motion: forces. By learning about forces, which you will do in the next several chapters, you will be able to explore a much wider range of problems in much more depth. As an example, think about the picture of a roller coaster with an inverted loop. How is it that riders can go through the loop and not fall out of their seats? This is just one of the problems that you will study once you know a bit about forces and the connection between forces and motion.

◀**Amusement park kinematics** Acceleration is fun—at least that's what the designer of this roller coaster seems to think! The coaster has ramps that give linear acceleration, parabolic segments in which the coaster follows a projectile path with a free-fall acceleration, and circular arcs in which the centripetal acceleration is greater than g. All of this acceleration means there are forces on the riders—and the coaster must be carefully designed so that these forces are well within safe limits.

STOP TO THINK 3.6   Which of the following particles has the greatest centripetal acceleration?

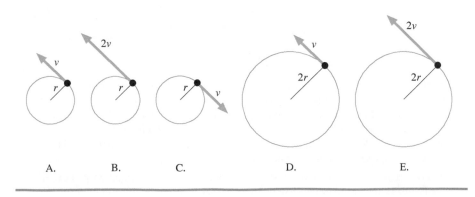

INTEGRATED EXAMPLE 3.16   **World-record jumpers**

Frogs, with their long, strong legs, are excellent jumpers. And thanks to the good folks of Calaveras County, California, who have a jumping frog contest every year in honor of a Mark Twain story, we have very good data as to just how far a determined frog can jump. The current record holder is Rosie the Ribeter, a bullfrog who made a leap of 6.5 m from a standing start. This compares favorably with the world record for a human, which is a mere 3.7 m.

Typical data for a serious leap by a bullfrog look like this: The frog goes into a crouch, then rapidly extends its legs by 15 cm as it pushes off, leaving the ground at an angle of 30° to the horizontal. It's in the air for 0.68 s before landing at the same height from which it took off. Given this leap, what is the acceleration while the frog is pushing off? How far does the frog jump?

PREPARE The problem really has two parts: the leap through the air and the acceleration required to produce this leap. We'll need to analyze the leap—the projectile motion—first, which will give us the frog's launch speed and the distance of the jump. Once we know the velocity with which the frog leaves the ground, we can calculate its acceleration while pushing off the ground. Let's start with a visual overview of the two parts, as shown in FIGURE 3.43. Notice that the second part of the problem uses a different x-axis, tilted as we did earlier for motion on a ramp.

SOLVE The "flying through the air" part of Figure 3.43a is projectile motion. The frog lifts off at a 30° angle with a speed v_i; the x- and y-components of the initial velocity are

$$(v_x)_i = v_i \cos (30°)$$
$$(v_y)_i = v_i \sin (30°)$$

The vertical motion can be analyzed as we did in Example 3.12. The kinematic equation is

$$y_f = y_i + (v_y)_i \Delta t + \tfrac{1}{2} a_y (\Delta t)^2$$

We know that $y_f = y_i = 0$, so this reduces to

$$(v_y)_i = -\tfrac{1}{2} a_y \Delta t = -\tfrac{1}{2}(-9.8 \text{ m/s}^2)(0.68 \text{ s}) = 3.3 \text{ m/s}$$

We know the y-component of the velocity and the angle, so we can find the magnitude of the velocity and the x-component:

$$v_i = \frac{(v_y)_i}{\sin 30°} = \frac{3.3 \text{ m/s}}{\sin 30°} = 6.6 \text{ m/s}$$

$$(v_x)_i = v_i \cos 30° = (6.6 \text{ m/s}) \cos 30° = 5.7 \text{ m/s}$$

The horizontal motion is uniform motion, so the frog's horizontal position when it returns to the ground is

$$x_f = x_i + (v_x)_i \Delta t = 0 + (5.7 \text{ m/s})(0.68 \text{ s}) = 3.9 \text{ m}$$

This is the length of the jump.

Now that we know how fast the frog is going when it leaves the ground, we can calculate the acceleration necessary to produce this jump—the "pushing off the ground" part of Figure 3.43b. We've drawn the x-axis along the direction of motion, as we did for problems of motion on a ramp. We know the displacement Δx of the jump but not the time, so we can use the third equation in Table 2.4:

$$(v_x)_f^2 = (v_x)_i^2 + 2a_x \Delta x$$

The initial velocity is zero, the final velocity is $(v_x)_f = 6.6$ m/s, and the displacement is the 15 cm (or 0.15 m) stretch of the legs during the jump. Thus the frog's acceleration while pushing off is

$$a_x = \frac{(v_x)_f^2}{2\Delta x} = \frac{(6.6 \text{ m/s})^2}{2(0.15 \text{ m})} = 150 \text{ m/s}^2$$

ASSESS A 3.9 m jump is more than a human can achieve, but it's less than the record for a frog, so the final result for the distance seems reasonable. Such a long jump must require a large acceleration during the pushing-off phase, which is what we found.

FIGURE 3.43 A visual overview for the leap of a frog.

(a) Flying through the air

(b) Pushing off the ground

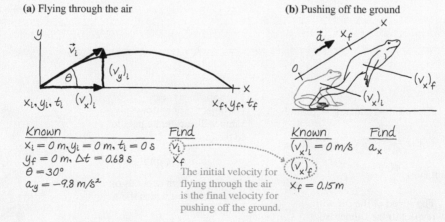

SUMMARY

The goals of Chapter 3 have been to learn more about vectors and to use vectors as a tool to analyze motion in two dimensions.

GENERAL PRINCIPLES

Projectile Motion

A projectile is an object that moves through the air under the influence of gravity and nothing else.

The path of the motion is a parabola.

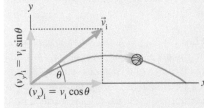

The motion consists of two pieces:

1. Vertical motion with free-fall acceleration, $a_y = -g$.

2. Horizontal motion with constant velocity.

Kinematic equations:

$$x_f = x_i + (v_x)_i \, \Delta t$$

$$(v_x)_f = (v_x)_i = \text{constant}$$

$$y_f = y_i + (v_y)_i \, \Delta t - \tfrac{1}{2} g (\Delta t)^2$$

$$(v_y)_f = (v_y)_i - g \, \Delta t$$

Circular Motion

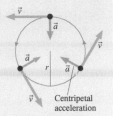

For an object moving in a circle at a constant speed:

- The period T is the time for one rotation.
- The frequency $f = 1/T$ is the number of revolutions per second.
- The velocity is tangent to the circular path.
- The acceleration points toward the center of the circle and has magnitude

$$a = \frac{v^2}{r}$$

IMPORTANT CONCEPTS

Vectors and Components

A vector can be decomposed into x- and y-**components**.

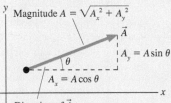

The magnitude and direction of a vector can be expressed in terms of its components.

The sign of the components depends on the direction of the vector:

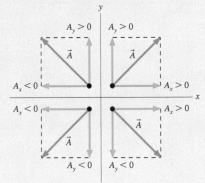

The Acceleration Vector

We define the acceleration vector as

$$\vec{a} = \frac{\vec{v}_f - \vec{v}_i}{t_f - t_i} = \frac{\Delta \vec{v}}{\Delta t}$$

We find the acceleration vector on a motion diagram as follows:

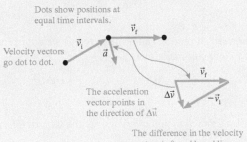

Dots show positions at equal time intervals.

Velocity vectors go dot to dot.

The acceleration vector points in the direction of $\Delta \vec{v}$.

The difference in the velocity vectors is found by adding the negative of $\vec{v}_i$ to $\vec{v}_f$.

APPLICATIONS

Relative motion
Velocities can be expressed relative to an observer. We can add relative velocities to convert to another observer's point of view.

c = car, r = runner, g = ground

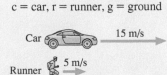

The speed of the car with respect to the runner is:

$$(v_x)_{cr} = (v_x)_{cg} + (v_x)_{gr}$$

Motion on a ramp
An object sliding down a ramp will accelerate parallel to the ramp:

$$a_x = \pm g \sin \theta$$

The correct sign depends on the direction in which the ramp is tilted.

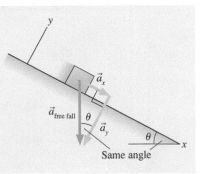

^{TM} For homework assigned on MasteringPhysics, go to
www.masteringphysics.com

Problems labeled **INT** integrate significant material from earlier
chapters; **BIO** are of biological or medical interest.

Problem difficulty is labeled as I (straightforward) to IIIII (challenging).

QUESTIONS

Conceptual Questions

1. a. Can a vector have nonzero magnitude if a component is
       zero? If no, why not? If yes, give an example.
    b. Can a vector have zero magnitude and a nonzero compo-
       nent? If no, why not? If yes, give an example.
2. Is it possible to add a scalar to a vector? If so, demonstrate. If
    not, explain why not.
3. Suppose two vectors have unequal magnitudes. Can their sum
    be $\vec{0}$? Explain.
4. Suppose $\vec{C} = \vec{A} + \vec{B}$
    a. Under what circumstances does $C = A + B$?
    b. Could $C = A - B$? If so, how? If not, why not?
5. For a projectile, which of the following quantities are constant
    during the flight: x, y, v_x, v_y, v, a_x, a_y? Which of the quantities
    are zero throughout the flight?
6. A baseball player throws a ball at a 40° angle to the ground. The
    ball lands on the ground some distance away.
    a. Is there any point on the trajectory where $\vec{v}$ and $\vec{a}$ are parallel
       to each other? If so, where?
    b. Is there any point where $\vec{v}$ and $\vec{a}$ are perpendicular to each
       other? If so, where?
7. An athlete performing the long
    jump tries to achieve the maxi-
    mum distance from the point of
    takeoff to the first point of touch-
    ing the ground. After the jump,
    rather than land upright, she
    extends her legs forward as in the
    photo. How does this affect the
    time in the air? How does this
    give the jumper a longer range?
8. A person trying to throw a ball as far as possible will run for-
    ward during the throw. Explain why this increases the distance
    of the throw.
9. A passenger on a jet airplane claims to be able to walk at a
    speed in excess of 500 mph. Can this be true? Explain.
10. If you go to a ski area, you'll likely find that the beginner's
    slope has the smallest angle. Use the concept of acceleration on
    a ramp to explain why this is so.
11. In an amusement-park ride, cars rolling along at high speed
    suddenly head up a long, straight ramp. They roll up the ramp,
    reverse direction at the highest point, then roll backward back
    down the ramp. In each of the following segments of the
    motion, are the cars accelerating, or is their acceleration zero? If
    accelerating, which way does their acceleration vector point?
    a. As the cars roll up the ramp.
    b. At the highest point on the ramp.
    c. As the cars roll back down the ramp.

12. There are competitions in which pilots fly small planes low
    over the ground and drop weights, trying to hit a target. A pilot
    flying low and slow drops a weight; it takes 2.0 s to hit the
    ground, during which it travels a horizontal distance of 100 m.
    Now the pilot does a run at the same height but twice the speed.
    How much time does it take the weight to hit the ground? How
    far does it travel before it lands?
13. A cyclist goes around a level, circular track at constant speed. Do
    you agree or disagree with the following statement: "Because the
    cyclist's speed is constant, her acceleration is zero." Explain.
14. You are driving your car in a circular path on level ground at a
    constant speed of 20 mph. At the instant you are driving north,
    and turning left, are you accelerating? If so, toward what point
    of the compass (N, S, E, W) does your acceleration vector
    point? If not, why not?
15. An airplane has been directed to fly in a clockwise circle, as seen
    from above, at constant speed until another plane has landed.
    When the plane is going north, is it accelerating? If so, in what
    direction does the acceleration vector point? If not, why not?
16. When you go around a corner in your car, your car follows a
    path that is a segment of a circle. To turn safely, you should
    keep your car's acceleration below some safe upper limit. If
    you want to make a "tighter" turn—that is, turn in a circle with
    a smaller radius—how should you adjust your speed? Explain.

Multiple-Choice Questions

17. II Which combination of the vectors shown in Figure Q3.17 has
    the largest magnitude?

    A. $\vec{A} + \vec{B} + \vec{C}$
    B. $\vec{B} + \vec{A} - \vec{C}$
    C. $\vec{A} - \vec{B} + \vec{C}$
    D. $\vec{C} - \vec{A} - \vec{C}$

    FIGURE Q3.17

18. II Two vectors appear as in Figure Q3.18. Which combination
    points directly to the left?

    A. $\vec{P} + \vec{Q}$
    B. $\vec{P} - \vec{Q}$
    C. $\vec{Q} - \vec{P}$
    D. $-\vec{Q} - \vec{P}$

    FIGURE Q3.18

19. I The gas pedal in a car is sometimes referred to as "the accel-
    erator." Which other controls on the vehicle can be used to pro-
    duce acceleration?
    A. The brakes.
    B. The steering wheel.
    C. The gear shift.
    D. All of the above.

20. | A car travels at constant speed along the curved path shown from above in Figure Q3.20. Five possible vectors are also shown in the figure; the letter E represents the zero vector. Which vector best represents

a. The car's *velocity* at position 1?
b. The car's *acceleration* at point 1?
c. The car's *velocity* at position 2?
d. The car's *acceleration* at point 2?
e. The car's *velocity* at position 3?
f. The car's *acceleration* at point 3?

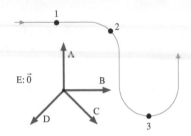

FIGURE Q3.20

21. | A ball is fired from a cannon at point 1 and follows the trajectory shown in Figure Q3.21. Air resistance may be neglected. Five possible vectors are also shown in the figure; the letter E represents the zero vector. Which vector best represents

a. The ball's *velocity* at position 2?
b. The ball's *acceleration* at point 2?
c. The ball's *velocity* at position 3?
d. The ball's *acceleration* at point 3?

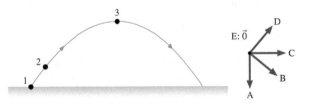

FIGURE Q3.21

22. | A ball thrown at an initial angle of 37.0° and initial velocity of 23.0 m/s reaches a maximum height h, as shown in Figure Q3.22. With what initial speed must a ball be thrown *straight up* to reach the same maximum height h?

A. 13.8 m/s   B. 17.3 m/s
C. 18.4 m/s   D. 23.0 m/s

FIGURE Q3.22

23. | A cannon, elevated at 40° is fired at a wall 300 m away on level ground, as shown in Figure Q3.23. The initial speed of the cannonball is 89 m/s

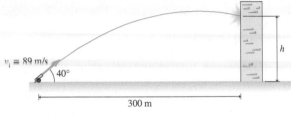

FIGURE Q3.23

a. How long does it take for the ball to hit the wall?
     A. 1.3 s   B. 3.3 s   C. 4.4 s
     D. 6.8 s   E. 7.2 s
b. At what height h does the ball hit the wall?
     A. 39 m   B. 47 m   C. 74 m
     D. 160 m   E. 210 m

24. | A car drives horizontally off a 73-m-high cliff at a speed of 27 m/s. Ignore air resistance.
a. How long will it take the car to hit the ground?
     A. 2.0 s   B. 3.2 s   C. 3.9 s
     D. 4.9 s   E. 5.0 s
b. How far from the base of the cliff will the car hit?
     A. 74 m   B. 88 m   C. 100 m
     D. 170 m   E. 280 m

25. | A football is kicked at an angle of 30° with a speed of 20 m/s. To the nearest second, how long will the ball stay in the air?
     A. 1 s   B. 2 s   C. 3 s   D. 4 s

26. | A football is kicked at an angle of 30° with a speed of 20 m/s. To the nearest 5 m, how far will the ball travel?
     A. 15 m   B. 25 m   C. 35 m   D. 45 m

27. | Riders on a Ferris wheel move in a circle with a speed of 4.0 m/s. As they go around, they experience a centripetal acceleration of 2.0 m/s². What is the diameter of this particular Ferris wheel?
     A. 4.0 m   B. 6.0 m   C. 8.0 m
     D. 16 m   E. 24 m

PROBLEMS

Section 3.1 Using Vectors

1. || Trace the vectors in Figure P3.1 onto your paper. Then use graphical methods to draw the vectors (a) $\vec{A} + \vec{B}$ and (b) $\vec{A} - \vec{B}$.

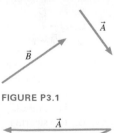

FIGURE P3.1

2. ||| Trace the vectors in Figure P3.2 onto your paper. Then use graphical methods to draw the vectors (a) $\vec{A} + \vec{B}$ and (b) $\vec{A} - \vec{B}$.

FIGURE P3.2

Section 3.2 Using Vectors on Motion Diagrams

3. | A car goes around a corner in a circular arc at constant speed. Draw a motion diagram including positions, velocity vectors, and acceleration vectors.

4. | a. Is the object's average speed between points 1 and 2 greater than, less than, or equal to its average speed between points 0 and 1? Explain how you can tell.
b. Find the average acceleration vector at point 1 of the three-point motion diagram in Figure P3.4.

2 ●

1 ●

0 ●

FIGURE P3.4

5. ‖‖ Figure 3.11 showed the motion diagram for Anne as she rode a Ferris wheel that was turning at a constant speed. The inset to the figure showed how to find the acceleration vector at the lowest point in her motion. Use a similar analysis to find Anne's acceleration vector at the 12 o'clock, 4 o'clock, and 8 o'clock positions of the motion diagram. Use a ruler so that your analysis is accurate.

Section 3.3 Coordinate Systems and Vector Components

6. ‖ A position vector with magnitude 10 m points to the right and up. Its x-component is 6.0 m. What is the value of its y-component?
7. ‖‖ A velocity vector 40° above the positive x-axis has a y component of 10 m/s. What is the value of its x-component?
8. ‖ Jack and Jill ran up the hill at 3.0 m/s. The horizontal component of Jill's velocity vector was 2.5 m/s.
   a. What was the angle of the hill?
   b. What was the vertical component of Jill's velocity?
9. ‖ A cannon tilted upward at 30° fires a cannonball with a speed of 100 m/s. At that instant, what is the component of the cannonball's velocity parallel to the ground?
10. ‖ a. What are the x- and y-components of vector $\vec{E}$ of Figure P3.10 in terms of the angle θ and the magnitude E?
    b. For the same vector, what are the x- and y-components in terms of the angle ϕ and the magnitude E?

FIGURE P3.10

11. ‖ Draw each of the following vectors, then find its x- and y-components.
    a. $\vec{d} = (100\ \text{m}, 45°\ \text{below} +x\text{-axis})$
    b. $\vec{v} = (300\ \text{m/s}, 20°\ \text{above} +x\text{-axis})$
    c. $\vec{a} = (5.0\ \text{m/s}^2, -y\text{-direction})$
12. ‖ Draw each of the following vectors, then find its x- and y-components.
    a. $\vec{d} = (2.0\ \text{km}, 30°\ \text{left of} +y\text{-axis})$
    b. $\vec{v} = (5.0\ \text{cm/s}, -x\text{-direction})$
    c. $\vec{a} = (10\ \text{m/s}^2, 40°\ \text{left of} -y\text{-axis})$
13. ‖ Each of the following vectors is given in terms of its x- and y-components. Draw the vector, label an angle that specifies the vector's direction, then find the vector's magnitude and direction.
    a. $v_x = 20\ \text{m/s}, v_y = 40\ \text{m/s}$
    b. $a_x = 2.0\ \text{m/s}^2, a_y = -6.0\ \text{m/s}^2$
14. ‖ Each of the following vectors is given in terms of its x- and y-components. Draw the vector, label an angle that specifies the vector's direction, then find the vector's magnitude and direction.
    a. $v_x = 10\ \text{m/s}, v_y = 30\ \text{m/s}$
    b. $a_x = 20\ \text{m/s}^2, a_y = 10\ \text{m/s}^2$
15. ‖‖ While visiting England, you decide to take a jog and find yourself in the neighborhood shown on the map in Figure P3.15. What is your displacement after running 2.0 km on Strawberry Fields, 1.0 km on Penny Lane, and 4.0 km on Abbey Road?

FIGURE P3.15

Section 3.4 Motion on a Ramp

16. ‖‖ You begin sliding down a 15° ski slope. Ignoring friction and air resistance, how fast will you be moving after 10 s?
17. ‖‖ A car traveling at 30 m/s runs out of gas while traveling up a 5.0° slope. How far will it coast before starting to roll back down?
18. ‖ In the Soapbox Derby, young participants build non-motorized cars with very low-friction wheels. Cars race by rolling down a hill. The track at Akron's Derby Downs, where the national championship is held, begins with a 55-ft-long section tilted 13° below horizontal.

   a. What is the maximum possible acceleration of a car moving down this stretch of track?
   b. If a car starts from rest and undergoes this acceleration for the full 55 ft, what is its final speed in m/s?
19. ‖‖ A piano has been pushed to the top of the ramp at the back of a moving van. The workers think it is safe, but as they walk away, it begins to roll down the ramp. If the back of the truck is 1.0 m above the ground and the ramp is inclined at 20°, how much time do the workers have to get to the piano before it reaches the bottom of the ramp?
20. ‖ Starting from rest, several toy cars roll down ramps of differing lengths and angles. Rank them according to their speed at the bottom of the ramp, from slowest to fastest. Car A goes down a 10 m ramp inclined at 15°, car B goes down a 10 m ramp inclined at 20°, car C goes down an 8.0 m ramp inclined at 20°, and car D goes down a 12 m ramp inclined at 12°.

Section 3.5 Relative Motion

21. ‖ Anita is running to the right at 5 m/s, as shown in Figure P3.21. Balls 1 and 2 are thrown toward her at 10 m/s by friends standing on the ground. According to Anita, what is the speed of each ball?

FIGURE P3.21

22. ‖ Anita is running to the right at 5 m/s, as shown in Figure P3.22. Balls 1 and 2 are thrown toward her by friends standing on the ground. According to Anita, both balls are approaching her at 10 m/s. According to her friends, with what speeds were the balls thrown?

FIGURE P3.22

23. ▮▮▮▮ A boat takes 3.0 h to travel 30 km down a river, then 5.0 h to return. How fast is the river flowing?

24. ▮▮ Two children who are bored while waiting for their flight at the airport decide to race from one end of the 20-m-long moving sidewalk to the other and back. Phillippe runs on the sidewalk at 2.0 m/s (relative to the sidewalk). Renee runs on the floor at 2.0 m/s. The sidewalk moves at 1.5 m/s relative to the floor. Both make the turn instantly with no loss of speed.
    a. Who wins the race?
    b. By how much time does the winner win?

25. ▮▮ A skydiver deploys his parachute when he is 1000 m directly above his desired landing spot. He then falls through the air at a steady 5.0 m/s. There is a breeze blowing to the west at 2.0 m/s.
    a. At what angle with respect to vertical does he fall?
    b. By what distance will he miss his desired landing spot?

Section 3.6 Motion in Two Dimensions: Projectile Motion

Section 3.7 Projectile Motion: Solving Problems

26. ▮▮▮▮ An object is launched with an initial velocity of 50.0 m/s at a launch angle of 36.9° above the horizontal.
    a. Make a table showing values of x, y, v_x, v_y, and the speed v every 1 s from $t = 0$ s to $t = 6$ s.
    b. Plot a graph of the object's trajectory during the first 6 s of motion.

27. ▮▮▮▮ A ball is thrown horizontally from a 20-m-high building with a speed of 5.0 m/s.
    a. Make a sketch of the ball's trajectory.
    b. Draw a graph of v_x, the horizontal velocity, as a function of time. Include units on both axes.
    c. Draw a graph of v_y, the vertical velocity, as a function of time. Include units on both axes.
    d. How far from the base of the building does the ball hit the ground?

28. ▮▮ A ball with a horizontal speed of 1.25 m/s rolls off a bench 1.00 m above the floor.
    a. How long will it take the ball to hit the floor?
    b. How far from a point on the floor directly below the edge of the bench will the ball land?

29. ▮▮▮▮▮ King Arthur's knights use a catapult to launch a rock from their vantage point on top of the castle wall, 12 m above the moat. The rock is launched at a speed of 25 m/s and an angle of 30° above the horizontal. How far from the castle wall does the launched rock hit the ground?

30. ▮ Two spheres are launched horizontally from a 1.0-m-high table. Sphere A is launched with an initial speed of 5.0 m/s. Sphere B is launched with an initial speed of 2.5 m/s.
    a. What are the times for each sphere to hit the floor?
    b. What are the distances that each travels from the edge of the table?

31. ▮▮▮ A rifle is aimed horizontally at a target 50 m away. The bullet hits the target 2.0 cm below the aim point.
    a. What was the bullet's flight time?
    b. What was the bullet's speed as it left the barrel?

32. ▮▮▮ A gray kangaroo can bound across a flat stretch of ground
BIO with each jump carrying it 10 m from the takeoff point. If the kangaroo leaves the ground at a 20° angle, what are its (a) takeoff speed and (b) horizontal speed?

33. ▮▮▮ On the Apollo 14 mission to the moon, astronaut Alan Shepard hit a golf ball with a golf club improvised from a tool. The free-fall acceleration on the moon is 1/6 of its value on earth. Suppose he hit the ball with a speed of 25 m/s at an angle 30° above the horizontal.
    a. How long was the ball in flight?
    b. How far did it travel?
    c. Ignoring air resistance, how much farther would it travel on the moon than on earth?

Section 3.8 Motion in Two Dimensions: Circular Motion

34. ▮ An old-fashioned LP record rotates at $33\frac{1}{3}$ rpm.
    a. What is its frequency, in rev/s?
    b. What is its period, in seconds?

35. ▮ A typical hard disk in a computer spins at 5400 rpm.
    a. What is the frequency, in rev/s?
    b. What is the period, in seconds?

36. ▮ Racing greyhounds are capable of rounding corners at very
BIO high speeds. A typical greyhound track has turns that are 45-m-diameter semicircles. A greyhound can run around these turns at a constant speed of 15 m/s. What is its acceleration in m/s² and in units of g?

37. ▮▮ A CD-ROM drive in a computer spins the 12-cm-diameter disks at 10,000 rpm.
    a. What are the disk's period (in s) and frequency (in rev/s)?
    b. What would be the speed of a speck of dust on the outside edge of this disk?
    c. What is the acceleration in units of g that this speck of dust experiences?

38. ▮▮ To withstand "g-forces" of up to 10 g's, caused by suddenly
BIO pulling out of a steep dive, fighter jet pilots train on a "human centrifuge." 10 g's is an acceleration of 98 m/s². If the length of the centrifuge arm is 12 m, at what speed is the rider moving when she experiences 10 g's?

39. ▮▮ A particle rotates in a circle with centripetal acceleration $a = 8.0$ m/s². What is a if
    a. The radius is doubled without changing the particle's speed?
    b. The speed is doubled without changing the circle's radius?

40. ▮▮ Entrance and exit ramps for freeways are often circular stretches of road. As you go around one at a constant speed, you will experience a constant acceleration. Suppose you drive through an entrance ramp at a modest speed and your acceleration is 3.0 m/s². What will be the acceleration if you double your speed?

41. ▮▮ A peregrine falcon in a tight, circular turn can attain a cen-
BIO tripetal acceleration 1.5 times the free-fall acceleration. If the falcon is flying at 20 m/s, what is the radius of the turn?

General Problems

42. ▮ Suppose $\vec{C} = \vec{A} + \vec{B}$ where vector $\vec{A}$ has components $A_x = 5$, $A_y = 2$ and vector $\vec{B}$ has components $B_x = -3$, $B_y = -5$.
    a. What are the x- and y-components of vector $\vec{C}$?
    b. Draw a coordinate system and on it show vectors $\vec{A}$, $\vec{B}$, and $\vec{C}$.
    c. What are the magnitude and direction of vector $\vec{C}$?

43. | Suppose $\vec{D} = \vec{A} - \vec{B}$ where vector $\vec{A}$ has components $A_x = 5$, $A_y = 2$ and vector $\vec{B}$ has components $B_x = -3$, $B_y = -5$.
   a. What are the x- and y-components of vector $\vec{D}$?
   b. Draw a coordinate system and on it show vectors $\vec{A}$, $\vec{B}$, and $\vec{D}$.
   c. What are the magnitude and direction of vector $\vec{D}$?

44. ‖ Suppose $\vec{E} = 2\vec{A} + 3\vec{B}$ where vector $\vec{A}$ has components $A_x = 5$, $A_y = 2$ and vector $\vec{B}$ has components $B_x = -3$, $B_y = -5$.
   a. What are the x- and y-components of vector $\vec{E}$?
   b. Draw a coordinate system and on it show vectors $\vec{A}$, $\vec{B}$, and $\vec{E}$.
   c. What are the magnitude and direction of vector $\vec{E}$?

45. ‖ For the three vectors shown in Figure P3.45, the vector sum $\vec{D} = \vec{A} + \vec{B} + \vec{C}$ has components $D_x = 2$ and $D_y = 0$.
   a. What are the x- and y-components of vector $\vec{B}$?
   b. Write $\vec{B}$ as a magnitude and a direction.

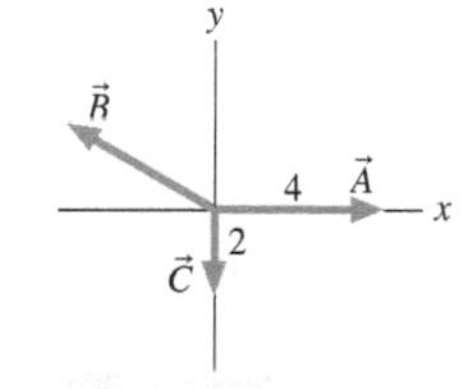

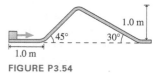

FIGURE P3.45

46. ‖ Let $\vec{A} = (3.0 \text{ m}, 20° \text{ south of east})$, $\vec{B} = (2.0 \text{ m, north})$, and $\vec{C} = (5.0 \text{ m}, 70° \text{ south of west})$.
   a. Draw and label $\vec{A}$, $\vec{B}$, and $\vec{C}$ with their tails at the origin. Use a coordinate system with the x-axis to the east.
   b. Write the x- and y-components of vectors $\vec{A}$, $\vec{B}$, and $\vec{C}$.
   c. Find the magnitude and the direction of $\vec{D} = \vec{A} + \vec{B} + \vec{C}$.

47. ‖ A typical set of stairs is angled at 38°. You climb a set of stairs at a speed of 3.5 m/s.
   a. How much height will you gain in 2.0 s?
   b. How much horizontal distance will you cover in 2.0 s?

48. ‖ The minute hand on a watch is 2.0 cm long. What is the displacement vector of the tip of the minute hand
   a. From 8:00 to 8:20 A.M.?
   b. From 8:00 to 9:00 A.M.?

49. ‖‖‖ A field mouse trying to escape a hawk runs east for 5.0 m, darts southeast for 3.0 m, then drops 1.0 m down a hole into its burrow. What is the magnitude of the net displacement of the mouse?

50. ‖‖ A pilot in a small plane encounters shifting winds. He flies 26.0 km northeast, then 45.0 km due north. From this point, he flies an additional distance in an unknown direction, only to find himself at a small airstrip that his map shows to be 70.0 km directly north of his starting point. What were the length and direction of the third leg of his trip?

51. ‖ A small plane is 100 km south of the equator. The plane is flying at 150 km/h at a heading of 30° to the west of north. In how many minutes will the plane cross the equator?

52. ‖ The bacterium *Escherichia coli* (or *E. coli*) is a single-
BIO celled organism that lives in the gut of healthy humans and animals. When grown in a uniform medium rich in salts and amino acids, these bacteria swim along zig-zag paths at a constant speed of 20 μm/s. Figure P3.52 shows the trajectory of an *E. coli* as it moves from point A to point E. Each segment of the motion can be identified by two letters, such as segment BC.
   a. For each of the four segments in the bacterium's trajectory, calculate the x- and y-components of its displacement and of its velocity.
   b. Calculate both the total distance traveled and the magnitude of the net displacement for the entire motion.
   c. What are the magnitude and the direction of the bacterium's average velocity for the entire trip?

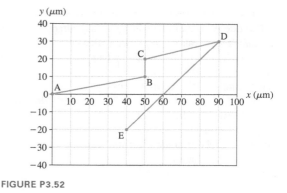

FIGURE P3.52

53. ‖‖‖ A skier is gliding along at 3.0 m/s on horizontal, frictionless snow. He suddenly starts down a 10° incline. His speed at the bottom is 15 m/s.
   a. What is the length of the incline?
   b. How long does it take him to reach the bottom?

54. ‖‖‖ A block slides along the frictionless track shown in Figure P3.54 with an initial speed of 5.0 m/s. Assume it turns all the corners smoothly, with no loss of speed.
   a. What is the block's speed as it goes over the top?
   b. What is its speed when it reaches the level track on the right side?
   c. By what percentage does the block's final speed differ from its initial speed? Is this surprising?

FIGURE P3.54

55. ‖ One game at the amusement park has you push a puck up a long, frictionless ramp. You win a stuffed animal if the puck, at its highest point, comes to within 10 cm of the end of the ramp without going off. You give the puck a push, releasing it with a speed of 5.0 m/s when it is 8.5 m from the end of the ramp. The puck's speed after traveling 3.0 m is 4.0 m/s. Are you a winner?

56. ‖‖‖ When the moving sidewalk at the airport is broken, as it often seems to be, it takes you 50 s to walk from your gate to the baggage claim. When it is working and you stand on the moving sidewalk the entire way, without walking, it takes 75 s to travel the same distance. How long will it take you to travel from the gate to baggage claim if you walk while riding on the moving sidewalk?

57. ‖‖‖ Ships A and B leave port together. For the next two hours, ship A travels at 20 mph in a direction 30° west of north while ship B travels 20° east of north at 25 mph.
   a. What is the distance between the two ships two hours after they depart?
   b. What is the speed of ship A as seen by ship B?

58. ‖‖‖ Mary needs to row her boat across a 100-m-wide river that is flowing to the east at a speed of 1.0 m/s. Mary can row the boat with a speed of 2.0 m/s relative to the water.
   a. If Mary rows straight north, how far downstream will she land?
   b. Draw a picture showing Mary's displacement due to rowing, her displacement due to the river's motion, and her net displacement.

59. ‖‖ A flock of ducks is trying to migrate south for the winter, but they keep being blown off course by a wind blowing from the west at 12 m/s. A wise elder duck finally realizes that the solution is to fly at an angle to the wind. If the ducks can fly at 16 m/s relative to the air, in what direction should they head in order to move directly south?

60. ||| A kayaker needs to paddle north across a 100-m-wide harbor. The tide is going out, creating a tidal current flowing east at 2.0 m/s. The kayaker can paddle with a speed of 3.0 m/s.
    a. In which direction should he paddle in order to travel straight across the harbor?
    b. How long will it take him to cross?

61. ||| A plane has an airspeed of 200 mph. The pilot wishes to reach a destination 600 mi due east, but a wind is blowing at 50 mph in the direction 30° north of east.
    a. In what direction must the pilot head the plane in order to reach her destination?
    b. How long will the trip take?

62. ||| The Gulf Stream off the east coast of the United States can flow at a rapid 3.6 m/s to the north. A ship in this current has a cruising speed of 10 m/s. The captain would like to reach land at a point due west from the current position.
    a. In what direction with respect to the water should the ship sail?
    b. At this heading, what is the ship's speed with respect to land?

63. || A physics student on Planet Exidor throws a ball, and it follows the parabolic trajectory shown in Figure P3.63. The ball's position is shown at 1.0 s intervals until $t = 3.0$ s. At $t = 1.0$ s, the ball's velocity has components $v_x = 2.0$ m/s, $v_y = 2.0$ m/s.

    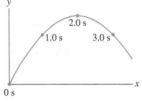

    FIGURE P3.63

    a. Determine the x- and y-components of the ball's velocity at $t = 0.0$ s, 2.0 s, and 3.0 s.
    b. What is the value of g on Planet Exidor?
    c. What was the ball's launch angle?

64. ||| A ball thrown horizontally at 25 m/s travels a horizontal distance of 50 m before hitting the ground. From what height was the ball thrown?

65. ||| In 1780, in what is now referred
BIO   to as "Brady's Leap," Captain Sam Brady of the U.S. Continental Army escaped certain death from his enemies by running over the edge of the cliff above Ohio's Cuyahoga River, which is confined at that spot to a gorge. He landed safely on the far side of the river. It was reported that he leapt 22 ft across while falling 20 ft.

    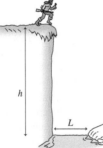

    FIGURE P3.65

    a. Representing the distance jumped as L and the vertical drop as h, as shown in Figure P3.65, derive an expression for the minimum speed v he would need to make his leap if he ran straight off the cliff.
    b. Evaluate your expression for a 22 ft jump with a 20 ft drop to the other side.
    c. Is it reasonable that a person could make this leap? Use the fact that the world record for the 100 m dash is approximately 10 s to estimate the maximum speed such a runner would have.

66. ||| The longest recorded pass in an NFL game traveled 83 yards in the air from the quarterback to the receiver. Assuming that the pass was thrown at the optimal 45° angle, what was the speed at which the ball left the quarterback's hand?

67. ||| A spring-loaded gun, fired vertically, shoots a marble 6.0 m straight up in the air. What is the marble's range if it is fired horizontally from 1.5 m above the ground?

68. || In a shot-put event, an athlete throws the shot with an initial speed of 12.0 m/s at a 40.0° angle from the horizontal. The shot leaves her hand at a height of 1.80 m above the ground.
    a. How far does the shot travel?
    b. Repeat the calculation of part (a) for angles 42.5°, 45.0°, and 47.5°. Put all your results, including 40.0°, in a table. At what angle of release does she throw the farthest?

69. ||| A tennis player hits a ball 2.0 m above the ground. The ball leaves his racquet with a speed of 20 m/s at an angle 5.0° above the horizontal. The horizontal distance to the net is 7.0 m, and the net is 1.0 m high. Does the ball clear the net? If so, by how much? If not, by how much does it miss?

70. ||| Water at the top of Horseshoe Falls (part of Niagara Falls) is moving horizontally at 9.0 m/s as it goes off the edge and plunges 53 m to the pool below. If you ignore air resistance, at what angle is the falling water moving as it enters the pool?

71. || Figure 3.37 shows that the range of a projectile launched at a 60° angle has the same range as a projectile launched at a 30° angle—but they won't be in the air for the same amount of time. Suppose a projectile launched at a 30° angle is in the air for 2.0 s. How long will the projectile be in the air if it is launched with the same speed at a 60° angle?

72. || A supply plane needs to drop a package of food to scientists working on a glacier in Greenland. The plane flies 100 m above the glacier at a speed of 150 m/s. How far short of the target should it drop the package?

73. ||| A child slides down a frictionless 3.0-m-long playground slide tilted upward at an angle of 40°. At the end of the slide, there is an additional section that curves so that the child is launched off the end of the slide horizontally.
    a. How fast is the child moving at the bottom of the slide?
    b. If the end of the slide is 0.40 m above the ground, how far from the end does she land?

74. ||| A sports car is advertised to be able to "reach 60 mph in 5 sec-
INT   onds flat, corner at 0.85g, and stop from 70 mph in only 168 feet."
    a. In which of those three situations is the magnitude of the car's acceleration the largest? In which is it the smallest?
    b. At 60 mph, what is the smallest turning radius that this car can navigate?

75. || A Ford Mustang can accelerate from 0 to 60 mph in a time of
INT   5.6 s. A Mini Cooper isn't capable of such a rapid start, but it can turn in a very small circle 34 ft in diameter. How fast would you need to drive the Mini Cooper in this tight circle to match the magnitude of the Mustang's acceleration?

76. || The "Screaming Swing" is a carnival ride that is—not surprisingly—a giant swing. It's actually two swings moving in opposite directions. At the bottom of its arc, riders are moving at 30 m/s with respect to the ground in a 50-m-diameter circle.
    a. What is the acceleration, in m/s² and in units of g, that riders experience?
    b. At the bottom of the ride, as they pass each other, how fast do the riders move with respect to each other?

77. || On an otherwise straight stretch of road near Moffat, Colorado, the road suddenly turns. This bend in the road is a segment of a circle with radius 110 m. Drivers are cautioned to slow down to 40 mph as they navigate the curve.
    a. If you heed the sign and slow to 40 mph, what will be your acceleration going around the curve at this constant speed? Give your answer in m/s² and in units of g.
    b. At what speed would your acceleration be double that at the recommended speed?

Passage Problems

Riding the Water Slide

A rider on a water slide goes through three different kinds of motion, as illustrated in Figure P3.78. Use the data and details from the figure to answer the following questions.

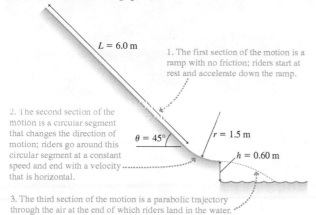

L = 6.0 m

1. The first section of the motion is a ramp with no friction; riders start at rest and accelerate down the ramp.

2. The second section of the motion is a circular segment that changes the direction of motion; riders go around this circular segment at a constant speed and end with a velocity that is horizontal.

$\theta = 45°$ $r = 1.5$ m

$h = 0.60$ m

3. The third section of the motion is a parabolic trajectory through the air at the end of which riders land in the water.

FIGURE P3.78

78. | At the end of the first section of the motion, riders are moving at what approximate speed?
    A. 3 m/s   B. 6 m/s   C. 9 m/s   D. 12 m/s

79. | Suppose the acceleration during the second section of the motion is too large to be comfortable for riders. What change could be made to decrease the acceleration during this section?
    A. Reduce the radius of the circular segment.
    B. Increase the radius of the circular segment.
    C. Increase the angle of the ramp.
    D. Increase the length of the ramp.

80. | What is the vertical component of the velocity of a rider as he or she hits the water?
    A. 2.4 m/s   B. 3.4 m/s   C. 5.2 m/s   D. 9.1 m/s

81. | Suppose the designers of the water slide want to adjust the height h above the water so that riders land twice as far away from the bottom of the slide. What would be the necessary height above the water?
    A. 1.2 m   B. 1.8 m   C. 2.4 m   D. 3.0 m

82. | During which section of the motion is the magnitude of the acceleration experienced by a rider the greatest?
    A. The first.   B. The second.
    C. The third.   D. It is the same in all sections.

STOP TO THINK ANSWERS

Stop to Think 3.1: A. The graphical construction of $2\vec{P} - \vec{Q}$ is shown at right.

Stop to Think 3.2: From the axes on the graph, we can see that the x- and y-components are -4 cm and $+2$ cm, respectively.

$2\vec{P} - \vec{Q}$ $-\vec{Q}$ $2\vec{P}$

Stop to Think 3.3: C. Vector $\vec{C}$ points to the left and down, so both C_x and C_y are negative. C_x is in the numerator because it is the side opposite ϕ.

Stop to Think 3.4: B. The angle of the slope is greatest in this case, leading to the greatest acceleration.

Stop to Think 3.5: D. Mass does not appear in the kinematic equations, so the mass has no effect; the balls will follow the same path.

Stop to Think 3.6: B. The magnitude of the acceleration is v^2/r. Acceleration is largest for the combination of highest speed and smallest radius.

4 Forces and Newton's Laws of Motion

These ice boats sail across the ice at great speeds. What gets the boats moving in the first place? What keeps them moving once they're going?

LOOKING AHEAD ▶

The goal of Chapter 4 is to establish a connection between force and motion.

What Causes Motion?

Galileo was the first to realize that objects in *uniform motion* require no "cause" for their motion. Only *changes* in motion—accelerations—require a cause: a *force*.

What is a Force?

We'll understand force by first examining the properties common to all forces, then by studying a number of forces we'll encounter often.

Forces are a *push* or a *pull*, act on an *object*, and have an identifiable *agent*. Forces are *vectors*.

Looking Back ◀◀
1.5 Vectors and motion

Newton's Third Law

When two objects interact, each exerts a force on the other. Newton's third law tells us that these two forces point in *opposite* directions but have the *same* magnitudes.

The force of the hammer on the nail has the same magnitude as the force of the nail on the hammer.

Some Important Forces

It's important to understand the characteristics of a number of important forces. Some of the forces you'll learn about in this chapter are . . .

Weight
The force of gravity acting on an object.

Spring force
The force exerted by a stretched or compressed spring.

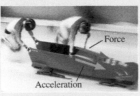

Normal force
A force that a surface exerts on an object.

Newton's Second Law

Newton's second law tells us what forces *do* when applied to an object. We'll find that forces act to *accelerate* objects. We will use Newton's second law throughout this textbook to solve a wide variety of physics problems.

An object's acceleration vector is in the same direction as the net force acting on the object.

Looking Back ◀◀
2.4 Acceleration

Looking Back ◀◀
3.2–3.3 Vectors and coordinate systems

Identifying and Representing Forces

One of the most important skills you'll learn in this chapter is to properly identify the forces that act on an object. Then you'll learn to organize these forces in a *free-body diagram*.

Other than the weight force, all forces acting on an object come from other objects that *touch* it.

We can represent all the forces acting on an object in a free-body diagram.

4.1 What Causes Motion?

The ice boats shown in the chapter-opening photo fly across the frozen lake at some 60 mph. We could use kinematics to describe the boats' motion with pictures, graphs, and equations. Kinematics provides a language to describe *how* something moves, but tells us nothing about *why* the boats accelerate briskly before reaching their top speed. For the more fundamental task of understanding the *cause* of motion, we turn our attention to **dynamics.** Dynamics joins with kinematics to form **mechanics,** the general science of motion. We study dynamics qualitatively in this chapter, then develop it quantitatively in the next four chapters.

As we remarked in Chapter 1, Aristotle (384–322 BC) and his contemporaries in the world of ancient Greece were very interested in motion. One question they asked was: What is the "natural state" of an object if left to itself? It does not take an expensive research program to see that every moving object on earth, if left to itself, eventually comes to rest. You must push a shopping cart to keep it rolling, but when you stop pushing, the cart soon comes to rest; a boulder bounds downhill and then tumbles to a halt. Having observed many such examples himself, Aristotle concluded that the natural state of an earthly object is to be *at rest*. An object at rest requires no explanation; it is doing precisely what comes naturally to it. We'll soon see, however, that this simple viewpoint is *incomplete*.

Aristotle further pondered moving objects. A moving object is *not* in its natural state and thus requires an explanation: Why is this object moving? What keeps it going and prevents it from being in its natural state? When a puck is sliding across the ice, what keeps it going? Why does an arrow fly through the air once it is no longer being pushed by the bowstring? Although these questions seem like reasonable ones to pose, it was Galileo who first showed that the questions being asked were, in fact, the wrong ones.

Galileo reopened the question of the "natural state" of objects. He suggested focusing on the *idealized case* in which resistance to the motion (e.g., friction or air resistance) is zero. He performed many experiments to study motion. Let's imagine a modern experiment of this kind, as shown in FIGURE 4.1.

The rocks in this rockslide quickly came to rest. Is this the "natural state" of objects?

FIGURE 4.1 Sleds sliding on increasingly smooth surfaces.

(a) Smooth snow

On smooth snow, the sled soon comes to rest.

(b) Slick ice

On slick ice, the sled slides farther.

(c) Frictionless surface

If friction could be reduced to zero, the sled would *never* stop.

▶ **Interstellar coasting** A nearly perfect example of Newton's first law is the pair of Voyager space probes launched in 1977. Both spacecraft long ago ran out of fuel and are now coasting through the frictionless vacuum of space. Although not entirely free of influence from the sun's gravity, they are now so far from the sun and other stars that gravitational influences are very nearly zero. Thus, according to the first law, they will continue at their current speed of about 40,000 miles per hour essentially forever. Billions of years from now, long after our solar system is dead, the Voyagers will still be drifting through the stars.

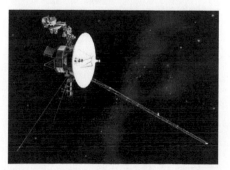

TRY IT YOURSELF

Getting the ketchup out The ketchup stuck at the bottom of the bottle is initially at rest. If you hit the bottom of the bottle, the bottle suddenly moves down, taking the ketchup on the bottom of the bottle with it, so that the ketchup just stays stuck to the bottom. But if instead you hit *up* on the bottle, as shown, you force the bottle rapidly upward. By the first law, the ketchup that was stuck to the bottom stays at rest, so it separates from the upward-moving bottle: The ketchup has moved forward with respect to the bottle!

FIGURE 4.2 Newton's first law tells us: Wear your seatbelts!

At the instant of impact, the car and driver are moving at the same speed.

The car slows as it hits, but the driver continues at the same speed . . .

. . . until he hits the now-stationary dashboard. Ouch!

Tyler slides down a hill on his sled, then out onto a horizontal patch of smooth snow, which is shown in Figure 4.1a. Even if the snow is quite smooth, the friction between the sled and the snow will soon cause the sled to come to rest. What if Tyler slides down the hill onto some very slick ice, as in Figure 4.1b? This gives very low friction, and the sled could slide for quite a distance before stopping. Galileo's genius was to imagine the case where *all* sources of friction, air resistance, and other retarding influences were removed, as for the sled in Figure 4.1c sliding on idealized *frictionless* ice. We can imagine in that case that the sled, once started in its motion, would continue in its motion *forever,* moving in a straight line with no loss of speed. In other words, **the natural state of an object—its behavior if free of external influences—is *uniform motion* with constant velocity!** Further, "at rest" has no special significance in Galileo's view of motion; it is simply uniform motion that happens to have a velocity of zero. This implies that an object at rest, in the absence of external influences, will remain at rest forever.

Galileo's ideas were completely counter to those of the ancient Greeks. We no longer need to explain why a sled continues to slide across the ice; that motion is its "natural" state. What needs explanation, in this new viewpoint, is why objects *don't* continue in uniform motion. Why does a sliding puck eventually slow to a stop? Why does a stone, thrown upward, slow and eventually fall back down? Galileo's new viewpoint was that the stone and the puck are *not* free of "influences": The stone is somehow pulled toward the earth, and some sort of retarding influence acted to slow the sled down. Today, we call such influences that lead to deviations from uniform motion **forces.**

Galileo's experiments were limited to motion along horizontal surfaces. It was left to Newton to generalize Galileo's conclusions, and today we call this generalization Newton's first law of motion.

> **Newton's first law** Consider an object with no force acting on it. If it is at rest, it will remain at rest; if it is moving, it will continue to move in a straight line at a constant speed.

As an important application of Newton's first law, consider the crash test of FIGURE 4.2. As the car contacts the wall, the wall exerts a force on the car and it begins to slow. But the wall is a force on the *car,* not on the dummy. In accordance with Newton's first law, the unbelted dummy continues to move straight ahead at his original speed. Only when he collides violently with the dashboard of the stopped car is there a force acting to halt the dummy's uniform motion. If he had been wearing a seatbelt, the influence (i.e., the force) of the seatbelt would have slowed the dummy at the much lower rate at which the car slows down. We'll study the forces of collisions in detail in Chapter 10.

4.2 Force

Newton's first law tells us that an object in motion subject to no forces will continue to move in a straight line forever. But this law does not explain in any detail exactly what a force *is.* Unfortunately, there is no simple one-sentence definition of force. The concept of force is best introduced by looking at examples of some common forces and considering the basic properties shared by all forces. This will be our task in the next two sections. Let's begin by examining the properties that all forces have in common, as presented in the table on the next page.

What is a force?

A force is a push or a pull.

Our commonsense idea of a **force** is that it is a *push* or a *pull.* We will refine this idea as we go along, but it is an adequate starting point. Notice our careful choice of words: We refer to "*a* force" rather than simply "force." We want to think of a force as a very specific *action,* so that we can talk about a single force or perhaps about two or three individual forces that we can clearly distinguish—hence the concrete idea of "a force" acting on an object.

A force acts on an object.

Implicit in our concept of force is that **a force acts on an object.** In other words, pushes and pulls are applied *to* something—an object. From the object's perspective, it has a force exerted on it. Forces do not exist in isolation from the object that experiences them.

A force requires an agent.

Every force has an **agent,** something that acts or pushes or pulls; that is, a force has a specific, identifiable *cause.* As you throw a ball, it is your hand, while in contact with the ball, that is the agent or the cause of the force exerted on the ball. *If* a force is being exerted on an object, you must be able to identify a specific cause (i.e., the agent) of that force. Conversely, a force is not exerted on an object *unless* you can identify a specific cause or agent. Note that an agent can be an inert object such as a tabletop or a wall. Such agents are the cause of many common forces.

A force is a vector.

If you push an object, you can push either gently or very hard. Similarly, you can push either left or right, up or down. To quantify a push, we need to specify both a magnitude *and* a direction. It should thus come as no surprise that a force is a vector quantity. The general symbol for a force is the vector symbol $\vec{F}$. The size or strength of such a force is its magnitude F.

A force can be either a contact force . . .

There are two basic classes of forces, depending on whether the agent touches the object or not. **Contact forces** are forces that act on an object by touching it at a point of contact. The bat must touch the ball to hit it. A string must be tied to an object to pull it. The majority of forces that we will examine are contact forces.

. . . or a long-range force.

Long-range forces are forces that act on an object without physical contact. Magnetism is an example of a long-range force. You have undoubtedly held a magnet over a paper clip and seen the paper clip leap up to the magnet. A coffee cup released from your hand is pulled to the earth by the long-range force of gravity.

Let's summarize these ideas as our definition of force:

- A force is a push or a pull on an object.
- A force is a vector. It has both a magnitude and a direction.
- A force requires an agent. Something does the pushing or pulling. The agent can be an inert object such as a tabletop or a wall.
- A force is either a contact force or a long-range force. Gravity is the only long-range force we will deal with until much later in the book.

There's one more important aspect of forces. If you push against a door (the object) to close it, the door pushes back against your hand (the agent). If a tow rope pulls on a car (the object), the car pulls back on the rope (the agent). In general, if an agent exerts a force on an object, the object exerts a force on the agent. We really need to think of a force as an *interaction* between two objects. Although the interaction perspective is a more exact way to view forces, it adds complications that we would like to avoid for now. Our approach will be to start by focusing on how a single object responds to forces exerted on it. Later in this chapter, we'll return to the larger issue of how two or more objects interact with each other.

Force Vectors

We can use a simple diagram to visualize how forces are exerted on objects. Because we are using the particle model, in which objects are treated as points, the process of drawing a force vector is straightforward. Here is how it goes:

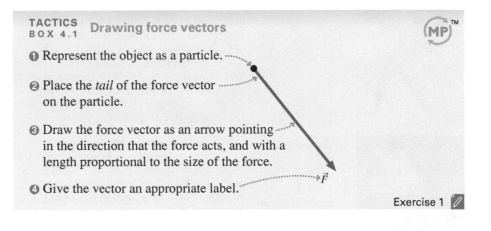

TACTICS BOX 4.1 Drawing force vectors

❶ Represent the object as a particle.

❷ Place the *tail* of the force vector on the particle.

❸ Draw the force vector as an arrow pointing in the direction that the force acts, and with a length proportional to the size of the force.

❹ Give the vector an appropriate label.

Exercise 1

Step 2 may seem contrary to what a "push" should do (it may look as if the force arrow is *pulling* the object rather than *pushing* it), but recall that moving a vector does not change it as long as the length and angle do not change. The vector $\vec{F}$ is the same regardless of whether the tail or the tip is placed on the particle. Our reason for using the tail will become clear when we consider how to combine several forces.

FIGURE 4.3 shows three examples of force vectors. One is a pull, one a push, and one a long-range force, but in all three the *tail* of the force vector is placed on the particle representing the object.

FIGURE 4.3 Three force vectors.

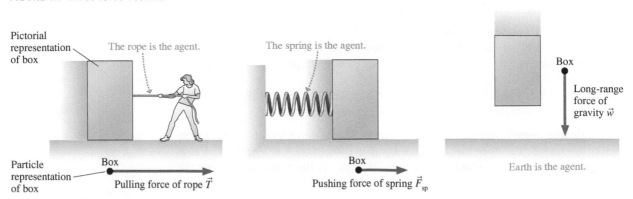

Pictorial representation of box — The rope is the agent.

The spring is the agent.

Box

Long-range force of gravity $\vec{w}$

Earth is the agent.

Particle representation of box

Box — Pulling force of rope $\vec{T}$

Box — Pushing force of spring $\vec{F}_{sp}$

Combining Forces

FIGURE 4.4a shows a top view of a box being pulled by two ropes, each exerting a force on the box. How will the box respond? Experimentally, we find that when several forces $\vec{F}_1, \vec{F}_2, \vec{F}_3, \ldots$ are exerted on an object, they combine to form a **net force** that is the *vector* sum of all the forces:

$$\vec{F}_{\text{net}} = \vec{F}_1 + \vec{F}_2 + \vec{F}_3 + \cdots \qquad (4.1)$$

That is, the single force $\vec{F}_{\text{net}}$ causes the exact same motion of the object as the combination of original forces $\vec{F}_1, \vec{F}_2, \vec{F}_3, \ldots$. Mathematically, this summation is called a *superposition* of forces. The net force is sometimes called the *resultant force*. FIGURE 4.4b shows the net force on the box.

> **NOTE** ▶ It is important to realize that the net force $\vec{F}_{\text{net}}$ is not a new force acting *in addition* to the original forces $\vec{F}_1, \vec{F}_2, \vec{F}_3, \ldots$. Instead, we should think of the original forces being *replaced* by $\vec{F}_{\text{net}}$. ◀

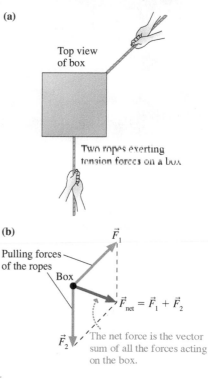

FIGURE 4.4 Two forces applied to a box.

(a)

Top view of box

Two ropes exerting tension forces on a box

(b)

Pulling forces of the ropes

Box

$\vec{F}_1$

$\vec{F}_{\text{net}} = \vec{F}_1 + \vec{F}_2$

$\vec{F}_2$

The net force is the vector sum of all the forces acting on the box.

STOP TO THINK 4.1   Two of the three forces exerted on an object are shown. The net force points directly to the left. Which is the missing third force?

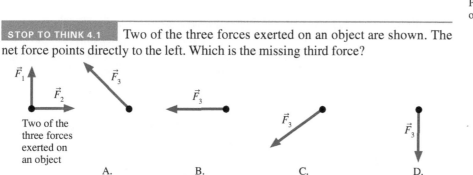

Two of the three forces exerted on an object

A.   B.   C.   D.

4.3 A Short Catalog of Forces

There are many forces we will deal with over and over. This section will introduce you to some of them and to the symbols we use to represent them.

Weight

A falling rock is pulled toward the earth by the long-range force of gravity. Gravity is what keeps you in your chair, keeps the planets in their orbits around the sun, and shapes the large-scale structure of the universe. We'll have a thorough look at gravity in Chapter 6. For now we'll concentrate on objects on or near the surface of the earth (or other planet).

The gravitational pull of the earth on an object on or near the surface of the earth is called **weight**. The symbol for weight is $\vec{w}$. Weight is the only long-range force we will encounter in the next few chapters. The agent for the weight force is the *entire earth* pulling on an object. The weight force is in some ways the simplest force we'll study. As FIGURE 4.5 shows, **an object's weight vector always points vertically downward**, no matter how the object is moving.

> **NOTE** ▶ We often refer to "the weight" of an object. This is an informal expression for w, the magnitude of the weight force exerted on the object. Note that **weight is not the same thing as mass.** We will briefly examine mass later in the chapter and explore the connection between weight and mass in Chapter 5. ◀

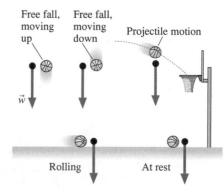

FIGURE 4.5 Weight always points vertically downward.

Free fall, moving up   Free fall, moving down   Projectile motion

$\vec{w}$

Rolling   At rest

Springs come in many forms. When deflected, they push or pull with a spring force.

Spring Force

Springs exert one of the most basic contact forces. A spring can either push (when compressed) or pull (when stretched). FIGURE 4.6 shows the **spring force.** In both cases, pushing and pulling, the tail of the force vector is placed on the particle in the force diagram. There is no special symbol for a spring force, so we simply use a subscript label: $\vec{F}_{sp}$.

FIGURE 4.6 The spring force is parallel to the spring.

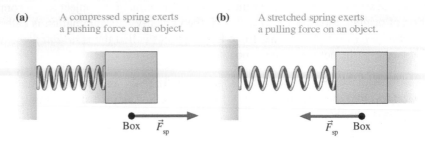

(a) A compressed spring exerts a pushing force on an object.

(b) A stretched spring exerts a pulling force on an object.

Box $\vec{F}_{sp}$ $\vec{F}_{sp}$ Box

Although you may think of a spring as a metal coil that can be stretched or compressed, this is only one type of spring. Hold a ruler, or any other thin piece of wood or metal, by the ends and bend it slightly. It flexes. When you let go, it "springs" back to its original shape. This is just as much a spring as is a metal coil.

Tension Force

FIGURE 4.7 Tension is parallel to the rope.

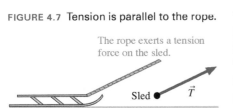

The rope exerts a tension force on the sled.

Sled $\vec{T}$

When a string or rope or wire pulls on an object, it exerts a contact force that we call the **tension force,** represented by $\vec{T}$. **The direction of the tension force is always in the direction of the string or rope,** as you can see in FIGURE 4.7. When we speak of "the tension" in a string, this is an informal expression for T, the size or magnitude of the tension force. Note that the tension force can only *pull* in the direction of the string; if you try to *push* with a string, it will go slack and be unable to exert a force.

We can think about the tension force using a microscopic picture. If you were to use a very powerful microscope to look inside a rope, you would "see" that it is made of *atoms* joined together by *molecular bonds*. Molecular bonds are not rigid connections between the atoms. They are more accurately thought of as tiny *springs* holding the atoms together, as in FIGURE 4.8. Pulling on the ends of a string or rope stretches the molecular springs ever so slightly. The tension within a rope and the tension force experienced by an object at the end of the rope are really the net spring force exerted by billions and billions of microscopic springs.

FIGURE 4.8 An atomic model of tension.

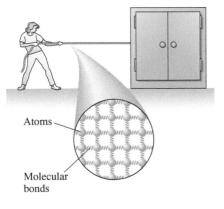

Atoms

Molecular bonds

This atomic-level view of tension introduces a new idea: a microscopic **atomic model** for understanding the behavior and properties of **macroscopic** (i.e., containing many atoms) objects. We will frequently use atomic models to obtain a deeper understanding of our observations.

The atomic model of tension also helps to explain one of the basic properties of ropes and strings. When you pull on a rope tied to a heavy box, the rope in turn exerts a tension force on the box. If you pull harder, the tension force on the box becomes greater. How does the box "know" that you are pulling harder on the other end of the rope? According to our atomic model, when you pull harder on the rope, its microscopic springs stretch a bit more, increasing the spring force they exert on each other—and on the box they're attached to.

Normal Force

If you sit on a bed, the springs in the mattress compress and, as a consequence of the compression, exert an upward force on you. Stiffer springs would show less compression but would still exert an upward force. The compression of extremely stiff springs might be measurable only by sensitive instruments. Nonetheless, the springs would compress ever so slightly and exert an upward spring force on you.

FIGURE 4.9 shows a book resting on top of a sturdy table. The table may not visibly flex or sag, but—just as you do to the bed—the book compresses the molecular springs in the table. The compression is very small, but it is not zero. As a consequence, the compressed molecular springs *push upward* on the book. We say that "the table" exerts the upward force, but it is important to understand that the pushing is *really* done by molecular springs. Similarly, an object resting on the ground compresses the molecular springs holding the ground together and, as a consequence, the ground pushes up on the object.

We can extend this idea. Suppose you place your hand on a wall and lean against it, as shown in FIGURE 4.10. Does the wall exert a force on your hand? As you lean, you compress the molecular springs in the wall and, as a consequence, they push outward *against* your hand. So the answer is Yes, the wall does exert a force on you. It's not hard to see this if you examine your hand as you lean: You can see that your hand is slightly deformed, and becomes more so the harder you lean. This deformation is direct evidence of the force that the wall exerts on your hand. Consider also what would happen if the wall suddenly vanished. Without the wall there to push against you, you would topple forward.

The force the table surface exerts is vertical, while the force the wall exerts is horizontal. In all cases, the force exerted on an object that is pressing against a surface is in a direction *perpendicular* to the surface. Mathematicians refer to a line that is perpendicular to a surface as being *normal* to the surface. In keeping with this terminology, we define the **normal force** as the force exerted by a surface (the agent) against an object that is pressing against the surface. The symbol for the normal force is $\vec{n}$.

We're not using the word "normal" to imply that the force is an "ordinary" force or to distinguish it from an "abnormal force." A surface exerts a force *perpendicular* (i.e., normal) to itself as the molecular springs press *outward*. FIGURE 4.11 shows an object on an inclined surface, a common situation. Notice how the normal force $\vec{n}$ is perpendicular to the surface.

The normal force is a very real force arising from the very real compression of molecular bonds. It is in essence just a spring force, but one exerted by a vast number of microscopic springs acting at once. The normal force is responsible for the "solidness" of solids. It is what prevents you from passing right through the chair you are sitting in and what causes the pain and the lump if you bang your head into a door. Your head can then tell you that the force exerted on it by the door was very real!

Friction

You've certainly observed that a rolling or sliding object, if not pushed or propelled, slows down and eventually stops. You've probably discovered that you can slide better across a sheet of ice than across asphalt. And you also know that most objects stay in place on a table without sliding off even if the table is tilted a bit. The force responsible for these sorts of behavior is **friction.** The symbol for friction is $\vec{f}$.

Friction, like the normal force, is exerted by a surface. Unlike the normal force, however, **the frictional force is always *parallel* to the surface,** not perpendicular to it. (In many cases, a surface will exert *both* a normal and a frictional force.) On a microscopic level, friction arises as atoms from the object and atoms on the surface run into each other. The rougher the surface is, the more these atoms are forced into close proximity and, as a result, the larger the friction force. We will develop a

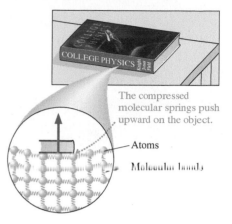
FIGURE 4.9 An atomic model of the force exerted by a table.

The compressed molecular springs push upward on the object.

Atoms

Molecular bonds

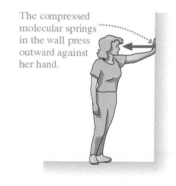
FIGURE 4.10 The wall pushes outward against your hand.

The compressed molecular springs in the wall press outward against her hand.

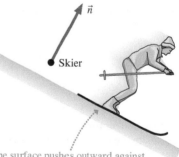
FIGURE 4.11 The normal force is perpendicular to the surface.

$\vec{n}$

Skier

The surface pushes outward against the bottom of the skis. The force is perpendicular to the surface.

simple model of friction in the next chapter that will be sufficient for our needs. For now, it is useful to distinguish between two kinds of friction:

- *Kinetic friction,* denoted $\vec{f}_k$, acts as an object slides across a surface. Kinetic friction is a force that always "opposes the motion," meaning that the friction force $\vec{f}_k$ on a sliding object points in the direction opposite the direction of the object's motion.
- *Static friction,* denoted $\vec{f}_s$, is the force that keeps an object "stuck" on a surface and prevents its motion relative to the surface. Finding the direction of $\vec{f}_s$ is a little trickier than finding it for $\vec{f}_k$. Static friction points opposite the direction in which the object *would* move if there were no friction. That is, it points in the direction necessary to *prevent* motion.

FIGURE 4.12 shows examples of kinetic and static friction.

FIGURE 4.12 Kinetic and static friction are parallel to the surface.

FIGURE 4.13 Air resistance is an example of drag.

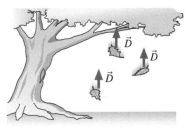

Air resistance is a significant force on falling leaves. It points opposite the direction of motion.

FIGURE 4.14 The thrust force on a rocket is opposite the direction of the expelled gases.

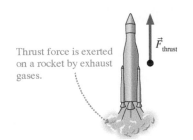

Thrust force is exerted on a rocket by exhaust gases.

Drag

Friction at a surface is one example of a *resistive force,* a force that opposes or resists motion. Resistive forces are also experienced by objects moving through *fluids*—gases (like air) and liquids (like water). This kind of resistive force—the force of a fluid on a moving object—is called **drag** and is symbolized as $\vec{D}$. Like kinetic friction, **drag points opposite the direction of motion.** FIGURE 4.13 shows an example of drag.

Drag can be a large force for objects moving at high speeds or in dense fluids. Hold your arm out the window as you ride in a car and feel how hard the air pushes against your arm; note also how the air resistance against your arm increases rapidly as the car's speed increases. Drop a lightweight bead into a beaker of water and watch how slowly it settles to the bottom. The drag force of the water on the bead is significant.

On the other hand, for objects that are heavy and compact, moving in air, and with a speed that is not too great, the drag force of air resistance is fairly small. To keep things as simple as possible, **you can neglect air resistance in all problems unless a problem explicitly asks you to include it.** The error introduced into calculations by this approximation is generally pretty small.

Thrust

A jet airplane obviously has a force that propels it forward; likewise for the rocket in FIGURE 4.14. This force, called **thrust,** occurs when a jet or rocket engine expels gas molecules at high speed. Thrust is a contact force, with the exhaust gas being the agent that pushes on the engine. The process by which thrust is generated is rather subtle and requires an appreciation of Newton's third law, introduced later in this chapter. For now, we need only consider that **thrust is a force opposite the direction in which the exhaust gas is expelled.** There's no special symbol for thrust, so we will call it $\vec{F}_{\text{thrust}}$.

Electric and Magnetic Forces

Electricity and magnetism, like gravity, exert long-range forces. The forces of electricity and magnetism act on charged particles. We will study electric and magnetic forces in detail in Part VI of this book. For now, it is worth noting that the forces holding molecules together—the molecular bonds—are not actually tiny springs. Atoms and molecules are made of charged particles—electrons and protons—and what we call a molecular bond is really an electric force between these particles. So when we say that the normal force and the tension force are due to "molecular springs," or that friction is due to atoms running into each other, what we're really saying is that these forces, at the most fundamental level, are actually electric forces between the charged particles in the atoms.

It's a drag At the high speeds attained by racing cyclists, air drag can become very significant. The world record for the longest distance traveled in one hour on an ordinary bicycle is 56.38 km, set by Chris Boardman in 1996. But a bicycle with an aerodynamic shell has a much lower drag force, allowing it to attain significantly higher speeds. The bike shown here was pedaled 84.22 km in one hour by Sam Whittingham in 2004, for an amazing average speed of 52.3 mph!

4.4 Identifying Forces

Force and motion problems generally have two basic steps:

1. Identify all of the forces acting on an object.
2. Use Newton's laws and kinematics to determine the motion.

Understanding the first step is the primary goal of this chapter. We'll turn our attention to step 2 in the next chapter.

A typical physics problem describes an object that is being pushed and pulled in various directions. Some forces are given explicitly, while others are only implied. In order to proceed, it is necessary to determine all the forces that act on the object. It is also necessary to avoid including forces that do not really exist. Now that you have learned the properties of forces and seen a catalog of typical forces, we can develop a step-by-step method for identifying each force in a problem. A list of the most common forces we'll come across in the next few chapters is given in Table 4.1.

TABLE 4.1 Common forces and their notation

Force	Notation
General force	$\vec{F}$
Weight	$\vec{w}$
Spring force	$\vec{F}_{\text{sp}}$
Tension	$\vec{T}$
Normal force	$\vec{n}$
Static friction	$\vec{f}_{\text{s}}$
Kinetic friction	$\vec{f}_{\text{k}}$
Drag	$\vec{D}$
Thrust	$\vec{F}_{\text{thrust}}$

TACTICS BOX 4.2 Identifying forces   (MP)™

❶ **Identify the object of interest.** This is the object whose motion you wish to study.

❷ **Draw a picture of the situation.** Show the object of interest and all other objects—such as ropes, springs, and surfaces—that touch it.

❸ **Draw a closed curve around the object.** Only the object of interest is inside the curve; everything else is outside.

❹ **Locate every point on the boundary of this curve where other objects touch the object of interest.** These are the points where *contact forces* are exerted on the object.

❺ **Name and label each contact force acting on the object.** There is at least one force at each point of contact; there may be more than one. When necessary, use subscripts to distinguish forces of the same type.

❻ **Name and label each long-range force acting on the object.** For now, the only long-range force is weight.

Exercises 4–8 ✏

CONCEPTUAL EXAMPLE 4.1 Identifying forces on a bungee jumper

A bungee jumper has leapt off a bridge and is nearing the bottom of her fall. What forces are being exerted on the bungee jumper?

REASON FIGURE 4.15 Forces on a bungee jumper.

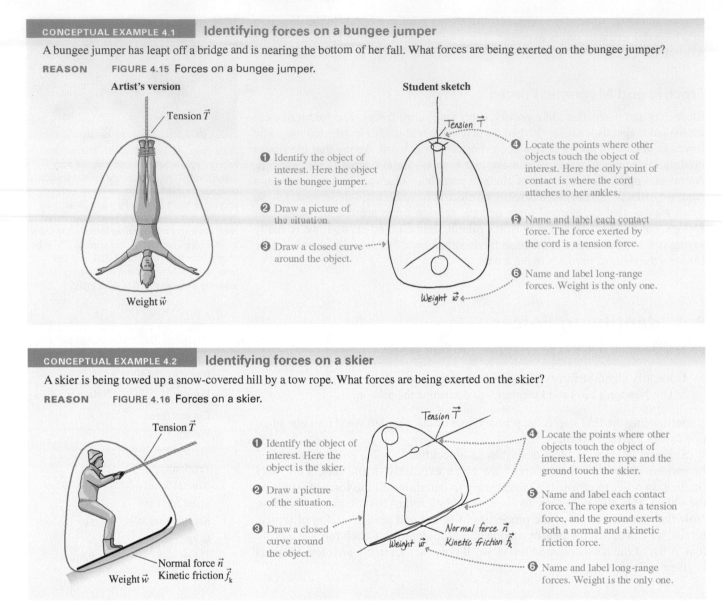

Artist's version

Tension $\vec{T}$

Weight $\vec{w}$

Student sketch

Tension $\vec{T}$

Weight $\vec{w}$

❶ Identify the object of interest. Here the object is the bungee jumper.

❷ Draw a picture of the situation.

❸ Draw a closed curve around the object.

❹ Locate the points where other objects touch the object of interest. Here the only point of contact is where the cord attaches to her ankles.

❺ Name and label each contact force. The force exerted by the cord is a tension force.

❻ Name and label long-range forces. Weight is the only one.

CONCEPTUAL EXAMPLE 4.2 Identifying forces on a skier

A skier is being towed up a snow-covered hill by a tow rope. What forces are being exerted on the skier?

REASON FIGURE 4.16 Forces on a skier.

Tension $\vec{T}$

Normal force $\vec{n}$
Weight $\vec{w}$ Kinetic friction $\vec{f}_k$

Tension $\vec{T}$

Weight $\vec{w}$ Normal force $\vec{n}$
Kinetic friction $\vec{f}_k$

❶ Identify the object of interest. Here the object is the skier.

❷ Draw a picture of the situation.

❸ Draw a closed curve around the object.

❹ Locate the points where other objects touch the object of interest. Here the rope and the ground touch the skier.

❺ Name and label each contact force. The rope exerts a tension force, and the ground exerts both a normal and a kinetic friction force.

❻ Name and label long-range forces. Weight is the only one.

NOTE ▶ You might have expected two friction forces and two normal forces in Example 4.2, one on each ski. Keep in mind, however, that we're working within the particle model, which represents the skier by a single point. A particle has only one contact with the ground, so there is a single normal force and a single friction force. The particle model is valid if we want to analyze the motion of the skier as a whole, but we would have to go beyond the particle model to find out what happens to each ski. ◀

CONCEPTUAL EXAMPLE 4.3 Identifying forces on a rocket

A rocket is being launched to place a new satellite in orbit. Air resistance is not negligible. What forces are being exerted on the rocket?

REASON

FIGURE 4.17 Forces on a rocket.

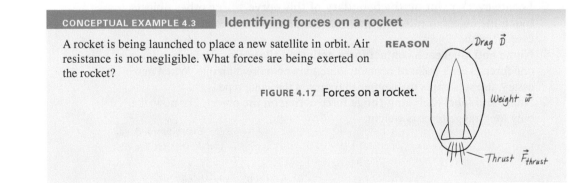

Drag $\vec{D}$

Weight $\vec{w}$

Thrust $\vec{F}_{thrust}$

STOP TO THINK 4.2 You've just kicked a rock, and it is now sliding across the ground about 2 meters in front of you. Which of these are forces acting on the rock? List all that apply.

A. Gravity, acting downward
B. The normal force, acting upward
C. The force of the kick, acting in the direction of motion
D. Friction, acting opposite the direction of motion
E. Air resistance, acting opposite the direction of motion

4.5 What Do Forces Do?

The fundamental question is: How does an object move when a force is exerted on it? The only way to answer this question is to do experiments. To do experiments, however, we need a way to reproduce the same force again and again, and we need a standard object so that our experiments are repeatable.

FIGURE 4.18 shows how you can use your fingers to stretch a rubber band to a certain length—say, 10 centimeters—that you can measure with a ruler. We'll call this the *standard length*. You know that a stretched rubber band exerts a force because your fingers *feel* the pull. Furthermore, this is a reproducible force. The rubber band exerts the same force every time you stretch it to the standard length. We'll call the magnitude of this force the *standard force F*. Not surprisingly, two identical rubber bands, each stretched to the standard length, exert twice the force of one rubber band; three rubber bands exert three times the force; and so on.

We'll also need several identical standard objects to which the force will be applied. As we learned in Chapter 1, the SI unit of mass is the kilogram (kg). The kilogram is defined in terms of a particular metal block kept in a vault in Paris. For our standard objects, we will make ourselves several identical copies, each with, by definition, a mass of 1 kg. At this point, you can think of mass as the "quantity of matter" in an object. This idea will suffice for now, but by the end of this section, we'll be able to give a more precise meaning to the concept of mass.

Now we're ready to start the virtual experiment. First, place one of the 1 kg blocks on a frictionless surface. (In a real experiment, we can nearly eliminate friction by floating the block on a cushion of air.) Second, attach a rubber band to the block and stretch the band to the standard length. Then the block experiences the same force *F* as your finger did. As the block starts to move, in order to keep the pulling force constant you must *move your hand* in just the right way to keep the length of the rubber band—and thus the force—*constant*. FIGURE 4.19 shows the experiment being carried out. Once the motion is complete, you can use motion diagrams and kinematics to analyze the block's motion.

FIGURE 4.18 A reproducible force.

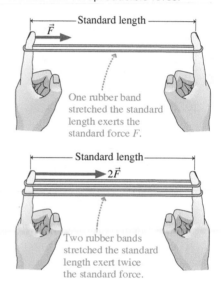

One rubber band stretched the standard length exerts the standard force *F*.

Two rubber bands stretched the standard length exert twice the standard force.

FIGURE 4.19 Measuring the motion of a 1 kg block that is pulled with a constant force.

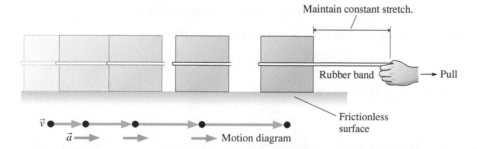

Maintain constant stretch.

Rubber band

Pull

Frictionless surface

$\vec{v}$

$\vec{a}$ Motion diagram

The motion diagram in Figure 4.19 shows that the velocity vectors are getting longer, so the velocity is increasing: The block is *accelerating*. Furthermore, a close inspection of the motion diagram shows that the acceleration vectors are all the same length. This is the first important finding of this experiment: **An object pulled with**

FIGURE 4.20 Graph of acceleration versus force.

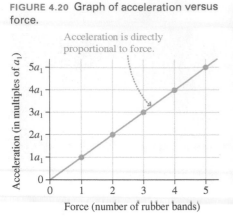

Force (number of rubber bands)

FIGURE 4.21 Graph of acceleration versus number of blocks.

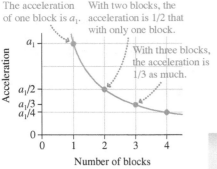

Number of blocks

a constant force moves with a constant acceleration. This finding could not have been anticipated in advance. It's conceivable that the object would speed up for a while and then move with a steady speed. Or that it would continue to speed up, but that the *rate* of increase, the acceleration, would steadily decline. But these descriptions do not match what happens. Instead, the object continues *with a constant acceleration* for as long as you pull it with a constant force. We'll call this constant acceleration of *one* block pulled by *one* band a_1.

What happens if you increase the force by using several rubber bands? To find out, use two rubber bands. Stretch both to the standard length to double the force to $2F$, then measure the acceleration. Measure the acceleration due to three rubber bands, then four, and so on. FIGURE 4.20 is a graph of the results. Force is the independent variable, the one you can control, so we've placed force on the horizontal axis to make an acceleration-versus-force graph. The graph reveals our second important finding: **Acceleration is directly proportional to force.**

The final question for our virtual experiment is: How does the acceleration of an object depend on the mass of the object, the "quantity of matter" that it contains? To find out, we'll glue two of our 1 kg blocks together, so that we have a block with twice as much matter as a 1 kg block—that is, a 2 kg block. Now apply the same force—a single rubber band—as you applied to the single 1 kg block. FIGURE 4.21 shows that the acceleration is *one-half* as great as that of the single block. If we glue three blocks together, making a 3 kg object, we find that the acceleration is only *one-third* of the 1 kg block's acceleration. In general, we find that the acceleration is proportional to the *inverse* of the mass of the object. So our third important result is: **Acceleration is *inversely proportional* to an object's mass.**

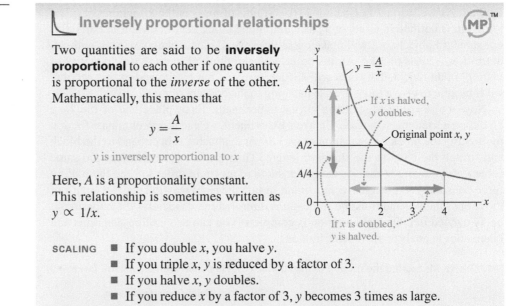

Inversely proportional relationships

Two quantities are said to be **inversely proportional** to each other if one quantity is proportional to the *inverse* of the other. Mathematically, this means that

$$y = \frac{A}{x}$$

 y is inversely proportional to x

Here, A is a proportionality constant. This relationship is sometimes written as $y \propto 1/x$.

SCALING
- If you double x, you halve y.
- If you triple x, y is reduced by a factor of 3.
- If you halve x, y doubles.
- If you reduce x by a factor of 3, y becomes 3 times as large.

RATIOS For any two values of x—say, x_1 and x_2—we have

$$y_1 = \frac{A}{x_1} \quad \text{and} \quad y_2 = \frac{A}{x_2}$$

Dividing the y_1 equation by the y_2 equation, we find

$$\frac{y_1}{y_2} = \frac{A/x_1}{A/x_2} = \frac{A}{x_1}\frac{x_2}{A} = \frac{x_2}{x_1}$$

That is, the ratio of y-values is the inverse of the ratio of the corresponding values of x.

LIMITS
- As x gets very large, y approaches zero.
- As x approaches zero, y gets very large.

Exercise 10

Our original idea of mass was that it was a measure of the "quantity of matter" that an object contains. Now we see that a more precise way of defining the mass of an object is in terms of its *acceleration*. You're familiar with this idea: It's much harder to get your car rolling by pushing it than to get your bicycle rolling; it's harder to stop a heavily loaded grocery cart than to stop a skateboard. This tendency to resist a change in velocity (i.e., to resist speeding up or slowing down) is called **inertia.** Thus we can say that more massive objects have more inertia.

These considerations allow us to unambiguously determine the mass of an object by measuring its acceleration, as the next example shows.

Feel the difference Because of its high sugar content, a can of regular soda has a mass about 4% greater than that of a can of diet soda. If you try to judge which can is more massive by simply holding one in each hand, this small difference is almost impossible to detect. If you *move* the cans up and down, however, the difference becomes subtly but noticeably apparent: People evidently are more sensitive to how the mass of each can resists acceleration than they are to the cans' weights alone.

EXAMPLE 4.4   **Finding the mass of an unknown block**

When a rubber band is stretched to pull on a 1.0 kg block with a constant force, the acceleration of the block is measured to be 3.0 m/s². When a block with an unknown mass is pulled with the same rubber band, using the same force, its acceleration is 5.0 m/s². What is the mass of the unknown block?

PREPARE Each block's acceleration is inversely proportional to its mass.

SOLVE We can use the result of the Inversely Proportional Relationships box to write

$$\frac{3.0 \text{ m/s}^2}{5.0 \text{ m/s}^2} = \frac{m}{1.0 \text{ kg}}$$

or

$$m = \frac{3.0 \text{ m/s}^2}{5.0 \text{ m/s}^2}(1.0 \text{ kg}) = 0.60 \text{ kg}$$

ASSESS With the same force applied, the unknown block had a *larger* acceleration than the 1.0 kg block. It makes sense, then, that its mass—its resistance to acceleration—is *less* than 1.0 kg.

STOP TO THINK 4.3   Two rubber bands stretched to the standard length cause an object to accelerate at 2 m/s². Suppose another object with twice the mass is pulled by four rubber bands stretched to the standard length. What is the acceleration of this second object?

A. 1 m/s²   B. 2 m/s²   C. 4 m/s²   D. 8 m/s²   E. 16 m/s²

4.6 Newton's Second Law

We can now summarize the results of our experiments. We've seen that **a force causes an object to accelerate. The acceleration *a* is directly proportional to the force *F* and inversely proportional to the mass *m*.** We can express both these relationships in equation form as

$$a = \frac{F}{m} \tag{4.2}$$

Note that if we double the size of the force *F*, the acceleration *a* will double, as we found experimentally. And if we triple the mass *m*, the acceleration will be only one-third as great, again agreeing with experiment.

Equation 4.2 tells us the magnitude of an object's acceleration in terms of its mass and the force applied. But our experiments also had another important finding: The *direction* of the acceleration was the same as the direction of the force. We can express this fact by writing Equation 4.2 in *vector* form as

$$\vec{a} = \frac{\vec{F}}{m} \tag{4.3}$$

Finally, our experiment was limited to looking at an object's response to a *single* applied force acting in a single direction. Realistically, an object is likely to be subjected to several distinct forces $\vec{F}_1, \vec{F}_2, \vec{F}_3, \ldots$ that may point in different directions. What happens then? Experiments show that the acceleration of the object is determined by the *net force* acting on it. Recall from Figure 4.4 and Equation 4.1 that the net force is the *vector sum* of all forces acting on the object. So if several forces are acting, we use the *net* force in Equation 4.4.

Newton was the first to recognize these connections between force and motion. This relationship is known today as Newton's second law.

> **Newton's second law** An object of mass m subjected to forces $\vec{F}_1, \vec{F}_2, \vec{F}_3, \ldots$ will undergo an acceleration $\vec{a}$ given by
>
> $$\vec{a} = \frac{\vec{F}_{net}}{m} \qquad (4.4)$$
>
> where the net force $\vec{F}_{net} = \vec{F}_1 + \vec{F}_2 + \vec{F}_3 + \cdots$ is the vector sum of all forces acting on the object. **The acceleration vector $\vec{a}$ points in the same direction as the net force vector $\vec{F}_{net}$.**

We'll use Newton's second law in Chapter 5 to solve many kinds of motion problems; for the moment, however, the critical idea is that an object accelerates in the direction of the net force acting on it.

The significance of Newton's second law cannot be overstated. There was no reason to suspect that there should be any simple relationship between force and acceleration. Yet a simple but exceedingly powerful equation relates the two. Newton's work, preceded to some extent by Galileo's, marks the beginning of a highly successful period in the history of science during which it was learned that the behavior of physical objects can often be described and predicted by mathematical relationships. While some relationships are found to apply only in special circumstances, others seem to have universal applicability. Those equations that appear to apply at all times and under all conditions have come to be called "laws of nature." Newton's second law is a law of nature; you will meet others as we go through this book.

We can rewrite Newton's second law in the form

$$\vec{F}_{net} = m\vec{a} \qquad (4.5)$$

which is how you'll see it presented in many textbooks and how, in practice, we'll often use the second law. Equations 4.4 and 4.5 are mathematically equivalent, but Equation 4.4 better describes the central idea of Newtonian mechanics: A force applied to an object causes the object to accelerate.

> NOTE ▶ When several forces act on an object, be careful not to think that the strongest force "overcomes" the others to determine the motion on its own. It is $\vec{F}_{net}$, the sum of *all* the forces, that determines the acceleration $\vec{a}$. ◄

An unfair advantage? Race car driver Danica Patrick was the subject of controversial comments by other drivers who thought her small mass of 45 kg gave her an advantage over heavier drivers; the next-lightest driver's mass was 61 kg. Because every driver's car must have the same mass, Patrick's overall racing mass was lower than any other driver's. Because a car's acceleration is inversely proportional to its mass, her car could be expected to have a slightly greater acceleration.

CONCEPTUAL EXAMPLE 4.5   **Acceleration of a wind-blown basketball**

A basketball is released from rest in a stiff breeze directed to the right. In what direction does the ball accelerate?

REASON As shown in FIGURE 4.22a, two forces are acting on the ball: its weight $\vec{w}$ directed downward and a wind force $\vec{F}_{wind}$ pushing the ball to the right. Newton's second law tells us that the direction of the acceleration is the same as the direction of the net force $\vec{F}_{net}$. In FIGURE 4.22b we find $\vec{F}_{net}$ by graphical vector addition of $\vec{w}$ and $\vec{F}_{wind}$. We see that $\vec{F}_{net}$ and therefore $\vec{a}$ point down and to the right.

FIGURE 4.22 A basketball falling in a strong breeze.

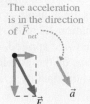

(a) The force of the wind is to the right.
$\vec{F}_{wind}$
The weight force points down.
$\vec{w}$

(b) The acceleration is in the direction of $\vec{F}_{net}$.
$\vec{a}$
$\vec{F}_{net}$

Units of Force

Because $\vec{F}_{net} = m\vec{a}$, the unit of force must be mass units multiplied by acceleration units. We've previously specified the SI unit of mass as the kilogram. We can now define the basic unit of force as "the force that causes a 1 kg mass to accelerate at 1 m/s^2." From Newton's second law, this force is

$$1 \text{ basic unit of force} = (1 \text{ kg}) \times (1 \text{ m/s}^2) = 1 \frac{\text{kg} \cdot \text{m}}{\text{s}^2}$$

This basic unit of force is called a *newton:* One **newton** is the force that causes a 1 kg mass to accelerate at 1 m/s^2. The abbreviation for newton is N. Mathematically, $1 \text{ N} = 1 \text{ kg} \cdot \text{m/s}^2$.

The newton is a *secondary unit,* meaning that it is defined in terms of the *primary units* of kilograms, meters, and seconds. We will introduce other secondary units as needed.

It is important to develop a feeling for what the size of forces should be. Table 4.2 lists some typical forces. As you can see, "typical" forces on "typical" objects are likely to be in the range 0.01–10,000 N. Forces less than 0.01 N are too small to consider unless you are dealing with very small objects. Forces greater than 10,000 N would make sense only if applied to very massive objects.

The unit of force in the English system is the *pound* (abbreviated lb). Although the definition of the pound has varied throughout history, it is now defined in terms of the newton:

$$1 \text{ pound} = 1 \text{ lb} = 4.45 \text{ N}$$

You very likely associate pounds with kilograms rather than with newtons. Everyday language often confuses the ideas of mass and weight, but we're going to need to make a clear distinction between them. We'll have more to say about this in the next chapter.

TABLE 4.2 Approximate magnitude of some typical forces

Force	Approximate magnitude (newtons)
Weight of a U.S. nickel	0.05
Weight of a 1-pound object	5
Weight of a 110-pound person	500
Propulsion force of a car	5000
Thrust force of a rocket motor	5,000,000

EXAMPLE 4.6 **Pulling an airplane**

In 2000, a team of 60 British police officers set a world record by pulling a Boeing 747, with a mass of 205,000 kg, a distance of 100 m in 53.3 s. Estimate the force with which each officer pulled on the plane.

PREPARE If we assume that the plane undergoes a constant acceleration, we can use kinematics to find the magnitude of that acceleration. Then we can use Newton's second law to find the force applied to the airplane. FIGURE 4.23 shows the visual overview of the airplane.

FIGURE 4.23 Visual overview of the airplane accelerating.

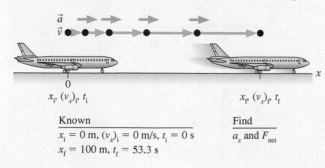

Known	Find
$x_i = 0 \text{ m}, (v_x)_i = 0 \text{ m/s}, t_i = 0 \text{ s}$	a_x and F_{net}
$x_f = 100 \text{ m}, t_f = 53.3 \text{ s}$	

SOLVE Because we know the net displacement of the plane and the time it took to move, we can use the kinematic equation

$$x_f = x_i + (v_x)_i \, \Delta t + \tfrac{1}{2} a_x (\Delta t)^2$$

to find the airplane's acceleration a_x. Using the known values $x_i = 0 \text{ m}$ and $(v_x)_i = 0 \text{ m/s}$, we can solve for the acceleration:

$$a_x = \frac{2x_f}{(\Delta t)^2} = \frac{2(100 \text{ m})}{(53.3 \text{ s})^2} = 0.0704 \text{ m/s}^2$$

Now we apply Newton's second law. The net force is

$$F_{net} = ma_x = (205,000 \text{ kg})(0.0704 \text{ m/s}^2) = 1.44 \times 10^4 \text{ N}$$

This is the force applied by all 60 men. Each man thus applies about 1/60th of this force, or around 240 N.

ASSESS Converting this force to pounds, we have

$$F = 240 \text{ N} \times \frac{1 \text{ lb}}{4.45 \text{ N}} = 54 \text{ lb}$$

Our answer is suspiciously low. Burly policemen can certainly apply a force greater than 54 lb. The fact that our calculation ended with a force that appears too small suggests we've overlooked something. In fact, we have. We've neglected the rolling friction of the plane's tires. We'll learn how to deal with friction in the next chapter, where we'll find that, because of the opposing friction force, the men have to pull harder than our estimate, in which we've ignored friction.

STOP TO THINK 4.4 Three forces act on an object. In which direction does the object accelerate?

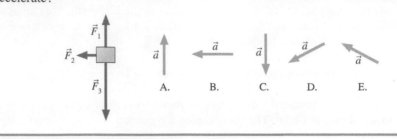

4.7 Free-Body Diagrams

Having discussed at length what is and is not a force, and what forces do to an object, we are ready to assemble our knowledge about force and motion into a single diagram called a **free-body diagram.** A free-body diagram represents the object as a particle and shows *all* of the forces acting on the object. Learning how to draw a correct free-body diagram is a very important skill, one that in the next chapter will become a critical part of our strategy for solving motion problems. For now, let's concentrate on the basic skill of constructing a correct free-body diagram.

TACTICS BOX 4.3 Drawing a free-body diagram

❶ **Identify all forces acting on the object.** This step was described in Tactics Box 4.2.
❷ **Draw a coordinate system.** Use the axes defined in your pictorial representation (Tactics Box 2.2). If those axes are tilted, for motion along an incline, then the axes of the free-body diagram should be similarly tilted.
❸ **Represent the object as a dot at the origin of the coordinate axes.** This is the particle model.
❹ **Draw vectors representing each of the identified forces.** This was described in Tactics Box 4.1. Be sure to label each force vector.
❺ **Draw and label the** *net force* **vector** $\vec{F}_{\text{net}}$. Draw this vector beside the diagram, not on the particle. Then check that $\vec{F}_{\text{net}}$ points in the same direction as the acceleration vector $\vec{a}$ on your motion diagram. Or, if appropriate, write $\vec{F}_{\text{net}} = \vec{0}$.

Exercises 17–22

EXAMPLE 4.7 **Forces on an upward-accelerating elevator**

An elevator, suspended by a cable, speeds up as it moves upward from the ground floor. Draw a free-body diagram of the elevator.

PREPARE FIGURE 4.24 illustrates the steps listed in Tactics Box 4.3.

FIGURE 4.24 Free-body diagram of an elevator accelerating upward.

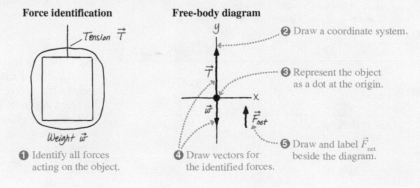

ASSESS The coordinate axes, with a vertical y-axis, are the ones we use in a pictorial representation of the motion. The elevator is accelerating upward, so $\vec{F}_{net}$ must point upward. For this to be true, the magnitude of $\vec{T}$ must be greater than the magnitude of $\vec{w}$. The diagram has been drawn accordingly.

EXAMPLE 4.8 **Forces on a rocket-propelled ice block**

Bobby straps a small model rocket to a block of ice and shoots it across the smooth surface of a frozen lake. Friction is negligible. Draw a visual overview—a motion diagram, force identification diagram, and free-body diagram—of the block of ice.

PREPARE We treat the block of ice as a particle. The visual overview consists of a motion diagram to determine $\vec{a}$, a force identification picture, and a free-body diagram. The statement of the situation tells us that friction is negligible. We can draw these three pictures using Problem-Solving Strategy 1.1 for the motion diagram, Tactics Box 4.2 to identify the forces, and Tactics Box

4.3 to draw the free-body diagrams. These pictures are shown in FIGURE 4.25.

ASSESS The motion diagram tells us that the acceleration is in the positive x-direction. According to the rules of vector addition, this can be true only if the upward-pointing n and the downward-pointing $\vec{w}$ are equal in magnitude and thus cancel each other. The vectors have been drawn accordingly, and this leaves the net force vector pointing toward the right, in agreement with $\vec{a}$ from the motion diagram.

FIGURE 4.25 Visual overview for a block of ice shooting across a frictionless frozen lake.

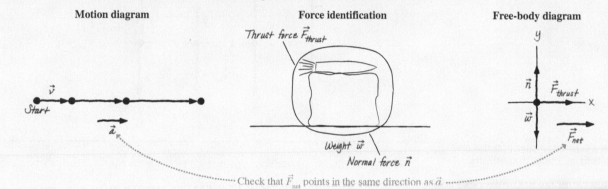

Check that $\vec{F}_{net}$ points in the same direction as $\vec{a}$

EXAMPLE 4.9 **Forces on a towed skier**

A tow rope pulls a skier up a snow-covered hill at a constant speed. Draw a full visual overview of the skier.

PREPARE This is Example 4.2 again with the additional information that the skier is moving at a constant speed. If we were doing a kinematics problem, the pictorial representation would

use a tilted coordinate system with the x-axis parallel to the slope, so we use these same tilted coordinate axes for the free-body diagram. The motion diagram, force identification diagram, and free-body diagram are shown in FIGURE 4.26.

FIGURE 4.26 Visual overview for a skier being towed at a constant speed.

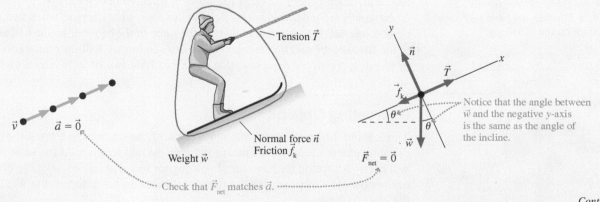

Check that $\vec{F}_{net}$ matches $\vec{a}$.

Continued

ASSESS We have shown $\vec{T}$ pulling parallel to the slope and $\vec{f}_k$, which opposes the direction of motion, pointing down the slope. The normal force $\vec{n}$ is perpendicular to the surface and thus along the y-axis. Finally, and this is important, the weight $\vec{w}$ is *vertically* downward, *not* along the negative y-axis.

The skier moves in a straight line with constant speed, so $\vec{a} = \vec{0}$. Newton's second law then tells us that $\vec{F}_{\text{net}} = m\vec{a} = \vec{0}$. Thus we have drawn the vectors such that the forces add to zero. We'll learn more about how to do this in Chapter 5.

Free-body diagrams will be our major tool for the next several chapters. Careful practice with the workbook exercises and homework in this chapter will pay immediate benefits in the next chapter. Indeed, it is not too much to assert that a problem is more than half solved when you correctly complete the free-body diagram.

STOP TO THINK 4.5 An elevator suspended by a cable is moving upward and slowing to a stop. Which free-body diagram is correct?

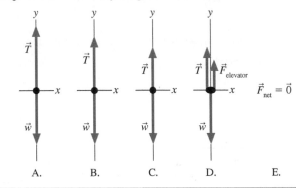

A.   B.   C.   D.   E.

FIGURE 4.27 The hammer and the nail are a system of interacting objects.

FIGURE 4.28 The hammer and nail each exert a force on the other.

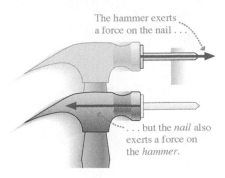

The hammer exerts a force on the nail . . .

. . . but the *nail* also exerts a force on the *hammer*.

4.8 Newton's Third Law

Thus far, we've focused on the motion of a single particle responding to well-defined forces exerted by other objects, or to long-range forces. A skier sliding downhill, for instance, is subject to frictional and normal forces from the slope, and the pull of gravity on his body. Once we have identified these forces, we can use Newton's second law to calculate the acceleration, and hence the overall motion, of the skier.

But motion in the real world often involves two or more objects *interacting* with each other. Consider the hammer and nail in FIGURE 4.27. As the hammer hits the nail, the nail pushes back on the hammer. A bat and a ball, your foot and a soccer ball, and the earth–moon system are other examples of interacting objects.

Newton's second law is not sufficient to explain what happens when two or more objects interact. It does not explain how the force of the hammer on the nail is related to the force of the nail on the hammer. In this section we will introduce another law of physics, Newton's *third* law, that describes how two objects interact with each other.

Interacting Objects

Think about the hammer and nail in Figure 4.27. As FIGURE 4.28 shows, the hammer certainly exerts a force on the nail as it drives the nail forward. At the same time, the nail exerts a force on the hammer. If you are not sure that it does, imagine hitting the nail with a glass hammer. It's the force of the nail on the hammer that would cause the glass to shatter.

Indeed, if you stop to think about it, any time that object A pushes or pulls on object B, object B pushes or pulls back on object A. As you push on a filing cabinet to move it, the cabinet pushes back on you. (If you pushed forward without the cabinet pushing back, you would fall forward in the same way you do if someone suddenly opens a door you're leaning against.) Your chair pushes upward on you (the normal force that keeps you from falling) while, at the same time, you push down on the chair, compressing the cushion. These are examples of what we call an *interaction*. An **interaction** is the mutual influence of two objects on each other.

These examples illustrate a key aspect of interactions: The forces involved in an interaction between two objects always occur as a *pair*. To be more specific, if object A exerts a force $\vec{F}_{\text{A on B}}$ on object B, then object B exerts a force $\vec{F}_{\text{B on A}}$ on object A. This pair of forces, shown in FIGURE 4.29, is called an **action/reaction pair**. Two objects interact by exerting an action/reaction pair of forces on each other. Notice the very explicit subscripts on the force vectors. The first letter is the *agent*—the source of the force—and the second letter is the *object* on which the force acts. $\vec{F}_{\text{A on B}}$ is thus the force exerted *by* A *on* B.

> NOTE ▶ The name "action/reaction pair" is somewhat misleading. The forces occur simultaneously, and we cannot say which is the "action" and which the "reaction." Neither is there any implication about cause and effect; the action does not cause the reaction. **An action/reaction pair of forces exists as a pair, or not at all.** For action/reaction pairs, the labels are the key: Force $\vec{F}_{\text{A on B}}$ is paired with force $\vec{F}_{\text{B on A}}$. ◀

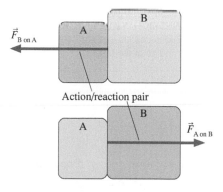

FIGURE 4.29 An action/reaction pair of forces.

Action/reaction pair

Reasoning with Newton's Third Law

We've discovered that two objects always interact via an action/reaction pair of forces. Newton was the first to recognize how the two members of an action/reaction pair of forces are related to each other. Today we know this as Newton's third law:

> **Newton's third law** Every force occurs as one member of an action/reaction pair of forces.
>
> - The two members of an action/reaction pair act on two *different* objects.
> - The two members of an action/reaction pair point in *opposite* directions and are *equal in magnitude*.

Newton's third law is often stated: "For every action there is an equal but opposite reaction." While this is a catchy phrase, it lacks the preciseness of our preferred version. In particular, it fails to capture an essential feature of the two members of an action/reaction pair—that each acts on a *different* object. This is shown in FIGURE 4.30, where a hammer hitting a nail exerts a force $\vec{F}_{\text{hammer on nail}}$ on the nail; by the third law, the nail must exert a force $\vec{F}_{\text{nail on hammer}}$ to complete the action/reaction pair.

Figure 4.30 also illustrates that these two forces point in *opposite directions*. This feature of the third law is also in accord with our experience. If the hammer hits the nail with a force directed to the right, the force of the nail on the hammer is directed to the left; if the force of my chair on me pushes up, the force of me on the chair pushes down.

Finally, Figure 4.30 shows that, according to Newton's third law, the two members of an action/reaction pair have *equal* magnitudes, so that $F_{\text{hammer on nail}} = F_{\text{nail on hammer}}$. This is something new, and it is by no means obvious. Indeed, this statement causes students the most trouble when applying the third law because it seems so counter to our intuition, as the following example shows.

FIGURE 4.30 Newton's third law.

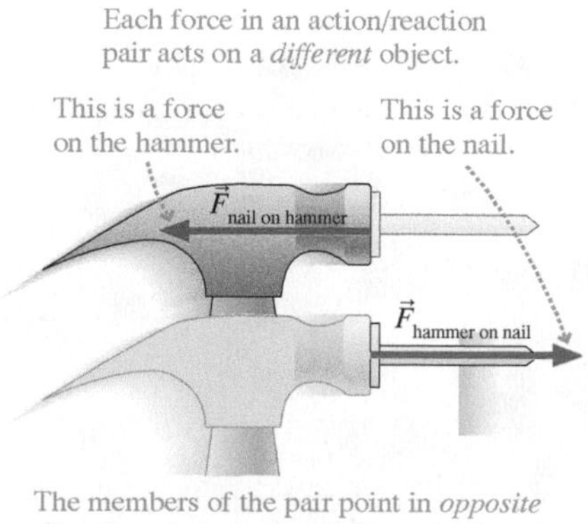

Each force in an action/reaction pair acts on a *different* object.

This is a force on the hammer.

This is a force on the nail.

$\vec{F}_{\text{nail on hammer}}$

$\vec{F}_{\text{hammer on nail}}$

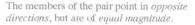

The members of the pair point in *opposite directions*, but are of *equal magnitude*.

Revenge of the target We normally think of the damage that the force of a bullet inflicts on its target. But according to Newton's third law, the target exerts an equal force on the bullet. The photo shows the damage sustained by bullets fired at 1600, 1800, and 2000 ft/s, after impacting a test target. The appearance of the bullet before firing is shown at the left.

CONCEPTUAL EXAMPLE 4.10   **The bug versus the windshield**

During the collision between a bug and the windshield of a fast-moving truck, which force has greater magnitude: the force of the windshield on the bug or the force of the bug on the windshield?

REASON The third law tells us that the magnitude of the force of the windshield on the bug must be *equal* to that of the bug on the windshield! How can this be, when the bug is so small compared to the truck? The source of puzzlement in problems like this is that Newton's third law equates the size of the *forces* acting on the two objects, not their *accelerations*. The acceleration of each object depends not only on the force applied to it, but also, according to Newton's second law, on its mass. The bug and the truck do in fact feel forces of equal strength from the other, but the bug, with its very small mass, undergoes an extreme acceleration from this force while the acceleration of the heavy truck is negligible.

ASSESS It is important to separate the *effects* of the forces (the accelerations) from the causes (the forces themselves). Because two interacting objects can have very different masses, their accelerations can be very different even though the interaction forces are of the same strength.

We'll return to Newton's third law in Chapter 5, where we'll use it to solve problems involving two or more interacting objects.

Propulsion

A sprinter accelerates out of the blocks. Because he's accelerating, there must be a force on him in the forward direction. For a system with an internal source of energy, a force that drives the system is a force of **propulsion.** Propulsion is an important feature not only of walking or running but also of the forward motion of cars, jets, and rockets. Propulsion is somewhat counterintuitive, so it is worth a closer look.

If you tried to walk across a frictionless floor, your foot would slip and slide *backward.* In order for you to walk, the floor needs to have friction so that your foot *sticks* to the floor as you straighten your leg, moving your body forward. The friction that prevents slipping is *static* friction. Static friction, you will recall, acts in the direction that prevents slipping, so the static friction force $\vec{f}_{\text{S on P}}$ (for **Surface** on **Person**) has to point in the *forward* direction to prevent your foot from slipping backward. As shown in FIGURE 4.31a, it is this forward-directed static friction force that propels you forward! The force of your foot on the floor, $\vec{f}_{\text{P on S}}$, is the other half of the action/reaction pair, and it points in the opposite direction as you push backward against the floor.

Similarly, the car in FIGURE 4.31b uses static friction to propel itself. The car uses its motor to turn the tires, causing the tires to push backward against the road ($\vec{f}_{\text{tire on road}}$). The road surface responds by pushing the car forward ($\vec{f}_{\text{road on tire}}$). This force of the road on the tire can be seen in photos of drag racers, where the forces are very great (FIGURE 4.32). Again, the forces involved are *static* friction forces. The tire is rolling, but the bottom of the tire, where it contacts the road, is instantaneously at rest. If it weren't, you would leave one giant skid mark as you drove and would burn off the tread within a few miles.

Rocket motors are somewhat different because they are not pushing *against* anything external. That's why rocket propulsion works in the vacuum of space. Instead, the rocket engine pushes hot, expanding gases out of the back of the rocket, as shown in FIGURE 4.33. In response, the exhaust gases push the rocket forward with the force we've called *thrust*.

FIGURE 4.31 Examples of propulsion.

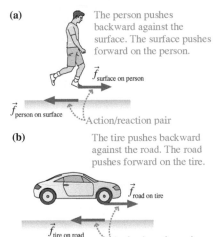

(a)
The person pushes backward against the surface. The surface pushes forward on the person.

$\vec{f}_{\text{surface on person}}$

$\vec{f}_{\text{person on surface}}$
Action/reaction pair

(b)
The tire pushes backward against the road. The road pushes forward on the tire.

$\vec{f}_{\text{road on tire}}$

$\vec{f}_{\text{tire on road}}$
Action/reaction pair

FIGURE 4.32 When the driver hits the gas, the force of the track on the tire is so great that the tire deforms.

$\vec{F}_{\text{road on tire}}$

You can *see* that the force of the road on the tire points forward by the way it twists the rubber of the tire.

Now we've assembled all the pieces we need in order to start solving problems in dynamics. We have seen what forces are and how to identify them, and we've learned how forces cause objects to accelerate according to Newton's second law. We've also found how Newton's third law governs the interaction forces between two objects. Our goal in the next several chapters is to apply Newton's laws to a variety of problems involving straight-line and circular motion.

FIGURE 4.33 Rocket propulsion.

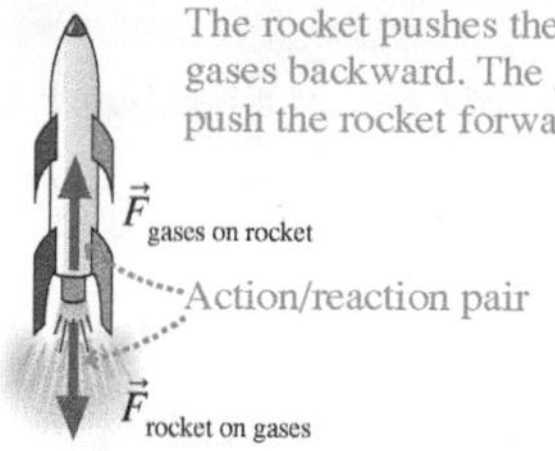

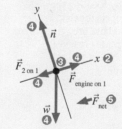

The rocket pushes the hot gases backward. The gases push the rocket forward.

$\vec{F}_{\text{gases on rocket}}$

Action/reaction pair

$\vec{F}_{\text{rocket on gases}}$

STOP TO THINK 4.6 A small car is pushing a larger truck that has a dead battery. The mass of the truck is greater than the mass of the car. Which of the following statements is true?

A. The car exerts a force on the truck, but the truck doesn't exert a force on the car.
B. The car exerts a larger force on the truck than the truck exerts on the car.
C. The car exerts the same amount of force on the truck as the truck exerts on the car.
D. The truck exerts a larger force on the car than the car exerts on the truck.
E. The truck exerts a force on the car, but the car doesn't exert a force on the truck.

INTEGRATED EXAMPLE 4.11   **Pulling an excursion train**

An engine slows as it pulls two cars of an excursion train up a mountain. Draw a visual overview (motion diagram, a force identification diagram, and free-body diagram) for the car just behind the engine. Ignore friction.

PREPARE Because the train is slowing down, the motion diagram consists of a series of particle positions that become closer together at successive times; the corresponding velocity vectors become shorter and shorter. To identify the forces acting on the car we use the steps of Tactics Box 4.2. Finally, we can draw a free-body diagram using Tactics Box 4.3.

SOLVE Finding the forces acting on car 1 can be tricky. The engine exerts a forward force $\vec{F}_{\text{engine on 1}}$ on car 1 where the engine touches the front of car 1. At its back, car 1 touches car 2, so car 2

must also exert a force on car 1. The direction of this force can be understood from Newton's third law. Car 1 exerts an uphill force on car 2 in order to pull it up the mountain. Thus, by Newton's third law, car 2 must exert an oppositely directed *downhill* force on car 1. This is the force we label $\vec{F}_{2\text{ on }1}$. The three diagrams that make up the full visual overview are shown in **FIGURE 4.34**.

ASSESS Correctly preparing the three diagrams illustrated in this example is critical for solving problems using Newton's laws. The motion diagram allows you to determine the direction of the acceleration and hence of $\vec{F}_{\text{net}}$. Using the force identification diagram, you will correctly identify all the forces acting on the object and, just as important, not add any extraneous forces. And by properly drawing these force vectors in a free-body diagram, you'll be ready for the quantitative application of Newton's laws that is the focus of Chapter 5.

FIGURE 4.34 Visual overview for a slowing train car being pulled up a mountain.

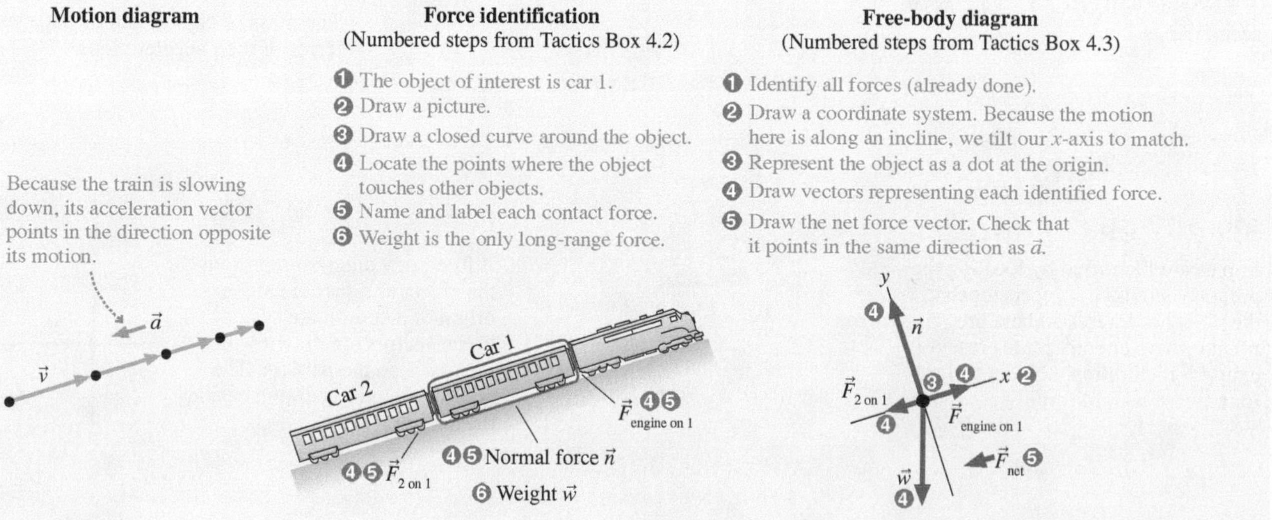

Motion diagram

Because the train is slowing down, its acceleration vector points in the direction opposite its motion.

$\vec{a}$

$\vec{v}$

Force identification
(Numbered steps from Tactics Box 4.2)

❶ The object of interest is car 1.
❷ Draw a picture.
❸ Draw a closed curve around the object.
❹ Locate the points where the object touches other objects.
❺ Name and label each contact force.
❻ Weight is the only long-range force.

Car 1

Car 2

$\vec{F}$ ❹❺ $_{\text{engine on 1}}$

❹❺ $\vec{F}_{2\text{ on }1}$

❹❺ Normal force $\vec{n}$

❻ Weight $\vec{w}$

Free-body diagram
(Numbered steps from Tactics Box 4.3)

❶ Identify all forces (already done).
❷ Draw a coordinate system. Because the motion here is along an incline, we tilt our x-axis to match.
❸ Represent the object as a dot at the origin.
❹ Draw vectors representing each identified force.
❺ Draw the net force vector. Check that it points in the same direction as $\vec{a}$.

y

❹ $\vec{n}$

$\vec{F}_{2\text{ on }1}$ ❸ ❹ x ❷

❹ $\vec{F}_{\text{engine on 1}}$

$\vec{F}_{\text{net}}$ ❺

$\vec{w}$ ❹

SUMMARY

The goal of Chapter 4 has been to establish a connection between force and motion.

GENERAL PRINCIPLES

Newton's First Law

Consider an object with no force acting on it. If it is at rest, it will remain at rest. If it is in motion, then it will continue to move in a straight line at a constant speed.

The first law tells us that no "cause" is needed for motion. Uniform motion is the "natural state" of an object.

Newton's Second Law

An object with mass m will undergo acceleration

$$\vec{a} = \frac{\vec{F}_{net}}{m}$$

where the net force $\vec{F}_{net} = \vec{F}_1 + \vec{F}_2 + \vec{F}_3 + \cdots$ is the vector sum of all the individual forces acting on the object.

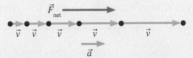

The second law tells us that a net force causes an object to accelerate. This is the connection between force and motion. The acceleration points in the direction of $\vec{F}_{net}$.

Newton's Third Law

Every force occurs as one member of an **action/reaction** pair of forces. The two members of an action/reaction pair:

- act on two *different* objects.
- point in opposite directions and are equal in magnitude:

$$\vec{F}_{A\ on\ B} = -\vec{F}_{B\ on\ A}$$

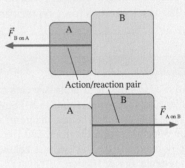

Action/reaction pair

IMPORTANT CONCEPTS

Force is a push or pull on an object.

- Force is a vector, with a magnitude and a direction.
- A force requires an agent.
- A force is either a contact force or a long-range force.

The SI unit of force is the **newton** (N). A 1 N force will cause a 1 kg mass to accelerate at 1 m/s².

Net force is the vector sum of all the forces acting on an object.

$$\vec{F}_{net} = \vec{F}_1 + \vec{F}_2 + \vec{F}_3$$

Mass is the property of an object that determines its resistance to acceleration.

If the same force is applied to objects A and B, then the ratio of their accelerations is related to the ratio of their masses as

$$\frac{a_A}{a_B} = \frac{m_B}{m_A}$$

The mass of objects can be determined in terms of their accelerations.

APPLICATIONS

Identifying Forces

Forces are identified by locating the points where other objects touch the object of interest. These are points where contact forces are exerted. In addition, objects feel a long-range weight force.

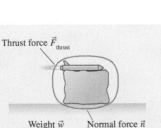

Thrust force $\vec{F}_{thrust}$

Weight $\vec{w}$ Normal force $\vec{n}$

Free-Body Diagrams

A free-body diagram represents the object as a particle at the origin of a coordinate system. Force vectors are drawn with their tails on the particle. The net force vector is drawn beside the diagram.

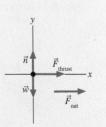

™ For homework assigned on MasteringPhysics, go to
www.masteringphysics.com

Problems labeled INT integrate significant material from earlier
chapters; BIO are of biological or medical interest.

Problem difficulty is labeled as | (straightforward) to |||| (challenging).

QUESTIONS

Conceptual Questions

1. A hockey puck slides along the surface of the ice. If friction and air resistance are negligible, what force is required to keep the puck moving?

2. If an object is not moving, does that mean that there are no forces acting on it? Explain.

3. An object moves in a straight line at a constant speed. Is it true that there must be no forces of any kind acting on this object? Explain.

4. A ball sits near the front of a child's wagon. As she pulls on the wagon and it begins to move forward, the ball rolls toward the back of the wagon. Explain why the ball rolls in this direction.

5. If you know all of the forces acting on a moving object, can you tell in which direction the object is moving? If the answer is Yes, explain how. If the answer is No, give an example.

6. Three arrows are shot horizontally. They have left the bow and are traveling parallel to the ground as shown in Figure Q4.6. Air resistance is negligible. Rank in order, from largest to smallest, the magnitudes of the *horizontal* forces F_1, F_2, and F_3 acting on the arrows. Some may be equal. State your reasoning.

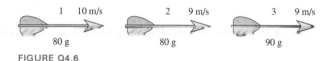

FIGURE Q4.6

7. A carpenter wishes to tighten the heavy head of his hammer onto its light handle. Which method shown in Figure Q4.7 will better tighten the head? Explain.

FIGURE Q4.7

8. BIO Internal injuries in vehicular accidents may be due to what is called the "third collision." The first collision is the vehicle hitting the external object. The second collision is the person hitting something on the inside of the car, such as the dashboard or windshield. This may cause external lacerations. The third collision, possibly the most damaging to the body, is when organs, such as the heart or brain, hit the ribcage, skull, or other confines of the body, bruising the tissues on the leading edge and tearing the organ from its supporting structures on the trailing edge.
   a. Why is there a third collision? In other words, why are the organs still moving after the second collision?
   b. If the vehicle was traveling at 60 mph before the first collision, would the organs be traveling more than, equal to, or less than 60 mph just before the third collision?

9. a. Give an example of the motion of an object in which the frictional force on the object is directed opposite to the motion.
   b. Give an example of the motion of an object in which the frictional force on the object is in the same direction as the motion.

10. Suppose you are an astronaut in deep space, far from any source of gravity. You have two objects that look identical, but one has a large mass and the other a small mass. How can you tell the difference between the two?

11. Jonathan accelerates away from a stop sign. His eight-year-old daughter sits in the passenger seat. On whom does the back of the seat exert a greater force?

12. The weight of a box sitting on the floor points directly down. The normal force of the floor on the box points directly up. Need these two forces have the same magnitude? Explain.

13. A ball weighs 2.0 N when placed on a scale. It is then thrown straight up. What is its weight at the very top of its motion? Explain.

14. Josh and Taylor, standing face-to-face on frictionless ice, push off each other, causing each to slide backward. Josh is much bigger than Taylor. After the push, which of the two is moving faster?

15. A person sits on a sloped hillside. Is it ever possible to have the static friction force on this person point down the hill? Explain.

16. BIO Walking without slipping requires a static friction force between your feet (or footwear) and the floor. As described in this chapter, the force on your foot as you push off the floor is forward while the force exerted by your foot on the floor is backward. But what about your *other* foot, the one moved during a stride? What is the direction of the force on that foot as it comes into contact with the floor? Explain.

17. Figure 4.31b showed a situation in which the force of the road on the car's tire points forward. In other situations, the force points backward. Give an example of such a situation.

18. Alyssa pushes to the right on a filing cabinet; the friction force from the floor pushes on it to the left. Because the cabinet doesn't move, these forces have the same magnitude. Do they form an action/reaction pair? Explain.

19. A very smart three-year-old child is given a wagon for her birthday. She refuses to use it. "After all," she says, "Newton's third law says that no matter how hard I pull, the wagon will exert an equal but opposite force on me. So I will never be able to get it to move forward." What would you say to her in reply?

20. Will hanging a magnet in front of an iron cart, as shown in Figure Q4.20, make it go? Explain why or why not.

FIGURE Q4.20

Multiple-Choice Questions

21. | Figure Q4.21 shows the view looking down onto a frictionless sheet of ice. A puck, tied with a string to point P, slides on the surface of the ice in the circular path shown. If the string suddenly snaps when the puck is in the position shown, which path best represents the puck's subsequent motion?

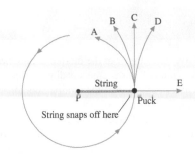

FIGURE Q4.21

22. | A block has acceleration a when pulled by a string. If two identical blocks are glued together and pulled with twice the original force, their acceleration will be
    A. $(1/4)a$ B. $(1/2)a$
    C. a D. $2a$
    E. $4a$

23. | A 5.0 kg block has an acceleration of 0.20 m/s² when a force is exerted on it. A second block has an acceleration of 0.10 m/s² when subject to the same force. What is the mass of the second block?
    A. 10 kg   B. 5.0 kg   C. 2.5 kg   D. 7.5 kg

24. | Tennis balls experience a large drag force. A tennis ball is hit so that it goes straight up and then comes back down. The direction of the drag force is
    A. Always up.
    B. Up and then down.
    C. Always down.
    D. Down and then up.

25. | A person gives a box a shove so that it slides up a ramp, then reverses its motion and slides down. The direction of the force of friction is
    A. Always down the ramp.
    B. Up the ramp and then down the ramp.
    C. Always down the ramp.
    D. Down the ramp and then up the ramp.

26. | A person is pushing horizontally on a box with a constant force, causing it to slide across the floor with a constant speed. If the person suddenly stops pushing on the box, the box will
    A. Immediately come to a stop.
    B. Continue moving at a constant speed for a while, then gradually slow down to a stop.
    C. Immediately change to a slower but constant speed.
    D. Immediately begin slowing down and eventually stop.

27. | Rachel is pushing a box across the floor while Jon, at the same time, is hoping to stop the box by pushing in the opposite direction. There is friction between the box and floor. If the box is moving at constant speed, then the magnitude of Rachel's pushing force is
    A. Greater than the magnitude of Jon's force.
    B. Equal to the magnitude of Jon's force.
    C. Less than the magnitude of Jon's force.
    D. The question can't be answered without knowing how large the friction force is.

28. ‖ Dave pushes his four-year-old son Thomas across the snow on a sled. As Dave pushes, Thomas speeds up. Which statement is true?
    A. The force of Dave on Thomas is larger than the force of Thomas on Dave.
    B. The force of Thomas on Dave is larger than the force of Dave on Thomas.
    C. Both forces have the same magnitude.
    D. It depends on how hard Dave pushes on Thomas.

29. | Figure Q4.29 shows block A sitting on top of block B. A constant force $\vec{F}$ is exerted on block B, causing block B to accelerate to the right. Block A rides on block B without slipping. Which statement is true?
    A. Block B exerts a friction force on block A, directed to the left.
    B. Block B exerts a friction force on block A, directed to the right.
    C. Block B does not exert a friction force on block A.

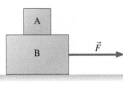

FIGURE Q4.29

PROBLEMS

Section 4.1 What Causes Motion?

1. | Whiplash injuries during an automobile accident are caused
BIO by the inertia of the head. If someone is wearing a seatbelt, her body will tend to move with the car seat. However, her head is free to move until the neck restrains it, causing damage to the neck. Brain damage can also occur.

   Figure P4.1 shows two sequences of head and neck motion for a passenger in an auto accident. One corresponds to a head-on collision, the other to a rear-end collision. Which is which? Explain.

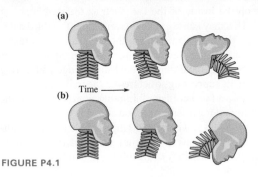

FIGURE P4.1

2. | An automobile has a head-on
BIO collision. A passenger in the car
experiences a compression injury
to the brain. Is this injury most
likely to be in the front or rear
portion of the brain? Explain.

3. | In a head-on collision, an infant
is much safer in a child safety seat
when the seat is installed facing
the rear of the car. Explain.

Section 4.2 Force

Problems 1 through 6 show two forces acting on an object at rest.
Redraw the diagram, then add a third force that will allow the object
to remain at rest. Label the new force $\vec{F}_3$.

4. ‖   5. ‖   6. ‖

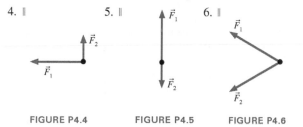

FIGURE P4.4   FIGURE P4.5   FIGURE P4.6

Section 4.3 A Short Catalog of Forces

Section 4.4 Identifying Forces

7. ‖ A mountain climber is hanging from a rope in the middle of a
crevasse. The rope is vertical. Identify the forces on the mountain climber.

8. ‖ A circus clown hangs from one end of a large spring. The
other end is anchored to the ceiling. Identify the forces on the
clown.

9. ‖ A baseball player is sliding into second base. Identify the
forces on the baseball player.

10. ‖‖ A jet plane is speeding down the runway during takeoff. Air
resistance is not negligible. Identify the forces on the jet.

11. | A skier is sliding down a 15° slope. Friction is not negligible.
Identify the forces on the skier.

12. ‖ A tennis ball is flying horizontally across the net. Air resistance is not negligible. Identify the forces on the ball.

Section 4.5 What Do Forces Do?

13. ‖‖ Figure P4.13 shows an acceleration-versus-force graph for
three objects pulled by rubber bands. The mass of object 2 is
0.20 kg. What are the masses of objects 1 and 3? Explain your
reasoning.

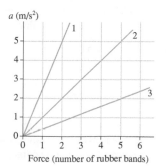

FIGURE P4.13   Force (number of rubber bands)

14. | A constant force applied to object A causes it to accelerate at
5 m/s². The same force applied to object B causes an acceleration
of 3 m/s². Applied to object C, it causes an acceleration of 8 m/s².
   a. Which object has the largest mass?
   b. Which object has the smallest mass?
   c. What is the ratio of mass A to mass B (m_A/m_B)?

15. | Two rubber bands pulling on an object cause it to accelerate
at 1.2 m/s².
   a. What will be the object's acceleration if it is pulled by four
   rubber bands?
   b. What will be the acceleration of two of these objects glued
   together if they are pulled by two rubber bands?

16. | A constant force is applied to an object, causing the object to
accelerate at 10 m/s². What will the acceleration be if
   a. The force is halved?
   b. The object's mass is halved?
   c. The force and the object's mass are both halved?
   d. The force is halved and the object's mass is doubled?

17. | A constant force is applied to an object, causing the object to
accelerate at 8.0 m/s². What will the acceleration be if
   a. The force is doubled?
   b. The object's mass is doubled?
   c. The force and the object's mass are both doubled?
   d. The force is doubled and the object's mass is halved?

18. ‖‖ A man pulling an empty wagon causes it to accelerate at
1.4 m/s². What will the acceleration be if he pulls with the same
force when the wagon contains a child whose mass is three
times that of the wagon?

19. | A car has a maximum acceleration of 5.0 m/s². What will the
maximum acceleration be if the car is towing another car of the
same mass?

Section 4.6 Newton's Second Law

20. ‖ Figure P4.20 shows an acceleration-versus-force graph for a
500 g object. Redraw this graph and add appropriate acceleration values on the vertical scale.

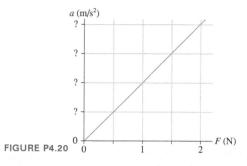

FIGURE P4.20

21. | Figure P4.21 shows an object's acceleration-versus-force
graph. What is the object's mass?

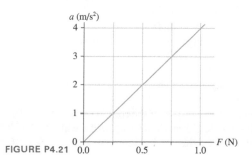

FIGURE P4.21

22. ‖ Two children fight over a 200 g stuffed bear. The 25 kg boy pulls to the right with a 15 N force and the 20 kg girl pulls to the left with a 17 N force. Ignore all other forces on the bear (such as its weight).
    a. At this instant, can you say what the velocity of the bear is? If so, what are the magnitude and direction of the velocity?
    b. At this instant, can you say what the acceleration of the bear is? If so, what are the magnitude and direction of the acceleration?

23. ‖ A 1500 kg car is traveling along a straight road at 20 m/s. INT Two seconds later its speed is 21 m/s. What is the magnitude of the net force acting on the car during this time?

24. ‖ Very small forces can have tremendous effects on the motion of very small objects. Consider a single electron, with a mass of 9.1×10^{-31} kg, subject to a single force equal to the weight of a penny, 2.5×10^{-2} N. What is the acceleration of the electron?

25. ‖ The motion of a very massive object is hardly affected by what would seem to be a substantial force. Consider a supertanker, with a mass of 3.0×10^8 kg. If it is pushed by a rocket motor (see Table 4.2) and is subject to no other forces, what will be the magnitude of its acceleration?

Section 4.7 Free-Body Diagrams

Problems 26 through 28 show a free-body diagram. For each, (a) Redraw the free-body diagram and (b) Write a short description of a real object for which this is the correct free-body diagram. Use Examples 4.3, 4.4, and 4.5 as models of what a description should be like.

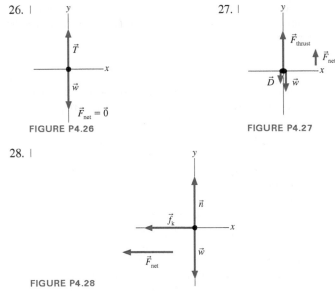

FIGURE P4.26   FIGURE P4.27

28. ‖

FIGURE P4.28

Problems 29 through 35 describe a situation. For each, identify all forces acting on the object and draw a free-body diagram of the object.

29. ‖ Your car is sitting in the parking lot.
30. ‖ Your car is accelerating from a stop.
31. ‖ Your car is slowing to a stop from a high speed.
32. ‖ Your physics textbook is sliding across the table.
33. ‖ An ascending elevator, hanging from a cable, is coming to a stop.
34. ‖ A skier slides down a slope at a constant speed.
35. ‖‖ You hold a picture motionless against a wall by pressing on it, as shown in Figure P4.35.

FIGURE P4.35

Section 4.8 Newton's Third Law

36. ‖ A weightlifter stands up from a squatting position while holding a heavy barbell across his shoulders. Identify all the action/reaction pairs of forces between the weight lifter and the barbell.

37. ‖ Three ice skaters, numbered 1, 2, and 3, stand in a line, each with her hands on the shoulders of the skater in front. Skater 3, at the rear, pushes on skater 2. Identify all the action/reaction pairs of forces between the three skaters. Draw a free-body diagram for skater 2, in the middle. Assume the ice is frictionless.

38. ‖ A girl stands on a sofa. Identify all the action/reaction pairs of forces between the girl and the sofa.

General Problems

39. ‖ Redraw the motion diagram INT shown in Figure P4.39, then draw a vector beside it to show the direction of the net force acting on the object. Explain your reasoning.

40. ‖ Redraw the motion diagram INT shown in Figure P4.40, then draw a vector beside it to show the direction of the net force acting on the object. Explain your reasoning.

41. ‖ Redraw the motion diagram INT shown in Figure P4.41, then draw a vector beside it to show the direction of the net force acting on the object. Explain your reasoning.

FIGURE P4.39   FIGURE P4.40

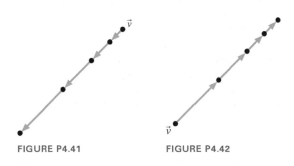

FIGURE P4.41   FIGURE P4.42

42. ‖ Redraw the motion diagram shown in Figure P4.42, then INT draw a vector beside it to show the direction of the net force acting on the object. Explain your reasoning.

Problems 43 through 49 show a free-body diagram. For each:

a. Redraw the diagram.
b. Identify the direction of the acceleration vector $\vec{a}$ and show it as a vector next to your diagram. Or, if appropriate, write $\vec{a} = \vec{0}$.
c. Write a short description of a real object for which this is the correct free-body diagram. Use Examples 4.7, 4.8, and 4.9 as models of what a description should be like.

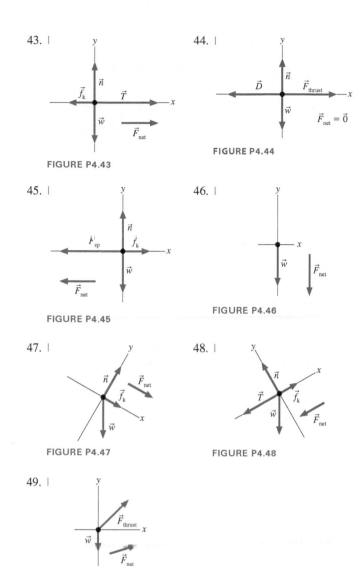

43. |

FIGURE P4.43

44. |

$\vec{F}_{net} = \vec{0}$

FIGURE P4.44

45. |

FIGURE P4.45

46. |

FIGURE P4.46

47. |

FIGURE P4.47

48. |

FIGURE P4.48

49. |

FIGURE P4.49

50. ‖‖‖ A student draws the flawed free-body diagram shown in Figure P4.50 to represent the forces acting on a car traveling at constant speed on a level road. Identify the errors in the diagram, then draw a correct free-body diagram for this situation.

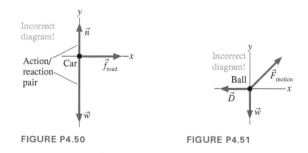

FIGURE P4.50

FIGURE P4.51

51. ‖‖ A student draws the flawed free-body diagram shown in Figure P4.51 to represent the forces acting on a golf ball that is traveling upward and to the right a very short time after being hit off the tee. Air resistance is assumed to be relevant. Identify the errors in the diagram, then draw a correct free-body diagram for this situation.

Problems 52 through 63 describe a situation. For each, draw a motion diagram, a force identification diagram, and a free-body diagram.

52. ‖ An elevator, suspended by a single cable, has just left the tenth floor and is speeding up as it descends toward the ground floor.

53. ‖‖ A rocket is being launched straight up. Air resistance is not negligible.

54. ‖‖ A jet plane is speeding down the runway during takeoff. Air resistance is not negligible.

55. ‖ You've slammed on the brakes and your car is skidding to a stop while going down a 20° hill.

56. ‖ A skier is going down a 20° slope. A *horizontal* headwind is blowing in the skier's face. Friction is small, but not zero.

57. ‖ A bale of hay sits on the bed of a trailer. The trailer is starting to accelerate forward, and the bale is slipping toward the back of the trailer.

58. ‖ A Styrofoam ball has just been shot straight up. Air resistance is not negligible.

59. ‖‖ A spring-loaded gun shoots a plastic ball. The trigger has just been pulled and the ball is starting to move down the barrel. The barrel is horizontal.

60. ‖ A person on a bridge throws a rock straight down toward the water. The rock has just been released.

61. ‖‖ A gymnast has just landed on a trampoline. She's still moving downward as the trampoline stretches.

62. ‖‖ A heavy box is in the back of a truck. The truck is accelerating to the right. Apply your analysis to the box.

63. ‖ A bag of groceries is on the back seat of your car as you stop for a stop light. The bag does not slide. Apply your analysis to the bag.

64. ‖ A rubber ball bounces. We'd like to understand *how* the ball bounces.

   a. A rubber ball has been dropped and is bouncing off the floor. Draw a motion diagram of the ball during the brief time interval that it is in contact with the floor. Show 4 or 5 frames as the ball compresses, then another 4 or 5 frames as it expands. What is the direction of $\vec{a}$ during each of these parts of the motion?

   b. Draw a picture of the ball in contact with the floor and identify all forces acting on the ball.

   c. Draw a free-body diagram of the ball during its contact with the ground. Is there a net force acting on the ball? If so, in which direction?

   d. During contact, is the force of the ground on the ball larger, smaller, or equal to the weight of the ball? Use your answers to parts a–c to explain your reasoning.

65. ‖ If a car stops suddenly, you feel "thrown forward." We'd like to understand what happens to the passengers as a car stops. Imagine yourself sitting on a *very* slippery bench inside a car. This bench has no friction, no seat back, and there's nothing for you to hold on to.

   a. Draw a picture and identify all of the forces acting on you as the car travels in a straight line at a perfectly steady speed on level ground.

   b. Draw your free-body diagram. Is there a net force on you? If so, in which direction?

   c. Repeat parts a and b with the car slowing down.

   d. Describe what happens to you as the car slows down.

   e. Use Newton's laws to explain why you seem to be "thrown forward" as the car stops. Is there really a force pushing you forward?

66. ⫴ The fastest pitched baseball was clocked at 46 m/s. If the
BIO   pitcher exerted his force (assumed to be horizontal and constant)
      over a distance of 1.0 m, and a baseball has a mass of 145 g,
      a. Draw a free-body diagram of the ball during the pitch.
      b. What force did the pitcher exert on the ball during this
         record-setting pitch?
      c. Estimate the force in part b as a fraction of the pitcher's
         weight.
67. ⎸ The froghopper, champion leaper of the insect world, can
BIO   jump straight up at 4.0 m/s. The jump itself lasts a mere 1.0 ms
      before the insect is clear of the ground.
      a. Draw a free-body diagram of this mighty leaper while the
         jump is taking place.
      b. While the jump is taking place, is the force that the ground
         exerts on the froghopper greater than, less than, or equal to
         the insect's weight? Explain.
68. ⫼ A beach ball is thrown straight up, and some time later it
      lands on the sand. Is the magnitude of the net force on the ball
      greatest when it is going up or when it is on the way down? Or
      is it the same in both cases? Explain. Air resistance should not
      be neglected for a large, light object.

Passage Problems

A Simple Solution for a Stuck Car

If your car is stuck in the mud and you don't have a winch to pull it
out, you can use a piece of rope and a tree to do the trick. First, you
tie one end of the rope to your car and the other to a tree, then pull as
hard as you can on the middle of the rope, as shown in Figure
P4.69a. This technique applies a force to the car much larger than the
force that you can apply directly. To see why the car experiences
such a large force, look at the forces acting on the center point of the
rope, as shown in Figure P4.69b. The sum of the forces is zero, thus
the tension is much greater than the force you apply. It is this tension
force that acts on the car and, with luck, pulls it free.

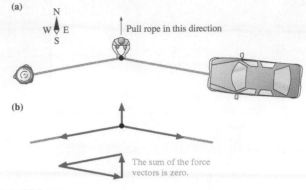

(a)

Pull rope in this direction

(b)

The sum of the force
vectors is zero.

FIGURE P4.69

69. ⎸ The sum of the three forces acting on the center point of the
    rope is assumed to be zero because
    A. This point has a very small mass.
    B. Tension forces in a rope always cancel.
    C. This point is not accelerating.
    D. The angle of deflection is very small.
70. ⎸ When you are pulling on the rope as shown, what is the
    approximate direction of the tension force on the tree?
    A. North   B. South   C. East   D. West
71. ⎸ Assume that you are pulling on the rope but the car is not
    moving. What is the approximate direction of the force of the
    mud on the car?
    A. North   B. South   C. East   D. West
72. ⎸ Suppose your efforts work, and the car begins to move for-
    ward out of the mud. As it does so, the force of the car on the
    rope is
    A. Zero.
    B. Less than the force of the rope on the car.
    C. Equal to the force of the rope on the car.
    D. Greater than the force of the rope on the car.

STOP TO THINK ANSWERS

Stop to Think 4.1: C.

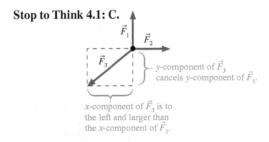

y-component of $\vec{F}_3$
cancels y-component of $\vec{F}_1$.

x-component of $\vec{F}_3$ is to
the left and larger than
the x-component of $\vec{F}_2$.

Stop to Think 4.2: A, B, and D. Friction and the normal force are
the only contact forces. Nothing is touching the rock to provide a
"force of the kick." We've agreed to ignore air resistance unless a
problem specifically calls for it.

Stop to Think 4.3: B. Acceleration is proportional to force, so doubling the number of rubber bands doubles the acceleration of the
original object from 2 m/s² to 4 m/s². But acceleration is also
inversely proportional to mass. Doubling the mass cuts the acceleration in half, back to 2 m/s².

Stop to Think 4.4: D

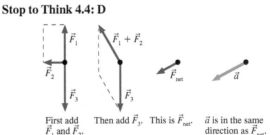

First add   Then add $\vec{F}_3$.   This is $\vec{F}_{net}$. $\vec{a}$ is in the same
$\vec{F}_1$ and $\vec{F}_2$.   direction as $\vec{F}_{net}$.

Stop to Think 4.5: C. The acceleration vector points downward as
the elevator slows. $\vec{F}_{net}$ points in the same direction as $\vec{a}$, so $\vec{F}_{net}$ also
points downward. This will be true if the tension is less than the
weight: $T < w$.

Stop to Think 4.6: C. Newton's third law says that the force of A on
B is *equal* and opposite to the force of B on A. This is always true. The
mass of the objects isn't relevant.

5 Applying Newton's Laws

Why does this sky surfer fall at a constant speed? And why does he suddenly slow down when his parachute opens?

LOOKING AHEAD ▶

The goal of Chapter 5 is to learn how to solve problems about motion along a straight line.

Equilibrium Problems

An object at rest or moving at a constant velocity has zero acceleration. According to Newton's second law, this means that the net force on it must also be zero.

This boulder is in *static equilibrium:* It remains at rest.

A ski lift, moving at a constant velocity, is in *dynamic equilibrium.*

> **Looking Back** ◀◀
> 4.4, 4.7 Identifying forces, free-body diagrams
> 4.6 Newton's second law

Interacting Objects

When two objects interact with each other, each exerts a force on the other. By Newton's third law, these forces are equal in magnitude but oppositely directed.

The barge pushes back on the tug just as hard as the tug pushes on the barge. Newton's third law will help you understand the motion of objects that are in contact with each other.

A common way for two objects to interact is with ropes or strings under tension. You'll learn how to solve problems involving tension and how pulleys act to change the direction of the tension force.

Applying Newton's Second Law

In this chapter, you'll learn how to use Newton's second law in component form to solve a variety of problems in mechanics.

What are the blocks' accelerations?

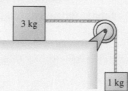

3 kg

1 kg

Friction, tension, gravity, and the pulley all act in this problem. You'll learn explicit strategies to solve problems like this.

> **Looking Back** ◀◀
> 2.5, 2.7 Constant acceleration and free fall
> 3.2–3.3 Vectors and components

Forces and Newton's Second Law

Chapter 4 introduced several important forces. Now you'll need to understand these forces in more detail, so that you can use them in Newton's second law. For example, you'll learn . . .

. . . that **mass and weight are not the same thing.** However, you'll find that there is a simple relationship between the two.

. . . a simple model for friction that provides a reasonably accurate description of how static and kinetic friction behave.

Static friction adjusts its magnitude as needed to keep the sofa from slipping.

Kinetic (sliding) friction does not depend on an object's speed.

This astronaut on the moon weighs only 1/6 of what he does on earth. His *mass*, however, is the same on both the moon and the earth.

This human tower is in equilibrium because the net force on each man is zero.

5.1 Equilibrium

Chapter 4 introduced Newton's three laws of motion. Now, in Chapter 5, we want to use these laws to solve force and motion problems. This chapter focuses on objects that are at rest or that move in a straight line, such as runners, bicycles, cars, planes, and rockets. Circular motion and rotational motion will be treated in Chapters 6 and 7.

The simplest applications of Newton's second law, $\vec{F}_{net} = m\vec{a}$, are those for which the acceleration $\vec{a}$ is *zero*. In such cases, the net force acting on the object must be zero as well. One way an object can have $\vec{a} = \vec{0}$ is to be at rest. An object that remains at rest is said to be in **static equilibrium**. A second way for an object to have $\vec{a} = \vec{0}$ is to move in a straight line at a constant speed. Such an object is in **dynamic equilibrium**. The key property of both these cases of **equilibrium** is that the net force acting on the object is $\vec{F}_{net} = \vec{0}$.

To use Newton's laws, we have to identify all the forces acting on an object and then evaluate $\vec{F}_{net}$. Recall that $\vec{F}_{net}$ is the vector sum

$$\vec{F}_{net} = \vec{F}_1 + \vec{F}_2 + \vec{F}_3 + \cdots$$

where $\vec{F}_1$, $\vec{F}_2$, and so on are the individual forces, such as tension or friction, acting on the object. We found in Chapter 3 that vector sums can be evaluated in terms of the x- and y-components of the vectors; that is, the x-component of the net force is $(F_{net})_x = F_{1x} + F_{2x} + F_{3x} + \cdots$. If we restrict ourselves to problems where all the forces are in the xy-plane, then the equilibrium requirement $\vec{F}_{net} = \vec{a} = \vec{0}$ is a shorthand way of writing two simultaneous equations:

$$(F_{net})_x = F_{1x} + F_{2x} + F_{3x} + \cdots = 0$$
$$(F_{net})_y = F_{1y} + F_{2y} + F_{3y} + \cdots = 0$$

Recall from your math classes that the Greek letter Σ (sigma) stands for "the sum of." It will be convenient to abbreviate the sum of the x-components of all forces as

$$F_{1x} + F_{2x} + F_{3x} + \cdots = \sum F_x$$

With this notation, Newton's second law for an object in equilibrium, with $\vec{a} = \vec{0}$, can be written as the two equations

$$\sum F_x = ma_x = 0 \quad \text{and} \quad \sum F_y = ma_y = 0 \qquad (5.1)$$

In equilibrium, the sums of the x- and y-components of the force are zero

Although this may look a bit forbidding, we'll soon see how to use a free-body diagram of the forces to help evaluate these sums.

When an object is in equilibrium, we are usually interested in finding the forces that keep it in equilibrium. Newton's second law is the basis for a strategy for solving equilibrium problems.

PROBLEM-SOLVING STRATEGY 5.1   Equilibrium problems   (MP)™

PREPARE First check that the object is in equilibrium: Does $\vec{a} = \vec{0}$?

■ An object at rest is in static equilibrium.
■ An object moving at a constant velocity is in dynamic equilibrium.

Then identify all forces acting on the object and show them on a free-body diagram. Determine which forces you know and which you need to solve for.

Continued

SOLVE An object in equilibrium must satisfy Newton's second law for the case where $\vec{a} = \vec{0}$. In component form, the requirement is

$$\sum F_x = ma_x = 0 \quad \text{and} \quad \sum F_y = ma_y = 0$$

You can find the force components that go into these sums directly from your free-body diagram. From these two equations, solve for the unknown forces in the problem.

ASSESS Check that your result has the correct units, is reasonable, and answers the question.

Static Equilibrium

EXAMPLE 5.1   Forces supporting an orangutan

An orangutan weighing 500 N hangs from a vertical vine. What is the tension in the vine?

PREPARE The orangutan is at rest, so it is in static equilibrium. The net force on it must then be zero. FIGURE 5.1 first identifies the forces acting on the orangutan: the upward force of the tension in the vine and the downward, long-range force of gravity. These forces are then shown on a free-body diagram, where it's noted that equilibrium requires $\vec{F}_{net} = \vec{0}$.

FIGURE 5.1 The forces on an orangutan.

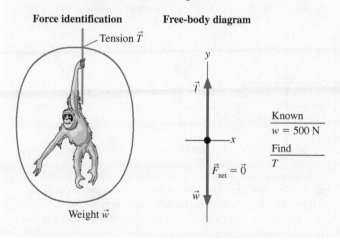

Force identification   **Free-body diagram**

Tension $\vec{T}$

Weight $\vec{w}$

$\vec{F}_{net} = \vec{0}$

Known
w = 500 N

Find
T

SOLVE Neither force has an x-component, so we need to examine only the y-components of the forces. In this case, the y-component of Newton's second law is

$$\sum F_y = T_y + w_y = ma_y = 0$$

You might have been tempted to write $T_y - w_y$ because the weight force points down. But remember that T_y and w_y are *components* of vectors, and can thus be positive (for a vector such as $\vec{T}$ that points up) or negative (for a vector such as $\vec{w}$ that points down). The fact that $\vec{w}$ points down is taken into account when we *evaluate* the components—that is, when we write them in terms of the *magnitudes* T and w of the vectors $\vec{T}$ and $\vec{w}$.

Because the tension vector $\vec{T}$ points straight up, in the positive y-direction, its y-component is $T_y = T$. Because the weight vector $\vec{w}$ points straight down, in the negative y-direction, its y-component is $w_y = -w$. This is where the signs enter. With these components, Newton's second law becomes

$$T - w = 0$$

This equation is easily solved for the tension in the vine:

$$T = w = 500 \text{ N}$$

ASSESS It's not surprising that the tension in the vine equals the weight of the orangutan. However, we'll soon see that this is *not* the case if the object is accelerating.

EXAMPLE 5.2   Readying a wrecking ball

A wrecking ball weighing 2500 N hangs from a cable. Prior to swinging, it is pulled back to a 20° angle by a second, horizontal cable. What is the tension in the horizontal cable?

PREPARE Because the ball is not moving, it hangs in static equilibrium, with $\vec{a} = \vec{0}$, until it is released. In FIGURE 5.2, we start by identifying all the forces acting on the ball: a tension force from each cable and the ball's weight. We've used different symbols $\vec{T}_1$ and $\vec{T}_2$ for the two different tension forces. We then construct a free-body diagram for these three forces, noting that $\vec{F}_{net} = m\vec{a} = \vec{0}$. We're looking for the magnitude T_1 of the tension force $\vec{T}_1$ in the horizontal cable.

FIGURE 5.2 Visual overview of a wrecking ball just before release.

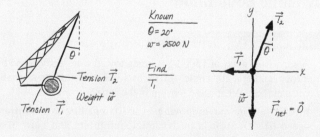

Tension $\vec{T}_2$

Weight $\vec{w}$

Tension $\vec{T}_1$

Known
$\theta = 20°$
$w = 2500$ N

Find
T_1

$\vec{F}_{net} = \vec{0}$

Continued

SOLVE The requirement of equilibrium is $\vec{F}_{net} = m\vec{a} = \vec{0}$. In component form, we have the two equations:

$$\sum F_x = T_{1x} + T_{2x} + w_x = ma_x = 0$$

$$\sum F_y = T_{1y} + T_{2y} + w_y = ma_y = 0$$

As always, we *add* the force components together. Now we're ready to write the components of each force vector in terms of the magnitudes and directions of those vectors. We learned how to do this in Section 3.3 of Chapter 3. With practice you'll learn to read the components directly off the free-body diagram, but to begin it's worthwhile to organize the components into a table.

Force	Name of x-component	Value of x component	Name of y-component	Value of y-component
$\vec{T}_1$	T_{1x}	$-T_1$	T_{1y}	0
$\vec{T}_2$	T_{2x}	$T_2\sin\theta$	T_{2y}	$T_2\cos\theta$
$\vec{w}$	w_x	0	w_y	$-w$

We see from the free-body diagram that $\vec{T}_1$ points along the negative x-axis, so $T_{1x} = -T_1$ and $T_{1y} = 0$. We need to be careful with our trigonometry as we find the components of $\vec{T}_2$. Remembering that the side adjacent to the angle is related to the cosine,

we see that the vertical (y) component of $\vec{T}_2$ is $T_2\cos\theta$. Similarly, the horizontal (x) component is $T_2\sin\theta$. The weight vector points straight down, so its y-component is $-w$. Notice that negative signs enter as we evaluate the components of the vectors, *not* when we write Newton's second law. This is a critical aspect of solving force and motion problems. With these components, Newton's second law now becomes

$$-T_1 + T_2\sin\theta + 0 = 0 \quad \text{and} \quad 0 + T_2\cos\theta - w = 0$$

We can rewrite these equations as

$$T_2\sin\theta = T_1 \quad \text{and} \quad T_2\cos\theta = w$$

These are two simultaneous equations with two unknowns: T_1 and T_2. To eliminate T_2 from the two equations, we solve the second equation for T_2, giving $T_2 = w/\cos\theta$. Then we insert this expression for T_2 into the first equation to get

$$T_1 = \frac{w}{\cos\theta}\sin\theta = \frac{\sin\theta}{\cos\theta}w = w\tan\theta = (2500\ \text{N})\tan 20° = 910\ \text{N}$$

where we made use of the fact that $\tan\theta = \sin\theta/\cos\theta$.

ASSESS It seems reasonable that to pull the ball back to this modest angle, a force substantially less than the ball's weight will be required.

CONCEPTUAL EXAMPLE 5.3   **Forces in static equilibrium**

A rod is free to slide on a frictionless sheet of ice. One end of the rod is lifted by a string. If the rod is at rest, which diagram in FIGURE 5.3 shows the correct angle of the string?

FIGURE 5.3 Which is the correct angle of the string?

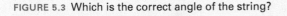
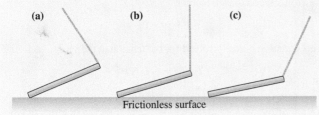

(a)   (b)   (c)

Frictionless surface

REASON If the rod is to hang motionless, it must be in static equilibrium with $\sum F_x = ma_x = 0$ and $\sum F_y = ma_y = 0$. FIGURE 5.4 shows free-body diagrams for the three string orientations. Remember that tension always acts along the direction of the string and that the weight force always points straight down. The

FIGURE 5.4 Free-body diagrams for three angles of the string.

ice pushes up with a normal force perpendicular to the surface, but frictionless ice cannot exert any horizontal force. If the string is angled, we see that its horizontal component exerts a net force on the rod. Only in case b, where the tension and the string are vertical, can the net force be zero.

ASSESS If friction were present, the rod could in fact hang as in cases a or c. But without friction, the rods in these cases would slide until they came to rest as in case b.

Dynamic Equilibrium

EXAMPLE 5.4   **Tension in towing a car**

A car with a mass of 1500 kg is being towed at a steady speed by a rope held at a 20° angle. A friction force of 320 N opposes the car's motion. What is the tension in the rope?

PREPARE The car is moving in a straight line at a constant speed ($\vec{a} = \vec{0}$) so it is in dynamic equilibrium and must have

$\vec{F}_{net} = m\vec{a} = \vec{0}$. FIGURE 5.5 shows three contact forces acting on the car—the tension force $\vec{T}$, friction $\vec{f}$, and the normal force $\vec{n}$—and the long-range force of gravity $\vec{w}$. These four forces are shown on the free-body diagram.

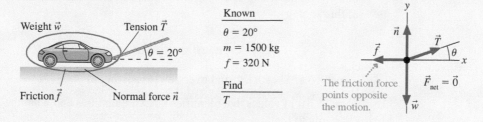

FIGURE 5.5 Visual overview of a car being towed.

SOLVE This is still an equilibrium problem, even though the car is moving, so our problem solving procedure is unchanged. With four forces, the requirement of equilibrium is

$$\sum F_x = n_x + T_x + f_x + w_x = ma_x = 0$$

$$\sum F_y = n_y + T_y + f_y + w_y = ma_y = 0$$

We can again determine the horizontal and vertical components of the forces by "reading" the free-body diagram. The results are shown in the table.

Force	Name of x-component	Value of x-component	Name of y-component	Value of y-component
$\vec{n}$	n_x	0	n_y	n
$\vec{T}$	T_x	$T\cos\theta$	T_y	$T\sin\theta$
$\vec{f}$	f_x	$-f$	f_y	0
$\vec{w}$	w_x	0	w_y	$-w$

With these components, Newton's second law becomes

$$T\cos\theta - f = 0$$

$$n + T\sin\theta - w = 0$$

The first equation can be used to solve for the tension in the rope:

$$T = \frac{f}{\cos\theta} = \frac{320\,\text{N}}{\cos 20°} = 340\,\text{N}$$

to two significant figures. It turned out that we did not need the y-component equation in this problem. We would need it if we wanted to find the normal force $\vec{n}$.

ASSESS Had we pulled the car with a horizontal rope, the tension would need to exactly balance the friction force of 320 N. Because we are pulling at an angle, however, part of the tension in the rope pulls *up* on the car instead of in the forward direction. Thus we need a little more tension in the rope when it's at an angle.

5.2 Dynamics and Newton's Second Law

Newton's second law is the essential link between force and motion. The essence of Newtonian mechanics can be expressed in two steps:

- The forces acting on an object determine its acceleration $\vec{a} = \vec{F}_{net}/m$.
- The object's motion can be found by using $\vec{a}$ in the equations of kinematics.

We want to develop a strategy to solve a variety of problems in mechanics, but first we need to write the second law in terms of its components. To do so, let's first rewrite Newton's second law in the form

$$\vec{F}_{net} = \vec{F}_1 + \vec{F}_2 + \vec{F}_3 + \cdots = m\vec{a}$$

where $\vec{F}_1, \vec{F}_2, \vec{F}_3$, and so on are the forces acting on an object. To write the second law in component form merely requires that we use the x- and y-components of the acceleration. Thus Newton's second law, $\vec{F}_{net} = m\vec{a}$, is

$$\sum F_x = ma_x \quad \text{and} \quad \sum F_y = ma_y \qquad (5.2)$$

Newton's second law in component form

The first equation says that **the component of the acceleration in the x-direction is determined by the sum of the x-components of the forces acting on the object.** A similar statement applies to the y-direction.

There are two basic types of problems in mechanics. In the first, you use information about forces to find an object's acceleration, then use kinematics to determine the object's motion. In the second, you use information about the object's motion to determine its acceleration, then solve for unknown forces. Either way, the two equations of Equation 5.2 are the link between force and motion, and they form the basis of a problem-solving strategy. The primary goal of this chapter is to illustrate the use of this strategy.

PROBLEM-SOLVING
STRATEGY 5.2   **Dynamics problems**

PREPARE   Sketch a visual overview consisting of:

- A list of values that identifies known quantities and what the problem is trying to find.
- A force identification diagram to help you identify all the forces acting on the object.
- A free-body diagram that shows all the forces acting on the object.

If you'll need to use kinematics to find velocities or positions, you'll also need to sketch:

- A motion diagram to determine the direction of the acceleration.
- A pictorial representation that establishes a coordinate system, shows important points in the motion, and defines symbols.

It's OK to go back and forth between these steps as you visualize the situation.

SOLVE   Write Newton's second law in component form as

$$\sum F_x = ma_x \quad \text{and} \quad \sum F_y = ma_y$$

You can find the components of the forces directly from your free-body diagram. Depending on the problem, either:

- Solve for the acceleration, then use kinematics to find velocities and positions.
- Use kinematics to determine the acceleration, then solve for unknown forces.

ASSESS   Check that your result has the correct units, is reasonable, and answers the question.

Exercise 24 🖉

EXAMPLE 5.5   Putting a golf ball

A golfer putts a 46 g ball with a speed of 3.0 m/s. Friction exerts a 0.020 N retarding force on the ball, slowing it down. Will her putt reach the hole, 10 m away?

PREPARE   FIGURE 5.6 is a visual overview of the problem. We've collected the known information, drawn a sketch, and identified what we want to find. The motion diagram shows that the ball is slowing down as it rolls to the right, so the acceleration vector points to the left. Next, we identify the forces acting on the ball and show them on a free-body diagram. Note that the net force points to the left, as it must because the acceleration points to the left.

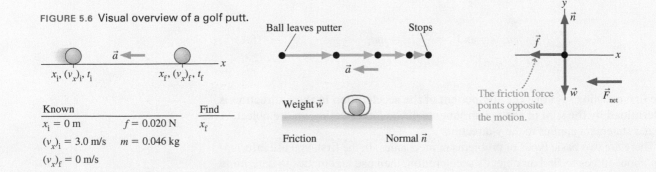

FIGURE 5.6 Visual overview of a golf putt.

Known		Find
$x_i = 0$ m	$f = 0.020$ N	x_f
$(v_x)_i = 3.0$ m/s	$m = 0.046$ kg	
$(v_x)_f = 0$ m/s		

SOLVE Newton's second law in component form is

$$\sum F_x = n_x + f_x + w_x = 0 - f + 0 = ma_x$$

$$\sum F_y = n_y + f_y + w_y = n + 0 - w = ma_y = 0$$

We've written the equations as sums, as we did with equilibrium problems, then "read" the values of the force components from the free-body diagram. The components are simple enough in this problem that we don't really need to show them in a table. It is particularly important to notice that we set $a_y = 0$ in the second equation. This is because the ball does not move in the y-direction, so it can't have any acceleration in the y-direction. This will be an important step in many problems.

The first equation is $f = ma_x$, from which we find

$$a_x = -\frac{f}{m} = \frac{-(0.020 \text{ N})}{0.046 \text{ kg}} = -0.43 \text{ m/s}^2$$

The negative sign shows that the acceleration is directed to the left, as expected.

Now that we know the acceleration, we can use kinematics to find how far the ball will roll before stopping. We don't have any information about the time it takes for the ball to stop, so we'll use the kinematic equation $(v_x)_f^2 = (v_x)_i^2 + 2a_x(x_f - x_i)$. This gives

$$x_f = x_i + \frac{(v_x)_f^2 - (v_x)_i^2}{2a_x} = 0 \text{ m} + \frac{(0 \text{ m/s})^2 - (3.0 \text{ m/s})^2}{2(-0.43 \text{ m/s}^2)} = 10.5 \text{ m}$$

If her aim is true, the ball will just make it into the hole.

ASSESS It seems reasonable that a ball putted on grass with an initial speed of 3 m/s—about jogging speed—would travel roughly 10 m.

EXAMPLE 5.6 **Finding a rocket cruiser's acceleration**

A rocket cruiser with a mass of 2200 kg and weighing 5000 N is flying horizontally over the surface of a distant planet. At its present speed, a 3000 N drag force acts on the cruiser. The cruiser's engines can be tilted so as to provide a thrust angled up or down. The pilot turns the thrust up to 14,000 N while pivoting the engines to continue flying horizontally. What is the cruiser's acceleration?

PREPARE FIGURE 5.7 is a visual overview in which we've listed the known information, identified the forces on the cruiser, and drawn a free-body diagram. (Because kinematics is not needed to find the acceleration, we don't need a pictorial diagram.) As discussed in Chapter 4, the thrust force points *opposite* the direction of the rocket exhaust, which we've shown at angle θ. The thrust must have an upward vertical component to balance the weight force; otherwise, the cruiser would fall. To continue flying horizontally requires the net force to be directed forward.

SOLVE Newton's second law in component form is

$$\sum F_x = (F_{\text{thrust}})_x + D_x + w_x = ma_x$$

$$\sum F_y = (F_{\text{thrust}})_y + D_y + w_y = ma_y$$

From the free-body diagram, we see that $(F_{\text{thrust}})_x = F_{\text{thrust}}\cos\theta$, $(F_{\text{thrust}})_y = F_{\text{thrust}}\sin\theta$, $D_x = -D$, $D_y = 0$, $w_x = 0$, and $w_y = -w$. We know that a_y must be zero because the cruiser is to accelerate *horizontally*. Thus the second law becomes

$$F_{\text{thrust}}\cos\theta - D = ma_x$$

$$F_{\text{thrust}}\sin\theta - w = 0$$

The first of these equations contains a_x, the quantity we want to find, but we can't solve for a_x without knowing what θ is. Fortunately, we can use the second equation to find θ, then use this value of θ in the first equation to find a_x.

The second equation gives

$$\sin\theta = \frac{w}{F_{\text{thrust}}} = \frac{5000 \text{ N}}{14,000 \text{ N}} = 0.357$$

$$\theta = \sin^{-1}(0.357) = 20.9°$$

Now we can use this value in the first equation to get

$$a_x = \frac{1}{m}(F_{\text{thrust}}\cos\theta - D)$$

$$= \frac{1}{2200 \text{ kg}}[(14,000 \text{ N})\cos(20.9°) - 3000 \text{ N}] = 4.6 \text{ m/s}^2$$

ASSESS An important key to solving this problem was to use the information that the cruiser accelerates only in the horizontal direction. Mathematically, this means that $a_y = 0$. Because the thrust is much greater than the weight, we need only a modest downward component of the thrust to cancel the weight and let the cruiser accelerate horizontally. So our engine tilt seems reasonable.

FIGURE 5.7 Visual overview of a rocket cruiser.

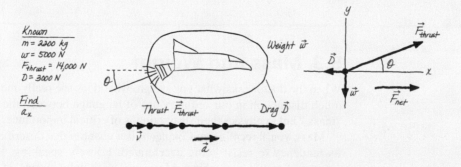

EXAMPLE 5.7   **Towing a car with acceleration**

A car with a mass of 1500 kg is being towed by a rope held at a 20° angle. A friction force of 320 N opposes the car's motion. What is the tension in the rope if the car goes from rest to 12 m/s in 10 s?

PREPARE You should recognize that this problem is almost identical to Example 5.4. The difference is that the car is now accelerating, so it is no longer in equilibrium. This means, as shown in FIGURE 5.8, that the net force is not zero. We've already identified all the forces in Example 5.4.

SOLVE Newton's second law in component form is

$$\sum F_x = n_x + T_x + f_x + w_x = ma_x$$

$$\sum F_y = n_y + T_y + f_y + w_y = ma_y = 0$$

We've again used the fact that $a_y = 0$ for motion that is purely along the x-axis. The components of the forces were worked out

in Example 5.4. With that information, Newton's second law in component form is

$$T\cos\theta - f = ma_x$$

$$n + T\sin\theta - w = 0$$

Because the car speeds up from rest to 12 m/s in 10 s, we can use kinematics to find the acceleration:

$$a_x = \frac{\Delta v_x}{\Delta t} = \frac{(v_x)_f - (v_x)_i}{t_f - t_i} = \frac{(12 \text{ m/s}) - (0 \text{ m/s})}{(10 \text{ s}) - (0 \text{ s})} = 1.2 \text{ m/s}^2$$

We can now use the first Newton's-law equation above to solve for the tension. We have

$$T = \frac{ma_x + f}{\cos\theta} = \frac{(1500 \text{ kg})(1.2 \text{ m/s}^2) + 320 \text{ N}}{\cos 20°} = 2300 \text{ N}$$

ASSESS The tension is substantially more than the 340 N found in Example 5.4. It takes a much more force to accelerate the car than to keep it rolling at a constant speed.

FIGURE 5.8 Visual overview of a car being towed.

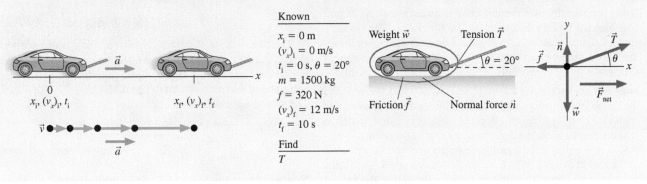

Known
$x_i = 0$ m
$(v_x)_i = 0$ m/s
$t_i = 0$ s, $\theta = 20°$
$m = 1500$ kg
$f = 320$ N
$(v_x)_f = 12$ m/s
$t_f = 10$ s

Find
T

These first examples have shown all the details of our problem-solving strategy. Our purpose has been to demonstrate how the strategy is put into practice. Future examples will be briefer, but the basic *procedure* will remain the same.

STOP TO THINK 5.1   A Martian lander is approaching the surface. It is slowing its descent by firing its rocket motor. Which is the correct free-body diagram for the lander?

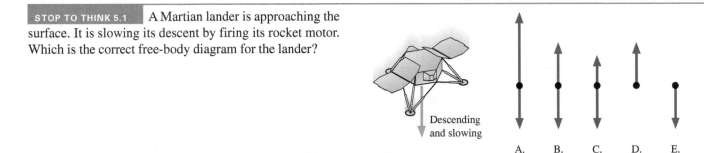

5.3 Mass and Weight

When the doctor asks what you weigh, what does she really mean? We do not make much distinction in our ordinary use of language between the terms "weight" and "mass," but in physics their distinction is of critical importance.

Mass, you'll recall from Chapter 4, is a quantity that describes an object's inertia, its tendency to resist being accelerated. Loosely speaking, it also describes the amount of matter in an object. Mass, measured in kilograms, is an intrinsic property of an object; it has the same value wherever the object may be and whatever forces might be acting on it.

Weight, on the other hand, is a *force*. Specifically, it is the gravitational force exerted on an object by a planet. Weight is a vector, not a scalar, and the vector's direction is always straight down. Weight is measured in newtons.

Mass and weight are not the same thing, but they are related. We can use Galileo's discovery about free fall to make the connection. FIGURE 5.9 shows the free-body diagram of an object in free fall. The *only* force acting on this object is its weight $\vec{w}$ the downward pull of gravity. Newton's second law for this object is

$$\vec{F}_{net} = \vec{w} = m\vec{a} \tag{5.3}$$

Recall Galileo's discovery that *any* object in free fall, regardless of its mass, has the same acceleration:

$$\vec{a}_{freefall} = (g, \text{downward}) \tag{5.4}$$

where $g = 9.80 \text{ m/s}^2$ is the free-fall acceleration at the earth's surface. So a_y in Equation 5.3 is equal to $-g$, and we have $-w = -mg$, or

$$w = mg \tag{5.5}$$

The magnitude of the weight force, which we call simply "the weight," is directly proportional to the mass, with g as the constant of proportionality. Thus, for example, the weight of a 3.6 kg book is $w = (3.6 \text{ kg})(9.8 \text{ m/s}^2) = 35 \text{ N}$.

NOTE ▶ Although we derived the relationship between mass and weight for an object in free fall, the weight of an object is *independent* of its state of motion. Equation 5.5 holds for an object at rest on a table, sliding horizontally, or moving in any other way. ◀

Because an object's weight depends on g, and the value of g varies from planet to planet, weight is not a fixed, constant property of an object. The value of g at the surface of the moon is about one-sixth its earthly value, so an object on the moon would have only one-sixth its weight on earth. The object's weight on Jupiter would be greater than its weight on earth. Its mass, however, would be the same. The amount of matter has not changed, only the gravitational force exerted on that matter.

So, when the doctor asks what you weigh, she really wants to know your *mass*. That's the amount of matter in your body. You can't really "lose weight" by going to the moon, even though you would weigh less there!

Measuring Mass and Weight

A *pan balance,* shown in FIGURE 5.10, is a device for measuring *mass.* You may have used a pan balance to "weigh" chemicals in a chemistry lab. An unknown mass is placed in one pan, then known masses are added to the other until the pans balance. Gravity pulls down on both sides, effectively *comparing* the masses, and the unknown mass equals the sum of the known masses that balance it. Although a pan balance requires gravity in order to function, it does not depend on the value of g. Consequently, the pan balance would give the same result on another planet.

A *spring scale* measures weight, not mass. A spring scale can be understood on the basis of Newton's second law. The object being weighed compresses the springs, as shown in FIGURE 5.11 on the following page, which then push up with force $\vec{F}_{sp}$. But because the object is at rest, in static equilibrium, the net force on it must be zero. Thus the upward spring force must exactly balance the downward weight force:

$$F_{sp} = w = mg \tag{5.6}$$

The *reading* of a spring scale is F_{sp}, the magnitude of the force that the spring is exerting. If the object is in equilibrium, then F_{sp} is exactly equal to the object's weight w. The scale does not "know" the weight of the object. All it can do is measure how much its spring is stretched or compressed. On a different planet, with a

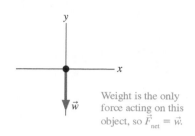

FIGURE 5.9 The free-body diagram of an object in free fall.

Weight is the only force acting on this object, so $\vec{F}_{net} = \vec{w}$.

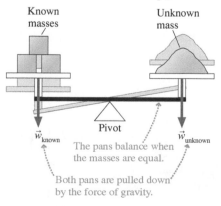

On the moon, astronaut John Young jumps 2 feet straight up, despite his spacesuit that weighs 370 pounds on earth. On the moon, where $g = 1.6 \text{ m/s}^2$, he and his suit together weighed only 90 pounds.

FIGURE 5.10 A pan balance measures mass.

If the unknown mass differs from the known masses, the beam will rotate about the pivot.

Known masses Unknown mass

$\vec{w}_{known}$ Pivot $\vec{w}_{unknown}$

The pans balance when the masses are equal.

Both pans are pulled down by the force of gravity.

FIGURE 5.11 A spring scale measures weight.

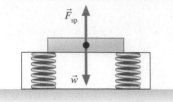

different value for g, the expansion or compression of the spring would be different and the scale's reading would be different.

The unit of force in the English system is the *pound*. We noted in Chapter 4 that the pound is defined as 1 lb = 4.45 N. An object whose weight $w = mg$ is 4.45 N has a mass

$$m = \frac{w}{g} = \frac{4.45 \text{ N}}{9.80 \text{ m/s}^2} = 0.454 \text{ kg} = 454 \text{ g}$$

You may have learned in previous science classes that "1 pound = 454 grams" or, equivalently, "1 kg = 2.2 lb." Strictly speaking, these well-known "conversion factors" are not true. They are comparing a weight (pounds) to a mass (kilograms). The correct statement is: "A mass of 1 kg has a weight on *earth* of 2.2 pounds." On another planet, the weight of a 1 kg mass would be something other than 2.2 pounds.

This popular amusement park ride shoots you straight up with an acceleration of $4g$. As a result, you feel five times as heavy as usual.

EXAMPLE 5.8 **Masses of people**

What is the mass, in kilograms, of a 90 pound gymnast, a 160 pound professor, and a 240 pound football player?

SOLVE We must convert their weights into newtons; then we can find their masses from $m = w/g$:

$$w_{\text{gymnast}} = 90 \text{ lb} \times \frac{4.45 \text{ N}}{1 \text{ lb}} = 400 \text{ N} \qquad m_{\text{gymnast}} = \frac{w_{\text{gymnast}}}{g} = \frac{400 \text{ N}}{9.80 \text{ m/s}^2} = 41 \text{ kg}$$

$$w_{\text{prof}} = 160 \text{ lb} \times \frac{4.45 \text{ N}}{1 \text{ lb}} = 710 \text{ N} \qquad m_{\text{prof}} = \frac{w_{\text{prof}}}{g} = \frac{710 \text{ N}}{9.80 \text{ m/s}^2} = 72 \text{ kg}$$

$$w_{\text{football}} = 240 \text{ lb} \times \frac{4.45 \text{ N}}{1 \text{ lb}} = 1070 \text{ N} \qquad m_{\text{football}} = \frac{w_{\text{football}}}{g} = \frac{1070 \text{ N}}{9.80 \text{ m/s}^2} = 110 \text{ kg}$$

ASSESS It's worth remembering that a *typical* adult has a mass in the range of 60 to 80 kg.

Apparent Weight

The weight of an object is the force of gravity on that object. You may never have thought about it, but gravity is not a force that you can feel or sense directly. Your *sensation* of weight—how heavy you *feel*—is due to *contact forces* pressing against you. Surfaces touch you and activate nerve endings in your skin. As you read this, your sensation of weight is due to the normal force exerted on you by the chair in which you are sitting. When you stand, you feel the contact force of the floor pushing against your feet.

When you stand on a scale, the contact force is the upward spring force F_{sp} acting on your feet. If you and the scale are in equilibrium, with $\vec{a} = \vec{0}$, this spring force and thus the scale reading are equal to your weight.

What would happen, however, if you stood on a scale while *accelerating* upward in an elevator? What would the scale read then? Recall the sensations you feel while being accelerated. You feel "heavy" when an elevator suddenly accelerates upward, and you feel lighter than normal as the upward-moving elevator brakes to a halt. Your true weight $w = mg$ has not changed during these events, but your *sensation* of your weight has.

To investigate this, imagine a man weighing himself by standing on a spring scale in an elevator as it accelerates upward. What does the scale read? As FIGURE 5.12 shows, the only forces acting on the man are the upward spring force of the scale and the downward weight force. Because the man now has an acceleration $\vec{a}$, according to Newton's second law there must be a net force acting on the man in the direction of $\vec{a}$.

FIGURE 5.12 A man weighing himself in an accelerating elevator.

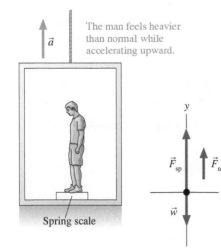

The man feels heavier than normal while accelerating upward.

Looking at the free-body diagram in Figure 5.12, we see that the y-component of Newton's second law is

$$\sum F_y = (F_{sp})_y + w_y = F_{sp} - w = ma_y \qquad (5.7)$$

where m is the man's mass. Solving Equation 5.7 for F_{sp} gives

$$F_{sp} = w + ma_y \qquad (5.8)$$

If the elevator is either at rest or moving with constant velocity, then $a_y = 0$ and the man is in equilibrium. In that case, $F_{sp} = w$ and the scale correctly reads his weight. But if $a_y \neq 0$, the scale's reading is *not* the man's true weight. If the elevator is accelerating upward, then $a_y = +a$, and Equation 5.8 reads $F_{sp} = w + a$. Thus $F_{sp} > w$ and the man *feels* heavier than normal. If the elevator is accelerating downward, the acceleration vector $\vec{a}$ points downward and $a_y = -a$. Thus $F_{sp} < w$ and the man feels lighter.

Let's define a person's **apparent weight** w_{app} as the magnitude of the contact force that supports him; in this case, this is the spring force F_{sp}. From Equation 5.8, the apparent weight is

$$\boxed{w_{app} = w + ma_y = mg + ma_y = m(g + a_y)} \qquad (5.9)$$

Thus, when the man accelerates upward, his apparent weight is greater than his true weight; when accelerating downward, his apparent weight is less than his true weight.

An object doesn't have to be on a scale for its apparent weight to differ from its true weight. An object's apparent weight is the magnitude of the contact force supporting it. It makes no difference whether this is the spring force of the scale or simply the normal force of the floor.

The idea of apparent weight has important applications. Astronauts are nearly crushed by their apparent weight during a rocket launch when a is much greater than g. Much of the thrill of amusement park rides, such as roller coasters, comes from rapid changes in your apparent weight.

Physics students can't jump The next time you ride up in an elevator, try jumping in the air just as the elevator starts to rise. You'll feel like you can hardly get off the ground. This is because with $a_y > 0$ your apparent weight is *greater* than your actual weight; for an elevator with a large acceleration it's like trying to jump while carrying an extra 20 pounds. What will happen if you jump as the elevator slows at the top?

EXAMPLE 5.9 Apparent weight in an elevator

Anjay's mass is 70 kg. He's standing on a scale in an elevator. As the elevator stops, the scale reads 750 N. Had the elevator been moving up or down? If the elevator had been moving at 5.0 m/s, how long does it take to stop?

PREPARE The scale reading as he stops is his apparent weight, so $w_{app} = 750$ N. Because we know his mass m, we can use Equation 5.9 to find the elevator's acceleration a_y. Then we can use kinematics to find the time it takes to stop the elevator.

SOLVE From Equation 5.9 we have $w_{app} = m(g + a_y)$, so that

$$a_y = \frac{w_{app}}{m} - g = \frac{750 \text{ N}}{70 \text{ kg}} - 9.80 \text{ m/s}^2 = 0.91 \text{ m/s}^2$$

This is a *positive* acceleration. If the elevator is stopping with a positive acceleration, it must have been moving *down*, with a negative velocity.

To find the stopping time, we can use the kinematic equation

$$(v_y)_f = (v_y)_i + a_y \Delta t$$

to get

$$\Delta t = \frac{(v_y)_f - (v_y)_i}{a_y} = \frac{(0 \text{ m/s}) - (-5.0 \text{ m/s})}{0.91 \text{ m/s}^2} = 5.5 \text{ s}$$

Notice that we used -5.0 m/s as the initial velocity because the elevator was moving down before it stopped.

ASSESS Anjay's true weight is $mg = (70 \text{ kg})(9.8 \text{ m/s}^2) = 670$ N. Thus his apparent weight is *greater* than his true weight. You have no doubt experienced this sensation in an elevator that is stopping as it reaches the ground floor. If it had stopped while going up, you'd feel *lighter* than your true weight.

Weightlessness

One last issue before leaving this topic: Suppose the elevator cable breaks and the elevator, along with the man and his scale, plunges straight down in free fall! What will the scale read? The acceleration in free fall is $a_y = -g$. When this acceleration is used in Equation 5.9, we find that $w_{app} = 0$! In other words, the man has *no sensation* of weight.

A weightless experience You probably wouldn't want to experience weightlessness in a falling elevator. But, as we learned in Chapter 3, objects undergoing projectile motion are in free fall as well. The special plane shown flies in the same parabolic trajectory as would a projectile with no air resistance. Objects inside, such as these passengers, are then moving along a perfect free-fall trajectory. Just as for the man in the elevator, they then float with respect to the plane's interior. Such flights can last up to 30 seconds.

Think about this carefully. Suppose, as the elevator falls, the man inside releases a ball from his hand. In the absence of air resistance, as Galileo discovered, both the man and the ball would fall at the same rate. From the man's perspective, the ball would appear to "float" beside him. Similarly, the scale would float beneath him and not press against his feet. He is what we call *weightless*.

Surprisingly, "weightless" does *not* mean "no weight." An object that is **weightless** has no *apparent* weight. The distinction is significant. The man's weight is still *mg* because gravity is still pulling down on him, but he has no *sensation* of weight as he free falls. The term "weightless" is a very poor one, likely to cause confusion because it implies that objects have no weight. As we see, that is not the case.

But isn't this exactly what happens to astronauts orbiting the earth? You've seen films of astronauts and various objects floating inside the Space Shuttle. If an astronaut tries to stand on a scale, it does not exert any force against her feet and reads zero. She is said to be weightless. But if the criterion to be weightless is to be in free fall, and if astronauts orbiting the earth are weightless, does this mean that they are in free fall? This is a very interesting question to which we shall return in Chapter 6.

STOP TO THINK 5.2 You're bouncing up and down on a trampoline. At the very highest point of your motion, your apparent weight is

A. More than your true weight.   B. Less than your true weight.
C. Equal to your true weight.   D. Zero.

5.4 Normal Forces

In Chapter 4 we saw that an object at rest on a table is subject to an upward force due to the table. This force is called the *normal force* because it is always directed normal, or perpendicular, to the surface of contact. As we saw, the normal force has its origin in the atomic "springs" that make up the surface. The harder the object bears down on the surface, the more these springs are compressed and the harder they push back. Thus the normal force *adjusts* itself so that the object stays on the surface without penetrating it. This fact is key in solving for the normal force.

EXAMPLE 5.10 | **Normal force on a pressed book**

A 1.2 kg book lies on a table. The book is pressed down from above with a force of 15 N. What is the normal force acting on the book from the table below?

PREPARE The book is not moving and is thus in static equilibrium. We need to identify the forces acting on the book, and prepare a free-body diagram showing these forces. These steps are illustrated in **FIGURE 5.13**.

FIGURE 5.13 Finding the normal force on a book pressed from above.

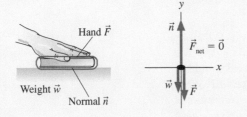

SOLVE Because the book is in static equilibrium, the net force on it must be zero. The only forces acting are in the *y*-direction, so Newton's second law is

$$\sum F_y = n_y + w_y + F_y = n - w - F = ma_y = 0$$

We learned in the last section that the weight force is $w = mg$. The weight of the book is thus

$$w = mg = (1.2 \text{ kg})(9.8 \text{ m/s}^2) = 12 \text{ N}$$

With this information, we see that the normal force exerted by the table is

$$n = F + w = 15 \text{ N} + 12 \text{ N} = 27 \text{ N}$$

ASSESS The magnitude of the normal force is *larger* than the weight of the book. From the table's perspective, the extra force from the hand pushes the book further into the atomic springs of the table. These springs then push back harder, giving a normal force that is greater than the weight of the book.

A common situation is an object on a ramp or incline. If friction is neglected, there are only two forces acting on the object: gravity and the normal force. However, we need to carefully work out the components of these two forces in order to solve dynamics problems. FIGURE 5.14a shows how. Be sure you avoid the two common errors shown in FIGURE 5.14b.

FIGURE 5.14 The forces on an object on an incline.

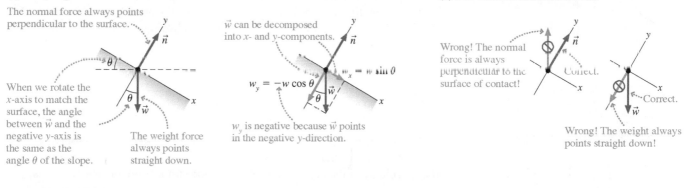

(a) Analyzing forces on an incline

The normal force always points perpendicular to the surface.

When we rotate the x-axis to match the surface, the angle between $\vec{w}$ and the negative y-axis is the same as the angle θ of the slope.

The weight force always points straight down.

$\vec{w}$ can be decomposed into x- and y-components.

$w_y = -w\cos\theta$

$w_x = w\sin\theta$

w_y is negative because $\vec{w}$ points in the negative y-direction.

(b) Two common mistakes to avoid

Wrong! The normal force is always perpendicular to the surface of contact!

Correct.

Correct.

Wrong! The weight always points straight down!

EXAMPLE 5.11 Acceleration of a downhill skier

A skier slides down a steep slope of 27° on ideal, frictionless snow. What is his acceleration?

PREPARE FIGURE 5.15 is a visual overview. We choose a coordinate system tilted so that the x-axis points down the slope. This greatly simplifies the analysis, because with this choice $a_y = 0$ (the skier does not move in the y-direction at all). The free-body diagram is based on the information in Figure 5.14.

FIGURE 5.15 Visual overview of a downhill skier.

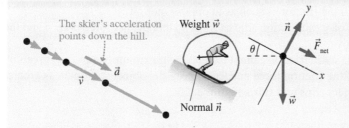

The skier's acceleration points down the hill.

Weight $\vec{w}$

Normal $\vec{n}$

$\vec{F}_{net}$

SOLVE We can now use Newton's second law in component form to find the skier's acceleration:

$$\sum F_x = w_x + n_x = ma_x$$
$$\sum F_y = w_y + n_y = ma_y$$

Because $\vec{n}$ points directly in the positive y-direction, $n_y = n$ and $n_x = 0$. Figure 5.14a showed the important fact that the angle between $\vec{w}$ and the negative y-axis is the *same* as the slope angle θ. With this information, the components of $\vec{w}$ are $w_x = w\sin\theta = mg\sin\theta$ and $w_y = -w\cos\theta = -mg\cos\theta$, where we used the fact that $w = mg$. With these components in hand, Newton's second law becomes

$$\sum F_x = w_x + n_x = mg\sin\theta = ma_x$$
$$\sum F_y = w_y + n_y = -mg\cos\theta + n = ma_y = 0$$

In the second equation we used the fact that $a_y = 0$. The m cancels in the first of these equations, leaving us with

$$a_x = g\sin\theta$$

This is the expression for acceleration on a frictionless surface that we presented, without proof, in Chapter 3. Now we've justified our earlier assertion. We can use this to calculate the skier's acceleration:

$$a_x = g\sin\theta = (9.8 \text{ m/s}^2)\sin(27°) = 4.4 \text{ m/s}^2$$

ASSESS Our result shows that when $\theta = 0$, so that the slope is horizontal, the skier's acceleration is zero, as it should be. Further, when $\theta = 90°$ (a vertical slope), his acceleration is g, which makes sense because he's in free fall when $\theta = 90°$. Notice that the mass canceled out, so we didn't need to know the skier's mass.

5.5 Friction

In everyday life, friction is everywhere. Friction is absolutely essential for many things we do. Without friction you could not walk, drive, or even sit down (you would slide right off the chair!). It is sometimes useful to think about idealized frictionless situations, but it is equally necessary to understand a real world where friction is present. Although friction is a complicated force, many aspects of friction can be described with a simple model.

FIGURE 5.16 Static friction keeps an object from slipping.

(a) Force identification

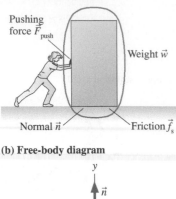

Pushing force $\vec{F}_{push}$

Weight $\vec{w}$

Normal $\vec{n}$ Friction $\vec{f}_s$

(b) Free-body diagram

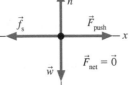

y

$\vec{n}$

$\vec{f}_s$ $\vec{F}_{push}$ x

$\vec{w}$ $\vec{F}_{net} = \vec{0}$

FIGURE 5.17 Static friction acts in *response* to an applied force.

(a) Pushing gently: friction pushes back gently.

$\vec{f}_s$ $\vec{F}_{push}$

$\vec{f}_s$ balances $\vec{F}_{push}$ and the box does not move.

(b) Pushing harder: friction pushes back harder.

$\vec{f}_s$ $\vec{F}_{push}$

$\vec{f}_s$ grows as $\vec{F}_{push}$ increases, but the two still cancel and the box remains at rest.

(c) Pushing harder still: $\vec{f}_s$ is now pushing back as hard as it can.

$\vec{f}_s$ $\vec{F}_{push}$

$f_{s\,max}$

Now the magnitude of f_s has reached its maximum value $f_{s\,max}$. If $\vec{F}_{push}$ gets any bigger, the forces will *not* cancel and the box will start to accelerate.

TABLE 5.1 Coefficients of friction

Materials	Static μ_s	Kinetic μ_k	Rolling μ_r
Rubber on concrete	1.00	0.80	0.02
Steel on steel (dry)	0.80	0.60	0.002
Steel on steel (lubricated)	0.10	0.05	
Wood on wood	0.50	0.20	
Wood on snow	0.12	0.06	
Ice on ice	0.10	0.03	

Static Friction

Chapter 4 defined static friction $\vec{f}_s$ as the force that a surface exerts on an object to keep it from slipping across that surface. Consider the woman pushing on the box in FIGURE 5.16a. Because the box is not moving with respect to the floor, the woman's push to the right must be balanced by a static friction force $\vec{f}_s$ pointing to the left. This is the general rule for finding the *direction* of $\vec{f}_s$: Decide which way the object *would* move if there were no friction. The static friction force $\vec{f}_s$ then points in the opposite direction, to prevent motion relative to the surface.

Determining the *magnitude* of $\vec{f}_s$ is a bit trickier. Because the box is at rest, it's in static equilibrium. From the free-body diagram of FIGURE 5.16b, this means that the static friction force must exactly balance the pushing force, so that $f_s = F_{push}$. As shown in FIGURES 5.17a and 5.17b, the harder the woman pushes, the harder the friction force from the floor pushes back. If she reduces her pushing force, the friction force will automatically be reduced to match. Static friction acts in *response* to an applied force.

But there's clearly a limit to how big $\vec{f}_s$ can get. If she pushes hard enough, the box will slip and start to move across the floor. In other words, the static friction force has a *maximum* possible magnitude $f_{s\,max}$, as illustrated in FIGURE 5.17c. Experiments with friction (first done by Leonardo da Vinci) show that $f_{s\,max}$ is proportional to the magnitude of the normal force between the surface and the object; that is,

$$f_{s\,max} = \mu_s n \qquad (5.10)$$

where μ_s is called the **coefficient of static friction**. The coefficient is a number that depends on the materials from which the object and the surface are made. The higher the coefficient of static friction, the greater the "stickiness" between the object and the surface, and the harder it is to make the object slip. Table 5.1 lists some approximate values of coefficients of friction.

NOTE ▶ Equation 5.10 does *not* say $f_s = \mu_s n$. The value of f_s depends on the force or forces that static friction has to balance to keep the object from moving. It can have any value from zero up to, but not exceeding, $\mu_s n$. ◀

So our rules for static friction are:

- The direction of static friction is such as to oppose motion.
- The magnitude f_s of static friction adjusts itself so that the net force is zero and the object doesn't move.
- The magnitude of static friction cannot exceed the maximum value $f_{s\,max}$ given by Equation 5.10. If the friction force needed to keep the object stationary is greater than $f_{s\,max}$, the object slips and starts to move.

Kinetic Friction

Once the box starts to slide, as in FIGURE 5.18, the static friction force is replaced by a kinetic (or sliding) friction force $\vec{f}_k$. Kinetic friction is in some ways simpler than static friction: The direction of $\vec{f}_k$ is always opposite the direction in which an object

FIGURE 5.18 The kinetic friction force is *opposite* the direction of motion.

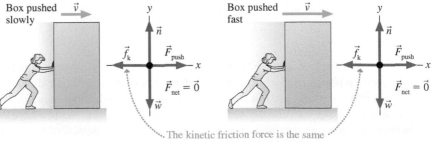

Box pushed slowly $\vec{v}$ y $\vec{n}$ $\vec{f}_k$ $\vec{F}_{push}$ x $\vec{F}_{net} = \vec{0}$ $\vec{w}$

Box pushed fast $\vec{v}$ y $\vec{n}$ $\vec{f}_k$ $\vec{F}_{push}$ x $\vec{F}_{net} = \vec{0}$ $\vec{w}$

The kinetic friction force is the same no matter how fast the object slides.

slides across the surface, and experiments show that kinetic friction, unlike static friction, has a nearly *constant* magnitude, given by

$$f_k = \mu_k n \qquad (5.11)$$

where μ_k is called the **coefficient of kinetic friction**. Equation 5.11 also shows that kinetic friction, like static friction, is proportional to the magnitude of the normal force n. Notice that **the magnitude of the kinetic friction force does not depend on how fast the object is sliding.**

Table 5.1 includes approximate values of μ_k. You can see that $\mu_k < \mu_s$, which explains why it is easier to keep a box moving than it was to start it moving.

Rolling Friction

If you slam on the brakes hard enough, your car tires slide against the road surface and leave skid marks. This is kinetic friction because the tire and the road are *sliding* against each other. A wheel *rolling* on a surface also experiences friction, but not kinetic friction: The portion of the wheel that contacts the surface is stationary with respect to the surface, not sliding. The photo in FIGURE 5.19 was taken with a stationary camera. Note how the part of the wheel touching the ground is not blurred, indicating that this part of the wheel is not moving with respect to the ground.

Textbooks draw wheels as circles, but no wheel is perfectly round. The weight of the wheel, and of any object supported by the wheel, causes the bottom of the wheel to flatten where it touches the surface, as FIGURE 5.20 shows. As a wheel rolls forward, the leading part of the tire must become deformed. This requires that the road push *backward* on the tire. In this way the road causes a backward force, even without slipping between the tire and the road.

The force of this *rolling friction* can be calculated in terms of a **coefficient of rolling friction** μ_r:

$$f_r = \mu_r n \qquad (5.12)$$

with the *direction* of the force opposing the direction of motion. Thus rolling friction acts very much like kinetic friction, but values of μ_r (see Table 5.1) are much lower than values of μ_k. This is why it is easier to roll an object on wheels than to slide it.

FIGURE 5.19 The bottom of the wheel is stationary.

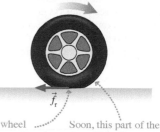

FIGURE 5.20 Rolling friction is due to deformation of a wheel.

The wheel flattens where it touches the road.

Soon, this part of the tire will be flattened. To flatten it, the road must push *back* on the tire.

STOP TO THINK 5.3   Rank in order, from largest to smallest, the size of the friction forces $\vec{f}_A$ to $\vec{f}_E$ in the five different situations (one or more friction forces could be zero). The box and the floor are made of the same materials in all situations.

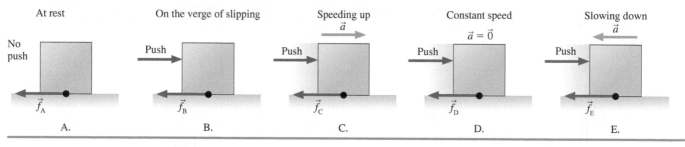

At rest	On the verge of slipping	Speeding up $\vec{a}$	Constant speed $\vec{a} = \vec{0}$	Slowing down $\vec{a}$
No push $\vec{f}_A$	Push $\vec{f}_B$	Push $\vec{f}_C$	Push $\vec{f}_D$	Push $\vec{f}_E$
A.	B.	C.	D.	E.

Working with Friction Forces

These ideas can be summarized in a *model* of friction:

Activ Physics ONLINE   2.5, 2.6

Static: $\vec{f}_s = $ (magnitude $\leq f_{s\,max} = \mu_s n$,
            direction as necessary to prevent motion)

Kinetic: $\vec{f}_k = (\mu_k n$, direction opposite the motion) (5.13)

Rolling: $\vec{f}_r = (\mu_r n$, direction opposite the motion)

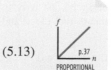

PROPORTIONAL   p.37

Here "motion" means "motion relative to the surface." The maximum value of static friction $f_{s\,max} = \mu_s n$ occurs at the point where the object slips and begins to move. Note that only one kind of friction force at a time can act on an object.

NOTE ▶ Equations 5.13 are a "model" of friction, not a "law" of friction. These equations provide a reasonably accurate, but not perfect, description of how friction forces act. They are a simplification of reality that works reasonably well, which is what we mean by a "model." They are not a "law of nature" on a level with Newton's laws. ◀

Optimized braking If you slam on your brakes, your wheels will lock up and you'll go into a skid. Then it is the *kinetic* friction force between the road and your tires that slows your car to a halt. If, however, you apply the brakes such that you don't quite skid and your tires continue to roll, the force stopping you is the *static* friction force between the road and your tires. This is a better way to brake, because the maximum static friction force is always greater than the kinetic friction force. *Antilock braking systems* (ABS) automatically do this for you when you slam on the brakes, stopping you in the shortest possible distance.

TACTICS BOX 5.1   Working with friction forces

❶ If the object is *not moving* relative to the surface it's in contact with, then the friction force is **static friction**. Draw a free-body diagram of the object. The *direction* of the friction force is such as to oppose sliding of the object relative to the surface. Then use Problem-Solving Strategy 5.1 to solve for f_s. If f_s is greater than $f_{s\,max} = \mu_s n$, then static friction cannot hold the object in place. The assumption that the object is at rest is not valid, and you need to redo the problem using kinetic friction.

❷ If the object is *sliding* relative to the surface, then **kinetic friction** is acting. From Newton's second law, find the normal force n. Equation 5.13 then gives the magnitude and direction of the friction force.

❸ If the object is *rolling* along the surface, then **rolling friction** is acting. From Newton's second law, find the normal force n. Equation 5.13 then gives the magnitude and direction of the friction force.

Exercises 20, 21

EXAMPLE 5.12   Finding the force to push a box

Carol pushes a 10.0 kg wood box across a wood floor at a steady speed of 2.0 m/s. How much force does Carol exert on the box?

PREPARE Let's assume the box slides to the right. In this case, a kinetic friction force $\vec{f}_k$, opposes the motion by pointing to the left. In **FIGURE 5.21** we identify the forces acting on the box and construct a free-body diagram.

FIGURE 5.21 Forces on a box being pushed across a floor.

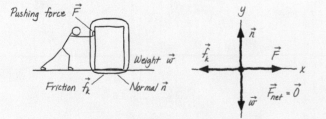

SOLVE The box is moving at a constant speed, so it is in dynamic equilibrium with $\vec{F}_{net} = \vec{0}$. This means that the x- and y-components of the net force must be zero:

$$\sum F_x = n_x + w_x + F_x + (f_k)_x = 0 + 0 + F - f_k = 0$$
$$\sum F_y = n_y + w_y + F_y + (f_k)_y = n - w + 0 + 0 = 0$$

In the first equation, the x-component of $\vec{f}_k$ is equal to $-f_k$ because $\vec{f}_k$ is directed to the left. Similarly, $w_y = -w$ because the weight force points down.

From the first equation, we see that Carol's pushing force is $F = f_k$. To evaluate this, we need f_k. Here we can use our model for kinetic friction:

$$f_k = \mu_k n$$

Because the friction is wood sliding on wood, we can use Table 5.1 to find $\mu_k = 0.20$. Further, we can use the second Newton's-law equation to find that the normal force is $n = w = mg$. Thus

$$F = f_k = \mu_k n = \mu_k mg$$
$$= (0.20)(10.0 \text{ kg})(9.80 \text{ m/s}^2) = 20 \text{ N}$$

This is the force that Carol needs to apply to the box to keep it moving at a steady speed.

ASSESS The speed of 2.0 m/s with which Carol pushes the box does not enter into the answer. This is because our model of kinetic friction does not depend on the speed of the sliding object.

CONCEPTUAL EXAMPLE 5.13   To push or pull a lawn roller?

A lawn roller is a heavy cylinder used to flatten a bumpy lawn, as shown in FIGURE 5.22. Is it easier to push or pull such a roller? Which is more effective for flattening the lawn: pushing or pulling? Assume that the pushing or pulling force is directed along the handle of the roller.

FIGURE 5.22 Pushing and pulling a lawn roller.

REASON FIGURE 5.23 shows free-body diagrams for the two cases. We assume that the roller is pushed at a constant speed so that it is in dynamic equilibrium with $\vec{F}_{net} = \vec{0}$. Because the roller does not move in the y-direction, the y-component of the net force must be zero. According to our model, the magnitude f_r of rolling friction is proportional to the magnitude n of the normal force. If we *push* on the roller, our pushing force $\vec{F}$ will have a downward y-component. To compensate for this, the normal force must increase and, because $f_r = \mu_r n$, the rolling friction will increase as well. This makes the roller harder to move. If we *pull* on the roller, the now upward y-component of $\vec{F}$ will lead to a

reduced value of n and hence of f_r. Thus the roller is easier to pull than to push.

FIGURE 5.23 Free-body diagrams for the lawn roller.

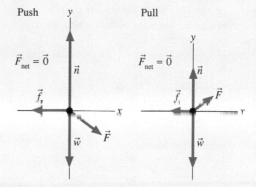

However, the purpose of the roller is to flatten the soil. If the normal force $\vec{n}$ of the ground on the roller is greater, then by Newton's third law the force of the roller on the ground will be greater as well. So for smoothing your lawn, it's better to push.

ASSESS You've probably experienced this effect while using an upright vacuum cleaner. The vacuum is harder to push on the forward stroke than when drawing it back.

EXAMPLE 5.14   How to dump a file cabinet

A 50.0 kg steel file cabinet is in the back of a dump truck. The truck's bed, also made of steel, is slowly tilted. What is the magnitude of the static friction force on the cabinet when the bed is tilted 20°? At what angle will the file cabinet begin to slide?

PREPARE We'll use our model of static friction. The file cabinet will slip when the static friction force reaches its maximum possible value f_{smax}. FIGURE 5.24 shows the visual overview when the truck bed is tilted at angle θ. We can make the analysis easier if we tilt the coordinate system to match the bed of the truck. To prevent the file cabinet from slipping, the static friction force must point *up* the slope.

SOLVE Before it slips, the file cabinet is in static equilibrium. Newton's second law gives

$$\sum F_x = n_x + w_x + (f_s)_x = 0$$
$$\sum F_y = n_y + w_y + (f_s)_y = 0$$

From the free-body diagram we see that f_s has only a negative x-component and that n has only a positive y-component. We also have $w_x = w\sin\theta$ and $w_y = -w\cos\theta$. Thus the second law becomes

$$\sum F_x = w\sin\theta - f_s = mg\sin\theta - f_s = 0$$
$$\sum F_y = n - w\cos\theta = n - mg\cos\theta = 0$$

FIGURE 5.24 Visual overview of a file cabinet in a tilted dump truck.

Known
$\mu_s = 0.80$ $m = 50.0$ kg
$\mu_k = 0.60$

Find
f_s when $\theta = 20°$
θ at which cabinet slips

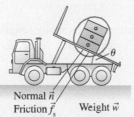

Normal $\vec{n}$
Friction $\vec{f}_s$ Weight $\vec{w}$

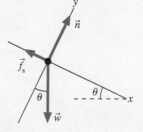

Continued

The x-component equation allows us to determine the magnitude of the static friction force when $\theta = 20°$:

$$f_s = mg\sin\theta = (50.0\text{ kg})(9.80\text{ m/s}^2)\sin 20° = 168\text{ N}$$

This value does not require that we know μ_s. The coefficient of static friction enters only when we want to find the angle at which the file cabinet slips. Slipping occurs when the static friction force reaches its maximum value:

$$f_s = f_{s\,max} = \mu_s n$$

From the y-component of Newton's second law we see that $n = mg\cos\theta$. Consequently,

$$f_{s\,max} = \mu_s mg\cos\theta$$

The x-component of the second law gave

$$f_s = mg\sin\theta$$

Setting $f_s = f_{s\,max}$ then gives

$$mg\sin\theta = \mu_s mg\cos\theta$$

The mg in both terms cancels, and we find

$$\frac{\sin\theta}{\cos\theta} = \tan\theta = \mu_s$$

$$\theta = \tan^{-1}\mu_s = \tan^{-1}(0.80) = 39°$$

ASSESS Steel doesn't slide all that well on unlubricated steel, so a fairly large angle is not surprising. The answer seems reasonable. It is worth noting that $n = mg\cos\theta$ in this example. A common error is to use simply $n = mg$. Be sure to evaluate the normal force within the context of each particular problem.

FIGURE 5.25 A microscopic view of friction.

Two surfaces in contact

Very few points are actually in contact.

Causes of Friction

It is worth a brief pause to look at the *causes* of friction. All surfaces, even those quite smooth to the touch, are very rough on a microscopic scale. When two objects are placed in contact, they do not make a smooth fit. Instead, as **FIGURE 5.25** shows, the high points on one surface become jammed against the high points on the other surface, while the low points are not in contact at all. Only a very small fraction (typically 10^{-4}) of the surface area is in actual contact. The amount of contact depends on how hard the surfaces are pushed together, which is why friction forces are proportional to n.

For an object to slip, you must push it hard enough to overcome the forces exerted at these contact points. Once the two surfaces are sliding against each other, their high points undergo constant collisions, deformations, and even brief bonding that lead to the resistive force of kinetic friction.

5.6 Drag

The air exerts a drag force on objects as they move through it. You experience drag forces every day as you jog, bicycle, ski, or drive your car. The drag force $\vec{D}$:

- Is opposite in direction to the velocity $\vec{v}$.
- Increases in magnitude as the object's speed increases.

At relatively low speeds, the drag force in air is small and can usually be neglected, but drag plays an important role as speeds increase. Fortunately, we can use a fairly simple *model* of drag if the following three conditions are met:

- The object's size (diameter) is between a few millimeters and a few meters.
- The object's speed is less than a few hundred meters per second.
- The object is moving through the air near the earth's surface.

These conditions are usually satisfied for balls, people, cars, and many other objects in our everyday experience. Under these conditions, the drag force can be written:

$$\vec{D} = \left(\tfrac{1}{2}C_D\rho Av^2,\text{ direction opposite the motion}\right) \qquad (5.14)$$

Drag force on an object of cross-section area A moving at speed v

QUADRATIC

Here, ρ is the density of air ($\rho = 1.22$ kg/m³ at sea level), A is the cross-section area of the object (in m²), and the **drag coefficient** C_D depends on the details of the object's shape. However, the value of C_D for everyday moving objects is roughly 1/2, so a good approximation to the drag force is

$$D \approx \tfrac{1}{4}\rho A v^2 \qquad (5.15)$$

This is the expression for the magnitude of the drag force that we'll use in this chapter.

The size of the drag force in air is proportional to the *square* of the object's speed: If the speed doubles, the drag increases by a factor of 4. This model of drag fails for objects that are very small (such as dust particles) or very fast (such as jet planes) or that move in other media (such as water).

FIGURE 5.26 shows that the area A in Equation 5.14 is the cross section of the object as it "faces into the wind." It's interesting to note that the magnitude of the drag force depends on the object's *size and shape* but not on its *mass*. This has important consequences for the motion of falling objects.

FIGURE 5.26 How to calculate the cross-section area A.

The cross-section area of a sphere is a circle. For this soccer ball, $A = \pi r^2$.

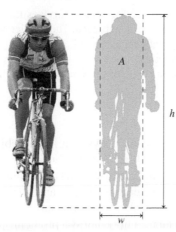

A is the cross-section area of the cyclist as seen from the front. This area is approximated by the rectangle shown, with area $A = h \times w$.

Terminal Speed

Just after an object is released from rest, its speed is low and the drag force is small (as shown in FIGURE 5.27a). Because the net force is nearly equal to the weight, the object will fall with an acceleration only a little less than g. As it falls farther, its speed and hence the drag force increase. Now the net force is smaller, so the acceleration is smaller (as shown in FIGURE 5.27b). It's still speeding up, but at a lower *rate*. Eventually the speed will increase to a point such that the magnitude of the drag force *equals* the weight (as shown in FIGURE 5.27c). The net force and hence the acceleration at this speed are then *zero,* and the object falls with a *constant* speed. The speed at which the exact balance between the upward drag force and the downward weight force causes an object to fall without acceleration is called the **terminal speed** v_{term}. **Once an object has reached terminal speed, it will continue falling at that speed until it hits the ground.**

It's straightforward to compute the terminal speed. It is the speed, by definition, at which $D = w$ or, equivalently, $\tfrac{1}{4}\rho A v^2 = mg$. This speed is then

$$v_{\text{term}} \approx \sqrt{\frac{4mg}{\rho A}} \qquad (5.16)$$

This equation shows that a more massive object has a greater terminal speed than a less massive object of equal size. A 10-cm-diameter lead ball, with a mass of 6 kg, has a terminal speed of 150 m/s, while a 10-cm-diameter Styrofoam ball, with a mass of 50 g, has a terminal speed of only 14 m/s.

FIGURE 5.27 A falling object eventually reaches terminal speed.

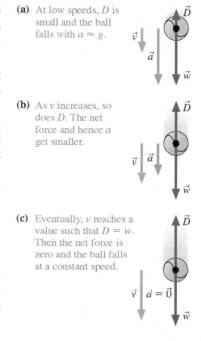

(a) At low speeds, D is small and the ball falls with $a \approx g$.

(b) As v increases, so does D. The net force and hence a get smaller.

(c) Eventually, v reaches a value such that $D = w$. Then the net force is zero and the ball falls at a constant speed.

EXAMPLE 5.15   **Terminal speeds of a skydiver and a mouse**

A skydiver and his pet mouse jump from a plane. Estimate their terminal speeds.

PREPARE To use Equation 5.16 we need to estimate the mass m and cross-section area A of both man and mouse. **FIGURE 5.28** shows how. A typical skydiver might be 1.8 m long and 0.4 m wide ($A = 0.72$ m^2) with a mass of 75 kg, while a mouse has a mass of perhaps 20 g (0.020 kg) and is 7 cm long and 3 cm wide ($A = 0.07$ m $\times$ 0.03 m $= 0.0021$ m^2).

FIGURE 5.28 The cross-section areas of a skydiver and a mouse.

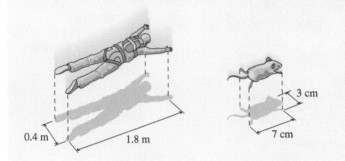

0.4 m   1.8 m   3 cm   7 cm

SOLVE We can use Equation 5.16 to find that for the skydiver

$$v_{\text{term}} \approx \sqrt{\frac{4mg}{\rho A}} = \sqrt{\frac{4(75 \text{ kg})(9.8 \text{ m/s}^2)}{(1.22 \text{ kg/m}^3)(0.72 \text{ m}^2)}} = 58 \text{ m/s}$$

This is roughly 130 mph. A higher speed can be reached by falling feet first or head first, which reduces the area A. Fortunately the skydiver can open his parachute, greatly increasing A. This brings his terminal speed down to a safe value.

For the mouse we have

$$v_{\text{term}} \approx \sqrt{\frac{4mg}{\rho A}} = \sqrt{\frac{4(0.020 \text{ kg})(9.8 \text{ m/s}^2)}{(1.22 \text{ kg/m}^2)(0.0021 \text{ m}^2)}} = 17 \text{ m/s}$$

The mouse has no parachute—nor does he need one! A mouse's terminal speed is slow enough that he can fall from any height, even out of an airplane, and survive. Cats, too, have relatively low terminal speeds. In a study of cats that fell from high rises, over 90% survived—including one that fell 45 stories!

ASSESS The mouse survives the fall not only because of its lower terminal speed. The smaller an animal's body, the proportionally more robust it is. Further, a small animal's low mass and terminal speed mean that it has a very small *kinetic energy,* an idea we'll study in Chapter 10.

Although we've focused our analysis on falling objects, the same ideas apply to objects moving horizontally. If an object is thrown or shot horizontally, $\vec{D}$ causes the object to slow down. An airplane reaches its maximum speed, which is analogous to the terminal speed, when the drag is equal to and opposite the thrust: $D = F_{\text{thrust}}$. The net force is then zero and the plane cannot go any faster.

We will continue to neglect drag unless a problem specifically calls for drag to be considered.

The terminal speed of a Styrofoam ball is 15 m/s. Suppose a Styrofoam ball is shot straight down with an initial speed of 30 m/s. Which velocity graph is correct?

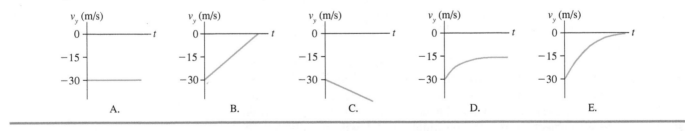

A.   B.   C.   D.   E.

5.7 Interacting Objects

2.7–2.9   Activ ONLINE Physics

Up to this point we have studied the dynamics of a single object subject to forces exerted on it by other objects. In Example 5.11, for instance, the box was acted upon by friction, normal, weight, and pushing forces that came from the floor, the earth, and the person pushing. As we've seen, such problems can be solved by an application of Newton's second law after all the forces have been identified.

But in Chapter 4 we found that real-world motion often involves two or more objects interacting with each other. We further found that forces always come in action/reaction *pairs* that are related by Newton's third law. To remind you, Newton's third law states:

- Every force occurs as one member of an action/reaction pair of forces. The two members of the pair always act on *different* objects.
- The two members of an action/reaction pair point in *opposite* directions and are *equal* in magnitude.

Our goal in this section is to learn how to apply the second *and* third laws to interacting objects.

Objects in Contact

One common way that two objects interact is via direct contact forces between them. Consider, for example, the two blocks being pushed across a frictionless table in FIGURE 5.29. To analyze block A's motion, we need to identify all the forces acting on it and then draw its free-body diagram. We repeat the same steps to analyze the motion of block B. However, the forces on A and B are *not* independent: Forces $\vec{F}_{\text{B on A}}$ acting on block A and $\vec{F}_{\text{A on B}}$ acting on block B are an action/reaction pair and thus have the same magnitude. Furthermore, because the two blocks are in contact, their *accelerations* must be the same, so that $a_{\text{A}x} = a_{\text{B}x} = a_x$. Because the accelerations of both blocks are equal, we can drop the subscripts A and B and call both accelerations a_x.

These observations suggest that we can't solve for the motion of one block without considering the motion of the other. The following revised version of our basic Problem-Solving Strategy 5.2 that was developed earlier in this chapter shows how to do this.

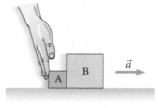

FIGURE 5.29 Two boxes moving together have the same acceleration.

**PROBLEM-SOLVING
STRATEGY 5.3** Objects-in-contact problems (MP)™

PREPARE Identify those objects whose motion you wish to study. Make simplifying assumptions.

Prepare a visual overview:

- Make a sketch of the situation. Define symbols and identify what the problem is trying to find. You may want to give each object its own coordinate system.
- Draw each object separately and prepare a *separate* force identification diagram for each object.
- Identify the action/reaction pairs of forces. If object A acts on object B with force $\vec{F}_{\text{A on B}}$, then identify the force $\vec{F}_{\text{B on A}}$ that B exerts on A.
- Draw a *separate* free-body diagram for each object. Use subscript labels to distinguish forces, such as $\vec{n}$ and $\vec{w}$, that act independently on more than one object.

SOLVE Use Newton's second and third laws:

- Write Newton's second law in component form for each object. Find the force components from the free-body diagrams.
- Equate the magnitudes of the two forces in each action/reaction pair.
- Determine how the accelerations of the objects are related to each other. Objects in contact will have the *same* acceleration; Section 5.8 shows how accelerations are related for objects connected by ropes or strings.
- Solve for the unknown forces or acceleration.

ASSESS Check that your result has the correct units, is reasonable, and answers the question.

NOTE ▶ Two steps are especially important when drawing the free-body diagrams. First, draw a *separate* diagram for each object. They need not have the same coordinate system. Second, show only the forces acting *on* that object. The force $\vec{F}_{\text{A on B}}$ goes on the free-body diagram of object B, but $\vec{F}_{\text{B on A}}$ goes on the diagram of object A. The two members of an action/reaction pair *always* appear on two different free-body diagrams—*never* on the same diagram. ◀

You might be puzzled that the Solve step calls for the use of the third law to equate just the *magnitudes* of action/reaction forces. What about the "opposite in direction" part of the third law? You have already used it! Your free-body diagrams should show the two members of an action/reaction pair to be opposite in direction, and that information will have been utilized in writing the second-law equations. Because the directional information has already been used, all that is left is the magnitude information.

EXAMPLE 5.16   **Pushing two blocks**

FIGURE 5.30 shows a 5.0 kg block A being pushed with a 3.0 N force. In front of this block is a 10 kg block B; the two blocks move together. What force does block A exert on block B?

PREPARE The visual overview of **FIGURE 5.31** lists the known information and identifies $F_{\text{A on B}}$ as what we're trying to find. Then, following the steps of Problem-Solving Strategy 5.3, we've drawn *separate* force identification diagrams and *separate* free-body diagrams for the two blocks. Both blocks have a weight force and a normal force, so we've used subscripts A and B to distinguish between them.

The force $\vec{F}_{\text{A on B}}$ is the contact force that block A exerts on B; it forms an action/reaction pair with the force $\vec{F}_{\text{B on A}}$ that block B exerts on A. Notice that force $\vec{F}_{\text{A on B}}$ is drawn acting on block B; it is the force *of* A *on* B. **Force vectors are always drawn on the free-body diagram of the object that *experiences* the force,** not the object exerting the force. Because action/reaction pairs act in opposite directions, force $\vec{F}_{\text{B on A}}$ pushes backward on block A and appears on A's free-body diagram.

SOLVE We begin by writing Newton's second law in component form for each block. Because the motion is only in the x-direction, we need only the x-component of the second law. For block A,

$$\sum F_x = (F_{\text{H}})_x + (F_{\text{B on A}})_x = m_{\text{A}}a_{\text{A}x}$$

FIGURE 5.30 Two blocks are pushed by a hand.

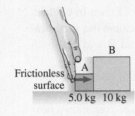

Frictionless surface

5.0 kg   10 kg

The force components can be "read" from the free-body diagram, where we see $\vec{F}_{\text{H}}$ pointing to the right and $\vec{F}_{\text{B on A}}$ pointing to the left. Thus

$$F_{\text{H}} - F_{\text{B on A}} = m_{\text{A}}a_{\text{A}x}$$

For B, we have

$$\sum F_x = (F_{\text{A on B}})_x = F_{\text{A on B}} = m_{\text{B}}a_{\text{B}x}$$

We have two additional pieces of information: First, Newton's third law tells us that $F_{\text{B on A}} = F_{\text{A on B}}$. Second, the boxes are in contact and must have the same acceleration a_x: that is, $a_{\text{A}x} = a_{\text{B}x} = a_x$. With this information, the two x-component equations become

$$F_{\text{H}} - F_{\text{A on B}} = m_{\text{A}}a_x$$
$$F_{\text{A on B}} = m_{\text{B}}a_x$$

Our goal is to find $F_{\text{A on B}}$, so we need to eliminate the unknown acceleration a_x. From the first equation, $a_x = F_{\text{A on B}}/m_{\text{B}}$. Substituting this into the second equation gives

$$F_{\text{H}} - F_{\text{A on B}} = \frac{m_{\text{A}}}{m_{\text{B}}}F_{\text{A on B}}$$

This can be solved for the force of block A on block B, giving

$$F_{\text{A on B}} = \frac{F_{\text{H}}}{1 + m_{\text{A}}/m_{\text{B}}} = \frac{3.0 \text{ N}}{1 + (5.0 \text{ kg})/(10 \text{ kg})} = \frac{3.0 \text{ N}}{1.5} = 2.0 \text{ N}$$

ASSESS Force F_{H} accelerates both blocks, a total mass of 15 kg, but force $F_{\text{A on B}}$ on B accelerates only block B, with a mass of 10 kg. Thus it makes sense that $F_{\text{A on B}} < F_{\text{H}}$.

FIGURE 5.31 A visual overview of the two blocks.

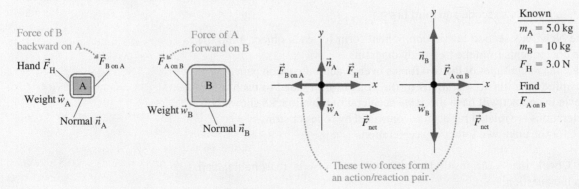

Force of B backward on A

Hand $\vec{F}_{\text{H}}$ $\vec{F}_{\text{B on A}}$

A

Weight $\vec{w}_{\text{A}}$

Normal $\vec{n}_{\text{A}}$

Force of A forward on B

$\vec{F}_{\text{A on B}}$

B

Weight $\vec{w}_{\text{B}}$

Normal $\vec{n}_{\text{B}}$

$\vec{F}_{\text{B on A}}$ $\vec{n}_{\text{A}}$ $\vec{F}_{\text{H}}$

$\vec{w}_{\text{A}}$ $\vec{F}_{\text{net}}$

$\vec{n}_{\text{B}}$ $\vec{F}_{\text{A on B}}$

$\vec{w}_{\text{B}}$ $\vec{F}_{\text{net}}$

These two forces form an action/reaction pair.

Known
$m_{\text{A}} = 5.0$ kg
$m_{\text{B}} = 10$ kg
$F_{\text{H}} = 3.0$ N

Find
$F_{\text{A on B}}$

Boxes P and Q are sliding to the right across a frictionless table. The hand H is slowing them down. The mass of P is larger than the mass of Q. Rank in order, from largest to smallest, the *horizontal* forces on P, Q, and H.

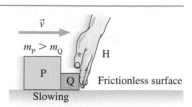

A. $F_{Q \text{ on } H} = F_{H \text{ on } Q} = F_{P \text{ on } Q} = F_{Q \text{ on } P}$

B. $F_{Q \text{ on } H} = F_{H \text{ on } Q} > F_{P \text{ on } Q} = F_{Q \text{ on } P}$

C. $F_{Q \text{ on } H} = F_{H \text{ on } Q} < F_{P \text{ on } Q} = F_{Q \text{ on } P}$

D. $F_{H \text{ on } Q} = F_{H \text{ on } P} > F_{P \text{ on } Q}$

5.8 Ropes and Pulleys

Many objects are connected by strings, ropes, cables, and so on. In single-particle dynamics, we defined *tension* as the force exerted on an object by a rope or string. We can learn several important facts about ropes and tension by considering the box being pulled by a rope in FIGURE 5.32; the rope in turn is being pulled by a hand that exerts a force $\vec{F}$ on the rope.

The box is pulled by the rope, so the box's free-body diagram shows a tension force $\vec{T}$. The *rope* is subject to two horizontal forces: the force $\vec{F}$ of the hand on the rope, and the force $\vec{F}_{\text{box on rope}}$ with which the box pulls back on the rope. $\vec{T}$ and $\vec{F}_{\text{box on rope}}$ form an action/reaction pair, so their magnitudes are equal: $F_{\text{box on rope}} = T$. Newton's second law *for the rope* is thus

$$\sum F_x = F - F_{\text{box on rope}} = F - T = m_{\text{rope}}a_x \qquad (5.17)$$

where m_{rope} is the rope's mass.

In many problems, the mass of a string or rope is significantly less than the mass of the objects it pulls on. In that case, it's reasonable to make the approximation—called the **massless string approximation**—that $m_{\text{rope}} = 0$. If $m_{\text{rope}} = 0$, then the right side of Equation 5.17 is zero and so $T = F$. In other words, **the tension in a massless string or rope equals the magnitude of the force pulling on the end of the string or rope.** As a result:

- A massless string or rope "transmits" a force undiminished from one end to the other: If you pull on one end of a rope with force F, the other end of the rope pulls on what it's attached to with a force of the same magnitude F.
- The tension in a massless string or rope is the same from one end to the other.

FIGURE 5.32 A box being pulled by a rope.

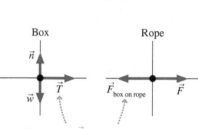

Box   Rope

The tension $\vec{T}$ is the force that the rope exerts on the box. Thus $\vec{T}$ and $\vec{F}_{\text{box on rope}}$ are an action/reaction pair and have the same magnitude.

Pulling a rope

FIGURE 5.33a shows a student pulling horizontally with a 100 N force on a rope that is attached to a wall. In FIGURE 5.33b, two students in a tug-of-war pull on opposite ends of a rope with 100 N each. Is the tension in the second rope larger, smaller, or the same as that in the first?

FIGURE 5.33 Pulling on a rope. Which produces a larger tension?

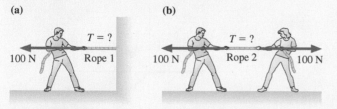

(a) $T = ?$ Rope 1   100 N

(b) $T = ?$ Rope 2   100 N

REASON Surely pulling on a rope from both ends causes more tension than pulling on one end. Right? Before jumping to

conclusions, let's analyze the situation carefully. We found above that the force pulling on the end of a rope—here, the 100 N force exerted by the student—and the tension in the rope have the same magnitude. Thus, the tension in rope 1 is 100 N, the force with which the student pulls on the rope.

To find the tension in the second rope, consider the force that the *wall* exerts on the *first* rope. The first rope is in equilibrium, so the 100 N force exerted by the student must be balanced by a 100 N force on the rope from the wall. The first rope is being pulled from *both* ends by a 100 N force—the exact same situation as for the second rope, pulled by the students. A rope doesn't care whether it's being pulled on by a wall or by a person, so the tension in the second rope is the *same* as that in the first, or 100 N.

ASSESS This example reinforces what we just learned about ropes: A rope pulls on the objects at each of its ends with a force equal in magnitude to the tension, and the external force applied to each end of the rope and the rope's tension have equal magnitude.

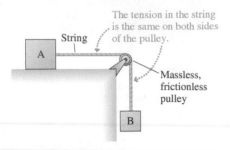

FIGURE 5.34 An ideal pulley changes the direction in which a tension force acts, but not its magnitude.

String

The tension in the string is the same on both sides of the pulley.

A

Massless, frictionless pulley

B

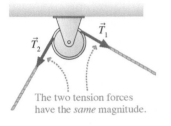

FIGURE 5.35 Tension forces on a pulley.

$\vec{T}_1$

$\vec{T}_2$

The two tension forces have the *same* magnitude.

Pulleys

Strings and ropes often pass over pulleys. FIGURE 5.34 shows a simple situation in which block B drags block A across a table as it falls. As the string moves, static friction between the string and the pulley causes the pulley to turn. If we assume that

- The string *and* the pulley are both massless, and
- There is no friction where the pulley turns on its axle,

then no net force is needed to accelerate the string or turn the pulley. In this case, **the tension in a massless string is unchanged by passing over a massless, frictionless pulley.** We'll assume such an ideal pulley for problems in this chapter. Later, when we study rotational motion in Chapter 8, we'll consider the effect of the pulley's mass.

In some situations we are interested in the force exerted on the pulley by the rope. Even though the pulley in FIGURE 5.35 is frictionless, the tension force still pulls on the pulley. Because the rope is under tension on *both* sides of the pulley, the pulley is subject to *two* tension forces, one from each side of the rope. The net force on the pulley due to the rope is then the vector sum of these two tension forces, both of which have the same magnitude, equal to the rope's tension.

We can collect all these observations about ropes, pulleys, and tension into a Tactics Box. We'll use these three rules extensively in solving problems with ropes, strings, and pulleys.

> **TACTICS BOX 5.2** **Working with ropes and pulleys** (MP)™
>
> For massless ropes or strings and massless, frictionless pulleys:
>
> - If a force pulls on one end of a rope, the tension in the rope equals the magnitude of the pulling force.
> - If two objects are connected by a rope, the tension is the same at both ends.
> - If the rope passes over a pulley, the tension in the rope is unaffected.
>
> Exercises 29–32 ✎

EXAMPLE 5.18 **Placing a leg in traction**

For serious fractures of the leg, the leg may need to have a stretching force applied to it to keep contracting leg muscles from forcing the broken bones together too hard. This is often done using *traction*, an arrangement of a rope, a weight, and pulleys as shown in FIGURE 5.36. The rope must make the same angle θ on

FIGURE 5.36 A leg in traction.

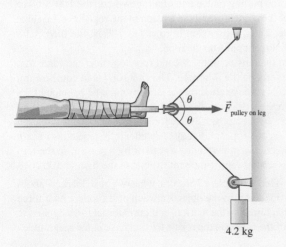

$\vec{F}_{\text{pulley on leg}}$

4.2 kg

both sides of the pulley so that the net force of the rope on the pulley is horizontally to the right, but θ can be adjusted to control the amount of traction. The doctor has specified 50 N of traction for this patient, with a 4.2 kg hanging mass. What is the proper angle θ?

PREPARE The pulley attached to the patient's leg is in static equilibrium, so the net force on it must be zero. FIGURE 5.37 shows a free-body diagram for the pulley, which we'll assume to be frictionless. Forces $\vec{T}_1$ and $\vec{T}_2$ are the tension forces of the rope as it

FIGURE 5.37 Free-body diagram for the pulley.

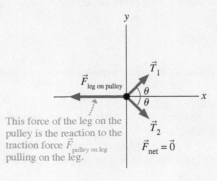

y

$\vec{T}_1$

$\vec{F}_{\text{leg on pulley}}$

θ
θ

x

This force of the leg on the pulley is the reaction to the traction force $\vec{F}_{\text{pulley on leg}}$ pulling on the leg.

$\vec{T}_2$

$\vec{F}_{\text{net}} = \vec{0}$

pulls on the pulley. These forces are equal in magnitude for a frictionless pulley, and their combined pull is to the right. This force is balanced by the force $\vec{F}_{\text{leg on pulley}}$ of the patient's leg pulling to the left. The traction force $\vec{F}_{\text{pulley on leg}}$ forms an action/reaction pair with $\vec{F}_{\text{leg on pulley}}$, so 50 N of traction means that $\vec{F}_{\text{leg on pulley}}$ also has a magnitude of 50 N.

SOLVE Two important properties of ropes, given in Tactics Box 5.2, are that (1) the tension equals the magnitude of the force pulling on its end and (2) the tension is the same throughout the rope. Thus, if a hanging mass m pulls on the rope with its weight mg, the tension along the entire rope is $T = mg$. For a 4.2 kg hanging mass, the tension is then $T = mg = 41$ N.

The pulley, in equilibrium, must satisfy Newton's second law for the case where $\vec{a} = \vec{0}$. Thus

$$\sum F_x = T_{1x} + T_{2x} + (F_{\text{leg on pulley}})_x = ma_x = 0$$

The tension forces both have the same magnitude T, and both are at angle θ from horizontal. The x-component of the leg force is negative because it's directed to the left. Then Newton's law becomes

$$2T\cos\theta - F_{\text{leg on pulley}} = 0$$

so that

$$\cos\theta = \frac{F_{\text{leg on pulley}}}{2T} = \frac{50 \text{ N}}{82 \text{ N}} = 0.61$$

$$\theta = \cos^{-1}(0.61) = 52°$$

ASSESS The traction force would approach $2mg = 82$ N if angle θ approached zero because the two tensions would pull in parallel. Conversely, the traction force would approach 0 N if θ approached 90°. Because the desired traction force is roughly halfway between 0 N and 82 N, an angle near 45° is reasonable.

EXAMPLE 5.19 **Lifting a stage set**

A 200 kg set used in a play is stored in the loft above the stage. The rope holding the set passes up and over a pulley, then is tied backstage. The director tells a 100 kg stagehand to lower the set. When he unties the rope, the set falls and the unfortunate man is hoisted into the loft. What is the stagehand's acceleration?

PREPARE FIGURE 5.38 shows the visual overview. The objects of interest are the stagehand M and the set S, for which we've drawn separate free-body diagrams. Assume a massless rope and a massless, frictionless pulley. Tension forces $\vec{T}_S$ and $\vec{T}_M$ are due to a massless rope going over an ideal pulley, so their magnitudes are the same.

FIGURE 5.38 Visual overview for the stagehand and set.

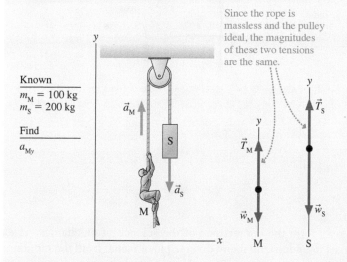

SOLVE From the two free-body diagrams, we can write Newton's second law in component form. For the man we have

$$\sum F_{My} = T_M - w_M = T_M - m_M g = m_M a_{My}$$

For the set we have

$$\sum F_{Sy} = T_S - w_S = T_S - m_S g = m_S a_{Sy}$$

Only the y-equations are needed. Because the stagehand and the set are connected by a rope, the upward distance traveled by one is the *same* as the downward distance traveled by the other. Thus the *magnitudes* of their accelerations must be the same, but, as Figure 5.38 shows, their *directions* are opposite. We can express this mathematically as $a_{Sy} = -a_{My}$. We also know that the two tension forces have equal magnitudes, which we'll call T. Inserting this information into the above equations gives

$$T - m_M g = m_M a_{My}$$

$$T - m_S g = -m_S a_{My}$$

These are simultaneous equations in the two unknowns T and a_{My}. We can solve for T in the first equation to get

$$T = m_M a_{My} + m_M g$$

Inserting this value of T into the second equation then gives

$$m_M a_{My} + m_M g - m_S g = -m_S a_{My}$$

which we can rewrite as

$$(m_S - m_M)g = (m_S + m_M)a_{My}$$

Finally, we can solve for the hapless stagehand's acceleration:

$$a_{My} = \frac{m_S - m_M}{m_S + m_M} g = \left(\frac{100 \text{ kg}}{300 \text{ kg}}\right) \times 9.80 \text{ m/s}^2 = 3.3 \text{ m/s}^2$$

This is also the acceleration with which the set falls. If the rope's tension was needed, we could now find it from $T = m_M a_{My} + m_M g$.

ASSESS If the stagehand weren't holding on, the set would fall with free-fall acceleration g. The stagehand acts as a *counterweight* to reduce the acceleration.

EXAMPLE 5.20 **A not-so-clever bank robbery**

Bank robbers have pushed a 1000 kg safe to a second-story floor-to-ceiling window. They plan to break the window, then lower the safe 3.0 m to their truck. Not being too clever, they stack up 500 kg of furniture, tie a rope between the safe and the furniture, and place the rope over a pulley. Then they push the safe out the window. What is the safe's speed when it hits the truck? The coefficient of kinetic friction between the furniture and the floor is 0.50.

PREPARE The visual overview in FIGURE 5.39 establishes a coordinate system and defines the symbols that will be needed to calculate the safe's motion. The objects of interest are the safe S and the furniture F, which we will model as particles. We will assume a massless rope and a massless, frictionless pulley; the tension is then the same everywhere in the rope.

SOLVE We can write Newton's second law directly from the free-body diagrams. For the furniture,

$$\sum F_{Fx} = T_F - f_k = T - f_k = m_F a_{Fx}$$

$$\sum F_{Fy} = n - w_F = n - m_F g = 0$$

And for the safe,

$$\sum F_{Sy} = T_S - w_S = T - m_S g = m_S a_{Sy}$$

The safe and the furniture are tied together, so their accelerations have the same magnitude. But as the furniture slides to the right with positive acceleration a_{Fx}, the safe falls in the negative y-direction, so its acceleration a_{Sy} is negative; we can express this mathematically as $a_{Fx} = -a_{Sy}$. We also have made use of the fact that $T_S = T_F = T$. We have one additional piece of information, the model of kinetic friction:

$$f_k = \mu_k n = \mu_k m_F g$$

where we used the y-equation of the furniture to deduce that $n = m_F g$. Substitute this result for f_k into the x-equation of the furniture, then rewrite the furniture's x-equation and the safe's y-equation:

$$T - \mu_k m_F g = -m_F a_{Sy}$$

$$T - m_S g = m_S a_{Sy}$$

We have succeeded in reducing our knowledge to two simultaneous equations in the two unknowns a_{Sy} and T. We subtract the second equation from the first to eliminate T:

$$(m_S - \mu_k m_F)g = -(m_S + m_F)a_{Sy}$$

Finally, we can solve for the safe's acceleration:

$$a_{Sy} = -\left(\frac{m_S - \mu_k m_F}{m_S + m_F}\right)g$$

$$= -\frac{1000 \text{ kg} - 0.5(500 \text{ kg})}{1000 \text{ kg} + 500 \text{ kg}} \times 9.80 \text{ m/s}^2 = -4.9 \text{ m/s}^2$$

Now we need to calculate the kinematics of the falling safe. Because the time of the fall is not known or needed, we can use

$$(v_y)_f^2 = (v_y)_i^2 + 2a_{Sy}\,\Delta y = 0 + 2a_{Sy}(y_f - y_i) = -2a_{Sy}y_i$$

$$(v_y)_f = \sqrt{-2a_{Sy}y_i} = \sqrt{-2(-4.9 \text{ m/s}^2)(3.0 \text{ m})} = 5.4 \text{ m/s}$$

The value of $(v_y)_f$ is negative, but we only needed to find the speed, so we took the absolute value. It seems unlikely that the truck will survive the impact of the 1000 kg safe!

FIGURE 5.39 Visual overview of the furniture and falling safe.

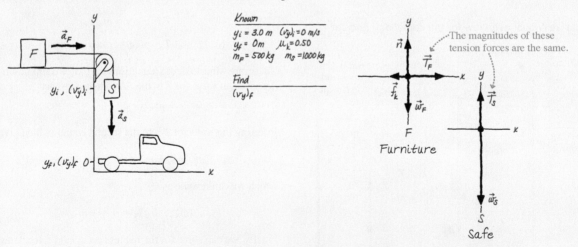

Newton's three laws form the cornerstone of the science of mechanics. These laws allowed scientists to understand many diverse phenomena, from the motion of a raindrop to the orbits of the planets. These laws were so precise at predicting motion that they went unchallenged for well over two hundred years. At the beginning of the twentieth century, however, it began to be apparent that the laws of mechanics and the laws of electricity and magnetism were somehow inconsistent. Bringing these two apparently disconnected theories into harmony required the genius of a young patent clerk named Albert Einstein. In doing so, he shook the foundations not only of Newtonian mechanics but also of our very notions of space and time. We will continue to develop Newtonian mechanics for the next few chapters because of its tremendous importance to the physics of everyday life. But it's worth keeping in the back of your mind that Newton's laws aren't the ultimate statement about motion. Later in this textbook we'll reexamine motion and mechanics from the perspective of Einstein's theory of relativity.

STOP TO THINK 5.6 All three 50 kg blocks are at rest. Is the tension in rope 2 greater than, less than, or equal to the tension in rope 1?

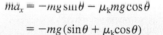

INTEGRATED EXAMPLE 5.21 Stopping distances

A 1500 kg car is traveling at a speed of 30 m/s when the driver slams on the brakes and skids to a halt. Determine the stopping distance if the car is traveling up a 10° slope, down a 10° slope, or on a level road.

PREPARE We'll represent the car as a particle and we'll use the model of kinetic friction. We want to solve the problem only once, not three separate times, so we'll leave the slope angle θ unspecified until the end.

FIGURE 5.40 shows the visual overview. We've shown the car sliding uphill, but these representations work equally well for a level or downhill slide if we let θ be zero or negative, respectively. We've used a tilted coordinate system so that the motion is along the x-axis. The car *skids* to a halt, so we've taken the coefficient of *kinetic* friction for rubber on concrete from Table 5.1.

SOLVE Newton's second law and the model of kinetic friction are

$$\sum F_x = n_x + w_x + (f_k)_x$$
$$= 0 - mg\sin\theta - f_k = ma_x$$

$$\sum F_y = n_y + w_y + (f_k)_y$$
$$= n - mg\cos\theta + 0 = ma_y = 0$$

We've written these equations by "reading" the motion diagram and the free-body diagram. Notice that both components of the weight vector $\vec{w}$ are negative. $a_y = 0$ because the motion is entirely along the x-axis.

The second equation gives $n = mg\cos\theta$. Using this in the friction model, we find $f_k = \mu_k mg\cos\theta$. Inserting this result back into the first equation then gives

$$ma_x = -mg\sin\theta - \mu_k mg\cos\theta$$
$$= -mg(\sin\theta + \mu_k\cos\theta)$$
$$a_x = -g(\sin\theta + \mu_k\cos\theta)$$

This is a constant acceleration. Constant-acceleration kinematics gives

$$(v_x)_f^2 = 0 = (v_x)_i^2 + 2a_x(x_f - x_i) = (v_x)_i^2 + 2a_x x_f$$

which we can solve for the stopping distance x_f:

$$x_f = -\frac{(v_x)_i^2}{2a_x} = \frac{(v_x)_i^2}{2g(\sin\theta + \mu_k\cos\theta)}$$

Notice how the minus sign in the expression for a_x canceled the minus sign in the expression for x_f. Evaluating our result at the three different angles gives the stopping distances:

$$x_f = \begin{cases} 48\text{ m} & \theta = 10° & \text{uphill} \\ 57\text{ m} & \theta = 0° & \text{level} \\ 75\text{ m} & \theta = -10° & \text{downhill} \end{cases}$$

The implications are clear about the danger of driving downhill too fast!

ASSESS 30m/s ≈ 60 mph and 57m ≈ 180 feet on a level surface. These are similar to the stopping distances you learned when you got your driver's license, so the results seem reasonable. Additional confirmation comes from noting that the expression for a_x becomes $-g\sin\theta$ if $\mu_k = 0$. This is what you learned in Chapter 3 for the acceleration on a frictionless inclined plane.

FIGURE 5.40 Visual overview for a skidding car.

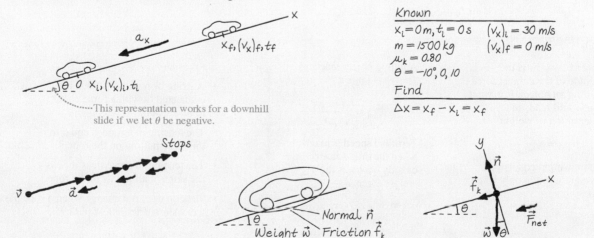

SUMMARY

The goal of Chapter 5 has been to learn how to solve problems about motion in a straight line.

GENERAL STRATEGY

All examples in this chapter follow a three-part strategy. You'll become a better problem solver if you adhere to it as you do the homework problems. The *Dynamics Worksheets* in the *Student Workbook* will help you structure your work in this way.

Equilibrium Problems

Object at rest or moving at constant velocity.

PREPARE Make simplifying assumptions.

- Check that the object is either at rest or moving with constant velocity ($\vec{a} = \vec{0}$).
- Identify forces and show them on a free-body diagram.

SOLVE Use Newton's second law in component form:

$$\sum F_x = ma_x = 0$$
$$\sum F_y = ma_y = 0$$

"Read" the components from the free-body diagram.

ASSESS Is your result reasonable?

Dynamics Problems

Object accelerating.

PREPARE Make simplifying assumptions. Make a **visual overview:**

- Sketch a pictorial representation.
- Identify known quantities and what the problem is trying to find.
- Identify all forces and show them on a free-body diagram.

SOLVE Use Newton's second law in component form:

$$\sum F_x = ma_x \text{ and } \sum F_y = ma_y$$

"Read" the components of the vectors from the free-body diagram. If needed, use kinematics to find positions and velocities.

ASSESS Is your result reasonable?

Objects in Contact

Two or more objects interacting.

PREPARE Make a **visual overview:**

- Sketch a pictorial representation.
- Identify all forces acting on *each* object.
- Identify action/reaction pairs of forces acting on objects in the system.
- Draw a *separate* free-body diagram for each object.

SOLVE Write Newton's second law for each object. Use Newton's third law to equate the magnitudes of action/reaction pairs. Determine how the accelerations of the objects are related to each other.

ASSESS Is your result reasonable?

IMPORTANT CONCEPTS

Specific information about three important forces:

Weight $\vec{w} = (mg, \text{downward})$

Friction $\vec{f}_s = (0 \text{ to } \mu_s n, \text{direction as necessary to prevent motion})$

$\vec{f}_k = (\mu_k n, \text{direction opposite the motion})$

$\vec{f}_r = (\mu_r n, \text{direction opposite the motion})$

Drag $\vec{D} \approx (\frac{1}{4}\rho A v^2, \text{direction opposite the motion})$ for motion in air

Newton's laws are vector expressions. You must write them out by **components:**

$$(F_{net})_x = \sum F_x = ma_x$$
$$(F_{net})_y = \sum F_y = ma_y$$

For equilibrium problems, $a_x = 0$ and $a_y = 0$.

APPLICATIONS

Apparent weight is the magnitude of the contact force supporting an object. It is what a scale would read, and it is your sensation of weight:

$$w_{app} = m(g + a_y)$$

Apparent weight equals your true weight $w = mg$ only when $a_y = 0$.

A falling object reaches **terminal speed**

$$v_{term} \approx \sqrt{\frac{4mg}{\rho A}}$$

Terminal speed is reached when the drag force exactly balances the weight force: $\vec{a} = \vec{0}$.

Strings and pulleys

- A string or rope pulls what it's connected to with a force equal to its tension.
- The tension in a rope is equal to the force pulling on the rope.
- The tension in a massless rope is the same at all points in the rope.
- Tension does not change when a rope passes over a massless, frictionless pulley.

™ For homework assigned on MasteringPhysics, go to www.masteringphysics.com

Problem difficulty is labeled as | (straightforward) to |||| (challenging).

Problems labeled 🖉 can be done on a Workbook Dynamics Worksheet; INT integrate significant material from earlier chapters; BIO are of biological or medical interest.

QUESTIONS

Conceptual Questions

1. An object is subject to two forces that do not point in opposite directions. Is it possible to choose their magnitudes so that the object is in equilibrium? Explain.

2. Are the objects described here in static equilibrium, dynamic equilibrium, or not in equilibrium at all?
   a. A girder is lifted at constant speed by a crane.
   b. A girder is lowered by a crane. It is slowing down.
   c. You're straining to hold a 200 lb barbell over your head.
   d. A jet plane has reached its cruising speed and altitude.
   e. A rock is falling into the Grand Canyon.
   f. A box in the back of a truck doesn't slide as the truck stops.

3. What forces are acting on you right now? What net force is acting on you right now?

4. Decide whether each of the following is true or false. Give a reason!
   a. The mass of an object depends on its location.
   b. The weight of an object depends on its location.
   c. Mass and weight describe the same thing in different units.

5. An astronaut takes his bathroom scale to the moon and then stands on it. Is the reading of the scale his true weight? Explain.

6. A light block of mass m and a heavy block of mass M are attached to the ends of a rope. A student holds the heavier block and lets the lighter block hang below it, as shown in Figure Q5.6. Then she lets go. Air resistance can be neglected.
   a. What is the tension in the rope while the blocks are falling, before either hits the ground?
   b. Would your answer be different if she had been holding the lighter block initially?

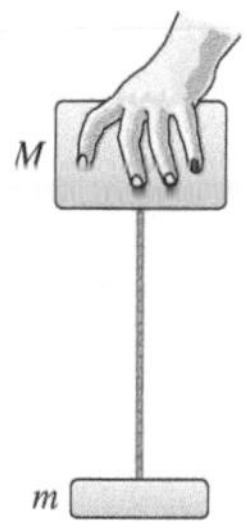

FIGURE Q5.6

7. Four balls are thrown straight up. Figure Q5.7 is a "snapshot" showing their velocities. They have the same size but different mass. Air resistance is negligible. Rank in order, from largest to smallest, the magnitudes of the net forces, F_{net1}, F_{net2}, F_{net3}, F_{net4}, acting on the balls. Some may be equal. Give your answer in the form A > B = C > D, and state your reasoning.

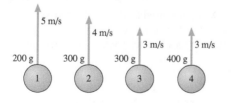

FIGURE Q5.7

8. Suppose you attempt to pour out 100 g of salt, using a pan balance for measurements, while in an elevator that is accelerating upward. Will the quantity of salt be too much, too little, or the correct amount? Explain.

9. a. Can the normal force on an object be directed horizontally? If not, why not? If so, provide an example.
   b. Can the normal force on an object be directed downward? If not, why not? If so, provide an example.

10. A ball is thrown straight up. Taking the drag force of air into account, does it take longer for the ball to travel to the top of its motion or for it to fall back down again?

11. Three objects move through the air as shown in Figure Q5.11. Rank in order, from largest to smallest, the three drag forces D_1, D_2, and D_3. Some may be equal. Give your answer in the form A > B = C and state your reasoning.

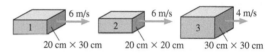

FIGURE Q5.11

12. A skydiver is falling at her terminal speed. Right after she opens her parachute, which has a very large area, what is the direction of the net force on her?

13. Raindrops can fall at different speeds; some fall quite quickly, others quite slowly. Why might this be true?

14. An airplane moves through the air at a constant speed. The jet engine's thrust applies a force in the direction of motion. Reducing thrust will cause the plane to fly at a slower—but still constant—speed. Explain why this is so.

15. Is it possible for an object to travel in air faster than its terminal speed? If not, why not? If so, explain how this might happen.

For Questions 16 through 19, determine the tension in the rope at the point indicated with a dot.

- All objects are at rest.
- The strings and pulleys are massless, and the pulleys are frictionless.

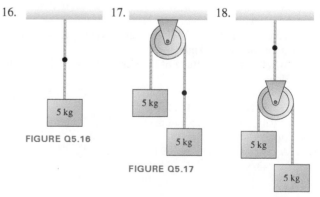

16.

FIGURE Q5.16

17.

FIGURE Q5.17

18.

FIGURE Q5.18

19.

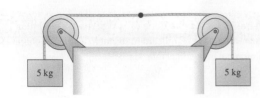

FIGURE Q5.19

20. The floor is frictionless. In which direction is the kinetic friction force on block 1 in Figure Q5.20? On block 2? Explain.

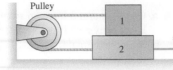

FIGURE Q5.20

Multiple-Choice Questions

21. ‖ The wood block in Figure Q5.21 is at rest on a wood ramp. In which direction is the static friction force on block 1?
   A. Up the slope.
   B. Down the slope.
   C. The friction force is zero.
   D. There's not enough information to tell.

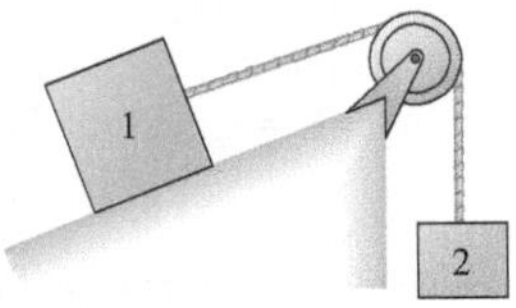

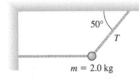

FIGURE Q5.21

22. ‖ A 2.0 kg ball is suspended by two light strings as shown in Figure Q5.22. What is the tension T in the angled string?
   A. 9.5 N   B. 15 N   C. 20 N
   D. 26 N   E. 30 N

50°

T

$m = 2.0$ kg

FIGURE Q5.22

23. | While standing in a low tunnel, you raise your arms and push against the ceiling with a force of 100 N. Your mass is 70 kg.
   a. What force does the ceiling exert on you?
      A. 10 N   B. 100 N   C. 690 N
      D. 790 N   E. 980 N
   b. What force does the floor exert on you?
      A. 10 N   B. 100 N   C. 690 N
      D. 790 N   E. 980 N

24. | A 5.0 kg dog sits on the floor of an elevator that is accelerating *downward* at 1.20 m/s².
   a. What is the magnitude of the normal force of the elevator floor on the dog?
      A. 34 N   B. 43 N   C. 49 N
      D. 55 N   E. 74 N
   b. What is the magnitude of the force of the dog on the elevator floor?
      A. 4.2 N   B. 49 N   C. 55 N
      D. 43 N   E. 74 N

25. | A 3.0 kg puck slides due east on a horizontal frictionless surface at a constant speed of 4.5 m/s. Then a force of magnitude 6.0 N, directed due north, is applied for 1.5 s. Afterward,
   a. What is the northward component of the puck's velocity?
      A. 0.50 m/s   B. 2.0 m/s   C. 3.0 m/s
      D. 4.0 m/s   E. 4.5 m/s
   b. What is the speed of the puck?
      A. 4.9 m/s   B. 5.4 m/s   C. 6.2 m/s
      D. 7.5 m/s   E. 11 m/s

26. | A rocket in space, initially at rest, fires its main engines at a constant thrust. As it burns fuel, the mass of the rocket decreases. Which of the graphs in Figure Q5.26 best represents the velocity of the rocket as a function of time?

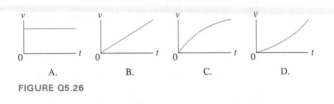

FIGURE Q5.26

27. | Eric has a mass of 60 kg. He is standing on a scale in an elevator that is accelerating downward at 1.7 m/s². What is the approximate reading on the scale?
   A. 0 N   B. 400 N   C. 500 N   D. 600 N

28. | The two blocks in Figure Q5.28 are at rest on frictionless surfaces. What must be the mass of the right block in order that the two blocks remain stationary?
   A. 4.9 kg   B. 6.1 kg   C. 7.9 kg
   D. 9.8 kg   E. 12 kg

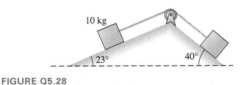

FIGURE Q5.28

29. | A football player at practice pushes a 60 kg blocking sled across the field at a constant speed. The coefficient of kinetic friction between the grass and the sled is 0.30. How much force must he apply to the sled?
   A. 18 N   B. 60 N   C. 180 N   D. 600 N

30. | Two football players are pushing a 60 kg blocking sled across the field at a constant speed of 2.0 m/s. The coefficient of kinetic friction between the grass and the sled is 0.30. Once they stop pushing, how far will the sled slide before coming to rest?
   A. 0.20 m   B. 0.68 m   C. 1.0 m   D. 6.6 m

31. ‖ Land Rover ads used to claim that their vehicles could climb a slope of 45°. For this to be possible, what must be the minimum coefficient of static friction between the vehicle's tires and the road?
   A. 0.5   B. 0.7   C. 0.9   D. 1.0

32. ‖ A truck is traveling at 30 m/s on a slippery road. The driver slams on the brakes and the truck starts to skid. If the coefficient of kinetic friction between the tires and the road is 0.20, how far will the truck skid before stopping?
   A. 230 m   B. 300 m   C. 450 m   D. 680 m

PROBLEMS

Section 5.1 Equilibrium

1. | The three ropes in Figure P5.1 are tied to a small, very light ring. Two of the ropes are anchored to walls at right angles, and the third rope pulls as shown. What are T_1 and T_2, the magnitudes of the tension forces in the first two ropes?

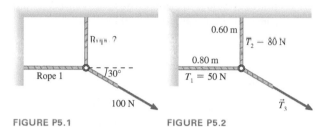

FIGURE P5.1   FIGURE P5.2

2. ||| The three ropes in Figure P5.2 are tied to a small, very light ring. Two of these ropes are anchored to walls at right angles with the tensions shown in the figure. What are the magnitude and direction of the tension $\vec{T}_3$ in the third rope?

3. |||| A 20 kg loudspeaker is suspended 2.0 m below the ceiling by two cables that are each 30° from vertical. What is the tension in the cables?

4. || A 1000 kg steel beam is supported by the two ropes shown in Figure P5.4. Each rope can support a maximum sustained tension of 5600 N. Do the ropes break?

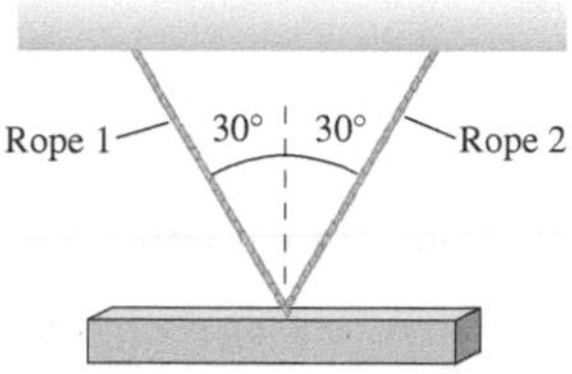

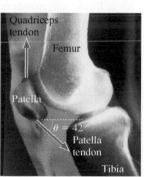

FIGURE P5.4

5. | A cable is used to raise a 25 kg urn from an underwater archeological site. There is a 25 N drag force from the water as the urn is raised at a constant speed. What is the tension in the cable?

6. |||| When you bend your knee, the quadriceps muscle is stretched. This increases the tension in the quadriceps tendon attached to your kneecap (patella), which, in turn, increases the tension in the patella tendon that attaches your kneecap to your lower leg bone (tibia). Simultaneously, the end of your upper leg bone (femur) pushes outward on the patella. Figure P5.6 shows how these parts of a knee joint are arranged. What size force does the femur exert on the kneecap if the tendons are oriented as in the figure and the tension in each tendon is 60 N?
BIO

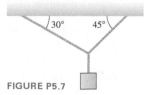

FIGURE P5.6

7. || The two angled ropes used to support the crate in Figure P5.7 can withstand a maximum tension of 1500 N before they break. What is the largest mass the ropes can support?

FIGURE P5.7

Section 5.2 Dynamics and Newton's Second Law

8. || A force with x-component F_x acts on a 500 g object as it moves along the x-axis. The object's acceleration graph (a_x versus t) is shown in Figure P5.8. Draw a graph of F_x versus t.

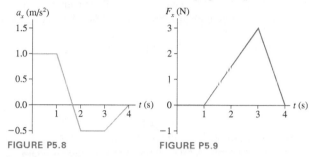

FIGURE P5.8   FIGURE P5.9

9. || A force with x-component F_x acts on a 2.0 kg object as it moves along the x-axis. A graph of F_x versus t is shown in Figure P5.9. Draw an acceleration graph (a_x versus t) for this object.

10. | A force with x-component F_x acts on a 500 g object as it moves along the x-axis. A graph of F_x versus t is shown in Figure P5.10. Draw an acceleration graph (a_x versus t) for this object.

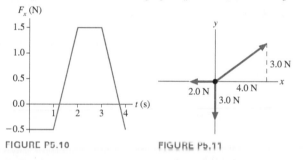

FIGURE P5.10   FIGURE P5.11

11. || The forces in Figure P5.11 are acting on a 2.0 kg object. Find the values of a_x and a_y, the x- and y-components of the object's acceleration.

12. | The forces in Figure P5.12 are acting on a 2.0 kg object. Find the values of a_x and a_y, the x- and y-components of the object's acceleration.

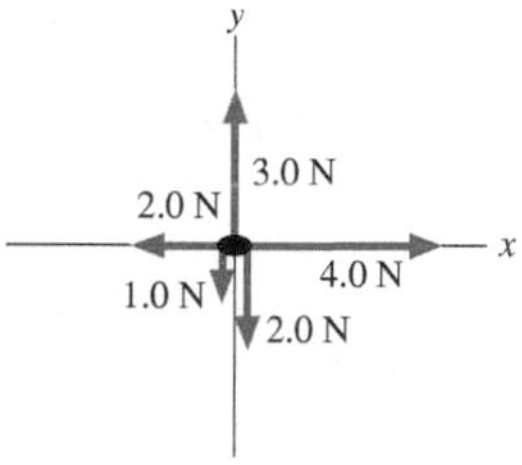

13. | A horizontal rope is tied to a 50 kg box on frictionless ice. What is the tension in the rope if
   a. The box is at rest?
   b. The box moves at a steady 5.0 m/s?
   c. The box has $v_x = 5.0$ m/s and $a_x = 5.0$ m/s²?

FIGURE P5.12

14. |||| A crate pushed along the floor with velocity $\vec{v}_i$ slides a distance d after the pushing force is removed.
   a. If the mass of the crate is doubled but the initial velocity is not changed, what distance does the crate slide before stopping? Explain.
   b. If the initial velocity of the crate is doubled to $2\vec{v}_i$ but the mass is not changed, what distance does the crate slide before stopping? Explain.

15. || In a head-on collision, a car stops in 0.10 s from a speed of 14 m/s. The driver has a mass of 70 kg, and is, fortunately, tightly strapped into his seat. What force is applied to the driver by his seat belt during that fraction of a second?

Section 5.3 Mass and Weight

16. | An astronaut's weight on earth is 800 N. What is his weight on Mars, where $g = 3.76$ m/s²?

17. | A woman has a mass of 55.0 kg.
    a. What is her weight on earth?
    b. What are her mass and her weight on the moon, where $g = 1.62$ m/s²?

18. ||| A box with a 75 kg passenger inside is launched straight up into the air by a giant rubber band. After the box has left the rubber band but is still moving *upward,*
    a. What is the passenger's true weight?
    b. What is the passenger's apparent weight?

19. || a. How much force does an 80 kg astronaut exert on his chair while sitting at rest on the launch pad?
    b. How much force does the astronaut exert on his chair while accelerating straight up at 10 m/s²?

20. | It takes the elevator in a skyscraper 4.0 s to reach its cruising speed of 10 m/s. A 60 kg passenger gets aboard on the ground floor. What is the passenger's apparent weight
    a. Before the elevator starts moving?
    b. While the elevator is speeding up?
    c. After the elevator reaches its cruising speed?

21. || Zach, whose mass is 80 kg, is in an elevator descending at 10 m/s. The elevator takes 3.0 s to brake to a stop at the first floor.
    a. What is Zach's apparent weight before the elevator starts braking?
    b. What is Zach's apparent weight while the elevator is braking?

22. ||| Figure P5.22 shows the velocity graph of a 75 kg passenger in an elevator. What is the passenger's apparent weight at $t = 1.0$ s? At 5.0 s? At 9.0 s?

FIGURE P5.22

Section 5.4 Normal Forces

23. || a. A 0.60 kg bullfrog is sitting at rest on a level log. How large is the normal force of the log on the bullfrog?
    b. A second 0.60 kg bullfrog is on a log tilted 30° above horizontal. How large is the normal force of the log on this bullfrog?

24. ||| A 23 kg child goes down a straight slide inclined 38° above horizontal. The child is acted on by his weight, the normal force from the slide, and kinetic friction.
    a. Draw a free-body diagram of the child.
    b. How large is the normal force of the slide on the child?

Section 5.5 Friction

25. ||| Bonnie and Clyde are sliding a 300 kg bank safe across the floor to their getaway car. The safe slides with a constant speed if Clyde pushes from behind with 385 N of force while Bonnie pulls forward on a rope with 350 N of force. What is the safe's coefficient of kinetic friction on the bank floor?

26. ||| A 4000 kg truck is parked on a 15° slope. How big is the friction force on the truck?

27. ||| A 1000 kg car traveling at a speed of 40 m/s skids to a halt on wet concrete where $\mu_k = 0.60$. How long are the skid marks?

28. | A stubborn 120 kg mule sits down and refuses to move. To drag the mule to the barn, the exasperated farmer ties a rope around the mule and pulls with his maximum force of 800 N.

The coefficients of friction between the mule and the ground are $\mu_s = 0.80$ and $\mu_k = 0.50$. Is the farmer able to move the mule?

29. ||| A 10 kg crate is placed on a horizontal conveyor belt. The materials are such that $\mu_s = 0.50$ and $\mu_k = 0.30$.
    a. Draw a free-body diagram showing all the forces on the crate if the conveyor belt runs at constant speed.
    b. Draw a free-body diagram showing all the forces on the crate if the conveyor belt is speeding up.
    c. What is the maximum acceleration the belt can have without the crate slipping?
    d. If acceleration of the belt exceeds the value determined in part c, what is the acceleration of the crate?

30. || What is the minimum downward force on the box in Figure P5.30 that will keep it from slipping? The coefficients of static and kinetic friction between the box and the floor are 0.35 and 0.25, respectively.

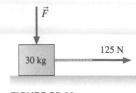

FIGURE P5.30

Section 5.6 Drag

31. || What is the drag force on a 1.6-m-wide, 1.4-m-high car traveling at
    a. 10 m/s (≈22 mph)?   b. 30 m/s (≈65 mph)?

32. |||| A 22-cm-diameter bowling ball has a terminal speed of 77 m/s. What is the ball's mass?

33. |||| A 75 kg skydiver can be modeled as a rectangular "box" with dimensions 20 cm × 40 cm × 1.8 m. What is his terminal speed if he falls feet first?

Section 5.7 Interacting Objects

34. ||| A 1000 kg car pushes a 2000 kg truck that has a dead battery. When the driver steps on the accelerator, the drive wheels of the car push backward against the ground with a force of 4500 N.
    a. What is the magnitude of the force of the car on the truck?
    b. What is the magnitude of the force of the truck on the car?

35. |||| Blocks with masses of 1.0 kg, 2.0 kg, and 3.0 kg are lined up in a row on a frictionless table. All three are pushed forward by a 12 N force applied to the 1.0 kg block. How much force does the 2.0 kg block exert on (a) the 3.0 kg block and (b) the 1.0 kg block?

Section 5.8 Ropes and Pulleys

36. ||| What is the tension in the rope of Figure P5.36?

37. || A 2.0-m-long, 500 g rope pulls a 10 kg block of ice across a horizontal, frictionless surface. The block accelerates at 2.0 m/s². How much force pulls forward on (a) the block of ice, (b) the rope?

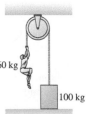

FIGURE P5.36

38. ||| Figure P5.38 shows two 1.00 kg blocks connected by a rope. A second rope hangs beneath the lower block. Both ropes have a mass of 250 g. The entire assembly is accelerated upward at 3.00 m/s² by force $\vec{F}$.
    a. What is F?
    b. What is the tension at the top end of rope 1?
    c. What is the tension at the bottom end of rope 1?
    d. What is the tension at the top end of rope 2?

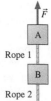

FIGURE P5.38

39. ‖ Each of 100 identical blocks sitting on a frictionless surface is connected to the next block by a massless string. The first block is pulled with a force of 100 N.
   a. What is the tension in the string connecting block 100 to block 99?
   b. What is the tension in the string connecting block 50 to block 51?
40. ‖ Two blocks on a frictionless table, A and B, are connected by a massless string. When block A is pulled with a certain force, dragging block B, the tension in the string is 24 N. When block B is pulled by the same force, dragging block A, the tension is 18 N. What is the ratio m_A/m_B of the blocks' masses?

General Problems

41. ‖‖ A 500 kg piano is being lowered into position by a crane while two people steady it with ropes pulling to the sides. Bob's rope pulls to the left, 15° below horizontal, with 500 N of tension. Ellen's rope pulls toward the right, 25° below horizontal.
   a. What tension must Ellen maintain in her rope to keep the piano descending vertically at constant speed?
   b. What is the tension in the vertical main cable supporting the piano?
42. ‖ Dana has a sports medal suspended by a long ribbon from her rearview mirror. As she accelerates onto the highway, she notices that the medal is hanging at an angle of 10° from the vertical.
   a. Does the medal lean toward or away from the windshield? Explain.
   b. What is her acceleration?
43. ‖ Figure P5.43 shows the velocity graph of a 2.0 kg object as it moves along the x-axis. What is the net force acting on this object at $t = 1$ s? At 4 s? At 7 s?

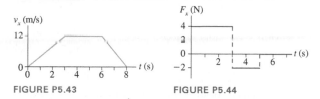

FIGURE P5.43   FIGURE P5.44

44. ‖ Figure P5.44 shows the net force acting on a 2.0 kg object as it moves along the x-axis. The object is at rest at the origin at $t = 0$ s. What are its acceleration and velocity at $t = 6.0$ s?
45. ‖ A 50 kg box hangs from a rope. What is the tension in the rope if
   a. The box is at rest?
   b. The box has $v_y = 5.0$ m/s and is speeding up at 5.0 m/s²?
46. ‖ A 50 kg box hangs from a rope. What is the tension in the rope if
   a. The box moves up at a steady 5.0 m/s?
   b. The box has $v_y = 5.0$ m/s and is slowing down at 5.0 m/s²?
47. ‖ Your forehead can withstand a force of about 6.0 kN before fracturing, while your cheekbone can only withstand about 1.3 kN.
   a. If a 140 g baseball strikes your head at 30 m/s and stops in 0.0015 s, what is the magnitude of the ball's acceleration?
   b. What is the magnitude of the force that stops the baseball?
   c. What force does the baseball apply to your head? Explain.
   d. Are you in danger of a fracture if the ball hits you in the forehead? In the cheek?
48. ‖‖ Seat belts and air bags save lives by reducing the forces exerted on the driver and passengers in an automobile collision. Cars are designed with a "crumple zone" in the front of the car.

In the event of an impact, the passenger compartment decelerates over a distance of about 1 m as the front of the car crumples. An occupant restrained by seat belts and air bags decelerates with the car. By contrast, an unrestrained occupant keeps moving forward with no loss of speed (Newton's first law!) until hitting the dashboard or windshield, as we saw in Figure 4.2. These are unyielding surfaces, and the unfortunate occupant then decelerates over a distance of only about 5 mm.
   a. A 60 kg person is in a head-on collision. The car's speed at impact is 15 m/s. Estimate the net force on the person if he or she is wearing a seat belt and if the air bag deploys.
   b. Estimate the net force that ultimately stops the person if he or she is not restrained by a seat belt or air bag.
   c. How do these two forces compare to the person's weight?
49. ‖‖‖ Bob, who has a mass of 75 kg, can throw a 500 g rock with a speed of 30 m/s. The distance through which his hand moves as he accelerates the rock forward from rest until he releases it is 1.0 m.
   a. What constant force must Bob exert on the rock to throw it with this speed?
   b. If Bob is standing on frictionless ice, what is his recoil speed after releasing the rock?
50. ‖‖‖ An 80 kg spacewalking astronaut pushes off a 640 kg satellite, exerting a 100 N force for the 0.50 s it takes him to straighten his arms. How far apart are the astronaut and the satellite after 1.0 min?
51. ‖ What thrust does a 200 g model rocket need in order to have a vertical acceleration of 10.0 m/s²
   a. On earth?
   b. On the moon, where $g = 1.62$ m/s²?
52. ‖‖ A 20,000 kg rocket has a rocket motor that generates 3.0×10^5 N of thrust.
   a. What is the rocket's initial upward acceleration?
   b. At an altitude of 5.0 km the rocket's acceleration has increased to 6.0 m/s². What mass of fuel has it burned?
53. ‖‖ You've always wondered about the acceleration of the elevators in the 101-story-tall Empire State Building. One day, while visiting New York, you take your bathroom scales into the elevator and stand on them. The scales read 150 lb as the door closes. The reading varies between 120 lb and 170 lb as the elevator travels 101 floors.
   a. What is the magnitude of the acceleration as the elevator starts upward?
   b. What is the magnitude of the acceleration as the elevator brakes to a stop?
54. ‖‖‖ A 23 kg child goes down a straight slide inclined 38° above horizontal. The child is acted on by his weight, the normal force from the slide, kinetic friction, and a horizontal rope exerting a 30 N force as shown in Figure P5.54. How large is the normal force of the slide on the child?

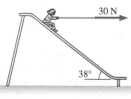

FIGURE P5.54

55. ‖ Josh starts his sled at the top of a 3.0-m-high hill that has a constant slope of 25°. After reaching the bottom, he slides across a horizontal patch of snow. The hill is frictionless, but the coefficient of kinetic friction between his sled and the snow is 0.05. How far from the base of the hill does he end up?
56. ‖ A wood block, after being given a starting push, slides down a wood ramp at a constant speed. What is the angle of the ramp above horizontal?

57. ‖ Researchers often use *force plates* to measure the forces
BIO that people exert against the floor during movement. A force
INT plate works like a bathroom scale, but it keeps a record of how
the reading changes with time. Figure P5.57 shows the data
from a force plate as a woman jumps straight up and then
lands.
    a. What was the vertical component of her acceleration during
       push-off?
    b. What was the vertical component of her acceleration while
       in the air?
    c. What was the vertical component of her acceleration during
       the landing?
    d. What was her speed as her feet left the force plate?
    e. How high did she jump?

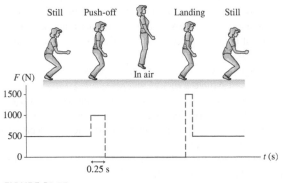

FIGURE P5.57

58. ‖‖‖ A 77 kg sprinter is running the 100 m dash. At one instant,
BIO early in the race, his acceleration is 4.7 m/s².
    a. What *total* force does the track surface exert on the sprinter?
       Assume his acceleration is parallel to the ground. Give
       your answer as a magnitude and an angle with respect to
       the horizontal.
    b. This force is applied to one foot (the other foot is in the air),
       which for a fraction of a second is stationary with respect to
       the track surface. Because the foot is stationary, the net force
       on it must be zero. Thus the force of the lower leg bone on
       the foot is equal but opposite to the force of the track on the
       foot. If the lower leg bone is 60° from horizontal, what are
       the components of the leg's force on the foot in the direc-
       tions parallel and perpendicular to the leg? (Force compo-
       nents perpendicular to the leg can cause dislocation of the
       ankle joint.)

59. ‖‖‖ Sam, whose mass is 75 kg, takes off across level snow on his
jet-powered skis. The skis have a thrust of 200 N and a coefficient of kinetic friction on snow of 0.10. Unfortunately, the skis
run out of fuel after only 10 s.
    a. What is Sam's top speed?
    b. How far has Sam traveled when he finally coasts to a
       stop?

60. ‖‖‖ A person with compromised pinch
strength in his fingers can only exert a nor-
BIO mal force of 6.0 N to either side of a pinch-
held object, such as the book shown in
Figure P5.60. What is the heaviest book he
can hold onto vertically before it slips out of
his fingers? The coefficient of static friction
of the surface between the fingers and the
book cover is 0.80.

FIGURE P5.60

61. ‖‖ A 1.0 kg wood block is pressed against a
vertical wood wall by a 12 N force as shown
in Figure P5.61. If the block is initially at
rest, will it move upward, move downward,
or stay at rest?

FIGURE P5.61

62. ‖‖‖‖ A 50,000 kg locomotive, with steel
wheels, is traveling at 10 m/s on steel rails
when its engine and brakes both fail. How far will the locomotive roll before it comes to a stop?

63. ‖ An Airbus A320 jetliner has a takeoff mass of 75,000 kg. It
reaches its takeoff speed of 82 m/s (180 mph) in 35 s. What is
the thrust of the engines? You can neglect air resistance but not
rolling friction.

64. ‖‖‖‖ A 2.0 kg wood block is launched up a wooden ramp that is
inclined at a 35° angle. The block's initial speed is 10 m/s.
    a. What vertical height does the block reach above its starting
       point?
    b. What speed does it have when it slides back down to its
       starting point?

65. ‖‖‖ Two blocks are at rest
on a frictionless incline,
as shown in Figure P5.65.
What are the tensions in
the two strings?

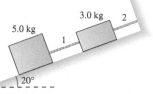

FIGURE P5.65

66. ‖ Two identical blocks
are stacked one on top
of the other. The bottom
block is free to slide on a frictionless surface. The coefficient
of static friction between the blocks is 0.35. What is the maximum horizontal force that can be applied to the lower block
without the upper block slipping?

67. ‖‖‖ A wood block is sliding up a wood ramp. If the ramp is very
steep, the block will reverse direction at its highest point and
slide back down. If the ramp is shallow, the block will stop
when it reaches its highest point. What is the smallest ramp
angle, measured from the horizontal, for which the block will
slide back down?

68. ‖‖‖‖ The fastest recorded skydive was by an Air Force officer
who jumped from a helium balloon at an elevation of
103,000 ft, three times higher than airliners fly. Because the
density of air is so low at these altitudes, he reached a speed
of 614 mph at an elevation of 90,000 ft, then gradually
slowed as the air became more dense. Assume that he fell in
the spread-eagle position of Example 5.15 and that his low-
altitude terminal speed is 125 mph. Use this information to
determine the density of air at 90,000 ft.

69. ‖‖‖‖ A 2.7 g Ping-Pong ball has a diameter of 4.0 cm.
    a. The ball is shot straight up at twice its terminal speed. What
       is its initial acceleration?
    b. The ball is shot straight down at twice its terminal speed.
       What is its initial acceleration?

70. ‖‖‖‖ Two blocks are connected by a string as in Figure P5.70.
What is the upper block's acceleration if the coefficient of
kinetic friction between the block and the table is 0.20?

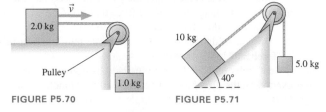

FIGURE P5.70   FIGURE P5.71

71. ||||| The 10 kg block in Figure P5.71 slides down a frictionless ramp. What is its acceleration?

72. || A 2.0 kg wood block is pulled along a wood floor at a steady speed. A second wood block, with mass 3.0 kg, is attached to the first by a horizontal string. What is the magnitude of the force pulling on the first block?

73. ||||| A magician pulls a tablecloth out from under some dishes. How far do the dishes move during the 0.25 s it takes to pull out the tablecloth? The coefficient of kinetic friction between the cloth and the dishes is $\mu_k = 0.12$.

74. || The 100 kg block in Figure P5.74 takes 6.0 s to reach the floor after being released from rest. What is the mass of the block on the left?

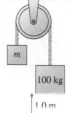
m
100 kg
1.0 m

FIGURE P5.74

Problems 75 and 76 show free-body diagrams. For each,

a. Write a realistic dynamics problem for which this is the correct free-body diagram. Your problem should ask a question that can be answered with a value of position or velocity (such as "How far?" or "How fast?"), and should give sufficient information to allow a solution.

b. Solve your problem!

75. |

76. ||||

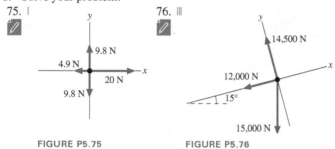

FIGURE P5.75   **FIGURE P5.76**

In Problems 77 through 79 you are given the dynamics equations that are used to solve a problem. For each of these, you are to

a. Write a realistic problem for which these are the correct equations.

b. Draw the free-body diagram and the pictorial representation for your problem.

c. Finish the solution of the problem.

77. || $-0.80n = (1500 \text{ kg})a_x$
    $n - (1500 \text{ kg})(9.8 \text{ m/s}^2) = 0$

78. || $T - 0.2n - (20 \text{ kg})(9.8 \text{ m/s}^2)\sin 20° = (20 \text{ kg})(2.0 \text{ m/s}^2)$
    $n - (20 \text{ kg})(9.8 \text{ m/s}^2)\cos 20° = 0$

79. || $(100 \text{ N})\cos 30° - f_k = (20 \text{ kg})a_x$
    $n + (100 \text{ N})\sin 30° - (20 \text{ kg})(9.8 \text{ m/s}^2) = 0$
    $f_k = 0.20n$

Passage Problems

Sliding on the Ice

In the winter sport of curling, players give a 20 kg stone a push across a sheet of ice. The stone moves approximately 40 m before coming to rest. The final position of the stone, in principle, only depends on the initial speed at which it is launched and the force of friction between the ice and the stone, but team members can use brooms to sweep the ice in front of the stone to adjust its speed and trajectory a bit; they must do this without touching the stone. Judicious sweeping can lengthen the travel of the stone by 3 m.

80. | A curler pushes a stone to a speed of 3.0 m/s over a time of 2.0 s. Ignoring the force of friction, how much force must the curler apply to the stone to bring it up to speed?
    A. 3.0 N   B. 15 N   C. 30 N   D. 150 N

81. | The sweepers in a curling competition adjust the trajectory of the stone by
    A. Decreasing the coefficient of friction between the stone and the ice.
    B. Increasing the coefficient of friction between the stone and the ice.
    C. Changing friction from kinetic to static.
    D. Changing friction from static to kinetic.

82. | Suppose the stone is launched with a speed of 3 m/s and travels 40 m before coming to rest. What is the *approximate* magnitude of the friction force on the stone?
    A. 0 N   B. 2 N   C. 20 N   D. 200 N

83. | Suppose the stone's mass is increased to 40 kg, but it is launched at the same 3 m/s. Which one of the following is true?
    A. The stone would now travel a longer distance before coming to rest.
    B. The stone would now travel a shorter distance before coming to rest.
    C. The coefficient of friction would now be greater.
    D. The force of friction would now be greater.

STOP TO THINK ANSWERS

Stop to Think 5.1: A. The lander is descending and slowing. The acceleration vector points upward, and so $\vec{F}_{net}$ points upward. This can be true only if the thrust has a larger magnitude than the weight.

Stop to Think 5.2: D. When you are in the air, there is *no* contact force supporting you, so your apparent weight is zero: You are weightless.

Stop to Think 5.3: $f_B > f_C = f_D = f_E > f_A$. Situations C, D, and E are all kinetic friction, which does not depend on either velocity or acceleration. Kinetic friction is less than the maximum static friction that is exerted in B. $f_A = 0$ because no friction is needed to keep the object at rest.

Stop to Think 5.4: D. The ball is shot *down* at 30 m/s, so $v_{0y} = -30$ m/s. This exceeds the terminal speed, so the upward drag force is *greater* than the downward weight force. Thus the ball *slows down* even though it is "falling." It will slow until $v_y = -15$ m/s, the terminal velocity, then maintain that velocity.

Stop to Think 5.5: B. $F_{QonH} = F_{HonQ}$ and $F_{PonQ} = F_{QonP}$ because these are action/reaction pairs. Box Q is slowing down and therefore must have a net force to the left. So from Newton's second law we also know that $F_{HonQ} > F_{PonQ}$.

Stop to Think 5.6: Equal to. Each block is hanging in equilibrium, with no net force, so the upward tension force is mg.

6 Circular Motion, Orbits, and Gravity

Motorcyclists in the "Globe of Death" ride their bikes on the inside of a spherical steel frame, seeming to defy gravity as they ride up the sides and upside down over the top. What prevents them from falling?

LOOKING AHEAD ▶

The goal of Chapter 6 is to learn about motion in a circle, including orbital motion under the influence of a gravitational force.

Uniform Circular Motion

A particle moving in a circle at a constant speed undergoes **uniform circular motion**. In this chapter you'll learn how to describe a particle's motion in terms of its *angular* position and *angular* velocity.

We'll also review the important idea that a particle moving in a circle has an acceleration directed toward the center of the circle.

> **Looking Back ◀◀**
> 2.2 Uniform motion
> 3.8 Circular motion

The acceleration points toward the center of the circle.

Dynamics of Uniform Circular Motion

Because a particle moving in a circle has an acceleration that points toward the center of the circle, there must be a net force toward the center to cause this acceleration.

> **Looking Back ◀◀**
> 5.2 Using Newton's second law

 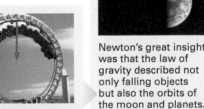

The net force on the girl is directed toward the center of the circle.

The normal force of the track and the car's weight combine to provide a net force toward the circle's center.

Apparent Forces in Circular Motion

An object moving in a circle appears to experience a force that "flings" it outward. You'll learn that these apparent forces are not real forces, but are in fact a consequence of Newton's first law.

> **Looking Back ◀◀**
> 5.3 Weight and apparent weight

What holds these riders in this carnival ride against the wall?

Newton's Law of Gravity

Newton discovered the law that governs gravity. You'll learn how it applies to an apple falling to earth or a rock falling on the moon, and how this law governs the motions of the moon, the planets, and even distant galaxies.

Newton's great insight was that the law of gravity described not only falling objects but also the orbits of the moon and planets.

Even the structure of distant galaxies is determined by Newton's law of gravity.

Gravity and Orbits

If an object moves fast enough, it can orbit the earth, the sun, or another planet.

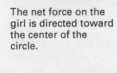 

An orbit can be thought of as projectile motion where the ground curves away just as fast as the object falls.

The space station appears weightless, but gravity still acts strongly on it; only its *apparent weight* is zero.

6.1 Uniform Circular Motion

We began our study of circular motion in Section 3.8. There, we learned how to describe the circular motion of a particle in terms of its period and frequency. We also learned that a particle moving in a circle has an acceleration—even if the particle's speed is constant—because the *direction* of its velocity is constantly changing.

In this chapter, we'll study the simplest kind of circular motion, in which a particle moves at a *constant* speed around its circular path. FIGURE 6.1 shows a particle undergoing this uniform circular motion. The particle might be a satellite moving in an orbit, a ball on the end of a string, or even just a dot painted on the side of a wheel. Regardless of what the particle represents, its velocity vector is always tangent to the circular path. The particle's speed v is constant, so the vector's length stays constant as the particle moves around the circle.

FIGURE 6.1 A particle in uniform circular motion.

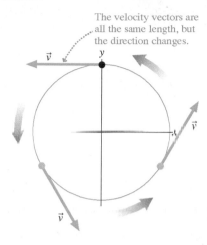

The velocity vectors are all the same length, but the direction changes.

Angular Position

In order to describe the position of a particle as it moves around the circle, it is convenient to use the angle θ from the positive x-axis. This is shown in FIGURE 6.2. Because the particle travels in a circle with a fixed radius r, specifying θ completely locates the position of the particle. Thus we call angle θ the **angular position** of the particle.

We define θ to be positive when measured *counterclockwise* from the positive x-axis. An angle measured *clockwise* from the positive x-axis has a negative value. "Clockwise" and "counterclockwise" in circular motion are analogous, respectively, to "left of the origin" and "right of the origin" in linear motion, which we associated with negative and positive values of x.

Rather than measure angles in degrees, mathematicians and scientists usually measure angle θ in the angular unit of *radians*. In Figure 6.2, we also show the **arc length** s, the distance that the particle has traveled along its circular path. We define the particle's angle θ in **radians** in terms of this arc length and the radius of the circle:

$$\theta \text{ (radians)} = \frac{s}{r} \qquad (6.1)$$

FIGURE 6.2 A particle's angular position is described by angle θ.

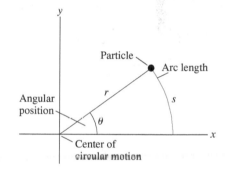

This is a sensible definition of an angle. The farther the particle has traveled around the circle (i.e., the greater s is), the larger the angle θ in radians. The radian, abbreviated rad, is the SI unit of angle. An angle of 1 rad has an arc length s exactly equal to the radius r. An important consequence of Equation 6.1 is that the arc length spanning the angle θ is

$$s = r\theta \qquad (6.2)$$

NOTE ▶ Equation 6.2 is valid only if θ is measured in radians, not degrees. This very simple relationship between angle and arc length is one of the primary motivations for using radians. ◀

When a particle travels all the way around the circle—completing one *revolution*, abbreviated rev—the arc length it travels is the circle's circumference $2\pi r$. Thus the angle of a full circle is

$$\theta_{\text{full circle}} = \frac{s}{r} = \frac{2\pi r}{r} = 2\pi \text{ rad}$$

We can use this fact to define conversion factors among revolutions, radians, and degrees:

$$1 \text{ rev} = 360° = 2\pi \text{ rad}$$

$$1 \text{ rad} = 1 \text{ rad} \times \frac{360°}{2\pi \text{ rad}} = 57.3°$$

We will often specify angles in degrees, but keep in mind that the SI unit is the radian. You can visualize angles in radians by remembering that 1 rad is just about 60°.

Angular Displacement and Angular Velocity

For the *linear* motion you studied in Chapters 1 and 2, a particle with a larger velocity undergoes a greater displacement in each second than one with a smaller velocity, as FIGURE 6.3a shows. FIGURE 6.3b shows two particles undergoing uniform *circular* motion. The particle on the left is moving slowly around the circle; it has gone only one-quarter of the way around after 5 seconds. The particle on the right is moving much faster around the circle, covering half of the circle in the same 5 seconds. You can see that the particle to the right undergoes twice the **angular displacement** $\Delta\theta$ during each interval as the particle to the left. Its **angular velocity,** the angular displacement through which the particle moves each second, is twice as large.

FIGURE 6.3 Comparing uniform linear and circular motion.

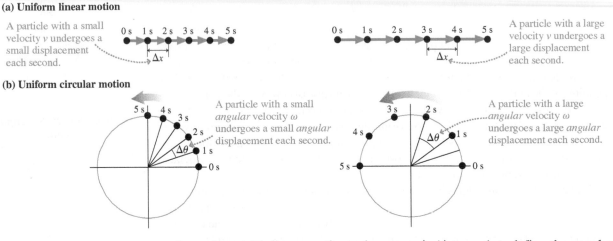

(a) Uniform linear motion

A particle with a small velocity *v* undergoes a small displacement each second.

A particle with a large velocity *v* undergoes a large displacement each second.

(b) Uniform circular motion

A particle with a small *angular* velocity ω undergoes a small *angular* displacement each second.

A particle with a large *angular* velocity ω undergoes a large *angular* displacement each second.

In analogy with linear motion, where $v_x = \Delta x/\Delta t$, we thus define the angular velocity as

$$\omega = \frac{\text{angular displacement}}{\text{time interval}} = \frac{\Delta\theta}{\Delta t} \qquad (6.3)$$

Angular velocity of a particle in uniform circular motion

The symbol ω is a lowercase Greek omega, *not* an ordinary *w*. The SI unit of angular velocity is rad/s.

Figure 6.3a shows that the displacement Δx of a particle in uniform linear motion changes by the same amount each second. Similarly, as Figure 6.3b shows, the *angular* displacement $\Delta\theta$ of a particle in uniform *circular* motion changes by the same amount each second. This means that **the angular velocity $\omega = \Delta\theta/\Delta t$ is constant for a particle moving with uniform circular motion.**

EXAMPLE 6.1   Comparing angular velocities

Find the angular velocities of the two particles in Figure 6.3b.

PREPARE For uniform circular motion, we can use any angular displacement $\Delta\theta$, as long as we use the corresponding time interval Δt. For each particle, we'll choose the angular displacement corresponding to the motion from $t = 0$ s to $t = 5$ s.

SOLVE The particle on the left travels one-quarter of a full circle during the 5 s time interval. We learned earlier that a full circle corresponds to an angle of 2π rad, so the angular displacement for this particle is $\Delta\theta = (2\pi \text{ rad})/4 = \pi/2$ rad. Thus its angular velocity is

$$\omega = \frac{\Delta\theta}{\Delta t} = \frac{\pi/2 \text{ rad}}{5 \text{ s}} = 0.31 \text{ rad/s}$$

The particle on the right travels halfway around the circle, or π rad, in the 5 s interval. Its angular velocity is

$$\omega = \frac{\Delta\theta}{\Delta t} = \frac{\pi \text{ rad}}{5 \text{ s}} = 0.63 \text{ rad/s}$$

ASSESS The angular velocity of the particle on the right is 0.63 rad/s, meaning that the particle travels through an angle of 0.63 rad each second. Because 1 rad $\approx 60°$, 0.63 rad is roughly 35°. In Figure 6.3b, the particle on the right appears to move through an angle of about this size during each 1 s time interval, so our answer is reasonable.

Angular velocity, like the velocity v_x of one-dimensional motion, can be positive or negative. The signs for ω noted in FIGURE 6.4 are based on the convention that angles are positive when measured counterclockwise from the positive x-axis.

We've already noted how circular motion is analogous to linear motion, with angular variables replacing linear variables. Thus much of what you learned about linear kinematics and dynamics carries over to circular motion. For example, Equation 2.4 gave us a formula for computing a linear displacement during a time interval:

$$x_f - x_i = \Delta x = v_x \Delta t$$

You can see from Equation 6.3 that we can write a similar equation for the angular displacement:

$$\theta_f - \theta_i = \Delta\theta = \omega \Delta t \qquad (6.4)$$

Angular displacement for uniform circular motion

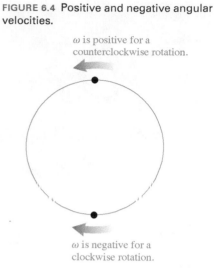

FIGURE 6.4 Positive and negative angular velocities.

ω is positive for a counterclockwise rotation.

ω is negative for a clockwise rotation.

For linear motion, we use the term *speed v* when we are not concerned with the direction of motion, *velocity v_x* when we are. For circular motion, we define the **angular speed** to be the absolute value of the angular velocity, so that it's a positive quantity irrespective of the particle's direction of rotation. Although potentially confusing, it is customary to use the symbol ω for angular speed *and* for angular velocity. If the direction of rotation is not important, we will interpret ω to mean angular speed. In kinematic equations, such as Equation 6.4, ω is always the angular velocity, and you need to use a negative value for clockwise rotation.

EXAMPLE 6.2   Kinematics at the roulette wheel

A small steel ball rolls counterclockwise around the inside of a 30.0-cm-diameter roulette wheel. The ball completes exactly 2 rev in 1.20 s.

a. What is the ball's angular velocity?
b. What is the ball's angular position at $t = 2.00$ s? Assume $\theta_i = 0$.

PREPARE Treat the ball as a particle in uniform circular motion.

SOLVE

a. The ball's angular velocity is $\omega = \Delta\theta/\Delta t$. We know that the ball completes 2 revolutions in 1.20 s, and that each revolution corresponds to an angular displacement $\Delta\theta = 2\pi$ rad. Thus

$$\omega = \frac{2(2\pi \text{ rad})}{1.20 \text{ s}} = 10.5 \text{ rad/s}$$

Because the rotation direction is counterclockwise, the angular velocity is positive.

b. The ball moves with constant angular velocity, so its angular position is given by Equation 6.4. Thus the ball's angular position at $t = 2.00$ s is

$$\theta_f = \theta_i + \omega \Delta t = 0 \text{ rad} + (10.5 \text{ rad/s})(2.00 \text{ s}) = 21.0 \text{ rad}$$

If we're interested in where the ball is in the wheel at $t = 2.00$ s, we can write its angular position as an integer multiple of 2π (representing the number of complete revolutions the ball has made) plus a remainder:

$$\theta_f = 21.0 \text{ rad} = 3.34 \times 2\pi \text{ rad}$$
$$= 3 \times 2\pi \text{ rad} + 0.34 \times 2\pi \text{ rad}$$
$$= 3 \times 2\pi \text{ rad} + 2.1 \text{ rad}$$

In other words, at $t = 2.00$ s, the ball has completed 3 rev and is 2.1 rad = 120° into its fourth revolution. An observer would say that the ball's angular position is $\theta = 120°$.

ASSESS Since the ball completes 2 revolutions in 1.20 s, it seems reasonable that it completes 3.34 revolutions in 2.00 s.

The angular speed ω is closely related to the period T and the frequency f of the motion. If a particle in uniform circular motion moves around a circle once, which by definition takes time T, its angular displacement is $\Delta\theta = 2\pi$ rad. The angular speed is thus

$$\omega = \frac{2\pi \text{ rad}}{T} \qquad (6.5)$$

◄ Why do clocks go clockwise? In the northern hemisphere, the rotation of the earth causes the sun to follow a circular arc through the southern sky, rising in the east and setting in the west. For millennia, humans have marked passing time by noting the position of shadows cast by the sun, which sweep in an arc from west to east—eventually leading to the development of the sundial, the first practical timekeeping device. In the northern hemisphere, sundials point north, and the shadow sweeps around the dial from left to right. Early clockmakers used the same convention, which is how it came to be clockwise.

We can also write the angular speed in terms of the frequency $f = 1/T$:

$$\omega = (2\pi \text{ rad})f \qquad (6.6)$$

where f must be in rev/s. For example, a particle in circular motion with frequency 10 rev/s would have angular speed $\omega = 20\pi$ rad/s = 62.8 rad/s.

EXAMPLE 6.3   Rotations in a car engine

The crankshaft in your car engine is turning at 3000 rpm. What is the shaft's angular velocity?

PREPARE We'll need to convert rpm to rev/s; then we can use Equation 6.6.

SOLVE We convert rpm to rev/s by

$$\left(3000 \, \frac{\text{rev}}{\text{min}}\right)\left(\frac{1 \text{ min}}{60 \text{ s}}\right) = 50 \text{ rev/s}$$

Thus the crankshaft's angular velocity is

$$\omega = (2\pi \text{ rad})f = (2\pi \text{ rad})(50 \text{ rev/s}) = 314 \text{ rad/s}$$

Angular-Position and Angular-Velocity Graphs

FIGURE 6.5 Angular position for the ball on the roulette wheel.

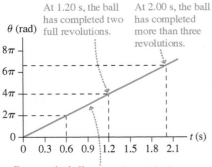

Because the ball moves at a constant angular velocity, a graph of the angular position versus time is a straight line.

For the one-dimensional motion you studied in Chapter 3, we found that position- and velocity-versus-time graphs were important and useful representations of motion. We can use the same kinds of graphs to represent angular motion. Let's begin by considering the motion of the roulette ball of Example 6.2. We found that it had angular velocity $\omega = 10.5$ rad/s, meaning that its angular *position* changed by $+10.5$ rad every second. This is exactly analogous to the one-dimensional motion problem of a car driving in a straight line with a velocity of 10.5 m/s, so that its position increases by 10.5 m each second. Using this analogy, we can construct the **angular position-versus-time graph** for the roulette ball shown in FIGURE 6.5.

The angular velocity is given by $\omega = \Delta\theta/\Delta t$. Graphically, this is the *slope* of the angular position-versus-time graph, just as the ordinary velocity is the slope of the position-versus-time graph. Thus we can create an **angular velocity-versus-time graph** by finding the slope of the corresponding angular position-versus-time graph.

EXAMPLE 6.4   Graphing a bike ride

Jake rides his bicycle home from campus. FIGURE 6.6 is the angular position-versus-time graph for a small rock stuck in the tread of his tire. First, draw the rock's angular velocity-versus-position graph, using rpm on the vertical axis. Then interpret the graphs with a story about Jake's ride.

PREPARE Angular velocity ω is the slope of the angular position-versus-time graph.

SOLVE We can see that $\omega = 0$ rad/s during the first and last 30 s of Jake's ride because the horizontal segments of the graph have zero slope. Between $t = 30$ s and $t = 150$ s, an interval of 120 s,

FIGURE 6.6 Angular position-versus-time graph for Jake's bike ride.

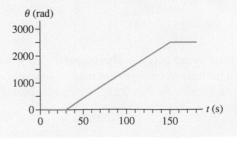

the rock's angular velocity (the slope of the angular position-versus-time graph) is

$$\omega = \text{slope} = \frac{2500 \text{ rad} - 0 \text{ rad}}{120 \text{ s}} = 20.8 \text{ rad/s}$$

We need to convert this to rpm:

$$\omega = \left(\frac{20.8 \text{ rad}}{1 \text{ s}}\right)\left(\frac{1 \text{ rev}}{2\pi \text{ rad}}\right)\left(\frac{60 \text{ s}}{1 \text{ min}}\right) = 200 \text{ rpm}$$

These values have been used to draw the angular velocity-versus-time graph of **FIGURE 6.7**. It looks like Jake waited 30 s for the light to change, then pedaled so that the bike wheel turned at a constant angular velocity of 200 rpm. 2.0 min later, he quickly braked to a stop for another 30-s-long red light.

FIGURE 6.7 Angular velocity-versus-time graph for Jake's bike ride.

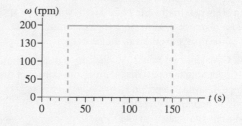

ASSESS At 200 rpm for 2 minutes, the wheel would turn roughly 400 times or, at ≈6 rad/rev, through about 2400 rad. Our answer seems reasonable.

STOP TO THINK 6.1   Which particle has angular position $5\pi/2$?

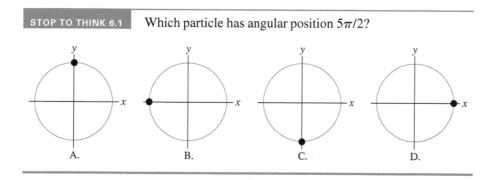

A.   B.   C.   D.

6.2 Speed, Velocity, and Acceleration in Uniform Circular Motion

The preceding section described uniform circular motion in terms of angular variables. In Chapter 3, we introduced a description of uniform circular motion in terms of velocity and acceleration vectors. We will now unite these two different descriptions, which will enable us to consider a much wider range of problems.

Speed

In Chapter 3, we found that the speed of a particle moving with frequency f around a circular path of radius r is $v = 2\pi f r$. If we combine this result with Equation 6.5 for the angular speed, we find that speed v and angular speed ω are related by

$$v = \omega r \qquad (6.7)$$

Relationship between speed and angular speed

NOTE ▶ In Equation 6.7, ω **must be in units of rad/s.** If you are given a frequency in rev/s or rpm, you should convert it to an angular speed in rad/s. ◀

EXAMPLE 6.5 **Finding the speed at two points on a CD**

The diameter of an audio compact disc is 12.0 cm. When the disc is spinning at its maximum rate of 540 rpm, what is the speed of a point (a) at a distance 3.0 cm from the center and (b) at the outside edge of the disc, 6.0 cm from the center?

PREPARE Consider two points A and B on the rotating compact disc in FIGURE 6.8. During one period T, the disc rotates once, and both points rotate through the same angle, 2π rad. Thus the angular speed, $\omega = 2\pi/T$, is the same for these two points; in fact, it is the same for all points on the disc. But as they go around one time, the two points move different *distances;* the outer point B goes around a larger circle. The two points thus have different *speeds.* We can solve this problem by first finding the angular speed of the disc and then computing the speeds at the two points.

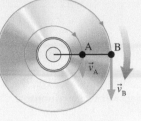
FIGURE 6.8 The rotation of an audio compact disc.

SOLVE We first convert the frequency of the disc from rpm to rev/s:

$$f = \left(540 \frac{\text{rev}}{\text{min}}\right) \times \left(\frac{1 \text{ min}}{60 \text{ s}}\right) = 9.00 \text{ rev/s}$$

We can compute the angular speed using Equation 6.6:

$$\omega = (2\pi \text{ rad})(9.00 \text{ rev/s}) = 56.5 \text{ rad/s}$$

We can now use Equation 6.7 to compute the speeds of points on the disc. At point A, $r = 3.0$ cm $= 0.030$ m, so the speed is

$$v_B = \omega r = (56.5 \text{ rad/s})(0.030 \text{ m}) = 1.7 \text{ m/s}$$

At point B, $r = 6.0$ cm $= 0.060$ m, so the speed at the outside edge is

$$v_B = \omega r = (56.5 \text{ rad/s})(0.060 \text{ m}) = 3.4 \text{ m/s}$$

ASSESS The speeds are a few meters per second, which seems reasonable. The point farther from the center is moving at a higher speed, as we expected.

FIGURE 6.9 Velocity and acceleration for uniform circular motion.

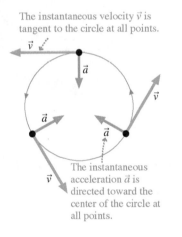

The instantaneous velocity $\vec{v}$ is tangent to the circle at all points.

The instantaneous acceleration $\vec{a}$ is directed toward the center of the circle at all points.

Velocity and Acceleration

Although the *speed* of a particle in uniform circular motion is constant, its *velocity* is not constant because the *direction* of the motion is always changing. As you learned in Chapter 3, and as FIGURE 6.9 reminds you, there is an acceleration at every point in the motion, with the acceleration vector $\vec{a}$ pointing toward the center of the circle. We called this the *centripetal acceleration,* and we showed that for uniform circular motion the acceleration was given by $a = v^2/r$. Because $v = \omega r$, we can also write this relationship in terms of the angular speed:

$$a = \frac{v^2}{r} = \omega^2 r \qquad (6.8)$$

Centripetal acceleration for uniform circular motion

QUADRATIC

Acceleration depends on speed, but also distance from the center of the circle.

CONCEPTUAL EXAMPLE 6.6 **Who has the larger acceleration?**

Two children are riding in circles on a merry-go-round, as shown in FIGURE 6.10. Which child experiences the larger acceleration?

FIGURE 6.10 Top view of a merry-go-round.

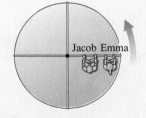

Jacob Emma

REASON As Example 6.2 showed, all points on the merry-go-round move at the same angular speed. The second expression for the acceleration in Equation 6.8 tells us that $a = \omega^2 r$. As the two children are moving with the same angular speed, Emma, with a larger value of r, experiences a larger acceleration.

ASSESS In Example 6.5, we saw that points farther from the center move at a higher speed. This would imply a higher acceleration as well, so our answer makes sense.

| EXAMPLE 6.7 | **Finding the period of a carnival ride** |

In the Quasar carnival ride, passengers travel in a horizontal 5.0-m-radius circle. For safe operation, the maximum sustained acceleration that riders may experience is 20 m/s², approximately twice the free-fall acceleration. What is the period of the ride when it is being operated at the maximum acceleration?

FIGURE 6.11 Visual overview for the Quasar carnival ride.

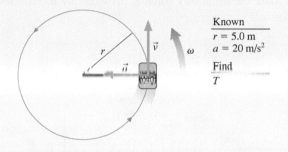

Known
$r = 5.0$ m
$a = 20$ m/s²

Find
T

PREPARE We will assume that the cars on the ride are in uniform circular motion. The visual overview of **FIGURE 6.11** shows a top view of the motion of the ride.

SOLVE The angular speed can be computed from the acceleration by rearranging Equation 6.8:

$$\omega = \sqrt{\frac{a}{r}} = \sqrt{\frac{20 \text{ m/s}^2}{5.0 \text{ m}}} = 2.0 \text{ rad/s}$$

At this angular speed, the period is $T = 2\pi/\omega = 3.1$ s.

ASSESS One rotation in just over 3 seconds seems reasonable for a pretty zippy carnival ride. The period for this particular ride is actually 3.7 s, so it runs a bit slower than the maximum safe speed.

| STOP TO THINK 6.2 | Rank in order, from largest to smallest, the centripetal accelerations of particles A to D.

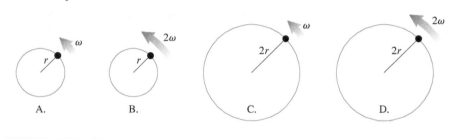

A.   B.   C.   D.

Hurling the heavy hammer This man is throwing a hammer that weighs over 30 pounds as far as he can by spinning the hammer around in a circle and then letting go. While he holds the handle, the hammer follows a circular path. He must provide a very large force directed toward the center of the circle to produce the centripetal acceleration, as you can see by how he is leaning away from the hammer. When he lets go, there is no longer a force directed toward the center, and the hammer will stop going in a circle and fly across the field.

6.3 Dynamics of Uniform Circular Motion

Riders traveling around on a circular carnival ride are accelerating, as we have just seen. Consequently, according to Newton's second law, the riders must have a net *force* acting on them. In this section, we'll look at the forces that cause uniform circular motion.

We've already determined the acceleration of a particle in uniform circular motion—the centripetal acceleration of Equation 6.8. Newton's second law tells us what the net force must be to cause this acceleration:

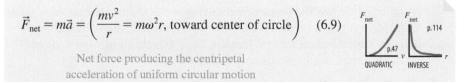

$$\vec{F}_{\text{net}} = m\vec{a} = \left(\frac{mv^2}{r} = m\omega^2 r, \text{ toward center of circle} \right) \quad (6.9)$$

Net force producing the centripetal acceleration of uniform circular motion

In other words, **a particle of mass *m* moving at constant speed *v* around a circle of radius *r* must always have a net force of magnitude $mv^2/r = m\omega^2 r$ pointing toward the center of the circle,** as in **FIGURE 6.12**. It is this net force that causes the centripetal acceleration of circular motion. Without such a net force, the particle would move off in a straight line tangent to the circle.

The force described by Equation 6.9 is not a *new* kind of force. The net force will be due to one or more of our familiar forces, such as tension, friction, or the normal

FIGURE 6.12 Net force for circular motion.

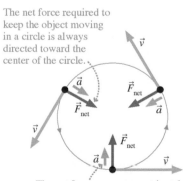

The net force required to keep the object moving in a circle is always directed toward the center of the circle.

The net force causes a centripetal acceleration.

force. Equation 6.9 simply tells us how the net force needs to act—how strongly and in which direction—to cause the particle to move with speed v in a circle of radius r.

In each example of circular motion that we will consider in this chapter, a physical force or a combination of forces directed toward the center produces the necessary acceleration. In some cases, the circular motion and the force are obvious, as in the hammer throw. Other cases are more subtle. For instance, for a car following a circular path on a level road, the necessary force is provided by the friction force between the tires and the road.

CONCEPTUAL EXAMPLE 6.8   **Forces on a car**

A car drives through a circularly shaped valley at a constant speed. At the very bottom of the valley, is the normal force of the road on the car greater than, less than, or equal to the car's weight?

REASON FIGURE 6.13 shows a visual overview of the situation. The car is accelerating, even though it is moving at a constant speed, because its direction is changing. When the car is at the bottom of the valley, the center of its circular path is directly above it and so its acceleration vector points straight up. The free-body diagram of Figure 6.13 identifies the only two forces acting on the car as the normal force, pointing upward, and its weight, pointing downward. Which is larger: n or w?

Because $\vec{a}$ points upward, by Newton's second law there must be a net force on the car that also points upward. In order for this to be the case, the free-body diagram shows that the magnitude of the normal force must be *greater* than the weight.

FIGURE 6.13 Visual overview for the car in the valley.

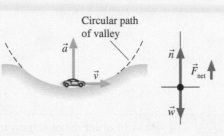

ASSESS You have probably experienced this situation. As you drive through a dip in the road, you feel "heavier" than normal. As discussed in Section 5.3, this is because your apparent weight—the normal force that supports you—is greater than your true weight.

Solving Circular Dynamics Problems

4.2–4.5   Activ Physics

We have one basic equation for circular dynamics problems, Equation 6.9, which is just a version of Newton's second law. The techniques for solving circular dynamics problems are thus quite similar to those we have used for solving other Newton's second-law problems.

PROBLEM-SOLVING STRATEGY 6.1   **Circular dynamics problems**   (MP)™

PREPARE Begin your visual overview with a pictorial representation in which you sketch the motion, define symbols, define axes, and identify what the problem is trying to find. There are two common situations:

■ If the motion is in a horizontal plane, like a tabletop, draw the free-body diagram with the circle viewed edge-on, the x-axis pointing toward the center of the circle, and the y-axis perpendicular to the plane of the circle.

■ If the motion is in a vertical plane, like a Ferris wheel, draw the free-body diagram with the circle viewed face-on, the x-axis pointing toward the center of the circle, and the y-axis tangent to the circle.

SOLVE Newton's second law for uniform circular motion, $\vec{F}_{net} = (mv^2/r$, toward center of circle), is a vector equation. Some forces act in the plane of the circle, some act perpendicular to the circle, and some may have components in both directions. In the coordinate system described above, with the x-axis pointing toward the center of the circle, Newton's second law is

$$\sum F_x = \frac{mv^2}{r} = m\omega^2 r \quad \text{and} \quad \sum F_y = 0$$

Continued

That is, the net force toward the center of the circle has magnitude $mv^2/r = m\omega^2 r$ while the net force perpendicular to the circle is zero. The components of the forces are found directly from the free-body diagram. Depending on the problem, either:

- Use the net force to determine the speed v, then use circular kinematics to find frequencies or angular velocities.
- Use circular kinematics to determine the speed v, then solve for unknown forces.

ASSESS Make sure your net force points toward the center of the circle. Check that your result has the correct units, is reasonable, and answers the question.

Exercise 13

EXAMPLE 6.9   **Analyzing the motion of a cart**

An energetic father places his 20 kg child on a 5.0 kg cart to which a 2.0-m-long rope is attached. He then holds the end of the rope and spins the cart and child around in a circle, keeping the rope parallel to the ground. If the tension in the rope is 100 N, how much time does it take for the cart to make one rotation?

PREPARE We proceed according to the steps of Problem-Solving Strategy 6.1. FIGURE 6.14 shows a visual overview of the problem. The main reason for the pictorial representation on the left is to illustrate the relevant geometry and to define the symbols that will be used. A circular dynamics problem usually does not have starting and ending points like a projectile problem, so subscripts such as x_i or y_f are usually not needed. Here we need to define the cart's speed v and the radius r of the circle.

The object moving in the circle is the cart plus the child, a total mass of 25 kg; the free-body diagram shows the forces. Because the motion is in a horizontal plane, Problem-Solving Strategy 6.1 tells us to draw the free-body diagram looking at the edge of the circle, with the x-axis pointing toward the center of the circle and the y-axis perpendicular to the plane of the circle. Three forces are acting on the cart: the weight force $\vec{w}$, the normal force of the ground $\vec{n}$, and the tension force of the rope $\vec{T}$.

Notice that there are two quantities for which we use the symbol T: the tension and the period. We will include additional information when necessary to distinguish the two.

SOLVE There is no net force in the y-direction, perpendicular to the circle, so $\vec{w}$ and $\vec{n}$ must be equal and opposite. There is a net force in the x-direction, toward the center of the circle, as there must be to cause the centripetal acceleration of circular motion. Only the tension force has an x-component, so Newton's second law is

$$\sum F_x = T = \frac{mv^2}{r}$$

We know the mass, the radius of the circle, and the tension, so we can solve for v:

$$v = \sqrt{\frac{Tr}{m}} = \sqrt{\frac{(100\ \text{N})(2.0\ \text{m})}{25\ \text{kg}}} = 2.83\ \text{m/s}$$

From this, we can compute the period with a slight rearrangement of Equation 3.27:

$$T = \frac{2\pi r}{v} = \frac{(2\pi)(2.0\ \text{m})}{2.83\ \text{m/s}} = 4.4\ \text{s}$$

ASSESS The speed is about 3 m/s. Because 1 m/s $\approx$ 2 mph, the child is going about 6 mph. A trip around the circle in just over 4 s at a speed of about 6 mph sounds reasonable; it's a fast ride, but not so fast as to be scary!

FIGURE 6.14 A visual overview of the cart spinning in a circle.

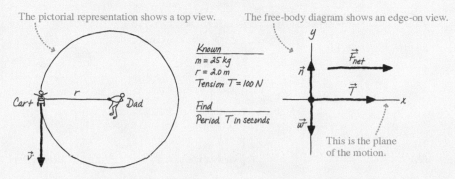

EXAMPLE 6.10 **Finding the maximum speed to turn a corner**

What is the maximum speed with which a 1500 kg car can make a turn around a curve of radius 20 m on a level (unbanked) road without sliding? (This radius turn is about what you might expect at a major intersection in a city.)

PREPARE We start with the visual overview in **FIGURE 6.15**. The car moves along a circular arc at a constant speed—uniform circular motion—for the quarter-circle necessary to complete the turn. The motion before and after the turn is not relevant to the problem. The more interesting issue is *how* a car turns a corner. What force or forces can we identify that cause the direction of the velocity vector to change? Imagine you are driving a car on a frictionless road, such as a very icy road. You would not be able to turn a corner. Turning the steering wheel would be of no use; the car would slide straight ahead, in accordance with both Newton's first law and the experience of anyone who has ever driven on ice! So it must be *friction* that causes the car to turn.

The top view of the tire in Figure 6.15 shows the force on one of the car's tires as it turns a corner. If the road surface were frictionless, the tire would slide straight ahead. The force that prevents an object from sliding across a surface is *static friction*. Static friction $\vec{f}_s$ pushes *sideways* on the tire, toward the center of the circle. How do we know the direction is sideways? If $\vec{f}_s$ had a component either parallel to $\vec{v}$ or opposite $\vec{v}$, it would cause the car to speed up or slow down. Because the car changes direction but not speed, static friction must be perpendicular to $\vec{v}$. Thus $\vec{f}_s$ causes the centripetal acceleration of circular motion around the curve. With this in mind, the free-body diagram, drawn from behind the car, shows the static friction force pointing toward the center of the circle. Because the motion is in a horizontal plane, we've again chosen an *x*-axis toward the center of the circle and a *y*-axis perpendicular to the plane of motion.

SOLVE The only force in the *x*-direction, toward the center of the circle, is static friction. Newton's second law along the *x*-axis is

$$\sum F_x = f_s = \frac{mv^2}{r}$$

The only difference between this example and the preceding one is that the tension force toward the center has been replaced by a static friction force toward the center.

Newton's second law in the *y*-direction is

$$\sum F_y = n - w = ma_y = 0$$

so that $n = w = mg$.

The net force toward the center of the circle is the force of static friction. Recall from Equation 5.10 in Chapter 5 that static friction has a maximum possible value:

$$f_{s\,max} = \mu_s n = \mu_s mg$$

Because the static friction force has a maximum value, there will be a maximum speed at which a car can turn without sliding. This speed is reached when the static friction force reaches its maximum value $f_{s\,max} = \mu_s mg$. If the car enters the curve at a speed higher than the maximum, static friction cannot provide the necessary centripetal acceleration and the car will slide.

Thus the maximum speed occurs at the maximum value of the force of static friction, or when

$$f_{s\,max} = \frac{mv_{max}^2}{r}$$

Using the known value of $f_{s\,max}$, we find

$$\frac{mv_{max}^2}{r} = f_{s\,max} = \mu_s mg$$

Rearranging, we get

$$v_{max}^2 = \mu_s gr$$

For rubber tires on pavement, we find from Table 5.1 that $\mu_s = 1.0$. We then have

$$v_{max} = \sqrt{\mu_s gr} = \sqrt{(1.0)(9.8 \text{ m/s}^2)(20 \text{ m})} = 14 \text{ m/s}$$

ASSESS 14 m/s $\approx$ 30 mph, which seems like a reasonable upper limit for the speed at which a car can go around a curve without sliding. There are two other things to note about the solution:

- The car's mass canceled out. The maximum speed *does not* depend on the mass of the vehicle, though this may seem surprising.
- The final expression for v_{max} *does* depend on the coefficient of friction and the radius of the turn. v_{max} decreases if μ is less (a slipperier road) or if r is smaller (a tighter turn). Both make sense.

FIGURE 6.15 Visual overview of a car turning a corner.

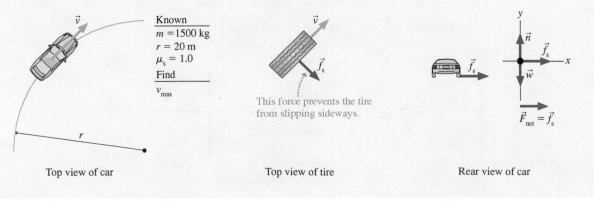

Known
$m = 1500$ kg
$r = 20$ m
$\mu_s = 1.0$

Find
v_{max}

This force prevents the tire from slipping sideways.

Top view of car   Top view of tire   Rear view of car

Because v_{max} depends on μ_s and because μ_s depends on road conditions, the maximum safe speed through turns can vary dramatically. Wet or icy roads lower the value of μ_s and thus lower the maximum speed of turns. A car that easily handles a curve in dry weather can suddenly slide out of control when the pavement is wet. Icy conditions are even worse. If you lower the value of the coefficient of friction in Example 6.10 from 1.0 (dry pavement) to 0.1 (icy pavement), the maximum speed for the turn goes down to 4.4 m/s—about 10 mph!

Race cars turn corners at much higher speeds than normal passenger vehicles. One design modification of the *cars* to allow this is the addition of wings, as on the car in FIGURE 6.16. The wings provide an additional force pushing the car *down* onto the pavement by deflecting air upward. This extra downward force increases the normal force, thus increasing the maximum static friction force and making faster turns possible.

There are also design modifications of the *track* to allow race cars to take corners at high speeds. If the track is banked by raising the outside edge of curved sections, the normal force can provide some of the force necessary to produce the centripetal acceleration, as we will see in the next example. The curves on racetracks may be quite sharply banked. Curves on ordinary highways are often banked as well, though at more modest angles suiting the lower speeds.

FIGURE 6.16 Wings on an Indy racer.

A banked turn on a racetrack.

EXAMPLE 6.11   **Finding speed on a banked turn**

A curve on a racetrack of radius 70 m is banked at a 15° angle. At what speed can a car take this curve without assistance from friction?

PREPARE After drawing the pictorial representation in FIGURE 6.17, we use the force identification diagram to find that, given that there is no friction acting, the only two forces are the normal force and the car's weight. We can then construct the free-body diagram, making sure that we draw the normal force perpendicular to the road's surface.

Even though the car is tilted, it is still moving in a *horizontal* circle. Thus, following Problem-Solving Strategy 6.1, we choose

FIGURE 6.17 Visual overview for the car on a banked turn.

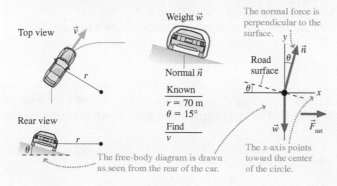

the x-axis to be horizontal and pointing toward the center of the circle.

SOLVE Without friction, $n_x = n\sin\theta$ is the only component of force toward the center of the circle. It is this inward component of the normal force on the car that causes it to turn the corner. Newton's second law is

$$\sum F_x = n\sin\theta = \frac{mv^2}{r}$$

$$\sum F_y = n\cos\theta - w = 0$$

where θ is the angle at which the road is banked, and we've assumed that the car is traveling at the correct speed v. From the y-equation,

$$n = \frac{w}{\cos\theta} = \frac{mg}{\cos\theta}$$

Substituting this into the x-equation and solving for v give

$$\left(\frac{mg}{\cos\theta}\right)\sin\theta = mg\tan\theta = \frac{mv^2}{r}$$

$$v = \sqrt{rg\tan\theta} = 14 \text{ m/s}$$

ASSESS This is $\approx$30 mph, a reasonable speed. Only at this exact speed can the turn be negotiated without reliance on friction forces.

Maximum Walking Speed

Humans and other two-legged animals have two basic gaits: walking and running. At slow speeds, you walk. When you need to go faster, you run. Why don't you just walk faster? There is an upper limit to the speed of walking, and this limit is set by the physics of circular motion.

FIGURE 6.18 Analysis of a walking stride.

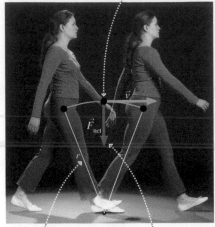

(a) Walking stride During each stride, her hip undergoes circular motion.

The radius of the circular motion is the length of the leg from the foot to the hip.

The circular motion requires a force directed toward the center of the circle.

(b) Forces in the stride Side view (same as photo)

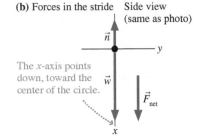

The x-axis points down, toward the center of the circle.

Think about the motion of your body as you take a walking stride. You put one foot forward, then push off with your rear foot. Your body pivots over your front foot, and you bring your rear foot forward to take the next stride. As you can see in **FIGURE 6.18a**, the path that your body takes during this stride is the arc of a circle. **In a walking gait, your body is in circular motion as you pivot on your forward foot.**

A force toward the center of the circle is required for this circular motion, as shown in Figure 6.18. **FIGURE 6.18b** shows the forces acting on the woman's body during the midpoint of the stride: her weight, directed down, and the normal force of the ground, directed up. Newton's second law for the x-axis is

$$\sum F_x = w - n = \frac{mv^2}{r}$$

Because of her circular motion, the net force must point toward the center of the circle, or, in this case, down. In order for the net force to point down, the normal force must be *less* than her weight. Your body tries to "lift off" as it pivots over your foot, decreasing the normal force exerted on you by the ground. The normal force becomes smaller as you walk faster, but n cannot be less than zero. Thus the maximum possible walking speed v_{max} occurs when $n = 0$. Setting $n = 0$ in Newton's second law gives

$$w = mg = \frac{mv_{max}^2}{r}$$

Thus

$$v_{max} = \sqrt{gr} \qquad (6.10)$$

The maximum possible walking speed is limited by r, the length of the leg, and g, the free-fall acceleration. This formula is a good approximation of the maximum walking speed for humans and other animals. The maximum walking speed is higher for animals with longer legs. Giraffes, with their very long legs, can walk at high speeds. Animals such as mice with very short legs have such a low maximum walking speed that they rarely use this gait. Mice generally run to get from one place to another.

For humans, the length of the leg is approximately 0.7 m, so we calculate a maximum speed of

$$v_{max} \approx 2.6 \text{ m/s} \approx 6 \text{ mph}$$

You *can* walk this fast, though it becomes energetically unfavorable to do so at speeds above 4 mph. Most people make a transition to a running gait at about this speed. Children, with their shorter legs, must make a transition to a running gait at a much lower speed.

STOP TO THINK 6.3 A block on a string spins in a horizontal circle on a frictionless table. Rank in order, from largest to smallest, the tensions T_A to T_E acting on the blocks A to E.

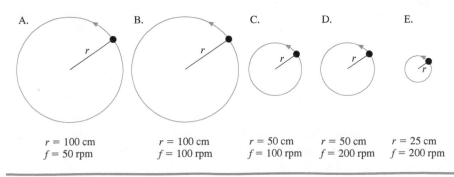

A.	B.	C.	D.	E.
$r = 100$ cm	$r = 100$ cm	$r = 50$ cm	$r = 50$ cm	$r = 25$ cm
$f = 50$ rpm	$f = 100$ rpm	$f = 100$ rpm	$f = 200$ rpm	$f = 200$ rpm

6.4 Apparent Forces in Circular Motion

FIGURE 6.19 shows a carnival ride that spins the riders around inside a large cylinder. The people are "stuck" to the inside wall of the cylinder! As you probably know from experience, the riders *feel* that they are being pushed outward, into the wall. But our analysis has found that an object in circular motion must have an *inward* force to create the centripetal acceleration. How can we explain this apparent difference?

Centrifugal Force?

If you are a passenger in a car that turns a corner quickly, you may feel "thrown" by some mysterious force against the door. But is there really such a force? FIGURE 6.20 shows a bird's-eye view of you riding in a car as it makes a left turn. You try to continue moving in a straight line, obeying Newton's first law, when—without having been provoked—the door starts to turn in toward you and so runs into you! You do then feel the force of the door because it is now the force of the door, pushing *inward* toward the center of the curve, that is causing you to turn the corner. But you were not "thrown" into the door; the door ran into you.

A "force" that *seems* to push an object to the outside of a circle is called a *centrifugal force*. Despite having a name, there really is no such force. What you feel is your body trying to move ahead in a straight line (which would take you away from the center of the circle) as outside forces act to turn you in a circle. The only real forces, those that appear on free-body diagrams, are the ones pushing inward toward the center. **A centrifugal force will never appear on a free-body diagram and never be included in Newton's laws.**

With this in mind, let's revisit the rotating carnival ride. A person watching from above would see the riders in the cylinder moving in a circle with the walls providing the inward force that causes their centripetal acceleration. The riders *feel* as if they're being pushed outward because their natural tendency to move in a straight line is being resisted by the wall of the cylinder, which keeps getting in the way. But feelings aren't forces. The only actual force is the contact force of the cylinder wall pushing *inward*.

Apparent Weight in Circular Motion

Imagine swinging a bucket of water over your head. If you swing the bucket quickly, the water stays in. But you'll get a shower if you swing too slowly. Why does the water stay in the bucket? Or think about a roller coaster that does a loop-the-loop. How does the car stay on the track when it's upside down? You might have said that there was a centrifugal force holding the water in the bucket and the car on the track, but we have seen that there really isn't a centrifugal force. Analyzing these questions will tell us a lot about forces in general and circular motion in particular.

FIGURE 6.21a shows a roller coaster car going around a vertical loop-the-loop of radius r. If you've ever ridden a roller coaster, you know that your sensation of weight changes as you go over the crests and through the dips. To understand why, let's look at the forces on passengers going through the loop. To simplify our analysis, we will assume that the speed of the car stays constant as it moves through the loop.

FIGURE 6.21b shows a passenger's free-body diagram at the top and the bottom of the loop. Let's start by examining the forces on the passenger at the bottom of the loop. The only forces acting on her are her weight $\vec{w}$ and the normal force $\vec{n}$ of the seat pushing up on her. Recall from Chapter 5 that a person's apparent weight is the magnitude of the force that supports her. Here the seat is supporting the passenger with the normal force $\vec{n}$, so her apparent weight is $w_{app} = n$. Based on our understanding of circular motion, we can say:

- She's moving in a circle, so there must be a net force directed toward the center of the circle—currently directly above her head—to provide the centripetal acceleration.

FIGURE 6.19 Inside the Gravitron, a rotating circular room.

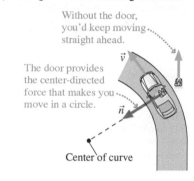

FIGURE 6.20 Bird's-eye view of a passenger in a car turning a corner.

Without the door, you'd keep moving straight ahead.

$\vec{v}$

The door provides the center-directed force that makes you move in a circle.

$\vec{n}$

Center of curve

FIGURE 6.21 A roller coaster car going around a loop-the-loop.

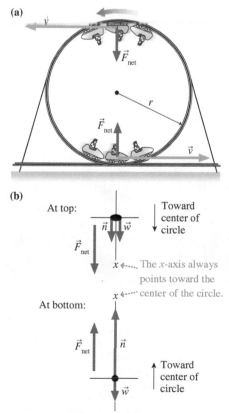

(a)

$\vec{v}$

$\vec{F}_{net}$

r

$\vec{F}_{net}$

$\vec{v}$

(b)

At top:

$\vec{n}$ $\vec{w}$

Toward center of circle

$\vec{F}_{net}$

x ←···· The x-axis always points toward the

x ←···· center of the circle.

At bottom:

$\vec{F}_{net}$ $\vec{n}$

Toward center of circle

$\vec{w}$

- The net force points *upward*, so it must be the case that $n > w$.
- Her apparent weight is $w_{app} = n$, so her apparent weight is greater than her true weight ($w_{app} > w$). Thus she "feels heavy" at the bottom of the circle.

This situation is the same as for the car driving through a valley in Conceptual Example 6.8. To analyze the situation quantitatively, we'll apply the steps of Problem-Solving Strategy 6.1. As always, we choose the x-axis to point toward the center of the circle or, in this case, vertically upward. Then Newton's second law is

$$\sum F_x = n_x + w_x = n - w = \frac{mv^2}{r}$$

From this equation, her apparent weight is

$$w_{app} = n = w + \frac{mv^2}{r} \tag{6.11}$$

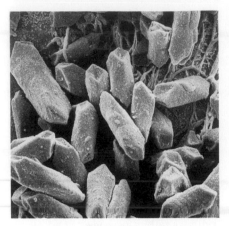

When "down" is up BIO You can tell, even with your eyes closed, what direction is down. This sense is due to small crystals of calcium carbonate, called *otoliths,* in your inner ears. Gravity pulls the otoliths down, so a normal force from a sensitive supporting membrane must push them up. Your brain interprets "down" as the opposite of this normal force. Normally, what your ears tell you is "down" is really down. But at the top of a loop in a roller coaster, the normal force is directed down, so your inner ear tells you that "down" is up! If your ears tell you one thing and your eyes another, it can be disorienting.

The passenger's apparent weight at the bottom is *greater* than her true weight w, which agrees with your experience when you go through a dip or a valley.

Now let's look at the roller coaster car as it crosses the top of the loop. Things are a little trickier here. As Figure 6.21b shows, whereas the normal force of the seat pushes up when the passenger is at the bottom of the circle, it pushes *down* when she is at the top and the seat is above her. It's worth thinking carefully about this diagram to make sure you understand what it is showing.

The passenger is still moving in a circle, so there must be a net force *downward,* toward the center of the circle, to provide her centripetal acceleration. As always, we define the x-axis to be toward the center of the circle, so here the x-axis points vertically downward. Newton's second law gives

$$\sum F_x = n_x + w_x = n + w = \frac{mv^2}{r}$$

Note that w_x is now *positive* because the x-axis is directed downward. We can solve for her apparent weight:

$$w_{app} = n = \frac{mv^2}{r} - w \tag{6.12}$$

If v is sufficiently large, her apparent weight can exceed the true weight, just as it did at the bottom of the track.

But let's look at what happens if the car goes slower. Notice from Equation 6.12 that, as v decreases, there comes a point when $mv^2/r = w$ and n becomes zero. At that point, the seat is *not* pushing against the passenger at all! Instead, she is able to complete the circle because her weight force alone provides sufficient centripetal acceleration.

The speed for which $n = 0$ is called the *critical speed* v_c. Because for n to be zero we must have $mv_c^2/r = w$, the critical speed is

$$v_c = \sqrt{\frac{rw}{m}} = \sqrt{\frac{rmg}{m}} = \sqrt{gr} \tag{6.13}$$

What happens if the speed is slower than the critical speed? In this case, Equation 6.12 gives a *negative* value for n if $v < v_c$. But that is physically impossible. The seat can push against the passenger ($n > 0$), but it can't *pull* on her, so the slowest possible speed is the speed for which $n = 0$ at the top. Thus, **the critical speed is the slowest speed at which the car can complete the circle.** If $v < v_c$, the passenger cannot turn the full loop but, instead, will fall from the car as a projectile! (This is why you're always strapped into a roller coaster.)

Water stays in a bucket swung over your head for the same reason. The bottom of the bucket pushes against the water to provide the inward force that causes circular motion. If you swing the bucket too slowly, the force of the bucket on the water drops to zero. At that point, the water leaves the bucket and becomes a projectile following a parabolic trajectory onto your head!

A fast-spinning world Saturn, a gas giant planet composed largely of fluid matter, is quite a bit larger than the earth. It also rotates much more quickly, completing one rotation in just under 11 hours. The rapid rotation decreases the apparent weight at the equator enough to distort the fluid surface; the planet is noticeably out of round, as the red circle shows. The diameter at the equator is 11% greater than the diameter at the poles.

EXAMPLE 6.12 How slow can you go?

A motorcyclist in the Globe of Death, pictured at the start of the chapter, rides in a 2.2-m-radius vertical loop. To keep control of the bike, the rider wants the normal force on his tires at the top of the loop to equal or exceed his and the bike's combined weight. What is the minimum speed at which the rider can take the loop?

PREPARE The visual overview for this problem is shown in FIGURE 6.22. At the top of the loop, the normal force of the cage on the tires is a *downward* force. In accordance with Problem-

FIGURE 6.22 Riding in a vertical loop around the Globe of Death.

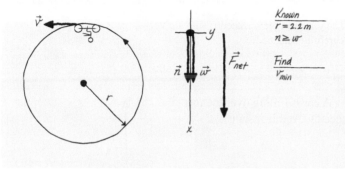

Solving Strategy 6.1, we've chosen the x-axis to point toward the center of the circle.

SOLVE We will consider the forces at the top point of the loop. Because the x-axis points downward, Newton's second law is

$$\sum F_x = w + n = \frac{mv^2}{r}$$

The minimum acceptable speed occurs when $n = w$; thus

$$2w = 2mg = \frac{mv_{min}^2}{r}$$

Solving for the speed, we find

$$v_{min} = \sqrt{2gr} = \sqrt{2(9.8 \text{ m/s}^2)(2.2 \text{ m})} = 6.6 \text{ m/s}$$

ASSESS The minimum speed is $\approx$15 mph, which isn't all that fast; the bikes can easily reach this speed. But normally several bikes are in the globe at one time. The big challenge is to keep all of the riders in the cage moving at this speed in synchrony. The period for the circular motion at this speed is $T = 2\pi r/v \approx 2$ s, leaving little room for error!

Centrifuges

The *centrifuge,* an important biological application of circular motion, is used to separate the components of a liquid with different densities. Typically these are different types of cells, or the components of cells, suspended in water. You probably know that small particles suspended in water will eventually settle to the bottom. However, the downward motion due to gravity for extremely small objects such as cells is so slow that it could take days or even months for the cells to settle out. It's not practical to wait for biological samples to separate due to gravity alone.

The separation would go faster if the force of gravity could be increased. Although we can't change gravity, we can increase the apparent weight of objects in the sample by spinning them very fast, and that is what the centrifuge in FIGURE 6.23 does. By using very high angular velocities, the centrifuge produces centripetal accelerations that are thousands of times greater than free-fall acceleration. As the centrifuge effectively increases gravity to thousands of times its normal value, the cells or cell components settle out and separate by density in a matter of minutes or hours.

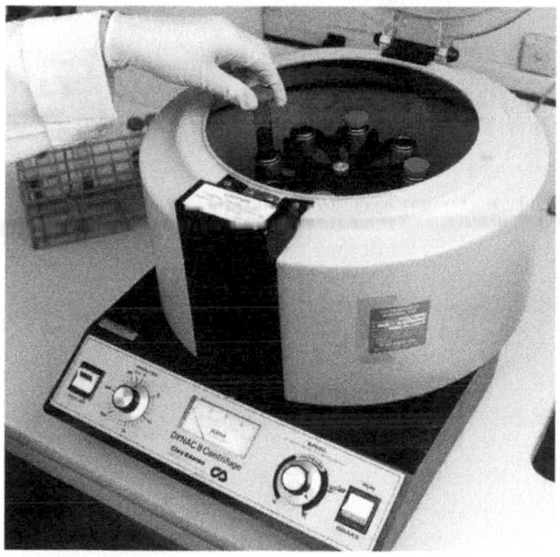

A centrifuge.

EXAMPLE 6.13 Analyzing the ultracentrifuge

An 18-cm-diameter ultracentrifuge produces an extraordinarily large centripetal acceleration of 250,000g, where g is the free-fall acceleration due to gravity. What is its frequency in rpm? What is the apparent weight of a sample with a mass of 0.0030 kg?

PREPARE The acceleration in SI units is

$$a = 250,000(9.80 \text{ m/s}^2) = 2.45 \times 10^6 \text{ m/s}^2$$

The radius is half the diameter, or $r = 9.0$ cm $= 0.090$ m.

SOLVE The centripetal acceleration is related to the angular speed by $a = \omega^2 r$. Thus

$$\omega = \sqrt{\frac{a}{r}} = \sqrt{\frac{2.45 \times 10^6 \text{ m/s}^2}{0.090 \text{ m}}} = 5.22 \times 10^3 \text{ rad/s}$$

FIGURE 6.23 The operation of a centrifuge.

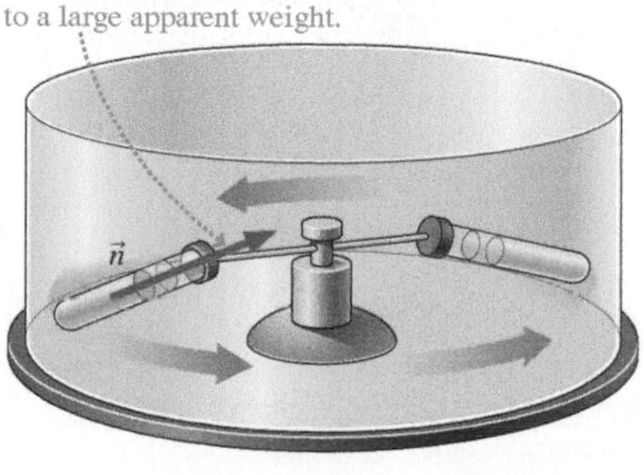

The high angular velocity requires a large normal force, which leads to a large apparent weight.

Continued

Human centrifuge BIO If you spin your arm rapidly in a vertical circle, the motion will produce an effect like that in a centrifuge. The motion will assist outbound blood flow in your arteries and retard inbound blood flow in your veins. There will be a buildup of fluid in your hand that you will be able to see (and feel!) quite easily.

By Equation 6.6, this corresponds to a frequency

$$f = \frac{\omega}{2\pi} = \frac{5.22 \times 10^3 \text{ rad/s}}{2\pi} = 830 \text{ rev/s}$$

Converting to rpm, we find

$$830 \, \frac{\text{rev}}{\text{s}} \times \frac{60 \text{ s}}{1 \text{ min}} = 50{,}000 \text{ rpm}$$

At this rotation rate, the 0.0030 kg mass has an apparent weight

$$w_{\text{app}} = ma = (3.0 \times 10^{-3} \text{ kg})(2.45 \times 10^6 \text{ m/s}^2) = 7.4 \times 10^3 \text{ N}$$

The three gram sample has an effective weight of about 1700 pounds!

ASSESS Because the acceleration is 250,000g, the apparent weight is 250,000 times the actual weight. The forces in the ultracentrifuge are very large and can destroy the machine if it is not carefully balanced.

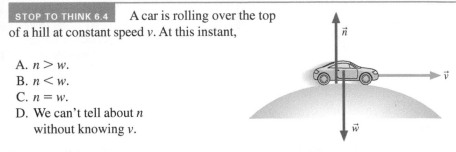

STOP TO THINK 6.4   A car is rolling over the top of a hill at constant speed v. At this instant,

A. $n > w$.
B. $n < w$.
C. $n = w$.
D. We can't tell about n without knowing v.

6.5 Circular Orbits and Weightlessness

The Space Shuttle orbits the earth in a circular path at a speed of over 15,000 miles per hour. What forces act on it? Why does it move in a circle? Before we start considering the physics of orbital motion, let's return, for a moment, to projectile motion. Projectile motion occurs when the only force on an object is gravity. Our analysis of projectiles made an implicit assumption that the earth is flat and that the free-fall acceleration, due to gravity, is everywhere straight down. This is an acceptable approximation for projectiles of limited range, such as baseballs or cannon balls, but there comes a point where we can no longer ignore the curvature of the earth.

Orbital Motion

FIGURE 6.24 Projectiles being launched at increasing speeds from height h on a smooth, airless planet.

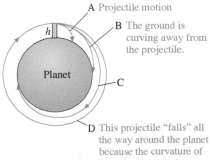

FIGURE 6.24 shows a perfectly smooth, spherical, airless planet with a vertical tower of height h. A projectile is launched from this tower with initial speed v_i parallel to the ground. If v_i is very small, as in trajectory A, the "flat-earth approximation" is valid and the problem is identical to Example 3.11 in which a car drove off a cliff. The projectile simply falls to the ground along a parabolic trajectory.

As the initial speed v_i is increased, it seems to the projectile that the ground is curving out from beneath it. It is still falling the entire time, always getting closer to the ground, but the distance that the projectile travels before finally reaching the ground—that is, its range—increases because the projectile must "catch up" with the ground that is curving away from it. Trajectories B and C are like this.

If the launch speed v_i is sufficiently large, there comes a point at which the curve of the trajectory and the curve of the earth are parallel. In this case, the projectile "falls" but it never gets any closer to the ground! This is the situation for trajectory D. The projectile returns to the point from which it was launched, at the same speed at which it was launched, making a closed trajectory. Such a closed trajectory around a planet or star is called an **orbit.**

The most important point of this qualitative analysis is that, in the absence of air resistance, **an orbiting projectile is in free fall.** This is, admittedly, a strange idea, but one worth careful thought. An orbiting projectile is really no different from a thrown baseball or a car driving off a cliff. The only force acting on it is gravity, but its tangential velocity is so great that the curvature of its trajectory matches the curvature of the earth. When this happens, the projectile "falls" under the influence of gravity but never gets any closer to the surface, which curves away beneath it.

When we first studied free fall in Chapter 2, we said that free-fall acceleration is always directed vertically downward. As we see in FIGURE 6.25, "downward" really means "toward the center of the earth." For a projectile in orbit, the direction of the force of gravity changes, always pointing toward the center of the earth.

FIGURE 6.25 The force of gravity is really directed toward the center of the earth.

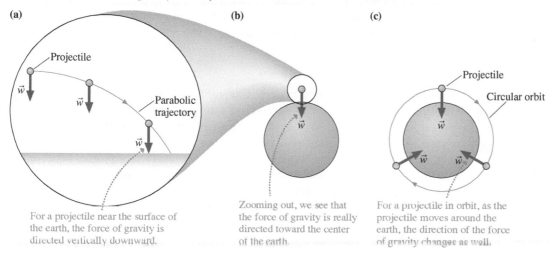

(a)

Projectile

Parabolic trajectory

For a projectile near the surface of the earth, the force of gravity is directed vertically downward.

(b)

Zooming out, we see that the force of gravity is really directed toward the center of the earth.

(c)

Projectile

Circular orbit

For a projectile in orbit, as the projectile moves around the earth, the direction of the force of gravity changes as well.

As you have learned, a force of constant magnitude that always points toward the center of a circle causes the centripetal acceleration of uniform circular motion. Because the only force acting on the orbiting projectile in Figure 6.25 is gravity, and we're assuming the projectile is very near the surface of the earth, we can write

$$a = \frac{F_{net}}{m} = \frac{w}{m} = \frac{mg}{m} = g \qquad (6.14)$$

An object moving in a circle of radius r at speed v_{orbit} will have this centripetal acceleration if

$$a = \frac{(v_{orbit})^2}{r} = g \qquad (6.15)$$

That is, if an object moves parallel to the surface with the speed

$$v_{orbit} = \sqrt{gr} \qquad (6.16)$$

then the free-fall acceleration provides exactly the centripetal acceleration needed for a circular orbit of radius r. An object with any other speed will not follow a circular orbit.

The earth's radius is $r = R_e = 6.37 \times 10^6$ m. The orbital speed of a projectile just skimming the surface of a smooth, airless earth is

$$v_{orbit} = \sqrt{gR_e} = \sqrt{(9.80 \text{ m/s}^2)(6.37 \times 10^6 \text{ m})} = 7900 \text{ m/s} \approx 18,000 \text{ mph}$$

We can use v_{orbit} to calculate the period of the satellite's orbit:

$$T = \frac{2\pi r}{v_{orbit}} = 2\pi\sqrt{\frac{r}{g}} \tag{6.17}$$

For this earth-skimming orbit, $T = 5065$ s $= 84.4$ min.

Of course, this orbit is unrealistic; even if there were no trees and mountains, a real projectile moving at this speed would burn up from the friction of air resistance. Suppose, however, that we launched the projectile from a tower of height $h = 200$ mi $\approx 3.2 \times 10^5$ m, above most of the earth's atmosphere. This is approximately the height of low-earth-orbit satellites, such as the Space Shuttle. Note that $h \ll R_e$, so the radius of the orbit $r = R_e + h = 6.69 \times 10^6$ m is only 5% larger than the earth's radius. Many people have a mental image that satellites orbit far above the earth, but in fact most satellites come pretty close to skimming the surface.

At this slightly larger value of r, Equation 6.17 gives $T = 87$ min. The actual period of the Space Shuttle at an altitude of 200 mi is about 91 minutes, so our calculation is very good—but not perfect. As we'll see in the next section, a correct calculation must take into account the fact that the force of gravity gradually gets weaker at higher elevations above the earth's surface.

Weightlessness in Orbit

When we discussed *weightlessness* in Chapter 5, we saw that it occurs during free fall. We asked the question, at the end of Section 5.4, whether astronauts and their spacecraft are in free fall. We can now give an affirmative answer: They are, indeed, in free fall. They are falling continuously around the earth, under the influence of only the gravitational force, but never getting any closer to the ground because the earth's surface curves beneath them. Weightlessness in space is no different from the weightlessness in a free-falling elevator. **Weightlessness does *not* occur from an absence of weight or an absence of gravity.** Instead, the astronaut, the spacecraft, and everything in it are "weightless" (i.e., their *apparent* weight is zero) because they are all falling together.

Zero apparent weight in the Space Shuttle.

The Orbit of the Moon

If a satellite is simply "falling" around the earth, with the gravitational force causing a centripetal acceleration, then what about the moon? Is it obeying the same laws of physics? Or do celestial objects obey laws that we cannot discover by experiments here on earth?

The radius of the moon's orbit around the earth is 3.84×10^8 m. If we use Equation 6.17 to calculate the period of the moon's orbit, the time the moon takes to circle the earth once, we get

$$T = 2\pi\sqrt{\frac{r}{g}} = 2\pi\sqrt{\frac{3.84 \times 10^8 \text{ m}}{9.80 \text{ m/s}^2}} = 655 \text{ min} \approx 11 \text{ h} \tag{6.18}$$

This is clearly wrong; the period of the moon's orbit is approximately one month.

Newton believed that the laws of motion he had discovered were *universal* and so should apply to the motion of the moon as well as to the motion of objects in the laboratory. But why should we assume that the free-fall acceleration g is the same at the distance of the moon as it is on or near the earth's surface? If gravity is the force of the earth pulling on an object, it seems plausible that the size of that force, and thus the size of g, should diminish with increasing distance from the earth.

Newton proposed the idea that the earth's force of gravity decreases with the square of the distance from the earth. This is the basis of *Newton's law of gravity*, a

Rotating space stations BIO The weightlessness astronauts experience in orbit has serious physiological consequences. Astronauts who spend time in weightless environments lose bone and muscle mass and suffer other adverse effects. One solution is to introduce "artificial gravity." On a space station, the easiest way to do this would be to make the station rotate, producing an apparent weight. The designers of this space station model for the movie *2001: A Space Odyssey* made it rotate for just that reason.

topic we will study in the next section. The force of gravity is less at the distance of the moon—exactly the strength needed to make the moon orbit at the observed rate. The moon, just like the Space Shuttle, is simply "falling" around the earth!

6.6 Newton's Law of Gravity

A popular image has Newton thinking of the idea of gravity after an apple fell on his head. This amusing story is at least close to the truth. Newton himself said that the "notion of gravitation" came to him as he "sat in a contemplative mood" and "was occasioned by the fall of an apple." It occurred to him that, perhaps, the apple was attracted to the center of the earth but was prevented from getting there by the earth's surface. And if the apple was so attracted, why not the moon? Newton's genius was his sudden realization that **the force that attracts the moon to the earth (and the planets to the sun) was identical to the force that attracts an apple to the earth.** In other words, gravitation is a *universal* force between all objects in the universe! This is not shocking today, but no one before Newton had ever thought that the mundane motion of objects on earth had any connection at all with the stately motion of the planets around the sun.

Gravity Obeys an Inverse-Square Law

Newton also recognized that the strength of gravity must decrease with distance. These two notions about gravity—that it is universal and that it decreases with distance—form the basis for Newton's law of gravity.

Newton proposed that *every* object in the universe attracts *every other* object with a force that has the following properties:

1. The force is inversely proportional to the square of the distance between the objects.
2. The force is directly proportional to the product of the masses of the two objects.

FIGURE 6.26 shows two spherical objects with masses m_1 and m_2 separated by distance r. Each object exerts an attractive force on the other, a force that we call the **gravitational force.** These two forces form an action/reaction pair, so $\vec{F}_{1\,on\,2}$ is equal in magnitude and opposite in direction to $\vec{F}_{2\,on\,1}$. The magnitude of the forces is given by Newton's law of gravity.

Isaac Newton was born to a poor farming family in 1642, the year of Galileo's death. He entered Trinity College at Cambridge University at age 19 as a "subsizar," a poor student who had to work his way through school. Newton graduated in 1665, at age 23, just as an outbreak of the plague in England forced the universities to close for two years. He returned to his family farm for that period, during which he made important experimental discoveries in optics, laid the foundations for his theories of mechanics and gravitation, and made major progress toward his invention of calculus as a whole new branch of mathematics.

FIGURE 6.26 The gravitational forces on masses m_1 and m_2.

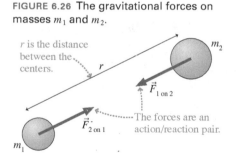

Newton's law of gravity If two objects with masses m_1 and m_2 are a distance r apart, the objects exert attractive forces on each other of magnitude

$$F_{1\,on\,2} = F_{2\,on\,1} = \frac{Gm_1m_2}{r^2} \qquad (6.19)$$

INVERSE-SQUARE

The forces are directed along the line joining the two objects.

The constant G is called the **gravitational constant.** In the SI system of units,

$$G = 6.67 \times 10^{-11} \ \text{N} \cdot \text{m}^2/\text{kg}^2$$

NOTE ▶ Strictly speaking, Newton's law of gravity applies to *particles* with masses m_1 and m_2. However, it can be shown that the law also applies to the force between two spherical objects if r is the distance between their centers. ◀

As the distance r between two objects increases, the gravitational force between them decreases. Because the distance appears squared in the denominator, Newton's law of gravity is what we call an **inverse-square** law. Doubling the distance between two masses causes the force between them to decrease by a factor of 4. This mathematical form is one we will see again, so it is worth our time to explore it in more detail.

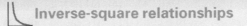

Inverse-square relationships

Two quantities have an **inverse-square relationship** if y is inversely proportional to the *square* of x. We write the mathematical relationship as

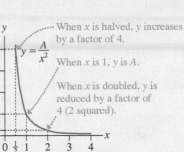

When x is halved, y increases by a factor of 4.

When x is 1, y is A.

When x is doubled, y is reduced by a factor of 4 (2 squared).

$$y = \frac{A}{x^2}$$

y is inversely proportional to x^2

Here, A is a constant. This relationship is sometimes written as $y \propto 1/x^2$.

SCALING As the graph shows, inverse-square scaling means, for example:

- If you double x, you decrease y by a factor of 4.
- If you halve x, you increase y by a factor of 4.
- If you increase x by a factor of 3, you decrease y by a factor of 9.
- If you decrease x by a factor of 3, you increase y by a factor of 9.

Generally, **if x increases by a factor of C, y decreases by a factor of C^2.** If x *decreases* by a factor of C, y *increases* by a factor of C^2.

RATIOS For any two values of x—say, x_1 and x_2—we have

$$y_1 = \frac{A}{x_1^2} \quad \text{and} \quad y_2 = \frac{A}{x_2^2}$$

Dividing the y_1-equation by the y_2-equation, we find

$$\frac{y_1}{y_2} = \frac{A/x_1^2}{A/x_2^2} = \frac{A}{x_1^2}\frac{x_2^2}{A} = \frac{x_2^2}{x_1^2}$$

That is, the ratio of y-values is the inverse of the ratio of the squares of the corresponding values of x.

LIMITS As x becomes large, y becomes very small; as x becomes small, y becomes very large.

Exercises 23, 24

CONCEPTUAL EXAMPLE 6.14   **Varying gravitational force**

The gravitational force between two giant lead spheres is 0.010 N when the centers of the spheres are 20 m apart. What is the distance between their centers when the gravitational force between them is 0.160 N?

REASON We can solve this problem without knowing the masses of the two spheres. The key is to consider the ratios of forces and distances. Gravity is an inverse-square relationship;

the force is related to the inverse square of the distance. The force *increases* by a factor of (0.160 N)/(0.010 N) = 16, so the distance must *decrease* by a factor of $\sqrt{16} = 4$. The distance is thus (20 m)/4 = 5.0 m.

ASSESS This type of ratio reasoning is a very good way to get a quick handle on the solution to a problem.

EXAMPLE 6.15 **Gravitational force between two people**

You are seated in your physics class next to another student 0.60 m away. Estimate the magnitude of the gravitational force between you. Assume that you each have a mass of 65 kg.

PREPARE We will model each of you as a sphere; this is not a particularly good model, but it will do for making an estimate. We will take the 0.60 m as the distance between your centers.

SOLVE The gravitational force is given by Equation 6.19:

$$F_{(\text{you})\text{on}(\text{other student})} = \frac{Gm_{\text{you}}m_{\text{other student}}}{r^2}$$

$$= \frac{(6.67 \times 10^{-11} \text{ N} \cdot \text{m}^2/\text{kg}^2)(65 \text{ kg})(65 \text{ kg})}{(0.60 \text{ m})^2}$$

$$= 7.8 \times 10^{-7} \text{ N}$$

ASSESS The force is quite small, roughly the weight of one hair on your head.

There is a gravitational force between all objects in the universe, but the gravitational force between two ordinary-sized objects is extremely small. Only when one (or both) of the masses is exceptionally large does the force of gravity become important. The downward force of the earth on you—your weight—is large because the earth has an enormous mass. And the attraction is mutual; by Newton's third law, you exert an upward force on the earth that is equal to your weight. However, the large mass of the earth makes the effect of this force on the earth negligible.

EXAMPLE 6.16 **Gravitational force of the earth on a person**

What is the magnitude of the gravitational force of the earth on a 60 kg person? The earth has mass 5.98×10^{24} kg and radius 6.37×10^{6} m.

PREPARE We'll again model the person as a sphere. The distance r in Newton's law of gravity is the distance between the *centers* of the two spheres. The size of the person is negligible compared to the size of the earth, so we can use the earth's radius as r.

SOLVE The force of gravity on the person due to the earth can be computed using Equation 6.19:

$$F_{\text{earth on person}} = \frac{GM_e m}{R_e^2} = \frac{(6.67 \times 10^{-11} \text{ N} \cdot \text{kg}^2/\text{m}^2)(5.98 \times 10^{24} \text{ kg})(60 \text{ kg})}{(6.37 \times 10^{6} \text{ m})^2}$$

$$= 590 \text{ N}$$

ASSESS This force is exactly the same as we would calculate using the formula for the weight force, $w = mg$. This isn't surprising, though. Chapter 5 introduced the weight of an object as simply the "force of gravity" acting on it. Newton's law of gravity is a more fundamental law for calculating the force of gravity, but it's still the same force that we earlier called "weight."

NOTE ▶ We will use uppercase R and M to represent the large mass and radius of a star or planet, as we did in Example 6.16. ◀

The force of gravitational attraction between the earth and you is responsible for your weight. If you were to venture to another planet, your *mass* would be the same but your *weight* would vary, as we discussed in Chapter 5. We will now explore this concept in more detail.

Gravity on Other Worlds

When astronauts ventured to the moon, television images showed them walking—and even jumping and skipping—with some ease, even though they were wearing life support systems with a mass of over 80 kg. This was a visible reminder that the weight of objects is less on the moon. Let's consider why this is so.

FIGURE 6.27 on the next page shows an astronaut on the moon weighing a rock of mass m. When we compute the weight of an object on the surface of the earth, we

Variable gravity When we calculated the force of the earth's gravity, we assumed that the earth's shape and composition are uniform. Neither is quite true, so there is a very small variation in gravity at the surface of the earth, as shown in this image. Red means slightly stronger surface gravity; blue, slightly weaker. These variations are caused by differing distances from the earth's center and by unevenness in the density of the earth's crust. Though these variations are important for scientists studying the earth, they are small enough that we can ignore them for the computations we'll do in this textbook.

FIGURE 6.27 An astronaut weighing a mass on the moon.

"Little g" perspective:
$F = mg_{moon}$

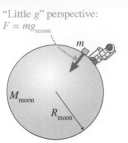

"Big G" perspective:
$F = \dfrac{GM_{moon}m}{R_{moon}^2}$

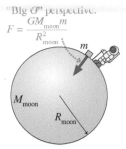

use the formula $w = mg$. We can do the same calculation for a mass on the moon, as long as we use the value of g on the moon:

$$w = mg_{moon} \tag{6.20}$$

This is the "little g" perspective. Falling-body experiments on the moon would give the value of g_{moon} as 1.62 m/s^2.

But we can also take a "big G" perspective. The weight of the rock comes from the gravitational attraction of the moon, and we can compute this weight using Equation 6.19. The distance r is the radius of the moon, which we'll call R_{moon}. Thus

$$F_{moon\,on\,m} = \frac{GM_{moon}m}{R_{moon}^2} \tag{6.21}$$

Because Equations 6.20 and 6.21 are two names and two expressions for the same force, we can equate the right-hand sides to find that

$$g_{moon} = \frac{GM_{moon}}{R_{moon}^2}$$

We have done this calculation for an object on the moon, but the result is completely general. At the surface of a planet (or a star), the free-fall acceleration g, a consequence of gravity, can be computed as

$$g_{planet} = \frac{GM_{planet}}{R_{planet}^2} \tag{6.22}$$

Free-fall acceleration on the surface of a planet

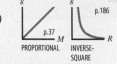

If we use values for the mass and the radius of the moon from the table inside the cover of the book, we can compute $g_{moon} = 1.62$ m/s^2. This means that an object would weigh less on the moon than it would on the earth, where g is 9.80 m/s^2. A 70 kg astronaut wearing an 80 kg spacesuit would weigh over 330 lb on the earth but only 54 lb on the moon.

The low lunar gravity makes walking very easy, but a walking pace on the moon would be very slow. Earlier in the chapter we found that the maximum walking speed is $v_{max} = \sqrt{gr}$, where r is the length of the leg. For a typical leg length of 0.7 m and the gravity of the moon, the *maximum* walking speed would be about 1 m/s, just over 2 mph—a very gentle stroll!

Equation 6.22 gives g at the surface of a planet. More generally, imagine an object at distance $r > R$ from the center of a planet. Its free-fall acceleration at this distance is

$$g = \frac{GM}{r^2} \tag{6.23}$$

This more general result agrees with Equation 6.22 if $r = R$, but it allows us to determine the "local" free-fall acceleration at distances $r > R$. Equation 6.23 expresses Newton's idea that the size of g should decrease as you get farther from the earth.

As you're flying in a jet airplane at a height of about 10 km, the free-fall acceleration is about 0.3% less than on the ground. At the height of the Space Shuttle, about 300 km, Equation 6.23 gives $g = 8.9$ m/s^2, about 10% less than the free-fall acceleration on the earth's surface. If you use this slightly smaller value of g in Equation 6.17 for the period of a satellite's orbit, you'll get the correct period of about 90 minutes. This value of g, only slightly less than the ground-level value, emphasizes the

◀ **Walking on the moon** BIO The low lunar gravity made walking at a reasonable pace difficult for the Apollo astronauts, but the reduced weight made jumping quite easy. Videos from the surface of the moon often show the astronauts getting from place to place by hopping or skipping—not for fun, but for speed and efficiency.

point that an object in orbit is not "weightless" due to the absence of gravity, but rather because it is in free fall.

EXAMPLE 6.17   **Gravity on Saturn**

Saturn, at 5.68×10^{26} kg, has nearly 100 times the mass of the earth. It is also much larger, with a radius of 5.85×10^7 m. What is the value of g on the surface of Saturn?

SOLVE We can use Equation 6.22 to compute the value of g_{Saturn}:

$$g_{Saturn} = \frac{GM_{Saturn}}{R_{Saturn}^2} = \frac{(6.67 \times 10^{-11}\ \text{N} \cdot \text{m}^2/\text{kg}^2)(5.68 \times 10^{26}\ \text{kg})}{(5.85 \times 10^7\ \text{m})^2} = 11.1\ \text{m/s}^2$$

ASSESS Even though Saturn is much more massive than the earth, its larger radius gives it a surface gravity that is not markedly different from that of the earth. If Saturn had a solid surface, you could walk and move around quite normally.

EXAMPLE 6.18   **Finding the speed to orbit Deimos**

Mars has two moons, each much smaller than the earth's moon. The smaller of these two bodies, Deimos, has an average radius of only 6.3 km and a mass of 1.8×10^{15} kg. At what speed would a projectile move in a very low orbit around Deimos?

SOLVE The free-fall acceleration at the surface of Deimos is quite small:

$$g_{Deimos} = \frac{GM_{Deimos}}{R_{Deimos}^2} = \frac{(6.67 \times 10^{-11}\ \text{N} \cdot \text{m}^2/\text{kg}^2)(1.8 \times 10^{15}\ \text{kg})}{(6.3 \times 10^3\ \text{m})^2}$$

$$= 0.0030\ \text{m/s}^2$$

Given this, we can use Equation 6.16 to calculate the orbital speed:

$$v_{orbit} = \sqrt{gr} = \sqrt{(0.0030\ \text{m/s}^2)(6.3 \times 10^3\ \text{m})} = 4.3\ \text{m/s} \approx 10\ \text{mph}$$

ASSESS This is quite slow. With a good jump, you could easily launch yourself into an orbit around Deimos!

STOP TO THINK 6.5   Rank in order, from largest to smallest, the free-fall accelerations on the surfaces of the following planets.

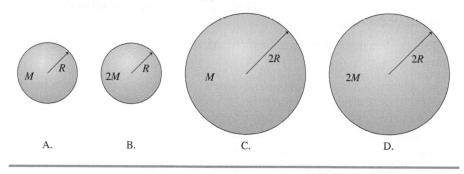

A.   B.   C.   D.

6.7 Gravity and Orbits

The planets of the solar system orbit the sun because the sun's gravitational pull, a force that points toward the center, causes the centripetal acceleration of circular motion. Mercury, the closest planet, experiences the largest acceleration, while Pluto, the most distant, has the smallest.

FIGURE 6.28 on the following page shows a large body of mass M, such as the earth or the sun, with a much smaller body of mass m orbiting it. The smaller body is called a **satellite**, even though it may be a planet orbiting the sun. Newton's second law tells us that $F_{M \text{on} m} = ma$, where $F_{M \text{on} m}$ is the gravitational force of the large body

Activ ONLINE Physics   4.6

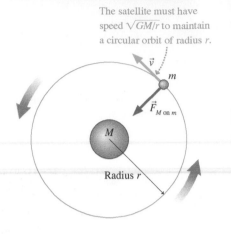

FIGURE 6.28 The orbital motion of a satellite is due to the force of gravity.

The satellite must have speed $\sqrt{GM/r}$ to maintain a circular orbit of radius r.

$\vec{v}$

m

$\vec{F}_{M \text{ on } m}$

M

Radius r

on the satellite and a is the satellite's acceleration. $F_{M \text{on} m}$ is given by Equation 6.19, and, because it's moving in a circular orbit, the satellite's acceleration is its centripetal acceleration, mv^2/r. Thus Newton's second law gives

$$F_{M \text{on} m} = \frac{GMm}{r^2} = ma = \frac{mv^2}{r} \tag{6.24}$$

Solving for v, we find that the speed of a satellite in a circular orbit is

$$v = \sqrt{\frac{GM}{r}} \tag{6.25}$$

Speed of a satellite in a circular orbit of radius r
about a star or planet of mass M

A satellite must have this specific speed in order to maintain a circular orbit of radius r about the larger mass M. If the velocity differs from this value, the orbit will become elliptical rather than circular. Notice that the orbital speed does not depend on the satellite's mass m. This is consistent with our previous discoveries that free-fall motion and projectile motion due to gravity are independent of the mass.

For a planet orbiting the sun, the period T is the time to complete one full orbit. The relationship among speed, radius, and period is the same as for any circular motion, $v = 2\pi r/T$. Combining this with the value of v for a circular orbit from Equation 6.25 gives

$$\sqrt{\frac{GM}{r}} = \frac{2\pi r}{T}$$

If we square both sides and rearrange, we find the period of a satellite:

$$T^2 = \left(\frac{4\pi^2}{GM}\right)r^3 \tag{6.26}$$

Relationship between the orbital period T and radius r for a
satellite in a circular orbit around an object of mass M

In other words, **the square of the period of the orbit is proportional to the cube of the radius of the orbit.**

> NOTE ▶ The mass M in Equation 6.26 is the mass of the object at the center of the orbit. ◀

This relationship between radius and period had been deduced from naked-eye observations of planetary motions by the 17th-century astronomer Johannes Kepler. One of Newton's major scientific accomplishments was to use his law of gravity and his laws of motion to prove what Kepler had deduced from observations. Even today, Newton's law of gravity and equations such as Equation 6.26 are essential tools for the NASA engineers who launch probes to other planets in the solar system.

The table inside the back cover of this book contains astronomical information about the sun and the planets that will be useful for many of the end-of-chapter problems. Note that planets farther from the sun have longer periods, in agreement with Equation 6.26.

EXAMPLE 6.19   Locating a geostationary satellite

Communication satellites appear to "hover" over one point on the earth's equator. A satellite that appears to remain stationary as the earth rotates is said to be in a *geostationary orbit*. What is the radius of the orbit of such a satellite?

PREPARE For the satellite to remain stationary with respect to the earth, the satellite's orbital period must be 24 hours; in seconds this is $T = 8.64 \times 10^4$ s.

SOLVE We solve for the radius of the orbit by rearranging Equation 6.26. The mass at the center of the orbit is the earth:

$$r = \left(\frac{GM_eT^2}{4\pi^2}\right)^{\frac{1}{3}} = \left(\frac{(6.67 \times 10^{-11} \text{ N} \cdot \text{m}^2/\text{kg}^2)(5.98 \times 10^{24} \text{ kg})(8.64 \times 10^4 \text{ s})^2}{4\pi^2}\right)^{\frac{1}{3}}$$

$$= 4.22 \times 10^7 \text{ m}$$

ASSESS This is a high orbit; the radius is about 7 times the radius of the earth. Recall that the radius of the Space Shuttle's orbit is only about 5% larger than that of the earth.

Gravity on a Grand Scale

Although relatively weak, gravity is a long-range force. No matter how far apart two objects may be, there is a gravitational attraction between them. Consequently, gravity is the most ubiquitous force in the universe. It not only keeps your feet on the ground, but also is at work on a much larger scale. The Milky Way galaxy, the collection of stars of which our sun is a part, is held together by gravity. But why doesn't the attractive force of gravity simply pull all of the stars together?

The reason is that all of the stars in the galaxy are in orbit around the center of the galaxy. The gravitational attraction keeps the stars moving in orbits around the center of the galaxy rather than falling inward, much as the planets orbit the sun rather than falling into the sun. In the nearly 5 billion years that our solar system has existed, it has orbited the center of the galaxy approximately 20 times.

The galaxy as a whole doesn't rotate at a fixed angular speed, though. All of the stars in the galaxy are different distances from the galaxy's center, and so orbit with different periods. Stars closer to the center complete their orbits in less time, as we would expect from Equation 6.26. As the stars orbit, their relative positions shift. Stars that are relatively near neighbors now could be on opposite sides of the galaxy at some later time.

The rotation of a *rigid body* like a wheel is much simpler. As a wheel rotates, all of the points keep the same relationship to each other; every point on the wheel moves with the same angular velocity. The rotational dynamics of such rigid bodies is a topic we will take up in the next chapter.

A spiral galaxy, similar to our Milky Way galaxy.

STOP TO THINK 6.6   If the mass of the moon were doubled but it stayed in its present orbit, how would its orbital period change?

A. The period would increase.
B. The period would decrease.
C. The period would stay the same.

INTEGRATED EXAMPLE 6.20   **A hunter and his sling**

A Stone Age hunter stands on a cliff overlooking a flat plain. He places a 1.0 kg rock in a sling, ties the sling to a 1.0-m-long vine, then swings the rock in a horizontal circle around his head. The plane of the motion is 25 m above the plain below. The tension in the vine increases as the rock goes faster and faster. Suddenly, just as the tension reaches 200 N, the vine snaps. If the rock is moving toward the cliff at this instant, how far out on the plain (from the base of the cliff) will it land?

PREPARE We model the rock as a particle in uniform circular motion. We can use Problem-Solving Strategy 6.1 to analyze this part of the motion. Once the vine breaks, the rock undergoes projectile motion with an initial velocity that is horizontal.

The force identification diagram of FIGURE 6.29a on the next page shows that the only contact force acting on the rock is the tension in the vine. Because the rock moves in a horizontal circle, you may be tempted to draw a free-body diagram like FIGURE 6.29b, on the next page where $\vec{T}$ is directed along the x-axis. You will quickly run into trouble, however, because in this diagram the net force has a downward y-component that would cause the rock to rapidly accelerate downward. But we know that it moves in a horizontal circle and that the net force must point toward the center of the circle. In this free-body diagram, the weight force $\vec{w}$ points straight down and is certainly correct, so the difficulty must be with $\vec{T}$.

Continued

FIGURE 6.29 Visual overview of a hunter swinging a rock.

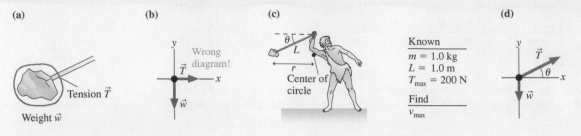

(a)   (b)   (c)   (d)

As an experiment, tie a small weight to a string, swing it over your head, and check the angle of the string. You will discover that the string is not horizontal but, instead, is angled downward. The sketch of FIGURE 6.29c labels this angle θ. Notice that the rock moves in a *horizontal* circle, so the center of the circle is not at his hand. The x-axis points horizontally, to the center of the circle, but the tension force is directed along the vine. Thus the correct free-body diagram is the one in FIGURE 6.29d.

Once the vine breaks, the visual overview of the situation is shown in FIGURE 6.30. The important thing to note here is that the initial x-component of velocity is the speed the rock had an instant before the vine broke.

SOLVE From the free-body diagram of Figure 6.29d, Newton's second law for circular motion is

$$\sum F_x = T\cos\theta = \frac{mv^2}{r}$$
$$\sum F_y = T\sin\theta - mg = 0$$

where θ is the angle of the vine below the horizontal. We can use the y-equation to find the angle of the vine:

$$\sin\theta = \frac{mg}{T}$$
$$\theta = \sin^{-1}\left(\frac{mg}{T}\right) = \sin^{-1}\left(\frac{(1.0\ \text{kg})(9.8\ \text{m/s}^2)}{200\ \text{N}}\right) = 2.81°$$

where we've evaluated the angle at the maximum tension of 200 N. The vine's angle of inclination is small but not zero.

Turning now to the x-equation, we find the rock's speed around the circle is

$$v = \sqrt{\frac{rT\cos\theta}{m}}$$

Be careful! The radius r of the circle is not the length L of the vine. You can see in Figure 6.29c that $r = L\cos\theta$. Thus

$$v = \sqrt{\frac{LT\cos^2\theta}{m}} = \sqrt{\frac{(1.0\ \text{m})(200\ \text{N})(\cos 2.81°)^2}{1.0\ \text{kg}}} = 14\ \text{m/s}$$

Because this is the horizontal speed of the rock just when the vine breaks, the initial velocity $(v_x)_i$ in the visual overview of the projectile motion, Figure 6.30, must be $(v_x)_i = 14\ \text{m/s}$. Recall that a projectile has no horizontal acceleration, so the rock's final position is

$$x_f = x_i + (v_x)_i\,\Delta t = 0\ \text{m} + (14\ \text{m/s})\Delta t$$

where Δt is the time the projectile is in the air. We're not given Δt, but we can find it from the vertical motion. For a projectile, the vertical motion is just free-fall motion, so we have

$$y_f = y_i + (v_y)_i\Delta t - \frac{1}{2}g(\Delta t)^2$$

The initial height is $y_i = 25$ m, the final height is $y_f = 0$ m, and the initial vertical velocity is $(v_y)_i = 0$ m/s. With these values, we have

$$0\ \text{m} = 25\ \text{m} + (0\ \text{m/s})\Delta t - \frac{1}{2}(9.8\ \text{m/s}^2)(\Delta t)^2$$

Solving this for Δt gives

$$\Delta t = \sqrt{\frac{2(25\ \text{m})}{9.8\ \text{m/s}^2}} = 2.3\ \text{s}$$

Now we can use this time to find

$$x_f = 0\ \text{m} + (14\ \text{m/s})(2.3\ \text{s}) = 32\ \text{m}$$

The rock lands 32 m from the base of the cliff.

ASSESS The circumference of the rock's circle is $2\pi r$, or about 6 m. At a speed of 14 m/s, the rock takes roughly half a second to go around once. This seems reasonable. The 32 m distance is about 100 ft, which seems easily attainable from a cliff over 75 feet high.

FIGURE 6.30 Visual overview of the rock in projectile motion.

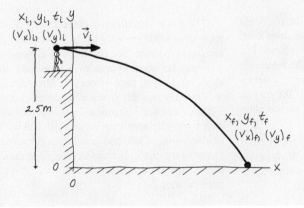

SUMMARY

The goal of Chapter 6 has been to learn about motion in a circle, including orbital motion under the influence of a gravitational force.

GENERAL PRINCIPLES

Uniform Circular Motion

An object moving in a circular path is in uniform circular motion if v is constant.

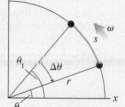

- The speed is constant, but the direction of motion is constantly changing.
- The **centripetal acceleration** is directed toward the center of the circle and has magnitude

$$a = \frac{v^2}{r}$$

- This acceleration requires a net force directed toward the center of the circle. Newton's second law for circular motion is

$$\vec{F}_{net} = m\vec{a} = \left(\frac{mv^2}{r}, \text{ toward center of circle}\right)$$

Universal Gravitation

Two objects with masses m_1 and m_2 that are distance r apart exert attractive gravitational forces on each other of magnitude

$$F_{1 on 2} = F_{2 on 1} = \frac{Gm_1m_2}{r^2}$$

where the gravitational constant is

$$G = 6.67 \times 10^{-11} \text{ N} \cdot \text{m}^2/\text{kg}^2$$

This is **Newton's law of gravity.** Gravity is an inverse-square law.

IMPORTANT CONCEPTS

Describing circular motion

We define new variables for circular motion. By convention, counterclockwise is positive.

Angular position: θ

Angular displacement: $\Delta\theta = \theta_f - \theta_i$

Angular velocity: $\omega = \dfrac{\Delta\theta}{\Delta t}$

Angles are measured in radians, where $1 \text{ rev} = 360° = 2\pi \text{ rad}$. The SI units of angular velocity are rad/s.

Period: $T = $ time for one complete circle.

Frequency: $f = \dfrac{1}{T}$

Uniform circular motion kinematics

For uniform circular motion:

$$\omega = 2\pi f \qquad \theta_f - \theta_i = \Delta\theta = \omega\,\Delta t$$

The velocity, acceleration, and circular motion variables are related as follows:

$$v = \frac{2\pi r}{T}$$

$$v = \omega r$$

$$a = \frac{v^2}{r} = \omega^2 r$$

APPLICATIONS

Apparent weight and weightlessness

Circular motion requires a net force pointing to the center. The apparent weight $w_{app} = n$ is usually not the same as the true weight w. n must be > 0 for the object to be in contact with a surface.

In orbital motion, the net force is provided by gravity. An astronaut and his spacecraft are both in free fall, so he feels weightless.

Planetary gravity and orbital motion

For a planet of mass M and radius R, the free-fall acceleration on the surface is

$$g = \frac{GM}{R^2}$$

The speed of a satellite in a low orbit is

$$v = \sqrt{gr}$$

A **satellite** in a circular orbit of radius r around an object of mass M moves at a speed v given by

$$v = \sqrt{\frac{GM}{r}}$$

The period and radius are related as follows:

$$T^2 = \left(\frac{4\pi^2}{GM}\right)r^3$$

QUESTIONS

Conceptual Questions

1. The batter in a baseball game hits a home run. As he circles the bases, is his angular velocity positive or negative?

2. Viewed from somewhere in space above the north pole, would a point on the earth's equator have a positive or negative angular velocity due to the earth's rotation?

3. A cyclist goes around a level, circular track at constant speed. Do you agree or disagree with the following statement? "Since the cyclist's speed is constant, her acceleration is zero." Explain.

4. In uniform circular motion, which of the following quantities are constant: speed, instantaneous velocity, angular velocity, centripetal acceleration, the magnitude of the net force?

5. A particle moving along a straight line can have nonzero acceleration even when its speed is zero (for instance, a ball in free fall at the top of its path). Can a particle moving in a circle have nonzero *centripetal* acceleration when its speed is zero? If so, give an example. If not, why not?

6. Would having four-wheel drive on a car make it possible to drive faster around corners on an icy road, without slipping, than the same car with two-wheel drive? Explain.

7. Large birds like pheasants often walk short distances. Small
BIO birds like chickadees never walk. They either hop or fly. Why might this be?

8. When you drive fast on the highway with muddy tires, you can hear the mud flying off the tires into your wheel wells. Why does the mud fly off?

9. A ball on a string moves in a vertical circle as in Figure Q6.9. When the ball is at its lowest point, is the tension in the string greater than, less than, or equal to the ball's weight? Explain. (You may want to include a free-body diagram as part of your explanation.)

FIGURE Q6.9

10. Give an everyday example of circular motion for which the centripetal acceleration is mostly or completely due to a force of the type specified: (a) Static friction. (b) Tension.

11. Give an everyday example of circular motion for which the centripetal acceleration is mostly or completely due to a force of the type specified: (a) Gravity. (b) Normal force.

12. It's been proposed that future space stations create "artificial gravity" by rotating around an axis. (The space station would have to be much larger than the present space station for this to be feasible.)
    a. How would this work? Explain.
    b. Would the artificial gravity be equally effective throughout the space station? If not, where in the space station would the residents want to live and work?

13. A car coasts at a constant speed over a circular hill. Which of the free-body diagrams in Figure Q6.13 is correct? Explain.

FIGURE Q6.13   A.   B.   C.

14. Riding in the back of a pickup truck can be very dangerous. If the truck turns suddenly, the riders can be thrown from the truck bed. Why are the riders ejected from the bed?

15. Variation in your apparent weight is desirable when you ride a roller coaster; it makes the ride fun. However, too much variation over a short period of time can be painful. For this reason, the loops of real roller coasters are not simply circles like Figure 6.21a. A typical loop is shown in Figure Q6.15. The radius of the circle that matches the track at the top of the loop is much smaller than that of a matching circle at other places on the track. Explain why this shape gives a more comfortable ride than a circular loop.

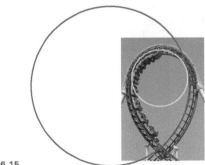

FIGURE Q6.15

16. A small projectile is launched parallel to the ground at height $h = 1$ m with sufficient speed to orbit a completely smooth, airless planet. A bug rides in a small hole inside the projectile. Is the bug weightless? Explain.

17. Why is it impossible for an astronaut inside an orbiting space shuttle to go from one end to the other by walking normally?

18. If every object in the universe feels an attractive gravitational force due to every other object, why don't you feel a pull from someone seated next to you?

19. A mountain climber's weight is less on the top of a tall mountain than at the base, though his mass is the same. Why?

20. Is the earth's gravitational force on the sun larger, smaller, or equal to the sun's gravitational force on the earth? Explain.

Multiple-Choice Questions

21. | A ball on a string moves around a complete circle, once a second, on a frictionless, horizontal table. The tension in the string is measured to be 6.0 N. What would the tension be if the ball went around in only half a second?
    A. 1.5 N   B. 3.0 N   C. 12 N   D. 24 N

22. | As seen from above, a car rounds the curved path shown in Figure Q6.22 at a constant speed. Which vector best represents the net force acting on the car?

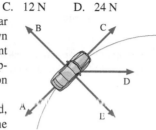

23. | Suppose you and a friend, each of mass 60 kg, go to the park and get on a 4.0-m-diameter merry-go-round. **FIGURE Q6.22** You stand on the outside edge of the merry-go-round, while your friend pushes so that it rotates once every 6.0 s. What is the magnitude of the (apparent) outward force that you feel?
    A. 7 N   B. 63 N   C. 130 N   D. 260 N

24. | The cylindrical space station in Figure Q6.24, 200 m in diameter, rotates in order to provide artificial gravity of g for the occupants. How much time does the station take to complete one rotation?
    A. 3 s   B. 20 s   C. 28 s   D. 32 s

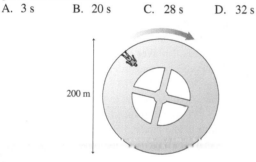

200 m

FIGURE Q6.24

25. ‖ Two cylindrical space stations, the second four times the diameter of the first, rotate so as to provide the same amount of artificial gravity. If the first station makes one rotation in the time T, then the second station makes one rotation in time
    A. $T/4$ B. $2T$ C. $4T$ D. $16T$

26. | A newly discovered planet has twice the mass and three times the radius of the earth. What is the free-fall acceleration at its surface, in terms of the free-fall acceleration g at the surface of the earth?
    A. $\frac{2}{9}g$ B. $\frac{2}{3}g$ C. $\frac{3}{4}g$ D. $\frac{4}{3}g$

27. ‖ Suppose one night the radius of the earth doubled but its mass stayed the same. What would be an approximate new value for the free-fall acceleration at the surface of the earth?
    A. 2.5 m/s²   B. 5.0 m/s²   C. 10 m/s²   D. 20 m/s²

28. | Currently, the moon goes around the earth once every 27.3 days. If the moon could be brought into a new circular orbit with a smaller radius, its orbital period would be
    A. More than 27.3 days.
    B. 27.3 days.
    C. Less than 27.3 days.

29. ‖ Two planets orbit a star. Planet 1 has orbital radius r_1 and planet 2 has $r_2 = 4r_1$. Planet 1 orbits with period T_1. Planet 2 orbits with period
    A. $T_2 = \frac{1}{2}T_1$ B. $T_2 = 2T_1$ C. $T_2 = 4T_1$ D. $T_2 = 8T_1$

30. | A particle undergoing circular motion in the xy-plane stops on the positive y-axis. Which of the following does *not* describe its angular position?
    A. $\pi/2$ rad   B. π rad   C. $5\pi/2$ rad   D. $-3\pi/2$ rad

Questions 31 through 33 concern a classic figure-skating jump called the axel. A skater starts the jump moving forward as shown in Figure Q6.31, leaps into the air, and turns one-and-a-half revolutions before landing. The typical skater is in the air for about 0.5 s, and the skater's hands are located about 0.8 m from the rotation axis.

FIGURE Q6.31

31. ‖ What is the approximate angular speed of the skater during the leap?
    A. 2 rad/s   B. 6 rad/s   C. 9 rad/s   D. 20 rad/s

32. | The skater's arms are fully extended during the jump. What is the approximate centripetal acceleration of the skater's hand?
    A. 10 m/s²   B. 30 m/s²   C. 300 m/s²   D. 450 m/s²

33. | What is the approximate speed of the skater's hand?
    A. 1 m/s   B. 3 m/s   C. 9 m/s   D. 15 m/s

PROBLEMS

Section 6.1 Uniform Circular Motion

1. ‖ What is the angular position in radians of the minute hand of a clock at (a) 5:00, (b) 7:15, and (c) 3:35?

2. | A child on a merry-go-round takes 3.0 s to go around once. What is his angular displacement during a 1.0 s time interval?

3. ‖ What is the angular speed of the tip of the minute hand on a clock, in rad/s?

4. ‖ An old-fashioned vinyl record rotates on a turntable at 45 rpm. What are (a) the angular speed in rad/s and (b) the period of the motion?

5. ‖ The earth's radius is about 4000 miles. Kampala, the capital of Uganda, and Singapore are both nearly on the equator. The distance between them is 5000 miles.
    a. Through what angle do you turn, relative to the earth, if you fly from Kampala to Singapore? Give your answer in both radians and degrees.
    b. The flight from Kampala to Singapore takes 9 hours. What is the plane's angular speed relative to the earth?

6. ‖ A Ferris wheel rotates at an angular velocity of 0.036 rad/s. At $t = 0$ min, your friend Seth is at the very top of the ride. What is Seth's angular position at $t = 3.0$ min, measured counterclockwise from the top? Give your answer as an angle in degrees between 0° and 360°.

7. ‖‖‖ A turntable rotates counterclockwise at 78 rpm. A speck of dust on the turntable is at $\theta = 0.45$ rad at $t = 0$ s. What is the angle of the speck at $t = 8.0$ s? Your answer should be between 0 and 2π rad.

8. ‖ A fast-moving superhero in a comic book runs around a circular, 70-m-diameter track five and a half times (ending up directly opposite her starting point) in 3.0 s. What is her angular speed, in rad/s?

9. ‖ Figure P6.9 shows the angular position of a potter's wheel.
   a. What is the angular displacement of the wheel between $t = 5$ s and $t = 15$ s?
   b. What is the angular velocity of the wheel at $t = 15$ s?

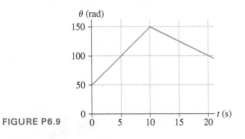

FIGURE P6.9

10. ‖ The angular velocity (in rpm) of the blade of a blender is given in Figure P6.10.
   a. If $\theta = 0$ rad at $t = 0$ s, what is the blade's angular position at $t = 20$ s?
   b. At what time has the blade completed 10 full revolutions?

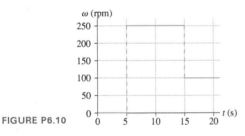

FIGURE P6.10

Section 6.2 Speed, Velocity, and Acceleration in Uniform Circular Motion

11. ‖ A 5.0-m-diameter merry-go-round is turning with a 4.0 s period. What is the speed of a child on the rim?

12. ‖ The blade on a table saw spins at 3450 rpm. Its diameter is 25.0 cm. What is the speed of a tooth on the edge of the blade, in both m/s and mph?

13. ‖ The horse on a carousel is 4.0 m from the central axis.
   a. If the carousel rotates at 0.10 rev/s, how long does it take the horse to go around twice?
   b. How fast is a child on the horse going (in m/s)?

14. ‖‖‖ The radius of the earth's very nearly circular orbit around the sun is 1.50×10^{11} m. Find the magnitude of the earth's (a) velocity, (b) angular velocity, and (c) centripetal acceleration as it travels around the sun. Assume a year of 365 days.

15. ‖ Your roommate is working on his bicycle and has the bike upside down. He spins the 60-cm-diameter wheel, and you notice that a pebble stuck in the tread goes by three times every second. What are the pebble's speed and acceleration?

16. ‖ To withstand "g-forces" of up to 10g, caused by suddenly pulling out of a steep dive, fighter jet pilots train on a "human centrifuge." 10g is an acceleration of 98 m/s². If the length of the centrifuge arm is 12 m, at what speed is the rider moving when she experiences 10g?

Section 6.3 Dynamics of Uniform Circular Motion

17. ‖‖‖ Figure P6.17 is a bird's-eye view of particles on a string moving in horizontal circles on a tabletop. All are moving at the same speed. Rank in order, from largest to smallest, the tensions T_1 to T_4.

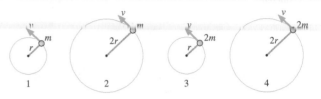

FIGURE P6.17

18. ‖ A 200 g block on a 50-cm-long string swings in a circle on a horizontal, frictionless table at 75 rpm.
   a. What is the speed of the block?
   b. What is the tension in the string?

19. ‖ A 1500 kg car drives around a flat 200-m-diameter circular track at 25 m/s. What are the magnitude and direction of the net force on the car? What causes this force?

20. ‖ A fast pitch softball player does a "windmill" pitch, illustrated in Figure P6.20, moving her hand through a circular arc to pitch a ball at 70 mph. The 0.19 kg ball is 50 cm from the pivot point at her shoulder. At the lowest point of the circle, the ball has reached its maximum speed.
   a. At the bottom of the circle, just before the ball leaves her hand, what is its centripetal acceleration?
   b. What are the magnitude and direction of the force her hand exerts on the ball at this point?

FIGURE P6.20

21. ‖ A baseball pitching machine works by rotating a light and stiff rigid rod about a horizontal axis until the ball is moving toward the target. Suppose a 144 g baseball is held 85 cm from the axis of rotation and released at the major league pitching speed of 85 mph.
   a. What is the ball's centripetal acceleration just before it is released?
   b. What is the magnitude of the net force that is acting on the ball just before it is released?

22. ‖ You're driving your pickup truck around a curve with a radius of 20 m. A box in the back of the truck is pressed up against the wall of the truck. How fast must you drive so that the force of the wall on the box equals the weight of the box?

Section 6.4 Apparent Forces in Circular Motion

23. ⫾⫾ The passengers in a roller coaster car feel 50% heavier than their true weight as the car goes through a dip with a 30 m radius of curvature. What is the car's speed at the bottom of the dip?

24. ⫾ You hold a bucket in one hand. In the bucket is a 500 g rock. You swing the bucket so the rock moves in a vertical circle 2.2 m in diameter. What is the minimum speed the rock must have at the top of the circle if it is to always stay in contact with the bottom of the bucket?

25. ⫾⫾ As a roller coaster car crosses the top of a 40-m-diameter loop-the-loop, its apparent weight is the same as its true weight. What is the car's speed at the top?

26. ⫾⫾ A typical laboratory centrifuge rotates at 4000 rpm. Test tubes have to be placed into a centrifuge very carefully because of the very large accelerations.
    a. What is the acceleration at the end of a test tube that is 10 cm from the axis of rotation?
    b. For comparison, what is the magnitude of the acceleration a test tube would experience if stopped in a 1.0-ms-long encounter with a hard floor after falling from a height of 1.0 m?

Section 6.5 Circular Orbits and Weightlessness

27. ⫾⫾ A satellite orbiting the moon very near the surface has a period of 110 min. Use this information, together with the radius of the moon from the table on the inside of the back cover, to calculate the free-fall acceleration on the moon's surface.

Section 6.6 Newton's Law of Gravity

28. ⫾⫾⫾ The centers of a 10 kg lead ball and a 100 g lead ball are separated by 10 cm.
    a. What gravitational force does each exert on the other?
    b. What is the ratio of this gravitational force to the weight of the 100 g ball?

29. ⫾ The gravitational force of a star on an orbiting planet 1 is F_1. Planet 2, which is twice as massive as planet 1 and orbits at twice the distance from the star, experiences gravitational force F_2. What is the ratio F_2/F_1?

30. ⫾ The free-fall acceleration at the surface of planet 1 is 20 m/s². The radius and the mass of planet 2 are twice those of planet 1. What is the free-fall acceleration on planet 2?

31. ⫾⫾⫾ What is the ratio of the sun's gravitational force on you to the earth's gravitational force on you?

32. ⫾⫾ Suppose the free-fall acceleration at some location on earth was exactly 9.8000 m/s². What would it be at the top of a 1000-m-tall tower at this location? (Give your answer to five significant figures.)

33. ⫾ a. What is the gravitational force of the sun on the earth?
    b. What is the gravitational force of the moon on the earth?
    c. The moon's force is what percent of the sun's force?

34. ⫾ What is the free-fall acceleration at the surface of (a) Mars and (b) Jupiter?

Section 6.7 Gravity and Orbits

35. ⫾⫾⫾ Planet X orbits the star Omega with a "year" that is 200 earth days long. Planet Y circles Omega at four times the distance of Planet X. How long is a year on Planet Y?

36. ⫾⫾⫾ Satellite A orbits a planet with a speed of 10,000 m/s. Satellite B is twice as massive as satellite A and orbits at twice the distance from the center of the planet. What is the speed of satellite B?

37. ⫾⫾⫾ The Space Shuttle is in a 250-mile-high orbit. What are the shuttle's orbital period, in minutes, and its speed?

38. ⫾ The *asteroid belt* circles the sun between the orbits of Mars and Jupiter. One asteroid has a period of 5.0 earth years. What are the asteroid's orbital radius and speed?

39. ⫾⫾⫾ An earth satellite moves in a circular orbit at a speed of 5500 m/s. What is its orbital period?

General Problems

40. ⫾ How fast must a plane fly along the earth's equator so that the sun stands still relative to the passengers? In which direction must the plane fly, east to west or west to east? Give your answer in both km/h and mph. The radius of the earth is 6400 km.

41. ⫾⫾⫾ The car in Figure P6.41 travels at a constant speed along the road shown. Draw vectors showing its acceleration at the three points A, B, and C, or write $\vec{a} = \vec{0}$. The lengths of your vectors should correspond to the magnitudes of the accelerations.

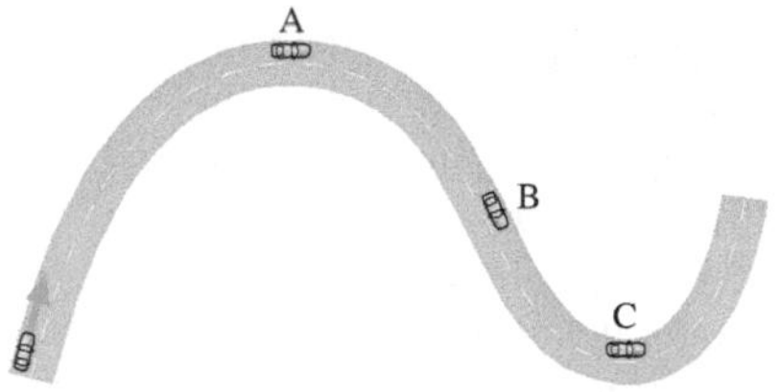

FIGURE P6.41

42. ⫾⫾⫾ In the Bohr model of the hydrogen atom, an electron (mass $m = 9.1 \times 10^{-31}$ kg) orbits a proton at a distance of 5.3×10^{-11} m. The proton pulls on the electron with an electric force of 8.2×10^{-8} N. How many revolutions per second does the electron make?

43. ⫾⫾ A 75 kg man weighs himself at the north pole and at the equator. Which scale reading is higher? By how much? Assume the earth is a perfect sphere. Explain why the readings differ.

44. ⫾ A 1500 kg car takes a 50-m-radius unbanked curve at 15 m/s. What is the size of the friction force on the car?

45. ⫾⫾⫾ A 500 g ball swings in a vertical circle at the end of a 1.5-m-long string. When the ball is at the bottom of the circle, the tension in the string is 15 N. What is the speed of the ball at that point?

46. ⫾⫾⫾ Suppose the moon were held in its orbit not by gravity but by a massless cable attached to the center of the earth. What would be the tension in the cable? See the inside of the back cover for astronomical data.

47. ⫾⫾⫾ A 30 g ball rolls around a 40-cm-diameter L-shaped track, shown in Figure P6.47, at 60 rpm. Rolling friction can be neglected.
    a. How many different contact forces does the track exert on the ball? Name them.
    b. What is the magnitude of the net force on the ball?

FIGURE P6.47

48. ⫾ A 5.0 g coin is placed 15 cm from the center of a turntable. The coin has static and kinetic coefficients of friction with the turntable surface of $\mu_s = 0.80$ and $\mu_k = 0.50$. The turntable very slowly speeds up to 60 rpm. Does the coin slide off?

49. ⫼ A *conical pendulum* is formed by attaching a 500 g ball to a 1.0-m-long string, then allowing the mass to move in a horizontal circle of radius 20 cm. Figure P6.49 shows that the string traces out the surface of a cone, hence the name.
    a. What is the tension in the string?
    b. What is the ball's angular velocity, in rpm?
    Hint: Determine the horizontal and vertical components of the forces acting on the ball, and use the fact that the vertical component of acceleration is zero since there is no vertical motion.

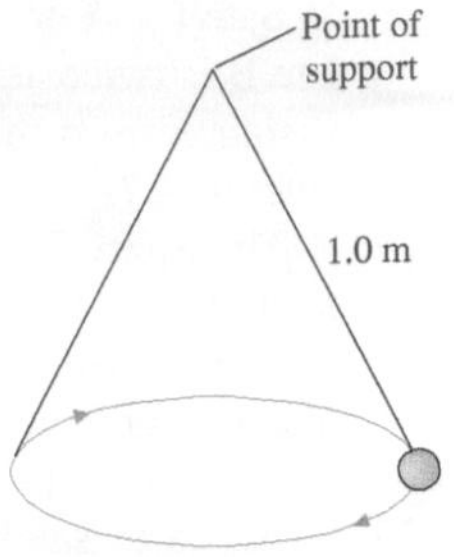

FIGURE P6.49

Point of support

1.0 m

50. ⫼ In an old-fashioned amusement park ride, passengers stand inside a 3.0-m-tall, 5.0-m-diameter hollow steel cylinder with their backs against the wall. The cylinder begins to rotate about a vertical axis. Then the floor on which the passengers are standing suddenly drops away! If all goes well, the passengers will "stick" to the wall and not slide. Clothing has a static coefficient of friction against steel in the range 0.60 to 1.0 and a kinetic coefficient in the range 0.40 to 0.70. What is the minimum rotational frequency, in rpm, for which the ride is safe?

51. ⫼ The 0.20 kg puck on the frictionless, horizontal table in Figure P6.51 is connected by a string through a hole in the table to a hanging 1.20 kg block. With what speed must the puck rotate in a circle of radius 0.50 m if the block is to remain hanging at rest?

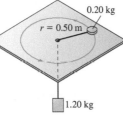

0.20 kg

$r = 0.50$ m

1.20 kg

FIGURE P6.51

52. ⫼ While at the county fair, you decide to ride the Ferris wheel. Having eaten too many candy apples and elephant ears, you find the motion somewhat unpleasant. To take your mind off your stomach, you wonder about the motion of the ride. You estimate the radius of the big wheel to be 15 m, and you use your watch to find that each loop around takes 25 s.
    a. What are your speed and magnitude of your acceleration?
    b. What is the ratio of your apparent weight to your true weight at the top of the ride?
    c. What is the ratio of your apparent weight to your true weight at the bottom?

53. ⫼ A car drives over the top of a hill that has a radius of 50 m. What maximum speed can the car have without flying off the road at the top of the hill?

54. ⫼ A 100 g ball on a 60-cm-long string is swung in a vertical circle whose center is 200 cm above the floor. The string suddenly breaks when it is parallel to the ground and the ball is moving upward. The ball reaches a height 600 cm above the floor. What was the tension in the string an instant before it broke?

55. ⫼ While a person is walking, his arms (each with typical length 70 cm measured from the shoulder joint) swing through approximately a 45° angle in 0.5 s. As a reasonable approximation, we can assume that the arm moves with constant speed during each swing.
    a. What is the acceleration of a 1.0 g drop of blood in the fingertips at the bottom of the swing?

b. Draw a free-body diagram for the drop of blood in part a.
    c. Find the magnitude and direction of the force that the blood vessel must exert on the drop of blood.
    d. What force would the blood vessel exert if the arm were not swinging?

56. ⫼ The two identical pucks in Figure P6.56 rotate together on a frictionless, horizontal table. They are tied together by strings 1 and 2, each of length *l*. If their common angular speed is ω, what are the tensions in the two strings?

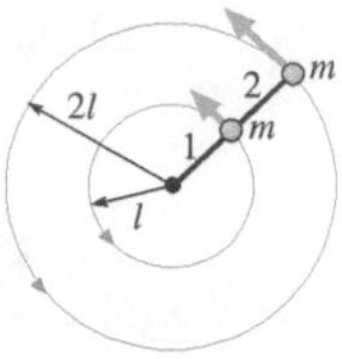

$2l$ 2 ⬤ m
        1 ⬤ m
    l

FIGURE P6.56

57. ⫼ The ultracentrifuge is an important tool for separating and analyzing proteins in biological research. Because of the enormous centripetal accelerations that can be achieved, the apparatus (see Figure 6.23) must be carefully balanced so that each sample is matched by another on the opposite side of the rotor shaft. Failure to do so is a costly mistake, as seen in Figure P6.57. Any difference in mass of the opposing samples will cause a net force in the horizontal plane on the shaft of the rotor. Suppose that a scientist makes a slight error in sample preparation, and one sample has a mass 10 mg greater than the opposing sample. If the samples are 10 cm from the axis of the rotor and the ultracentrifuge spins at 70,000 rpm, what is the magnitude of the net force on the rotor due to the unbalanced samples?

FIGURE P6.57

58. ⫼ The Space Shuttle orbits 300 km above the surface of the earth.
    a. What is the force of gravity on a 1.0 kg sphere inside the Space Shuttle?
    b. The sphere floats around inside the Space Shuttle, apparently "weightless." How is this possible?

59. ⫼ A sensitive gravimeter at a mountain observatory finds that the free-fall acceleration is 0.0075 m/s² less than that at sea level. What is the observatory's altitude?

60. ⫼ Suppose we could shrink the earth without changing its mass. At what fraction of its current radius would the free-fall acceleration at the surface be three times its present value?

61. ⫼ Planet Z is 10,000 km in diameter. The free-fall acceleration on Planet Z is 8.0 m/s².
    a. What is the mass of Planet Z?
    b. What is the free-fall acceleration 10,000 km above Planet Z's north pole?

62. ⫼ What are the speed and altitude of a geostationary satellite (see Example 6.19) orbiting Mars? Mars rotates on its axis once every 24.8 hours.

63. ⫼ a. What is the free-fall acceleration on Mars?
    b. Estimate the maximum speed at which an astronaut can walk on the surface of Mars.

64. ⫼ How long will it take a rock dropped from 2.0 m above the surface of Mars to reach the ground?

65. ⫾ A 20 kg sphere is at the origin and a 10 kg sphere is at
INT (x, y) = (20 cm, 0 cm). At what point or points could you place
a small mass such that the net gravitational force on it due to the
spheres is zero?

66. ⫾ a. At what height above the earth is the free-fall acceleration
10% of its value at the surface?

   b. What is the speed of a satellite orbiting at that height?

67. ⏐ Mars has a small moon, Phobos, that orbits with a period of 7 h
39 min. The radius of Phobos' orbit is 9.4×10^6 m. Use only this
information (and the value of G) to calculate the mass of Mars.

68. ⫾ You are the science officer on a visit to a distant solar system.
Prior to landing on a planet you measure its diameter to be
1.80×10^7 m and its rotation period to be 22.3 h. You have previously determined that the planet orbits 2.20×10^{11} m from its
star with a period of 402 earth days. Once on the surface you
find that the free-fall acceleration is 12.2 m/s². What are the
masses of (a) the planet and (b) the star?

69. ⫾⫾ Europa, a satellite of Jupiter,
BIO is believed to have a liquid
ocean of water (with a possibil-
ity of life) beneath its icy surface. In planning a future mission
to Europa, what is the fastest
that an astronaut with legs of
length 0.70 m could walk on the
surface of Europa? Europa is
3100 km in diameter and has a
mass of 4.8×10^{22} kg.

In Problems 70 through 73 you are given the equation (or equations)
used to solve a problem. For each of these, you are to

a. Write a realistic problem for which this is the correct equation.
The last two questions should involve real planets. Be sure that
the answer your problem requests is consistent with the equation
given.

b. Finish the solution of the problem.

70. ⫾ $60 \text{ N} = (0.30 \text{ kg})\omega^2(0.50 \text{ m})$

71. ⫾ $(1500 \text{ kg})(9.80 \text{ m/s}^2) - 11{,}760 \text{ N} = (1500 \text{ kg})v^2/(200 \text{ m})$

72. ⫾ $\dfrac{(6.67 \times 10^{-11} \text{ N} \cdot \text{m}^2/\text{kg}^2)(1.90 \times 10^{27} \text{ kg})}{r^2}$

   $= \dfrac{(6.67 \times 10^{-11} \text{ N} \cdot \text{m}^2/\text{kg}^2)(5.98 \times 10^{24} \text{ kg})}{(6.37 \times 10^6 \text{ m})^2}$

73. ⫾ $\dfrac{(6.67 \times 10^{-11} \text{ N} \cdot \text{m}^2/\text{kg}^2)(5.98 \times 10^{24} \text{ kg})(1000 \text{ kg})}{r^2}$

   $= \dfrac{(1000 \text{ kg})(1997 \text{ m/s})^2}{r}$

Passage Problems

Orbiting the Moon

Suppose a spacecraft orbits the moon in a very low, circular orbit,
just a few hundred meters above the lunar surface. The moon has a
diameter of 3500 km, and the free-fall acceleration at the surface is
1.6 m/s².

74. ⏐ The direction of the net force on the craft is
   A. Away from the surface of the moon.
   B. In the direction of motion.
   C. Toward the center of the moon.
   D. Nonexistent, because the net force is zero.

75. ⏐ How fast is this spacecraft moving?
   A. 53 m/s   B. 75 m/s   C. 1700 m/s   D. 2400 m/s

76. ⏐ How much time does it take for the spacecraft to complete
one orbit?
   A. 38 min   B. 76 min   C. 110 min   D. 220 min

77. ⏐ The material that comprises the side of the moon facing the
earth is actually slightly more dense than the material on the far
side. When the spacecraft is above a more dense area of the surface, the moon's gravitational force on the craft is a bit stronger. In
order to stay in a circular orbit of constant height and speed, the
spacecraft could fire its rockets while passing over the denser
area. The rockets should be fired so as to generate a force on the
craft
   A. Away from the surface of the moon.
   B. In the direction of motion.
   C. Toward the center of the moon.
   D. Opposite the direction of motion.

| STOP TO THINK ANSWERS |

Stop to Think 6.1: A. Because $5\pi/2$ rad $= 2\pi$ rad $+ \pi/2$ rad, the
particle's position is one complete revolution (2π rad) plus an extra
$\pi/2$ rad. This extra $\pi/2$ rad puts the particle at position A.

Stop to Think 6.2: D > B > C > A. The centripetal acceleration
is $\omega^2 r$. Changing r by a factor of 2 changes the centripetal acceleration by a factor of 2, but changing ω by a factor of 2 changes the centripetal acceleration by a factor of 4.

Stop to Think 6.3: $T_D > T_B = T_E > T_C > T_A$. The center-
directed force is $m\omega^2 r$. Changing r by a factor of 2 changes the tension by a factor of 2, but changing f (and thus ω) by a factor of 2
changes the tension by a factor of 4.

Stop to Think 6.4: B. The car is moving in a circle, so there must
be a net force toward the center of the circle. The center of the circle
is below the car, so the net force must point downward. This can be
true only if $w > n$.

Stop to Think 6.5: B > A > D > C. The free-fall acceleration is
proportional to the mass, but inversely proportional to the square of
the radius.

Stop to Think 6.6: C. The period of the orbit does not depend on the
mass of the orbiting object.

7 Rotational Motion

To get the roulette wheel spinning, the croupier must give the wheel a push in the direction of its motion. Does it matter if she pushes closer to the rim or nearer the center?

LOOKING AHEAD ▶

The goal of Chapter 7 is to understand the physics of rotating objects.

The Rotation of a Rigid Body

A **rigid body** is an extended object whose size and shape do not change as it moves.

Boomerangs and bicycle wheels are examples of rigid bodies.

A rigid body whose angular velocity is changing has an **angular acceleration.**

The angular velocity is increasing.

Looking Back ◀◀
6.1–6.2 Uniform circular motion

Newton's Second Law for Rotational Motion

You've learned Newton's second law of motion for *translational* motion: **A net force causes an object to accelerate.** In this chapter, we'll study Newton's second law for *rotational* motion: **A net torque causes an object to have an *angular* acceleration.**

To make the merry-go-round speed up, the girl has to apply a torque to it by pushing at its edge.

Looking Back ◀◀
4.6 Newton's second law

Torque

Torque is the rotational equivalent of force. To get an object rotating, you need to apply a torque to it. The farther from the axis of rotation a force is applied, the greater the torque.

By applying forces at the edge of the large wheel, the sailor can exert a large torque upon it.

Gravitational Torque

For the purpose of calculating torque, the entire weight of an object can be considered as acting at a single point, the **center of gravity.**

The weight of this tree, acting at its center of gravity, tries to rotate the tree about its base.

Moment of Inertia

We have learned that *mass* is the property of an object that resists acceleration. The property of an object that resists angular acceleration is its *moment of inertia.* The moment of inertia of an object depends not only on its mass but also on how that mass is distributed.

By extending its tail, this cat increases its moment of inertia. This increases its resistance to angular acceleration, making it harder for it to fall.

7.1 The Rotation of a Rigid Body

So far, our study of physics has focused almost exclusively on the *particle model* in which an entire object is represented as a single point in space. The particle model is entirely adequate for understanding motion in a wide variety of situations, but there are also cases for which we need to consider the motion of an *extended object*—a system of particles for which the size and shape *do* make a difference and cannot be neglected.

A **rigid body** is an extended object whose size and shape do not change as it moves. For example, a bicycle wheel can be thought of as a rigid body. FIGURE 7.1 shows a rigid body as a collection of atoms held together by the rigid "massless rods" of molecular bonds.

Real molecular bonds are, of course, not perfectly rigid. That's why an object seemingly as rigid as a bicycle wheel can flex and bend. Thus Figure 7.1 is really a simplified *model* of an extended object, the **rigid-body model.** The rigid-body model is a very good approximation for many real objects of practical interest, such as wheels and axles. Even nonrigid objects can often be modeled as rigid bodies during segments of their motion. For example, a diver is well described as a rotating rigid body while she's in the tuck position.

FIGURE 7.2 illustrates the three basic types of motion of a rigid body: **translational motion, rotational motion,** and **combination motion.** We've already studied translational motion of a rigid body using the particle model. If a rigid body doesn't rotate, this model is often adequate for describing its motion. The rotational motion of a rigid body will be the main focus of this chapter. We'll also discuss an important case of combination motion—that of a *rolling* object—later in this chapter.

Acti**v**
Physics ONLINE 7.7

FIGURE 7.1 The rigid-body model of an extended object.

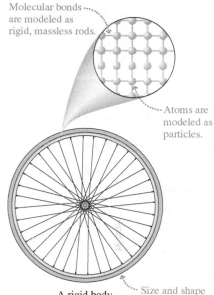

Molecular bonds are modeled as rigid, massless rods.

Atoms are modeled as particles.

A rigid body ···· Size and shape do not change as the object moves.

FIGURE 7.2 Three basic types of motion of a rigid body.

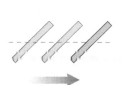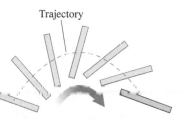

Trajectory

Translational motion: The object as a whole moves along a trajectory but does not rotate.

Rotational motion: The object rotates about a fixed point. Every point on the object moves in a circle.

Combination motion: An object rotates as it moves along a trajectory.

Rotational Motion of a Rigid Body

FIGURE 7.3 shows a wheel rotating on an axle. Notice that as the wheel rotates for a time interval Δt, two points 1 and 2 on the wheel, marked with dots, turn through the *same angle*, even through their distances r from the axis of rotation may be different; that is, $\Delta\theta_1 = \Delta\theta_2$ during the time interval Δt. As a consequence, the two points have equal angular velocities: $\omega_1 = \omega_2$. In general, **every point on a rotating rigid body has the same angular velocity.** Because of this, we can refer to the angular velocity ω *of the wheel.*

Recall from Chapter 6 that the speed of a particle moving in a circle is $v = \omega r$, so two points of a rotating object will have different *speeds* if they have different distances from the axis of rotation, but *all* points have the *same* angular velocity ω. Thus angular velocity is one of the most important parameters of a rotating object.

Because every point on a rotating object moves in a circle, we can carry forward all the results for circular motion from Chapter 6. Thus the angular displacement of any point on the wheel shown in Figure 7.3 is found from Equation 6.4 as $\Delta\theta = \omega\,\Delta t$; the speed of any particle in the wheel is $v = \omega r$, where r is the particle's distance from the axis; and the particle's centripetal acceleration is $a = \omega^2 r$.

FIGURE 7.3 All points on a wheel rotate with the same angular velocity.

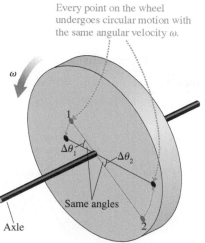

Every point on the wheel undergoes circular motion with the same angular velocity ω.

ω

1

$\Delta\theta_1$ $\Delta\theta_2$

Same angles

Axle

2

FIGURE 7.4 A rotating wheel with a changing angular velocity.

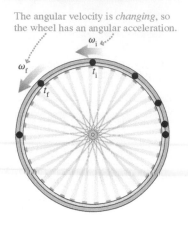

The angular velocity is *changing*, so the wheel has an angular acceleration.

FIGURE 7.5 Determining the sign of the angular acceleration.

α is *positive* when the rigid body is . . .

. . . rotating counter–clockwise and speeding up.   . . . rotating clockwise and slowing down.

α is *negative* when the rigid body is . . .

. . . rotating counter–clockwise and slowing down.   . . . rotating clockwise and speeding up.

Angular Acceleration

If you push on the edge of a bicycle wheel, it begins to rotate. If you continue to push, it rotates ever faster. Its angular velocity is *changing*. To understand the dynamics of rotating objects, we'll need to be able to describe this case of changing angular velocity—that is, the case of *nonuniform* circular motion.

FIGURE 7.4 shows a bicycle wheel whose angular velocity is changing. The dot represents a particular point on the wheel at successive times. At time t_i the angular velocity is ω_i; at a later time $t_f = t_i + \Delta t$ the angular velocity has changed to ω_f. The change in angular velocity during this time interval is

$$\Delta\omega = \omega_f - \omega_i$$

Recall that in Chapter 2 we defined the *linear* acceleration as

$$a_x = \frac{\Delta v_x}{\Delta t} = \frac{(v_x)_f - (v_x)_i}{\Delta t}$$

By analogy, we now define the **angular acceleration** as

$$\alpha = \frac{\text{change in angular velocity}}{\text{time interval}} = \frac{\Delta\omega}{\Delta t} \tag{7.1}$$

Angular acceleration for a particle in nonuniform circular motion

We use the symbol α (Greek alpha) for angular acceleration. Because the units of ω are rad/s, the units of angular acceleration are (rad/s)/s, or rad/s². From Equation 7.1, the sign of α is the same as the sign of $\Delta\omega$. **FIGURE 7.5** shows how to determine the sign of α. Be careful with the sign of α; just as with linear acceleration, positive and negative values of α can't be interpreted as simply "speeding up" and "slowing down." Like ω, the angular acceleration α is the same for every point on a rotating rigid body.

In Chapter 6 we found analogies between linear and angular positions and velocities. Here we've extended those analogies to include linear and angular accelerations. Table 7.1 summarizes all of these analogies between linear and circular motion.

NOTE ▶ Don't confuse the angular acceleration with the centripetal acceleration introduced in Chapter 6. The angular acceleration indicates how rapidly the *angular* velocity is changing. The centripetal acceleration is a vector quantity that points toward the center of a particle's circular path; it is nonzero even if the angular velocity is constant. ◀

In addition, the various equations of one-dimensional kinematics have analogs for rotational or circular motion. Table 7.2 lists the equations for one-dimensional motion and the analogous equations for the kinematics of circular motion.

TABLE 7.1 Linear and circular motion variables

Linear motion	Circular motion
Position x	Angular position θ
Velocity $v_x = \Delta x/\Delta t$	Angular velocity $\omega = \Delta\theta/\Delta t$
Acceleration $a_x = \Delta v_x/\Delta t$	Angular acceleration $\alpha = \Delta\omega/\Delta t$

TABLE 7.2 Linear and circular motion equations

Linear motion	Circular motion
Displacement at constant speed: $\Delta x = v\,\Delta t$	Angular displacement at constant angular speed: $\Delta\theta = \omega\,\Delta t$
Change in velocity at constant acceleration: $\Delta v = a\,\Delta t$	Change in angular velocity at constant angular acceleration: $\Delta\omega = \alpha\,\Delta t$
Displacement at constant acceleration: $\Delta x = v_i\,\Delta t + \frac{1}{2}a\,\Delta t^2$	Angular displacement at constant angular acceleration: $\Delta\theta = \omega_i\,\Delta t + \frac{1}{2}\alpha\,\Delta t^2$

EXAMPLE 7.1 **Spinning up a computer disk**

The disk in a computer disk drive spins up to 5400 rpm in 2.00 s. What is the angular acceleration of the disk? At the end of 2.00 s, how many revolutions has the disk made?

PREPARE The initial angular velocity is $\omega_i = 0$ rad/s. The final angular velocity is $\omega_f = 5400$ rpm. However, this value is not in the correct SI units of rad/s. The conversion is

$$\omega_f = \frac{5400 \text{ rev}}{\text{min}} \times \frac{1 \text{ min}}{60 \text{ s}} \times \frac{2\pi \text{ rad}}{1 \text{ rev}} = 565 \text{ rad/s}$$

SOLVE From the definition of angular acceleration, we have

$$\alpha = \frac{\Delta\omega}{\Delta t} = \frac{565 \text{ rad/s} - 0 \text{ rad/s}}{2.00 \text{ s}} = 283 \text{ rad/s}^2$$

We can compute the angular displacement during this acceleration by using the angular displacement equation from Table 7.2:

$$\Delta\theta = \omega_i \Delta t + \tfrac{1}{2}\alpha \, \Delta t^2$$

$$= (0 \text{ rad/s})(2.00 \text{ s}) + \tfrac{1}{2}(283 \text{ rad/s}^2)(2.00 \text{ s})^2$$

$$= 566 \text{ rad}$$

Each revolution corresponds to an angular displacement of 2π, so we have

$$\text{number of revolutions} = \frac{566 \text{ rad}}{2\pi \text{ rad/revolution}}$$

$$= 90 \text{ revolutions}$$

The disk completes 90 revolutions during the first 2 seconds.

ASSESS It seems reasonable that a fast-spinning disk would turn 90 times in a few seconds.

Graphs for Rotational Motion with Constant Angular Acceleration

In Chapter 2 we studied position, velocity, and acceleration graphs for motion with constant acceleration. A review of Section 2.5 is highly recommended. Because of the analogies between linear and angular quantities in Table 7.1, the rules for graphing angular variables are identical with those for linear variables. In particular, **the angular velocity is the slope of the angular position-versus-time graph** (as we discussed in Chapter 6), and **the angular acceleration is the slope of the angular velocity-versus-time graph.** When the angular acceleration is constant, the equations for circular motion in Table 7.2 show that the angular velocity graph is linear while the angular position graph is parabolic.

EXAMPLE 7.2 **Graphing angular quantities**

FIGURE 7.6 shows the angular velocity-versus-time graph for the propeller of a ship.

a. Describe the motion of the propeller.
b. Draw the angular acceleration graph for the propeller.

FIGURE 7.6 The propeller's angular velocity.

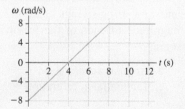

PREPARE The angular acceleration graph is the slope of the angular velocity graph.

SOLVE

a. Initially the propeller has a negative angular velocity, so it is turning clockwise. It slows down until, at $t = 4$ s, it is instantaneously stopped. It then speeds up in the opposite direction until it is turning counterclockwise at a constant angular velocity.

b. The angular acceleration graph is the slope of the angular velocity graph. From $t = 0$ s, to $t = 8$ s, the slope is

$$\frac{\Delta\omega}{\Delta t} = \frac{\omega_f - \omega_i}{\Delta t} = \frac{(8.0 \text{ rad/s}) - (-8.0 \text{ rad/s})}{8.0 \text{ s}} = 2.0 \text{ rad/s}^2$$

After $t = 8$ s, the slope is zero, so the angular acceleration is zero. This graph is plotted in FIGURE 7.7.

FIGURE 7.7 Angular acceleration graph for a propeller.

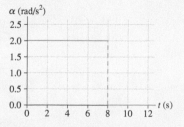

ASSESS A comparison of these graphs with their linear analogs in Figure 2.24 suggests that we're on the right track.

FIGURE 7.8 Uniform and nonuniform circular motion.

(a) Uniform circular motion

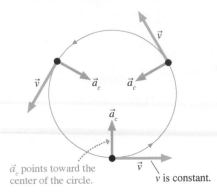

$\vec{a}_c$ points toward the center of the circle.

v is constant.

(b) Nonuniform circular motion

The tangential acceleration $\vec{a}_t$ causes the particle's *speed* to change. There's a tangential acceleration *only* when the particle is speeding up or slowing down.

v is increasing.

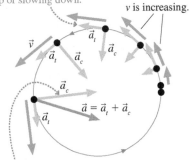

$\vec{a} = \vec{a}_t + \vec{a}_c$

The centripetal acceleration $\vec{a}_c$ causes the particle's *direction* to change. As the particle speeds up, a_c gets larger. Circular motion *always* has a centripetal acceleration.

Tangential Acceleration

As you learned in Chapter 6, and as FIGURE 7.8a reminds you, a particle undergoing uniform circular motion has an acceleration directed inward toward the center of the circle. This centripetal acceleration $\vec{a}_c$ is due to the change in the *direction* of the particle's velocity. Recall that the magnitude of the centripetal acceleration is $a_c = v^2/r = \omega^2 r$.

> NOTE ▶ Centripetal acceleration will now be denoted a_c to distinguish it from tangential acceleration a_t, discussed below. ◀

If the particle's circular motion is *nonuniform*, so that the particle's speed is changing, then the particle will have another component to its acceleration. FIGURE 7.8b shows a particle whose speed is increasing as it moves around its circular path. Because the *magnitude* of the velocity is increasing, this second component of the acceleration is directed *tangentially* to the circle, in the same direction as the velocity. This component of acceleration is called the **tangential acceleration.** As shown in Figure 7.8b, **the full acceleration $\vec{a}$ is then the vector sum of these two components:** the centripetal acceleration $\vec{a}_c$ and the tangential acceleration $\vec{a}_t$.

The tangential acceleration measures the rate at which the particle's speed around the circle increases. Thus its magnitude is

$$a_t = \frac{\Delta v}{\Delta t}$$

We can relate the tangential acceleration to the *angular* acceleration by using the relation $v = \omega r$ between the speed of a particle moving in a circle of radius r and its angular velocity ω. We have

$$a_t = \frac{\Delta v}{\Delta t} = \frac{\Delta(\omega r)}{\Delta t} = \frac{\Delta \omega}{\Delta t} r$$

or, because $\alpha = \Delta \omega / \Delta t$ from Equation 7.1,

$$a_t = \alpha r \qquad (7.2)$$

Relationship between tangential and angular acceleration

We've seen that all points on a rotating rigid body have the same angular acceleration. From Equation 7.2, however, the centripetal and tangential accelerations of a point on a rotating object depends on the point's distance r from the axis, so that these accelerations are *not* the same for all points.

STOP TO THINK 7.1   A ball on the end of a string swings in a horizontal circle once every second. State whether the magnitude of each of the following quantities is zero, constant (but not zero), or changing.

a. Velocity
b. Angular velocity
c. Centripetal acceleration
d. Angular acceleration
e. Tangential acceleration

7.2 Torque

Newton's genius, summarized in his second law of motion, was to recognize force as the cause of acceleration. But what about *angular* acceleration? What do Newton's laws tell us about rotational motion? To begin our study of rotational motion, we'll need to find a rotational equivalent of force.

Consider the common experience of pushing open a heavy door. FIGURE 7.9 is a top view of a door that is hinged on the left. Four forces are shown, all of equal strength. Which of these will be most effective at opening the door?

Force $\vec{F}_1$ will open the door, but force $\vec{F}_2$, which pushes straight at the hinge, will not. Force $\vec{F}_3$ will open the door, but not as easily as $\vec{F}_1$. What about $\vec{F}_4$? It is perpendicular to the door and it has the same magnitude as $\vec{F}_1$, but you know from experience that pushing close to the hinge is not as effective as pushing at the outer edge of the door.

The ability of a force to cause a rotation thus depends on three factors:

1. The magnitude F of the force
2. The distance r from the pivot—the axis about which the object can rotate—to the point at which the force is applied
3. The angle at which the force is applied

We can incorporate these three observations into a single quantity called the **torque** τ (Greek tau). Loosely speaking, τ measures the "effectiveness" of a force at causing an object to rotate about a pivot. **Torque is the rotational equivalent of force.** In Figure 7.9, for instance, the torque τ_1 due to $\vec{F}_1$ is greater than τ_4 due to $\vec{F}_4$.

To make these ideas specific, FIGURE 7.10 shows a force $\vec{F}$ applied at one point of a wrench that's loosening a nut. Figure 7.10 defines the distance r from the pivot to the point at which the force is applied; the **radial line,** the line starting at the pivot and extending through this point; and the angle ϕ (Greek phi) measured from the radial line to the direction of the force.

We saw in Figure 7.9 that force $\vec{F}_1$, which was directed perpendicular to the door, was effective in opening it, but force $\vec{F}_2$, directed toward the hinges, had no effect on its rotation. As shown in FIGURE 7.11, this suggests breaking the force $\vec{F}$ applied to the wrench into two component vectors: $\vec{F}_\perp$ directed perpendicular to the radial line, and $\vec{F}_\parallel$ directed parallel to it. Because $\vec{F}_\parallel$ points either directly toward or away from the pivot, it has no effect on the wrench's rotation, and thus contributes nothing to the torque. Only $\vec{F}_\perp$ tends to cause rotation of the wrench, so it is this component of the force that determines the torque.

NOTE ▶ The perpendicular component $\vec{F}_\perp$ is pronounced "F perpendicular" and the parallel component $\vec{F}_\parallel$ is "F parallel." ◀

We've seen that a force applied at a greater distance r from the pivot has a greater effect on rotation, so we expect a larger value of r to give a greater torque. We also saw that only $\vec{F}_\perp$ contributes to the torque. Both these observations are contained in our first expression for torque:

$$\tau = rF_\perp \qquad (7.3)$$

Torque due to a force with perpendicular component $F_\perp$
acting at a distance r from the pivot

From this equation, we see that the SI units of torque are newton-meters, abbreviated N·m.

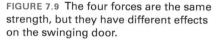
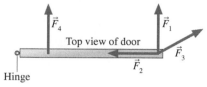

FIGURE 7.9 The four forces are the same strength, but they have different effects on the swinging door.

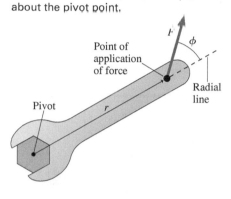

FIGURE 7.10 Force $\vec{F}$ exerts a torque about the pivot point.

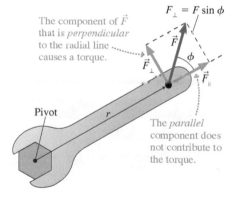

FIGURE 7.11 Torque is due to the component of the force perpendicular to the radial line.

The component of $\vec{F}$ that is *perpendicular* to the radial line causes a torque.

$F_\perp = F \sin \phi$

The *parallel* component does not contribute to the torque.

Activ ONLINE Physics 7.1

EXAMPLE 7.3 Torque in opening a door

In trying to open a stuck door, Ryan pushes it at a point 0.75 m from the hinges with a 240 N force directed 20° away from being perpendicular to the door. What torque does Ryan exert on the door?

PREPARE In FIGURE 7.12 on the next page the radial line is shown drawn from the pivot—the hinge—through the point at

which the force $\vec{F}$ is applied. We see that the component of $\vec{F}$ that is perpendicular to the radial line is $F_\perp = F \cos 20° = 226$ N. The distance from the hinge to the point at which the force is applied is $r = 0.75$ m.

Continued

FIGURE 7.12 Ryan's force exerts a torque on the door.

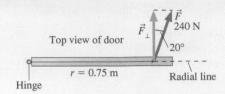

Top view of door

$\vec{F}$
240 N
$\vec{F}_\perp$
20°

$r = 0.75$ m

Hinge

Radial line

SOLVE We can find the torque on the door from Equation 7.3:

$$\tau = rF_\perp = (0.75 \text{ m})(226 \text{ N}) = 170 \text{ N} \cdot \text{m}$$

ASSESS Ryan could slightly increase the torque he exerts by pushing with the same force but exactly perpendicular to the door.

FIGURE 7.13 You can also calculate torque in terms of the moment arm between the pivot and the line of action.

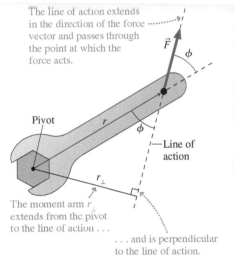

The line of action extends in the direction of the force vector and passes through the point at which the force acts.

$\vec{F}$
ϕ

Pivot

r

ϕ

Line of action

$r_\perp$

The moment arm $r_\perp$ extends from the pivot to the line of action . . .

. . . and is perpendicular to the line of action.

FIGURE 7.13 shows an alternative way to calculate torque. The line that is in the direction of the force, and passes through the point at which the force acts, is called the *line of action*. The perpendicular distance from this line to the pivot is called the moment arm (or *lever arm*) $r_\perp$. You can see from the figure that $r_\perp = r\sin\phi$. Further, Figure 7.11 showed that $F_\perp = F\sin\phi$. We can then write Equation 7.3 as $\tau = rF\sin\phi = F(r\sin\phi) = Fr_\perp$. Thus an equivalent expression for the torque is

$$\tau = r_\perp F \tag{7.4}$$

Torque due to a force F with moment arm $r_\perp$

CONCEPTUAL EXAMPLE 7.4 | Starting a bike

It is hard to get going if you try to start your bike with the pedal at the highest point. Why is this?

REASON Aided by the weight of the body, the greatest force can be applied to the pedal straight down. But with the pedal at the top, this force is exerted almost directly toward the pivot, causing only a small torque. We could say either that the perpendicular component of the force is small or that the moment arm is small.

ASSESS If you've ever climbed a steep hill while standing on the pedals, you know that you get the greatest forward motion when one pedal is completely forward with the crank parallel to the ground. This gives the maximum possible torque because the force you apply is entirely perpendicular to the radial line, and the moment arm is as long as it can be.

We've seen that Equation 7.3 can be written as $\tau = rF_\perp = r(F\sin\phi)$, and Equation 7.4 as $\tau = r_\perp F = (r\sin\phi)F$. This shows that both methods of calculating torque lead to the same expression for torque—namely:

$$\tau = rF\sin\phi \tag{7.5}$$

Torque due to a force F applied at a distance r from the pivot, at an angle ϕ to the radial line

◄ Torque versus speed To start and stop quickly, the basketball player needs to apply a large torque to her wheel. To make the torque as large as possible, the handrim—the outside wheel that she actually grabs—is almost as big as the wheel itself. The racer needs to move continuously at high speed, so his wheel spins much faster. To allow his hands to keep up, his handrim is much smaller than his chair's wheel, making its linear velocity correspondingly lower. The smaller radius means, however, that the torque he can apply is lower as well.

NOTE ► Torque differs from force in a very important way. Torque is calculated or measured *about a particular point*. To say that a torque is 20 N · m is meaningless without specifying the point about which the torque is calculated. Torque can be calculated about any point, but its value depends on the point chosen because this choice determines r and ϕ. In practice, we usually calculate torques about a hinge, pivot, or axle. ◄

Equations 7.3–7.5 are three different ways of thinking about—and calculating—the torque due to a force. Depending on the problem at hand, one might be easier to use than the others. But they all calculate the *same* torque, and all will give the same value for the torque.

These equations give only the magnitude of the torque. But torque, like a force component, has a sign. **A torque that tends to rotate the object in a counterclockwise direction is positive, while a torque that tends to rotate the object in a clockwise direction is negative.** FIGURE 7.14 summarizes the signs. Notice that a force pushing straight toward the pivot or pulling straight out from the pivot exerts *no* torque.

NOTE ► When calculating a torque, you must supply the appropriate sign by observing the direction in which the torque acts. ◄

FIGURE 7.14 Signs and strengths of the torque.

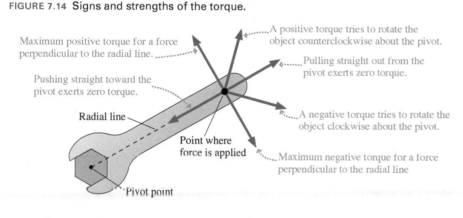

Maximum positive torque for a force perpendicular to the radial line.

A positive torque tries to rotate the object counterclockwise about the pivot.

Pushing straight toward the pivot exerts zero torque.

Pulling straight out from the pivot exerts zero torque.

Radial line

A negative torque tries to rotate the object clockwise about the pivot.

Point where force is applied

Maximum negative torque for a force perpendicular to the radial line

Pivot point

EXAMPLE 7.5 **Calculating the torque on a nut**

Luis uses a 20-cm-long wrench to turn a nut. The wrench handle is tilted 30° above the horizontal, and Luis pulls straight down on the end with a force of 100 N. How much torque does Luis exert on the nut?

PREPARE FIGURE 7.15 shows the situation. The two illustrations correspond to two methods of calculating torque, corresponding to Equations 7.3 and 7.4.

FIGURE 7.15 A wrench being used to turn a nut.

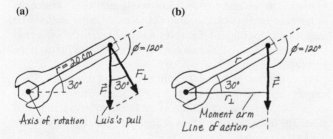

(a)   (b)

SOLVE According to Equation 7.3 and 7.5, the torque can be calculated as $\tau = rF_{\perp} = rF \sin \phi$. From Figure 7.15a we see that

the angle between the force and the radial line is $\phi = 30° + 90° = 120°$. The torque is then

$$\tau = -rF \sin \phi = -(0.20 \text{ m})(100 \text{ N})(\sin 120°) = -17 \text{ N} \cdot \text{m}$$

We put in the minus sign because the torque is negative—it tries to rotate the nut in a *clockwise* direction.

Alternatively, we can use Equation 7.4 to find the torque. Figure 7.15b shows the moment arm $r_{\perp}$, the perpendicular distance from the pivot to the line of action. From the figure we see that

$$r_{\perp} = r \cos 30° = (0.20 \text{ m})(\cos 30°) = 0.17 \text{ m}$$

Then the torque is

$$\tau = -r_{\perp} F = -(0.17 \text{ m})(100 \text{ N}) = -17 \text{ N} \cdot \text{m}$$

Again, we insert the minus sign because the torque acts to give a clockwise rotation.

ASSESS Both methods give the same answer for the torque, as expected. In general, however, you need use only one of Equations 7.3–7.5 to find the torque in any given situation. In using any of these methods to find the torque, remember to include the minus sign if the torque acts to rotate the object in a clockwise direction.

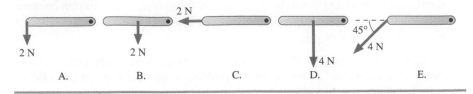

STOP TO THINK 7.2   Rank in order, from largest to smallest, the five torques τ_A to τ_E. The rods all have the same length and are pivoted at the dot.

A.   B.   C.   D.   E.

Net Torque

FIGURE 7.16 The forces exert a net torque about the pivot point.

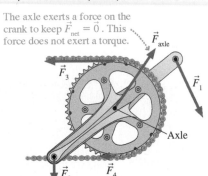

The axle exerts a force on the crank to keep $\vec{F}_{net} = \vec{0}$. This force does not exert a torque.

FIGURE 7.16 shows the forces acting on the crankset of a bicycle. Forces $\vec{F}_1$ and $\vec{F}_2$ are due to the rider pushing on the pedals, and $\vec{F}_3$ and $\vec{F}_4$ are tension forces from the chain. The crankset is free to rotate about a fixed axle, but the axle prevents it from having any translational motion with respect to the bike frame. It does so by exerting force $\vec{F}_{axle}$ on the object to balance the other forces and keep $\vec{F}_{net} = \vec{0}$.

Forces $\vec{F}_1$, $\vec{F}_2$, $\vec{F}_3$, and $\vec{F}_4$ exert torques τ_1, τ_2, τ_3, and τ_4 on the crank (measured about the axle), but $\vec{F}_{axle}$ does *not* exert a torque because it is applied at the pivot point—the axle—and so has zero moment arm. Thus the *net* torque about the axle is the sum of the torques due to the *applied* forces:

$$\tau_{net} = \tau_1 + \tau_2 + \tau_3 + \tau_4 + \cdots = \sum \tau \tag{7.6}$$

EXAMPLE 7.6   Force in turning a capstan

A capstan is a device used on old sailing ships to raise the anchor. A sailor pushes the long lever, turning the capstan and winding up the anchor rope. If the capstan turns at a constant speed, the net torque on it, as we'll learn later in the chapter, is zero.

Suppose the rope tension due to the weight of the anchor is 1500 N. If the distance from the axis to the point on the lever where the sailor pushes is exactly seven times the radius of the capstan around which the rope is wound, with what force must the sailor push if the net torque on the capstan is to be zero?

PREPARE Shown in **FIGURE 7.17** is a view looking down from above the capstan. The rope pulls with a tension force $\vec{T}$ at distance R from the axis of rotation. The sailor pushes with a force $\vec{F}$ at distance $7R$ from the axis. Both forces are perpendicular to their radial lines, so ϕ in Equation 7.5 is 90°.

FIGURE 7.17 Top view of a sailor turning a capstan.

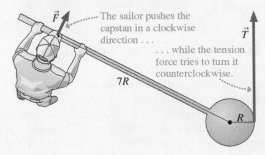

The sailor pushes the capstan in a clockwise direction . . .

. . . while the tension force tries to turn it counterclockwise.

SOLVE The torque due to the tension in the rope is

$$\tau_T = RT\sin 90° = RT$$

We don't know the capstan radius, so we'll just leave it as R for now. This torque is positive because it tries to turn the capstan counterclockwise. The torque due to the sailor is

$$\tau_S = -(7R)F\sin 90° = -7RF$$

We put the minus sign in because this torque acts in the clockwise (negative) direction. The net torque is zero, so we have $\tau_T + \tau_S = 0$, or

$$RT - 7RF = 0$$

Note that the radius R cancels, leaving

$$F = \frac{T}{7} = \frac{1500 \text{ N}}{7} = 210 \text{ N}$$

ASSESS 210 N is about 50 lb, a reasonable number. The force the sailor must exert is one-seventh the force the rope exerts: The long lever helps him lift the heavy anchor. In the HMS *Warrior*, built in 1860, it took 200 men turning the capstan to lift the huge anchor that weighed close to 55,000 N!

Note that forces $\vec{F}$ and $\vec{T}$ point in different directions. Their torques depend only on their directions with respect to their own radial lines, not on the directions of the forces with respect to each other. The force the sailor needs to apply remains unchanged as he circles the capstan.

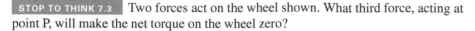

STOP TO THINK 7.3 Two forces act on the wheel shown. What third force, acting at point P, will make the net torque on the wheel zero?

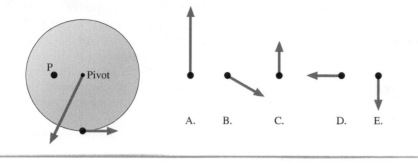

A.   B.   C.   D.   E.

FIGURE 7.18 The center of gravity is the point where the weight appears to act.

(a) Gravity exerts a force and a torque on each particle that makes up the gymnast.⋯ Rotation axis

7.3 Gravitational Torque and the Center of Gravity

As the gymnast in FIGURE 7.18 pivots around the bar, a torque due to the force of gravity causes her to rotate toward a vertical position. A falling tree and a car hood slamming shut are other examples where gravity exerts a torque on an object. Stationary objects can also experience a torque due to gravity. A diving board experiences a gravitational torque about its fixed end. It doesn't rotate because of a counteracting torque provided by forces from the base at its fixed end.

We've learned how to calculate the torque due to a single force acting on an object. But gravity doesn't act at a single point on an object. It pulls downward on *every particle* that makes up the object, as shown for the gymnast in Figure 7.18a, and so each particle experiences a small torque due to the force of gravity that acts upon it. The gravitational torque on the object as a whole is then the *net* torque exerted on all the particles. We won't prove it, but the gravitational torque can be calculated by assuming that the net force of gravity—that is, the object's weight $\vec{w}$ acts at a single special point on the object called its **center of gravity** (symbol �). Then we can calculate the torque due to gravity by the methods learned earlier for a single force ($\vec{w}$) acting at a single point (the center of gravity). Figure 7.18b shows how we can consider the gymnast's weight as acting at her center of gravity.

(b) The weight force provides a torque about the rotation axis.⋯

Center of gravity

$\vec{w}$

The gymnast responds *as if* her entire weight acts at her center of gravity.

EXAMPLE 7.7 **The torque on a flagpole**

A 3.2 kg flagpole extends from a wall at an angle of 25° from the horizontal. Its center of gravity is 1.6 m from the point where the pole is attached to the wall. What is the gravitational torque on the flagpole about the point of attachment?

PREPARE FIGURE 7.19 shows the situation. For the purpose of calculating torque, we can consider the entire weight of the pole as acting at the center of gravity. We can use any of the three

FIGURE 7.19 Visual overview of the flagpole.

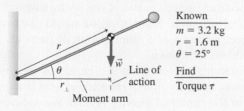

Known
$m = 3.2$ kg
$r = 1.6$ m
$\theta = 25°$

Find
Torque τ

methods discussed in Section 7.2 to calculate the torque. Because the moment arm $r_\perp$ is simple to visualize here, we'll use Equation 7.4 for the torque.

SOLVE From Figure 7.19, we see that the moment arm is $r_\perp = (1.6 \text{ m})\cos 25° = 1.5$ m. Thus the gravitational torque on the flagpole, about the point where it attaches to the wall, is

$$\tau = -r_\perp w = -r_\perp mg = -(1.5 \text{ m})(3.2 \text{ kg})(9.8 \text{ m/s}^2) = -47 \text{ N} \cdot \text{m}$$

We inserted the minus sign because the torque tries to rotate the pole in a clockwise direction.

ASSESS If the pole were attached to the wall by a hinge, the gravitational torque would cause the pole to fall. However, the actual rigid connection provides a counteracting (positive) torque to the pole that prevents this.

FIGURE 7.20 Method for finding the center of gravity of an object.

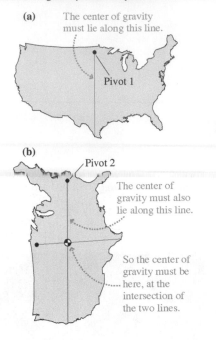

Finding the Center of Gravity

To calculate the gravitational torque, we need to locate the object's center of gravity. There is a simple experimental method for finding the center of gravity of any object, based on the observation that **any object free to rotate about a pivot will come to rest with its center of gravity directly below the pivot.** To see this, consider the cutout map of the continental United States in FIGURE 7.20a. If the center of gravity is to the right or left of the blue line, a gravitational torque will cause the map to swing. If the center of gravity lies directly *below* the pivot, however, the weight force lies along the line of action and the torque is zero. The map can then remain at rest with no tendency to swing.

We know that the center of gravity lies somewhere along the blue line, but we don't yet know where. To find out, we need to suspend the map from a second pivot, as shown in FIGURE 7.20b. Then the center of gravity will fall somewhere along the red line shown. Because the center of gravity must lie on both the blue and red lines, it must be at their *intersection*. Interestingly, the geographical center of the continental United States is defined in just this way, as the center of gravity of a map of the contiguous United States. This point is one mile northwest of Lebanon, Kansas.

For a simple symmetrical object, such as a rod, sphere, or cube made of a uniform material, FIGURE 7.21 shows that **the center of gravity of a symmetrical object lies at its geometrical center.** A particularly simple case of this is a point particle, whose center of gravity lies at the position of the particle.

FIGURE 7.21 The center of gravity of a symmetrical object lies at its center.

FIGURE 7.22 Balancing a ruler.

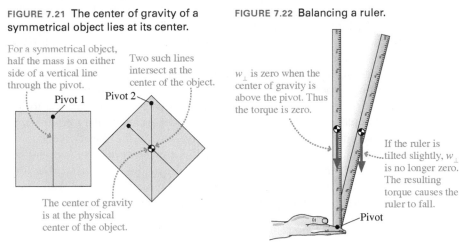

As we've seen, an object free to pivot will rotate until its center of gravity is directly below the pivot. If the center of gravity lies directly *above* the pivot, as in FIGURE 7.22, there is no torque due to the object's weight and it can remain balanced. However, if the object is even slightly displaced to either side, the gravitational torque will no longer be zero and the object will begin to rotate. This question of *balance*—the behavior of an object whose center of gravity lies above the pivot—will be explored in depth in Chapter 8.

Calculating the Position of the Center of Gravity

It is nice to know you can locate an object's center of gravity by suspending it from a pivot, but it is rarely a practical technique. More often, we would like to calculate the center of gravity of an object made up of a combination of particles and objects whose center-of-gravity positions are known.

Because there's no gravitational torque when the center of gravity lies either directly above or directly below the pivot, it must be the case that **the torque due to gravity when the pivot is *at* the center of gravity is zero.** We can use this fact to find a general expression for the position of the center of gravity.

Consider the dumbbell shown in FIGURE 7.23. If we slide the triangular pivot back and forth until the dumbbell balances, the pivot must then be at the center of gravity (at position x_{cg}), and the torque due to gravity must therefore be zero. But we can calculate the gravitational torque directly by calculating and summing the torques about this point due to the two individual weights. Gravity acts on weight 1 with moment arm r_1, so the torque about the pivot at position x_{cg} is

$$\tau_1 = r_1 w_1 = (x_{cg} - x_1)m_1 g$$

Similarly, the torque due to weight 2 is

$$\tau_2 = -r_2 w_2 = -(x_2 - x_{cg})m_2 g$$

This torque is negative because it tends to rotate the dumbbell in a clockwise direction. We've just argued that the net torque must be zero because the pivot is directly under the center of gravity, so

$$\tau_{net} = 0 = \tau_1 + \tau_2 = (x_{cg} - x_1)m_1 g - (x_2 - x_{cg})m_2 g$$

We can solve this equation for the position of the center of gravity x_{cg}:

$$x_{cg} = \frac{x_1 m_1 + x_2 m_2}{m_1 + m_2} \tag{7.7}$$

The following Tactics Box shows how Equation 7.7 can be generalized to find the center of gravity of *any* number of particles. If the particles don't all lie along the x-axis, then we'll also need to find the y-coordinate of the center of gravity.

FIGURE 7.23 Finding the center of gravity of a dumbbell.

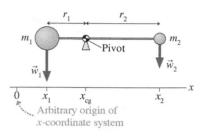

TACTICS BOX 7.1 Finding the center of gravity (MP)™

❶ Choose an origin for your coordinate system. You can choose any convenient point as the origin.
❷ Determine the coordinates (x_1, y_1), (x_2, y_2), (x_3, y_3), ... for the particles of masses $m_1, m_2, m_3, \ldots$, respectively.
❸ The x-coordinate of the center of gravity is

$$x_{cg} = \frac{x_1 m_1 + x_2 m_2 + x_3 m_3 + \cdots}{m_1 + m_2 + m_3 + \cdots} \tag{7.8}$$

❹ Similarly, the y-coordinate of the center of gravity is

$$y_{cg} = \frac{y_1 m_1 + y_2 m_2 + y_3 m_3 + \cdots}{m_1 + m_2 + m_3 + \cdots} \tag{7.9}$$

Exercises 12–15 ✐

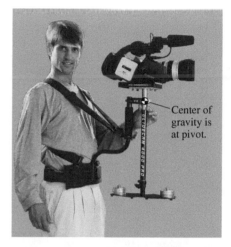

Holding steady Many movie-making scenes require handheld shots for which the cameraman must walk along, following the action. The stabilizer shown reduces unwanted camera motion as the cameraman walks. The center of gravity of the camera and its hanging weight arm is located exactly at a pivot that can swing freely in any direction. The frictionless pivot exerts no torque on the camera and arm. Neither does the weight, because it acts at the pivot. With no torque acting on it, the camera has no tendency to rotate. The long arm also increases the system's *moment of inertia*, further decreasing unwanted rotations. More about this later!

Because the center of gravity depends on products such as $x_1 m_1$, objects with large masses count more heavily than objects with small masses. Consequently, **the center of gravity tends to lie closer to the heavier objects or particles** that make up the entire object.

EXAMPLE 7.8 **Where should the dumbbell be lifted?**

A 1.0-m-long dumbbell has a 10 kg mass on the left and a 5.0 kg mass on the right. Find the position of the center of gravity, the point where the dumbbell should be lifted in order to remain balanced.

PREPARE We'll treat the two masses as point particles separated by a massless rod. Then we can use the steps from Tactics

Box 7.1 to find the center of gravity. Let's choose the origin to be at the position of the 10 kg mass on the left, making $x_1 = 0$ m and $x_2 = 1.0$ m. Because the dumbbell masses lie on the x-axis, the y-coordinate of the center of gravity must also lie on the x-axis. Thus we only need to solve for the x-coordinate of the center of gravity.

Continued

SOLVE The x-coordinate of the center of gravity is found from Equation 7.8:

$$x_{cg} = \frac{x_1 m_1 + x_2 m_2}{m_1 + m_2} = \frac{(0 \text{ m})(10 \text{ kg}) + (1.0 \text{ m})(5.0 \text{ kg})}{(10 \text{ kg}) + (5.0 \text{ kg})}$$

$$= 0.33 \text{ m}$$

The center of gravity is 0.33 m from the 10 kg mass or, equivalently, 0.17 m left of the center of the bar.

ASSESS The position of the center of gravity is closer to the larger mass. This agrees with our general statement that the center of gravity tends to lie closer to the heavier particles.

FIGURE 7.24 Body segment masses and centers of gravity.

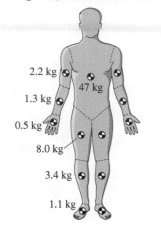

2.2 kg
47 kg
1.3 kg
0.5 kg
8.0 kg
3.4 kg
1.1 kg

The center of gravity of an extended object can often be found by considering the object as made up of pieces, each with mass and center of gravity that are known or can be found. Then the coordinates of the entire object's center of gravity are given by Equations 7.8 and 7.9, with $(x_1, y_1), (x_2, y_2), (x_3, y_3), \ldots$ the coordinates of the center of gravity of each piece and $m_1, m_2, m_3, \ldots$ their masses.

This method is widely used in biomechanics and kinesiology to calculate the center of gravity of the human body. **FIGURE 7.24** shows how the body can be considered to be made of segments, each of whose mass and center of gravity have been measured. The numbers shown are appropriate for a man with a total mass of 80 kg. For a given posture the positions of the segments and their centers of gravity can be found, and thus the whole-body center of gravity from Equations 7.8 and 7.9 (and a third equation for the z-coordinate). Example 7.9 explores a simplified version of this method.

EXAMPLE 7.9   **Finding the center of gravity of a gymnast**

A gymnast performing on the rings holds himself in the pike position. **FIGURE 7.25** shows how we can consider his body to be made up of two segments whose masses and center-of-gravity positions are shown. The upper segment includes his head, trunk, and arms, while the lower segment consists of his legs. Locate the overall center of gravity of the gymnast.

PREPARE From Figure 7.25 we can find the x- and y-coordinates of the segment centers of gravity:

$$x_{\text{trunk}} = 15 \text{ cm} \qquad y_{\text{trunk}} = 50 \text{ cm}$$
$$x_{\text{legs}} = 30 \text{ cm} \qquad y_{\text{legs}} = 20 \text{ cm}$$

SOLVE The x- and y-coordinates of the center of gravity are given by Equations 7.8 and 7.9:

$$x_{cg} = \frac{x_{\text{trunk}} m_{\text{trunk}} + x_{\text{legs}} m_{\text{legs}}}{m_{\text{trunk}} + m_{\text{legs}}}$$

$$= \frac{(15 \text{ cm})(45 \text{ kg}) + (30 \text{ cm})(30 \text{ kg})}{45 \text{ kg} + 30 \text{ kg}} = 21 \text{ cm}$$

and

$$y_{cg} = \frac{y_{\text{trunk}} m_{\text{trunk}} + y_{\text{legs}} m_{\text{legs}}}{m_{\text{trunk}} + m_{\text{legs}}}$$

$$= \frac{(50 \text{ cm})(45 \text{ kg}) + (20 \text{ cm})(30 \text{ kg})}{45 \text{ kg} + 30 \text{ kg}} = 38 \text{ cm}$$

FIGURE 7.25 Centers of gravity of two segments of a gymnast.

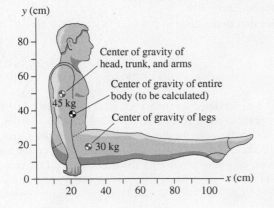

y (cm)

80
60
40
20
0

Center of gravity of head, trunk, and arms
Center of gravity of entire body (to be calculated)
Center of gravity of legs
45 kg
30 kg

20   40   60   80   100 x (cm)

ASSESS The center-of-gravity position of the entire body, shown in Figure 7.25, is closer to that of the heavier trunk segment than to that of the lighter legs. It also lies along a line connecting the two segment centers of gravity, just as it would for the center of gravity of two point particles. Note also that the gymnast's hands—the pivot point—must lie directly below his center of gravity. Otherwise he would rotate forward or backward.

STOP TO THINK 7.4 The balls are connected by very lightweight rods pivoted at the point indicated by a dot. The rod lengths are all equal except for A, which is twice as long. Rank in order, from least to greatest, the magnitudes of the gravitational torques about the pivots for arrangements A to E.

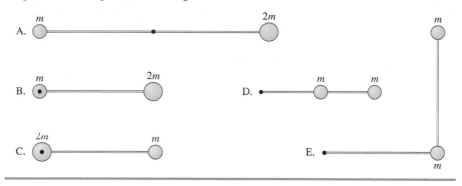

7.4 Rotational Dynamics and Moment of Inertia

In Section 7.2 we asked: What do Newton's laws tell us about rotational motion? We can now answer that question: **A torque causes an angular acceleration.** This is the rotational equivalent of our earlier discovery, for motion along a line, that a force causes an acceleration.

To see where this connection between torque and angular acceleration comes from, let's start by examining a *single particle* subject to a torque. FIGURE 7.26 shows a particle of mass m attached to a lightweight, rigid rod of length r that constrains the particle to move in a circle. The particle is subject to two forces. Because it's moving in a circle, there must be a force—here, the tension $\vec{T}$ from the rod—directed toward the center of the circle. As we learned in Chapter 6, this is the force responsible for changing the *direction* of the particle's velocity. The acceleration associated with this change in the particle's velocity is the centripetal acceleration $\vec{a}_c$.

But the particle in Figure 7.26 is also subject to the force $\vec{F}$ that changes the *speed* of the particle. This force causes a tangential acceleration $\vec{a}_t$. Applying Newton's second law in the direction tangent to the circle gives

$$a_t = \frac{F}{m} \qquad (7.10)$$

Now the tangential and angular accelerations are related by $a_t = \alpha r$, so we can rewrite Equation 7.10 as $\alpha r = F/m$, or

$$\alpha = \frac{F}{mr} \qquad (7.11)$$

We can now connect this angular acceleration to the torque because force $\vec{F}$, which is perpendicular to the radial line, exerts torque

$$\tau = rF$$

With this relation between F and τ, we can write Equation 7.11 as

$$\alpha = \frac{\tau}{mr^2} \qquad (7.12)$$

Equation 7.12 gives a relationship between the torque on a single particle and its angular acceleration. Now all that remains is to expand this idea from a single particle to an extended object.

FIGURE 7.26 A tangential force $\vec{F}$ exerts a torque on the particle and causes an angular acceleration.

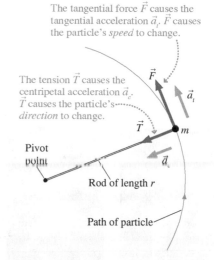

This large granite ball, with a mass of 26,400 kg, floats with nearly zero friction on a thin layer of pressurized water. Even though the girl exerts a large torque on the ball, its angular acceleration is small because of its large moment of inertia.

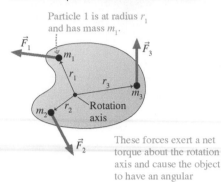

Particle 1 is at radius r_1 and has mass m_1.

These forces exert a net torque about the rotation axis and cause the object to have an angular acceleration.

Newton's Second Law for Rotational Motion

FIGURE 7.27 shows a rigid body that undergoes rotation about a fixed and unmoving axis. According to the rigid-body model, we can think of the object as consisting of particles with masses $m_1, m_2, m_3, \ldots$ at fixed distances $r_1, r_2, r_3, \ldots$ from the axis. Suppose forces $\vec{F}_1, \vec{F}_2, \vec{F}_3, \ldots$ act on these particles. These forces exert torques around the rotation axis, so the object will undergo an angular acceleration α. Because all the particles that make up the object rotate together, each particle has this *same* angular acceleration α. Rearranging Equation 7.12 slightly, we can write the torques on the particles as

$$\tau_1 = m_1 r_1^2 \alpha \qquad \tau_2 = m_2 r_2^2 \alpha \qquad \tau_3 = m_3 r_3^2 \alpha$$

and so on for every particle in the object. If we add up all these torques, the *net* torque on the object is

$$\tau_{\text{net}} = \tau_1 + \tau_2 + \tau_3 + \cdots = m_1 r_1^2 \alpha + m_2 r_2^2 \alpha + m_3 r_3^2 \alpha + \cdots$$
$$= \alpha(m_1 r_1^2 + m_2 r_2^2 + m_3 r_3^2 + \cdots) = \alpha \sum m_i r_i^2 \qquad (7.13)$$

By factoring α out of the sum, we're making explicit use of the fact that every particle in a rotating rigid body has the *same* angular acceleration α.

7.6   Activ
ONLINE
Physics

The quantity $\sum mr^2$ in Equation 7.13, which is the proportionality constant between angular acceleration and net torque, is called the object's **moment of inertia** I:

$$I = m_1 r_1^2 + m_2 r_2^2 + m_3 r_3^2 + \cdots = \sum m_i r_i^2 \qquad (7.14)$$

Moment of inertia of a collection of particles

The units of moment of inertia are mass times distance squared, or $\text{kg} \cdot \text{m}^2$. An object's moment of inertia, like torque, *depends on the axis of rotation.* Once the axis is specified, allowing the values of $r_1, r_2, r_3, \ldots$ to be determined, the moment of inertia *about that axis* can be calculated from Equation 7.14.

NOTE ▶ The word "moment" in "moment of inertia" and "moment arm" has nothing to do with time. It stems from the Latin *momentum,* meaning "motion." ◀

Substituting the moment of inertia into Equation 7.13 puts the final piece of the puzzle into place, giving us the fundamental equation for rigid-body dynamics:

Newton's second law for rotation An object that experiences a net torque τ_{net} about the axis of rotation undergoes an angular acceleration

$$\alpha = \frac{\tau_{\text{net}}}{I} \qquad (7.15)$$

where I is the moment of inertia of the object *about the rotation axis.*

In practice we often write $\tau_{\text{net}} = I\alpha$, but Equation 7.15 better conveys the idea that **a net torque is the cause of angular acceleration.** In the absence of a net torque ($\tau_{\text{net}} = 0$), the object has zero angular acceleration α, so it either does not rotate ($\omega = 0$) or rotates with *constant* angular velocity ($\omega = $ constant).

Interpreting the Moment of Inertia

Before rushing to calculate moments of inertia, let's get a better understanding of its meaning. First, notice that **moment of inertia is the rotational equivalent of mass.** It plays the same role in Equation 7.15 as does mass m in the now-familiar $\vec{a} = \vec{F}_{\text{net}}/m$. Recall that objects with larger mass have a larger *inertia,* meaning that they're harder to accelerate. Similarly, an object with a larger moment of inertia is

TRY IT YOURSELF

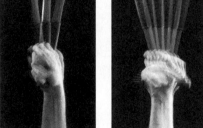

Hammering home inertia Most of the mass of a hammer is in its head, so the hammer's moment of inertia is large when calculated about an axis passing through the end of the handle (far from the head), but small when calculated about an axis passing through the head itself. You can *feel* this difference by attempting to wave a hammer back and forth about the handle end and the head end. It's much harder to do about the handle end because the large moment of inertia keeps the angular acceleration small.

harder to get rotating: It takes a larger torque to spin up an object with a larger moment of inertia than an object with a smaller moment of inertia. The fact that "moment of inertia" retains the word "inertia" reminds us of this.

But why does the moment of inertia depend on the distances r from the rotation axis? Think about trying to start a merry-go-round from rest, as shown in FIGURE 7.28. By pushing on the rim of the merry-go-round, you exert a torque on it, and its angular velocity begins to increase. If your friends sit at the rim of the merry-go-round, as in Figure 7.28a, their distances r from the axle are large. The moment of inertia is large, according to Equation 7.14, and it will be difficult to get the merry-go-round rotating. If, however, your friends sit near the axle, as in Figure 7.28b, then r and the moment of inertia are small. You'll find it's much easier to get the merry-go-round going.

Thus an object's moment of inertia depends not only on the object's mass but also on *how the mass is distributed* around the rotation axis. This is well known to bicycle racers. Every time a cyclist accelerates, she has to "spin up" the wheels and tires. The larger the moment of inertia, the more effort it takes and the slower her acceleration. For this reason, racers use the lightest possible tires, and they put those tires on wheels that have been designed to keep the mass as close as possible to the center without sacrificing the necessary strength and rigidity.

Table 7.3 summarizes the analogies between linear and rotational dynamics.

FIGURE 7.28 Moment of inertia depends on both the mass and how the mass is distributed.

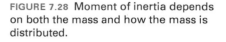

(a) Mass concentrated around the rim

(b) Mass concentrated at the center

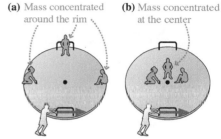

Larger moment of inertia, harder to get rotating

Smaller moment of inertia, easier to get rotating

TABLE 7.3 Rotational and linear dynamics

Rotational dynamics		Linear dynamics	
Torque	τ_{net}	Force	$\vec{F}_{net}$
Moment of inertia	I	Mass	m
Angular acceleration	α	Acceleration	$\vec{a}$
Second law	$\alpha = \tau_{net}/I$	Second law	$\vec{a} = \vec{F}_{net}/m$

EXAMPLE 7.10 **Calculating the moment of inertia**

Your friend is creating an abstract sculpture that consists of three small, heavy spheres attached by very lightweight 10-cm-long rods as shown in FIGURE 7.29. The spheres have masses $m_1 = 1.0$ kg, $m_2 = 1.5$ kg, and $m_3 = 1.0$ kg. What is the object's moment of inertia if it is rotated about axis a? About axis b?

FIGURE 7.29 Three point particles separated by lightweight rods.

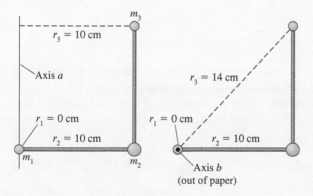

PREPARE We'll use Equation 7.14 for the moment of inertia:

$$I = m_1 r_1^2 + m_2 r_2^2 + m_3 r_3^2$$

In this expression, r_1, r_2, and r_3 are the distances of each particle from the axis of rotation, so they depend on the axis chosen. Particle 1 lies on both axes, so $r_1 = 0$ cm in both cases. Particle 2 lies

10 cm (0.10 m) from both axes. Particle 3 is 10 cm from axis a, but farther from axis b. We can find r_3 for axis b by using the Pythagorean theorem, which gives $r_3 = 14$ cm. These distances are indicated in the figure.

SOLVE For each axis, we can prepare a table of the values of r, m, and mr^2 for each particle, then add the values of mr^2. For axis a we have

Particle	r	m	mr^2
1	0 m	1.0 kg	0 kg $\cdot$ m^2
2	0.10 m	1.5 kg	0.015 kg $\cdot$ m^2
3	0.10 m	1.0 kg	0.010 kg $\cdot$ m^2
			$I_a = 0.025$ kg $\cdot$ m^2

For axis b we have

Particle	r	m	mr^2
1	0 m	1.0 kg	0 kg $\cdot$ m^2
2	0.10 m	1.5 kg	0.015 kg $\cdot$ m^2
3	0.14 m	1.0 kg	0.020 kg $\cdot$ m^2
			$I_b = 0.035$ kg $\cdot$ m^2

ASSESS We've already noted that the moment of inertia of an object is higher when its mass is distributed farther from the axis of rotation. Here, m_3 is farther from axis b than from axis a, leading to a higher moment of inertia about that axis.

The Moments of Inertia of Common Shapes

Newton's second law for rotational motion is easy to write, but we can't make use of it without knowing an object's moment of inertia. Unlike mass, we can't measure moment of inertia by putting an object on a scale. And although we can guess that the center of gravity of a symmetrical object is at the physical center of the object, we can *not* guess the moment of inertia of even a simple object.

For an object consisting of only a few point particles connected by massless rods, we can use Equation 7.14 to directly calculate I. But such an object is pretty unrealistic. All real objects are made up of solid material that is itself composed of countless atoms. To calculate the moment of inertia of even a simple object requires integral calculus and is beyond the scope of this text. A short list of common moments of inertia is given in Table 7.4. We use a capital M for the total mass of an extended object.

TABLE 7.4 Moments of inertia of objects with uniform density and total mass M

Object and axis	Picture	I	Object and axis	Picture	I
Thin rod (of any cross section), about center		$\frac{1}{12}ML^2$	Cylinder or disk, about center		$\frac{1}{2}MR^2$
Thin rod (of any cross section), about end		$\frac{1}{3}ML^2$	Cylindrical hoop, about center		MR^2
Plane or slab, about center		$\frac{1}{12}Ma^2$	Solid sphere, about diameter		$\frac{2}{5}MR^2$
Plane or slab, about edge		$\frac{1}{3}Ma^2$	Spherical shell, about diameter		$\frac{2}{3}MR^2$

We can make some general observations about the moments of inertia in Table 7.4. For instance, the cylindrical hoop is composed of particles that are all the same distance R from the axis. Thus each particle of mass m makes the *same* contribution mR^2 to the hoop's moment of inertia. Adding up all these contributions gives

$$I = m_1R^2 + m_2R^2 + m_3R^2 + \cdots = (m_1 + m_2 + m_3 + \cdots)R^2 = MR^2$$

as given in the table. The solid cylinder of the same mass and radius has a *lower* moment of inertia than the hoop because much of the cylinder's mass is nearer its center. In the same way we can see why a slab rotated about its center has a lower moment of inertia than the same slab rotated about its edge: In the latter case, some of the mass is twice as far from the axis as the farthest mass in the former case. Those particles contribute *four times* as much to the moment of inertia, leading to an overall larger moment of inertia for the slab rotated about its edge.

▶ **Novel golf clubs** The latest craze in golf putters is heads with high moments of inertia. When the putter hits the ball, the ball—by Newton's third law—exerts a force on the putter and thus exerts a torque that causes the head of the putter to rotate around the shaft. Any rotation while the putter is still in contact with the ball will affect the ball's direction. If the putter's mass is largely placed rather far from the shaft (the rotation axis), the moment of inertia about the shaft can be greatly increased. The large moment of inertia of the head will keep its angular acceleration small—reducing unwanted rotation and allowing a truer putt.

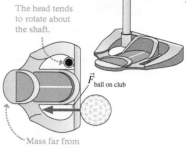

The head tends to rotate about the shaft.

$\vec{F}_{\text{ball on club}}$

Mass far from pivot gives a large moment of inertia.

STOP TO THINK 7.5 Four very lightweight disks of equal radii each have three identical heavy marbles glued to them as shown. Rank in order, from largest to smallest, the moments of inertia of the disks about the indicated axis.

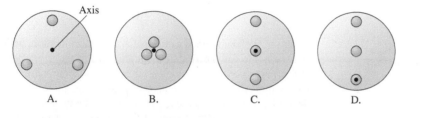

Axis

A.   B.   C.   D.

7.5 Using Newton's Second Law for Rotation

In this section we'll look at several examples of rotational dynamics for rigid bodies that rotate about a *fixed axis*. The restriction to a fixed axis avoids complications that arise for an object undergoing a combination of rotational and translational motion. The problem-solving strategy for rotational dynamics is very similar to that for linear dynamics in Chapter 5.

Activ
Physics ONLINE   7.8–7.10

PROBLEM-SOLVING STRATEGY 7.1   **Rotational dynamics problems**   (MP)™

PREPARE Model the object as a simple shape. Draw a pictorial representation to clarify the situation, define coordinates and symbols, and list known information.

■ Identify the axis about which the object rotates.
■ Identify the forces and determine their distance from the axis.
■ Calculate the torques caused by the forces, and find the signs of the torques.

SOLVE The mathematical representation is based on Newton's second law for rotational motion:

$$\tau_{\text{net}} = I\alpha \qquad \text{or} \qquad \alpha = \frac{\tau_{\text{net}}}{I}$$

■ Find the moment of inertia either by direct calculation using Equation 7.14 or from Table 7.4 for common shapes of objects.
■ Use rotational kinematics to find angular positions and velocities.

ASSESS Check that your result has the correct units, is reasonable, and answers the question.

Exercise 25 ✐

EXAMPLE 7.11 **Starting an airplane engine**

The engine in a small airplane is specified to have a torque of 500 N · m. This engine drives a 2.0-m-long, 40 kg single-blade propeller. On start-up, how long does it take the propeller to reach 2000 rpm?

PREPARE The propeller can be modeled as a rod that rotates about its center. The engine exerts a torque on the propeller. FIGURE 7.30 shows the propeller and the rotation axis.

FIGURE 7.30 A rotating airplane propeller.

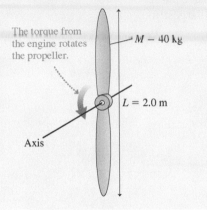

The torque from the engine rotates the propeller.

$M - 40$ kg

$L = 2.0$ m

Axis

SOLVE The moment of inertia of a rod rotating about its center is found from Table 7.4:

$$I = \tfrac{1}{12}ML^2 = \tfrac{1}{12}(40 \text{ kg})(2.0 \text{ m})^2 = 13.3 \text{ kg} \cdot \text{m}^2$$

The 500 N · m torque of the engine causes an angular acceleration of

$$\alpha = \frac{\tau}{I} = \frac{500 \text{ N} \cdot \text{m}}{13.3 \text{ kg} \cdot \text{m}^2} = 37.5 \text{ rad/s}^2$$

The time needed to reach $\omega_f = 2000$ rpm $= 33.3$ rev/s $= 209$ rad/s is

$$\Delta t = \frac{\Delta \omega}{\alpha} = \frac{\omega_f - \omega_i}{\alpha} = \frac{209 \text{ rad/s} - 0 \text{ rad/s}}{37.5 \text{ rad/s}^2} = 5.6 \text{ s}$$

ASSESS We've assumed a constant angular acceleration, which is reasonable for the first few seconds while the propeller is still turning slowly. Eventually, air resistance and friction will cause opposing torques and the angular acceleration will decrease. At full speed, the negative torque due to air resistance and friction cancels the torque of the engine. Then $\tau_{net} = 0$ and the propeller turns at *constant* angular velocity with no angular acceleration.

EXAMPLE 7.12 **Angular acceleration of a falling pole**

A 7.0-m-tall telephone pole with a mass of 260 kg has just been placed in the ground. Before the wires can be connected, the pole is hit by lightning, nearly severing the pole at its base. The pole begins to fall, rotating about the part still connected to the base. Estimate the pole's angular acceleration when it has fallen by 25° from the vertical.

PREPARE The situation is shown in FIGURE 7.31, where we define our symbols and list the known information. Two forces are acting on the pole: the pole's weight $\vec{w}$, which acts at the center of gravity, and the force of the base on the pole (not shown).

FIGURE 7.31 A falling telephone pole undergoes an angular acceleration due to a gravitational torque.

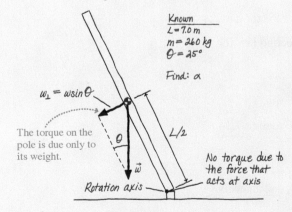

Known
$L = 7.0$ m
$m = 260$ kg
$\theta = 25°$

Find: α

$w_\perp = w\sin\theta$

The torque on the pole is due only to its weight.

$\vec{w}$

$L/2$

No torque due to the force that acts at axis

Rotation axis

This second force exerts no torque because it acts at the axis of rotation. The torque on the pole is thus due only to gravity. From the figure we see that this torque tends to rotate the pole in a counterclockwise direction, so the torque is positive.

SOLVE We'll model the pole as a uniform thin rod rotating about one end. Its center of gravity is at its center, a distance $L/2$ from the axis. You can see from the figure that the perpendicular component of $\vec{w}$ is $w_\perp = w\sin\theta$. Thus the torque due to gravity is

$$\tau_{net} = \left(\frac{L}{2}\right)w_\perp = \left(\frac{L}{2}\right)w\sin\theta = \frac{mgL}{2}\sin\theta$$

From Table 7.4, the moment of inertia of a thin rod rotated about its end is $I = \tfrac{1}{3}mL^2$. Thus, from Newton's second law for rotational motion, the angular acceleration is

$$\alpha = \frac{\tau_{net}}{I} = \frac{\tfrac{1}{2}mgL\sin\theta}{\tfrac{1}{3}mL^2} = \frac{3g\sin\theta}{2L}$$

$$= \frac{3(9.8 \text{ m/s}^2)\sin 25°}{2(7.0 \text{ m})} = 0.9 \text{ rad/s}^2$$

ASSESS The answer is given to only one significant figure because the problem asked for an *estimate* of the angular acceleration. This is usually a hint that you should make some simplifying assumptions, as we did here in modeling the pole as a thin rod.

CONCEPTUAL EXAMPLE 7.13 **Balancing a meter stick**

You've probably tried balancing a rod-shaped object vertically on your fingertip. If the object is very long, like a meter stick or a baseball bat, it's not too hard. But if it's short, like a pencil, it's almost impossible. Why is this?

REASON Suppose you've managed to balance a vertical stick on your fingertip, but then it starts to fall. You'll need to quickly adjust your finger to bring the stick back into balance. As Example 7.12 showed, the angular acceleration α of a thin rod is *inversely proportional* to L. Thus a long object like a meter stick

topples much more slowly than a short one like a pencil. Your reaction time is fast enough to correct for a slowly falling meter stick but not for a rapidly falling pencil.

ASSESS If we double the length of a rod, its mass doubles and its center of gravity is twice as high, so the gravitational torque τ on it is four times as much. But because a rod's moment of inertia is $I = \frac{1}{3}ML^2$, the longer rod's moment of inertia will be *eight* times greater, so the angular acceleration will be only half as large.

Constraints Due to Ropes and Pulleys

Many important applications of rotational dynamics involve objects that are attached to ropes that pass over pulleys. FIGURE 7.32 shows a rope passing over a pulley and connected to an object in linear motion. If the pulley turns *without the rope slipping on it,* then the rope's speed v_{rope} must exactly match the speed of the rim of the pulley, which is $v_{rim} = \omega R$. If the pulley has an angular acceleration, the rope's acceleration a_{rope} must match the *tangential* acceleration of the rim of the pulley, $a_t = \alpha R$.

The object attached to the other end of the rope has the same speed and acceleration as the rope. Consequently, the object must obey the constraints

FIGURE 7.32 The rope's motion must match the motion of the rim of the pulley.

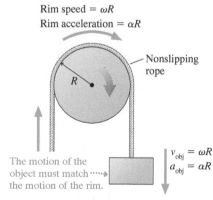

$$v_{obj} = \omega R$$
$$a_{obj} = \alpha R$$

(7.16)

Motion constraints for an object connected to a pulley of radius R by a nonslipping rope

These constraints are similar to the acceleration constraints introduced in Chapter 5 for two objects connected by a string or rope.

NOTE ▶ The constraints are given as magnitudes. Specific problems will require you to specify signs that depend on the direction of motion and on the choice of coordinate system. ◀

EXAMPLE 7.14 **Time for a bucket to fall**

Josh has just raised a 2.5 kg bucket of water using a well's winch when he accidentally lets go of the handle. The winch consists of a rope wrapped around a 3.0 kg, 4.0-cm-diameter cylinder, which rotates on an axle through the center. The bucket is released from rest 4.0 m above the water level of the well. How long does it take to reach the water?

PREPARE Assume the rope is massless and does not slip. FIGURE 7.33a gives a visual overview of the falling bucket. FIGURE 7.33b shows the free-body diagrams for the cylinder and the bucket. The rope tension exerts an upward force on the bucket and a downward force on the outer edge of the cylinder. The rope is massless, so these two tension forces have equal magnitudes, which we'll call T.

FIGURE 7.33 Visual overview of a falling bucket.

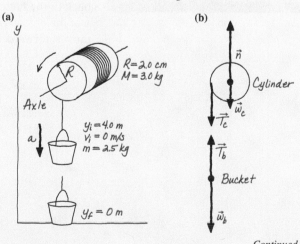

Continued

SOLVE Newton's second law applied to the linear motion of the bucket is

$$ma_y = T - mg$$

where, as usual, the y-axis points upward. What about the cylinder? There is a normal force $\vec{n}$ on the cylinder due to the axle and the weight of the cylinder $\vec{w}_c$. However, neither of these forces exerts a torque because each passes through the rotation axis. The only torque comes from the rope tension. The moment arm for the tension is $r_\perp = R$, and the torque is positive because the rope turns the cylinder counterclockwise. Thus $\tau_{\text{rope}} = TR$, and Newton's second law for the rotational motion is

$$\alpha = \frac{\tau_{\text{net}}}{I} = \frac{TR}{\frac{1}{2}MR^2} = \frac{2T}{MR}$$

The moment of inertia of a cylinder rotating about a center axis was taken from Table 7.4.

The last piece of information we need is the constraint due to the fact that the rope doesn't slip. Equation 7.16 relates only the magnitudes of the linear and angular accelerations, but in this problem α is positive (counterclockwise acceleration), while a_y is negative (downward acceleration). Hence

$$a_y = -\alpha R$$

Using α from the cylinder's equation in the constraint, we find

$$a_y = -\alpha R = -\frac{2T}{MR}R = -\frac{2T}{M}$$

Thus the tension is $T = -\frac{1}{2}Ma_y$. If we use this value of the tension in the bucket's equation, we can solve for the acceleration:

$$ma_y = -\frac{1}{2}Ma_y - mg$$

$$a_y = -\frac{g}{(1 + M/2m)} = -6.1 \text{ m/s}^2$$

The time to fall through $\Delta y = y_f - y_i = -4.0$ m is found from kinematics:

$$\Delta y = \frac{1}{2}a_y(\Delta t)^2$$

$$\Delta t = \sqrt{\frac{2\Delta y}{a_y}} = \sqrt{\frac{2(-4.0 \text{ m})}{-6.1 \text{ m/s}^2}} = 1.1 \text{ s}$$

ASSESS The expression for the acceleration gives $a_y = -g$ if $M = 0$. This makes sense because the bucket would be in free fall if there were no cylinder. When the cylinder has mass, the downward force of gravity on the bucket has to accelerate the bucket *and* spin the cylinder. Consequently, the acceleration is reduced and the bucket takes longer to fall.

7.6 Rolling Motion

FIGURE 7.34 The trajectories of the center of a wheel and of a point on the rim are seen in a time-exposure photograph.

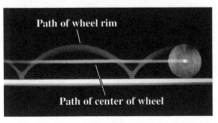

Rolling is a *combination motion* in which an object rotates about an axis that is moving along a straight-line trajectory. For example, FIGURE 7.34 is a time-exposure photo of a rolling wheel with one lightbulb on the axis and a second lightbulb at the edge. The axis light moves straight ahead, but the edge light follows a curve called a *cycloid*. Let's see if we can understand this interesting motion. We'll consider only objects that roll without slipping.

To understand rolling motion, consider FIGURE 7.35, which shows a round object—a wheel or a sphere—that rolls forward, *without slipping*, exactly one revolution. The point initially at the bottom follows the blue curve to the top and then back to the bottom. The overall position of the object is measured by the position x of the object's center. Because the object doesn't slip, in one revolution the center moves forward exactly one circumference, so that $\Delta x = 2\pi R$. The time for the

FIGURE 7.35 An object rolling through one revolution.

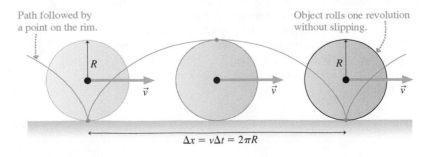

object to turn one revolution is its period T, so we can compute the speed of the object's center as

$$v = \frac{\Delta x}{T} = \frac{2\pi R}{T} \tag{7.17}$$

But $2\pi/T$ is the angular velocity ω, as you learned in Chapter 6, which leads to

$$v = \omega R \tag{7.18}$$

Equation 7.18 is the **rolling constraint,** the basic link between translation and rotation for objects that roll without slipping.

We can find the velocity for any point on a rolling object by adding the velocity of that point when the object is in pure translation, without rolling, to the velocity of the point when the object is in pure rotation, without translating. FIGURE 7.36 shows how the velocity vectors at the top, center, and bottom of a rotating wheel are found in this way.

Ancient movers The great stone *moai* of Easter Island were moved as far as 16 km from a quarry to their final positions. Archeologists believe that one possible method of moving these 14 ton statues was to place them on rollers. One disadvantage of this method is that the statues, placed on top of the rollers, move twice as fast as the rollers themselves. Thus rollers are continuously left behind and have to be carried back to the front and reinserted. Sadly, the indiscriminate cutting of trees for moving *moai* may have hastened the demise of this island civilization.

FIGURE 7.36 Rolling is a combination of translation and rotation.

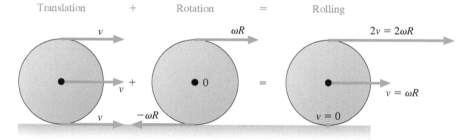

Thus the point at the top of the wheel has a forward speed of v due to its translational motion plus a forward speed of $\omega R = v$ due to its rotational motion. The speed of a point at the top of a wheel is then $2v = 2\omega R$, or *twice* the speed of its center of mass. On the other hand, the point at the bottom of the wheel, where it touches the ground, still has a forward speed of v due to its translational motion. But its velocity due to rotation points *backward* with a magnitude of $\omega R = v$. Adding these, we find that the velocity of this lowest point is *zero*. In other words, **the point on the bottom of a rolling object is instantaneously at rest.**

Although this seems surprising, it is really what we mean by "rolling without slipping." If the bottom point had a velocity, it would be moving horizontally relative to the surface. In other words, it would be slipping or sliding across the surface. To roll without slipping, the bottom point, the point touching the surface, must be at rest.

EXAMPLE 7.15 **Rotating your tires**

The diameter of your tires is 0.60 m. You take a 60 mile trip at a speed of 45 mph.

a. During this trip, what was your tires' angular speed?
b. How many times did they revolve?

PREPARE The angular speed is related to the speed of a wheel's center by Equation 7.18: $v = \omega R$. Because the center of the wheel turns on an axle fixed to the car, the speed v of the wheel's center is the same as that of the car. We prepare by converting the car's speed to SI units:

$$v = (45 \text{ mph}) \times \left(0.447 \frac{\text{m/s}}{\text{mph}}\right) = 20 \text{ m/s}$$

Once we know the angular speed, we can find the number of times the tires turned from the rotational-kinematic equation $\Delta\theta = \omega \Delta t$. We'll need to find the time traveled Δt from $v = \Delta x/\Delta t$.

SOLVE a. From Equation 7.18 we have

$$\omega = \frac{v}{R} = \frac{20 \text{ m/s}}{0.30 \text{ m}} = 67 \text{ rad/s}$$

b. The time of the trip is

$$\Delta t = \frac{\Delta x}{v} = \frac{60 \text{ mi}}{45 \text{ mi/h}} = 1.33 \text{ h} \times \frac{3600 \text{ s}}{1 \text{ h}} = 4800 \text{ s}$$

Continued

Thus the total angle through which the tires turn is

$$\Delta\theta = \omega \, \Delta t = (67 \text{ rad/s})(4800 \text{ s}) = 3.2 \times 10^5 \text{ rad}$$

Because each turn of the wheel is 2π rad, the number of turns is

$$\frac{3.2 \times 10^5 \text{ rad}}{2\pi \text{ rad}} = 51,000 \text{ turns}$$

ASSESS You probably know from seeing tires on passing cars that a tire rotates several times a second at 45 mph. Because there are 3600 s in an hour, and your 60 mile trip at 45 mph is going to take over an hour—say, $\approx$5000 s—you would expect the tire to make many thousands of revolutions. So 51,000 turns seems to be a reasonable answer. You can see that your tires rotate roughly a thousand times per mile. During the lifetime of a tire, about 50,000 miles, it will rotate about 50 million times!

STOP TO THINK 7.6 A wheel rolls without slipping. Which is the correct velocity vector for point P on the wheel?

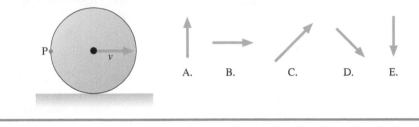

INTEGRATED EXAMPLE 7.16   **Spinning a gyroscope**

A gyroscope is a top-like toy consisting of a heavy ring attached by light spokes to a central axle. The axle and ring are free to turn on bearings. To get the gyroscope spinning, a 30-cm-long string is wrapped around the 2.0-mm-diameter axle, then pulled with a constant force of 5.0 N. If the ring's diameter is 5.0 cm and its mass is 30 g, at what rate is it spinning, in rpm, once the string is completely unwound?

PREPARE Because the ring is heavy compared to the spokes and the axle, we'll model it as a cylindrical hoop, taking its moment of inertia from Table 7.4 to be $I = MR^2$. FIGURE 7.37 shows a visual overview of the problem. Two points are worth noting. First, rule 2 of Tactics Box 5.2 tells us that the tension in the string has the same magnitude as the force that pulls on the string, so the tension is $T = 5.0$ N. Second, it is a good idea to convert all the known quantities in the problem statement to SI units, and to collect them all in one place as we have done in the visual overview of Figure 7.37. Here, radius R is half the 5.0 cm ring diameter, and radius r is half the 2.0 mm axle diameter.

We are asked at what rate the ring is spinning when the string is unwound. This is a question about the ring's final *angular velocity*, which we've labeled ω_f. We've assumed that the initial angular velocity is $\omega_i = 0$ rad/s. Because the angular velocity is changing, the ring must have an angular acceleration that, as we know, is caused by a torque. So a good strategy will be to find the torque on the ring, from which we can find its angular acceleration and, using kinematics, the final angular velocity.

FIGURE 7.37 Visual overview of a gyroscope being spun.

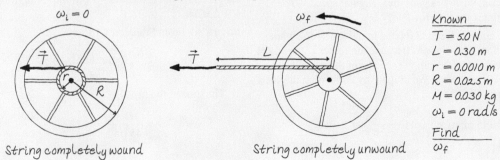

SOLVE The torque on the ring is due to the tension in the string. Because the string—and the line of action of the tension—is tangent to the axle, the moment arm of the tension force is the radius r of the axle. Thus $\tau = r_\perp T = rT$. Now we can apply Newton's second law for rotational motion, Equation 7.15, to find the angular acceleration:

$$\alpha = \frac{\tau_{net}}{I} = \frac{rT}{MR^2} = \frac{(0.0010\ \text{m})(5.0\ \text{N})}{(0.030\ \text{kg})(0.025\ \text{m})^2} = 267\ \text{rad/s}^2$$

We next use constant-angular-acceleration kinematics to find the final angular velocity. For the equation $\Delta\theta = \omega_i \Delta t + \frac{1}{2}\alpha \Delta t^2$ of Table 7.2, we know α and ω_i, and we should be able to find $\Delta\theta$ from the length of string unwound, but we don't know Δt. For the equation $\Delta\omega = \omega_f - \omega_i = \alpha \Delta t$, we know α and ω_i, and ω_f is what we want to find, but again we don't know Δt. To find an equation that doesn't contain Δt, we first write

$$\Delta t = \frac{\omega_f - \omega_i}{\alpha}$$

from the second kinematic equation. Inserting this value for Δt into the first equation gives

$$\Delta\theta = \omega_i \frac{\omega_f - \omega_i}{\alpha} + \frac{1}{2}\alpha\left(\frac{\omega_f - \omega_i}{\alpha}\right)^2$$

which can be simplified to

$$\omega_f^2 = \omega_i^2 + 2\alpha\,\Delta\theta$$

This equation, which is the rotational analog of the linear motion Equation 2.13, will allow us to find ω_f once $\Delta\theta$ is known.

FIGURE 7.38 shows how to find $\Delta\theta$. As a segment of string of length s unwinds, the axle turns through an angle (based on the

FIGURE 7.38 Relating the angle turned to the length of string unwound.

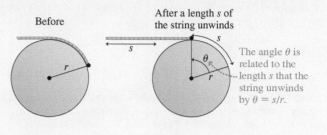

definition of radian measure) $\theta = s/r$. Thus as the whole string, of length L, unwinds, the axle (and the ring) turns through an angular displacement

$$\Delta\theta = \frac{L}{r} = \frac{0.30\ \text{m}}{0.0010\ \text{m}} = 300\ \text{rad}$$

Now we can use our kinematic equation to find that

$$\omega_f^2 = \omega_i^2 + 2\alpha\Delta\theta = (0\ \text{rad/s})^2 + 2(267\ \text{rad/s}^2)(300\ \text{rad})$$

$$= 160{,}000\ (\text{rad/s})^2$$

from which we find that $\omega_f = 400\ \text{rad/s}$. Converting rad/s to rpm, we find that the gyroscope ring is spinning at

$$400\ \text{rad/s} = \left(\frac{400\ \text{rad}}{\text{s}}\right)\left(\frac{60\ \text{s}}{1\ \text{min}}\right)\left(\frac{1\ \text{rev}}{2\pi\ \text{rad}}\right) = 3800\ \text{rpm}$$

ASSESS This is fast, about the speed of your car engine when its on the highway, but if you've ever played with a gyroscope or a string-wound top, you know you can really get it spinning fast.

SUMMARY

The goal of Chapter 7 has been to understand the physics of rotating objects.

GENERAL PRINCIPLES

Newton's Second Law for Rotational Motion

If a net torque τ_{net} acts on an object, the object will experience an angular acceleration given by $\alpha = \tau_{net}/I$, where I is the object's moment of inertia about the rotation axis.

This law is analogous to Newton's second law for linear motion, $\vec{a} = \vec{F}_{net}/m$.

IMPORTANT CONCEPTS

Torque is the rotational analog of force. Just as a force causes an object to undergo a linear acceleration, a torque causes an object to undergo an angular acceleration.

There are two interpretations of torque:

Interpretation 1: $\tau = rF_\perp$ Interpretation 2: $\tau = r_\perp F$

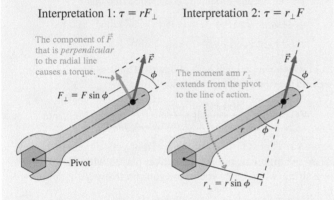

The component of $\vec{F}$ that is *perpendicular* to the radial line causes a torque.

$F_\perp = F\sin\phi$

The moment arm $r_\perp$ extends from the pivot to the line of action.

$r_\perp = r\sin\phi$

Pivot

Both interpretations give the same expression for the magnitude of the torque: $\tau = rF\sin\phi$.

A torque is positive if it tends to rotate the object counterclockwise; negative if it tends to rotate the object clockwise.

The **moment of inertia** is the rotational equivalent of mass. The larger an object's moment of inertia, the more difficult it is to get the object rotating. For an object made up of particles of masses $m_1, m_2, \ldots$ at distances $r_1, r_2, \ldots$ from the axis, the moment of inertia is

$$I = m_1 r_1^2 + m_2 r_2^2 + m_3 r_3^2 + \cdots = \sum mr^2$$

Angular and tangential acceleration

A particle moving in a circle has

- A velocity tangent to the circle.

- A centripetal acceleration $\vec{a}_c$ directed toward the center of the circle.

Centripetal acceleration

Angular velocity

Tangential acceleration

Velocity

If the particle's speed is increasing, it will also have

- A tangential acceleration $\vec{a}_t$ directed tangent to the circle.

- An angular acceleration α.

The angular and tangential accelerations are related by $a_t = \alpha r$.

For a **rigid body,** the angular velocity and angular acceleration are the same for every point on the object.

Center of gravity

The **center of gravity** of an object is the point at which gravity can be considered as acting.

Gravity acts on each particle that makes up the object.

The object responds *as if* its entire weight acts at the center of gravity.

$\vec{w}$

The **position of the center of gravity** depends on the distance $x_1, x_2, \ldots$ of each particle of mass $m_1, m_2, \ldots$ from the origin:

$$x_{cg} = \frac{x_1 m_1 + x_2 m_2 + x_3 m_3 + \cdots}{m_1 + m_2 + m_3 + \cdots}$$

APPLICATIONS

Moments of inertia of common shapes

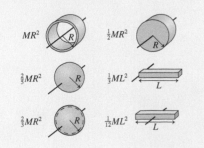

MR^2 $\frac{1}{2}MR^2$

$\frac{2}{5}MR^2$ $\frac{1}{3}ML^2$

$\frac{2}{3}MR^2$ $\frac{1}{12}ML^2$

Rotation about a fixed axis

When a net torque is applied to an object that rotates about a fixed axis, the object will undergo an **angular acceleration** given by

$$\alpha = \frac{\tau_{net}}{I}$$

If a rope unwinds from a pulley of radius R, the linear motion of an object tied to the rope is related to the angular motion of the pulley by

$$a_{obj} = \alpha R \qquad v_{obj} = \omega R$$

Rolling motion

For an object that rolls without slipping,

$$v = \omega R$$

The velocity of a point at the top of the object is twice that of the center.

$2\vec{v}$

$\vec{v}$

QUESTIONS

Conceptual Questions

1. Figure Q7.1 shows four pulleys, each with a heavy and a light block strung over them. The blocks' velocities are shown. What are the signs (+ or −) of the angular velocity and angular acceleration of the pulley in each case?

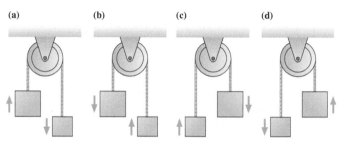

(a)   **(b)**   **(c)**   **(d)**

FIGURE Q7.1

2. If you are using a wrench to loosen a very stubborn nut, you can make the job easier by using a "cheater pipe." This is a piece of pipe that slides over the handle of the wrench, as shown in Figure Q7.2, making it effectively much longer. Explain why this would help you loosen the nut.

FIGURE Q7.2

3. Five forces are applied to a door, as seen from above in Figure Q7.3. For each force, is the torque about the hinge positive, negative, or zero?

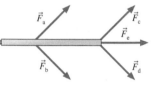

FIGURE Q7.3

4. A screwdriver with a very thick handle requires less force to operate than one with a very skinny handle. Explain why this is so.

5. If you have ever driven a truck, you likely found that it had a steering wheel with a larger diameter than that of a passenger car. Why is this?

6. A common type of door stop is a wedge made of rubber. Is such a stop more effective when jammed under the door near or far from the hinges? Why?

7. Suppose you are hanging from a tree branch. If you move out along the branch, farther away from the trunk, the branch will be more likely to break. Explain why this is so.

8. A student gives a quick push to a ball at the end of a massless, rigid rod, causing the ball to rotate clockwise in a *horizontal* circle as shown in Figure Q7.8. The rod's pivot is frictionless.

a. As the student is pushing, is the torque about the pivot positive, negative, or zero?

b. After the push has ended, what does the ball's angular velocity do? Steadily increase? Increase for a while, then hold steady? Hold steady? Decrease for a while, then hold steady? Steadily decrease? Explain.

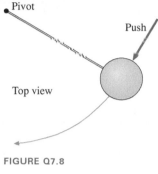

FIGURE Q7.8

c. Right after the push has ended, is the torque positive, negative, or zero?

9. The two ends of the dumbbell shown in Figure Q7.9 are made of the same material. Is the dumbbell's center of gravity at point 1, 2, or 3? Explain.

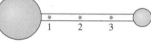

FIGURE Q7.9

10. When you rise from a chair, you have to lean quite far forward (try it!). Why is this?

11. Suppose you have two identical-looking metal spheres of the same size and the same mass. One of them is solid, the other is hollow. How can you tell which is which?

12. The moment of inertia of a uniform rod about an axis through its center is $ML^2/12$. The moment of inertia about an axis at one end is $ML^2/3$. Explain *why* the moment of inertia is larger about the end than about the center.

13. A heavy steel rod, 1.0 m long, and a light pencil, 0.15 m long, are held 15° from the vertical with one end on a table, then released simultaneously. Which will hit the table first? Or will it be a tie? Explain.

14. The wheel in Figure Q7.14 is rolling to the right without slipping. Rank in order, from fastest to slowest, the *speeds* of the points labeled 1 through 5. Explain your reasoning.

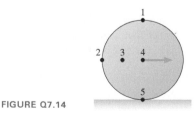

FIGURE Q7.14

15. A car traveling at 60 mph has a pebble stuck in one of its tires. Eventually the pebble works loose, and at the instant of release it is at the top of the tire. Explain why the pebble then slams *hard* into the *front* of the wheel well.

Multiple-Choice Questions

16. | A nut needs to be tightened with a wrench. Which force shown in Figure Q7.16 will apply the greatest torque to the nut?

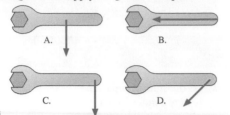

FIGURE Q7.16

17. | Suppose a bolt on your car engine needs to be tightened to a torque of 20 N·m. You are using a 15-cm-long wrench, and you apply a force at the very end in the direction that produces maximum torque. What force should you apply?
A. 1300 N   B. 260 N   C. 130 N   D. 26 N

18. | A machine part is made up of two pieces, with centers of gravity shown in Figure Q7.18. Which point could be the center of gravity of the entire part?

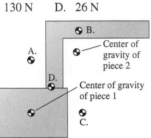

Center of gravity of piece 2

Center of gravity of piece 1

FIGURE Q7.18

19. ‖ A typical compact disk has a mass of 15 g and a diameter of 120 mm. What is its moment of inertia about an axis through its center, perpendicular to the disk?
A. 2.7×10^{-5} kg·m²   B. 5.4×10^{-5} kg·m²
C. 1.1×10^{-4} kg·m²   D. 2.2×10^{-4} kg·m²

20. ‖ Suppose you make a new kind of compact disk that is the same thickness as a current disk but twice the diameter. By what factor will the moment of inertia increase?
A. 2   B. 4   C. 8   D. 16

21. | Doors 1 and 2 have the same mass, height, and thickness. Door 2 is twice as wide as door 1. Bob pushes straight against the outer edge of door 2 with force F, and Barb pushes straight against the outer edge of door 1 with force $2F$. How do the angular accelerations α_1 and α_2 of the two doors compare?
A. $\alpha_1 > \alpha_2$ B. $\alpha_1 = \alpha_2$ C. $\alpha_1 < \alpha_2$

22. | A baseball bat has a heavy barrel and a thin handle. If you want to hold a baseball bat on your palm so that it balances vertically, you should
A. Put the end of the handle in your palm, with the barrel up.
B. Put the end of the barrel in your palm, with the handle up.
C. The bat will be equally easy to balance in either configuration.

23. | A car traveling at a steady 30 m/s has 74-cm-diameter tires. What is the approximate acceleration of a piece of the tread on any of the tires?
A. 24 m/s²   B. 48 m/s²   C. 2400 m/s²   D. 4800 m/s²

PROBLEMS

Section 7.1 The Rotation of a Rigid Body

1. ‖ To throw a discus, the thrower holds it with a fully outstretched arm. Starting from rest, he begins to turn with a constant angular acceleration, releasing the discus after making one complete revolution. The diameter of the circle in which the discus moves is about 1.8 m. If the thrower takes 1.0 s to complete one revolution, starting from rest, what will be the speed of the discus at release?

2. ‖ A computer hard disk starts from rest, then speeds up with an angular acceleration of 190 rad/s² until it reaches its final angular speed of 7200 rpm. How many revolutions has the disk made 10.0 s after it starts up?

3. ‖ The crankshaft in a race car goes from rest to 3000 rpm in 2.0 s.
   a. What is the crankshaft's angular acceleration?
   b. How many revolutions does it make while reaching 3000 rpm?

Section 7.2 Torque

4. | Reconsider the situation in Example 7.5. If Luis pulls straight down on the end of a wrench that is in the same orientation but is 35 cm long, rather than 20 cm, what force must he apply to exert the same torque?

5. ‖ Balls are attached to light rods and can move in horizontal circles as shown in Figure P7.5. Rank in order, from smallest to largest, the torques τ_1 to τ_4 about the centers of the circles. Explain.

6. ‖‖ Six forces, each of magnitude either F or $2F$, are applied to a door as seen from above in Figure P7.6. Rank in order, from smallest to largest, the six torques τ_1 to τ_6 about the hinge.

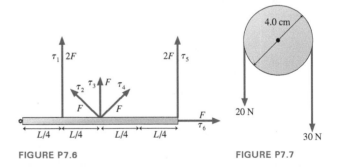

FIGURE P7.6   **FIGURE P7.7**

7. | What is the net torque about the axle on the pulley in Figure P7.7?

8. ‖ The tune-up specifications of a car call for the spark plugs to be tightened to a torque of 38 N·m. You plan to tighten the plugs by pulling on the end of a 25-cm-long wrench. Because of the cramped space under the hood, you'll need to pull at an angle of 120° with respect to the wrench shaft. With what force must you pull?

9. ‖ A professor's office door is 0.91 m wide, 2.0 m high, and 4.0 cm thick; has a mass of 25 kg; and pivots on frictionless hinges. A "door closer" is attached to the door and the top of the door frame. When the door is open and at rest, the door closer exerts a torque of 5.2 N·m. What is the least force that you need to apply to the door to hold it open?

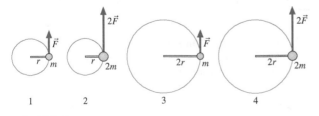

FIGURE P7.5

10. ‖ In Figure P7.10, force $\vec{F}_2$ acts half as far from the pivot as $\vec{F}_1$. What magnitude of $\vec{F}_2$ causes the net torque on the rod to be zero?

FIGURE P7.10

11. ‖ Tom and Jerry both push on the 3.00-m-diameter merry-go-round shown in Figure P7.11.
    a. If Tom pushes with a force of 10.0 N and Jerry pushes with a force of 35.2 N, what is the net torque on the merry-go-round?

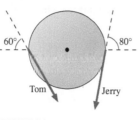

    FIGURE P7.11

    b. What is the net torque if Jerry reverses the direction he pushes by 180° without changing the magnitude of his force?

12. ‖ What is the net torque of the bar shown in Figure P7.12, about the axis indicated by the dot?

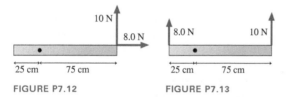

FIGURE P7.12   **FIGURE P7.13**

13. ‖ What is the net torque of the bar shown in Figure P7.13, about the axis indicated by the dot?

14. ‖ What is the net torque of the bar shown in Figure P7.14, about the axis indicated by the dot?

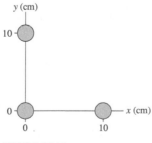

FIGURE P7.14

15. ‖ A 1.7-m-long barbell has a 20 kg weight on its left end and a 35 kg weight on its right end.
    a. If you ignore the weight of the bar itself, how far from the left end of the barbell is the center of gravity?
    b. Where is the center of gravity if the 8.0 kg mass of the barbell itself is taken into account?

Section 7.3 Gravitational Torque and the Center of Gravity

16. ‖ Three identical coins lie on three corners of a square 10.0 cm on a side, as shown in Figure P7.16. Determine the x and y coordinates of the center of gravity of the three coins.

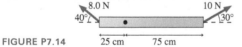

17. ‖ Hold your arm outstretched so that it is horizontal. Estimate the mass of your arm and the position of its center of gravity. What is the gravitational torque on your arm in this position, computed around the shoulder joint?
    BIO

FIGURE P7.16

18. ‖ A solid cylinder sits on top of a solid cube as shown in Figure P7.18. How far above the table's surface is the center of gravity of the combined object?

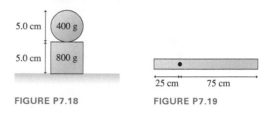

FIGURE P7.18   **FIGURE P7.19**

19. ‖ The 2.0 kg, uniform, horizontal rod in Figure P7.19 is seen from the side. What is the gravitational torque about the point shown?

20. ‖ A 4.00-m-long, 500 kg steel beam extends horizontally from the point where it has been bolted to the framework of a new building under construction. A 70.0 kg construction worker stands at the far end of the beam. What is the magnitude of the torque about the point where the beam is bolted into place?

21. ‖ An athlete at the gym holds a 3.0 kg steel ball in his hand.
    BIO His arm is 70 cm long and has a mass of 4.0 kg. What is the magnitude of the torque about his shoulder if he holds his arm
    a. Straight out to his side, parallel to the floor?
    b. Straight, but 45° below horizontal?

22. ‖ The 2.0-m-long, 15 kg beam in Figure P7.22 is hinged at its left end. It is "falling" (rotating clockwise, under the influence of gravity), and the figure shows its position at three different times. What is the gravitational torque on the beam about an axis through the hinged end when the beam is at the
    a. Upper position?
    b. Middle position?
    c. Lower position?

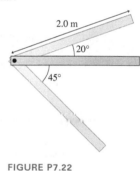

FIGURE P7.22

23. ‖ Two thin beams are joined end-to-end as shown in Figure P7.23 to make a single object. The left beam is 10.0 kg and 1.00 m long and the right one is 40.0 kg and 2.00 m long.
    a. How far from the left end of the left beam is the center of gravity of the object?
    b. What is the gravitational torque on the object about an axis through its left end? The object is seen from the side.

FIGURE P7.23

24. ‖ Figure P7.24 shows two thin beams joined at right angles. The vertical beam is 15.0 kg and 1.00 m long and the horizontal beam is 25.0 kg and 2.00 m long.
    a. Find the center of gravity of the two joined beams. Express your answer in the form (x, y), taking the origin at the corner where the beams join.
    b. Calculate the gravitational torque on the joined beams about an axis through the corner. The beams are seen from the side.

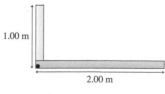

FIGURE P7.24

Section 7.4 Rotational Dynamics and Moment of Inertia

25. ‖‖ A regulation table tennis ball has a mass of 2.7 g and is 40 mm in diameter. What is its moment of inertia about an axis that passes through its center?

26. ‖ Three pairs of balls are connected by very light rods as shown in Figure P7.26. Rank in order, from smallest to largest, the moments of inertia I_1, I_2, and I_3 about axes through the centers of the rods.

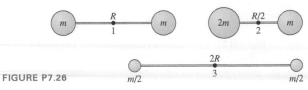

FIGURE P7.26

27. ‖ A playground toy has four seats, each 5.0 kg, attached to very light, 1.5-m-long rods, as seen from above in Figure P7.27. If two children, with masses of 15 kg and 20 kg, sit in seats opposite one another, what is the moment of inertia about the rotation axis?

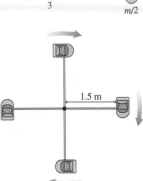

FIGURE P7.27

28. ‖‖ A solid cylinder with a radius of 4.0 cm has the same mass as a solid sphere of radius R. If the cylinder and sphere have the same moment of inertia about their centers, what is the sphere's radius?

29. ‖ A bicycle rim has a diameter of 0.65 m and a moment of inertia, measured about its center, of 0.19 kg · m². What is the mass of the rim?

Section 7.5 Using Newton's Second Law for Rotation

30. ‖ The left part of Figure P7.30 shows a bird's-eye view of two identical balls connected by a light rod that rotates about a vertical axis through its center. The right part shows a ball of twice the mass connected to a light rod of half the length, that rotates about its left end. If equal forces are applied as shown in the figure, which of the two rods will have the greater angular acceleration?

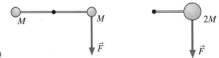

FIGURE P7.30

31. ‖‖ a. What is the moment of inertia of the door in Problem 9?
    b. If you let go of the open door, what is its angular acceleration immediately afterward?

32. ‖ A small grinding wheel has a moment of inertia of 4.0×10^{-5} kg · m². What net torque must be applied to the wheel for its angular acceleration to be 150 rad/s²?

33. ‖ While sitting in a swivel chair, you push against the floor with your heel to make the chair spin. The 7.0 N frictional force is applied at a point 40 cm from the chair's rotation axis, in the direction that causes the greatest angular acceleration. If that angular acceleration is 1.8 rad/s², what is the total moment of inertia about the axis of you and the chair?

34. ‖ An object's moment of inertia is 2.0 kg · m². Its angular velocity is increasing at the rate of 4.0 rad/s per second. What is the net torque on the object?

35. ‖‖ A 200 g, 20-cm-diameter plastic disk is spun on an axle through its center by an electric motor. What torque must the motor supply to take the disk from 0 to 1800 rpm in 4.0 s?

36. ‖‖ The 2.5 kg object shown in Figure P7.36 has a moment of inertia about the rotation axis of 0.085 kg · m². The rotation axis is horizontal. When released, what will be the object's initial angular acceleration?

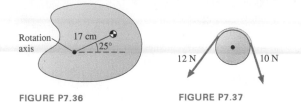

FIGURE P7.36   **FIGURE P7.37**

37. ‖‖ A frictionless pulley, which can be modeled as a 0.80 kg solid cylinder with a 0.30 m radius, has a rope going over it, as shown in Figure P7.37. The tension in the rope is 10 N on one side and 12 N on the other. What is the angular acceleration of the pulley?

38. ‖‖ If you lift the front wheel of a poorly maintained bicycle off the ground and then start it spinning at 0.72 rev/s, friction in the bearings causes the wheel to stop in just 12 s. If the moment of inertia of the wheel about its axle is 0.30 kg · m², what is the magnitude of the frictional torque?

39. ‖‖‖ A toy top with a spool of diameter 5.0 cm has a moment of inertia of 3.0×10^{-5} kg · m² about its rotation axis. To get the top spinning, its string is pulled with a tension of 0.30 N. How long does it take for the top to complete the first five revolutions? The string is long enough that it is wrapped around the top more than five turns.

40. ‖ A 34-cm-diameter potter's wheel with a mass of 20 kg is spinning at 180 rpm. Using her hands, a potter forms a pot, centered on the wheel, with a 14 cm diameter. Her hands apply a net friction force of 1.3 N to the edge of the pot. If the power goes out, so that the wheel's motor no longer provides any torque, how long will it take for the wheel to come to a stop in her hands?

41. ‖‖‖ A 1.5 kg block and a 2.5 kg block are attached to opposite ends of a light rope. The rope hangs over a solid, frictionless pulley that is 30 cm in diameter and has a mass of 0.75 kg. When the blocks are released, what is the acceleration of the lighter block?

Section 7.6 Rolling Motion

42. ‖‖ A bicycle with 0.80-m-diameter tires is coasting on a level road at 5.6 m/s. A small blue dot has been painted on the tread of the rear tire.
    a. What is the angular speed of the tires?
    b. What is the speed of the blue dot when it is 0.80 m above the road?
    c. What is the speed of the blue dot when it is 0.40 m above the road?

43. ‖‖‖ A 1.2 g pebble is stuck in a tread of a 0.76-m-diameter automobile tire, held in place by static friction that can be at most 3.6 N. The car starts from rest and gradually accelerates on a straight road. How fast is the car moving when the pebble flies out of the tire tread?

General Problems

44. | Figure P7.44 shows the angular position-versus-time graph
INT for a particle moving in a circle.
   a. Write a description of the particle's motion.
   b. Draw the angular velocity-versus-time graph.

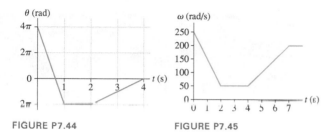

FIGURE P7.44   FIGURE P7.45

45. | The graph in Figure P7.45 shows the angular velocity of the
INT crankshaft in a car. Draw a graph of the angular acceleration
versus time. Include appropriate numerical scales on both axes.

46. ‖ A computer disk is 8.0 cm in diameter. A reference dot on the
edge of the disk is initially located at $\theta = 45°$. The disk accelerates steadily for 0.50 s, reaching 2000 rpm, then coasts at steady
angular velocity for another 0.50 s.
   a. What is the tangential acceleration of the reference dot at
      $t = 0.25$ s?
   b. What is the centripetal acceleration of the reference dot at
      $t = 0.25$ s?
   c. What is the angular position of the reference dot at $t = 1.0$ s?
   d. What is the speed of the reference dot at $t = 1.0$ s?

47. ‖ A car with 58-cm-diameter tires accelerates uniformly from
INT rest to 20 m/s in 10 s. How many times does each tire rotate?

48. ‖ The cable lifting an elevator is wrapped around a 1.0-m-
diameter cylinder that is turned by the elevator's motor. The
elevator is moving upward at a speed of 1.6 m/s. It then slows to
a stop, while the cylinder turns one complete revolution. How
long does it take for the elevator to stop?

49. ‖ The 20-cm-diameter disk
in Figure P7.49 can rotate on
an axle through its center.
What is the net torque about
the axle?

50. ‖ A combination lock has a
INT 1.0-cm-diameter knob that is
part of the dial you turn to
unlock the lock. To turn that
knob, you grip it between
your thumb and forefinger
with a force of 0.60 N as you
twist your wrist. Suppose the
coefficient of static friction between the knob and your fingers
is only 0.12 because some oil accidentally got onto the knob.
What is the most torque you can exert on the knob without having it slip between your fingers?

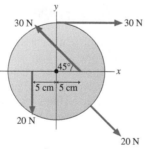

FIGURE P7.49

51. ‖‖ A 70 kg man's arm, including the hand, can be modeled as a
BIO 75-cm-long uniform cylinder with a mass of 3.5 kg. In raising
both his arms, from hanging down to straight up, by how much
does he raise his center of gravity?

52. ‖ A penny has a mass of 2.5 g and is 1.5 mm thick; a nickel has a
mass of 5.7 g and is 1.9 mm thick. If you make a stack of coins on
a table, starting with five nickels and finishing with four pennies,
how far above the tabletop is the center of gravity of the stack?

53. ‖‖ The   machinist's
square   shown   in
Figure P7.53 consists
of a thin, rectangular
blade connected to a
rectangular handle.
   a. Determine the x
      and y coordinates
      of the center of
      gravity. Let the lower left corner be $x = 0, y = 0$.
   b. Sketch how the tool would hang if it were allowed to freely
      pivot about the point $x = 0, y = 0$.
   c. When hanging from that point, what angle would the long
      side of the blade make with the vertical?

FIGURE P7.53

54. ‖‖ The four masses shown in
Figure P7.54 are connected by
massless, rigid rods.
   a. Find the coordinates of the
      center of gravity.
   b. Find the moment of inertia
      about an axis that passes
      through mass A and is per-
      pendicular to the page.
   c. Find the moment of inertia
      about a diagonal axis that
      passes through masses B
      and D.

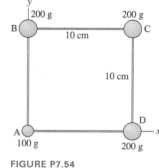

FIGURE P7.54

55. ‖‖ Three 0.10 kg balls are connected by light rods to form an
equilateral triangle with a side length of 0.30 m. What is the
moment of inertia of this triangle about an axis perpendicular to
its plane and passing through one of the balls?

56. ‖‖ The three masses shown in
Figure P7.56 are connected by
massless, rigid rods.
   a. Find the coordinates of the
      center of gravity.
   b. Find the moment of inertia
      about an axis that passes
      through mass A and is per-
      pendicular to the page.
   c. Find the moment of inertia
      about an axis that passes
      through masses B and C.

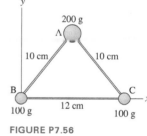

FIGURE P7.56

57. ‖ A reasonable estimate of the moment of inertia of an ice
BIO skater spinning with her arms at her sides can be made by modeling most of her body as a uniform cylinder. Suppose the
skater has a mass of 64 kg. One-eighth of that mass is in her
arms, which are 60 cm long and 20 cm from the vertical axis
about which she rotates. The rest of her mass is approximately
in the form of a 20-cm-radius cylinder.
   a. Estimate the skater's moment of inertia to two significant
      figures.
   b. If she were to hold her arms outward, rather than at her
      sides, would her moment of inertia increase, decrease, or
      remain unchanged? Explain.

58. ‖ Starting from rest, a 12-cm-diameter compact disk takes 3.0 s
to reach its operating angular velocity of 2000 rpm. Assume
that the angular acceleration is constant. The disk's moment of
inertia is 2.5×10^{-5} kg · m².
   a. How much torque is applied to the disk?
   b. How many revolutions does it make before reaching full speed?

59. ⦀ The ropes in Figure P7.59 are each wrapped around a cylinder, and the two cylinders are fastened together. The smaller cylinder has a diameter of 10 cm and a mass of 5.0 kg; the larger cylinder has a diameter of 20 cm and a mass of 20 kg. What is the angular acceleration of the cylinders? Assume that the cylinders turn on a frictionless axle.

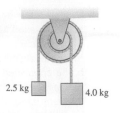

2.5 kg   4.0 kg

FIGURE P7.59

60. ⦀ Flywheels are large, massive wheels used to store energy. They can be spun up slowly, then the wheel's energy can be released quickly to accomplish a task that demands high power. An industrial flywheel has a 1.5 m diameter and a mass of 250 kg. A motor spins up the flywheel with a constant torque of 50 N·m. How long does it take the flywheel to reach top angular speed of 1200 rpm?

61. ⦀ A 1.0 kg ball and a 2.0 kg ball are connected by a 1.0-m-long rigid, massless rod. The rod and balls are rotating clockwise about their center of gravity at 20 rpm. What torque will bring the balls to a halt in 5.0 s?

62. ⦀ A 1.5 kg block is connected by a rope across a 50-cm-diameter, 2.0 kg, frictionless pulley, as shown in Figure P7.62. A constant 10 N tension is applied to the other end of the rope. Starting from rest, how long does it take the block to move 30 cm?

10 N

1.5 kg

FIGURE P7.62

63. ⦀ The two blocks in Figure P7.63 are connected by a massless rope that passes over a pulley. The pulley is 12 cm in diameter and has a mass of 2.0 kg. As the pulley turns, friction at the axle exerts a torque of magnitude 0.50 N·m. If the blocks are released from rest, how long does it take the 4.0 kg block to reach the floor?

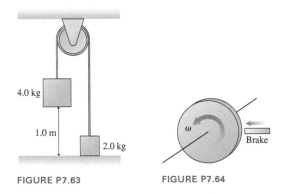

4.0 kg

1.0 m

2.0 kg

ω

Brake

FIGURE P7.63   **FIGURE P7.64**

64. ⦀ The 2.0 kg, 30-cm-diameter disk in Figure P7.64 is spinning at 300 rpm. How much friction force must the brake apply to the rim to bring the disk to a halt in 3.0 s?

65. ⦀ A tradesman sharpens a knife by pushing it against the rim of a grindstone. The 30-cm-diameter stone is spinning at 200 rpm and has a mass of 28 kg. The coefficient of kinetic friction between the knife and the stone is 0.20. If the stone loses 10% of its speed in 10 s of grinding, what is the force with which the man presses the knife against the stone?

66. ⦀ The bunchberry flower has the fastest-moving parts ever seen in a plant. Initially, the stamens are held by the petals in a bent position, storing elastic energy like a coiled spring. As the petals release, the tips of the stamens act like medieval catapults, flipping through a 60° angle in just 0.30 ms to launch pollen from the anther sacs at their ends. The human eye just sees a burst of pollen; careful photography (see Figure P7.66a) reveals the details. As shown in Figure P7.66b, we can model a stamen tip as a 1.0-mm-long, 10 μg rigid rod with a 10 μg anther sac at one end and a pivot point at the opposite end. Although oversimplifying, we will assume that the angular acceleration is constant throughout the motion.

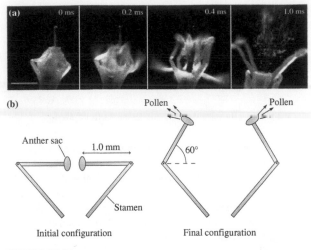

Anther sac   1.0 mm   60°

Stamen

Initial configuration   Final configuration

FIGURE P7.66

a. What is the tangential acceleration of the anther sac during the motion?
b. What is the speed of the anther sac as it releases its pollen?
c. How large is the "straightening torque"? Neglect gravitational forces in your calculation.
d. Compute the gravitational torque on the stamen tip (including the anther sac) in its initial orientation. Was it reasonable to neglect the gravitational torque in part c?

Passage Problems

The Illusion of Flight

The grand jeté is a classic ballet maneuver in which a dancer executes a horizontal leap while moving her arms and legs up and then down. At the center of the leap, the arms and legs are gracefully extended, as we see in Figure P7.67a. The goal of the leap is to create the illusion of flight. As discussed in Section 7.3, the center of mass—and hence the center of gravity—of an extended object follows a parabolic trajectory when undergoing projectile motion. But when you watch a dancer leap through the air, you don't watch her center of gravity, you watch her head. If the translational motion of her head is horizontal—not parabolic—this creates the illusion that she is flying through the air, held up by unseen forces.

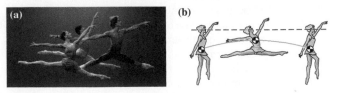

FIGURE P7.67

Figure P7.67b illustrates how the dancer creates this illusion. While in the air, she changes the position of her center of gravity relative to her body by moving her arms and legs up, then down. Her center of gravity moves in a parabolic path, but her head moves in a straight line. It's not flight, but it will appear that way, at least for a moment.

67. | To perform this maneuver, the dancer relies on the fact that the position of her center of gravity
    A. Is near the center of the torso.
    B. Is determined by the positions of her arms and legs.
    C. Moves in a horizontal path.
    D. Is outside of her body.

68. | Suppose you wish to make a vertical leap with the goal of getting your head as high as possible above the ground. At the top of your leap, your arms should be
    A. Held at your sides.
    B. Raised above your head.
    C. Outstretched, away from your body.

69. | When the dancer is in the air, is there a gravitational torque on her? Take the dancer's rotation axis to be through her center of gravity.
    A. Yes, there is a gravitational torque.
    B. No, there is not a gravitational torque.
    C. It depends on the positions of her arms and legs.

70. | In addition to changing her center of gravity, a dancer may change her moment of inertia. Consider her moment of inertia about a vertical axis through the center of her body. When she raises her arms and legs, this
    A. Increases her moment of inertia.
    B. Decreases her moment of inertia.
    C. Does not change her moment of inertia

STOP TO THINK ANSWERS

Stop to Think 7.1: a. changing, b. constant (but not zero), c. constant (but not zero), d. zero, e. zero. The angular velocity ω is constant. Thus the magnitude of the velocity $v = \omega r$ and the centripetal acceleration $a_c = \omega^2 r$ are constant. This also means that the ball's angular acceleration α and tangential acceleration $a_t = \alpha r$ are both zero.

Stop to Think 7.2: $\tau_E > \tau_A = \tau_D > \tau_B > \tau_C$. The perpendicular component in E is larger than 2 N.

Stop to Think 7.3: A. The force acting at the axis exerts no torque. Thus the third force needs to exert an equal but opposite torque to that exerted by the force acting at the rim. Force A, which

has twice the magnitude but acts at half the distance from the axis, does so.

Stop to Think 7.4: $\tau_E = \tau_B > \tau_D > \tau_A = \tau_C$. The torques are $\tau_B = \tau_E = 2mgL$, $\tau_D = \frac{3}{2}mgL$, and $\tau_A = \tau_C = mgL$, where L is the length of the rod in B.

Stop to Think 7.5: $I_D > I_A > I_C > I_B$. The moments of inertia are $I_B \approx 0$, $I_C = 2mr^2$, $I_A = 3mr^2$, and $I_D = mr^2 + m(2r)^2 = 5mr^2$.

Stop to Think 7.6: C. The velocity of P is the vector sum of $\vec{v}$ directed to the right and an upward velocity of the same magnitude due to the rotation of the wheel.

8 Equilibrium and Elasticity

How does a dancer balance so gracefully *en pointe*? And how does her foot withstand the great stresses concentrated on her toes? In this chapter we'll find answers to both these questions.

LOOKING AHEAD ►

The goals of Chapter 8 are to learn about the static equilibrium of extended objects and to understand the basic properties of springs and elastic materials.

Torque and Static Equilibrium

In Chapter 5 we found that a particle can be in static equilibrium only if the net force acting on it is zero. For an extended object such as the dancer shown above, we'll learn that the net torque on the object must also be zero for it to be in equilibrium.

Looking Back ◄◄
5.1 Equilibrium

For this cyclist and his bike to stand motionless, the net force *and* net torque on them must be zero.

Springs

We'll study springs and similar elastic objects, and we'll find the important result that the spring force is proportional to the distance the spring is stretched or compressed from its natural length.

Looking Back ◄◄
4.3 Spring forces

You can get a better workout by stretching the band farther, because the farther it stretches, the harder it is to pull.

Stability and Balance

Why are some objects more *stable* than others; that is, why are some easy to tip over while others are more solidly planted? We'll learn that an object is more stable when its center of gravity is low and its contact points with the ground are widely separated.

For maximal stability, this football player keeps his center of gravity low and his stance wide.

The girls on this tree trunk have a hard time balancing because of their tall stance and narrow footprint.

Looking Back ◄◄
7.2–7.3 Torque, center of gravity, gravitational torque

Elastic Materials

All materials, even seemingly rigid ones like glass or steel, stretch slightly when you pull on them—they act like very stiff springs. We'll learn how to calculate the amount a solid object stretches or compresses as forces are applied to it.

Each of the steel cables suspending this bridge is 24" in diameter, yet the designers must carefully compensate for the slight stretch in each cable due to the enormous load of the bridge.

Biological Materials

The elastic properties of biological materials such as bone, tendon, and even spider silk play an important role in the world of living things. Bone, of course, is quite rigid, but did you know that spider silk is as strong as steel?

8.1 Torque and Static Equilibrium

We have now spent several chapters studying motion and its causes. In many disciplines, it is just as important to understand the conditions under which objects do *not* move. In structural engineering, buildings and dams must be designed such that they remain motionless, even when huge forces act on them. In sports science, a correct stationary position is often the starting point for a successful athletic event. And joints in the body must sustain large forces when the body is supporting heavy loads, as in holding or carrying heavy objects.

Recall from Section 5.1 that an object at rest is in *static equilibrium.* As long as an object can be modeled as a *particle,* the condition necessary for static equilibrium is that the net force $\vec{F}_{net}$ on the particle is zero. Such a situation is shown in FIGURE 8.1a, where the two forces applied to the particle balance and the particle can remain at rest.

But in Chapter 7 we moved beyond the particle model to study extended objects that can rotate. Consider, for example, the block in FIGURE 8.1b. In this case the two forces act along the same line, the net force is zero, and the block is in equilibrium. But what about the block in FIGURE 8.1c? The net force is still zero, but this time the block begins to rotate because the two forces exert a net *torque*. For an extended object, $\vec{F}_{net} = \vec{0}$ is not by itself enough to ensure static equilibrium. There is a second condition for static equilibrium of an extended object: The net torque τ_{net} on the object must also be zero.

If we write the net force in component form, the conditions for static equilibrium of an extended object are

$$\left.\begin{matrix}\sum F_x = 0 \\ \sum F_y = 0\end{matrix}\right\} \text{ No net force}$$

$$\sum \tau = 0 \ \ \} \ \text{ No net torque} \tag{8.1}$$

Conditions for static equilibrium of an extended object

If motion is possible in the z-direction, we'd also require that $\sum F_z = 0$. In this chapter, however, we'll consider only motion restricted to the xy-plane.

FIGURE 8.1 A block with no net force acting on it may still be out of equilibrium.

(a) When the net force on a particle is zero, the particle is in static equilibrium.

(b) Both the net force and the net torque are zero, so the block is in static equilibrium.

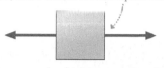

(c) The net force is still zero, but the net torque is *not* zero. The block is not in equilibrium.

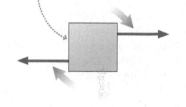

EXAMPLE 8.1	Finding the force from the biceps tendon

Weightlifting can exert extremely large forces on the body's joints and tendons. In the *strict curl* event, a standing athlete lifts a barbell by moving only his forearms, which pivot at the elbow. The record weight lifted in the strict curl is over 200 pounds (about 900 N). FIGURE 8.2 shows the arm bones and the main lifting muscle when the forearm is horizontal. The distance from the tendon to the elbow joint is 4.0 cm, and from the barbell to the elbow 35 cm.

a. What is the tension in the tendon connecting the biceps muscle to the bone while a 900 N barbell is held stationary in this position?

b. What is the force exerted by the elbow on the forearm bones?

PREPARE FIGURE 8.3 shows a simplified model of the arm and the forces acting on the forearm. $\vec{F}_t$ is the tension force due to the muscle, $\vec{F}_b$ is the downward force of the barbell, and $\vec{F}_e$ is the force of the elbow joint on the forearm. As a simplification, we've neglected the weight of the arm itself because it is so much less than the weight of the barbell. Because $\vec{F}_t$ and $\vec{F}_b$ have no x-component, neither can $\vec{F}_e$. If it did, the net force in the x-direction would not be zero, and the forearm could not be in equilibrium. Because each arm supports half the weight of the barbell, the magnitude of the barbell force is $F_b = 450$ N.

FIGURE 8.2 An arm holding a barbell.

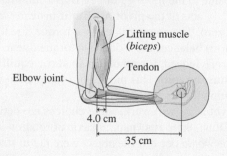

Lifting muscle (*biceps*)

Tendon

Elbow joint

4.0 cm

35 cm

Continued

FIGURE 8.3 Visual overview of holding a barbell.

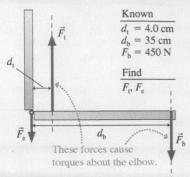

Known
$d_t = 4.0$ cm
$d_b = 35$ cm
$F_b = 450$ N

Find
F_t, F_e

These forces cause
torques about the elbow.

due to each of the three forces in terms of their magnitudes F and moment arms $r_\perp$ as $\tau = r_\perp F$. The moment arm is the perpendicular distance between the pivot and the "line of action" along which the force is applied. Figure 8.3 shows that the moment arms for $\vec{F}_t$ and $\vec{F}_b$ are the distances d_t and d_b, respectively, measured along the beam representing the forearm. The moment arm for $\vec{F}_e$ is zero, because this force acts directly at the pivot. Thus we have

$$\tau_{net} = F_e \times 0 + F_t d_t - F_b d_b = 0$$

The tension in the tendon tries to rotate the arm counterclockwise, so it produces a positive torque; the torque due to the barbell, which tries to rotate the arm in a clockwise direction, is negative. We can solve the torque equation for F_t:

$$F_t = F_b \frac{d_b}{d_t} = (450 \text{ N})\frac{35 \text{ cm}}{4.0 \text{ cm}} = 3900 \text{ N}$$

SOLVE a. For the forearm to be in static equilibrium, the net force and net torque on it must both be zero. Setting the net force to zero gives

$$\sum F_y = F_t - F_e - F_b = 0$$

We don't know either of the forces F_t and F_e, nor does the force equation give us enough information to find them. But the fact that in static equilibrium the torque also must be zero gives us the extra information that we need.

Recall that the torque must be calculated about a particular point. Here, a natural choice is the elbow joint, about which the forearm can pivot. Given this pivot, we can calculate the torque

b. We now need to make use of the force equation:

$$F_e = F_t - F_b = 3900 \text{ N} - 450 \text{ N} = 3450 \text{ N}$$

ASSESS This large value for F_t makes sense: The short distance d_t from the tendon to the elbow joint means that the force supplied by the biceps has to be very large to counter the torque generated by a force applied at the opposite end of the forearm.

STOP TO THINK 8.1 Which of these objects is in static equilibrium?

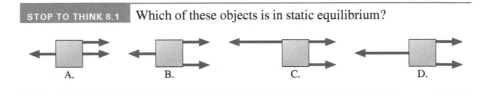

A.   B.   C.   D.

Choosing the Pivot Point

In Example 8.1, we calculated the net torque using the elbow joint as the axis of rotation or pivot point. But we learned in Chapter 7 that the torque depends on which point is chosen as the pivot point. Was there something special about our choice of the elbow joint?

FIGURE 8.4 A hammer resting on two pegs.

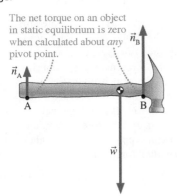

The net torque on an object in static equilibrium is zero when calculated about *any* pivot point.

Consider the hammer shown in FIGURE 8.4, supported on a pegboard by two pegs A and B. Because the hammer is in static equilibrium, the net torque around the pivot at peg A must be zero: The clockwise torque due to the weight $\vec{w}$ is exactly balanced by the counterclockwise torque due to the force $\vec{n}_B$ of peg B. (Recall that the torque due to $\vec{n}_A$ is zero, because here $\vec{n}_A$ acts at the pivot A.) But if instead we take B as the pivot, the net torque is still zero. The counterclockwise torque due to $\vec{w}$ (with a large force but small moment arm) balances the clockwise torque due to $\vec{n}_A$ (with a small force but large moment arm). Indeed, **for an object in static equilibrium, the net torque about *every* point must be zero.** This means you can pick *any* point you wish as a pivot point for calculating the torque.

Although any choice of a pivot point will work, some choices are better because they simplify the calculations. Often, there is a "natural" axis of rotation in the problem, an axis about which rotation *would* occur if the object were not in static equilibrium. Example 8.1 is of this type, with the elbow joint as a natural axis of rotation.

If no point naturally suggests itself as an axis, look for a point on the object at which several forces act, or at which a force acts whose magnitude you don't know. Such a point is a good choice because any force acting at that point does not contribute to the torque. For instance, the woman in FIGURE 8.5 is in equilibrium as she rests on the rock wall. A good choice of pivot point would be where her foot contacts the wall because this choice eliminates the torque due to the force $\vec{F}$ of the wall on her foot. But don't agonize over the choice of a pivot point! You can still solve the problem no matter which point you choose.

FIGURE 8.5 Choosing the pivot for a woman rappelling down a rock wall.

The torque due to $\vec{F}$ about this point is zero. This makes this point a good choice as the pivot.

PROBLEM-SOLVING
STRATEGY 8.1   **Static equilibrium problems**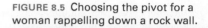

PREPARE Model the object as a simple shape. Draw a visual overview that shows all forces and distances. List known information.

■ Pick an axis or pivot about which the torques will be calculated.
■ Determine the torque about this pivot point due to each force acting on the object. The torques due to any forces acting *at* the pivot are zero.
■ Determine the sign of each torque about this pivot point.

SOLVE The mathematical steps are based on the fact that an object in static equilibrium has no net force and no net torque:

$$\vec{F}_{net} = \vec{0} \quad \text{and} \quad \tau_{net} = 0$$

■ Write equations for $\sum F_x = 0$, $\sum F_y = 0$, and $\sum \tau = 0$.
■ Solve the resulting equations.

ASSESS Check that your result is reasonable and answers the question.

Activ Physics   7.2–7.5

EXAMPLE 8.2   **Forces on a board on sawhorses**

A board weighing 100 N sits across two sawhorses, as shown in FIGURE 8.6. What are the magnitudes of the normal forces of the sawhorses acting on the board?

FIGURE 8.6 A board sitting on two sawhorses.

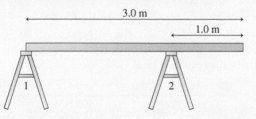

PREPARE The board and the forces acting on it are shown in FIGURE 8.7. $\vec{n}_1$ and $\vec{n}_2$ are the normal forces on the board due to the sawhorses, and $\vec{w}$ is the weight of the board acting at the center of gravity. The distance d_1 to the center of the board is half the board's length, or 1.5 m. Then d_2 is $d_1 - 1.0$ m, or 0.5 m.

As discussed above, a good choice for the pivot is a point at which an unknown force acts, because that force contributes nothing to the torque. Either the point where $\vec{n}_1$ acts or the point where $\vec{n}_2$ acts will work; let's choose the left end of the board, where $\vec{n}_1$ acts, for this example. With this choice of pivot point, the moment arm for $\vec{w}$ is $d_1 = 1.5$ m. Because $\vec{w}$ tends to rotate

the board clockwise, its torque is negative. The moment arm for $\vec{n}_2$ is the distance $d_1 + d_2 = 2.0$ m, and its torque is positive.

FIGURE 8.7 Visual overview of a board on two sawhorses.

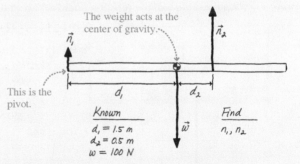

The weight acts at the center of gravity.

This is the pivot.

Known
$d_1 = 1.5$ m
$d_2 = 0.5$ m
$w = 100$ N

Find
n_1, n_2

SOLVE The board is in static equilibrium, so the net force $\vec{F}_{net}$ and the net torque τ_{net} must both be zero. The forces have only y-components, so the force equation is

$$\sum F_y = n_1 - w + n_2 = 0$$

The torque equation, computed around the left end of the board, is

$$\tau_{net} = -d_1 w + (d_1 + d_2)n_2 = 0$$

Continued

We now have two simultaneous equations with the two unknowns n_1 and n_2. To solve these, let's solve for n_2 in the torque equation and then substitute that result into the force equation. From the torque equation,

$$n_2 = \frac{d_1 w}{d_1 + d_2} = \frac{(1.5 \text{ m})(100 \text{ N})}{2.0 \text{ m}} = 75 \text{ N}$$

The force equation is then $n_1 - 100 \text{ N} + 75 \text{ N} = 0$, which we can solve for n_1:

$$n_1 = w - n_2 = 100 \text{ N} - 75 \text{ N} = 25 \text{ N}$$

ASSESS It seems reasonable that $n_2 > n_1$ because more of the board sits over the right sawhorse.

STOP TO THINK 8.2 A beam with a pivot on its left end is suspended from a rope. In which direction is the force of the pivot on the beam?

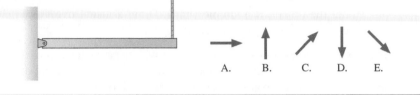

A.   B.   C.   D.   E.

An interesting application of static equilibrium is to find the center of gravity of the human body. Because the human body is highly flexible, the position of the center of gravity is quite variable and depends on just how the body is posed. The horizontal position of the body's center of gravity can be located accurately from simple measurements with a *reaction board* and a scale. The following example shows how this is done.

EXAMPLE 8.3 **Finding the center of gravity of the human body**

A woman weighing 600 N lies on a 2.5-m-long, 60 N reaction board with her feet over the pivot. The scale on the right reads 250 N. What is the distance d from the woman's feet to her center of gravity?

PREPARE The forces and distances in the problem are shown in FIGURE 8.8. We'll consider the board and woman as a single object. We've assumed that the board is uniform, so its center of gravity is at its midpoint. To eliminate the unknown magnitude of

FIGURE 8.8 Visual overview of the reaction board and woman.

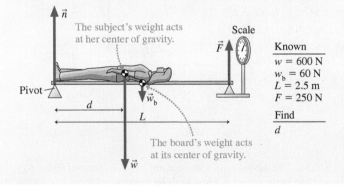

The subject's weight acts at her center of gravity.

Scale

Pivot

d

L

The board's weight acts at its center of gravity.

Known
$w = 600$ N
$w_b = 60$ N
$L = 2.5$ m
$F = 250$ N

Find
d

$\vec{n}$ from the torque equation, we'll choose the pivot to be the left end of the board. The torque due to $\vec{F}$ is positive, and those due to $\vec{w}$ and $\vec{w}_b$ are negative.

SOLVE Because the board and woman are in static equilibrium, the net force and net torque on them must be zero. The force equation reads

$$\sum F_y = n - w_b - w + F = 0$$

and the torque equation gives

$$\sum \tau = -\frac{L}{2} w_b - dw + LF = 0$$

In this case, the force equation isn't needed because we can solve the torque equation for d:

$$d = \frac{LF - \frac{1}{2}Lw_b}{w} = \frac{(2.5 \text{ m})(250 \text{ N}) - \frac{1}{2}(2.5 \text{ m})(60 \text{ N})}{600 \text{ N}}$$
$$= 0.92 \text{ m}$$

ASSESS If the woman is 5′ 6″ (1.68 m) tall, her center of gravity is $(0.92 \text{ m})/(1.68 \text{ m}) = 55\%$ of her height, or a little more than halfway up her body. This seems reasonable.

EXAMPLE 8.4 **Will the ladder slip?**

A 3.0-m-long ladder leans against a frictionless wall at an angle of 60° with respect to the floor. What is the minimum value of μ_s, the coefficient of static friction with the ground, that will prevent the ladder from slipping?

PREPARE The ladder is a rigid rod of length L. To not slip, both the net force and net torque on the ladder must be zero. FIGURE 8.9 shows the ladder and the forces acting on it. The bottom corner of the ladder is a good choice of a pivot point because two of the

FIGURE 8.9 Visual overview of a ladder in static equilibrium.

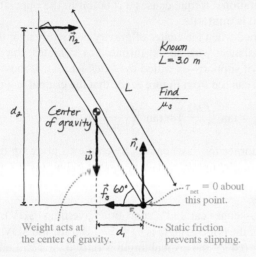

Known
$L = 3.0$ m

Find
μ_s

$\tau_{net} = 0$ about
this point.

Weight acts at
the center of gravity.

Static friction
prevents slipping.

forces pass through this point and thus produce no torque about it. With this choice, the weight of the ladder, acting at the center of gravity, exerts torque $d_1 w$ and the force of the wall exerts torque $-d_2 n_2$. The signs are based on the observation that $\vec{w}$ would cause the ladder to rotate counterclockwise, while $\vec{n}_2$ would cause it to rotate clockwise.

SOLVE The x- and y-components of $\vec{F}_{net} = \vec{0}$ are

$$\sum F_x = n_2 - f_s = 0$$
$$\sum F_y = n_1 - w = n_1 - Mg = 0$$

The torque about the bottom corner is

$$\tau_{net} = d_1 w - d_2 n_2 = \frac{1}{2}(L\cos 60°)Mg - (L\sin 60°)n_2 = 0$$

Altogether, we have three equations with the three unknowns n_1, n_2, and f_s. If we solve the third equation for n_2,

$$n_2 = \frac{\frac{1}{2}(L\cos 60°)Mg}{L\sin 60°} = \frac{Mg}{2\tan 60°}$$

we can then substitute this into the first equation to find

$$f_s = \frac{Mg}{2\tan 60°}$$

Our model of static friction is $f_s \leq f_{smax} = \mu_s n_1$. We can find n_1 from the second equation: $n_1 = Mg$. From this, the model of friction tells us that

$$f_s \leq \mu_s Mg$$

Comparing these two expressions for f_s, we see that μ_s must obey

$$\mu_s \geq \frac{1}{2\tan 60°} = 0.29$$

Thus the minimum value of the coefficient of static friction is 0.29.

ASSESS You know from experience that you can lean a ladder or other object against a wall if the ground is "rough," but it slips if the surface is too smooth. 0.29 is a "medium" value for the coefficient of static friction, which is reasonable.

8.2 Stability and Balance

If you tilt a box up on one edge by a small amount and let go, it falls back down. If you tilt it too much, it falls over. And if you tilt it "just right," you can get the box to balance on its edge. What determines these three possible outcomes?

FIGURE 8.10 illustrates the idea with a car, but the results are general and apply in many situations. An extended object, whether it's a car, a box, or a person, has a *base of support* on which it rests when in static equilibrium. If you tilt the object, one edge of the base of support becomes a pivot point. As long as the object's center of gravity remains over the base of support, torque due to gravity will rotate the object back toward its stable equilibrium position; we say that the object is **stable.** This is the

FIGURE 8.10 A car—or any object—will fall over when tilted too far.

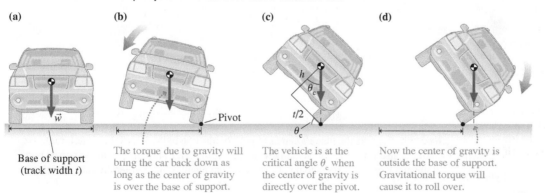

(a)

$\vec{w}$

Base of support
(track width t)

(b)

Pivot

The torque due to gravity will bring the car back down as long as the center of gravity is over the base of support.

(c)

h
θ_c
$t/2$
θ_c

The vehicle is at the critical angle θ_c when the center of gravity is directly over the pivot.

(d)

Now the center of gravity is outside the base of support. Gravitational torque will cause it to roll over.

FIGURE 8.11 Compared to a passenger car, an SUV has a high center of gravity relative to its width.

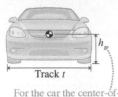

Track *t*

For the car the center-of-gravity height *h* is 33% of *t*.

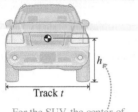

Track *t*

For the SUV, the center-of-gravity height *h* is 47% of *t*.

situation in Figure 8.10b. But if the center of gravity gets outside the base of support, as in Figure 8.10d, the gravitational torque causes a rotation in the opposite direction. Now the car rolls over; it is **unstable.**

A *critical angle* θ_c is reached when the center of gravity is directly over the pivot point. This is the point of balance, with no net torque. For vehicles, the distance between the tires—the base of support—is called the *track width t*. If the height of the center of gravity is *h*, you can see from Figure 8.10c that the critical angle is

$$\theta_c = \tan^{-1}\left(\frac{t/2}{h}\right) = \tan^{-1}\left(\frac{t}{2h}\right) \tag{8.2}$$

If an accident (or taking a corner too fast) causes a vehicle to pivot up onto two wheels, it will roll back to an upright position as long as $\theta < \theta_c$ but it will roll over if $\theta > \theta_c$. Notice that it's the height-to-width ratio that's important, not the absolute height of the center of gravity.

FIGURE 8.11 compares a passenger car and a sport utility vehicle (SUV). For the passenger car, with $h \approx 0.33t$, the critical angle is $\theta_c \approx 57°$. But for the SUV, with its higher center of gravity ($h \approx 0.47t$), the critical angle is only $\theta_c \approx 47°$. Loading an SUV with cargo further raises the center of gravity, especially if the roof rack is used, thus reducing θ_c even more. Various automobile safety groups have determined that a vehicle with $\theta_c > 50°$ is unlikely to roll over in an accident. A rollover becomes increasingly likely when θ_c is less than 50°. The same argument that leads to Equation 8.2 for tilted vehicles can be made for any object, leading to the general rule that **a wider base of support and/or a lower center of gravity improve stability.**

CONCEPTUAL EXAMPLE 8.5 **How far to walk the plank?**

A cat walks along a plank that extends out from a table. If the cat walks too far out on the plank, the plank will begin to tilt. What determines when this happens?

REASON An object is stable if its center of gravity lies over its base of support, and unstable otherwise. Let's take the cat and the plank to be one combined object whose center of gravity lies along a line between the cat's center of gravity and that of the plank.

In **FIGURE 8.12a,** when the cat is near the left end of the plank, the combined center of gravity is over the base of support and the plank is stable. As the cat moves to the right, he reaches a point where the combined center of gravity is directly over the edge of the table, as shown in **FIGURE 8.12b.** If the cat takes one more step, the cat and plank will become unstable and the plank will begin to tilt.

FIGURE 8.12 Changing stability as a cat walks on a plank.

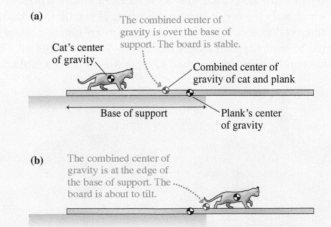

(a) The combined center of gravity is over the base of support. The board is stable.

Cat's center of gravity

Combined center of gravity of cat and plank

Base of support

Plank's center of gravity

(b) The combined center of gravity is at the edge of the base of support. The board is about to tilt.

ASSESS Because the plank's center of gravity must be to the left of the edge for it to be stable by itself, the cat can actually walk a short distance out onto the unsupported part of the plank before it starts to tilt. The heavier the plank is, the farther the cat can walk.

TRY IT YOURSELF

Balancing a soda can Try to balance a soda can—full or empty—on the narrow bevel at the bottom. It can't be done because, either full or empty, the center of gravity is near the center of the can. If the can is tilted enough to sit on the bevel, the center of gravity lies far outside this small base of support. But if you put about 2 ounces (60 ml) of water in an empty can, the center of gravity will be right over the bevel and the can will balance.

Stability and Balance of the Human Body

The human body is remarkable for its ability to constantly adjust its stance to remain stable on just two points of support. In walking, running, or even in the simple act of rising from a chair, the position of the body's center of gravity is constantly changing. To maintain stability, we unconsciously adjust the positions of our arms and legs to keep our center of gravity over our base of support.

A simple example of how the body naturally realigns its center of gravity is found in the act of standing up on tiptoes. FIGURE 8.13a shows the body in its normal standing position. Notice that the center of gravity is well centered over the base of support (the feet), ensuring stability. If the subject were now to stand on tiptoes *without* otherwise adjusting the body position, her center of gravity would fall behind the base of support, which is now the balls of the feet, and she would fall backward. To prevent this, as shown in FIGURE 8.13b, the body naturally leans forward, regaining stability by moving the center of gravity over the balls of the feet.

FIGURE 8.13 Standing on tiptoes.

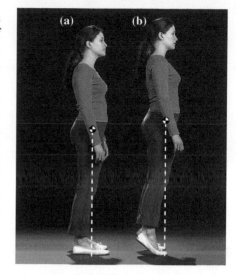

> **STOP TO THINK 8.3** Rank in order, from least stable to most stable, the three objects shown in the figure. The positions of their centers of gravity are marked. (For the centers of gravity to be positioned like this, the objects must have a nonuniform composition.)

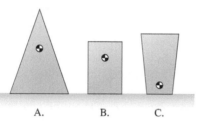

A.   B.   C.

8.3 Springs and Hooke's Law

We have assumed that objects in equilibrium maintain their shape as forces and torques are applied to them. In reality this is an oversimplification. Every solid object stretches, compresses, or deforms when a force acts upon it. This change is easy to see when you press on a green twig on a tree, but even the largest branch on the tree will bend slightly under your weight.

If you stretch a rubber band, there is a force that tries to pull the rubber band back to its equilibrium, or unstretched, length. A force that restores a system to an equilibrium position is called a **restoring force**. Systems that exhibit such restoring forces are called **elastic**. The most basic examples of **elasticity** are things like springs and rubber bands. If you stretch a spring, a tension-like force pulls back. Similarly, a compressed spring tries to re-expand to its equilibrium length. Elasticity and restoring forces are properties of much stiffer systems as well. The steel beams of a bridge bend slightly as you drive your car over it, but they are restored to equilibrium after your car passes by. Your leg bones flex a bit during each step you take. Nearly everything that stretches, compresses, bends, or twists exhibits a restoring force and can be called elastic.

The behavior of a simple spring illustrates the basic ideas of elasticity. When no forces act on a spring to compress or extend it, it will relax to its **equilibrium length**. If we now stretch the spring by a displacement Δx, how hard does it pull back? FIGURE 8.14 shows what happens: The farther we stretch the spring, the harder the restoring force of the spring pulls back.

FIGURE 8.14 The spring force depends on how far the spring is stretched.

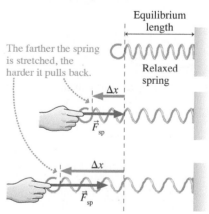

FIGURE 8.15 Measured data for the restoring force of a real spring.

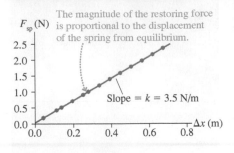

FIGURE 8.16 The spring force is always directed opposite the displacement.

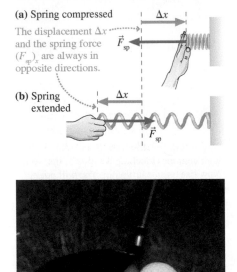

(a) Spring compressed

The displacement Δx and the spring force $(F_{sp})_x$ are always in opposite directions.

(b) Spring extended

Elasticity in action A golf ball compresses quite a bit when struck. The restoring force that pushes the ball back into its original shape helps launch the ball off the face of the club, making for a longer drive.

In FIGURE 8.15, data for the magnitude of the restoring force of a real spring show that **the force of the spring is *proportional* to the displacement of the end of the spring.** That is, compressing or stretching the spring twice as far results in a restoring force that is twice as large. This is a *linear relationship,* and the slope k of the line is the proportionality constant:

$$F_{sp} = k\,\Delta x \qquad (8.3)$$

A second important fact about spring forces is illustrated in FIGURE 8.16. If the spring is compressed, as in Figure 8.16a, Δx is positive and, because $\vec{F}_{sp}$ points to the left, its component $(F_{sp})_x$ is negative. If, however, the spring is stretched, as in Figure 8.16b, Δx is negative and, because $\vec{F}_{sp}$ points to the right, its component $(F_{sp})_x$ is positive. In general, **the spring force always points in the opposite direction to the displacement from equilibrium.** We can express this fact, along with what we've learned about the magnitude of the spring force, by rewriting Equation 8.3 in terms of the *component* of the spring force:

$$(F_{sp})_x = -k\,\Delta x \qquad (8.4)$$

Hooke's law for the force due to a spring

The minus sign in Equation 8.4 reflects the fact that $(F_{sp})_x$ and Δx are always of opposite sign. (For motion in the vertical (y) direction, Hooke's law is $(F_{sp})_y = -k\,\Delta y$.)

The proportionality constant k is called the **spring constant.** The units of the spring constant are N/m. The spring constant k is a property that characterizes a spring, just as mass m characterizes a particle. If k is large, it takes a large pull to cause a significant stretch, and we call the spring a "stiff" spring. If k is small, we can stretch the spring with very little force, and we call it a "soft" spring. Every spring has its own, unique value of k. The spring constant for the spring in Figure 8.15 can be determined from the slope of the straight line to be $k = 3.5$ N/m.

Equation 8.4 for the restoring force of a spring was first suggested by Robert Hooke, a contemporary (and sometimes bitter rival) of Newton. Hooke's law is not a true "law of nature," in the sense that Newton's laws are, but is actually just a *model* of a restoring force. It works extremely well for some springs, as in Figure 8.15, but less well for others. Hooke's law will fail for any spring if it is compressed or stretched too far.

NOTE ▶ Just as we used massless strings, we will adopt the idealization of a *massless spring.* Though not a perfect description, it is a good approximation if the mass attached to a spring is much greater than the mass of the spring itself. ◀

EXAMPLE 8.6 **Weighing a fish**

A scale used to weigh fish consists of a spring connected to the ceiling. The spring's equilibrium length is 30 cm. When a 4.0 kg fish is suspended from the end of the spring, it stretches to a length of 42 cm.

a. What is the spring constant k for this spring?
b. If an 8.0 kg fish is suspended from the spring, what will be the length of the spring?

PREPARE The visual overview in FIGURE 8.17 shows the details for the first part of the problem. The fish hangs in static equilibrium, so the net force in the y-direction and the net torque must be zero.

FIGURE 8.17 Visual overview of a mass suspended from a spring.

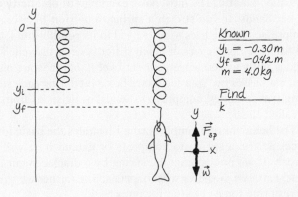

Known
$y_i = -0.30$ m
$y_f = -0.42$ m
$m = 4.0$ kg

Find
k

SOLVE a. Because the fish is in static equilibrium, we have

$$\sum F_y = (F_{sp})_y + w_y = -k\,\Delta y - mg = 0$$

so that $k = -mg/\Delta y$. (The net torque is zero because the fish's center of gravity comes to rest directly under the pivot point of the hook.) From Figure 8.17, the displacement of the spring from equilibrium is $\Delta y = y_f - y_i = (-0.42 \text{ m}) - (-0.30 \text{ m}) = -0.12 \text{ m}$. This displacement is *negative* because the fish moves in the $-y$-direction. We can now solve for the spring constant:

$$k = -\frac{mg}{\Delta y} = -\frac{(4.0 \text{ kg})(9.8 \text{ m/s}^2)}{-0.12 \text{ m}} = 330 \text{ N/m}$$

b. The restoring force is proportional to the displacement of the spring from its equilibrium length. If we double the mass (and thus the weight) of the fish, the displacement of the end of the spring will double as well, to $\Delta y = -0.24 \text{ m}$. Thus the spring will be 0.24 m longer, so its new length is 0.30 m + 0.24 m = 0.54 m.

ASSESS A spring constant of 330 N/m means that when the spring is stretched by 1.0 m it will exert a force of 330 N (about 75 lb). This seems reasonable for a spring used to weigh objects of 10 or 20 lb.

EXAMPLE 8.7 **When does the block slip?**

FIGURE 8.18 shows a spring attached to a 2.0 kg block. The other end of the spring is pulled by a motorized toy train that moves forward at 5.0 cm/s. The spring constant is 50 N/m, and the coefficient of static friction between the block and the surface is 0.60. The spring is at its equilibrium length at $t = 0$ s when the train starts to move. When does the block slip?

FIGURE 8.18 A toy train stretches the spring until the block slips.

5.0 cm/s

2.0 kg

PREPARE We model the block as a particle and the spring as a massless spring. **FIGURE 8.19** is a free-body diagram for the block. We convert the speed of the train into m/s: $v = 0.050$ m/s.

FIGURE 8.19 Free-body diagram for the block.

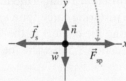

When the spring force exceeds the maximum force of static friction, the block will slip.

y

$\vec{f_s}$ $\vec{n}$

x

$\vec{w}$ $\vec{F}_{sp}$

SOLVE Recall that the tension in a massless string pulls equally at *both* ends of the string. The same is true for the spring force: It pulls (or pushes) equally at *both* ends. Imagine holding a rubber band with your left hand and stretching it with your right hand. Your left hand feels the pulling force, even though it was the right end of the rubber band that moved.

This is the key to solving the problem. As the right end of the spring moves, stretching the spring, the spring pulls backward on the train *and* forward on the block with equal strength. The train is moving to the right, and so the spring force pulls to the left on the train—as we would expect. But the block is at the other end of the spring; the spring force pulls to the right on the block, as shown in Figure 8.19. As the spring stretches, the static friction force on the block increases in magnitude to keep the block at rest. The block is in static equilibrium, so

$$\sum F_x = (F_{sp})_x + (f_s)_x = F_{sp} - f_s = 0$$

where F_{sp} is the magnitude of the spring force. This magnitude is $F_{sp} = k\,\Delta x$, where $\Delta x = vt$ is the distance the train has moved. Thus

$$f_s = F_{sp} = k\,\Delta x$$

The block slips when the static friction force reaches its maximum value $f_{s\,max} = \mu_s n = \mu_s mg$. This occurs when the train has moved a distance

$$\Delta x = \frac{f_{s\,max}}{k} = \frac{\mu_s mg}{k} = \frac{(0.60)(2.0 \text{ kg})(9.8 \text{ m/s}^2)}{50 \text{ N/m}} = 0.235 \text{ m}$$

The time at which the block slips is

$$t = \frac{\Delta x}{v} = \frac{0.235 \text{ m}}{0.050 \text{ m/s}} = 4.7 \text{ s}$$

ASSESS The result of about 5 s seems reasonable for a slowly moving toy train to stretch the spring enough for the block to slip.

STOP TO THINK 8.4 A 1.0 kg weight is suspended from a spring, stretching it by 5.0 cm. How much does the spring stretch if the 1.0 kg weight is replaced by a 3.0 kg weight?

A. 5.0 cm   B. 10.0 cm   C. 15.0 cm   D. 20.0 cm

8.4 Stretching and Compressing Materials

In Chapter 4 we noted that we could model most solid materials as being made of particle-like atoms connected by spring-like bonds. We can model a steel rod this way, as illustrated in FIGURE 8.20a. The spring-like bonds between the atoms in steel are quite stiff, but they can be stretched or compressed, meaning that even a steel rod is elastic. If you pull on the end of a steel rod, as in Figure 8.20a, you will slightly stretch the bonds between the particles that make it up, and the rod itself will stretch. The stretched bonds pull back on your hand with a restoring force that causes the rod to return to its original length when released. In this sense, the entire rod acts like a very stiff spring. As is the case for a spring, a restoring force is also produced by compressing the rod.

In FIGURE 8.20b, real data for a 1.0-m-long, 1.0-cm-diameter steel rod show that, just as for a spring, the restoring force is proportional to the change in length. However, the *scale* of the stretch of the rod and the restoring force is much different from that for a spring. It would take a force of 16,000 N to stretch the rod by only 1 mm, corresponding to a spring constant of 1.6×10^7 N/m! Steel is elastic, but under normal forces, it experiences only very small changes in dimension. Materials of this sort are called **rigid**.

The behavior of other materials, such as the rubber in a rubber band, can be quite different. A rubber band can be stretched quite far—several times its equilibrium length—with a very small force, and then snaps back to its original shape when released. Materials that show large deformations with small forces are called **pliant**.

A rod's spring constant depends on several factors, as shown in FIGURE 8.21. First, we expect that a thick rod, with a large cross-section area A, will be more difficult to stretch than a thinner rod. Second, a rod with a long length L will be easier to stretch by a given amount than a short rod (think of trying to stretch a rope by 1 cm—this would be easy to do for a 10-m-long rope, but it would be pretty hard for a piece of rope only 10 cm long). Finally, the stiffness of the rod will depend on the material that it's made of. Experiments bear out these observations, and it is found that the spring constant of the rod can be written as

$$k = \frac{YA}{L} \tag{8.5}$$

where the constant Y is called **Young's modulus**. Young's modulus is a property of the *material* from which the rod is made—it does not depend on the object's shape or size. All rods made from steel have the same Young's modulus, regardless of their length or area, while aluminum rods have a different Young's modulus.

From Equation 8.3, the magnitude of the restoring force for a spring is related to the change in its length as $F_{sp} = k \Delta x$. Writing the change in the length of a rod as ΔL, as shown in Figure 8.21, we can use Equation 8.5 to write the restoring force F of a rod as

$$F = \frac{YA}{L} \Delta L \tag{8.6}$$

Equation 8.6 applies both to elongation (stretching) and to compression.

It's useful to rearrange Equation 8.6 in terms of two new ratios, the *stress* and the *strain*:

The ratio of force to cross-section area is called **stress**. $\dashrightarrow$ $$\frac{F}{A} = Y\left(\frac{\Delta L}{L}\right) \tag{8.7}$$ $\dashleftarrow$ The ratio of the change in length to the original length is called **strain**.

The unit of stress is N/m^2. If the stress is due to stretching, we call it a **tensile stress**. The strain is the fractional change in the rod's length. If the rod's length changes by 1%, the strain is 0.01. Because strain is dimensionless, Young's modulus Y has the same units as stress. Table 8.1 gives values of Young's modulus for several

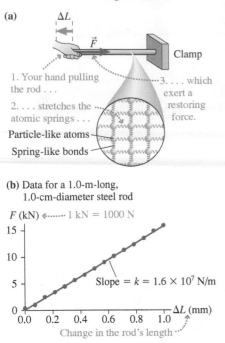

FIGURE 8.20 Stretching a steel rod.

(a)

ΔL

$\vec{F}$ Clamp

1. Your hand pulling the rod . . .
2. . . . stretches the atomic springs . . .
3. . . . which exert a restoring force.

Particle-like atoms
Spring-like bonds

(b) Data for a 1.0-m-long, 1.0-cm-diameter steel rod

F (kN) $\dashleftarrow$ 1 kN = 1000 N

15
10
5
0

Slope = $k = 1.6 \times 10^7$ N/m

0.0   0.2   0.4   0.6   0.8   1.0 ΔL (mm)

Change in the rod's length

FIGURE 8.21 A rod stretched by length ΔL.

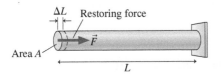

ΔL Restoring force
$\vec{F}$
Area A

L

TABLE 8.1 Young's modulus for rigid materials

Material	Young's modulus (10^{10} N/m^2)
Cast iron	20
Steel	20
Silicon	13
Copper	11
Aluminum	7
Glass	7
Concrete	3
Wood (Douglas Fir)	1

rigid materials. Large values of Y characterize materials that are stiff. "Softer" materials have smaller values of Y. Because the values of Young's modulus for materials such as steel or aluminum are very large, it takes a significant stress to produce even a small strain.

EXAMPLE 8.8 **Finding the stretch of a wire**

A *Foucault pendulum* in a physics department (used to prove that the earth rotates) consists of a 120 kg steel ball that swings at the end of a 6.0-m-long steel cable. The cable has a diameter of 2.5 mm. When the ball was first hung from the cable, by how much did the cable stretch?

PREPARE The amount by which the cable stretches depends on the elasticity of the steel cable. Young's modulus for steel is given in Table 8.1 as $Y = 20 \times 10^{10}$ N/m².

SOLVE Equation 8.7 relates the stretch of the cable ΔL to the restoring force F and to the properties of the cable. Rearranging terms, we find that the cable stretches by

$$\Delta L = \frac{LF}{AY}$$

The cross-section area of the cable is

$$A = \pi r^2 = \pi(0.00125 \text{ m})^2 = 4.91 \times 10^{-6} \text{ m}^2$$

The restoring force of the cable is equal to the ball's weight:

$$F = w = mg = (120 \text{ kg})(9.8 \text{ m/s}^2) \quad 1180 \text{ N}$$

The change in length is thus

$$\Delta L = \frac{(6.0 \text{ m})(1180 \text{ N})}{(4.91 \times 10^{-6} \text{ m}^2)(20 \times 10^{10} \text{ N/m}^2)}$$

$$= 0.0072 \text{ m} = 7.2 \text{ mm}$$

ASSESS If you've ever strung a guitar with steel strings, you know that the strings stretch several millimeters with the force you can apply by turning the tuning pegs. So a stretch of 7 mm under a 120 kg load seems reasonable.

Beyond the Elastic Limit

In the previous section, we found that if we stretch a rod by a small amount ΔL, it will pull back with a restoring force F, according to Equation 8.6. But if we continue to stretch the rod, this simple linear relationship between ΔL and F will eventually break down. FIGURE 8.22 is a graph of the rod's restoring force from the start of the stretch until the rod finally breaks.

As you can see, the graph has a *linear region,* the region where F and ΔL are proportional to each other, obeying Hooke's law: $F = k \, \Delta L$. **As long as the stretch stays within the linear region, a solid rod acts like a spring and obeys Hooke's law.**

How far can you stretch the rod before damaging it? As long as the stretch is less than the **elastic limit,** the rod will return to its initial length L when the force is removed. The elastic limit is the end of the **elastic region.** Stretching the rod beyond the elastic limit will permanently deform it, and the rod won't return to its original length. Finally, at a certain point the rod will reach a breaking point, where it will snap in two. The maximum stress that a material can be subjected to before failing is called the **tensile strength.** Table 8.2 lists values of tensile strength for rigid materials. When we speak of the *strength* of a material, we are referring to its tensile strength.

FIGURE 8.22 Stretch data for a steel rod.

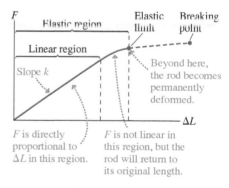

EXAMPLE 8.9 **Breaking a pendulum cable**

After a late night of studying physics, several 80 kg students decide it would be fun to swing on the Foucault pendulum of Example 8.8. What's the maximum number of students that the pendulum cable could support?

PREPARE The tensile strength, given for steel in Table 8.2 as 1000×10^6 N/m², or 1.0×10^9 N/m², is the largest stress the cable can sustain. Because the stress in the cable is F/A, we can find the maximum force F_{max} that can be applied to the cable before it fails.

Continued

TABLE 8.2 Tensile strengths of rigid materials

Material	Tensile strength (N/m²)
Polypropylene	20×10^6
Glass	60×10^6
Cast iron	150×10^6
Aluminum	400×10^6
Steel	1000×10^6

Spider silk BIO The glands on the abdomen of a spider produce different kinds of silk. The silk that is used in webs can be quite stretchy; that used to subdue prey is generally not. An individual strand of silk may be a mix of fibers of different types, allowing spiders great flexibility in their material.

FIGURE 8.23 Stress-versus-strain graphs for steel and spider silk.

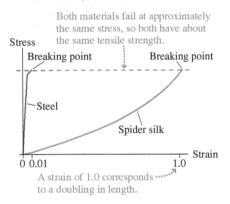

Both materials fail at approximately the same stress, so both have about the same tensile strength.

A strain of 1.0 corresponds to a doubling in length.

FIGURE 8.24 Cross section of a long bone.

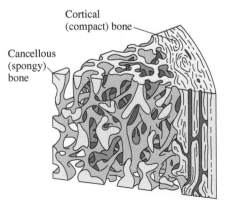

SOLVE We have

$$F_{max} = A(1.0 \times 10^9 \text{ N/m}^2)$$

From Example 8.8, the diameter of the cable is 2.5 mm, so its radius is 0.00125 m. Thus

$$F_{max} = \left(\pi(0.00125 \text{ m})^2\right)(1.0 \times 10^9 \text{ N/m}^2) = 4.9 \times 10^3 \text{ N}$$

This force is the weight of the heaviest mass the cable can support: $w = m_{max}g$. The maximum mass that can be supported is

$$m_{max} = \frac{F_{max}}{g} = 500 \text{ kg}$$

The ball has a mass of 120 kg, leaving 380 kg for the students. Four students have a mass of 320 kg, which is less than this value. But five students, totaling 400 kg, would cause the cable to break.

ASSESS Steel has a very large tensile strength. This very narrow wire can still support 4900 N ≈ 1100 lb.

Biological Materials

Suppose we take equal lengths of spider silk and steel wire, stretch each, and measure the restoring force of each until it breaks. The graph of stress versus strain might appear as in FIGURE 8.23.

The spider silk is certainly less stiff: For a given stress, the silk will stretch about 100 times farther than steel. Interestingly, though, spider silk and steel eventually fail at approximately the same stress. In this sense, spider silk is "as strong as steel." Many pliant biological materials share this combination of low stiffness and large tensile strength. These materials can undergo significant deformations without failing. Tendons, the walls of arteries, and the web of a spider are all quite strong but nonetheless capable of significant stretch.

Bone is an interesting example of a rigid biological material. Most bones in your body are made of two different kinds of bony material: dense and rigid cortical (or compact) bone on the outside, and porous, flexible cancellous (or spongy) bone on the inside. FIGURE 8.24 shows a cross section of a typical bone. Cortical and cancellous bones have very different values of Young's modulus. Young's modulus for cortical bone approaches that of concrete, so it is very rigid with little ability to stretch or compress. In contrast, cancellous bone has a much lower Young's modulus. Consequently, the elastic properties of bones can be well modeled as those of a hollow cylinder.

The structure of bones in birds actually approximates a hollow cylinder quite well. FIGURE 8.25 shows that a typical bone is a thin-walled tube of cortical bone with a tenuous structure of cancellous bone inside. Most of a cylinder's rigidity comes from the material near its surface. A hollow cylinder retains most of the rigidity of a solid one, but it is much lighter. Bird bones carry this idea to its extreme.

FIGURE 8.25 Section of a bone from a bird.

Table 8.3 gives values of Young's modulus for biological materials. Note the large difference between pliant and rigid materials. Table 8.4 shows the tensile strengths for biological materials. Interestingly, spider silk, a pliant material, has a greater tensile strength than bone!

The values in Table 8.4 are for static forces—forces applied for a long time in a testing machine. Bone can withstand significantly greater stresses if the forces are applied for only a very short period of time.

| EXAMPLE 8.10 | **Finding the compression of a bone** |

The femur, the long bone in the thigh, can be modeled as a tube of cortical bone for most of its length. A 70 kg person has a femur with a cross-section area (of the cortical bone) of 4.8×10^{-4} m^2, a typical value.

a. If this person supports his entire weight on one leg, what fraction of the tensile strength of the bone does this stress represent?
b. By what fraction of its length does the femur shorten?

PREPARE The stress on the femur is F/A. Here F, the force compressing the femur, is the person's weight, so $F = mg$. The fractional change $\Delta L/L$ in the femur is the strain, which we can find using Equation 8.7, taking the value of Young's modulus for cortical bone from Table 8.3.

SOLVE

a. The person's weight is $mg = (70 \text{ kg})(9.8 \text{ m/s}^2) = 690$ N. The resulting stress on the femur is

$$\frac{F}{A} = \frac{690 \text{ N}}{4.8 \times 10^{-4} \text{ m}^2} = 1.4 \times 10^6 \text{ N/m}^2$$

A stress of 1.4×10^6 N/m^2 is 1.4% of the tensile strength of cortical bone given in Table 8.4.

b. We can compute the strain as

$$\frac{\Delta L}{L} = \left(\frac{1}{Y}\right)\frac{F}{A} = \left(\frac{1}{1.6 \times 10^{10} \text{ N/m}^2}\right)(1.4 \times 10^6 \text{ N/m}^2) = 8.8 \times 10^{-5} \approx 0.0001$$

The femur compression is $\Delta L \approx 0.0001L$, or $\approx 0.01\%$ of its length.

ASSESS It makes sense that, under ordinary standing conditions, the stress on the femur is only a percent or so of the maximum value it can sustain.

TABLE 8.3 Young's modulus for biological materials

Material	Young's modulus (10^{10} N/m^2)
Tooth enamel	6
Cortical bone	1.6
Cancellous bone	0.02–0.3
Spider silk	0.2
Tendon	0.15
Cartilage	0.0001
Blood vessel (aorta)	0.00005

TABLE 8.4 Tensile strength of biological materials

Material	Tensile strength (N/m^2)
Cancellous bone	5×10^6
Cortical bone	100×10^6
Tendon	100×10^6
Spider silk	1000×10^6

The dancer in the chapter-opening photo stands *en pointe,* balanced delicately on the tip of her shoe with her entire weight supported on a very small area. The stress on the bones in her toes is very large, but it is still much less than the tensile strength of bone.

| STOP TO THINK 8.5 | A 10 kg mass is hung from a 1-m-long cable, causing the cable to stretch by 2 mm. Suppose a 10 kg mass is hung from a 2 m length of the same cable. By how much does the cable stretch?

A. 0.5 mm   B. 1 mm   C. 2 mm   D. 3 mm   E. 4 mm

| INTEGRATED EXAMPLE 8.11 | **Holding a barrel on a hill** |

FIGURE 8.26 shows a 60-cm-diameter barrel of sand, with a mass of 600 kg, being held in place on a hill by a polypropylene rope wrapped around the barrel. The coefficient of static friction between the barrel and the hill is 0.25.

a. What is the tension in the rope?
b. What is the steepest hill that the barrel could rest on without slipping?

FIGURE 8.26 A barrel being held by a rope.

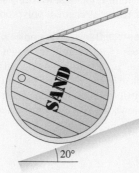

c. What is the smallest-diameter rope that can be used without the rope breaking?

PREPARE We'll follow Problem-Solving Strategy 8.1: For an object in static equilibrium, the net torque is zero, $\Sigma \tau = 0$, and the net force is zero, $\Sigma F_x = 0$ and $\Sigma F_y = 0$. To find the net torque on the barrel, we'll redraw it in FIGURE 8.27 on the next page with all the forces shown at the points at which they act. To find the components of the net force, we'll draw the free-body diagram of Figure 8.27. As usual, we tilt our x-axis so that it's parallel to the surface of the hill. Recall from Figure 5.14 that the angle between the weight vector and the $-y$-axis is the same as the angle of the slope.

The direction of the static friction force is chosen to keep the bottom of the barrel from slipping down the hill. Imagine what

Continued

FIGURE 8.27 Visual overview of the barrel.

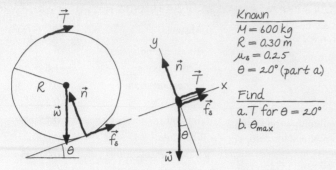

Known

$M = 600 \text{ kg}$
$R = 0.30 \text{ m}$
$\mu_s = 0.25$
$\theta = 20° \text{ (part a)}$

Find

a. T for $\theta = 20°$
b. θ_{max}

would happen if friction suddenly vanished while the rope was holding the top of the barrel in place.

We need to pick a pivot about which the torque will be calculated. If we choose the point of contact of the barrel with the hill as our pivot, then the unknown forces $\vec{n}$ and $\vec{f}_s$, which act at that point, make no contribution to the torque. Only the weight, whose magnitude we know, and the tension, which is what we want to find, contribute to the torque.

For part c, the rope will fail if the stress exceeds the tensile strength of polypropylene, given in Table 8.2 as $2.0 \times 10^7 \text{ N/m}^2$.

SOLVE

a. FIGURE 8.28 shows how to calculate the torque. Forces $\vec{n}$ and $\vec{f}_s$ are not shown because, as just discussed, they act at the pivot and do not contribute to the torque. In Figure 8.28a, the tension $\vec{T}$ acts perpendicular to the radial line, at a distance $2R$ from the pivot, so the torque due to the tension is $\tau_T = -2RT$. It's negative because the tension tries to rotate the barrel clockwise.

FIGURE 8.28 Calculating the torque.

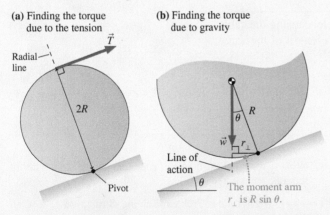

(a) Finding the torque due to the tension

(b) Finding the torque due to gravity

Radial line

$\vec{T}$

$2R$

Pivot

R

θ

$\vec{w}$ $r_\perp$

Line of action

θ

The moment arm $r_\perp$ is $R \sin \theta$.

We'll use Equation 7.4, $\tau = r_\perp F$, to find the torque due to the weight, which acts at the center of gravity. From Figure 8.28b we see that the moment arm $r_\perp$, the perpendicular distance from the line of action to the pivot, is $r_\perp = R \sin \theta$. The magnitude of the weight force is Mg, so the torque due to the weight is $\tau_w = MgR \sin \theta$.

We can now write the condition that the net torque is zero as

$$\tau_{net} = \tau_w + \tau_T = MgR \sin \theta - 2RT = 0$$

Solving this equation for the tension gives

$$T = \tfrac{1}{2} Mg \sin \theta = \frac{(600 \text{ kg})(9.8 \text{ m/s}^2)}{2} \sin 20° = 1000 \text{ N}$$

Note that R cancels, so the tension does not depend on the radius of the barrel.

b. Part a was solved using only the net torque equation. For this part, we'll need the two force equations as well. From the free-body diagram of Figure 8.27, we can write

$$\sum F_x = T + f_s - Mg \sin \theta = 0$$

$$\sum F_y = n - Mg\cos\theta = 0$$

We can solve the first of these equations for the friction force:

$$f_s = Mg \sin \theta - T = Mg \sin \theta - \tfrac{1}{2} Mg \sin \theta = \tfrac{1}{2} Mg \sin \theta$$

Here we used the result for the tension T found in part a.

The static friction must have this value to keep the barrel from slipping. But static friction can't exceed the maximum possible value, $f_{s\,max} = \mu_s n$. From the y force equation, the normal force is $n = Mg \cos \theta$, so $f_{s\,max} = \mu_s Mg \cos \theta$. The barrel will slip when the friction force equals its maximum possible value, or when

$$f_s = \tfrac{1}{2} Mg \sin \theta = f_{s\,max} = \mu_s Mg \cos \theta$$

The factor Mg cancels from both sides of this equation, giving $\tfrac{1}{2} \sin \theta = \mu_s \cos \theta$, which, after dividing both sides by $\cos \theta$, can be written as $\tfrac{1}{2} \tan \theta = \mu_s$. Thus the angle at which the barrel will slip is given by $\tan \theta = 2\mu_s$, or

$$\theta = \tan^{-1}(2\mu_s) = \tan^{-1}(2 \cdot 0.25) = 27°$$

c. The maximum possible stress in the rope, when it is at its breaking point, is

$$\frac{F}{A} = \frac{T}{\pi r^2} = \frac{1000 \text{ N}}{\pi r^2} = 2.0 \times 10^7 \text{ N/m}^2$$

The radius of the rope at this level of stress is

$$r = \sqrt{\frac{1000 \text{ N}}{\pi (2.0 \times 10^7 \text{ N/m}^2)}} = 4.0 \times 10^{-3} \text{ m}$$

The minimum rope diameter is twice this radius, or 8.0 mm. If the rope were any smaller, the stress would exceed the tensile strength of polypropylene and the rope would break.

ASSESS Back in Example 5.14, we found that an object will *slide* (without rolling) down a slope when the angle exceeds $\tan^{-1}\mu_s$, a *smaller* angle than for our rolling object. This makes sense because for the barrel there is an extra uphill force—the tension—that is absent for a sliding object. This uphill force allows the slope to be steeper before a round object begins to slip.

SUMMARY

The goals of Chapter 8 have been to learn about the static equilibrium of extended objects and to understand the basic properties of springs and elastic materials.

GENERAL PRINCIPLES

Static Equilibrium

An object in **static equilibrium** must have no net force on it and no net torque. Mathematically, we express this as

$$\sum F_x = 0$$

$$\sum F_y = 0$$

$$\sum \tau = 0$$

Since the net torque is zero about *any* point, the pivot point for calculating the torque can be chosen at any convenient location.

Springs and Hooke's Law

When a spring is stretched or compressed, it exerts a force proportional to the change Δx in its length but in the opposite direction. This is known as **Hooke's law:**

$$(F_{sp})_x = -k\,\Delta x$$

The constant of proportionality k is called the **spring constant.** It is larger for a "stiff" spring.

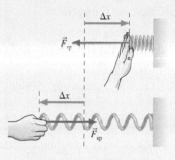

IMPORTANT CONCEPTS

Stability

An object is **stable** if its center of gravity is over its base of support; otherwise, it is **unstable.**

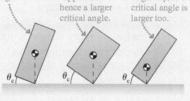

If an object is tipped, it will reach the limit of its stability when its center of gravity is over the edge of the base. This defines the **critical angle** θ_c.

Greater stability is possible with a lower center of gravity or a broader base of support.

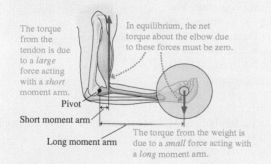

This object is at its critical angle.

This object has a wider base of support and hence a larger critical angle.

This object has a lower center of gravity, so its critical angle is larger too.

Elastic materials and Young's modulus

A solid rod illustrates how materials respond when stretched or compressed.

Stress is the restoring force of the rod divided by its cross-section area.

$$\left(\frac{F}{A}\right) = Y\left(\frac{\Delta L}{L}\right)$$

Strain is the fractional change in the rod's length.

Young's modulus

This equation can also be written as

This is the "spring constant" k for the rod.

$$F = \left(\frac{YA}{L}\right)\Delta L$$

showing that a rod obeys Hooke's law and acts like a very stiff spring.

APPLICATIONS

Forces in the body

Muscles and tendons apply the forces and torques needed to maintain static equilibrium. These forces may be quite large.

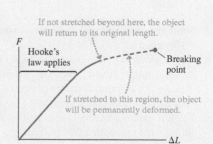

The torque from the tendon is due to a *large* force acting with a *short* moment arm.

In equilibrium, the net torque about the elbow due to these forces must be zero.

Pivot

Short moment arm

Long moment arm

The torque from the weight is due to a *small* force acting with a *long* moment arm.

The elastic limit and beyond

If a rod or other object is not stretched too far, when released it will return to its original shape.

If stretched too far, an object will permanently deform, and finally break. The stress at which an object breaks is its **tensile stress.**

If not stretched beyond here, the object will return to its original length.

Hooke's law applies

Breaking point

If stretched to this region, the object will be permanently deformed.

™ For homework assigned on MasteringPhysics, go to
www.masteringphysics.com

Problem difficulty is labeled as I (straightforward) to IIII (challenging).

Problems labeled INT integrate significant material from earlier
chapters; BIO are of biological or medical interest.

QUESTIONS

Conceptual Questions

1. An object is acted upon by two (and only two) forces that are of
   equal magnitude and oppositely directed. Is the object necessarily in static equilibrium?
2. Sketch a force acting at point P in Figure
   Q8.2 that would make the rod be in static
   equilibrium. Is there only one such force?
3. Could a ladder on a level floor lean against a
   wall in static equilibrium if there were no
   friction forces? Explain.
4. Suppose you are hanging from a tree branch.
   If you move out the branch, farther away
   from the trunk, the branch will be more likely
   to break. Explain why this is so.

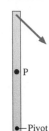

FIGURE Q8.2

5. As divers stand on tiptoes on
   the edge of a diving platform, in
   preparation for a high dive, as
   shown in Figure Q8.5, they usually extend their arms in front of
   them. Why do they do this?
6. Where are the centers of gravity
   of the two people doing the classic yoga poses shown in Figure
   Q8.6?

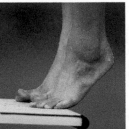

FIGURE Q8.5

FIGURE Q8.6

7. You must lean quite far forward as you rise from a chair (try
   it!). Explain why.
8. A spring exerts a 10 N force after being stretched by 1 cm from
   its equilibrium length. By how much will the spring force
   increase if the spring is stretched from 4 cm away from equilibrium to 5 cm from equilibrium?
9. The left end of a spring is attached to a wall. When Bob pulls
   on the right end with a 200 N force, he stretches the spring by
   20 cm. The same spring is then used for a tug-of-war between
   Bob and Carlos. Each pulls on his end of the spring with a
   200 N force.
   a. How far does Bob's end of the spring move? Explain.
   b. How far does Carlos's end of the spring move? Explain.

10. A spring is attached to the floor and pulled straight up by a
    string. The string's tension is measured. The graph in Figure
    Q8.10 shows the tension in the spring as a function of the
    spring's length L.
    a. Does this spring obey Hooke's law? Explain.
    b. If it does, what is the spring constant?

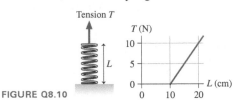

FIGURE Q8.10

11. Take a spring and cut it in half to make two springs. Is the
    spring constant of these smaller springs larger, smaller, or the
    same as the spring constant of the original spring? Explain.
12. A wire is stretched right to its breaking point by a 5000 N force.
    A longer wire made of the same material has the same diameter.
    Is the force that will stretch it right to its breaking point larger
    than, smaller than, or equal to 5000 N? Explain.
13. Steel nails are rigid and unbending. Steel wool is soft and
    squishy. How would you account for this difference?

Multiple-Choice Questions

14. II Two children carry a lightweight 1.8-m-long horizontal pole
    with a water bucket hanging from it. The older child supports
    twice as much weight as the younger child. How far is the
    bucket from the older child?
    A. 0.3 m   B. 0.6 m
    C. 0.9 m   D. 1.2 m
15. II The uniform rod in Figure Q8.15 has a
    weight of 14.0 N. What is the magnitude
    of the normal force exerted on the rod by
    the surface?
    A. 7 N   B. 14 N
    C. 20 N   D. 28 N

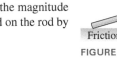

FIGURE Q8.15

16. I A student lies on a very
    light, rigid board with a scale
    under each end. Her feet are
    directly over one scale, and
    her body is positioned as
    shown in Figure Q8.16. The
    two scales read the values
    shown in the figure. What is
    the student's weight?
    A. 65 lb   B. 75 lb
    C. 100 lb   D. 165 lb

FIGURE Q8.16

17. I For the student in Figure Q8.16, approximately how far from
    her feet is her center of gravity?
    A. 0.6 m   B. 0.8 m
    C. 1.0 m   D. 1.2 m

Questions 18 through 20 use the information in the following paragraph and figure.

Suppose you stand on one foot while holding your other leg up behind you. Your muscles will have to apply a force to hold your leg in this raised position. We can model this situation as in Figure Q8.18. The leg pivots at the knee joint, and the force to hold the leg up is provided by a tendon attached to the lower leg as shown. Assume that the lower leg and the foot together have a combined mass of 4.0 kg, and that their combined center of gravity is at the center of the lower leg.

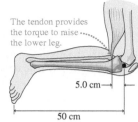

The tendon provides the torque to raise the lower leg.

5.0 cm

50 cm

FIGURE Q8.18

18. | How much force must the tendon exert to keep the leg in this BIO position?
   A. 40 N   B. 200 N   C. 400 N   D. 1000 N

19. | As you hold your leg in this position, the upper leg exerts a BIO force on the lower leg at the knee joint. What is the direction of this force?
   A. Up   B. Down   C. Right   D. Left

20. | What is the magnitude of the force of the upper leg on the BIO lower leg at the knee joint?
   A. 40 N   B. 160 N   C. 200 N   D. 240 N

21. ||| You have a heavy piece of equipment hanging from a 1.0-mm-diameter wire. Your supervisor asks that the length of the wire be doubled without changing how far the wire stretches. What diameter must the new wire have?
   A. 1.0 mm   B. 1.4 mm   C. 2.0 mm   D. 4.0 mm

22. ||| A 30.0-cm-long board is placed on a table such that its right end hangs over the edge by 8.0 cm. A second identical board is stacked on top of the first, as shown in Figure Q8.22. What is the largest that the distance x can be before both boards topple over?
   A. 4.0 cm   B. 8.0 cm
   C. 14 cm   D. 15 cm

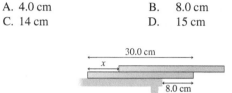

30.0 cm

x

8.0 cm

FIGURE Q8.22

23. || Two 20 kg blocks are connected by a 2.0-m-long, 5.0-mm-diameter rope. Young's modulus for this rope is 1.5×10^9 N/m². The rope is then hung over a pulley, so that the blocks, hanging from each side of the pulley, are in static equilibrium. By how much does the rope stretch?
   A. 3.0 mm   B. 6.3 mm
   C. 9.3 mm   D. 13 mm

PROBLEMS

Section 8.1 Torque and Static Equilibrium

1. || A 64 kg woman stands on a very light, rigid board that rests on a bathroom scale at each end, as shown in Figure P8.1. What is the reading on each of the scales?

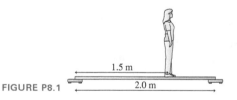

1.5 m

FIGURE P8.1

2.0 m

2. ||| Suppose the woman in Figure P8.1 is 54 kg, and the board she is standing on has a 10 kg mass. What is the reading on each of the scales?

3. ||| How close to the right edge of the 56 kg picnic table shown in Figure P8.3 can a 70 kg man stand without the table tipping over?

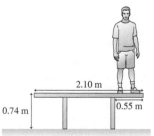

2.10 m

0.74 m

0.55 m

FIGURE P8.3

4. || In Figure P8.4, a 70 kg man walks out on a 10 kg beam that rests on, but is not attached to, two supports. When the beam just starts to tip, what is the force exerted on the beam by the right support?

FIGURE P8.4

5. ||| You're carrying a 3.6-m-long, 25 kg pole to a construction site when you decide to stop for a rest. You place one end of the pole on a fence post and hold the other end of the pole 35 cm from its tip. How much force must you exert to keep the pole motionless in a horizontal position?

6. ||| How much torque must the pin exert to keep the rod in Figure P8.6 from rotating? Calculate this torque about an axis that passes through the point where the pin enters the rod and is perpendicular to the plane of the figure.

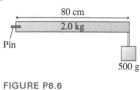

80 cm

2.0 kg

Pin

500 g

FIGURE P8.6

7. ||| Is the object in Figure P8.7 in equilibrium? Explain.

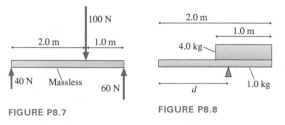

100 N

2.0 m   1.0 m

40 N   Massless   60 N

FIGURE P8.7

2.0 m

1.0 m

4.0 kg

d

1.0 kg

1.0 kg

FIGURE P8.8

8. ||| The two objects in Figure P8.8 are balanced on the pivot. What is distance d?

9. ⫴ A 60 kg diver stands at the end of a 30 kg spring-board, as shown in Figure P8.9. The board is attached to a hinge at the left end but simply rests on the right support. What is the magnitude of the vertical force exerted by the hinge on the board?

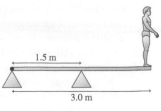

1.5 m

3.0 m

FIGURE P8.9

10. ⫴ A uniform beam of length 1.0 m and mass 10 kg is attached to a wall by a cable, as shown in Figure P8.10. The beam is free to pivot at the point where it attaches to the wall. What is the tension in the cable?

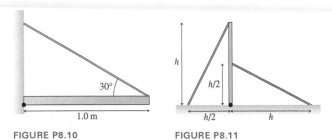

FIGURE P8.10   FIGURE P8.11

11. ‖ Figure P8.11 shows a vertical pole of height h that can rotate about a hinge at the bottom. The pole is held in position by two wires under tension. What is the ratio of the tension in the left wire to the tension in the right wire?

Section 8.2 Stability and Balance

12. ‖ You want to slowly push a stiff board across a 20 cm gap between two tabletops that are at the same height. If you apply only a horizontal force, how long must the board be so that it doesn't tilt down into the gap before reaching the other side?

13. | A magazine rack has a center of gravity 16 cm above the floor, as shown in Figure P8.13. Through what maximum angle, in degrees, can the rack be tilted without falling over?

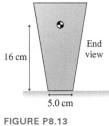

16 cm   End view

5.0 cm

FIGURE P8.13

14. ‖ A car manufacturer claims that you can drive its new vehicle across a hill with a 47° slope before the vehicle starts to tip. If the vehicle is 2.0 m wide, how high is its center of gravity?

15. ‖ A thin 2.00 kg box rests on a 6.00 kg board that hangs over the end of a table, as shown in Figure P8.15. How far can the center of the box be from the end of the table before the board begins to tilt?

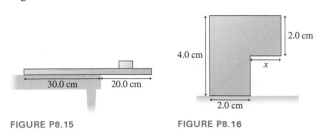

30.0 cm   20.0 cm

4.0 cm   2.0 cm

x

2.0 cm

FIGURE P8.15   FIGURE P8.16

16. ⫴ The object shown in Figure P8.16 is made of a uniform material. What is the greatest that x can be without the object tipping over?

Section 8.3 Springs and Hooke's Law

17. | One end of a spring is attached to a wall. A 25 N pull on the other end causes the spring to stretch by 3.0 cm. What is the spring constant?

18. | Experiments using "optical tweezers" measure the elasticity of individual DNA molecules. For small enough changes in length, the elasticity has the same form as that of a spring. A DNA molecule is anchored at one end, then a force of 1.5 nN (1.5×10^{-9} N) pulls on the other end, causing the molecule to stretch by 5.0 nm (5.0×10^{-9} m). What is the spring constant of that DNA molecule?

19. ‖ A spring has an unstretched length of 10 cm. It exerts a restoring force F when stretched to a length of 11 cm.
    a. For what total stretched length of the spring is its restoring force $3F$?
    b. At what compressed length is the restoring force $2F$?

20. ‖ A 10-cm-long spring is attached to the ceiling. When a 2.0 kg mass is hung from it, the spring stretches to a length of 15 cm.
    a. What is the spring constant?
    b. How long is the spring when a 3.0 kg mass is suspended from it?

21. ‖ A spring stretches 5.0 cm when a 0.20 kg block is hung from it. If a 0.70 kg block replaces the 0.20 kg block, how far does the spring stretch?

22. ‖ A 1.2 kg block is hung from a vertical spring, causing the spring to stretch by 2.4 cm. How much farther will the spring stretch if a 0.60 kg block is added to the 1.2 kg block?

23. ‖ A runner wearing spiked shoes pulls a 20 kg sled across frictionless ice using a horizontal spring with spring constant 1.5×10^2 N/m. The spring is stretched 20 cm from its equilibrium length. What is the acceleration of the sled?

24. | You need to make a spring scale to measure the mass of objects hung from it. You want each 1.0 cm length along the scale to correspond to a mass difference of 0.10 kg. What should be the value of the spring constant?

Section 8.4 Stretching and Compressing Materials

25. ‖ A force stretches a wire by 1.0 mm.
    a. A second wire of the same material has the same cross section and twice the length. How far will it be stretched by the same force?
    b. A third wire of the same material has the same length and twice the diameter as the first. How far will it be stretched by the same force?

26. ⫼ What hanging mass will stretch a 2.0-m-long, 0.50-mm-diameter steel wire by 1.0 mm?

27. ⫴ How much force does it take to stretch a 10-m-long, 1.0-cm-diameter steel cable by 5.0 mm?

28. ⫴ An 80-cm-long, 1.0-mm-diameter steel guitar string must be tightened to a tension of 2.0 kN by turning the tuning screws. By how much is the string stretched?

29. ⫴ A 2000 N force stretches a wire by 1.0 mm.
    a. A second wire of the same material is twice as long and has twice the diameter. How much force is needed to stretch it by 1.0 mm? Explain.
    b. A third wire of the same material is twice as long as the first and has the same diameter. How far is it stretched by a 4000 N force?

30. ⫴ A 1.2-m-long steel rod with a diameter of 0.50 cm hangs vertically from the ceiling. An auto engine weighing 4.7 kN is hung from the rod. By how much does the rod stretch?

31. ⫼ A mine shaft has an elevator hung from a single steel-wire cable of diameter 2.5 cm. When the cable is fully extended, the end of the cable is 500 m below the support. How much does the fully extended cable stretch when 3000 kg of ore is loaded into the elevator?

32. ⫼ The normal force of the ground on the foot can reach three
BIO times a runner's body weight when the foot strikes the pavement. By what amount does the 52-cm-long femur of an 80 kg runner compress at this moment? The cross-section area of the bone of the femur can be taken as $5.2 \times 10^{-4} \text{ m}^2$.

33. ⫼ A three-legged wooden bar stool made out of solid Douglas fir has legs that are 2.0 cm in diameter. When a 75 kg man sits on the stool, by what percent does the length of the legs decrease? Assume, for simplicity, that the stool's legs are vertical and that each bears the same load.

34. ⫼ A 3.0-m-tall, 50-cm-diameter concrete column supports a 200,000 kg load. By how much is the column compressed?

General Problems

35. ⫼ A 3.0-m-long rigid beam with a mass of 100 kg is supported at each end, as shown in Figure P8.35. An 80 kg student stands 2.0 m from support 1. How much upward force does each support exert on the beam?

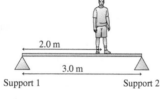

FIGURE P8.35

36. ⫼ An 80 kg construction worker sits down 2.0 m from the end of a 1450 kg steel beam to eat his lunch, as shown in Figure P8.36. The cable supporting the beam is rated at 15,000 N. Should the worker be worried?

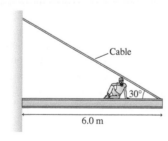

FIGURE P8.36

37. ⫼ Using the information in Figure 8.2, calculate the tension in
BIO the biceps tendon if the hand is holding a 10 kg ball while the forearm is held 45° below horizontal.

38. ⫼ A woman weighing 580 N does a
BIO pushup from her knees, as shown in Figure P8.38. What are the normal forces of the floor on (a) each of her hands and (b) each of her knees?

FIGURE P8.38

39. ⫼ When you bend over, a series of large
BIO muscles, the erector spinae, pull on your spine to hold you up. Figure P8.39 shows a simplified model of the spine as a rod of length L that pivots at its lower end. In this model, the center of gravity of the 320 N weight of the upper torso is at the center of the spine. The 160 N weight of the head and arms acts at the top of the spine. The erector spinae muscles are modeled as a single muscle that acts at an 12° angle to the spine. Suppose the

person in Figure P8.39 bends over to an angle of 30° from the horizontal.
a. What is the tension in the erector muscle?
Hint: Align your x-axis with the axis of the spine.
b. A force from the pelvic girdle acts on the base of the spine. What is the component of this force in the direction of the spine? (This large force is the cause of many back injuries).

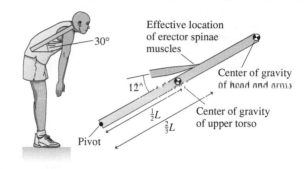

FIGURE P8.39

40. ⎮ The woman lying on the reaction board in Example 8.3 spreads her arms out in the plane of the board. The reading of the scale is observed to increase by 10 N. By how much does the distance from her feet to her center of gravity change?

41. ⫼ A man is attempting to raise a 7.5-m-long, 28 kg flagpole that has a hinge at the base by pulling on a rope attached to the top of the pole, as shown in Figure P8.41. With what force does the man have to pull on the rope to hold the pole motionless in this position?

FIGURE P8.41

42. ⫼ A library ladder of length L rolls on wheels as shown in Figure P8.42. The two legs of the ladder freely pivot at the hinge at the top. The legs are kept from splaying apart by a lightweight chain that is attached halfway up the ladder. If the ladder weighs 200 N, and the angle between each leg and the vertical is 25°, what is the tension in the chain?

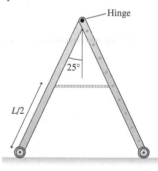

FIGURE P8.42

43. ⫼ A 40 kg, 5.0-m-long beam is supported by, but not attached to, the two posts in Figure P8.43. A 20 kg boy starts walking along the beam. How close can he get to the right end of the beam without it tipping?

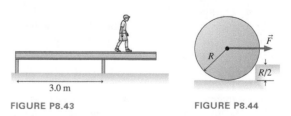

FIGURE P8.43

FIGURE P8.44

44. ⫼ The wheel of mass m in Figure P8.44 is pulled on by a horizontal force applied at its center. The wheel is touching a curb whose height is half the wheel's radius. What is the minimum force required to just raise the wheel off the ground?

45. ‖ A 5.0 kg mass hanging from a spring scale is slowly lowered onto a vertical spring, as shown in Figure P8.45. The scale reads in newtons.

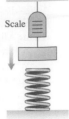

a. What does the spring scale read just before the mass touches the lower spring?

b. The scale reads 20 N when the lower spring has been compressed by 2.0 cm. What is the value of the spring constant for the lower spring?

c. At what compression distance will the scale read zero?

FIGURE P8.45

46. ‖ Two identical, side-by-side springs with spring constant 240 N/m support a 2.00 kg hanging box. By how much is each spring stretched?

47. | Two springs have the same equilibrium length but different spring constants. They are arranged as shown in Figure P8.47, then a block is pushed against them, compressing both by 1.00 cm. With what net force do they push back on the block?

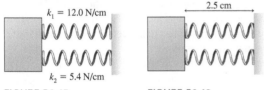

FIGURE P8.47   **FIGURE P8.48**

48. ‖ Two springs have the same spring constant $k = 130$ N/m but different equilibrium lengths, 3.0 cm and 5.0 cm. They are arranged as shown in Figure P8.48, then a block is pushed against them, compressing both to a length of 2.5 cm. With what net force do they push back on the block?

49. ‖ Figure P8.49 shows two springs attached to a block that can slide on a frictionless surface. In the block's equilibrium position, the left spring is compressed by 2.0 cm.

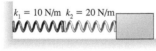

FIGURE P8.49

a. By how much is the right spring compressed?

b. What is the net force on the block if it is moved 15 cm to the right of its equilibrium position?

50. ‖ Figure P8.50 shows two springs attached to each other, and also attached to a box that can slide on a frictionless surface. In the block's equilibrium position,

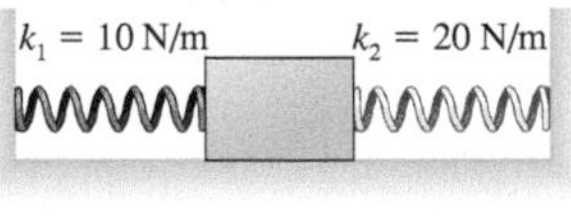

$k_1 = 10$ N/m $k_2 = 20$ N/m

FIGURE P8.50

neither spring is stretched. What is the net force on the block if it is moved 15 cm to the right of its equilibrium position?
Hint: There is zero net force on the point where the two springs meet. This implies a relationship between the amounts the two springs stretch.

51. ‖ A 60 kg student is standing atop a spring in an elevator that is accelerating upward at 3.0 m/s². The spring constant is 2.5×10^3 N/m. By how much is the spring compressed?

52. ‖‖ A 25 kg child bounces on a pogo stick. The pogo stick has a spring with spring constant 2.0×10^4 N/m. When the child makes a nice big bounce, she finds that at the bottom of the

bounce she is accelerating *upward* at 9.8 m/s². How much is the spring compressed?

53. ‖‖‖ Two 3.0 kg blocks on a level, frictionless surface are connected by a spring with spring constant 1000 N/m, as shown in Figure P8.53.

FIGURE P8.53

The left block is pushed by a horizontal force $\vec{F}$. At $t = 0$ s, both blocks have velocity 3.2 m/s to the right. For the next second, the spring's compression is a constant 1.5 cm.

a. What is the velocity of the right block at $t = 1.0$ s?

b. What is the magnitude of $\vec{F}$ during that 1.0 s interval?

54. ‖ What is the effective spring constant (that is, the ratio of force to change in length) of a copper cable that is 5.0 mm in diameter and 5.0 m long?

55. ‖‖ Figure P8.55 shows a 100 kg plank supported at its right end by a 7.0-mm-diameter rope with a tensile strength of 6.0×10^7 N/m². How far along the plank, measured from the pivot, can the center of gravity of an 800 kg piece of heavy machinery be placed before the rope snaps?

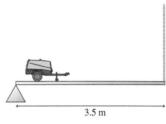

FIGURE P8.55

56. ‖‖ When you walk, your Achilles tendon, which connects your heel to your calf muscles, repeatedly stretches and contracts, much like a spring. This helps make walking more efficient. Suppose your Achilles tendon is 15 cm long and has a cross-section area of 110 mm², typical values. If you model the Achilles tendon as a spring, what is its spring constant?

57. ‖‖ There is a disk of cartilage between each pair of vertebrae in your spine. Suppose a disk is 0.50 cm thick and 4.0 cm in diameter. If this disk supports half the weight of a 65 kg person, by what fraction of its thickness does the disk compress?

58. ‖ In Example 8.1, the tension in the biceps tendon for a person doing a strict curl of a 900 N barbell was found to be 3900 N. What fraction does this represent of the maximum possible tension the biceps tendon can support? You can assume a typical cross-section area of 130 mm².

59. ‖‖ Larger animals have sturdier bones than smaller animals. A mouse's skeleton is only a few percent of its body weight, compared to 16% for an elephant. To see why this must be so, recall, from Example 8.10, that the stress on the femur for a man standing on one leg is 1.4% of the bone's tensile strength. Suppose we scale this man up by a factor of 10 in all dimensions, keeping the same body proportions. Use the data for Example 8.10 to compute the following.

a. Both the inside and outside diameter of the femur, the region of cortical bone, will increase by a factor of 10. What will be the new cross-section area?

b. The man's body will increase by a factor of 10 in each dimension. What will be his new mass?

c. If the scaled-up man now stands on one leg, what fraction of the tensile strength is the stress on the femur?

60. ‖ Orb spiders make silk with a typical diameter of 0.15 mm.

a. A typical large orb spider has a mass of 0.50 g. If this spider suspends itself from a single 12-cm-long strand of silk, by how much will the silk stretch?

b. What is the maximum weight that a single thread of this silk could support?

Passage Problems

Standing on Tiptoes BIO

When you stand on your tiptoes, your feet pivot about your ankle. As shown in Figure P8.61, the forces on your foot are an upward force on your toes from the floor, a downward force on your ankle from the lower leg bone, and an upward force on the heel of your foot from your Achilles tendon. Suppose a 60 kg woman stands on tiptoes with the sole of her foot making a 25° angle with the floor. Assume that each foot supports half her weight.

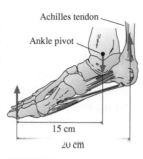

Achilles tendon
Ankle pivot

15 cm

20 cm

FIGURE P8.61

61. ⫼ What is the upward force of the floor on the toes of one foot?
    A. 140 N   B. 290 N
    C. 420 N   D. 590 N

62. ⫼ What upward force does the Achilles tendon exert on the heel of her foot?
    A. 290 N   B. 420 N
    C. 590 N   D. 880 N

63. ⫼ The tension in the Achilles tendon will cause it to stretch. If the Achilles tendon is 15 cm long and has a cross-section area of 110 mm^2, by how much will it stretch under this force?
    A. 0.2 mm   B. 0.8 mm
    C. 2.3 mm   D. 5.2 mm

STOP TO THINK ANSWERS

Stop to Think 8.1: D. Only object D has both zero net force and zero net torque.

Stop to Think 8.2: B. The tension in the rope and the weight have no horizontal component. To make the net force zero, the force due to the pivot must also have no horizontal component, so we know it points either up or down. Now consider the torque about the point where the rope is attached. The tension provides no torque. The weight exerts a counterclockwise torque. To make the net torque zero, the pivot force must exert a *clockwise* torque, which it can do only if it points *up*.

Stop to Think 8.3: B, A, C. The critical angle θ_c, shown in the figure, measures how far the object can be tipped before falling. B has the smallest critical angle, followed by A, then C.

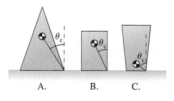

A.   B.   C.

Stop to Think 8.4: C. The restoring force of the spring is proportional to the stretch. Increasing the restoring force by a factor of 3 requires increasing the stretch by a factor of 3.

Stop to Think 8.5: E. The cables have the same diameter, and the force is the same, so the stress is the same in both cases. This means that the strain, $\Delta L/L$, is the same. The 2 m cable will experience twice the change in length of the 1 m cable.

Force and Motion

The goal of Part I has been to discover the connection between force and motion. We started with kinematics, the mathematical description of motion; then we proceeded to dynamics, the explanation of motion in terms of forces. We then used these descriptions to analyze and explain motions ranging from the motion of the moon about the earth to the forces in your elbow when you lift a weight. Newton's three laws of motion formed the basis of all of our explanations.

The table below is a *knowledge structure* for force and motion. The knowledge structure does not represent everything you have learned over the past eight chapters. It's a summary of the "big picture," outlining the basic goals, the general principles, and the primary applications of the part of the book we have just finished. When you are immersed in a chapter, it may be hard to see the connections among all

of the different topics. Before we move on to new topics, we will finish each part of the book with a knowledge structure to make these connections clear.

Work through the knowledge structure from top to bottom. First are the goals and general principles. There aren't that many general principles, but we can use them along with the general problem-solving strategy to solve a wide range of problems. Once you recognize a problem as a dynamics problem, you immediately know to start with Newton's laws. You can then determine the category of motion and apply Newton's second law in the appropriate form. The kinematic equations for that category of motion then allow you to reach the solution you seek. These equations and other detailed information from the chapters are summarized in the bottom section.

KNOWLEDGE STRUCTURE I Force and Motion

BASIC GOALS	How can we describe motion? How does an object respond to a force?
	How do systems interact? What is the nature of the force of gravity?
	How can we analyze the motion and deformation of extended objects?

GENERAL PRINCIPLES	**Newton's first law**	An object with no forces acting on it will remain at rest or move in a straight line at a constant speed.
	Newton's second law	$\vec{F}_{net} = m\vec{a}$
	Newton's third law	$\vec{F}_{A\,on\,B} = -\vec{F}_{B\,on\,A}$
	Newton's law of gravity	$F_{1\,on\,2} = F_{2\,on\,1} = \dfrac{Gm_1 m_2}{r^2}$

BASIC PROBLEM-SOLVING STRATEGY

Use Newton's second law for each particle or system. Use Newton's third law to equate the magnitudes of the two members of an action/reaction pair.

Types of forces:
$$\vec{w} = (mg, \text{downward})$$
$$\vec{f}_k = (\mu_k n, \text{opposite motion})$$
$$(F_{sp})_x = -k\,\Delta x$$

Linear and projectile motion:

$$\left.\begin{matrix}\sum F_x = ma_x \\ \sum F_y = 0\end{matrix}\right\} \text{ or } \left\{\begin{matrix}\sum F_x = 0 \\ \sum F_y = ma_y\end{matrix}\right.$$

Circular motion:

The force is directed to the center:

$$\vec{F}_{net} = \left(\frac{mv^2}{r}, \text{toward center of circle}\right)$$

Rigid-body motion:

When a torque is exerted on an object with moment of inertia I,

$$\tau_{net} = I\alpha$$

Equilibrium:

For an object at rest,

$$\sum F_x = 0 \quad \sum \tau = 0$$
$$\sum F_y = 0$$

Linear and projectile kinematics

Uniform motion: $x_f = x_i + v_x\,\Delta t$
($a_x = 0$, $v_x = $ constant)

Constant acceleration: $(v_x)_f = (v_x)_i + a_x\,\Delta t$
($a_x = $ constant)

$$x_f = x_i + (v_x)_i\,\Delta t + \tfrac{1}{2}a_x(\Delta t)^2$$

$$(v_x)_f^2 = (v_x)_i^2 + 2a_x\,\Delta x$$

Velocity is the slope of the position-versus-time graph.
Acceleration is the slope of the velocity-versus-time graph.

Projectile motion:
Projectile motion is uniform horizontal motion and constant-acceleration vertical motion with $a_y = -g$.

Circular kinematics

Uniform circular motion:

$$f = \frac{1}{T} \qquad \omega = 2\pi f$$

$$v = \frac{2\pi r}{T} = \omega r \qquad a = \frac{v^2}{r} = \omega^2 r$$

Rigid bodies

Torque $\tau = rF_\perp = r_\perp F$

Center of gravity $x_{cg} = \dfrac{x_1 m_1 + x_2 m_2 + \cdots}{m_1 + m_2 + \cdots}$

Moment of inertia $I = \sum mr^2$

Dark Matter and the Structure of the Universe

The idea that the earth exerts a gravitational force on us is something we now accept without questioning. But when Isaac Newton developed this idea to show that the gravitational force also holds the moon in its orbit, it was a remarkable, ground-breaking insight. It changed the way that we look at the universe we live in.

Newton's laws of motion and gravity are tools that allow us to continue Newton's quest to better understand our place in the cosmos. But it sometimes seems that the more we learn, the more we realize how little we actually know and understand.

Here's an example. Advances in astronomy over the past 100 years have given us great insight into the structure of the universe. But everything our telescopes can see appears to be only a small fraction of what is out there. As much as 90% of the mass in the universe is *dark matter*—matter that gives off no light or other radiation that we can detect. Everything that we have ever seen through a telescope is merely the tip of the cosmic iceberg.

What is this dark matter? Black holes? Neutrinos? Some form of exotic particle? No one knows. It could be any of these, or all of them—or something entirely different that no one has yet dreamed of. You might wonder how we know that such matter exists if no one has seen it. Even though we can't directly observe dark matter, we see its effects. And you now know enough physics to understand why.

Whatever dark matter is, it has mass, and so it has gravity. This picture of the Andromeda galaxy shows a typical spiral galaxy structure: a dense collection of stars in the center surrounded by a disk of stars and other matter. This is the shape of our own Milky Way galaxy.

The spiral Andromeda galaxy.

This structure is reminiscent of the structure of the solar system: a dense mass (the sun) in the center surrounded by a disk of other matter (the planets, asteroids, and comets). The sun's gravity keeps the planets in their orbits, but the planets would fall into the sun unless they were in constant motion around it. The same is true of a spiral galaxy; everything in the galaxy orbits its center. Our solar system orbits the center of our galaxy with a period of about 200 million years.

The orbital speed of an object depends on the mass that pulls on it. If you analyze our sun's motion about the center of the Milky Way, or the motion of stars in the Andromeda galaxy about its center, you find that the orbits are much faster than they should be, based on how many stars we see. There must be some other mass present.

There's another problem with the orbital motion of stars around the center of their galaxies. We know that the orbital speeds of planets decrease with distance from the sun; Neptune orbits at a much slower speed than the earth. We might expect something similar for galaxies: Stars farther from the center should orbit at reduced speeds. But they don't. As we measure outward from the center of the galaxy, the orbital speed stays about the same—even as we get to the edge of the visible disk. There must be some other mass—the invisible dark matter—exerting a gravitational force on the stars. This dark matter, which far outweighs the matter we can see, seems to form a halo around the centers of galaxies, providing the gravitational force necessary to produce the observed rotation. Other observations of the motions of galaxies with respect to each other verify this basic idea.

On a cosmic scale, the picture is even stranger. The universe is currently expanding. The mutual gravitational attraction of all matter—regular and dark—in the universe should slow this expansion. But recent observations of the speeds of distant galaxies imply that the expansion of the universe is accelerating, so there must be yet another component to the universe, something that "pushes out". The best explanation at present is that the acceleration is caused by *dark energy*. The nature of dark matter isn't known, but the nature of dark energy is even more mysterious. If current theories hold, it's the most abundant stuff in the universe. And we don't know what it is.

This sort of mystery is what drives scientific investigation. It's what drove Newton to wonder about the connection between the fall of an apple and the motion of the moon, and what drove investigators to develop all of the techniques and theories you will learn about in the coming chapters.

PART I PROBLEMS

The following questions are related to the passage "Dark Matter and the Structure of the Universe" on the previous page.

1. As noted in the passage, our solar system orbits the center of the Milky Way galaxy in about 200 million years. If there were no dark matter in our galaxy, this period would be
   A. Longer.
   B. The same.
   C. Shorter.

2. Saturn is approximately 10 times as far away from the sun as the earth. This means that its orbital acceleration is _____ that of the earth.
   A. 1/10
   B. 1/100
   C. 1/1000
   D. 1/10,000

3. Saturn is approximately 10 times as far away from the sun as the earth. If dark matter changed the orbital properties of the planets so that Saturn had the same orbital speed as the earth, Saturn's orbital acceleration would be _____ that of the earth.
   A. 1/10
   B. 1/100
   C. 1/1000
   D. 1/10,000

4. Which of the following might you expect to be an additional consequence of the fact that galaxies contain more mass than expected?
   A. The gravitational force between galaxies is greater than expected.
   B. Galaxies appear less bright than expected.
   C. Galaxies are farther away than expected.
   D. There are more galaxies than expected.

The following passages and associated questions are based on the material of Part I.

Animal Athletes BIO

Different animals have very different capacities for running. A horse can maintain a top speed of 20 m/s for a long distance but has a maximum acceleration of only 6.0 m/s², half what a good human sprinter can achieve with a block to push against. Greyhounds, dogs especially bred for feats of running, have a top speed of 17 m/s, but their acceleration is much greater than that of the horse. Greyhounds are particularly adept at turning corners at a run.

FIGURE I.1

5. If a horse starts from rest and accelerates at the maximum value until reaching its top speed, how much time elapses, to the nearest second?
   A. 1 s   B. 2 s
   C. 3 s   D. 4 s

6. If a horse starts from rest and accelerates at the maximum value until reaching its top speed, how far does it run, to the nearest 10 m?
   A. 40 m   B. 30 m
   C. 20 m   D. 10 m

7. A greyhound on a racetrack turns a corner at a constant speed of 15 m/s with an acceleration of 7.1 m/s². What is the radius of the turn?
   A. 40 m   B. 30 m
   C. 20 m   D. 10 m

8. A human sprinter of mass 70 kg starts a run at the maximum possible acceleration, pushing backward against a block set in the track. What is the force of his foot on the block?
   A. 1500 N   B. 840 N
   C. 690 N   D. 420 N

9. In the photograph of the greyhounds in Figure I.1, what is the direction of the net force on each dog?
   A. Up
   B. Down
   C. Left, toward the outside of the turn
   D. Right, toward the inside of the turn

Sticky Liquids BIO

The drag force on an object moving in a liquid is quite different from that in air. Drag forces in air are largely the result of the object having to push the air out of its way as it moves. For an object moving slowly through a liquid, however, the drag force is mostly due to the *viscosity* of the liquid, a measure of how much resistance to flow the fluid has. Honey, which drizzles slowly out of its container, has a much higher viscosity than water, which flows fairly freely.

The *viscous drag* force in a liquid depends on the shape of the object, but there is a simple result called *Stokes's law* for the drag on a sphere. The drag force on a sphere of radius r moving at speed v through a fluid with viscosity η is

$$\vec{D} = (6\pi\eta r v, \text{ direction opposite motion})$$

At small scales, viscous drag becomes very important. To a paramecium (Figure I.2), a single-celled animal that can propel itself through water with fine hairs on its body, swimming through water feels like swimming through honey would to you. We can model a paramecium as a sphere of diameter 50 μm, with a mass of 6.5×10^{-11} kg. Water has a viscosity of 0.0010 N·s/m².

FIGURE I.2

10. A paramecium swimming at a constant speed of 0.25 mm/s ceases propelling itself and slows to a stop. At the instant it stops swimming, what is the magnitude of its acceleration?
    A. 0.2g B. 0.5g
    C. 2g D. 5g

11. If the acceleration of the paramecium in Problem 10 were to stay constant as it comes to rest, approximately how far would it travel before stopping?
    A. 0.02 μm   B. 0.2 μm
    C. 2 μm   D. 20 μm

12. If the paramecium doubles its swimming speed, how does this change the drag force?
    A. The drag force decreases by a factor of 2.
    B. The drag force is unaffected.
    C. The drag force increases by a factor of 2.
    D. The drag force increases by a factor of 4.

13. You can test the viscosity of a liquid by dropping a steel sphere into it and measuring the speed at which it sinks. For viscous fluids, the sphere will rapidly reach a terminal speed. At this terminal speed, the net force on the sphere is
   A. Directed downward.
   B. Zero.
   C. Directed upward.

Pulling Out of a Dive BIO

Falcons are excellent fliers that can reach very high speeds by diving nearly straight down. To pull out of such a dive, a falcon extends its wings and flies through a circular arc that redirects its motion. The forces on the falcon that control its motion are its weight and an upward lift force—like an airplane—due to the air flowing over its wings. At the bottom of the arc, as in Figure I.3, a falcon can easily achieve an acceleration of 15 m/s².

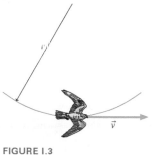

FIGURE I.3

14. At the bottom of the arc, as in Figure I.3, what is the direction of the net force on the falcon?
   A. To the left, opposite the motion
   B. To the right, in the direction of the motion
   C. Up
   D. Down
   E. The net force is zero.
15. Suppose the falcon weighs 8.0 N and is turning with an acceleration of 15 m/s² at the lowest point of the arc. What is the magnitude of the upward lift force at this instant?
   A. 8.0 N   B. 12 N
   C. 16 N   D. 20 N
16. A falcon starts from rest, does a free-fall dive from a height of 30 m, and then pulls out by flying in a circular arc of radius 50 m. Which segment of the motion has a higher acceleration?
   A. The free-fall dive
   B. The circular arc
   C. The two accelerations are equal.

Bending Beams

If you bend a rod down, it compresses the lower side of the rod and stretches the top, resulting in a restoring force. Figure I.4 shows a

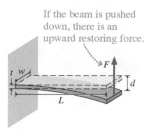

If the beam is pushed down, there is an upward restoring force.

FIGURE I.4

beam of length L, width w, and thickness t fixed at one end and free to move at the other. Deflecting the end of the beam causes a restoring force F at the end of the beam. The magnitude of the restoring force F depends on the dimensions of the beam, the Young's modulus Y for the material, and the deflection d. For small values of the deflection, the restoring force is

$$F = \left[\frac{Ywt^3}{4L^3} \right] d$$

This is similar to the formula for the restoring force of a spring, with the quantity in brackets playing the role of the spring constant k.
   When a 70 kg man stands on the end of a springboard (a type of diving board), the board deflects by 4.0 cm.
17. If a 35 kg child stands at the end of the board, the deflection is
   A. 1.0 cm.   B. 2.0 cm.
   C. 3.0 cm.   D. 4.0 cm.
18. A 70 kg man jumps up and lands on the end of the board, deflecting it by 12 cm. At this instant, what is the approximate magnitude of the upward force the board exerts on his feet?
   A. 700 N   B. 1400 N
   C. 2100 N   D. 2800 N
19. If the board is replaced by one that is half the length but otherwise identical, how much will it deflect when a 70 kg man stands on the end?
   A. 0.50 cm   B. 1.0 cm
   C. 2.0 cm   D. 4.0 cm

Additional Integrated Problems

20. You go to the playground and slide down the slide, a 3.0-m-long ramp at an angle of 40° with respect to horizontal. The pants that you've worn aren't very slippery; the coefficient of kinetic friction between your pants and the slide is $\mu_k = 0.45$. A friend gives you a very slight push to get you started. How long does it take you to reach the bottom of the slide?
21. If you stand on a scale at the equator, the scale will read slightly less than your true weight due to your circular motion with the rotation of the earth.
   a. Draw a free-body diagram to show why this is so.
   b. By how much is the scale reading reduced for a person with a true weight of 800 N?
22. Dolphins and other sea creatures can leap to great heights by swimming straight up and exiting the water at a high speed. A 210 kg dolphin leaps straight up to a height of 7.0 m. When the dolphin reenters the water, drag from the water brings it to a stop in 1.5 m. Assuming that the force of the water on the dolphin stays constant as it slows down,
   a. How much time does it take for the dolphin to come to rest?
   b. What is the force of the water on the dolphin as it is coming to rest?

Conservation Laws

The kestrel is pulling in its wings to begin a steep dive, in which it can achieve a speed of 60 mph. How does the bird achieve such a speed, and why does this speed help the kestrel catch its prey? Such questions are best answered by considering the conservation of energy and momentum.

Why Some Things Stay the Same

Part I of this textbook was about *change*. Simple observations show us that most things in the world around us are changing. Even so, there are some things that *don't* change even as everything else is changing around them. Our emphasis in Part II will be on things that stay the same.

Consider, for example, a strong, sealed box in which you have replaced all the air with a mixture of hydrogen and oxygen. The mass of the box plus the gases inside is 600.0 g. Now, suppose you use a spark to ignite the hydrogen and oxygen. As you know, this is an explosive reaction, with the hydrogen and oxygen combining to create water—and quite a bang. But the strong box contains the explosion and all of its products.

What is the mass of the box after the reaction? The gas inside the box is different now, but a careful measurement would reveal that the mass hasn't changed—it's still 600.0 g! We say that the mass is *conserved*. Of course, this is true only if the box has stayed sealed. For conservation of mass to apply, the system must be *closed*.

Conservation Laws

A closed system of interacting particles has another remarkable property. Each system is characterized by a certain number, and no matter how complex the interactions, the value of this number never changes. This number is called the *energy* of the system, and the fact that it never changes is called the *law of conservation of energy*. It is, perhaps, the single most important physical law ever discovered.

The law of conservation of energy is much more general than Newton's laws. Energy can be converted to many different forms, and, in all cases, the total energy stays the same:

- Gasoline, diesel, and jet engines convert the energy of a fuel into the mechanical energy of moving pistons, wheels, and gears.
- A solar cell converts the electromagnetic energy of light into electrical energy.
- An organism converts the chemical energy of food into a variety of other forms of energy, including kinetic energy, sound energy, and thermal energy.

Energy will be *the* most important concept throughout the remainder of this textbook, and much of Part II will focus on understanding what energy is and how it is used.

But energy is not the only conserved quantity. We will begin Part II with the study of two other quantities that are conserved in a closed system: *momentum* and *angular momentum*. Their conservation will help us understand a wide range of physical processes, from the forces when two rams butt heads to the graceful spins of ice skaters.

Conservation laws will give us a new and different *perspective* on motion. Some situations are most easily analyzed from the perspective of Newton's laws, but others make much more sense when analyzed from a conservation-law perspective. An important goal of Part II is to learn which perspective is best for a given problem.

9 Momentum

Male rams butt heads at high speeds in a ritual to assert their dominance. How can the force of this collision be minimized so as to avoid damage to their brains?

LOOKING AHEAD ▶

The goals of Chapter 9 are to introduce the ideas of impulse, momentum, and angular momentum and to learn a new problem-solving strategy based on conservation laws.

Impulse

We'll begin by studying what happens to an object subject to a strong but short-duration **impulsive force.**

We say that the club has delivered an **impulse** to the ball.

> **Looking Back** ◀◀
> 5.2 Newton's second law

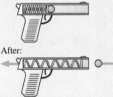

A golf ball being struck by a club is subject to a brief but very large force.

Momentum

The **momentum** of an object is the product of its mass and its velocity. A heavy, fast-moving object such as a car has much greater momentum than a light, slow-moving one such as a falling raindrop.

The momentum of a moving car is a billion times greater than that of a falling raindrop.

Momentum and Impulse

We'll discover how an impulse delivered to an object *changes* the object's momentum.

The player's head delivers an impulse to the ball, changing its momentum and thus its direction.

Conservation of Momentum

When two or more objects interact only with each other, the total momentum of these objects is conserved—it is the same after the interaction as it was before. This **law of conservation of momentum** will lead us to a powerful new *before-and-after* problem-solving strategy.

Before:

After:

Conservation of momentum is an important tool for analyzing *explosions*, like the ball shot from this toy gun, or *collisions*, like two pool balls hitting and flying apart.

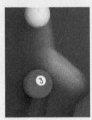

> **Looking Back** ◀◀
> 4.8 Newton's third law
> 5.7 Interacting objects

Angular Momentum

Rotating objects have *angular* momentum. Angular momentum is changed by an applied torque. When no torques act on a rotating object, its angular momentum is conserved.

Conservation of angular momentum causes this skater's spin to increase as she pulls her arms in toward her body.

> **Looking Back** ◀◀
> 7.2, 7.4 Torque and moment of inertia

9.1 Impulse

Suppose that two or more objects have an intense and perhaps complex interaction, such as a collision or an explosion. Our goal is to find a relationship between the velocities of the objects before the interaction and their velocities after the interaction. We'll start by looking at collisions.

A **collision** is a short-duration interaction between two objects. The collision between a tennis ball and a racket, or a baseball and a bat, may seem instantaneous to your eye, but that is a limitation of your perception. A careful look at the tennis ball/racket collision in FIGURE 9.1 reveals that the right side of the ball is flattened and pressed up against the strings of the racket. It takes time to compress the ball, and more time for the ball to re-expand as it leaves the racket.

The duration of a collision depends on the materials from which the objects are made, but 1 to 10 ms (0.001 to 0.010 s) is typical. This is the time during which the two objects are in contact with each other. The harder the objects, the shorter the contact time. A collision between two steel balls lasts less than 1 ms, while that between a tennis ball and racket might last 10 ms.

FIGURE 9.2 A sequence of high-speed photos of a soccer ball being kicked.

Let's begin our discussion by considering a collision that most of us have experienced: kicking a soccer ball. A sequence of high-speed photos of a soccer kick is shown in FIGURE 9.2. As the foot and the ball just come into contact, as shown in the left frame, the ball is just beginning to compress. By the middle frame of Figure 9.2, the ball has sped up and become greatly compressed. Finally, as shown in the right frame, the ball, now moving very fast, is again only slightly compressed.

The amount by which the ball is compressed is a measure of the magnitude of the force the foot exerts on the ball; more compression indicates a greater force. If we were to graph this force versus time, it would look something like FIGURE 9.3. The force is zero until the foot first contacts the ball, rises quickly to a maximum value, and then falls back to zero as the ball leaves the foot. Thus there is a well-defined duration Δt of the force. A large force like this exerted during a short interval of time is called an **impulsive force**. The forces of a hammer on a nail and of a bat on a baseball are other examples of impulsive forces.

A harder kick (i.e., a taller force curve) or a kick of longer duration (a wider force curve) causes the ball to leave the kicker's foot with a higher speed; that is, the *effect* of the kick is larger. Now a taller or wider force-versus-time curve has a larger *area* between the curve and the axis (i.e., the area "under" the force curve is larger), so we can say that **the effect of an impulsive force is proportional to the area under the force-versus-time curve**. This area, shown in FIGURE 9.4a, is called the **impulse J** of the force.

Impulsive forces can be complex, and the shape of the force-versus-time graph often changes in a complicated way. Consequently, it is often useful to think of the collision in terms of an *average* force F_{avg}. As FIGURE 9.4b shows, F_{avg} is defined to be the constant force that has the same duration Δt and the same area under the force curve as the real force. You can see from the figure that the area under the force curve can be written simply as $F_{avg} \Delta t$. Thus

$$\text{impulse } J = \text{area under the force curve} = F_{avg} \Delta t \qquad (9.1)$$

Impulse due to a force acting for a duration t

FIGURE 9.1 A tennis ball collides with a racket. Notice that the right side of the ball is flattened.

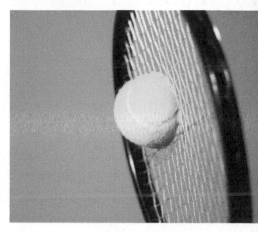

FIGURE 9.3 The force on a soccer ball changes rapidly.

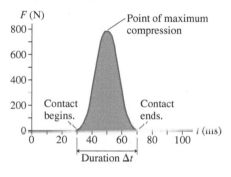

FIGURE 9.4 Looking at the impulse graphically.

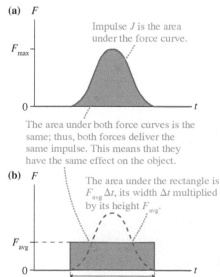

(a) F

Impulse J is the area under the force curve.

F_{max}

The area under both force curves is the same; thus, both forces deliver the same impulse. This means that they have the same effect on the object.

(b) F

The area under the rectangle is $F_{avg} \Delta t$, its width Δt multiplied by its height F_{avg}.

F_{avg}

Same duration Δt

From Equation 9.1 we see that impulse has units of N · s, but you should be able to show that N · s are equivalent to kg · m/s. We'll see shortly why the latter are the preferred units for impulse.

So far, we've been assuming the force is directed along a coordinate axis, such as the x-axis. In this case impulse is a *signed* quantity—it can be positive or negative. A positive impulse results from an average force directed in the positive x-direction (that is, F_{avg} is positive), while a negative impulse is due to a force directed in the negative x-direction (F_{avg} is negative). More generally, the impulse is a *vector* quantity pointing in the direction of the average force vector:

$$\vec{J} = \vec{F}_{avg} \, \Delta t \tag{9.2}$$

EXAMPLE 9.1   **Finding the impulse on a bouncing ball**

A rubber ball experiences the force shown in FIGURE 9.5 as it bounces off the floor.

a. What is the impulse on the ball?
b. What is the average force on the ball?

PREPARE The impulse is the area under the force curve. Here the shape of the graph is triangular, so we'll need to use the fact that the area of a triangle is $\frac{1}{2} \times$ height $\times$ base.

FIGURE 9.5 The force of the floor on a bouncing ball.

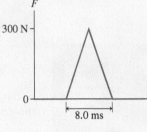

SOLVE a. The impulse is

$$J = \tfrac{1}{2}(300 \text{ N})(0.0080 \text{ s}) = 1.2 \text{ N} \cdot \text{s} = 1.2 \text{ kg} \cdot \text{m/s}$$

b. From Equation 9.1, $J = F_{avg} \, \Delta t$, we can find the average force that would give this same impulse:

$$F_{avg} = \frac{J}{\Delta t} = \frac{1.2 \text{ N} \cdot \text{s}}{0.0080 \text{ s}} = 150 \text{ N}$$

ASSESS In this particular example, the average value of the force is half the maximum value. This is not surprising for a triangular force because the area of a triangle is *half* the base times the height.

9.2 Momentum and the Impulse-Momentum Theorem

We've noted that the effect of an impulsive force depends on the impulse delivered to the object. The effect also depends on the object's mass. Our experience tells us that giving a kick to a heavy object will change its velocity much less than giving the same kick to a light object. We want now to find a quantitative relationship for impulse, mass, and velocity change.

Consider the puck of mass m in FIGURE 9.6, sliding with an initial velocity $\vec{v}_i$. It is struck by a hockey stick that delivers an impulse $\vec{J} = \vec{F}_{avg} \, \Delta t$ to the puck. After the impulse, the puck leaves the stick with a final velocity $\vec{v}_f$. How is this final velocity related to the initial velocity?

From Newton's second law, the average acceleration of the puck during the time the stick is in contact with it is

$$\vec{a}_{avg} = \frac{\vec{F}_{avg}}{m} \tag{9.3}$$

The average acceleration is related to the change in the velocity by

$$\vec{a}_{avg} = \frac{\Delta \vec{v}}{\Delta t} = \frac{\vec{v}_f - \vec{v}_i}{\Delta t} \tag{9.4}$$

Combining Equations 9.3 and 9.4, we have

$$\frac{\vec{F}_{avg}}{m} = \vec{a}_{avg} = \frac{\vec{v}_f - \vec{v}_i}{\Delta t}$$

or, rearranging,

$$\vec{F}_{avg} \, \Delta t = m\vec{v}_f - m\vec{v}_i \tag{9.5}$$

FIGURE 9.6 The stick exerts an impulse on the puck, changing its speed.

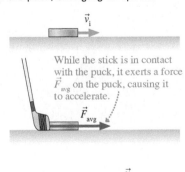

While the stick is in contact with the puck, it exerts a force $\vec{F}_{avg}$ on the puck, causing it to accelerate.

We recognize the left side of this equation as the impulse $\vec{J}$. The right side is the *change* in the quantity $m\vec{v}$. This quantity, the product of the object's mass and velocity, is called the **momentum** of the object. The symbol for momentum is $\vec{p}$:

$$\vec{p} = m\vec{v} \qquad (9.6)$$

Momentum of an object of mass m and velocity $\vec{v}$

From Equation 9.6, the units of momentum are those of mass times velocity, or kg · m/s. We noted above that kg · m/s are the preferred units of impulse. Now we see that the reason for that preference is to match the units of momentum.

FIGURE 9.7 shows that the momentum $\vec{p}$ is a *vector* quantity that points in the same direction as the velocity vector $\vec{v}$. Like any vector, $\vec{p}$ can be decomposed into x- and y-components. Equation 9.6, which is a vector equation, is a shorthand way to write the two equations

$$\begin{aligned} p_x &= mv_x \\ p_y &= mv_y \end{aligned} \qquad (9.7)$$

NOTE ▶ One of the most common errors in momentum problems is failure to use the correct signs. The momentum component p_x has the same sign as v_x. Just like velocity, momentum is positive for a particle moving to the right (on the x-axis) or up (on the y-axis), but *negative* for a particle moving to the left or down. ◀

The *magnitude* of an object's momentum is simply the product of the object's mass and speed, or $p = mv$. A heavy, fast-moving object will have a great deal of momentum, while a light, slow-moving object will have very little. Two objects with very different masses can have similar momenta if their speeds are very different as well. Table 9.1 gives some typical values of the momenta (the plural of *momentum*) of various moving objects. You can see that the momenta of a bullet and a fastball are similar. The momentum of a moving car is almost a billion times greater than that of a falling raindrop.

The Impulse-Momentum Theorem

We can now write Equation 9.5 in terms of impulse and momentum:

$$\vec{J} = \vec{p}_f - \vec{p}_i = \Delta\vec{p} \qquad (9.8)$$

Impulse-momentum theorem

where $\vec{p}_i = m\vec{v}_i$ is the object's initial momentum, $\vec{p}_f = m\vec{v}_f$ is its final momentum after the impulse, and $\Delta\vec{p} = \vec{p}_f - \vec{p}_i$ is the *change* in its momentum. This expression is known as the **impulse-momentum theorem**. It states that **an impulse delivered to an object causes the object's momentum to change.** That is, the *effect* of an impulsive force is to change the object's momentum from $\vec{p}_i$ to

$$\vec{p}_f = \vec{p}_i + \vec{J} \qquad (9.9)$$

Equation 9.8 can also be written in terms of its x- and y-components as

$$\begin{aligned} J_x &= \Delta p_x = (p_x)_f - (p_x)_i = m(v_x)_f - m(v_x)_i \\ J_y &= \Delta p_y = (p_y)_f - (p_y)_i = m(v_y)_f - m(v_y)_i \end{aligned} \qquad (9.10)$$

The impulse-momentum theorem is illustrated by two examples in FIGURE 9.8 on the next page. In the first, the putter strikes the ball, exerting a force on it and delivering an impulse $\vec{J} = \vec{F}_{avg}\,\Delta t$. Notice that the direction of the impulse is the same as

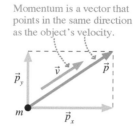

FIGURE 9.7 A particle's momentum vector $\vec{p}$ can be decomposed into x- and y-components.

Momentum is a vector that points in the same direction as the object's velocity.

TABLE 9.1 Some typical momenta (approximate)

Object	Mass (kg)	Speed (m/s)	Momentum (kg · m/s)
Falling raindrop	2×10^{-5}	5	10^{-4}
Bullet	0.004	500	2
Pitched baseball	0.15	40	6
Running person	70	3	200
Car on highway	1000	30	3×10^4

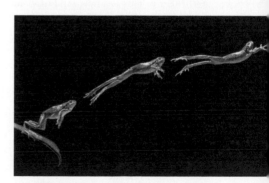

Legging it BIO A frog making a jump wants to gain as much momentum as possible before leaving the ground. This means that he wants the greatest impulse $J = F_{avg}\,\Delta t$ delivered to him by the ground. There is a maximum force that muscles can exert, limiting F_{avg}. But the time interval Δt over which the force is exerted can be greatly increased by having long legs. Many animals that are good jumpers have particularly long legs.

FIGURE 9.8 Impulse causes a *change* in momentum.

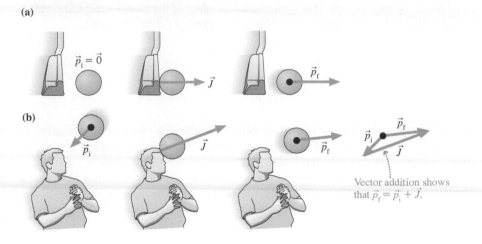

that of the force. Because $\vec{p}_i = \vec{0}$ in this situation, we can use the impulse-momentum theorem to find that the ball leaves the putter with momentum $\vec{p}_f = \vec{p}_i + \vec{J} = \vec{J}$.

NOTE ▶ You can think of the putter as changing the ball's momentum by transferring momentum to it as an impulse. Thus we say the putter *delivers* an impulse to the ball, and the ball *receives* an impulse from the putter. ◀

The soccer player in Figure 9.8b presents a more complicated case. Here, the initial momentum of the ball is directed downward to the left. The impulse delivered to it by the player's head, upward to the right, is strong enough to reverse the ball's motion and send it off in a new direction. The graphical addition of vectors in Figure 9.8b again shows that $\vec{p}_f = \vec{p}_i + \vec{J}$.

EXAMPLE 9.2   **Calculating the change in momentum**

A ball of mass $m = 0.25$ kg rolling to the right at 1.3 m/s strikes a wall and rebounds to the left at 1.1 m/s. What is the change in the ball's momentum? What is the impulse delivered to it by the wall?

PREPARE A visual overview of the ball bouncing is shown in FIGURE 9.9. This is a new kind of visual overview, one in which we show the situation "before" and "after" the interaction. We'll have more to say about before-and-after pictures in the next section. The ball is moving along the x-axis, so we'll write the momentum in component form, as in Equation 9.7. The change in

FIGURE 9.9 Visual overview for a ball bouncing off a wall.

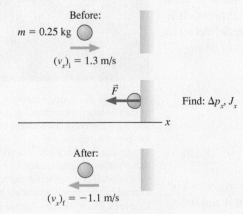

momentum is then the difference between the final and initial values of the momentum. By the impulse-momentum theorem, the impulse is equal to this change in momentum.

SOLVE The x-component of the initial momentum is

$$(p_x)_i = m(v_x)_i = (0.25 \text{ kg})(1.3 \text{ m/s}) = 0.33 \text{ kg} \cdot \text{m/s}$$

The y-component of the momentum is zero both before and after the bounce. After the ball rebounds, the x-component of its momentum is

$$(p_x)_f = m(v_x)_f = (0.25 \text{ kg})(-1.1 \text{ m/s}) = -0.28 \text{ kg} \cdot \text{m/s}$$

It is particularly important to notice that the x-component of the momentum, like that of the velocity, is negative. This indicates that the ball is moving to the *left*. The change in momentum is

$$\Delta p_x = (p_x)_f - (p_x)_i = (-0.28 \text{ kg} \cdot \text{m/s}) - (0.33 \text{ kg} \cdot \text{m/s})$$

$$= -0.61 \text{ kg} \cdot \text{m/s}$$

The change in the momentum is negative. By the impulse-momentum theorem, the impulse delivered to the ball by the wall is equal to this change, so

$$J_x = \Delta p_x = -0.61 \text{ kg} \cdot \text{m/s}$$

ASSESS The impulse is negative, indicating that the force causing the impulse is pointing to the left, which makes sense.

▶ **Water balloon catch** If you've ever tried to catch a water balloon, you may have learned the hard way not to catch it with your arms rigidly extended. The brief collision time implies a large, balloon-bursting force. A better way to catch a water balloon is to pull your arms in toward your body as you catch it, lengthening the collision time and hence reducing the force on the balloon.

An interesting application of the impulse-momentum theorem is to the question of how to slow down a fast-moving object in the gentlest possible way. For instance, a car is headed for a collision with a bridge abutment. How can this crash be made survivable? How do the rams in the chapter-opening photo avoid injury when they collide?

In these examples, the object has momentum $\vec{p}_i$ just before impact and zero momentum after (i.e., $\vec{p}_f = \vec{0}$). The impulse-momentum theorem tells us that

$$\vec{J} = \vec{F}_{avg}\,\Delta t = \Delta\vec{p} = \vec{p}_f - \vec{p}_i = -\vec{p}_i$$

or

$$\vec{F}_{avg} = -\frac{\vec{p}_i}{\Delta t} \qquad (9.11)$$

That is, the average force needed to stop an object is *inversely proportional* to the duration Δt of the collision. **If the duration of the collision can be increased, the force of the impact will be decreased.** This is the principle used in most impact-lessening techniques.

For example, obstacles such as bridge abutments are made safer by placing a line of water-filled barrels in front of them. Water is heavy but deformable. In case of a collision, the time it takes for the car to plow through these barrels is much longer than the time it would take it to stop if it hit the abutment head-on. The force on the car (and on the driver from his or her seat belt) is greatly reduced by the longer-duration collision with the barrels.

The spines of a hedgehog obviously help protect it from predators. But they serve another function as well. If a hedgehog falls from a tree—a not uncommon occurrence—it simply rolls itself into a ball before it lands. Indeed, hedgehogs have been observed to purposely descend to the ground by simply dropping from the tree. Its thick spines then cushion the blow by increasing the time it takes for the animal to come to rest. Along with its small size, this adaptation allows the hedgehog to easily survive long falls unhurt.

The butting rams shown in the photo at the beginning of this chapter also have adaptations that allow them to collide at high speeds without injury to their brains. The cranium has a double wall to prevent skull injuries, and there is a thick spongy mass that increases the time it takes for the brain to come to rest upon impact, again reducing the magnitude of the force on the brain.

Total Momentum

If we have more than one object moving—a *system* of particles—then the system as a whole has an overall momentum. The **total momentum** $\vec{P}$ (note the capital P) of a system of particles is the vector sum of the momenta of the individual particles:

$$\vec{P} = \vec{p}_1 + \vec{p}_2 + \vec{p}_3 + \cdots$$

FIGURE 9.10 shows how the momentum vectors of three moving pool balls are graphically added to find the total momentum. The concept of total momentum will be of key importance when we discuss the conservation law for momentum in Section 9.4.

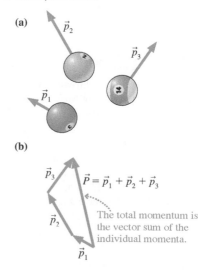

A hedgehog is its own crash cushion!

FIGURE 9.10 The total momentum of three pool balls.

(a)

(b)

$$\vec{P} = \vec{p}_1 + \vec{p}_2 + \vec{p}_3$$

The total momentum is the vector sum of the individual momenta.

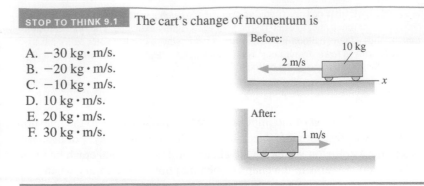

STOP TO THINK 9.1   The cart's change of momentum is

A. $-30 \text{ kg} \cdot \text{m/s}$.
B. $-20 \text{ kg} \cdot \text{m/s}$.
C. $-10 \text{ kg} \cdot \text{m/s}$.
D. $10 \text{ kg} \cdot \text{m/s}$.
E. $20 \text{ kg} \cdot \text{m/s}$.
F. $30 \text{ kg} \cdot \text{m/s}$.

9.3 Solving Impulse and Momentum Problems

Visual overviews have become an important problem-solving tool. The visual overviews and free-body diagrams that you learned to draw in Chapters 1–8 were oriented toward the use of Newton's laws and a subsequent kinematical analysis. Now we are interested in making a connection between "before" and "after."

TACTICS
BOX 9.1   **Drawing a before-and-after visual overview**   (MP)™

❶ **Sketch the situation.** Use two drawings, labeled "Before" and "After," to show the objects *immediately before* they interact and again *immediately after* they interact.
❷ **Establish a coordinate system.** Select your axes to match the motion.
❸ **Define symbols.** Define symbols for the masses and for the velocities before and after the interaction. Position and time are not needed.
❹ **List known information.** List the values of quantities known from the problem statement or that can be found quickly with simple geometry or unit conversions. Before-and-after pictures are usually simpler than the pictures you used for dynamics problems, so listing known information on the sketch is often adequate.
❺ **Identify the desired unknowns.** What quantity or quantities will allow you to answer the question? These should have been defined as symbols in step 3.

Exercises 9–11

EXAMPLE 9.3   **Force in hitting a baseball**

A 150 g baseball is thrown with a speed of 20 m/s. It is hit straight back toward the pitcher at a speed of 40 m/s. The impulsive force of the bat on the ball has the shape shown in FIGURE 9.11. What is the *maximum* force F_{max} that the bat exerts on the ball? What is the *average* force that the bat exerts on the ball?

FIGURE 9.11 The interaction force between the baseball and the bat.

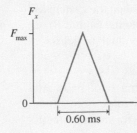

PREPARE We can model the interaction as a collision. FIGURE 9.12 is a before-and-after visual overview in which the steps from Tactics Box 9.1 are explicitly noted. Because F_x is positive (a force to the right), we know the ball was initially moving toward the left and is hit back toward the right. Thus we converted the statements about *speeds* into information about *velocities*, with $(v_x)_i$ negative.

SOLVE In the last several chapters we've started the mathematical solution with Newton's second law. Now we want to use the impulse-momentum theorem:

$$\Delta p_x = J_x = \text{area under the force curve}$$

FIGURE 9.12 A before-and-after visual overview.

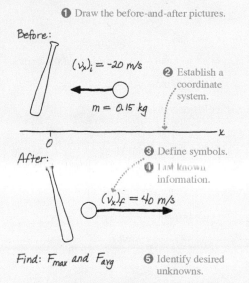

❶ Draw the before-and-after pictures.

Before:

$(v_x)_i = -20$ m/s

❷ Establish a coordinate system.

$m = 0.15$ kg

❸ Define symbols.

After:

❹ List known information.

$(v_x)_f = 40$ m/s

Find: F_{max} and F_{avg}

❺ Identify desired unknowns.

We know the velocities before and after the collision, so we can find the change in the ball's momentum:

$$\Delta p_x = m(v_x)_f - m(v_x)_i = (0.15 \text{ kg})(40 \text{ m/s} - (-20 \text{ m/s}))$$

$$= 9.0 \text{ kg} \cdot \text{m/s}$$

The force curve is a triangle with height F_{max} and width 0.60 ms. As in Example 9.1, the area under the curve is

$$J_x = \text{area} = \tfrac{1}{2} \times F_{max} \times (6.0 \times 10^{-4} \text{ s})$$

$$= (F_{max})(3.0 \times 10^{-4})$$

According to the impulse-momentum theorem, $\Delta p_x = J_x$, so we have

$$9.0 \text{ kg} \cdot \text{m/s} = (F_{max})(3.0 \times 10^{-4} \text{ s})$$

Thus the *maximum* force is

$$F_{max} = \frac{9.0 \text{ kg} \cdot \text{m/s}}{3.0 \times 10^{-4} \text{ s}} = 30,000 \text{ N}$$

Using Equation 9.1, we find that the *average* force, which depends on the collision duration $\Delta t = 6.0 \times 10^{-4}$ s, has the smaller value:

$$F_{avg} = \frac{J_x}{\Delta t} = \frac{\Delta p_x}{\Delta t} = \frac{9.0 \text{ kg} \cdot \text{m/s}}{6.0 \times 10^{-4} \text{ s}} = 15,000 \text{ N}$$

ASSESS F_{max} is a large force, but quite typical of the impulsive forces during collisions.

The Impulse Approximation

When two objects interact during a collision or other brief interaction, such as that between the bat and ball of Example 9.3, the forces *between* them are generally quite large. Other forces may also act on the interacting objects, but usually these forces are *much* smaller than the interaction forces. In Example 9.3, for example, the 1.5 N weight of the ball is vastly less than the 30,000 N force of the bat on the ball. We can reasonably neglect these small forces *during* the brief time of the impulsive force. Doing so is called the **impulse approximation.**

When we use the impulse approximation, $(p_x)_i$ and $(p_x)_f$—and $(v_x)_i$ and $(v_x)_f$—are then the momenta (and velocities) *immediately* before and *immediately* after the collision. For example, the velocities in Example 9.3 are those of the ball just before and after it collides with the bat. We could then do a follow-up problem, including weight and drag, to find the ball's speed a second later as the second baseman catches it.

EXAMPLE 9.4 **Height of a bouncing ball**

A 100 g rubber ball is thrown straight down onto a hard floor so that it strikes the floor with a speed of 11 m/s. FIGURE 9.13 shows the force that the floor exerts on the ball. Estimate the height of the ball's bounce.

PREPARE The ball experiences an impulsive force while in contact with the

FIGURE 9.13 The force of the floor on a bouncing rubber ball.

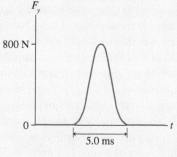

floor. Using the impulse approximation, we'll neglect the ball's weight during these 5.0 ms. The ball's rise after the bounce is free-fall motion—that is, motion subject only to the force of gravity. We'll use free-fall kinematics to describe the motion after the bounce.

FIGURE 9.14 on the next page is a visual overview. Here we have a two-part problem, an impulsive collision followed by upward free fall. The overview thus shows the ball just before the collision, where we label its velocity as v_{1y}; just after the collision, where its velocity is v_{2y}; and at the highest point of its rising free fall, where its velocity is $v_{3y} = 0$.

Continued

FIGURE 9.14 Before-and-after visual overview for a bouncing ball.

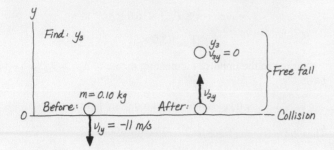

J_y = area under the force curve $\approx$ (400 N) $\times$ (0.0050 s)

$$= 2.0 \text{ N} \cdot \text{s} = 2.0 \text{ kg} \cdot \text{m/s}$$

Thus

$$p_{2y} = p_{1y} + J_y = (-1.1 \text{ kg} \cdot \text{m/s}) + 2.0 \text{ kg} \cdot \text{m/s}$$

$$= 0.9 \text{ kg} \cdot \text{m/s}$$

and the post-collision velocity is

$$v_{2y} = \frac{p_{2y}}{m} = \frac{0.9 \text{ kg} \cdot \text{m/s}}{0.10 \text{ kg}} = 9 \text{ m/s}$$

The rebound speed is less than the impact speed, as expected. Finally, we can use free-fall kinematics to find

$$v_{3y}^2 = 0 = v_{2y}^2 - 2g \, \Delta y = v_{2y}^2 - 2gy_3$$

$$y_3 = \frac{v_{2y}^2}{2g} = \frac{(9 \text{ m/s})^2}{2(9.8 \text{ m/s}^2)} = 4 \text{ m}$$

We estimate that the ball bounces to a height of 4 m.

ASSESS This is a reasonable height for a rubber ball thrown down quite hard.

SOLVE The impulse-momentum theorem tells us that $J_y = \Delta p_y = p_{2y} - p_{1y}$, so that $p_{2y} = p_{1y} + J_y$. The initial momentum, just before the collision, is $p_{1y} = mv_{1y} = (0.10 \text{ kg})(-11 \text{ m/s}) = -1.1 \text{ kg} \cdot \text{m/s}$.

Next, we need to find the impulse J_y, which is the area under the curve in Figure 9.13. Because the force is given as a smooth curve, we'll have to *estimate* this area. Recall that the area can be written as $F_{avg} \, \Delta t$. From the curve, we might estimate F_{avg} to be about 400 N, or half the maximum value of the force. With this estimate we have

---

STOP TO THINK 9.2 A 10 g rubber ball and a 10 g clay ball are each thrown at a wall with equal speeds. The rubber ball bounces; the clay ball sticks. Which ball receives the greater impulse from the wall?

A. The clay ball receives a greater impulse because it sticks.
B. The rubber ball receives a greater impulse because it bounces.
C. They receive equal impulses because they have equal momenta.
D. Neither receives an impulse because the wall doesn't move.

FIGURE 9.15 A collision between two balls.

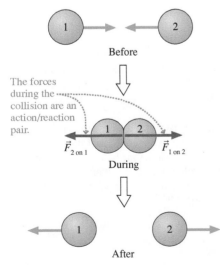

The forces during the collision are an action/reaction pair.

9.4 Conservation of Momentum

The impulse-momentum theorem was derived from Newton's second law and is really just an alternative way of looking at that law. It is used in the context of single-particle dynamics, much as we used Newton's law in Chapters 4–7.

However, consider two objects, such as the rams shown in the opening photo of this chapter, that interact during the brief moment of a collision. During a collision, two objects exert forces on each other that vary in a complex way. We usually don't even know the magnitudes of these forces. Using Newton's second law alone to predict the outcome of such a collision would thus be a daunting challenge. However, by using Newton's *third* law in the language of impulse and momentum, we'll find that it's possible to describe the *outcome* of a collision—the final speeds and directions of the colliding objects—in a simple way. Newton's third law will lead us to one of the most important conservation laws in physics.

FIGURE 9.15 shows two balls initially headed toward each other. The balls collide, then bounce apart. The forces during the collision, when the balls are interacting, are the action/reaction pair $\vec{F}_{1\text{ on }2}$ and $\vec{F}_{2\text{ on }1}$. For now, we'll continue to assume that the motion is one dimensional along the x-axis.

During the collision, the impulse J_{2x} delivered to ball 2 by ball 1 is the average value of $\vec{F}_{1\,\text{on}\,2}$ multiplied by the collision time Δt. Likewise, the impulse J_{1x} delivered to ball 1 by ball 2 is the average value of $\vec{F}_{2\,\text{on}\,1}$ multiplied by Δt. Because $\vec{F}_{1\,\text{on}\,2}$ and $\vec{F}_{2\,\text{on}\,1}$ form an action/reaction pair, they have equal magnitudes but opposite directions. As a result, the two impulses J_{1x} and J_{2x} are also equal in magnitude but opposite in sign, so that $J_{1x} = -J_{2x}$.

According to the impulse-momentum theorem, the change in the momentum of ball 1 is $\Delta p_{1x} = J_{1x}$ and the change in the momentum of ball 2 is $\Delta p_{2x} = J_{2x}$. Because $J_{1x} = -J_{2x}$, the change in the momentum of ball 1 is equal in magnitude but opposite in sign to the change in momentum of ball 2. If ball 1's momentum increases by a certain amount during the collision, ball 2's momentum will *decrease* by exactly the same amount. This implies that **the total momentum $P_x = p_{1x} + p_{2x}$ of the two balls is *unchanged* by the collision;** that is,

$$(P_x)_\text{f} = (P_x)_\text{i} \tag{9.12}$$

Because it doesn't change during the collision, we say that the *x*-component of total momentum is *conserved*. Equation 9.12 is our first example of a *conservation law*.

Law of Conservation of Momentum

The same arguments just presented for the two colliding balls can be extended to systems containing any number of objects. FIGURE 9.16 shows the idea. Each pair of particles in the system (the boundary of which is denoted by the red line) interacts via forces that are an action/reaction pair. Exactly as for the two-particle collision, the change in momentum of particle 2 due to the force from particle 3 is equal in magnitude, but opposite in direction, to the change in particle 3's momentum due to particle 2. The *net* change in the momentum of these two particles due to their interaction forces is thus zero. The same argument holds for every pair, with the result that, no matter how complicated the forces between the particles, **there is no change in the *total* momentum $\vec{P}$ of the system.** The total momentum of the system remains constant: It is *conserved*.

Figure 9.16 showed particles interacting only with other particles inside the system. Forces that act only between particles within the system are called **internal forces.** As we've just seen, **the total momentum of a system subject only to internal forces is conserved.**

Most systems are also subject to forces from agents outside the system. These forces are called **external forces.** For example, the system consisting of a student on a skateboard is subject to three external forces—the normal force of the ground on the skateboard, the force of gravity on the student, and the force of gravity on the board. How do external forces affect the momentum of a system of particles?

In FIGURE 9.17 we show the same three-particle system of Figure 9.16, but now with *external* forces acting on the three particles. These external forces *can* change the momentum of the system. During a time interval Δt, for instance, the external force $\vec{F}_{\text{ext on}\,1}$ acting on particle 1 changes its momentum, according to the impulse-momentum theorem, by $\Delta \vec{p}_1 = (\vec{F}_{\text{ext on}\,1})\Delta t$. The momenta of the other two particles change similarly. Thus the change in the total momentum is

$$
\begin{aligned}
\Delta \vec{P} &= \Delta \vec{p}_1 + \Delta \vec{p}_2 + \Delta \vec{p}_3 \\
&= (\vec{F}_{\text{ext on}\,1}\Delta t) + (\vec{F}_{\text{ext on}\,2}\Delta t) + (\vec{F}_{\text{ext on}\,3}\Delta t) \\
&= (\vec{F}_{\text{ext on}\,1} + \vec{F}_{\text{ext on}\,2} + \vec{F}_{\text{ext on}\,3})\Delta t \\
&= \vec{F}_{\text{net}}\Delta t
\end{aligned}
\tag{9.13}
$$

where $\vec{F}_{\text{net}}$ is the net force due to *external forces*.

Equation 9.13 has a very important implication in the case where the net force on a system is zero: **If $\vec{F}_{\text{net}} = \vec{0}$ the *total* momentum $\vec{P}$ of the system does not change.** The total momentum remains constant, *regardless* of whatever interactions are going on *inside* the system.

FIGURE 9.16 A system of three particles.

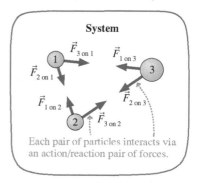

Each pair of particles interacts via an action/reaction pair of forces.

FIGURE 9.17 A system of particles subject to external forces.

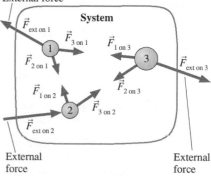

Earlier, we found that a system's total momentum is conserved when the system has no external forces acting on it. Now we've found that the system's total momentum is also conserved when the net external force acting on it is zero. With no external forces acting that can change its momentum, we call a system with $\vec{F}_{net} = \vec{0}$ an **isolated system.**

The importance of these results is sufficient to elevate them to a law of nature, alongside Newton's laws.

> **Law of conservation of momentum** The total momentum $\vec{P}$ of an isolated system is a constant. Interactions within the system do not change the system's total momentum.

NOTE ▶ It is worth emphasizing the critical role of Newton's third law in the derivation of Equation 9.13. The law of conservation of momentum is a direct consequence of the fact that interactions within an isolated system are action/reaction pairs. ◄

Mathematically, the law of conservation of momentum for an isolated system is

$$\vec{P}_f = \vec{P}_i \tag{9.14}$$

Law of conservation of momentum for an isolated system

The total momentum after an interaction is equal to the total momentum before the interaction. Because Equation 9.14 is a vector equation, the equality is true for each of the components of the momentum vector; that is,

$$
\begin{array}{c}
\overbrace{}^{\text{Final momentum}} \qquad \overbrace{}^{\text{Initial momentum}} \\
x\text{-component} \cdots\cdots\blacktriangleright (p_{1x})_f + (p_{2x})_f + (p_{3x})_f + \cdots = (p_{1x})_i + (p_{2x})_i + (p_{3x})_i + \cdots \\
\underbrace{\uparrow \qquad \uparrow \qquad \uparrow}_{\text{Particle 1 Particle 2 Particle 3}} \\
y\text{-component} \cdots\cdots\blacktriangleright (p_{1y})_f + (p_{2y})_f + (p_{3y})_f + \cdots = (p_{1y})_i + (p_{2y})_i + (p_{3y})_i + \cdots
\end{array}
\tag{9.15}
$$

EXAMPLE 9.5   Speed of ice skaters pushing off

Two ice skaters, Sandra and David, stand facing each other on frictionless ice. Sandra has a mass of 45 kg, David a mass of 80 kg. They then push off from each other. After the push, Sandra moves off at a speed of 2.2 m/s. What is David's speed?

PREPARE The two skaters interact with each other, but they form an isolated system because, for each skater, the upward normal force of the ice balances their downward weight force to make $\vec{F}_{net} = \vec{0}$. Thus the total momentum of the system of the two skaters is conserved.

FIGURE 9.18 shows a before-and-after visual overview for the two skaters. The total momentum before they push off is $\vec{P}_i = \vec{0}$ because both skaters are at rest. Consequently, the total momentum will still be $\vec{0}$ *after* they push off.

SOLVE Since the motion is only in the x-direction, we'll only need to consider x-components of momentum. We write Sandra's initial momentum as $(p_{Sx})_i = m_S(v_{Sx})_i$, where m_S is her mass and

FIGURE 9.18 Before-and-after visual overview for two skaters pushing off from each other.

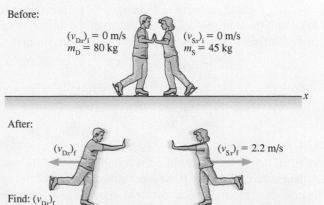

Before:

$(v_{Dx})_i = 0$ m/s
$m_D = 80$ kg

$(v_{Sx})_i = 0$ m/s
$m_S = 45$ kg

After:

$(v_{Dx})_f$

$(v_{Sx})_f = 2.2$ m/s

Find: $(v_{Dx})_f$

$(v_{Sx})_i$ her initial velocity. Similarly, we write David's initial momentum as $(p_{Dx})_i = m_D(v_{Dx})_i$. Both these momenta are zero because both skaters are initially at rest.

We can now apply the mathematical statement of momentum conservation, Equation 9.15. Writing the final momentum of Sandra as $m_S(v_{Sx})_f$ and that of David as $m_D(v_{Dx})_f$, we have

$$\underbrace{m_S(v_{Sx})_f + m_D(v_{Dx})_f}_{\substack{\text{The skaters' final} \\ \text{momentum} \dots}} = \underbrace{m_S(v_{Sx})_i + m_D(v_{Dx})_i}_{\substack{\dots \text{equals their initial} \\ \text{momentum} \dots}} = \underbrace{0}_{\substack{\dots \text{which} \\ \text{was zero.}}}$$

Solving for $(v_{Dx})_f$, we find

$$(v_{Dx})_f = -\frac{m_S}{m_D}(v_{Sx})_f = -\frac{45 \text{ kg}}{80 \text{ kg}} \times 2.2 \text{ m/s} = -1.2 \text{ m/s}$$

David moves backward with a *speed* of 1.2 m/s.

Notice that we didn't need to know any details about the force between David and Sandra in order to find David's final speed. Conservation of momentum *mandates* this result.

ASSESS The *total* momentum of the system is zero both before and after they push off, but the individual momenta are not zero. Because $(p_{Sx})_f$ is positive (Sandra moves to the right), $(p_{Dx})_f$ must have the same magnitude but the opposite sign (David moves to the left).

A Strategy for Conservation of Momentum Problems

Our derivation of the law of conservation of momentum, and the conditions under which it holds, suggests a problem-solving strategy.

Activ ONLINE Physics   6.3, 6.4, 6.6, 6.7, 6.10

PROBLEM-SOLVING STRATEGY 9.1   Conservation of momentum problems   (MP)™

PREPARE Clearly define *the system*.

■ If possible, choose a system that is isolated ($\vec{F}_{net} = \vec{0}$) or within which the interactions are sufficiently short and intense that you can ignore external forces for the duration of the interaction (the impulse approximation). Momentum is then conserved.

■ If it's not possible to choose an isolated system, try to divide the problem into parts such that momentum is conserved during one segment of the motion. Other segments of the motion can be analyzed using Newton's laws or, as you'll learn in Chapter 10, conservation of energy.

Following Tactics Box 9.1, draw a before-and-after visual overview. Define symbols that will be used in the problem, list known values, and identify what you're trying to find.

SOLVE The mathematical representation is based on the law of conservation of momentum: $\vec{P}_f = \vec{P}_i$. In component form, this is

$$(p_{1x})_f + (p_{2x})_f + (p_{3x})_f + \cdots = (p_{1x})_i + (p_{2x})_i + (p_{3x})_i + \cdots$$

$$(p_{1y})_f + (p_{2y})_f + (p_{3y})_f + \cdots = (p_{1y})_i + (p_{2y})_i + (p_{3y})_i + \cdots$$

ASSESS Check that your result has the correct units, is reasonable, and answers the question.

Exercise 17

EXAMPLE 9.6   **Getaway speed of a cart**

Bob is running from the police and thinks he can make a faster getaway by jumping on a stationary cart in front of him. He runs toward the cart, jumps on, and rolls along the horizontal street. Bob has a mass of 75 kg and the cart's mass is 25 kg. If Bob's speed is 4.0 m/s when he jumps onto the cart, what is the cart's speed after Bob jumps on?

PREPARE When Bob lands on and sticks to the cart, a "collision" occurs between Bob and the cart. If we take Bob and the cart together to be the system, the forces involved in this collision—friction forces between Bob's feet and the cart—are internal forces. Because the normal force balances the weight of both Bob and the cart, the net external force on the system is zero, so the

Continued

total momentum of Bob + cart is conserved: It is the same before and after the collision.

The visual overview in FIGURE 9.19 shows the important point that Bob and the cart move together after he lands on the cart, so $(v_x)_f$ is their common final velocity.

FIGURE 9.19 Before-and-after visual overview of Bob and the cart.

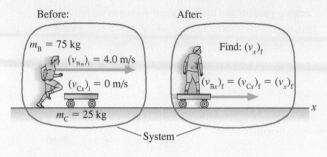

SOLVE To solve for the final velocity of Bob and the cart, we'll use conservation of momentum: $(P_x)_f = (P_x)_i$. Written in terms of the individual momenta, we have

$$(P_x)_i = m_B(v_{Bx})_i + m_C \underbrace{(v_{Cx})_i}_{0 \text{ m/s}} = m_B(v_{Bx})_i$$

$$(P_x)_f = m_B(v_x)_f + m_C(v_x)_f = (m_B + m_C)(v_x)_f$$

In the second equation, we've used the fact that both Bob and the cart travel at the common velocity of $(v_x)_f$. Equating the final and initial total momenta gives

$$(m_B + m_C)(v_x)_f = m_B(v_{Bx})_i$$

Solving this for $(v_x)_f$, we find

$$(v_x)_f = \frac{m_B}{m_B + m_C}(v_{Bx})_i = \frac{75 \text{ kg}}{100 \text{ kg}} \times 4.0 \text{ m/s} = 3.0 \text{ m/s}$$

The cart's speed is 3.0 m/s immediately after Bob jumps on.

ASSESS It makes sense that Bob has *lost* speed because he had to share his initial momentum with the cart. Not a good way to make a getaway!

Notice how easy this was! No forces, no kinematic equations, no simultaneous equations. Why didn't we think of this before? Although conservation laws are indeed powerful, they can answer only certain questions. Had we wanted to know how far Bob slid across the cart before sticking to it, how long the slide took, or what the cart's acceleration was during the collision, we would not have been able to answer such questions on the basis of the conservation law. There is a price to pay for finding a simple connection between before and after, and that price is the loss of information about the details of the interaction. If we are satisfied with knowing only about before and after, then conservation laws are a simple and straightforward way to proceed. But many problems *do* require us to understand the interaction, and for these there is no avoiding Newton's laws and all they entail.

It Depends on the System

The first step in the problem-solving strategy asks you to clearly define *the system*. This is worth emphasizing, because many problem-solving errors arise from trying to apply momentum conservation to an inappropriate system. **The goal is to choose a system whose momentum will be conserved.** Even then, it is the *total* momentum of the system that is conserved, not the momenta of the individual particles within the system.

In Example 9.6, we chose the system to be Bob and the cart. Why this choice? Let's see what would happen if we had chosen the system to be Bob alone, as shown in FIGURE 9.20. As the free-body diagram shows, as Bob lands on the cart, there are three forces acting on him: the normal force $\vec{n}$ of the cart on Bob, his weight $\vec{w}$, and a friction force $\vec{f}_{C \text{ on } B}$ of the cart on Bob. This last force is subtle. We know that Bob's feet must exert a rightward-directed friction force $\vec{f}_{B \text{ on } C}$ *on the cart* as he lands; it is this friction force that causes the cart to speed up. By Newton's third law, then, the cart exerts a leftward directed force $\vec{f}_{C \text{ on } B}$ on Bob.

The free-body diagram of Figure 9.20 then shows that there is a net force on Bob directed to the left. Thus the system consisting of Bob alone is *not* isolated, and Bob's momentum will not be conserved. Indeed, we know that Bob slows down after landing on the cart, so that his momentum clearly *decreases*.

If we had chosen the cart to be the system, the unbalanced rightward force $\vec{f}_{B \text{ on } C}$ of Bob on the cart would also lead to a nonzero net force. Thus the cart's momentum would not be conserved; in fact, we know it *increases* because the cart speeds up.

Only by choosing the system to be Bob and the cart *together* is the net force on the system zero and the total momentum conserved. The momentum lost by Bob is gained by the cart, so the total momentum of the two is unchanged.

FIGURE 9.20 An analysis of the system consisting of Bob alone.

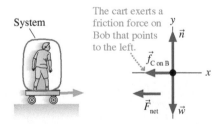

The cart exerts a friction force on Bob that points to the left.

Explosions

An **explosion,** where the particles of the system move apart after a brief, intense interaction, is the opposite of a collision. The explosive forces, which could be from an expanding spring or from expanding hot gases, are *internal* forces. If the system is isolated, its total momentum during the explosion will be conserved.

EXAMPLE 9.7   **Recoil speed of a rifle**

A 30 g ball is fired from a 1.2 kg spring-loaded toy rifle with a speed of 15 m/s. What is the recoil speed of the rifle?

PREPARE As the ball moves down the barrel, there are complicated forces exerted on the ball and on the rifle. However, if we take the system to be the ball + rifle, these are *internal* forces that do not change the total momentum.

The *external* forces of the rifle's and ball's weights are balanced by the external force exerted by the person holding the

FIGURE 9.21 Before-and-after visual overview for a toy rifle.

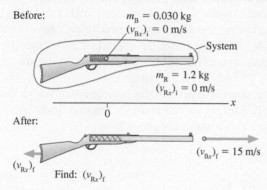

rifle, so $\vec{F}_{net} = \vec{0}$. This is an isolated system and the law of conservation of momentum applies.

FIGURE 9.21 shows a visual overview before and after the ball is fired. We'll assume the ball is fired in the $+x$ direction.

SOLVE The x-component of the total momentum is $P_x = p_{Bx} + p_{Rx}$. Everything is at rest before the trigger is pulled, so the initial momentum is zero. After the trigger is pulled, the internal force of the spring pushes the ball down the barrel *and* pushes the rifle backward. Conservation of momentum gives

$$(P_x)_f = m_B(v_{Bx})_f + m_R(v_{Rx})_f = (P_x)_i = 0$$

Solving for the rifle's velocity, we find

$$(v_{Rx})_f = -\frac{m_B}{m_R}(v_{Bx})_f = -\frac{0.030 \text{ kg}}{1.2 \text{ kg}} \times 15 \text{ m/s} = -0.38 \text{ m/s}$$

The minus sign indicates that the rifle's recoil is to the left. The recoil *speed* is 0.38 m/s.

ASSESS Real rifles fire their bullets at much higher velocities, and their recoil is correspondingly higher. Shooters need to brace themselves against the "kick" of the rifle back against their shoulder.

We would not know where to begin to solve a problem such as this using Newton's laws. But Example 9.7 is a simple problem when approached from the before-and-after perspective of a conservation law. The selection of ball + rifle as "the system" was the critical step. For momentum conservation to be a useful principle, we had to select a system in which the complicated forces due to the spring and to friction were all internal forces. The rifle by itself is *not* an isolated system, so its momentum is *not* conserved.

Much the same reasoning explains how a rocket or jet aircraft accelerates. **FIGURE 9.22** shows a rocket with a parcel of fuel on board. Burning converts the fuel to hot gases that are expelled from the rocket motor. If we choose rocket + gases to be the system, then the burning and expulsion are internal forces. In deep space there are no other forces, so the total momentum of the rocket + gases system must be conserved. The rocket gains forward velocity and momentum as the exhaust gases are shot out the back, but the *total* momentum of the system remains zero.

Many people find it hard to understand how a rocket can accelerate in the vacuum of space because there is nothing to "push against." Thinking in terms of momentum, you can see that the rocket does not push against anything *external,* but only against the gases that it pushes out the back. In return, in accordance with Newton's third law, the gases push forward on the rocket.

FIGURE 9.22 Rocket propulsion is an example of conservation of momentum.

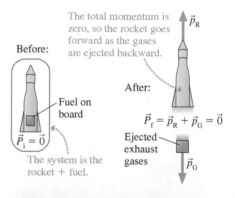

▶ **Squid propulsion** BIO Squids use a form of "rocket propulsion" to make quick movements to escape enemies or catch prey. The squid draws in water through a pair of valves in its outer sheath, or mantle, and then quickly expels the water through a funnel, propelling the squid backward. The funnel's direction is adjustable, allowing the squid to move in any backward direction.

An explosion in a rigid pipe shoots three balls out of its ends. A 6 g ball comes out the right end. A 4 g ball comes out the left end with twice the speed of the 6 g ball. From which end, left or right, does the third ball emerge?

9.5 Inelastic Collisions

Collisions can have different possible outcomes. A rubber ball dropped on the floor bounces—it's *elastic*—but a ball of clay sticks to the floor without bouncing; we call such a collision *inelastic*. A golf club hitting a golf ball causes the ball to rebound away from the club (elastic), but a bullet striking a block of wood becomes embedded in the block (inelastic).

A collision in which the two objects stick together and move with a common final velocity is called a **perfectly inelastic collision**. The clay hitting the floor and the bullet embedding itself in the wood are examples of perfectly inelastic collisions. Other examples include railroad cars coupling together upon impact and darts hitting a dart board. FIGURE 9.23 emphasizes the fact that the two objects have a common final velocity after they collide. (We have drawn the combined object moving to the right, but it could have ended up moving to the left, depending on the objects' masses and initial velocities.)

In an *elastic collision,* by contrast, the two objects bounce apart. We've looked at some examples of elastic collisions, but a full analysis requires some ideas about energy. We will return to elastic collisions in Chapter 10.

FIGURE 9.23 A perfectly inelastic collision.

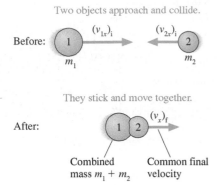

Two objects approach and collide.

Before: m_1 $(v_{1x})_i$ $(v_{2x})_i$ m_2

They stick and move together.

After: 1 2 $(v_x)_f$

Combined mass $m_1 + m_2$ Common final velocity

EXAMPLE 9.8   **Speeds in a perfectly inelastic glider collision**

In a laboratory experiment, a 200 g air-track glider and a 400 g air-track glider are pushed toward each other from opposite ends of the track. The gliders have Velcro tabs on their fronts so that they will stick together when they collide. The 200 g glider is pushed with an initial speed of 3.0 m/s. The collision causes it to reverse direction at 0.50 m/s. What was the initial speed of the 400 g glider?

PREPARE We model the gliders as particles and define the two gliders as the system. This is an isolated system, so its total momentum is conserved in the collision. The gliders stick together, so this is a perfectly inelastic collision.

FIGURE 9.24 Before-and-after visual overview for two gliders colliding on an air track.

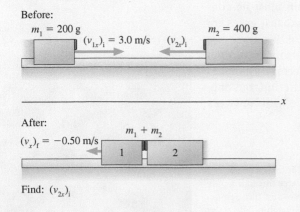

Before:

$m_1 = 200$ g $m_2 = 400$ g
$(v_{1x})_i = 3.0$ m/s $(v_{2x})_i$

After:

$(v_x)_f = -0.50$ m/s $m_1 + m_2$
1 2

Find: $(v_{2x})_i$

FIGURE 9.24 shows a visual overview. We've chosen to let the 200 g glider (glider 1) start out moving to the right, so $(v_{1x})_i$ is a positive 3.0 m/s. The gliders move to the left after the collision, so their common final velocity is $(v_x)_f = -0.50$ m/s. You can see that velocity $(v_{2x})_i$ must be negative in order to "turn around" both gliders.

SOLVE The law of conservation of momentum, $(P_x)_f = (P_x)_i$, is

$$(m_1 + m_2)(v_x)_f = m_1(v_{1x})_i + m_2(v_{2x})_i$$

where we made use of the fact that the combined mass $m_1 + m_2$ moves together after the collision. We can easily solve for the initial velocity of the 400 g glider:

$$(v_{2x})_i = \frac{(m_1 + m_2)(v_x)_f - m_1(v_{1x})_i}{m_2}$$

$$= \frac{(0.60 \text{ kg})(-0.50 \text{ m/s}) - (0.20 \text{ kg})(3.0 \text{ m/s})}{0.40 \text{ kg}}$$

$$= -2.3 \text{ m/s}$$

The negative sign, which we anticipated, indicates that the 400 g glider started out moving to the left. The initial *speed* of the glider, which we were asked to find, is 2.3 m/s.

ASSESS The key step in solving inelastic collision problems is that both objects move after the collision with the same velocity. You should thus choose a single symbol (here, $(v_x)_f$) for this common velocity.

STOP TO THINK 9.4   The two particles shown collide and stick together. After the collision, the combined particles

A. Move to the right as shown.
B. Move to the left.
C. Are at rest.

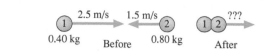

9.6 Momentum and Collisions in Two Dimensions

Our examples thus far have been confined to motion along a one-dimensional axis. Many practical examples of momentum conservation involve motion in a plane. The total momentum $\vec{P}$ is the *vector* sum of the momenta $\vec{p} = m\vec{v}$ of the individual particles. Consequently, as Equation 9.15 showed, momentum is conserved only if each component of $\vec{P}$ is conserved:

$$(p_{1x})_f + (p_{2x})_f + (p_{3x})_f + \cdots = (p_{1x})_i + (p_{2x})_i + (p_{3x})_i + \cdots$$

$$(p_{1y})_f + (p_{2y})_f + (p_{3y})_f + \cdots = (p_{1y})_i + (p_{2y})_i + (p_{3y})_i + \cdots \tag{9.16}$$

In this section we'll apply momentum conservation to motion in two dimensions.

Collisions and explosions often involve motion in two dimensions.

EXAMPLE 9.9   Analyzing a peregrine falcon strike

Peregrine falcons often grab their prey from above while both falcon and prey are in flight. A falcon, flying at 18 m/s, swoops down at a 45° angle from behind a pigeon flying horizontally at 9.0 m/s. The falcon has a mass of 0.80 kg and the pigeon a mass of 0.36 kg. What are the speed and direction of the falcon (now holding the pigeon) immediately after impact?

PREPARE This is a perfectly inelastic collision because after the collision the falcon and pigeon move at a common velocity. The total momentum of the falcon + pigeon system is conserved. For a two-dimensional collision, this means that the x-component of the total momentum before the collision must equal the x-component

FIGURE 9.25 Before-and-after visual overview for a falcon catching a pigeon.

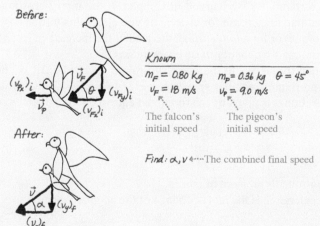

of the total momentum after the collision, and similarly for the y-components. FIGURE 9.25 is a before-and-after visual overview.

SOLVE We'll start by finding the x- and y-components of the momentum before the collision. For the x-component we have

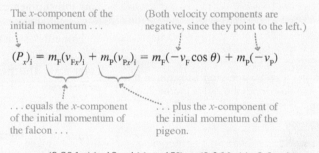

The x-component of the initial momentum . . .   (Both velocity components are negative, since they point to the left.)

$$(P_x)_i = m_F(v_{Fx})_i + m_P(v_{Px})_i = m_F(-v_F \cos\theta) + m_P(-v_P)$$

. . . equals the x-component of the initial momentum of the falcon . . .   . . plus the x-component of the initial momentum of the pigeon.

$$= (0.80 \text{ kg})(-18 \text{ m/s})(\cos 45°) + (0.36 \text{ kg})(-9.0 \text{ m/s})$$

$$= -13.4 \text{ kg} \cdot \text{m/s}$$

Similarly, for the y-component of the initial momentum we have

$$(P_y)_i = m_F(v_{Fy})_i + m_P(v_{Py})_i = m_F(-v_F \sin\theta) + 0$$

$$= (0.80 \text{ kg})(-18.0 \text{ m/s})(\sin 45°) = -10.2 \text{ kg} \cdot \text{m/s}$$

After the collision, the two birds move with a common velocity $\vec{v}$ that is directed at an angle α from the horizontal. The x-component of the final momentum is then

$$(P_x)_f = (m_F + m_P)(v_x)_f$$

Continued

Momentum conservation requires $(P_x)_f = (P_x)_i$, so

$$(v_x)_f = \frac{(P_x)_i}{m_F + m_P} = \frac{-13.4 \text{ kg} \cdot \text{m/s}}{(0.80 \text{ kg}) + (0.36 \text{ kg})} = -11.6 \text{ m/s}$$

Similarly, $(P_y)_f = (P_y)_i$ gives

$$(v_y)_f = \frac{(P_y)_i}{m_F + m_P} = \frac{-10.2 \text{ kg} \cdot \text{m/s}}{(0.80 \text{ kg}) + (0.36 \text{ kg})} = -8.79 \text{ m/s}$$

From the figure we see that $\tan\alpha = (v_y)_f/(v_x)_f$, so that

$$\alpha = \tan^{-1}\left(\frac{(v_y)_f}{(v_x)_f}\right) = \tan^{-1}\left(\frac{-8.79 \text{ m/s}}{-11.6 \text{ m/s}}\right) = 37°$$

The magnitude of the final velocity (i.e., the speed) can be found from the Pythagorean theorem as

$$v = \sqrt{(v_x)_f^2 + (v_y)_f^2}$$
$$= \sqrt{(-11.6 \text{ m/s})^2 + (-8.79 \text{ m/s})^2} = 15 \text{ m/s}$$

Thus immediately after impact the falcon, with its meal, is moving 37° below horizontal at a speed of 15 m/s.

ASSESS It makes sense that the falcon slows down after catching the slower-moving pigeon. Also, the final angle is closer to the horizontal than the falcon's initial angle. This seems reasonable because the pigeon was initially flying horizontally, making the total momentum vector more horizontal than the direction of the falcon's initial momentum.

FIGURE 9.26 The momentum vectors of the falcon strike.

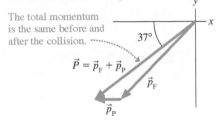

The total momentum is the same before and after the collision.

It's instructive to examine this collision with a picture of the momentum vectors. The vectors $\vec{p}_F$ and $\vec{p}_P$ before the collision, and their sum $\vec{P} = \vec{p}_F + \vec{p}_P$, are shown in **FIGURE 9.26**. You can see that the total momentum vector makes a 53° angle with the negative y-axis. The individual momenta change in the collision, *but the total momentum does not.*

9.7 Angular Momentum

For a single particle, we can think of the law of conservation of momentum as an alternative way of stating Newton's first law. Rather than saying that a particle will continue to move in a straight line at constant velocity unless acted on by a net force, we can say that the momentum of an isolated particle is conserved. Both express the idea that a particle moving in a straight line tends to "keep going" unless something acts on it to change its motion.

Another important motion you've studied is motion in a circle. The momentum $\vec{p}$ is *not* conserved for a particle undergoing circular motion. Momentum is a vector, and the momentum of a particle in circular motion changes as the direction of motion changes.

Nonetheless, a spinning bicycle wheel would keep turning if it were not for friction, and a ball moving in a circle at the end of a string tends to "keep going" in a circular path. The quantity that expresses this idea for circular motion is called *angular momentum.*

Let's start by looking at an example from everyday life: pushing a merry-go-round, as in **FIGURE 9.27**. If you push tangentially to the rim, you are applying a *torque* to the merry-go-round. As we learned in Chapter 7, the merry-go-round's angular speed will continue to increase for as long as you apply this torque. If you push *harder* (greater torque) or for a *longer time*, the greater the increase in its angular velocity will be. How can we quantify these observations?

Let's apply a constant torque τ_{net} to the merry-go-round for a time Δt. By how much will the merry-go-round's angular speed increase? In Section 7.4 we found that the angular acceleration α is given by the rotational equivalent of Newton's second law, or

$$\alpha = \frac{\tau_{net}}{I} \tag{9.17}$$

where I is the merry-go-round's moment of inertia.

Now the angular acceleration is the rate of change of the angular velocity, so

$$\alpha = \frac{\Delta\omega}{\Delta t} \tag{9.18}$$

FIGURE 9.27 By applying a torque to the merry-go-round, the girl is increasing its angular momentum.

Setting Equations 9.17 and 9.18 equal to each other gives

$$\frac{\Delta \omega}{\Delta t} = \frac{\tau_{net}}{I}$$

or, rearranging,

$$\tau_{net}\,\Delta t = I\,\Delta \omega \qquad (9.19)$$

If you recall the impulse-momentum theorem for *linear* motion, which is

$$\vec{F}_{net}\,\Delta t = m\,\Delta \vec{v} = \Delta \vec{p} \qquad (9.20)$$

you can see that Equation 9.19 is an analogous statement about rotational motion. Because the quantity $I\omega$ is evidently the rotational equivalent of mv, the linear momentum $\vec{p}$, it seems reasonable to define the **angular momentum** L to be

$$L = I\omega \qquad (9.21)$$

Angular momentum of an object with moment
of inertia I rotating at angular velocity ω

The SI units of angular momentum are those of moment of inertia times angular velocity, or kg · m²/s.

Just as an object in linear motion can have a large momentum by having either a large mass or a high speed, a rotating object can have a large angular momentum by having a large moment of inertia or a large angular velocity. The merry-go-round in Figure 9.27 has a larger angular momentum if it's spinning fast than if it's spinning slowly. Also, the merry-go-round (large I) has a much larger angular momentum than a toy top (small I) spinning with the same angular velocity.

Table 9.2 summarizes the analogies between linear and rotational quantities that you learned in Chapter 7 and adds the analogy between linear momentum and angular momentum.

TABLE 9.2 Rotational and linear dynamics

Rotational dynamics	Linear dynamics
Torque τ_{net}	Force $\vec{F}_{net}$
Moment of inertia I	Mass m
Angular velocity ω	Velocity $\vec{v}$
Angular momentum $L = I\omega$	Linear momentum $\vec{p} = m\vec{v}$

Conservation of Angular Momentum

Having now defined angular momentum, we can write Equation 9.19 as

$$\tau_{net}\,\Delta t = \Delta L \qquad (9.22)$$

in exact analogy with its linear dynamics equivalent, Equation 9.20. This equation states that the change in the angular momentum of an object is proportional to the net torque applied to the object. If the net external torque on an object is *zero*, the rotational analog of an isolated system, then the change in the angular momentum is zero as well. That is, a rotating object will continue to rotate with *constant* angular velocity—to "keep going"—unless acted upon by an external torque. We can state this conclusion as the *law of conservation of angular momentum*:

 7.14

Law of conservation of angular momentum The angular momentum of a rotating object subject to no net external torque ($\tau_{net} = 0$) is a constant. The final angular momentum L_f is equal to the initial angular momentum L_i.

This law is analogous to that for the conservation of linear momentum; there, linear momentum is conserved if the net *force* is zero. Because the angular momentum is $L = I\omega$, the mathematical statement of the law of conservation of angular momentum is

$$I_f \omega_f = I_i \omega_i \qquad (9.23)$$

EXAMPLE 9.10   **Period of a merry-go-round**

Joey, whose mass is 36 kg, stands at the center of a 200 kg merry-go-round that is rotating once every 2.5 s. While it is rotating, Joey walks out to the edge of the merry-go-round, 2.0 m from its center. What is the rotational period of the merry-go-round when Joey gets to the edge?

PREPARE Take the system to be Joey + merry-go-round and assume frictionless bearings. There is no external torque on this system, so the angular momentum of the system will be conserved. As shown in the visual overview of FIGURE 9.28, we model the merry-go-round as a uniform disk of radius $R = 2.0$ m. From Table 7.2, the moment of inertia of a disk is $I_{disk} = \frac{1}{2}MR^2$. If we model Joey as a particle of mass m, his moment of inertia is zero when he is at the center, but it increases to mR^2 when he reaches the edge.

FIGURE 9.28 Visual overview of the merry-go-round.

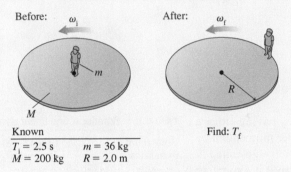

Before: ω_i After: ω_f

m

R

M

Known		Find: T_f
$T_i = 2.5$ s	$m = 36$ kg	
$M = 200$ kg	$R = 2.0$ m	

SOLVE The mathematical statement of the law of conservation of momentum is $L_i = L_f$ or, from Equation 9.23, $I_f \omega_f = I_i \omega_i$, which we can rewrite as

$$\omega_f = \frac{I_i}{I_f}\omega_i$$

As Joey moves out to the edge, the moment of inertia of the system increases and, as a result, the angular velocity decreases. Initially, the moment of inertia of the system is just that of the merry-go-round because Joey's contribution is zero. Thus

$$I_i = I_{disk} = \tfrac{1}{2}MR^2 = \tfrac{1}{2}(200 \text{ kg})(2.0 \text{ m})^2 = 400 \text{ kg} \cdot \text{m}^2$$

When Joey reaches the edge, the total moment of inertia becomes

$$I_f = I_{disk} + mR^2 = 400 \text{ kg} \cdot \text{m}^2 + (36 \text{ kg})(2.0 \text{ m})^2$$
$$= 540 \text{ kg} \cdot \text{m}^2$$

The initial angular velocity is related to the initial period of rotation T_i by

$$\omega_i = \frac{2\pi}{T_i} = \frac{2\pi}{2.5 \text{ s}} = 2.5 \text{ rad/s}$$

Thus the final angular velocity is

$$\omega_f = \frac{I_i}{I_f}\omega_i = \frac{400 \text{ kg} \cdot \text{m}^2}{540 \text{ kg} \cdot \text{m}^2}(2.5 \text{ rad/s}) = 1.9 \text{ rad/s}$$

When Joey reaches the edge, the period of the merry-go-round has increased to

$$T_f = \frac{2\pi}{\omega_f} = \frac{2\pi}{1.9 \text{ rad/s}} = 3.3 \text{ s}$$

ASSESS The merry-go-round rotates *more slowly* after Joey moves out to the edge. This makes sense because if the system's moment of inertia increases, as it does when Joey moves out, the angular velocity must decrease to keep the angular momentum constant.

FIGURE 9.29 A spinning figure skater.

Large moment of inertia; slow spin

Small moment of inertia; fast spin

Conservation of momentum enters into many aspects of sports. Because no external torques act, the angular momentum of a platform diver is conserved while she's in the air. Just as for Joey and the merry-go-round of Example 9.10, she spins slowly when her moment of inertia is large; by decreasing her moment of inertia, she increases her rate of spin. Divers can thus markedly increase their spin rate by changing their body from an extended posture to a tuck position. Figure skaters also increase their spin rate by decreasing their moment of inertia, as shown in FIGURE 9.29. The following example gives a simplified treatment of this process.

EXAMPLE 9.11   **Analyzing a spinning ice skater**

An ice skater spins around on the tips of his blades while holding a 5.0 kg weight in each hand. He begins with his arms straight out from his body and his hands 140 cm apart. While spinning at 2.0 rev/s, he pulls the weights in and holds them 50 cm apart against his shoulders. If we neglect the mass of the skater, how fast is he spinning after pulling the weights in?

PREPARE Although the mass of the skater is larger than the mass of the weights, neglecting the skater's mass is not a bad approximation. Moment of inertia depends on the *square* of the distance of the mass from the axis of rotation. The skater's mass is concentrated in his torso, which has an effective radius (i.e., where most of the mass is concentrated) of only 9 or 10 cm. The weights move in much larger circles and have a disproportionate influence on his motion. The skater's arms exert radial forces on the weights just to keep them moving in circles, and even larger radial forces as he pulls them in. But there is no external torque on the weights, so their total angular momentum is conserved. FIGURE 9.30 shows a before-and-after visual overview, as seen from above.

FIGURE 9.30 Top view visual overview of the spinning ice skater.

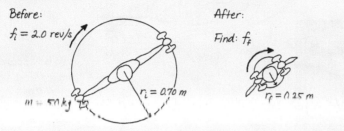

Before:

$f_i = 2.0$ rev/s

$r_i = 0.70$ m

$m = 50$ kg

After:

Find: f_f

$r_f = 0.25$ m

SOLVE The two weights have the same mass, move in circles with the same radius, and have the same angular velocity. Thus the total angular momentum is twice that of one weight. The mathematical statement of angular momentum conservation, $I_f \omega_f = I_i \omega_i$, is

There are two weights.

$$(2 \, mr_f^2)\omega_f = (2 \, mr_i^2)\omega_i$$
$$\underbrace{}_{I_f} \qquad \underbrace{}_{I_i}$$

Because the angular velocity is related to the rotation frequency f by $\omega = 2\pi f$, this equation simplifies to

$$f_f = \left(\frac{r_i}{r_f}\right)^2 f_i$$

When he pulls the weights in, his rotation frequency increases to

$$f_f = \left(\frac{0.70 \text{ m}}{0.25 \text{ m}}\right)^2 \times 2.0 \text{ rev/s} = 16 \text{ rev/s}$$

ASSESS Pulling in the weights increases the skater's spin from 2 rev/s to 16 rev/s. This is somewhat high, because we neglected the mass of the skater, but it illustrates how skaters do "spin up" by pulling their mass in toward the rotation axis.

Solving either of these two examples using Newton's laws would be quite difficult. We would have to deal with internal forces, such as Joey's feet against the merry-go-round, and other complications. For problems like these, where we're interested only in the before-and-after aspects of the motion, using a conservation law makes the solution much simpler.

▶ **The eye of a hurricane** As air masses from the slowing rotating outer zones are drawn toward the low-pressure center, their moment of inertia decreases. Because the angular momentum of these air masses is conserved, their speed must *increase* as they approach the center, leading to the high wind speeds near the center of the storm.

STOP TO THINK 9.5 The left figure shows two boys of equal mass standing halfway to the edge on a turntable that is freely rotating at angular speed ω_i. They then walk to the positions shown in the right figure. The final angular speed ω_f is

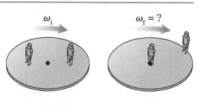

A. Greater than ω_i. B. Less than ω_i. C. Equal to ω_i.

Aerial firefighting

A forest fire is easiest to attack when it's just getting started. In remote locations, this often means using airplanes to rapidly deliver large quantities of water and fire suppressant to the blaze.

The "Superscooper" is an amphibious aircraft that can pick up a 6000 kg load of water by skimming over the surface of a river or lake and scooping water directly into its storage tanks. As it approaches the water's surface at a speed of 35 m/s, an empty Superscooper has a mass of 13,000 kg.

a. It takes the plane 12 s to pick up a full load of water. If we ignore the force on the plane due to the thrust of its propellers, what is its speed immediately after picking up the water?
b. What is the impulse delivered to the plane by the water?
c. What is the average force of the water on the plane?
d. The plane then flies over the fire zone at 40 m/s. It releases water by opening doors in the belly of the plane, allowing the water to fall straight down with respect to the plane. What is the plane's speed after dropping the water if it takes 5.0 s to do so?

PREPARE We can solve part a, and later part d, using conservation of momentum, following Problem-Solving Strategy 9.1. We'll need to choose the system with care, so that $\vec{F}_{net} = \vec{0}$. The plane alone is not an appropriate system for using conservation of momentum: As the plane scoops up the water, the water exerts a large external drag force on the plane, so $\vec{F}_{net}$ is definitely not zero. Instead, we should choose the plane *and* the water it is going to scoop up as the system. Then there are no external forces in the x-direction, and the net force in the y-direction is zero, since neither plane nor water accelerates appreciably in this direction during the scooping process. The complicated forces between plane and water are now *internal* forces that do not change the total momentum of the plane + water system.

With the system chosen, we follow the steps of Tactics Box 9.1 to prepare the before-and-after visual overview shown in FIGURE 9.31.

Parts b and c are impulse-and-momentum problems, so to solve them we'll use the impulse-momentum theorem, Equation 9.8. The impulse-momentum theorem considers the dynamics of a *single* object—here, the plane—subject to external forces—in this case, from the water.

FIGURE 9.31 Visual overview of the plane and water.

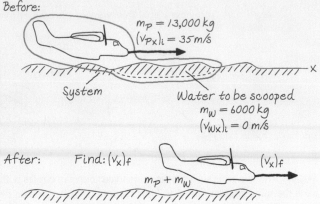

SOLVE a. Conservation of momentum in the x-direction is

$$(P_x)_f = (P_x)_i$$

or

$$(m_P + m_W)(v_x)_f = m_P(v_{Px})_i + m_W(v_{Wx})_i = m_P(v_{Px})_i + 0$$

Here we've used the facts that the initial velocity of the water is zero and that the final situation, as in an inelastic collision, has the combined mass of the plane and water moving with the same velocity $(v_x)_f$. Solving for $(v_x)_f$, we find

$$(v_x)_f = \frac{m_P(v_{Px})_i}{m_P + m_W} = \frac{(13,000 \text{ kg})(35 \text{ m/s})}{(13,000 \text{ kg}) + (6000 \text{ kg})} = 24 \text{ m/s}$$

b. The impulse-momentum theorem is $J_x = \Delta p_x$, where $\Delta p_x = m_P \Delta v_x$ is the change in the plane's momentum. Thus

$$J_x = m_P \Delta v_x = m_P[(v_x)_f - (v_{Px})_i]$$
$$= (13,000 \text{ kg})(24 \text{ m/s} - 35 \text{ m/s}) = -1.4 \times 10^5 \text{ kg} \cdot \text{m/s}$$

c. From Equation 9.1, the definition of impulse, we have

$$(F_{avg})_x = \frac{J_x}{\Delta t} = \frac{-1.4 \times 10^5 \text{ kg} \cdot \text{m/s}}{12 \text{ s}} = -12,000 \text{ N}$$

d. Because the water drops straight down *relative to the plane*, it has the same x-component of velocity immediately after being dropped as before being dropped. That is, simply opening the doors doesn't cause the water to speed up or slow down horizontally, so the water's horizontal momentum doesn't change upon being dropped. Because the total momentum of the plane + water system is conserved, the momentum of the plane doesn't change either. The plane's speed after the drop is still 40 m/s.

ASSESS The mass of the water is nearly half that of the plane, so the significant decrease in the plane's velocity as it scoops up the water is reasonable. The force of the water on the plane is large, but is still only about 10% of the plane's weight, $mg = 130,000$ N, so the answer seems to be reasonable.

SUMMARY

The goals of Chapter 9 have been to introduce the ideas of impulse, momentum, and angular momentum and to learn a new problem-solving strategy based on conservation laws.

GENERAL PRINCIPLES

Law of Conservation of Momentum

The total momentum $\vec{P} = \vec{p}_1 + \vec{p}_2 + \cdots$ of an isolated system is a constant. Thus

$$\vec{P}_f = \vec{P}_i$$

Conservation of Angular Momentum

The angular momentum L of a rotating object subject to zero external torque does not change. Thus

$$L_f = L_i$$

This can be written in terms of the moment of inertia and angular velocity as

$$I_f\omega_f = I_i\omega_i$$

Solving Momentum Conservation Problems

PREPARE Choose an isolated system or a system that is isolated during at least part of the problem. Draw a visual overview of the system before and after the interaction.

SOLVE Write the law of conservation of momentum in terms of vector components:

$$(p_{1x})_f + (p_{2x})_f + \cdots = (p_{1x})_i + (p_{2x})_i + \cdots$$
$$(p_{1y})_f + (p_{2y})_f + \cdots = (p_{1y})_i + (p_{2y})_i + \cdots$$

In terms of masses and velocities, this is

$$m_1(v_{1x})_f + m_2(v_{2x})_f + \cdots = m_1(v_{1x})_i + m_2(v_{2x})_i + \cdots$$
$$m_1(v_{1y})_f + m_2(v_{2y})_f + \cdots = m_1(v_{1y})_i + m_2(v_{2y})_i + \cdots$$

ASSESS Is the result reasonable?

IMPORTANT CONCEPTS

Momentum $\vec{p} = m\vec{v}$

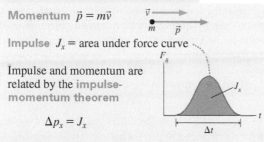

Impulse J_x = area under force curve

Impulse and momentum are related by the impulse-momentum theorem

$$\Delta p_x = J_x$$

This is an alternative statement of Newton's second law.

Angular momentum $L = I\omega$ is the rotational analog of linear momentum $\vec{p} = m\vec{v}$.

System A group of interacting particles.

Isolated system A system on which the net external force is zero.

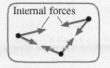

Before-and-after visual overview

- Define the system.

- Use two drawings to show the system *before* and *after* the interaction.

- List known information and identify what you are trying to find.

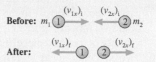

APPLICATIONS

Collisions Two or more particles come together. In a perfectly inelastic collision, they stick together and move with a common final velocity.

Explosions Two or more particles move away from each other.

Two dimensions Both the x- and y-components of the total momentum P must be conserved, giving two simultaneous equations.

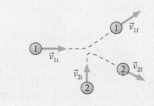

For homework assigned on MasteringPhysics, go to
www.masteringphysics.com

Problem difficulty is labeled as I (straightforward) to IIII (challenging).

Problems labeled can be done on a Workbook Momentum
Worksheet; INT integrate significant material from earlier chapters;
BIO are of biological or medical interest.

QUESTIONS

Conceptual Questions

1. Rank in order, from largest to smallest, the momenta p_{1x} through p_{5x} of the objects presented in Figure Q9.1. Explain.

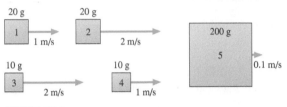

FIGURE Q9.1

2. Starting from rest, object 1 is subject to a 12 N force for 2.0 s. Object 2, with twice the mass, is subject to a 15 N force for 3.0 s. Which object has the greater final speed? Explain.

3. A 0.2 kg plastic cart and a 20 kg lead cart can roll without friction on a horizontal surface. Equal forces are used to push both carts forward for a time of 1 s, starting from rest. After the force is removed at $t = 1$ s, is the momentum of the plastic cart greater than, less than, or equal to the momentum of the lead cart? Explain.

4. Two pucks, of mass m and $4m$, lie on a frictionless table. Equal forces are used to push both pucks forward a distance of 1 m.
   a. Which puck takes longer to travel the distance? Explain.
   b. Which puck has the greater momentum upon completing the distance? Explain.

5. A stationary firecracker explodes into three pieces. One piece travels off to the east; a second travels to the north. Which of the vectors of Figure Q9.5 could be the velocity of the third piece? Explain.

6. Two students stand at rest, facing each other on frictionless skates. They then start tossing a heavy ball back and forth between them. Describe their subsequent motion.

7. Two particles collide, one of which was initially moving and the other initially at rest.
   a. Is it possible for *both* particles to be at rest after the collision? Give an example in which this happens, or explain why it can't happen.
   b. Is it possible for *one* particle to be at rest after the collision? Give an example in which this happens, or explain why it can't happen.

8. Automobiles are designed with "crumple zones" intended to collapse in a collision. Why would a manufacturer design part of a car so that it collapses in a collision?

9. You probably know that it feels better to catch a baseball if you are wearing a padded glove. Explain why this is so, using the ideas of momentum and impulse.

10. In the early days of rocketry, some people claimed that rockets couldn't fly in outer space as there was no air for the rockets to push against. Suppose you were an early investigator in the field of rocketry and met someone who made this argument. How would you convince the person that rockets could travel in space?

11. Two ice skaters, Megan and Jason, push off from each other on frictionless ice. Jason's mass is twice that of Megan.
    a. Which skater, if either, experiences the greater impulse during the push? Explain.
    b. Which skater, if either, has the greater speed after the push-off? Explain.

12. Suppose a rubber ball and a steel ball collide. Which, if either, receives the larger impulse? Explain.

13. While standing still on a basketball court, you throw the ball to a teammate. Why do you not move backward as a result? Is the law of conservation of momentum violated?

14. To win a prize at the county fair, you're trying to knock down a heavy bowling pin by hitting it with a thrown object. Should you choose to throw a rubber ball or a beanbag of equal size and weight? Explain.

15. Rank in order, from largest to smallest, the angular momenta L_1 through L_5 of the balls shown in Figure Q9.15. Explain.

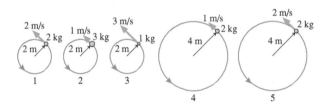

FIGURE Q9.15

16. Figure Q9.16 shows two masses held together by a thread on a rod that is rotating about its center with angular velocity ω. If the thread breaks, the masses will slide out to the ends of the rod. If that happens, will the rod's angular velocity increase, decrease, or remain unchanged? Explain.

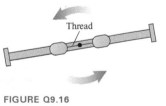

FIGURE Q9.16

17. If the earth warms significantly, the polar ice caps will melt. Water will move from the poles, near the earth's rotation axis, and will spread out around the globe. In principle, this will change the length of the day. Why? Will the length of the day increase or decrease?

18. The disks shown in Figure Q9.18 have equal mass. Is the angular momentum of disk 2, on the right, larger than, smaller than, or equal to the angular momentum of disk 1? Explain.

FIGURE Q9.18

Multiple-Choice Questions

19. | Curling is a sport played with 20 kg stones that slide across an ice surface. Suppose a curling stone sliding at 1 m/s strikes another stone and comes to rest in 2 ms. Approximately how much force is there on the stone during the impact?
    A. 200 N   B. 1000 N   C. 2000 N   D. 10,000 N

20. | Two balls are hung from cords. The first ball, of mass 1.0 kg, is pulled to the side and released, reaching a speed of 2.0 m/s at the bottom of its arc. Then, as shown in Figure Q9.20, it hits and sticks to another ball. The speed of the pair just after the collision is 1.2 m/s. What is the mass of the second ball?
    A. 0.67 kg
    B. 2.0 kg
    C. 1.7 kg
    D. 1.0 kg

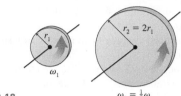

FIGURE Q9.20

21. | Figure Q9.21 shows two blocks sliding on a frictionless surface. Eventually the smaller block overtakes the larger one, collides with it, and sticks. What is the speed of the two blocks after the collision?
    A. $v_i/2$ B. $4v_i/5$ C. v_i D. $5v_i/4$ E. $2v_i$

FIGURE Q9.21

22. | Two friends are sitting in a stationary canoe. At $t = 3.0$ s the person at the front tosses a sack to the person in the rear, who catches the sack 0.2 s later. Which plot in Figure Q9.22 shows

the velocity of the boat as a function of time? Positive velocity is forward, negative velocity is backward. Neglect any drag force on the canoe from the water.

23. ‖ Two blocks, with masses $m_1 = 2.5$ kg and $m_2 = 14$ kg, approach each other along a horizontal, frictionless track. The initial velocities of the blocks are $v_1 = 12.0$ m/s to the right and $v_2 = 3.4$ m/s to the left. The two blocks then collide and stick together. Which of the graphs could represent the force of block 1 on block 2 during the collision?

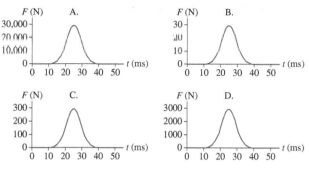

FIGURE Q9.23

24. | A small puck is sliding to the right with momentum $\vec{p}_i$ on a horizontal, frictionless surface, as shown in Figure Q9.24. A force is applied to the puck for a short time and its momentum afterward is $\vec{p}_f$. Which lettered arrow shows the direction of the impulse that was delivered to the puck?

FIGURE Q9.24

25. | A red ball, initially at rest, is simultaneously hit by a blue ball traveling from west to east at 3 m/s and a green ball traveling east to west at 3 m/s. All three balls have equal mass. Afterward, the red ball is traveling south and the green ball is moving to the east. In which direction is the blue ball traveling?
    A. West
    B. North
    C. Between north and west
    D. Between north and east
    E. Between south and west

26. | A 24 g, 3-cm-diameter thin, hollow sphere rotates at 30 rpm about a vertical, frictionless axis through its center. A 4 g bug stands at the top of the sphere. He then walks along the surface of the sphere until he reaches its "equator." When he reaches the equator, the sphere is rotating at
    A. 15 rpm
    B. 24 rpm
    C. 30 rpm
    D. 37 rpm
    E. 45 rpm

27. | A 5.0 kg solid cylinder of radius 12 cm rotates with $\omega_i = 3.7$ rad/s about an axis through its center. A torque of 0.040 N·m is applied to the cylinder for 5.0 s. By how much does the cylinder's angular momentum change?
    A. 0.12 kg·m²/s
    B. 0.20 kg·m²/s
    C. 0.38 kg·m²/s
    D. 0.52 kg·m²/s
    E. 0.88 kg·m²/s

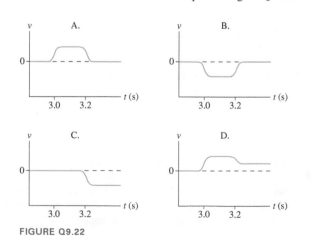

FIGURE Q9.22

PROBLEMS

Section 9.1 Impulse
Section 9.2 Momentum and the Impulse-Momentum Theorem

1. | At what speed do a bicycle and its rider, with a combined mass of 100 kg, have the same momentum as a 1500 kg car traveling at 5.0 m/s?

2. | A 57 g tennis ball is served at 45 m/s. If the ball started from rest, what impulse was applied to the ball by the racket?

3. || A student throws a 120 g snowball at 7.5 m/s at the side of the schoolhouse, where it hits and sticks. What is the magnitude of the average force on the wall if the duration of the collision is 0.15 s?

4. |||| In Figure P9.4, what value of F_{max} gives an impulse of 6.0 N · s?

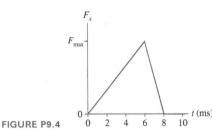

FIGURE P9.4

5. | A sled and rider, gliding over horizontal, frictionless ice at 4.0 m/s, have a combined mass of 80 kg. The sled then slides over a rough spot in the ice, slowing down to 3.0 m/s. What impulse was delivered to the sled by the friction force from the rough spot?

Section 9.3 Solving Impulse and Momentum Problems

6. || Use the impulse-momentum theorem to find how long a stone falling straight down takes to increase its speed from 5.5 m/s to 10.4 m/s.

7. || a. A 2.0 kg object is moving to the right with a speed of 1.0 m/s when it experiences the force shown in Figure P9.7a. What are the object's speed and direction after the force ends?

   b. Answer this question for the force shown in Figure P9.7b.

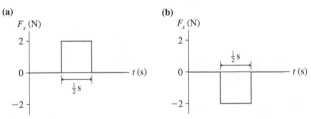

FIGURE P9.7

8. |||| A 60 g tennis ball with an initial speed of 32 m/s hits a wall and rebounds with the same speed. Figure P9.8 shows the force of the wall on the ball during the collision. What is the value of F_{max}, the maximum value of the contact force during the collision?

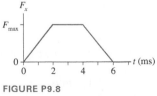

FIGURE P9.8

9. || A child is sliding on a sled at 1.5 m/s to the right. You stop the sled by pushing on it for 0.50 s in a direction opposite to its motion. If the mass of the child and sled is 35 kg, what average force do you need to apply to stop the sled? Use the concepts of impulse and momentum.

10. ||| An ice hockey puck slides along the ice at 12 m/s. A hockey stick delivers an impulse of 4.0 kg · m/s, causing the puck to move off in the opposite direction with the same speed. What is the mass of the puck?

11. | As part of a safety investigation, two 1400 kg cars traveling at 20 m/s are crashed into different barriers. Find the average forces exerted on (a) the car that hits a line of water barrels and takes 1.5 s to stop, and (b) the car that hits a concrete barrier and takes 0.1 s to stop.

12. || In a Little League baseball game, the 145 g ball enters the strike zone with a speed of 15.0 m/s. The batter hits the ball, and it leaves his bat with a speed of 20.0 m/s in exactly the opposite direction.

   a. What is the magnitude of the impulse delivered by the bat to the ball?

   b. If the bat is in contact with the ball for 1.5 ms, what is the magnitude of the average force exerted by the bat on the ball?

Section 9.4 Conservation of Momentum

13. |||| A small, 100 g cart is moving at 1.20 m/s on an air track when it collides with a larger, 1.00 kg cart at rest. After the collision, the small cart recoils at 0.850 m/s. What is the speed of the large cart after the collision?

14. || A man standing on very slick ice fires a rifle horizontally. The mass of the man together with the rifle is 70 kg, and the mass of the bullet is 10 g. If the bullet leaves the muzzle at a speed of 500 m/s, what is the final speed of the man?

15. ||| A 2.7 kg block of wood sits on a table. A 3.0 g bullet, fired horizontally at a speed of 500 m/s, goes completely through the block, emerging at a speed of 220 m/s. What is the speed of the block immediately after the bullet exits?

16. | A strong man is compressing a lightweight spring between two weights. One weight has a mass of 2.3 kg, the other a mass of 5.3 kg. He is holding the weights stationary, but then he loses his grip and the weights fly off in opposite directions. The lighter of the two is shot out at a speed of 6.0 m/s. What is the speed of the heavier weight?

17. || A 10,000 kg railroad car is rolling at 2.00 m/s when a 4000 kg load of gravel is suddenly dropped in. What is the car's speed just after the gravel is loaded?

18. | A 5000 kg open train car is rolling on frictionless rails at 22.0 m/s when it starts pouring rain. A few minutes later, the car's speed is 20.0 m/s. What mass of water has collected in the car?

19. || A 50.0 kg archer, standing on frictionless ice, shoots a 40 g arrow at a speed of 60 m/s. What is the recoil speed of the archer?

20. || A 9.5 kg dog takes a nap in a canoe and wakes up to find the canoe has drifted out onto the lake but now is stationary. He walks along the length of the canoe at 0.50 m/s, relative to the water, and the canoe simultaneously moves in the opposite direction at 0.15 m/s. What is the mass of the canoe?

Section 9.5 Inelastic Collisions

21. ‖ A 300 g bird flying along at 6.0 m/s sees a 10 g insect heading straight toward it with a speed of 30 m/s. The bird opens its mouth wide and enjoys a nice lunch. What is the bird's speed immediately after swallowing?

22. ‖ A 71 kg baseball player jumps straight up to catch a line drive. If the 140 g ball is moving horizontally at 28 m/s, and the catch is made when the ballplayer is at the highest point of his leap, what is his speed immediately after stopping the ball?

23. ‖‖ A kid at the junior high cafeteria wants to propel an empty milk carton along a lunch table by hitting it with a 3.0 g spit ball. If he wants the speed of the 20 g carton just after the spit ball hits it to be 0.30 m/s, at what speed should his spit ball hit the carton?

24. ‖ The parking brake on a 2000 kg Cadillac has failed, and it is rolling slowly, at 1 mph, toward a group of small children. Seeing the situation, you realize you have just enough time to drive your 1000 kg Volkswagen head-on into the Cadillac and save the children. With what speed should you impact the Cadillac to bring it to a halt?

25. ‖ A 2.0 kg block slides along a frictionless surface at 1.0 m/s. A second block, sliding at a faster 4.0 m/s, collides with the first from behind and sticks to it. The final velocity of the combined blocks is 2.0 m/s. What was the mass of the second block?

Section 9.6 Momentum and Collisions in Two Dimensions

26. ‖‖ A 20 g ball of clay traveling east at 3.0 m/s collides with a 30 g ball of clay traveling north at 2.0 m/s. What are the speed and the direction of the resulting 50 g ball of clay?

27. ‖ Two particles collide and bounce apart. Figure P9.27 shows the initial momenta of both and the final momentum of particle 2. What is the final momentum of particle 1? Show your answer by copying the figure and drawing the final momentum vector on the figure.

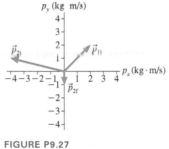

FIGURE P9.27

28. ‖ A 20 g ball of clay traveling east at 2.0 m/s collides with a 30 g ball of clay traveling 30° south of west at 1.0 m/s. What are the speed and direction of the resulting 50 g blob of clay?

29. ‖ A firecracker in a coconut blows the coconut into three pieces. Two pieces of equal mass fly off south and west, perpendicular to each other, at 20 m/s. The third piece has twice the mass as the other two. What are the speed and direction of the third piece?

Section 9.7 Angular Momentum

30. ‖‖ What is the angular momentum of the moon around the earth? The moon's mass is 7.4×10^{22} kg and it orbits 3.8×10^8 m from the earth.

31. ‖‖ A little girl is going on the merry-go-round for the first time, and wants her 47 kg mother to stand next to her on the ride, 2.6 m from the merry-go-round's center. If her mother's speed is 4.2 m/s when the ride is in motion, what is her angular momentum around the center of the merry-go-round?

32. ‖ What is the angular momentum about the axle of the 500 g rotating bar in Figure P9.32?

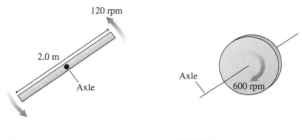

FIGURE P9.32   FIGURE P9.33

33. ‖‖ What is the angular momentum about the axle of the 2.0 kg, 4.0-cm-diameter rotating disk in Figure P9.33?

34. ‖ Divers change their body position in midair while rotating about their center of mass. In one dive, the diver leaves the board with her body nearly straight, then tucks into a somersault position. If the moment of inertia of the diver in a straight position is 14 kg · m² and in a tucked position is 4.0 kg · m², by what factor is her angular velocity when tucked greater than when straight?

35. ‖ Ice skaters often end their performances with spin turns, where they spin very fast about their center of mass with their arms folded in and legs together. Upon ending, their arms extend outward, proclaiming their finish. Not quite as noticeably, one leg goes out as well. Suppose that the moment of inertia of a skater with arms out and one leg extended is 3.2 kg · m² and for arms and legs in is 0.80 kg · m². If she starts out spinning at 5.0 rev/s, what is her angular speed (in rev/s) when her arms and one leg open outward?

General Problems

36. ‖‖ What is the impulse on a 3.0 kg particle that experiences the force described by the graph in Figure P9.36?

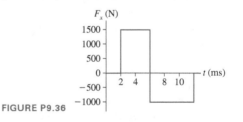

FIGURE P9.36

37. ‖‖ A 600 g air-track glider collides with a spring at one end of the track. Figure P9.37 shows the glider's velocity and the force exerted on the glider by the spring. How long is the glider in contact with the spring?

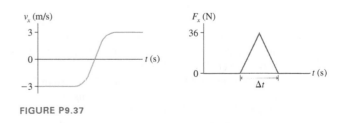

FIGURE P9.37

38. ‖ Far in space, where gravity is negligible, a 425 kg rocket traveling at 75.0 m/s in the positive x-direction fires its engines. Figure P9.38 shows the thrust force as a function of time. The mass lost by the rocket during these 30.0 s is negligible.
    a. What impulse does the engine impart to the rocket?
    b. At what time does the rocket reach its maximum speed? What is the maximum speed?

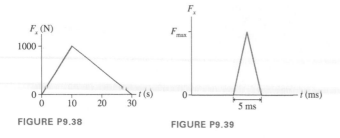

FIGURE P9.38   FIGURE P9.39

39. ‖‖‖ A 200 g ball is dropped from a height of 2.0 m, bounces on a hard floor, and rebounds to a height of 1.5 m. Figure P9.39 shows the impulse received from the floor. What maximum force does the floor exert on the ball?

40. ‖‖‖ A 200 g ball is dropped from a height of 2.0 m and bounces on a hard floor. The force on the ball from the floor is shown in Figure P9.40. How high does the ball rebound?

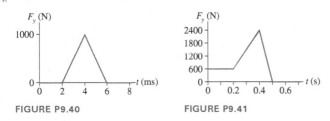

FIGURE P9.40   FIGURE P9.41

41. ‖ Figure P9.41 is a graph of the force exerted by the floor on a woman making a vertical jump. At what speed does she leave the ground?
    Hint: The force of the floor is not the only force acting on the woman.

42. ‖ A sled slides along a horizontal surface for which the coefficient of kinetic friction is 0.25. Its velocity at point A is 8.0 m/s and at point B is 5.0 m/s. Use the impulse-momentum theorem to find how long the sled takes to travel from A to B.

43. ‖‖‖ A 140 g baseball is moving horizontally to the right at 35 m/s when it is hit by the bat. The ball flies off to the left at 55 m/s, at an angle of 25° above the horizontal. What are the magnitude and direction of the impulse that the bat delivers to the ball?

44. ‖ Squids rely on jet propulsion, a versatile technique to move around in water. A 1.5 kg squid at rest suddenly expels 0.10 kg of water backward to quickly get itself moving forward at 3.0 m/s. If other forces (such as the drag force on the squid) are ignored, what is the speed with which the squid expels the water?

45. ‖‖‖ The flowers of the bunchberry plant open with astonishing force and speed, causing the pollen grains to be ejected out of the flower in a mere 0.30 ms at an acceleration of 2.5×10^4 m/s². If the acceleration is constant, what impulse is delivered to a pollen grain with a mass of 1.0×10^{-7} g?

46. ‖ a. With what speed are pollen grains ejected from a bunchberry flower? See Problem 45 for information.
      b. Suppose that 1000 ejected pollen grains slam into the abdomen of a 5.0 g bee that is hovering just above the flower. If the collision is perfectly inelastic, what is the bee's speed immediately afterward? Is the bee likely to notice?

47. ‖‖‖ A tennis player swings her 1000 g racket with a speed of 10 m/s. She hits a 60 g tennis ball that was approaching her at a speed of 20 m/s. The ball rebounds at 40 m/s.
    a. How fast is her racket moving immediately after the impact? You can ignore the interaction of the racket with her hand for the brief duration of the collision.
    b. If the tennis ball and racket are in contact for 10 ms, what is the average force that the racket exerts on the ball?

48. ‖ A 20 g ball of clay is thrown horizontally at 30 m/s toward a 1.0 kg block sitting at rest on a frictionless surface. The clay hits and sticks to the block.
    a. What is the speed of the block and clay right after the collision?
    b. Use the block's initial and final speeds to calculate the impulse the clay exerts on the block.
    c. Use the clay's initial and final speeds to calculate the impulse the block exerts on the clay.
    d. Does $\vec{J}_{\text{block on clay}} = -\vec{J}_{\text{clay on block}}$?

49. ‖ Dan is gliding on his skateboard at 4.0 m/s. He suddenly jumps backward off the skateboard, kicking the skateboard forward at 8.0 m/s. How fast is Dan going as his feet hit the ground? Dan's mass is 50 kg and the skateboard's mass is 5.0 kg.

50. ‖ James and Sarah stand on a stationary cart with frictionless wheels. The total mass of the cart and riders is 130 kg. At the same instant, James throws a 1.0 kg ball to Sarah at 4.5 m/s, while Sarah throws a 0.50 kg ball to James at 1.0 m/s. James's throw is to the right and Sarah's is to the left.
    a. While the two balls are in the air, what are the speed and direction of the cart and its riders?
    b. After the balls are caught, what are the speed and direction of the cart and riders?

51. ‖‖‖ Ethan, whose mass is 80 kg, stands at one end of a very long, stationary wheeled cart that has a mass of 500 kg. He then starts sprinting toward the other end of the cart. He soon reaches his top speed of 8.0 m/s, measured relative to the cart. What is the speed of the cart when Ethan has reached his top speed?

52. ‖ The cars of a long coal train are filled by pulling them under a hopper, from which coal falls into the cars at a rate of 10,000 kg/s. Ignoring friction due to the rails, what is the average force that the engine must exert on the coal train to keep it moving under the hopper at a speed of 0.50 m/s?

53. ‖ Three identical train cars, coupled together, are rolling east at 2.0 m/s. A fourth car traveling east at 4.0 m/s catches up with the three and couples to make a four-car train. A moment later, the train cars hit a fifth car that was at rest on the tracks, and it couples to make a five-car train. What is the speed of the five-car train?

54. ‖ A 110 kg linebacker running at 2.0 m/s and an 82 kg quarterback running at 3.0 m/s have a head-on collision in midair. The linebacker grabs and holds onto the quarterback. Who ends up moving forward after they hit?

55. ‖ Most geologists believe that the dinosaurs became extinct 65 million years ago when a large comet or asteroid struck the earth, throwing up so much dust that the sun was blocked out for a period of many months. Suppose an asteroid with a diameter of 2.0 km and a mass of 1.0×10^{13} kg hits the earth with an impact speed of 4.0×10^4 m/s.
    a. What is the earth's recoil speed after such a collision? (Use a reference frame in which the earth was initially at rest.)
    b. What percentage is this of the earth's speed around the sun? (Use the astronomical data inside the back cover.)

56. ▥ At the center of a 50-m-diameter circular ice rink, a 75 kg skater traveling north at 2.5 m/s collides with and holds onto a 60 kg skater who had been heading west at 3.5 m/s.
   a. How long will it take them to glide to the edge of the rink?
   b. Where will they reach it? Give your answer as an angle north of west.

57. ▥ Two ice skaters, with masses of 50 kg and 75 kg, are at the center of a 60-m-diameter circular rink. The skaters push off against each other and glide to opposite edges of the rink. If the heavier skater reaches the edge in 20 s, how long does the lighter skater take to reach the edge?

58. ▥ One billiard ball is shot east at 2.00 m/s. A second, identical billiard ball is shot west at 1.00 m/s. The balls have a glancing collision, not a head-on collision, deflecting the second ball by 90° and sending it north at 1.41 m/s. What are the speed and direction of the first ball after the collision?

59. ▥ A 10 g bullet is fired into a 10 kg wood block that is at rest on a wood table. The block, with the bullet embedded, slides 5.0 cm across the table. What was the speed of the bullet?

60. ▥ You are part of a search-and-rescue mission that has been called out to look for a lost explorer. You've found the missing explorer, but you're separated from him by a 200-m-high cliff and a 30-m-wide raging river, as shown in Figure P9.60. To save his life, you need to get a 5.0 kg package of emergency supplies across the river. Unfortunately, you can't throw the package hard enough to make it across. Fortunately, you happen to have a 1.0 kg rocket intended for launching flares. Improvising quickly, you attach a sharpened stick to the front of the rocket, so that it will impale itself into the package of supplies, then fire the rocket at ground level toward the supplies. What minimum speed must the rocket have just before impact in order to save the explorer's life?

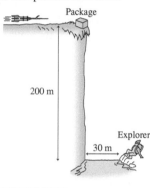

Package

200 m

Explorer

30 m

FIGURE P9.60

61. ▥ A 1500 kg weather rocket accelerates upward at 10.0 m/s². It explodes 2.00 s after liftoff and breaks into two fragments, one twice as massive as the other. Photos reveal that the lighter fragment traveled straight up and reached a maximum height of 530 m. What were the speed and direction of the heavier fragment just after the explosion?

62. ▥ Two 500 g blocks of wood are 2.0 m apart on a frictionless table. A 10 g bullet is fired at 400 m/s toward the blocks. It passes all the way through the first block, then embeds itself in the second block. The speed of the first block immediately afterward is 6.0 m/s. What is the speed of the second block after the bullet stops?

63. ▯ A 500 kg cannon fires a 10 kg cannonball with a speed of 200 m/s relative to the muzzle. The cannon is on wheels that roll without friction. When the cannon fires, what is the speed of the cannonball relative to the earth?

64. ▥ Laura, whose mass is 35 kg, jumps horizontally off a 55 kg canoe at 1.5 m/s relative to the canoe. What is the canoe's speed just after she jumps?

65. ▥ A spaceship of mass 2.0×10^6 kg is cruising at a speed of 5.0×10^6 m/s when the antimatter reactor fails, blowing the ship into three pieces. One section, having a mass of 5.0×10^5 kg, is blown straight backward with a speed of 2.0×10^6 m/s. A second piece, with mass 8.0×10^5 kg, continues forward at 1.0×10^6 m/s. What are the direction and speed of the third piece?

66. ▥ A proton is shot at 5.0×10^7 m/s toward a gold target. The nucleus of a gold atom, with a mass 197 times that of the proton, repels the proton and deflects it straight back with 90% of its initial speed. What is the recoil speed of the gold nucleus?

67. ▥ Figure P9.67 shows a collision between three balls of clay. The three hit simultaneously and stick together. What are the speed and direction of the resulting blob of clay?

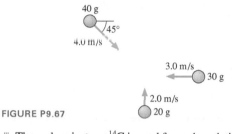

40 g
45°
4.0 m/s

3.0 m/s
30 g

2.0 m/s
20 g

FIGURE P9.67

68. ▥ The carbon isotope ^{14}C is used for carbon dating of archeological artifacts. ^{14}C (mass 2.34×10^{-26} kg) decays by the process known as *beta decay* in which the nucleus emits an electron (the beta particle) and a subatomic particle called a neutrino. In one such decay, the electron and the neutrino are emitted at right angles to each other. The electron (mass 9.11×10^{-31} kg) has a speed of 5.00×10^7 m/s and the neutrino has a momentum of 8.00×10^{-24} kg · m/s. What is the recoil speed of the nucleus?

69. ▥ A 1.0-m-long massless rod is pivoted at one end and swings around in a circle on a frictionless table. A block with a hole through the center can slide in and out along the rod. Initially, a small piece of wax holds the block 30 cm from the pivot. The block is spun at 50 rpm, then the temperature of the rod is slowly increased. When the wax melts, the block slides out to the end of the rod. What is the final angular speed? Give your answer in rpm.

70. ▥ A 200 g puck revolves in a circle on a frictionless table at the end of a 50.0-cm-long string. The puck's angular momentum about the center of the circle is 3.00 kg · m²/s. What is the tension in the string?

71. ▥ Figure P9.71 shows a 100 g puck revolving in a 20-cm-radius circle on a frictionless table. The string passes through a hole in the center of the table and is tied to two 200 g weights.
   a. What speed does the puck need to support the two weights?

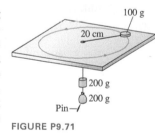

100 g
20 cm

200 g
200 g
Pin

FIGURE P9.71

   b. The lower weight is a light bag filled with sand. Suppose a pin pokes a hole in the bag and the sand slowly leaks out while the puck is revolving. What will be the puck's speed and the radius of its trajectory after all of the sand is gone?

72. ▥ A 2.0 kg, 20-cm-diameter turntable rotates at 100 rpm on frictionless bearings. Two 500 g blocks fall from above, hit the turntable simultaneously at opposite ends of a diagonal, and stick. What is the turntable's angular speed, in rpm, just after this event?

73. ▥ Joey, from Example 9.10, stands at rest at the outer edge of the frictionless merry-go-round of Figure 9.28. The merry-go-round is also at rest. Joey then begins to run around the perimeter of the merry-go-round, finally reaching a constant speed, measured relative to the ground, of 5.0 m/s. What is the final angular speed of the merry-go-round?

74. ⫼ A 3.0-m-diameter merry-go-round with a mass of 250 kg is spinning at 20 rpm. John runs around the merry-go-round at 5.0 m/s, in the same direction that it is turning, and jumps onto the outer edge. John's mass is 30 kg. What is the merry-go-round's angular speed, in rpm, after John jumps on?

75. ⫼ Disk A, with a mass of 2.0 kg and a radius of 40 cm, rotates clockwise about a frictionless vertical axle at 30 rev/s. Disk B, also 2.0 kg but with a radius of 20 cm, rotates counterclockwise about that same axle, but at a greater height than disk A, at 30 rev/s. Disk B slides down the axle until it lands on top of disk A, after which they rotate together. After the collision, what is their common angular speed (in rev/s) and in which direction do they rotate?

Passage Problems

Hitting a Golf Ball

Consider a golf club hitting a golf ball. To a good approximation, we can model this as a collision between the rapidly moving head of the golf club and the stationary golf ball, ignoring the shaft of the club and the golfer.

A golf ball has a mass of 46 g. Suppose a 200 g club head is moving at a speed of 40 m/s just before striking the golf ball. After the collision, the golf ball's speed is 60 m/s.

76. ⎮ What is the momentum of the club + ball system right before the collision?
    A. 1.8 kg · m/s   B. 8.0 kg · m/s
    C. 3220 kg · m/s   D. 8000 kg · m/s

77. ⎮ Immediately after the collision, the momentum of the club + ball system will be
    A. Less than before the collision.
    B. The same as before the collision.
    C. More than before the collision.

78. ⎮ A manufacturer makes a golf ball that compresses more than a traditional golf ball when struck by a club. How will this affect the average force during the collision?
    A. The force will decrease.
    B. The force will not be affected.
    C. The force will increase.

79. ⎮ By approximately how much does the club head slow down as a result of hitting the ball?
    A. 4 m/s   B. 6 m/s   C. 14 m/s   D. 26 m/s

STOP TO THINK ANSWERS

Stop to Think 9.1: F. The cart is initially moving in the negative x-direction, so $(p_x)_i = -20$ kg · m/s. After it bounces, $(p_x)_f = 10$ kg · m/s. Thus $\Delta p = (10$ kg · m/s$) - (-20$ kg · m/s$) = 30$ kg · m/s.

Stop to Think 9.2: B. The clay ball goes from $(v_x)_i = v$ to $(v_x)_f = 0$, so $J_{clay} = \Delta p_x = -mv$. The rubber ball rebounds, going from $(v_x)_i = v$ to $(v_x)_f = -v$ (same speed, opposite direction). Thus $J_{rubber} = \Delta p_x = -2mv$. The rubber ball has a greater momentum change, and this requires a greater impulse.

Stop to Think 9.3: Right end. The balls started at rest, so the total momentum of the system is zero. It's an isolated system, so the total momentum after the explosion is still zero. The 6 g ball has momentum $6v$. The 4 g ball, with velocity $-2v$, has momentum $-8v$. The combined momentum of these two balls is $-2v$. In order for P to be zero, the third ball must have a *positive* momentum $(+2v)$ and thus a positive velocity.

Stop to Think 9.4: B. The momentum of particle 1 is $(0.40$ kg$)(2.5$ m/s$) = 1.0$ kg · m/s, while that of particle 2 is $(0.80$ kg$)(-1.5$ m/s$) = -1.2$ kg · m/s. The total momentum is then 1.0 kg · m/s $- 1.2$ kg · m/s $= -0.2$ kg · m/s. Because it's negative, the total momentum, and hence the final velocity of the particles, is directed to the left.

Stop to Think 9.5: B. Angular momentum $L = I\omega$ is conserved. Both boys have mass m and initially stand distance $R/2$ from the axis. Thus the initial moment of inertia is $I_i = I_{disk} + 2 \times m(R/2)^2 = I_{disk} + \frac{1}{2}mR^2$. The final moment of inertia is $I_f = I_{disk} + 0 + mR^2$, because the boy standing at the axis contributes nothing to the moment of inertia. Because $I_f > I_i$ we must have $\omega_f < \omega_i$.

10 Energy and Work

As this bungee jumper falls, he gains kinetic energy, the energy of motion. Where does this energy come from? And where does it go as he slows at the bottom of his fall?

LOOKING AHEAD ▸

The goals of Chapter 10 are to introduce the concept of energy and to learn a new problem-solving strategy based on conservation of energy.

Forms of Energy

A principal goal of this chapter is to learn about several important forms of energy.

Kinetic energy is the energy of motion. This heavy, fast-moving elephant has lots of kinetic energy.

These passengers gain **potential energy**, the energy of position, as they ride up the escalator.

The **thermal energy** of this red-hot horseshoe is associated with the microscopic motion of its molecules.

> **Looking Back** ◂◂
> 2.5 Motion with constant acceleration
> 7.1, 7.4 Rotation and moment of inertia
> 8.3 Hooke's law

▸ The Law of Conservation of Energy

One of the most fundamental laws of physics, the **law of conservation of energy** states that the total energy of an isolated system is a constant.

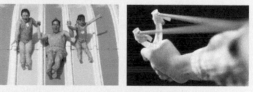

How fast are these water sliders moving at the bottom? How fast does the rock fly out of the slingshot? We'll use conservation of energy and the before-and-after analysis introduced in Chapter 9 to solve these kinds of problems.

> **Looking Back** ◂◂
> 9.2–9.3 Before-and after visual overviews

Transferring Energy

Energy can be *transferred* into a system by pushing on it, a process called **work.**

The bobsledders do work on the sled, *transferring* energy to it and causing it to speed up.

Transforming Energy

Energy of one kind can change into energy of a different kind. These **energy transformations** are what make the world an interesting place.

As this race car skids to a stop, its kinetic energy is being *transformed* into thermal energy, making the tires hot enough to smoke.

▸ Power

We're very often interested in **power,** the *rate* at which energy is transformed from one kind into another.

As they climb, this truck and these jets both transform the chemical energy of their fuel into potential energy. But the jet engines transform energy at a rate 70 times that of the truck's engine—their *power* is much greater.

10.1 The Basic Energy Model

Energy. It's a word you hear all the time. We use chemical energy to heat our homes and bodies, electric energy to run our lights and computers, and solar energy to grow our crops and forests. We're told to use energy wisely and not to waste it. Athletes and weary students consume "energy bars" and "energy drinks."

But just what is energy? The concept of energy has grown and changed over time, and it is not easy to define in a general way just what energy is. Rather than starting with a formal definition, we'll let the concept of energy expand slowly over the course of several chapters. In this chapter we introduce several fundamental forms of energy, including kinetic energy, potential energy, and thermal energy. Our goal is to understand the characteristics of energy, how energy is used, and, especially important, how energy is transformed from one form into another. Much of modern technology is concerned with transforming energy, such as changing the chemical energy of oil molecules into electric energy or into the kinetic energy of your car.

We'll also learn how energy can be transferred to or from a system by the application of mechanical forces. By pushing on a sled, you increase its speed, and hence its energy of motion. By lifting a heavy object, you increase its gravitational potential energy.

These observations will lead us to discover a very powerful conservation law for energy. Energy is neither created nor destroyed: If one form of energy in a system decreases, it must appear in an equal amount in another form. Many scientists consider the law of conservation of energy to be the most important of all the laws of nature. This law will have implications throughout the rest of this book.

Systems and Energy

In Chapter 9 we introduced the idea of a *system* of interacting objects. A system can be as simple as a falling acorn or as complex as a city. But whether simple or complex, every system in nature has associated with it a quantity we call its **total energy** E. The total energy is the sum of the different kinds of energies present in the system. In the table below, we give a brief overview of some of the more important forms of energy; in the rest of the chapter, we'll look at several of these forms of energy in much greater detail.

A system may have many of these kinds of energy at one time. For instance, a moving car has kinetic energy of motion, chemical energy stored in its gasoline, thermal energy in its hot engine, and many other forms of energy. The total energy of the system, E, is the *sum* of all the different energies present in the system:

$$E = K + U_g + U_s + E_{th} + E_{chem} + \cdots \tag{10.1}$$

The energies shown in this sum are the forms of energy in which we'll be most interested in this and the next chapter. The ellipses ($\cdots$) stand for other forms of energy, such as nuclear or electric, that also might be present. We'll treat these and others in later chapters.

Some important forms of energy

Kinetic energy K	Gravitational potential energy U_g	Elastic or spring potential energy U_s

Kinetic energy is the energy of *motion*. All moving objects have kinetic energy. The heavier an object and the faster it moves, the more kinetic energy it has. The wrecking ball in this picture is effective in part because of its large kinetic energy.	Gravitational potential energy is *stored* energy associated with an object's *height above the ground*. As this coaster ascends, energy is stored as gravitational potential energy. As it descends, this stored energy is converted into kinetic energy.	Elastic potential energy is energy stored when a spring or other elastic object, such as this archer's bow, is *stretched*. This energy can later be transformed into the kinetic energy of the arrow.

Continued

Thermal energy E_{th}

Hot objects have more *thermal energy* than cold ones because the molecules in a hot object jiggle around more than those in a cold object. Thermal energy is the sum of the microscopic kinetic and potential energies of all the molecules in an object. In boiling water, some molecules have enough energy to escape the water as steam.

Chemical energy E_{chem}

Electric forces cause atoms to bind together to make molecules. Energy can be stored in these bonds, energy that can later be released as the bonds are rearranged during chemical reactions. When we burn fuel to run our car or eat food to power our bodies, we are using *chemical energy*.

Nuclear energy $E_{nuclear}$

An enormous amount of energy is stored in the *nucleus,* the tiny core of an atom. Certain nuclei can be made to break apart, releasing some of this *nuclear energy,* which is transformed into the kinetic energy of the fragments and then into thermal energy. The ghostly blue glow of a nuclear reactor results from high-energy fragments as they travel through water.

Energy Transformations

We've seen that all systems contain energy in many different forms. But if the amounts of each form of energy never changed, the world would be a very dull place. What makes the world interesting is that **energy of one kind can be** *transformed* **into energy of another kind.** The gravitational potential energy of the roller coaster at the top of the track is rapidly transformed into kinetic energy as the coaster descends; the chemical energy of gasoline is transformed into the kinetic energy of your moving car. The following table illustrates a few common energy transformations. In this table, we use an arrow $\rightarrow$ as a shorthand way of representing an energy transformation.

Some energy transformations

A weightlifter lifts a barbell over her head
The barbell has much more gravitational potential energy when high above her head than when on the floor. To lift the barbell, she is transforming chemical energy in her body into gravitational potential energy of the barbell.

$$E_{chem} \rightarrow U_g$$

A base runner slides into the base
When running, he has lots of kinetic energy. After sliding, he has none. His kinetic energy is transformed mainly into thermal energy: The ground and his legs are slightly warmer.

$$K \rightarrow E_{th}$$

A burning campfire
The wood contains considerable chemical energy. When the carbon in the wood combines chemically with oxygen in the air, this chemical energy is transformed largely into thermal energy of the hot gases and embers.

$$E_{chem} \rightarrow E_{th}$$

A springboard diver
Here's a two-step energy transformation. At the instant shown, the board is flexed to its maximum extent, so that elastic potential energy stored in the board. Soon this energy will begin to be transformed into kinetic energy; as the diver rises into the air and slows, this kinetic energy will be transformed into gravitational potential energy.

$$U_s \rightarrow K \rightarrow U_g$$

FIGURE 10.1 Energy transformations occur within the system.

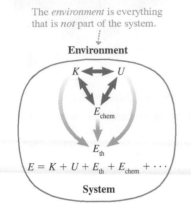

The *environment* is everything that is *not* part of the system.

Environment

$E = K + U + E_{th} + E_{chem} + \cdots$

System

FIGURE 10.1 reinforces the idea that **energy transformations are changes of energy *within* the system from one form to another.** (The U in this figure is a generic potential energy; it could be gravitational potential energy U_g, spring potential energy U_s, or some other form of potential energy.) Note that it is easy to convert kinetic, potential, and chemical energies into thermal energy, but converting thermal energy back into these other forms is not so easy. How it can be done, and what possible limitations there might be in doing so, will form a large part of the next chapter.

Energy Transfers and Work

We've just seen that energy *transformations* occur between forms of energy *within* a system. But every physical system also interacts with the world around it—that is, with its *environment*. In the course of these interactions, the system can exchange energy with the environment. **An exchange of energy between system and environment is called an energy *transfer*.** There are two primary energy-transfer processes: **work,** the *mechanical* transfer of energy to or from a system by pushing or pulling on it, and **heat,** the *nonmechanical* transfer of energy from the environment to the system (or vice versa) because of a temperature difference between the two.

FIGURE 10.2, which we call the **basic energy model,** shows how our energy model is modified to include energy transfers into and out of the system as well as energy transformations within the system. In this chapter we'll consider only energy transfers by means of work; the concept of heat will be developed much further in Chapters 11 and 12.

"Work" is a common word in the English language, with many meanings. When you first think of work, you probably think of physical effort or the job you do to make a living. After all, we talk about "working out," or we say, "I just got home from work." But that is not what work means in physics.

In physics, "work" is the process of *transferring* energy from the environment to a system, or from a system to the environment, by the application of mechanical forces—pushes and pulls—to the system. Once the energy has been transferred to the system, it can appear in many forms. Exactly what form it takes depends on the details of the system and how the forces are applied. The table below gives three examples of energy transfers due to work. We use W as the symbol for work.

FIGURE 10.2 The basic energy model shows that work and heat are energy transfers into and out of the system, while energy transformations occur within the system.

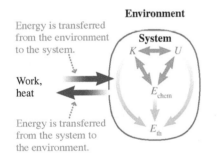

Energy is transferred from the environment to the system.

Environment

System

Work, heat

Energy is transferred from the system to the environment.

Energy transfers: work

Putting a shot

The system: The shot

The environment: The athlete

As the athlete pushes on the shot to get it moving, he is doing work on the system; that is, he is transferring energy from himself to the ball. The energy transferred to the system appears as kinetic energy.

The transfer: $W \rightarrow K$

Striking a match

The system: The match and matchbox

The environment: The hand

As the hand quickly pulls the match across the box, the hand does work on the system, increasing its thermal energy. The match head becomes hot enough to ignite.

The transfer: $W \rightarrow E_{th}$

Firing a slingshot

The system: The slingshot

The environment: The boy

As the boy pulls back on the elastic bands, he does work on the system, increasing its elastic potential energy.

The transfer: $W \rightarrow U_s$

Notice that in each example on the previous page, the environment applies a force while the system undergoes a *displacement*. Energy is transferred as work only when the system *moves* while the force acts. A force applied to a stationary object, such as when you push against a wall, transfers no energy to the object and thus does no work.

NOTE ▶ In the table on the previous page, energy is being transferred *from* the athlete *to* the shot by the force of his hand. We say he "does work" on the shot, or "work is done" by the force of his hand. ◀

The Law of Conservation of Energy

Work done on a system represents energy that is transferred into or out of the system. This transferred energy *changes* the system's energy by exactly the amount of work W that was done. Writing the change in the system's energy as ΔE, we can represent this idea mathematically as

$$\Delta E = W \qquad (10.2)$$

Now the total energy E of a system is, according to Equation 10.1, the sum of the different energies present in the system. Thus the change in E is the sum of the *changes* of the different energies present. Then Equation 10.2 gives what is called the *work-energy equation:*

The work-energy equation The total energy of a system changes by the amount of work done on it:

$$\Delta E = \Delta K + \Delta U_g + \Delta U_s + \Delta E_{th} + \Delta E_{chem} + \cdots = W \qquad (10.3)$$

NOTE ▶ Equation 10.3, the work-energy equation, is the mathematical representation of the basic energy model of Figure 10.2. Together, they are the heart of what the subject of energy is all about. ◀

Suppose now we have an **isolated system,** one that is separated from its surrounding environment in such a way that no energy is transferred into or out of the system. This means that *no work is done on the system.* The energy within the system may be transformed from one form into another, but it is a deep and remarkable fact of nature that, during these transformations, the total energy of an isolated system—the *sum* of all the individual kinds of energy—remains *constant,* as shown in FIGURE 10.3. We say that **the total energy of an isolated system is *conserved.***

For an isolated system, we must set $W = 0$ in Equation 10.3, leading to the following *law of conservation of energy:*

Law of conservation of energy The total energy of an isolated system remains constant:

$$\Delta E = \Delta K + \Delta U_g + \Delta U_s + \Delta E_{th} + \Delta E_{chem} + \cdots = 0 \qquad (10.4)$$

The law of conservation of energy is similar to the law of conservation of momentum. Momentum changes when an impulse acts on a system; the total momentum of an isolated system doesn't change. Similarly, energy changes when external forces do work on a system; the total energy of an isolated system doesn't change.

In solving momentum problems, we adopted a new before-and-after perspective: The momentum *after* an interaction was the same as the momentum *before* the interaction. We will introduce a similar before-and-after perspective for energy that will lead to an extremely powerful problem-solving strategy.

FIGURE 10.3 An isolated system.

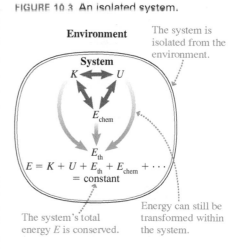

Before using energy ideas to solve problems, however, we first need to develop quantitative expressions for work, kinetic energy, potential energy, and thermal energy. This will be our task in the next several sections.

STOP TO THINK 10.1   A child slides down a playground slide at constant speed. The energy transformation is

A. $U_g \rightarrow K$ B. $K \rightarrow U_g$ C. $W \rightarrow K$ D. $U_g \rightarrow E_{th}$ E. $K \rightarrow E_{th}$

10.2 Work

Our first task is to learn how work is calculated. We've just seen that work is the transfer of energy to or from a system by the application of forces exerted on the system by the environment. Thus work is done on a system by forces from *outside* the system; we call such forces *external forces*. Only external forces can change the energy of a system. *Internal forces*—forces between objects *within* the system—cause energy transformations within the system but don't change the system's total energy.

We also learned that in order for energy to be transferred as work, the system must undergo a displacement—it must *move*—during the time that the force is applied. Let's further investigate the relationship among work, force, and displacement.

Consider a system consisting of a windsurfer at rest, as shown on the left in FIGURE 10.4. Let's assume that there is no friction between his board and the water. Initially the system has no kinetic energy. But if a force from outside the system, such as the force due to the wind, begins to act on the system, the surfer will begin to speed up, and his kinetic energy will increase. In terms of energy transfers, we would say that the energy of the system has increased because of the work done on the system by the force of the wind.

What determines how much work is done by the force of the wind? First, we note that the greater the distance over which the wind pushes the surfer, the faster the surfer goes, and the more his kinetic energy increases. This implies a greater transfer of energy. So, **the larger the displacement, the greater the work done.** Second, if the wind pushes with a stronger force, the surfer speeds up more rapidly, and the change in his kinetic energy is greater than with a weaker force. **The stronger the force, the greater the work done.**

This experiment suggests that the amount of energy transferred to a system by a force $\vec{F}$—that is, the amount of work done by $\vec{F}$—depends on both the magnitude F of the force *and* the displacement d of the system. Many experiments of this kind have established that the amount of work done by $\vec{F}$ is *proportional* to both F and d. For the simplest case described above, where the force $\vec{F}$ is constant and points in the direction of the object's displacement, the expression for the work done is found to be

$$W = Fd \qquad (10.5)$$

Work done by a constant force $\vec{F}$ in the direction of a displacement $\vec{d}$

The unit of work, that of force multiplied by distance, is N · m. This unit is so important that it has been given its own name, the **joule** (rhymes with *tool*). We define:

$$1 \text{ joule} = 1 \text{ J} = 1 \text{ N} \cdot \text{m}$$

Because work is simply energy being transferred, **the joule is the unit of *all* forms of energy.** Note that work is a *scalar* quantity.

FIGURE 10.4 The force of the wind does work on the system, increasing its kinetic energy K.

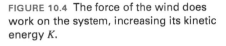
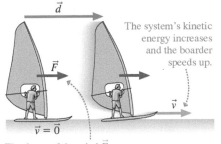

The system's kinetic energy increases and the boarder speeds up.

$\vec{v} = 0$

The force of the wind $\vec{F}$ does work on the system.

EXAMPLE 10.1 Work done in pushing a crate

Sarah pushes a heavy crate 3.0 m along the floor at a constant speed. She pushes with a constant horizontal force of magnitude 70 N. How much work does Sarah do on the crate?

PREPARE We begin with the visual overview in FIGURE 10.5. Sarah pushes with a constant force in the direction of the crate's motion, so we can use Equation 10.5 to find the work done.

FIGURE 10.5 Sarah pushing a crate.

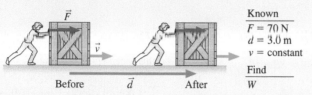

Known
$F = 70$ N
$d = 3.0$ m
$v =$ constant

Find
W

Before $\vec{d}$ After

SOLVE The work done by Sarah is

$$W = Fd = (70 \text{ N})(3.0 \text{ m}) = 210 \text{ J}$$

ASSESS Work represents a transfer of energy into a system, so here the energy of the system—the box and the floor—increases. Unlike the windsurfer, the box doesn't speed up, so its kinetic energy doesn't increase. Instead, the work increases the thermal energy in the crate and the part of the floor along which it slides, increasing the temperature of both. Using the notation of Equation 10.3, we can write this energy transfer as $\Delta E_{\text{th}} = W$.

Force at an Angle to the Displacement

A force does the greatest possible amount of work on an object when the force points in the same direction as the object's displacement. Less work is done when the force acts at an angle to the displacement. To see this, consider the kite buggy of FIGURE 10.6a, pulled along a horizontal path by the angled force of the kite string $\vec{F}$. As shown in FIGURE 10.6b, we can divide $\vec{F}$ into a component $F_\perp$ perpendicular to the motion, and a component $F_\parallel$ parallel to the motion. Only the parallel component acts to accelerate the rider and increase his kinetic energy, so only the parallel component does work on the rider. From Figure 10.6b, we see that if the angle between $\vec{F}$ and the displacement is θ, then the parallel component is $F_\parallel = F\cos\theta$. So, when the force acts at an angle θ to the direction of the displacement, we have

$$W = F_\parallel d = Fd\cos\theta \qquad (10.6)$$

Work done by a constant force $\vec{F}$ at an angle θ to the displacement $\vec{d}$

Notice that this more general definition of work agrees with Equation 10.5 if $\theta = 0°$.

Tactics Box 10.1 shows how to calculate the work done by a force at any angle to the direction of motion. The system illustrated is a block sliding on a frictionless, horizontal surface, so that only the kinetic energy is changing. However, the same relationships hold for any object undergoing a displacement.

The quantities F and d are always positive, so **the sign of W is determined entirely by the angle θ between the force and the displacement.** Note that Equation 10.6, $W = Fd\cos\theta$, is valid for any angle θ. In three special cases, $\theta = 0°$, $\theta = 90°$, and $\theta = 180°$, however, there are simple versions of Equation 10.6 that you can use. These are noted in Tactics Box 10.1.

FIGURE 10.6 Finding the work done when the force is at an angle to the displacement.

(a)

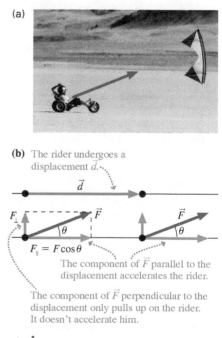

(b) The rider undergoes a displacement $\vec{d}$.

$\vec{d}$

$F_\perp$ $\vec{F}$ $\vec{F}$

θ θ

$F_\parallel = F\cos\theta$

The component of $\vec{F}$ parallel to the displacement accelerates the rider.

The component of $\vec{F}$ perpendicular to the displacement only pulls up on the rider. It doesn't accelerate him.

5.1

TACTICS BOX 10.1 Calculating the work done by a constant force

Direction of force relative to displacement	Angles and work done	Sign of W	Energy transfer
Before: $\vec{v}_i$ **After:** $\vec{v}_f$ $\vec{d}$ $\vec{F}$ $\theta = 0°$	$\theta = 0°$ $\cos\theta = 1$ $W = Fd$	+	The force is in the direction of motion. The block has its greatest positive acceleration. K increases the most: **Maximum energy transfer to system.**
$\theta < 90°$ $\vec{d}$ $\vec{F}$	$\theta < 90°$ $W = Fd\cos\theta$	+	The component of force parallel to the displacement is less than F. The block has a smaller positive acceleration. K increases less: **Decreased energy transfer to system.**
$\theta = 90°$ $\vec{d}$ $\vec{F}$	$\theta = 90°$ $\cos\theta = 0$ $W = 0$	0	There is no component of force in the direction of motion. The block moves at constant speed. No change in K: **No energy transferred.**
$\theta > 90°$ $\vec{F}$ $\vec{d}$	$\theta > 90°$ $W = Fd\cos\theta$	−	The component of force parallel to the displacement is opposite the motion. The block slows down, and K decreases: **Decreased energy transfer *out* of system.**
$\theta = 180°$ $\vec{F}$ $\vec{d}$	$\theta = 180°$ $\cos\theta = -1$ $W = -Fd$	−	The force is directly opposite the motion. The block has its greatest deceleration. K decreases the most: **Maximum energy transfer *out* of system.**

Exercises 5–6

EXAMPLE 10.2 Work done in pulling a suitcase

A strap inclined upward at a 45° angle pulls a suitcase through the airport. The tension in the strap is 20 N. How much work does the tension do if the suitcase is pulled 100 m at a constant speed?

PREPARE FIGURE 10.7 shows a visual overview. Since the suitcase moves at a constant speed, there must be a rolling friction force acting to the left.

SOLVE We can use Equation 10.6, with force $F = T$, to find that the tension does work:

$$W = Td\cos\theta = (20\text{ N})(100\text{ m})\cos 45° = 1400\text{ J}$$

ASSESS Because a person is pulling on the other end of the strap, causing the tension, we would say informally that the person does 1400 J of work on the suitcase. This work represents

FIGURE 10.7 A suitcase pulled by a strap.

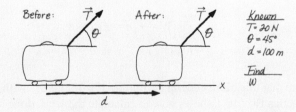

Before: $\vec{T}$ θ After: $\vec{T}$ θ

Known
$T = 20$ N
$\theta = 45°$
$d = 100$ m

Find
W

energy transferred into the suitcase + floor system. Since the suitcase moves at a constant speed, the system's kinetic energy doesn't change. Thus, just as for Sarah pushing the crate in Example 10.1, the work done goes entirely into increasing the thermal energy E_{th} of the suitcase and the floor.

CONCEPTUAL EXAMPLE 10.3   Work done by a parachute

A drag racer is slowed by a parachute. What is the sign of the work done?

REASON The drag force on the drag racer is shown in **FIGURE 10.8**, along with the dragster's displacement as it slows. The force points in the direction opposite the displacement, so that the angle θ in

FIGURE 10.8 The force acting on a drag racer.

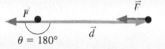

$$\theta = 180°$$

Equation 10.6 is 180°. Then $\cos\theta = \cos(180°) = -1$. Because F and d in Equation 10.6 are magnitudes, and hence positive, the work $W = Fd\cos\theta = -Fd$ done by the drag force is *negative*.

ASSESS Applying Equation 10.3 to this situation, we have

$$\Delta K = W$$

because the only system energy that changes is the racer's kinetic energy K. Because the kinetic energy is decreasing, its change ΔK is negative. This agrees with the sign of W. This example illustrates the general principle that **negative work represents a transfer of energy out of the system.**

If several forces act on an object that undergoes a displacement, each does work on the object. The **total** (or **net**) **work** W_{total} is the sum of the work done by each force. The total work represents the total energy transfer *to* the system from the environment (if $W_{total} > 0$) or *from* the system to the environment (if $W_{total} < 0$).

Forces That Do No Work

The fact that a force acts on an object doesn't mean that the force will do work on the object. The table below shows three common cases where a force does no work.

Forces that do no work

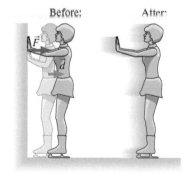

If the object undergoes no displacement while the force acts, no work is done.	**A force perpendicular to the displacement does no work.**	**If the part of the object on which the force acts undergoes no displacement, no work is done.**
This can sometimes seem counterintuitive. The weightlifter struggles mightily to hold the barbell over his head. But during the time the barbell remains stationary, he does no work on it because its displacement is zero. Why then is it so hard for him to hold it there? We'll see in Chapter 11 that it takes a rapid conversion of his internal chemical energy to keep his arms extended under this great load.	The woman exerts only a vertical force on the briefcase she's carrying. This force has no component in the direction of the displacement, so the briefcase moves at a constant velocity and its kinetic energy remains constant. Since the energy of the briefcase doesn't change, it must be that no energy is being transferred to it as work. (This is the case where $\theta = 90°$ in Tactics Box 10.1.)	Even though the wall pushes on the skater with a normal force $\vec{n}$ and she undergoes a displacement $\vec{d}$, the wall does no work on her, because the point of her body on which $\vec{n}$ acts—her hands—undergoes no displacement. This makes sense: How could energy be transferred as work from an inert, stationary object? So where does her kinetic energy come from? This will be the subject of much of Chapter 11. Can you guess?

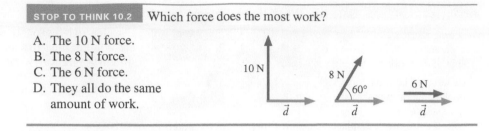

STOP TO THINK 10.2 Which force does the most work?

A. The 10 N force.
B. The 8 N force.
C. The 6 N force.
D. They all do the same amount of work.

10.3 Kinetic Energy

FIGURE 10.9 The work done by the tow rope increases the car's kinetic energy.

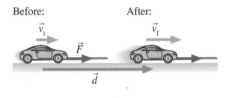

Before:

After:

We've already qualitatively discussed kinetic energy, an object's energy of motion. Let's now use what we've learned about work, and some simple kinematics, to find a quantitative expression for kinetic energy. Consider a car being pulled by a tow rope, as in FIGURE 10.9. The rope pulls with a constant force $\vec{F}$ while the car undergoes a displacement $\vec{d}$, so the force does work $W = Fd$ on the car. If we ignore friction and drag, the work done by $\vec{F}$ is transferred entirely into the car's energy of motion—its kinetic energy. In this case, the change in the car's kinetic energy is given by the work-energy equation, Equation 10.3, as

$$W = \Delta K = K_f - K_i \qquad (10.7)$$

Using kinematics, we can find another expression for the work done, in terms of the car's initial and final speeds. Recall from Chapter 2 the kinematic equation

$$v_f^2 = v_i^2 + 2a\Delta x$$

Applied to the motion of our car, $\Delta x = d$ is the car's displacement and, from Newton's second law, the acceleration is $a = F/m$. Thus we can write

$$v_f^2 = v_i^2 + \frac{2Fd}{m} = v_i^2 + \frac{2W}{m}$$

where we have replaced Fd with the work W. If we now solve for the work, we find

$$W = \frac{1}{2}m\left(v_f^2 - v_i^2\right) = \frac{1}{2}mv_f^2 - \frac{1}{2}mv_i^2$$

If we compare this result with Equation 10.7, we see that

$$K_f = \frac{1}{2}mv_f^2 \qquad \text{and} \qquad K_i = \frac{1}{2}mv_i^2$$

6.1 Activ ONLINE Physics

In general, then, an object of mass m moving with speed v has kinetic energy

$$K = \frac{1}{2}mv^2 \qquad (10.8)$$

Kinetic energy of an object of mass m moving with speed v

QUADRATIC

TABLE 10.1 Some approximate kinetic energies

Object	Kinetic energy
Ant walking	1×10^{-8} J
Penny dropped 1 m	2.5×10^{-3} J
Person walking	70 J
Fastball, 100 mph	150 J
Bullet	5000 J
Car, 60 mph	5×10^5 J
Supertanker, 20 mph	2×10^{10} J

From Equation 10.8, the units of kinetic energy are those of mass times speed squared, or kg $\cdot$ (m/s)^2. But

$$1 \text{ kg} \cdot (\text{m/s})^2 = \underbrace{1 \text{ kg} \cdot (\text{m/s}^2)}_{1\text{ N}} \cdot \text{m} = 1 \text{ N} \cdot \text{m} = 1 \text{ J}$$

We see that the units of kinetic energy are the same as those of work, as they must be. Table 10.1 gives some approximate kinetic energies. Everyday kinetic energies range from a tiny fraction of a fraction of a joule to nearly a million joules for a speeding car.

CONCEPTUAL EXAMPLE 10.4 **Kinetic energy changes for a car**

Compare the increase in a 1000 kg car's kinetic energy as it speeds up by 5.0 m/s, starting from 5.0 m/s, to its increase in kinetic energy as it speeds up by 5.0 m/s, starting from 10 m/s.

REASON The change in the car's kinetic energy in going from 5.0 m/s to 10 m/s is

$$\Delta K_{5\to10} = \frac{1}{2}mv_f^2 - \frac{1}{2}mv_i^2$$

This gives

$$\Delta K_{5\to10} = \frac{1}{2}(1000 \text{ kg})(10 \text{ m/s})^2 - \frac{1}{2}(1000 \text{ kg})(5.0 \text{ m/s})^2$$

$$= 3.8 \times 10^4 \text{ J}$$

Similarly, increasing from 10 m/s to 15 m/s requires

$$\Delta K_{10\to15} = \frac{1}{2}(1000 \text{ kg})(15 \text{ m/s})^2 - \frac{1}{2}(1000 \text{ kg})(10 \text{ m/s})^2$$

$$= 6.3 \times 10^4 \text{ J}$$

Even though the increase in the car's *speed* is the same in both cases, the increase in kinetic energy is substantially greater in the second case.

ASSESS Kinetic energy depends on the *square* of the speed v. In FIGURE 10.10, which plots kinetic energy versus speed, we see that the energy of the car increases rapidly with speed. We can also see graphically why the change in K for a 5 m/s change in v is greater at high speeds than at low speeds. In part this is why it's harder to accelerate your car at high speeds than at low speeds.

FIGURE 10.10 The kinetic energy increases as the *square* of the speed.

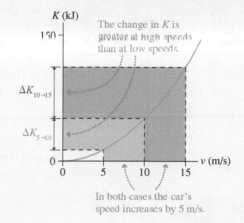

EXAMPLE 10.5 **Speed of a bobsled after pushing**

A two-man bobsled has a mass of 390 kg. Starting from rest, the two racers push the sled for the first 50 m with a net force of 270 N. Neglecting friction, what is the sled's speed at the end of the 50 m?

PREPARE We can find the sled's final speed if we can find its final kinetic energy. We can do so by equating the work done by the racers as they push on the sled to the change in its kinetic energy. FIGURE 10.11 lists the known quantities and the quantity (v_f) that we want to find.

FIGURE 10.11 The work done by the pushers increases the sled's kinetic energy.

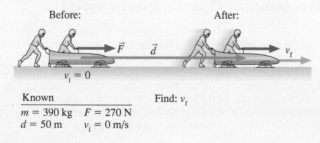

Before:
After:
$\vec{F}$ $\vec{d}$ v_f
$v_i = 0$

Find: v_f

Known
$m = 390 \text{ kg}$ $F = 270 \text{ N}$
$d = 50 \text{ m}$ $v_i = 0 \text{ m/s}$

SOLVE From Equation 10.3, the work-energy equation, the change in the sled's kinetic energy is $\Delta K = K_f - K_i = W$. The sled's final kinetic energy is thus

$$K_f = K_i + W$$

Using our expressions for kinetic energy and work, we get

$$\frac{1}{2}mv_f^2 = \frac{1}{2}mv_i^2 + Fd$$

Because $v_i = 0$, the work-energy equation reduces to

$$\frac{1}{2}mv_f^2 = Fd$$

We can solve for the final speed to get

$$v_f = \sqrt{\frac{2Fd}{m}} = \sqrt{\frac{2(270 \text{ N})(50 \text{ m})}{390 \text{ kg}}} = 8.3 \text{ m/s}$$

ASSESS 8.3 m/s, about 18 mph, seems a reasonable speed for two fast pushers to attain.

STOP TO THINK 10.3 Rank in order, from greatest to least, the kinetic energies of the sliding pucks.

FIGURE 10.12 The large rotating blades of a windmill have a great deal of kinetic energy.

Rotational Kinetic Energy

We've just found an expression for the kinetic energy of an object moving along a line or some other path. This energy is called **translational kinetic energy.** Consider now an object rotating about a fixed axis, such as the windmill blades in FIGURE 10.12. Although the blades have no overall translational motion, each particle in the blade is moving and hence has kinetic energy. Adding up the kinetic energy for each particle that makes up the blades, we find that the blades have **rotational kinetic energy,** the kinetic energy due to rotation.

FIGURE 10.13 shows two of the particles making up a windmill blade that rotates with angular velocity ω. Recall from Section 6.2 that a particle moving with angular velocity ω in a circle of radius r has a speed $v = \omega r$. Thus particle 1, which rotates in a circle of radius r_1, moves with speed $v_1 = r_1\omega$ and so has kinetic energy $\frac{1}{2}m_1 v_1^2 = \frac{1}{2}m_1 r_1^2\omega^2$. Similarly, particle 2, which rotates in a circle with a larger radius r_2, has kinetic energy $\frac{1}{2}m_2 r_2^2\omega^2$. The object's rotational kinetic energy is the sum of the kinetic energies of *all* the particles:

FIGURE 10.13 Rotational kinetic energy is due to the circular motion of the particles.

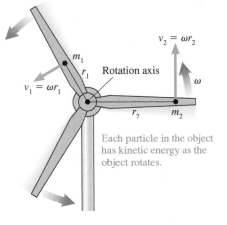

Each particle in the object has kinetic energy as the object rotates.

$$K_{\text{rot}} = \frac{1}{2}m_1 r_1^2\omega^2 + \frac{1}{2}m_2 r_2^2\omega^2 + \cdots = \frac{1}{2}\left(\sum mr^2\right)\omega^2$$

You will recognize the term in parentheses as our old friend, the moment of inertia I. Thus the rotational kinetic energy is

$$K_{\text{rot}} = \frac{1}{2}I\omega^2 \qquad (10.9)$$

Rotational kinetic energy of an object with moment of inertia I and angular velocity ω

NOTE ▶ Rotational kinetic energy is *not* a new form of energy. It is the ordinary kinetic energy of motion, only now expressed in a form that is especially convenient for rotational motion. Comparison with the familiar $\frac{1}{2}mv^2$ shows again that the moment of inertia I is the rotational equivalent of mass. ◀

A rolling object, such as a wheel, is undergoing both rotational *and* translational motions. Consequently, its total kinetic energy is the sum of its rotational and translational kinetic energies:

$$K = K_{\text{trans}} + K_{\text{rot}} = \frac{1}{2}mv^2 + \frac{1}{2}I\omega^2 \qquad (10.10)$$

This illustrates an important fact: **The kinetic energy of a rolling object is always greater than that of a nonrotating object moving at the same speed.**

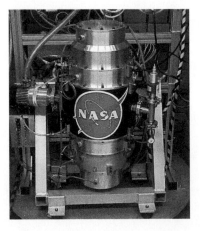

◀ **Rotational recharge** The International Space Station (ISS) gets its electric power from solar panels. But during each 92-minute orbit, the ISS is in the earth's shadow for 30 minutes. The batteries that currently provide power during these blackouts need periodic replacement, which is very expensive in space. A promising new technology would replace the batteries with a *flywheel*—a cylinder rotating at a very high angular speed. Energy from the solar panels is used to speed up the flywheel, storing energy as rotational kinetic energy, which can then be converted back into electric energy when the ISS is in shadow.

EXAMPLE 10.6 | **Kinetic energy of a bicycle**

Bike 1 has a 10.0 kg frame and 1.00 kg wheels; bike 2 has a 9.00 kg frame and 1.50 kg wheels. Both bikes thus have the same 12.0 kg total mass. What is the kinetic energy of each bike when they are ridden at 12.0 m/s? Model each wheel as a hoop of radius 35.0 cm.

PREPARE Each bike's frame has only translational kinetic energy $K_{\text{frame}} = \frac{1}{2}mv^2$, where m is the mass of the frame. The kinetic energy of each rolling wheel is given by Equation 10.10. From Table 7.4, we find that I for a hoop is MR^2, where M is the mass of one wheel.

SOLVE From Equation 10.10 the kinetic energy of each rolling wheel is

$$K_{\text{wheel}} = \frac{1}{2}Mv^2 + \frac{1}{2}I\omega^2 = \frac{1}{2}Mv^2 + \frac{1}{2}\underbrace{(MR^2)}_{I}\underbrace{\left(\frac{v}{R}\right)^2}_{\omega^2} = Mv^2$$

Then the total kinetic energy of a bike is

$$K = K_{\text{frame}} + 2K_{\text{wheel}} = \frac{1}{2}mv^2 + 2Mv^2$$

The factor of 2 in the second term occurs because each bike has two wheels. Thus the kinetic energies of the two bikes are

$$K_1 = \frac{1}{2}(10.0 \text{ kg})(12.0 \text{ m/s})^2 + 2(1.00 \text{ kg})(12.0 \text{ m/s})^2$$
$$= 1010 \text{ J}$$

$$K_2 = \frac{1}{2}(9.00 \text{ kg})(12.0 \text{ m/s})^2 + 2(1.50 \text{ kg})(12.0 \text{ m/s})^2$$
$$= 1080 \text{ J}$$

The kinetic energy of bike 2 is about 7% higher than that of bike 1. Note that the radius of the wheels was not needed in this calculation.

ASSESS As the cyclists on these bikes accelerate from rest to 12 m/s, they must convert some of their internal chemical energy into the kinetic energy of the bikes. Racing cyclists want to use as little of their own energy as possible. Although both bikes have the same total mass, the one with the lighter wheels will take less energy to get it moving. Shaving a little extra weight off your wheels is more useful than taking that same weight off your frame.

It's important that racing bike wheels are as light as possible.

10.4 Potential Energy

When two or more objects in a system interact, it is sometimes possible to *store* energy in the system in a way that the energy can be easily recovered. For instance, the earth and a ball interact by the gravitational force between them. If the ball is lifted up into the air, energy is stored in the ball + earth system, energy that can later be recovered as kinetic energy when the ball is released and falls. Similarly, a spring is a system made up of countless atoms that interact via their atomic "springs." If we push a box against a spring, energy is stored that can be recovered when the spring later pushes the box across the table. This sort of stored energy is called **potential energy,** since it has the *potential* to be converted into other forms of energy, such as kinetic or thermal energy.

The forces due to gravity and springs are special in that they allow for the storage of energy. Other interaction forces do not. When a crate is pushed across the floor, the crate and the floor interact via the force of friction, and the work done on the system is converted into thermal energy. But this energy is *not* stored up for later recovery—it slowly diffuses into the environment and cannot be recovered.

Interaction forces that can store useful energy are called **conservative forces.** The name comes from the important fact that, as we'll see, the mechanical energy of a system is *conserved* when only conservative forces act. Gravity and elastic forces are conservative forces, and later we'll find that the electric force is a conservative force as well. Friction, on the other hand, is a **nonconservative force.** When two objects interact via a friction force, energy is not stored. It is usually transformed into thermal energy.

Let's look more closely at the potential energies associated with the two conservative forces—gravity and springs—that we'll study in this chapter.

Gravitational Potential Energy

To find an expression for gravitational potential energy, let's consider the system of the book and the earth shown in **FIGURE 10.14a** on the next page. The book is lifted at a constant speed from its initial position at y_i to a final height y_f. The lifting force of the hand is external to the system and so does work W on the system, increasing its energy. The book is lifted at a constant speed, so its kinetic energy doesn't change. Because there's no friction, the book's thermal energy doesn't change either. Thus

(a)

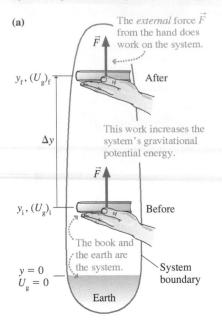

The *external* force $\vec{F}$ from the hand does work on the system.

$y_f, (U_g)_f$ — After

This work increases the system's gravitational potential energy.

Δy

$y_i, (U_g)_i$ — Before

The book and the earth are the system.

$y = 0$
$U_g = 0$

System boundary

Earth

(b) Because the book is being lifted at a constant speed, it is in dynamic equilibrium with $\vec{F}_{net} = \vec{0}$. Thus $F = w = mg$.

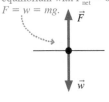

the work done goes entirely into increasing the gravitational potential energy of the system. According to Equation 10.3, the work-energy equation, $\Delta U_g = W$. Because $\Delta U_g = (U_g)_f - (U_g)_i$, Equation 10.3 can be written

$$(U_g)_f = (U_g)_i + W \tag{10.11}$$

The work done is $W = Fd$, where $d = \Delta y = y_f - y_i$ is the vertical distance that the book is lifted. From the free-body diagram of FIGURE 10.14b, we see that $F = mg$. Thus $W = mg\Delta y$, and so

$$(U_g)_f = (U_g)_i + mg\Delta y \tag{10.12}$$

Because our final height was greater than our initial height, Δy is positive and $(U_g)_f > (U_g)_i$. **The higher the object is lifted, the greater the gravitational potential energy in the object + earth system.**

Equation 10.12 gives the final gravitational potential energy $(U_g)_f$ in terms of its initial value $(U_g)_i$. But what is the value of $(U_g)_i$? We can gain some insight by writing Equation 10.12 in terms of energy *changes*:

$$(U_g)_f - (U_g)_i = \Delta U_g = mg\Delta y$$

For example, if we lift a 1.5 kg book up by $\Delta y = 2.0$ m, we increase the system's gravitational potential energy by $\Delta U_g = (1.5 \text{ kg})(9.8 \text{ m/s}^2)(2.0 \text{ m}) = 29.4$ J. This increase is *independent* of the book's starting height: The gravitational potential energy increases by 29.4 J whether we lift the book 2.0 m starting at sea level or starting at the top of the Washington Monument. This illustrates an important general fact about *every* form of potential energy: **Only *changes* in potential energy are significant.**

Because of this fact, we are free to choose a *reference level* where we define U_g to be zero. Our expression for U_g is particularly simple if we choose this reference level to be at $y = 0$. We then have

$$U_g = mgy \tag{10.13}$$

Gravitational potential energy of an object of mass m at height y
(assuming $U_g = 0$ when the object is at $y = 0$)

NOTE ▶ We've emphasized that gravitational potential energy is an energy of the earth + object *system*. In solving problems using the law of conservation of energy, you'll need to include the earth as part of your system. For simplicity, we'll usually speak of "the gravitational potential energy of the ball," but what we really mean is the potential energy of the earth + ball system. ◀

EXAMPLE 10.7 **Racing up a skyscraper**

In the Empire State Building Run-Up, competitors race up the 1576 steps of the Empire State Building, climbing a total vertical distance of 320 m. How much gravitational potential energy does a 70 kg racer gain during this race?

Racers head up the staircase in the Empire State Building Run-Up.

PREPARE We choose $y = 0$ m and $U_g = 0$ J at the ground floor of the building.

SOLVE At the top, the racer's gravitational potential energy is

$$U_g = mgy = (70 \text{ kg})(9.8 \text{ m/s}^2)(320 \text{ m}) = 2.2 \times 10^5 \text{ J}$$

Because the racer's gravitational potential energy was 0 J at the ground floor, the change in his potential energy is 2.2×10^5 J.

ASSESS This is a large amount of energy. According to Table 10.1, it's comparable to the energy of a speeding car. But if you think how hard it would be to climb the Empire State Building, it seems like a plausible result.

An important conclusion from Equation 10.13 is that gravitational potential energy depends only on the height of the object above the reference level $y = 0$, not on the object's horizontal position. To understand why, consider carrying a briefcase while walking on level ground at a constant speed. As shown in the table on page 297, the vertical force of your hand on the briefcase is *perpendicular* to the displacement. *No work* is done on the briefcase, so its gravitational potential energy remains constant as long as its height above the ground doesn't change.

This idea can be applied to more complicated cases, such as the 82 kg hiker in FIGURE 10.15. His gravitational potential energy depends *only* on his height y above the reference level. Along path A, it's the same value $U_g = mgy = 80$ kJ at any point where he is at height $y = 100$ m above the reference level. If he had instead taken path B, his gravitational potential energy at $y = 100$ m would be the same 80 kJ. It doesn't matter *how* he gets to the 100 m elevation; his potential energy at that height is always the same. **Gravitational potential energy depends only on the *height* of an object and not on the path the object took to get to that position.** This fact will allow us to use the law of conservation of energy to easily solve a variety of problems that would be very difficult to solve using Newton's laws alone.

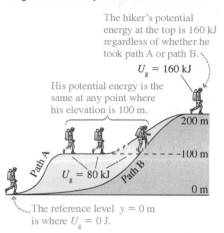

FIGURE 10.15 The hiker's gravitational potential energy depends only on his height above the $y = 0$ m reference level.

The hiker's potential energy at the top is 160 kJ regardless of whether he took path A or path B.

$U_g = 160$ kJ

His potential energy is the same at any point where his elevation is 100 m.

$U_g = 80$ kJ

200 m

100 m

0 m

The reference level $y = 0$ m is where $U_g = 0$ J.

STOP TO THINK 10.4 Rank in order, from largest to smallest, the gravitational potential energies of identical balls 1 through 4.

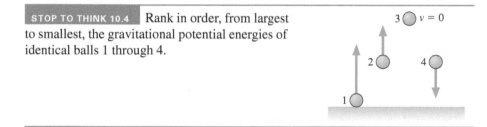

$3 \quad v = 0$

2

4

1

Elastic Potential Energy

Energy can also be stored in a compressed or extended spring as **elastic** (or **spring**) **potential energy** U_s. We can find out how much energy is stored in a spring by using an external force to slowly compress the spring. This external force does work on the spring, transferring energy to the spring. Since only the elastic potential energy of the spring is changing, Equation 10.3 reads

$$\Delta U_s = W \qquad (10.14)$$

That is, we can find out how much elastic potential energy is stored in the spring by calculating the amount of work needed to compress the spring.

FIGURE 10.16 shows a spring being compressed by a hand. In Section 8.3 we found that the force the spring exerts on the hand is $F_s = -k\Delta x$ (Hooke's law), where Δx is the displacement of the end of the spring from its equilibrium position and k is the spring constant. In Figure 10.16 we have set the origin of our coordinate system at the equilibrium position. The displacement from equilibrium Δx is therefore equal to x, and the spring force is then $-kx$. By Newton's third law, the force that the hand exerts on the spring is thus $F = +kx$.

As the hand pushes the end of the spring from its equilibrium position to a final position x, the applied force increases from 0 to kx. This is not a constant force, so we can't use Equation 10.5, $W = Fd$, to find the work done. However, it seems reasonable to calculate the work by using the *average* force in Equation 10.5. Because the force varies from $F_i = 0$ to $F_f = kx$, the average force used to compress the spring is $F_{avg} = \frac{1}{2}kx$. Thus the work done by the hand is

$$W = F_{avg}d = F_{avg}x = \left(\frac{1}{2}kx\right)x = \frac{1}{2}kx^2$$

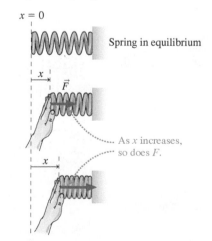

FIGURE 10.16 The force required to compress a spring is not constant.

$x = 0$

Spring in equilibrium

x

$\vec{F}$

As x increases, so does F.

x

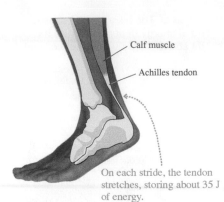

Calf muscle

Achilles tendon

On each stride, the tendon stretches, storing about 35 J of energy.

Spring in your step BIO As you run, you lose some of your mechanical energy each time your foot strikes the ground; this energy is transformed into unrecoverable thermal energy. Luckily, about 35% of the decrease of your mechanical energy when your foot lands is stored as elastic potential energy in the stretchable Achilles tendon of the lower leg. On each plant of the foot, the tendon is stretched, storing some energy. The tendon springs back as you push off the ground again, helping to propel you forward. This recovered energy reduces the amount of internal chemical energy you use, increasing your efficiency.

This work is stored as potential energy in the spring, so we can use Equation 10.14 to find that as the spring is compressed, the elastic potential energy increases by

$$\Delta U_s = \frac{1}{2}kx^2$$

Just as in the case of gravitational potential energy, we have found an expression for the *change* in U_s, not U_s itself. Again, we are free to set $U_s = 0$ at any convenient spring extension. An obvious choice is to set $U_s = 0$ at the point where the spring is in equilibrium, neither compressed nor stretched—that is, at $x = 0$. With this choice we have

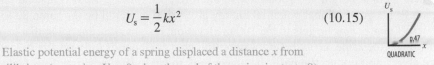

$$U_s = \frac{1}{2}kx^2 \qquad (10.15)$$

Elastic potential energy of a spring displaced a distance x from equilibrium (assuming $U_s = 0$ when the end of the spring is at $x = 0$)

p.47

QUADRATIC

NOTE ▶ Because U_s depends on the *square* of the displacement x, U_s is the same whether x is positive (the spring is compressed as in Figure 10.16) or negative (the spring is stretched). ◀

EXAMPLE 10.8   **Pulling back on a bow**

An archer pulls back the string on her bow to a distance of 70 cm from its equilibrium position. To hold the string at this position takes a force of 140 N. How much elastic potential energy is stored in the bow?

PREPARE A bow is an elastic material, so we will model it as obeying Hooke's law, $F_s = -kx$, where x is the distance the string is pulled back. We can use the force required to hold the string, and the distance it is pulled back, to find the bow's spring constant k. Then we can use Equation 10.15 to find the elastic potential energy.

SOLVE From Hooke's law, the spring constant is

$$k = \frac{F}{x} = \frac{140 \text{ N}}{0.70 \text{ m}} = 200 \text{ N/m}$$

Then the elastic potential energy of the flexed bow is

$$U_s = \frac{1}{2}kx^2 = \frac{1}{2}(200 \text{ N/m})(0.70 \text{ m})^2 = 49 \text{ J}$$

ASSESS When the arrow is released, this elastic potential energy will be transformed into the kinetic energy of the arrow. Because arrows are quite light, 49 J of kinetic energy will correspond to a very high speed.

FIGURE 10.17 A molecular view of thermal energy.

Hot object: Fast-moving molecules have lots of kinetic and elastic potential energy.

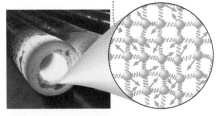

Cold object: Slow-moving molecules have little kinetic and elastic potential energy.

STOP TO THINK 10.5   When a spring is stretched by 5 cm, its elastic potential energy is 1 J. What will its elastic potential energy be if it is *compressed* by 10 cm?

A. −4 J   B. −2 J   C. 2 J   D. 4 J

10.5 Thermal Energy

We noted earlier that thermal energy is related to the microscopic motion of the molecules of an object. As FIGURE 10.17 shows, the molecules in a hot object jiggle around their average positions more than the molecules in a cold object. This has two consequences. First, each atom is on average moving faster in the hot object. This means that each atom has a higher *kinetic energy*. Second, each atom in the hot object tends to stray farther from its equilibrium position, leading to a greater stretching or compressing of the spring-like molecular bonds. This means that each atom has on average a higher *potential energy*. The potential energy stored in any one bond and the kinetic energy of any one atom are both exceedingly small, but there are incredibly many bonds and atoms. The sum of all these microscopic potential and kinetic energies is what we call **thermal energy**. Increasing an object's thermal energy corresponds to increasing its temperature.

Creating Thermal Energy

FIGURE 10.18 shows a thermogram of a heavy box and the floor across which it has just been dragged. In this image, warmer areas appear light blue or green. You can see that the bottom of the box and the region of the floor that the box moved over are noticeably warmer than their surroundings. In the process of dragging the box, thermal energy has appeared in the box and the floor.

We can find a quantitative expression for the change in thermal energy by considering such a box pulled by a rope at a constant speed. As the box is pulled across the floor, the rope exerts a constant forward force $\vec{F}$ on the box, while the friction force $\vec{f}_k$ exerts a constant force on the box that is directed backward. Because the box moves at a constant speed, the magnitudes of these two forces are equal: $F = f_k$.

As the box moves through a displacement $d = \Delta x$, the rope does work $W = F\Delta x$ on the box. This work represents energy transferred into the system, so the system's energy must *increase*. In what form is this increased energy? The box's speed remains constant, so there is no change in its kinetic energy ($\Delta K = 0$). And its height doesn't change, so its gravitational potential energy is unchanged as well ($\Delta U_g = 0$). Instead, the increased energy must be in the form of *thermal* energy E_{th}. As Figure 10.18 shows, this energy appears as an increased temperature of both the box *and* the floor across which it was dragged.

We can write the work-energy equation, Equation 10.3, for the case where only thermal energy changes:

$$\Delta E_{th} = W$$

or, because the work is $W = F\Delta x = f_k\Delta x$,

$$\Delta E_{th} = f_k\Delta x \tag{10.16}$$

This increase in thermal energy is a general feature of any system where friction between sliding objects is present. An atomic-level explanation is shown in FIGURE 10.19. Although we arrived at Equation 10.16 by considering energy transferred into the system via work done by an external force, the equation is equally valid for the transformation of mechanical energy into thermal energy when, for instance, an object slides to a halt on a rough surface. Equation 10.16 also applies to rolling friction; we need only replace f_k by f_r.

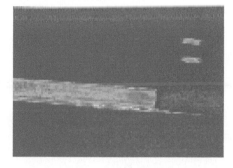

FIGURE 10.18 A thermograph of a box that's been dragged across the floor.

FIGURE 10.19 How friction causes an increase in thermal energy.

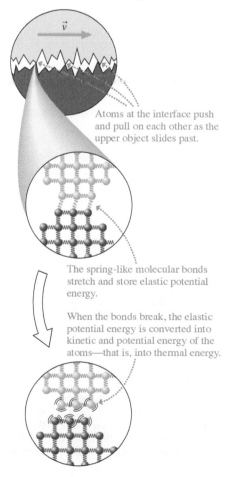

Atoms at the interface push and pull on each other as the upper object slides past.

The spring-like molecular bonds stretch and store elastic potential energy.

When the bonds break, the elastic potential energy is converted into kinetic and potential energy of the atoms—that is, into thermal energy.

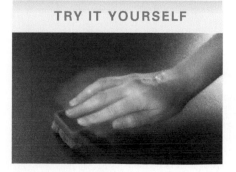

TRY IT YOURSELF

◀**Agitating atoms** Vigorously rub a somewhat soft object such as a blackboard eraser on your desktop for about 10 seconds. If you then pass your fingers over the spot where you rubbed, you'll feel a distinct warm area. Congratulations: You've just set some 100,000,000,000,000,000,000,000 atoms into motion!

EXAMPLE 10.9 **Creating thermal energy by rubbing**

A 0.30 kg block of wood is rubbed back and forth against a wood table 30 times in each direction. The block is moved 8.0 cm during each stroke and pressed against the table with a force of 22 N. How much thermal energy is created in this process?

PREPARE The hand holding the block does work to push the block back and forth. Work transfers energy into the block + table system, where it appears as thermal energy according to Equation 10.16. The force of friction can be found from the model of kinetic friction introduced in Chapter 5, $f_k = \mu_k n$; from Table 5.1 the coefficient of kinetic friction for wood sliding on wood is $\mu_k = 0.20$. To find the normal force n acting on the block, we draw the free-body diagram of FIGURE 10.20, which shows only the *vertical* forces acting on the block.

FIGURE 10.20 Free-body diagram (vertical forces only) for a block being rubbed against a table.

SOLVE From Equation 10.16 we have $\Delta E_{th} = f_k \Delta x$, where $f_k = \mu_k n$. The block is not accelerating in the y-direction, so from the free-body diagram Newton's second law gives

$$\sum F_y = n - w - F = ma_y = 0$$

or

$$n = w + F = mg + F = (0.30 \text{ kg})(9.8 \text{ m/s}^2) + 22 \text{ N} = 25 \text{ N}$$

The friction force is then $f_k = \mu_k n = (0.20)(25 \text{ N}) = 5.0 \text{ N}$. The total displacement of the block is $2 \times 30 \times 8.0 \text{ cm} = 4.8 \text{ m}$. Thus the thermal energy created is

$$\Delta E_{th} = f_k \Delta x = (5.0 \text{ N})(4.8 \text{ m}) = 24 \text{ J}$$

ASSESS This modest amount of thermal energy seems reasonable for a person to create by rubbing.

10.6 Using the Law of Conservation of Energy

The law of conservation of energy, Equation 10.4, states that **the total energy of an *isolated system* is conserved** so that its change is zero:

$$\Delta E = \Delta K + \Delta U_g + \Delta U_s + \Delta E_{th} + \Delta E_{chem} + \cdots = 0 \qquad (10.17)$$

This law applies to every form of energy, from kinetic to chemical to nuclear. For the rest of this chapter, however, we'll narrow our focus and concern ourselves with only the forms of energy typically transformed during the motion of ordinary objects. These forms are kinetic energy K, gravitational and elastic potential energies U_g and U_s, and thermal energy E_{th}.

We defined an isolated system as one on which external forces do no work, so that no energy is transferred into or out of the system. The following table shows how to choose an isolated system for four common situations.

TABLE 10.2 Choosing an isolated system

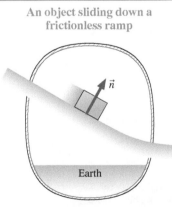

An object in free fall	An object sliding down a frictionless ramp	An object compressing a spring	An object sliding along a surface with friction
We choose the ball *and* the earth as the system, so that the forces between them are *internal* forces. There are no external forces to do work, so the system is isolated.	The external force the ramp exerts on the object is perpendicular to the motion, and so does no work. The object and the earth together form an isolated system.	We choose the object and the spring to be the system. The forces between them are internal forces, so no work is done.	The block and the surface interact via kinetic friction forces, but these forces are internal to the system. There are no external forces to do work, so the system is isolated.

Just as for momentum conservation, we wish to develop a before-and-after perspective for energy conservation. We can do so by noting that $\Delta K = K_f - K_i$, $\Delta U_g = (U_g)_f - (U_g)_i$, and so on. Then Equation 10.17 can be written as

$$K_f + (U_g)_f + (U_s)_f + \Delta E_{th} = K_i + (U_g)_i + (U_s)_i \qquad (10.18)$$

Equation 10.18 is the before-and-after version of the law of conservation of energy: It equates the final value of an isolated system's energy to its initial energy. This equation will be the basis for a powerful problem-solving strategy.

NOTE ▶ We don't write ΔE_{th} as $(E_{th})_f - (E_{th})_i$ because the initial and final values of the thermal energy are typically unknown; only their *difference* ΔE_{th} can be measured. ◀

Conservation of Mechanical Energy

If we further restrict ourselves to cases where friction can be neglected, so that $\Delta E_{th} = 0$, the law of conservation of energy, Equation 10.18, becomes

$$K_f + (U_g)_f + (U_s)_f = K_i + (U_g)_i + (U_s)_i \qquad (10.19)$$

Activ Physics ONLINE 5.2–5.7, 7.11–7.13

The sum of the kinetic and potential energies, $K + U_g + U_s$, is called the **mechanical energy** of the system, so Equation 10.19 says that **the mechanical energy is conserved for an isolated system without friction.**

These observations about the conservation of energy suggest the following problem-solving strategy.

PROBLEM-SOLVING STRATEGY 10.1 **Conservation of energy problems** (MP)™

PREPARE Referring to Table 10.2, choose your system so that it is isolated. Draw a before-and-after visual overview, as was outlined in Tactics Box 9.1. Note the known quantities, and identify what you're trying to find.

SOLVE There are two important situations:

- If the system is isolated *and* there's no friction, the mechanical energy is conserved:

$$K_f + (U_g)_f + (U_s)_f = K_i + (U_g)_i + (U_s)_i$$

- If the system is isolated but there is friction within the system, the total energy is conserved:

$$K_f + (U_g)_f + (U_s)_f + \Delta E_{th} = K_i + (U_g)_i + (U_s)_i$$

Depending on the problem, you'll need to calculate the initial and/or final values of these energies; you can then solve for the unknown energies, and from these any unknown speeds (from K), heights (from U_g and U_s), or displacements or friction forces (from $\Delta E_{th} = f_k \Delta x$).

ASSESS Check the signs of your energies. Kinetic energy is always positive, as is the change in thermal energy. Check that your result has the correct units, is reasonable, and answers the question.

Exercise 23

Spring into action BIO A locust can jump as far as 1 meter, an impressive distance for such a small animal. To make such a jump, its legs must extend much more rapidly than muscles can ordinarily contract. Thus, instead of using its muscles to make the jump directly, the locust uses them to more slowly stretch an internal "spring" near its knee joint. This stores elastic potential energy in the spring. When the muscles relax, the spring is suddenly released, and its energy is rapidly converted into kinetic energy of the insect.

EXAMPLE 10.10 **Hitting the bell**

At the county fair, Katie tries her hand at the ring-the-bell attraction, as shown in FIGURE 10.21 on the next page. She swings the mallet hard enough to give the ball an initial upward speed of 8.0 m/s. Will the ball ring the bell, 3.0 m from the bottom?

PREPARE We'll follow the steps of Problem-Solving Strategy 10.1. From Table 10.2, we see that once the ball is in the air, the system consisting of the ball and the earth is isolated. If we assume that the track along which the ball moves is frictionless, then the

Continued

system's mechanical energy is conserved. Figure 10.21 shows a before-and-after visual overview in which we've chosen $y = 0$ m to be at the ball's starting point. We can then use conservation of mechanical energy, Equation 10.19.

FIGURE 10.21 Before-and-after visual overview of the ring-the-bell attraction.

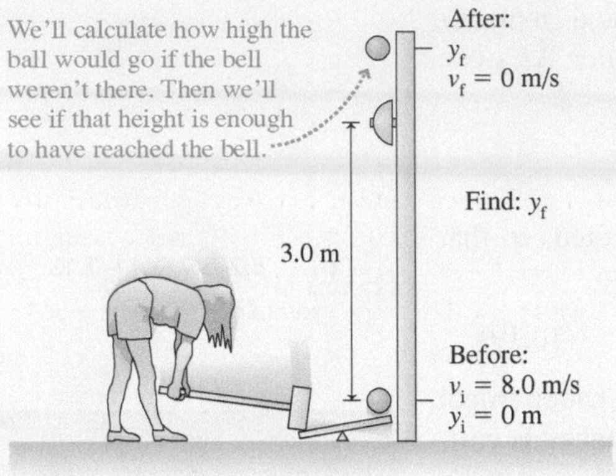

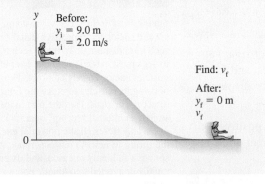

We'll calculate how high the ball would go if the bell weren't there. Then we'll see if that height is enough to have reached the bell.

After:
y_f
$v_f = 0$ m/s

Find: y_f

3.0 m

Before:
$v_i = 8.0$ m/s
$y_i = 0$ m

SOLVE Equation 10.19 tells us that $K_f + (U_g)_f = K_i + (U_g)_i$. We can use our expressions for kinetic and potential energy to write this as

$$\frac{1}{2}mv_f^2 + mgy_f = \frac{1}{2}mv_i^2 + mgy_i$$

Let's ignore the bell for the moment and figure out how far the ball would rise if there were nothing in its way. We know that the ball starts at $y_i = 0$ m and that its speed v_f at the highest point is 0 m/s. Thus the energy equation simplifies to

$$mgy_f = \frac{1}{2}mv_i^2$$

This is easily solved for the height y_f:

$$y_f = \frac{v_i^2}{2g} = \frac{(8.0 \text{ m/s})^2}{2(9.8 \text{ m/s}^2)} = 3.3 \text{ m}$$

This is higher than the point where the bell sits, so the ball would actually hit it on the way up.

ASSESS It seems reasonable that Katie could swing the mallet hard enough to make the ball rise by about 3 m.

EXAMPLE 10.11 **Speed at the bottom of a water slide**

Still at the county fair, Katie tries the water slide, whose shape is shown in **FIGURE 10.22**. The starting point is 9.0 m above the ground. She pushes off with an initial speed of 2.0 m/s. If the slide is frictionless, how fast will Katie be traveling at the bottom?

PREPARE Table 10.2 showed that the system consisting of Katie and the earth is isolated because the normal force of the slide is perpendicular to Katie's motion and does no work. If we assume the slide is frictionless, we can use the conservation of mechanical energy equation. Figure 10.22 is a visual overview of the problem.

FIGURE 10.22 Before-and-after visual overview of Katie on the water slide.

y

Before:
$y_i = 9.0$ m
$v_i = 2.0$ m/s

Find: v_f

After:
$y_f = 0$ m
v_f

0

SOLVE Conservation of mechanical energy gives

$$K_f + (U_g)_f = K_i + (U_g)_i$$

or

$$\frac{1}{2}mv_f^2 + mgy_f = \frac{1}{2}mv_i^2 + mgy_i$$

Taking $y_f = 0$ m, we have

$$\frac{1}{2}mv_f^2 = \frac{1}{2}mv_i^2 + mgy_i$$

which we can solve to get

$$v_f = \sqrt{v_i^2 + 2gy_i}$$
$$= \sqrt{(2.0 \text{ m/s})^2 + 2(9.8 \text{ m/s}^2)(9.0 \text{ m})} = 13 \text{ m/s}$$

ASSESS This speed is about 30 mph. This is probably faster than you really would go on a water slide but, because we have ignored friction, our answer is reasonable. It is important to realize that the *shape* of the slide does not matter because gravitational potential energy depends only on the *height* above a reference level. **If you slide down any (frictionless) slide of the same height, your speed at the bottom is the same.**

EXAMPLE 10.12 **Speed of a spring-launched ball**

A spring-loaded toy gun is used to launch a 10 g plastic ball. The spring, which has a spring constant of 10 N/m, is compressed by 10 cm as the ball is pushed into the barrel. When the trigger is pulled, the spring is released and shoots the ball back out. What is the ball's speed as it leaves the barrel? Assume that friction is negligible.

PREPARE Assume the spring obeys Hooke's law, $F_s = -kx$, and is massless so that it has no kinetic energy of its own. Using Table 10.2, we choose the isolated system to be the spring and the ball. There's no friction; hence the system's mechanical energy $K + U_s$ is conserved.

FIGURE 10.23 Before-and-after visual overview of a ball being shot out of a spring-loaded toy gun.

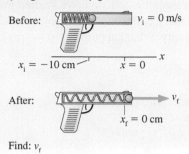

Before: $v_i = 0$ m/s

$x_i = -10$ cm $x = 0$

After: v_f

$x_f = 0$ cm

Find: v_f

FIGURE 10.23 shows a before-and-after visual overview. The compressed spring will push on the ball until the spring has returned to its equilibrium length. We have chosen the origin of the coordinate system at the equilibrium position of the free end of the spring, making $x_i = -10$ cm and $x_f = 0$ cm.

SOLVE The energy conservation equation is $K_f + (U_s)_f = K_i + (U_s)_i$. We can use the elastic potential energy of the spring, Equation 10.15, to write this as

$$\tfrac{1}{2}mv_f^2 + \tfrac{1}{2}kx_f^2 = \tfrac{1}{2}mv_i^2 + \tfrac{1}{2}kx_i^2$$

We know that $x_f = 0$ m and $v_i = 0$ m/s, so this simplifies to

$$\tfrac{1}{2}mv_f^2 = \tfrac{1}{2}kx_i^2$$

It is now straightforward to solve for the ball's speed:

$$v_f = \sqrt{\frac{kx_i^2}{m}} = \sqrt{\frac{(10 \text{ N/m})(-0.10 \text{ m})^2}{0.010 \text{ kg}}} = 3.2 \text{ m/s}$$

ASSESS This is *not* a problem that we could have easily solved with Newton's laws. The acceleration is not constant, and we have not learned how to handle the kinematics of nonconstant acceleration. But with conservation of energy—it's easy!

Friction and Thermal Energy

Thermal energy is always created when kinetic friction is present, so we must use the more general conservation of energy equation, Equation 10.18, which includes thermal-energy changes ΔE_{th}. Furthermore, we know from Section 10.5 that the change in the thermal energy when an object slides a distance Δx while subject to a friction force f_k is $\Delta E_{th} = f_k \Delta x$.

EXAMPLE 10.13   **Where will the sled stop?**

A sledder, starting from rest, slides down a 10-m-high hill. At the bottom of the hill is a long horizontal patch of rough snow. The hill is nearly frictionless, but the coefficient of friction between the sled and the rough snow at the bottom is $\mu_k = 0.30$. How far will the sled slide along the rough patch?

PREPARE In order to be isolated, the system must include the sled, the earth, *and* the rough snow. As Table 10.2 shows, this makes the friction force an internal force so that no work is done on the system. We can use conservation of energy, but we will need to include thermal energy. A visual overview of the problem is shown in **FIGURE 10.24**.

FIGURE 10.24 Visual overview of a sledder sliding downhill.

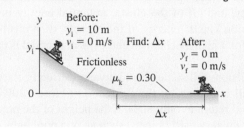

Before:
$y_i = 10$ m
$v_i = 0$ m/s   Find: Δx After:
Frictionless $y_f = 0$ m
$\mu_k = 0.30$ $v_f = 0$ m/s

Δx

SOLVE At the top of the hill the sled has only gravitational potential energy $(U_g)_i = mgy_i$. It has no kinetic or potential energy after stopping at the bottom of the hill, so $K_f = (U_g)_f = 0$. However, friction in the rough patch causes an increase in thermal energy. Thus our conservation of energy equation $K_f + (U_g)_f + \Delta E_{th} = K_i + (U_g)_i$ is

$$\Delta E_{th} = (U_g)_i = mgy_i$$

The change in thermal energy is $\Delta E_{th} = f_k \Delta x = \mu_k n \Delta x$. The normal force $\vec{n}$ balances the sled's weight $\vec{w}$ as it crosses the rough patch, so $n = w = mg$. Thus

$$\Delta E_{th} = \mu_k n \Delta x = \mu_k (mg) \Delta x = mgy_i$$

from which we find

$$\Delta x = \frac{y_i}{\mu_k} = \frac{10 \text{ m}}{0.30} = 33 \text{ m}$$

ASSESS It seems reasonable that the sledder would slide a distance that is greater than the height of the hill he started down.

10.7 Energy in Collisions

In Chapter 9 we studied collisions between two objects. We found that if no external forces are acting on the objects, the total *momentum* of the objects will be conserved. Now we wish to study what happens to *energy* in collisions. The energetics of

Activ Physics ONLINE   6.2, 6.5, 6.8, 6.9

collisions are important in many applications in biokinetics, such as designing safer automobiles and bicycle helmets.

Let's first re-examine a perfectly inelastic collision. We studied just such a collision in Example 9.8. Recall that in such a collision the two objects stick together and then move with a common final velocity. What happens to the energy?

EXAMPLE 10.14 **Energy transformations in a perfectly inelastic collision**

FIGURE 10.25 shows two air-track gliders that are pushed toward each other, collide, and stick together. In Example 9.8, we used conservation of momentum to find the final velocity shown in Figure 10.25 from the given initial velocities. How much thermal energy is created in this collision?

FIGURE 10.25 Before-and-after visual overview of a completely inelastic collision.

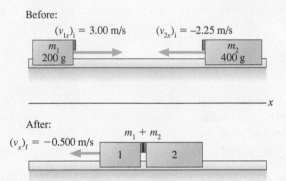

PREPARE We'll choose our system to be the two gliders. Because the track is horizontal, there is no change in potential energy. Thus the law of conservation of energy, Equation 10.18, is $K_f + \Delta E_{th} = K_i$. The total energy before the collision must equal the total energy afterward, but the *mechanical* energies need not be equal.

SOLVE The initial kinetic energy is

$$K_i = \frac{1}{2}m_1(v_{1x})_i^2 + \frac{1}{2}m_2(v_{2x})_i^2$$

$$= \frac{1}{2}(0.200 \text{ kg})(3.00 \text{ m/s})^2 + \frac{1}{2}(0.400 \text{ kg})(-2.25 \text{ m/s})^2$$

$$= 1.91 \text{ J}$$

Because the gliders stick together and move as a single object with mass $m_1 + m_2$, the final kinetic energy is

$$K_f = \frac{1}{2}(m_1 + m_2)(v_x)_f^2$$

$$= \frac{1}{2}(0.600 \text{ kg})(-0.500 \text{ m/s})^2 = 0.0750 \text{ J}$$

From the conservation of energy equation above, we find that the thermal energy increases by

$$\Delta E_{th} = K_i - K_f = 1.91 \text{ J} - 0.075 \text{ J} = 1.84 \text{ J}$$

This amount of the initial kinetic energy is transformed into thermal energy during the impact of the collision.

ASSESS About 96% of the initial kinetic energy is transformed into thermal energy. This is typical of many real-world collisions.

Elastic Collisions

Figure 9.1 showed a collision of a tennis ball with a racket. The ball is compressed and the racket strings stretch as the two collide, then the ball expands and the strings relax as the two are pushed apart. In the language of energy, the kinetic energy of the objects is transformed into the elastic potential energy of the ball and strings, then back into kinetic energy as the two objects spring apart. If *all* of the kinetic energy is stored as elastic potential energy, and *all* of the elastic potential energy is transformed back into the post-collision kinetic energy of the objects, then mechanical energy is conserved. A collision for which mechanical energy is conserved is called a **perfectly elastic collision.**

Needless to say, most real collisions fall somewhere between perfectly elastic and perfectly inelastic. A rubber ball bouncing on the floor might "lose" 20% of its kinetic energy on each bounce and return to only 80% of the height of the preceding bounce. But collisions between two very hard objects, such as two pool balls or two steel balls, come close to being perfectly elastic. And collisions between microscopic particles, such as atoms or electrons, can be perfectly elastic.

FIGURE 10.26 on the next page shows a head-on, perfectly elastic collision of a ball of mass m_1, having initial velocity $(v_{1x})_i$, with a ball of mass m_2 that is initially at rest. The balls' velocities after the collision are $(v_{1x})_f$ and $(v_{2x})_f$. These are velocities, not speeds, and have signs. Ball 1, in particular, might bounce backward and have a negative value for $(v_{1x})_f$.

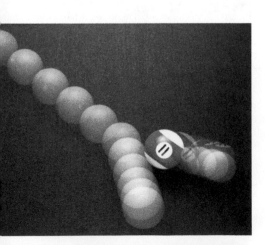

In a collision between a cue ball and a stationary ball, the mechanical energy of the balls is almost perfectly conserved.

The collision must obey two conservation laws: conservation of momentum (obeyed in any collision) and conservation of mechanical energy (because the collision is perfectly elastic). Although the energy is transformed into potential energy during the collision, the mechanical energy before and after the collision is purely kinetic energy. Thus,

momentum conservation: $\quad m_1(v_{1x})_i = m_1(v_{1x})_f + m_2(v_{2x})_f$

energy conservation: $\quad \dfrac{1}{2}m_1(v_{1x})_i^2 = \dfrac{1}{2}m_1(v_{1x})_f^2 + \dfrac{1}{2}m_2(v_{2x})_f^2$

Momentum conservation alone is not sufficient to analyze the collision because there are two unknowns: the two final velocities. That is why we did not consider perfectly elastic collisions in Chapter 9. Energy conservation gives us another condition. The complete solution of these two equations involves straightforward but rather lengthy algebra. We'll just give the solution here:

$$(v_{1x})_f = \frac{m_1 - m_2}{m_1 + m_2}(v_{1x})_i \qquad (v_{2x})_f = \frac{2m_1}{m_1 + m_2}(v_{1x})_i \qquad (10.20)$$

Perfectly elastic collision with object 2 initially at rest

Equations 10.20 allow us to compute the final velocity of each object. Let's look at a common and important example: a perfectly elastic collision between two objects of equal mass.

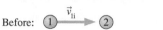

FIGURE 10.26 A perfectly elastic collision.

Before: ① $\vec{v}_{1i}$ ② $\quad K_i$

Energy is stored in compressed molecular bonds, then released as the bonds re-expand.

During: ①②

After: ① ② $\quad K_f = K_i$
$\vec{v}_{1f}$ $\vec{v}_{2f}$

EXAMPLE 10.15 **Velocities in an air hockey collision**

On an air hockey table, a moving puck, traveling to the right at 2.3 m/s, makes a head-on collision with an identical puck at rest. What is the final velocity of each puck?

PREPARE The before-and-after visual overview is shown in FIGURE 10.27. We've shown the final velocities in the picture, but we don't really know yet which way the pucks will move. Because one puck was initially at rest, we can use Equation 10.20 to find the final velocities of the pucks. The pucks are identical, so we have $m_1 = m_2 = m$.

SOLVE We use Equation 10.20 with $m_1 = m_2 = m$ to get

$$(v_{1x})_f = \frac{m - m}{m + m}(v_{1x})_i = 0 \text{ m/s}$$

$$(v_{2x})_f = \frac{2m}{m + m}(v_{1x})_i = (v_{1x})_i = 2.3 \text{ m/s}$$

The incoming puck stops dead, and the initially stationary puck goes off with the same velocity that the incoming one had.

ASSESS You can see that momentum and energy are conserved: The incoming puck's momentum and energy are completely transferred to the outgoing puck. If you've ever played pool, you've probably seen this sort of collision when you hit a ball head-on with the cue ball. The cue ball stops and the other ball picks up the cue ball's velocity.

FIGURE 10.27 A moving puck collides with a stationary puck.

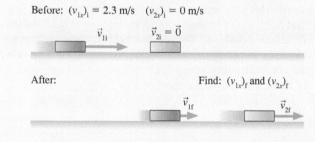

Before: $(v_{1x})_i = 2.3$ m/s $(v_{2x})_i = 0$ m/s

$\vec{v}_{1i}$ $\vec{v}_{2i} = \vec{0}$

After: Find: $(v_{1x})_f$ and $(v_{2x})_f$

$\vec{v}_{1f}$ $\vec{v}_{2f}$

Other cases where the colliding objects have unequal masses will be treated in the end-of-chapter problems.

Forces in Collisions

The collision between two pool balls occurs very quickly, and the forces are typically very large and difficult to calculate. Fortunately, by using the concepts of momentum and energy conservation, we can often calculate the final velocities of the balls without having to know the forces between them. There are collisions, however, where knowing the forces involved is of critical importance. The following example shows how a helmet helps protect the head from the large forces involved in a bicycle accident.

EXAMPLE 10.16 **Protecting your head**

A bike helmet—basically a shell of hard, crushable foam—is tested by being strapped onto a 5.0 kg headform and dropped from a height of 2.0 m onto a hard anvil. What force is encountered by the headform if the impact crushes the foam by 3.0 cm?

The foam inside a bike helmet is designed to crush upon impact.

PREPARE A before-and-after visual overview of the test is shown in FIGURE 10.28. We've chosen the endpoint of the problem to be when the headform comes to rest with the foam crushed. We can use the work-energy equation, Equation 10.3, to calculate the force on the headform. We'll choose the headform and the earth to be the system; the foam in the helmet is part

of the environment. We make this choice so that the force on the headform due to the foam is an *external* force that does work W on the headform.

SOLVE The work-energy equation $\Delta K + \Delta U_g + \Delta E_{th} = W$ tells us that the work done by external forces—in this case, the force of the foam on the headform—changes the energy of the system. The headform starts at rest, speeds up as it falls, then returns to rest during the impact. Overall, then, $\Delta K = 0$. Furthermore, $\Delta E_{th} = 0$ because there's no friction to increase the thermal energy. Only the gravitational potential energy changes, giving

$$\Delta U_g = (U_g)_f - (U_g)_i = W$$

The upward force of the foam on the headform is opposite the downward displacement of the headform. Referring to Tactics Box 10.1, we see that the work done is negative: $W = -Fd$, where we've assumed that the force is relatively constant. Using this result in the work-energy equation and solving for F, we find

$$F = -\frac{(U_g)_f - (U_g)_i}{d} = \frac{(U_g)_i - (U_g)_f}{d}$$

Taking our reference height to be $y = 0$ m at the anvil, we have $(U_g)_f = 0$. We're left with $(U_g)_i = mgy_i$, so

$$F = \frac{mgy_i}{d} = \frac{(5.0 \text{ kg})(9.8 \text{ m/s})(2.0 \text{ m})}{0.030 \text{ m}} = 3300 \text{ N}$$

This is the force that acts on the head to bring it to a halt in 3.0 cm. More important from the perspective of possible brain injury is the head's *acceleration*:

$$a = \frac{F}{m} = \frac{3300 \text{ N}}{5.0 \text{ kg}} = 660 \text{ m/s}^2 = 67g$$

ASSESS The accepted threshold for serious brain injury is around $300g$, so this helmet would protect the rider in all but the most serious accidents. Without the helmet, the rider's head would come to a stop in a much shorter distance and thus be subjected to a much larger acceleration.

FIGURE 10.28 Before-and-after visual overview of the bike helmet test.

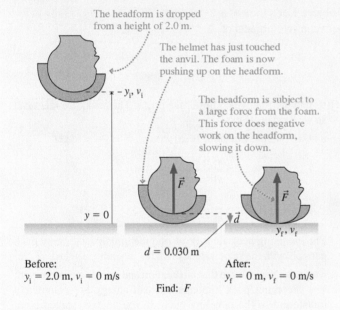

The headform is dropped from a height of 2.0 m.

The helmet has just touched the anvil. The foam is now pushing up on the headform.

$-y_i, v_i$

The headform is subject to a large force from the foam. This force does negative work on the headform, slowing it down.

$y = 0$

$\vec{F}$

$\vec{F}$

$\vec{d}$

y_f, v_f

$d = 0.030 \text{ m}$

Before:
$y_i = 2.0 \text{ m}, v_i = 0 \text{ m/s}$

After:
$y_f = 0 \text{ m}, v_f = 0 \text{ m/s}$

Find: F

10.8 Power

We've now studied how energy can be transformed from one kind into another and how it can be transferred between the environment and the system as work. In many situations we would like to know *how quickly* the energy is transformed or transferred. Is a transfer of energy very rapid, or does it take place over a long time? In passing a truck, your car needs to transform a certain amount of the chemical energy in its fuel into kinetic energy. It makes a *big* difference whether your engine can do this in 20 s or 60 s!

The question How quickly? implies that we are talking about a *rate*. For example, the velocity of an object—how fast it is going—is the *rate of change* of position. So, when we raise the issue of how fast the energy is transformed, we are talking about the *rate of transformation* of energy. Suppose in a time interval Δt an amount of energy ΔE is transformed from one form to another. The rate at which this energy is transformed is called the **power** P and is defined as

$$P = \frac{\Delta E}{\Delta t} \qquad (10.21)$$

Power when an amount of energy ΔE is transformed in a time interval Δt

The unit of power is the **watt,** which is defined as 1 watt = 1 W = 1 J/s.

Power also measures the rate at which energy is transferred into or out of a system as work W. If work W is done in time interval Δt, the rate of energy *transfer* is

$$P = \frac{W}{\Delta t} \qquad (10.22)$$

Power when an amount of work W is done in a time interval Δt

A force that is doing work (i.e., transferring energy) at a rate of 3 J/s has an "output power" of 3 W. A system that is gaining energy at the rate of 3 J/s is said to "consume" 3 W of power. Common prefixes used for power are mW (milliwatts), kW (kilowatts), and MW (megawatts).

We can express Equation 10.22 in a different form. If in the time interval Δt an object undergoes a displacement Δx, the work done by a force acting on the object is $W = F\Delta x$. Then Equation 10.22 can be written as

$$P = \frac{W}{\Delta t} = \frac{F\Delta x}{\Delta t} = F\frac{\Delta x}{\Delta t} = Fv$$

The rate at which energy is transferred to an object as work—the power—is the product of the force that does the work and the velocity of the object:

$$P = Fv \qquad (10.23)$$

Rate of energy transfer due to a force F acting on an object moving at velocity v

Both these cars take about the same energy to reach 60 mph, but the race car gets there in a much shorter time, so its *power* is much greater.

The English unit of power is the *horsepower.* The conversion factor to watts is

1 horsepower = 1 hp = 746 W

Many common appliances, such as motors, are rated in hp.

EXAMPLE 10.17   Power to pass a truck

Your 1500 kg car is behind a truck traveling at 60 mph (27 m/s). To pass it, you speed up to 75 mph (34 m/s) in 6.0 s. What engine power is required to do this?

PREPARE Your engine is transforming the chemical energy of its fuel into the kinetic energy of the car. We can calculate the rate of transformation by finding the change ΔK in the kinetic energy and using the known time interval.

SOLVE We have

$$K_i = \frac{1}{2}mv_i^2 = \frac{1}{2}(1500 \text{ kg})(27 \text{ m/s})^2 = 5.47 \times 10^5 \text{ J}$$

$$K_f = \frac{1}{2}mv_f^2 = \frac{1}{2}(1500 \text{ kg})(34 \text{ m/s})^2 = 8.67 \times 10^5 \text{ J}$$

so that

$$\Delta K = K_f - K_i$$
$$= (8.67 \times 10^5 \text{ J}) - (5.47 \times 10^5 \text{ J}) = 3.20 \times 10^5 \text{ J}$$

To transform this amount of energy in 6 s, the power required is

$$P = \frac{\Delta K}{\Delta t} = \frac{3.20 \times 10^5 \text{ J}}{6.0 \text{ s}} = 53,000 \text{ W} = 53 \text{ kW}$$

This is about 71 hp. This power is in addition to the power needed to overcome drag and friction and cruise at 60 mph, so the total power required from the engine will be even greater than this.

ASSESS You use a large amount of energy to perform a simple driving maneuver such as this. 3.20×10^5 J is enough energy to lift an 80 kg person 410 m in the air—the height of a tall skyscraper. And 53 kW would lift him there in only 6 s!

STOP TO THINK 10.6   Four students run up the stairs in the times shown. Rank in order, from largest to smallest, their power outputs P_A through P_D.

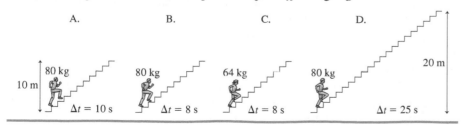

INTEGRATED EXAMPLE 10.18   **Stopping a runaway truck**

A truck's brakes can overheat and fail while descending mountain highways, leading to an extremely dangerous runaway truck. Some highways have *runaway-truck ramps* to safely bring out-of-control trucks to a stop. These uphill ramps are covered with a deep bed of gravel. The uphill slope and the large coefficient of rolling friction as the tires sink into the gravel bring the truck to a safe halt.

A runaway-truck ramp along Interstate 70 in Colorado.

A 22,000 kg truck heading down a 3.5° slope at 20 m/s (≈45 mph) suddenly has its brakes fail. Fortunately, there's a runaway-truck ramp 600 m ahead. The ramp slopes upward at an angle of 10°, and the coefficient of rolling friction between the truck's tires and the loose gravel is $\mu_r = 0.40$. Ignore air resistance and rolling friction as the truck rolls down the highway.

a. Use conservation of energy to find how far along the ramp the truck travels before stopping.
b. By how much does the thermal energy of the truck and ramp increase as the truck stops?

PREPARE   Parts a and b can be solved using energy conservation by following Problem-Solving Strategy 10.1. **FIGURE 10.29** shows a before-and-after visual overview. Because we're going to need to determine friction forces to calculate the increase in thermal energy, we've also drawn a free-body diagram for the truck as it moves up the ramp. One slight complication is that the y-axis of free-body diagrams is drawn perpendicular to the slope, whereas the calculation of gravitational potential energy needs a vertical y-axis to measure height. We've dealt with this by labeling the free-body diagram axis the y'-axis.

FIGURE 10.29   Visual overview of the runaway truck.

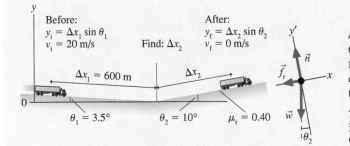

SOLVE   a. The law of conservation of energy for the motion of the truck, from the moment its brakes fail to when it finally stops, is

$$K_f + (U_g)_f + \Delta E_{th} = K_i + (U_g)_i$$

Because friction is present only along the ramp, thermal energy will be created only as the truck moves up the ramp. This thermal energy is then given by $\Delta E_{th} = f_r \Delta x_2$, because Δx_2 is the length of the ramp. The conservation of energy equation then is

$$\frac{1}{2}mv_f^2 + mgy_f + f_r\Delta x_2 = \frac{1}{2}mv_i^2 + mgy_i$$

From Figure 10.29 we have $y_i = \Delta x_1 \sin\theta_1$, $y_f = \Delta x_2 \sin\theta_2$, and $v_f = 0$, so the equation becomes

$$mg\Delta x_2 \sin\theta_2 + f_r\Delta x_2 = \frac{1}{2}mv_i^2 + mg\Delta x_1 \sin\theta_1$$

To find $f_r = \mu_r n$ we need to find the normal force n. The free-body diagram shows that

$$\sum F_{y'} = n - mg\cos\theta_2 = a_{y'} = 0$$

from which $f_r = \mu_r n = \mu_r mg\cos\theta_2$. With this result for f_r, our conservation of energy equation is

$$mg\Delta x_2 \sin\theta_2 + \mu_r mg\cos\theta_2\Delta x_2 = \frac{1}{2}mv_i^2 + mg\Delta x_1 \sin\theta_1$$

which, after we divide both sides by mg, simplifies to

$$\Delta x_2 \sin\theta_2 + \mu_r\cos\theta_2\Delta x_2 = \frac{v_i^2}{2g} + \Delta x_1 \sin\theta_1$$

Solving this for Δx_2 gives

$$\Delta x_2 = \frac{\dfrac{v_i^2}{2g} + \Delta x_1\sin\theta_1}{\sin\theta_2 + \mu_r\cos\theta_2}$$

$$= \frac{\dfrac{(20 \text{ m/s})^2}{2(9.8 \text{ m/s}^2)} + (600 \text{ m})(\sin 3.5°)}{\sin 10° + 0.40(\cos 10°)} = 100 \text{ m}$$

b. We know that $\Delta E_{th} = f_r\Delta x_2 = (\mu_r mg\cos\theta_2)\Delta x_2$, so that

$$\Delta E_{th} = (0.40)(22,000 \text{ kg})(9.8 \text{ m/s}^2)(\cos 10°)(100 \text{ m})$$

$$= 8.5 \times 10^6 \text{ J}$$

ASSESS   It seems reasonable that a truck that speeds up as it rolls 600 m downhill takes only 100 m to stop on a steeper, high-friction ramp. We also expect the thermal energy to be roughly comparable to the kinetic energy of the truck, since it's largely the kinetic energy that is transformed into thermal energy. At the top of the hill the truck's kinetic energy is $K_i = \frac{1}{2}mv_i^2 = \frac{1}{2}(22,000 \text{ kg})(20 \text{ m/s})^2 = 4.4 \times 10^6$ J, which is of the same order of magnitude as ΔE_{th}. Our answer is reasonable.

SUMMARY

The goals of Chapter 10 are to introduce the concept of energy and to learn a new problem-solving strategy based on conservation of energy.

GENERAL PRINCIPLES

Basic Energy Model

Within a system, energy can be **transformed** between various forms.

Energy can be **transferred** into or out of a system in two basic ways:

- **Work:** The transfer of energy by mechanical forces.

- **Heat:** The nonmechanical transfer of energy from a hotter to a colder object.

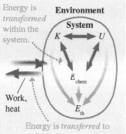

Energy is *transformed* within the system.

Environment
System

Work, heat

Energy is *transferred* to or from the system from or to the environment.

Conservation of Energy

When work W is done on a system, the system's total energy changes by the amount of work done. In mathematical form, this is the **work-energy equation:**

$$\Delta E = \Delta K + \Delta U_g + \Delta U_s + \Delta E_{th} + \Delta E_{chem} + \cdots = W$$

A system is **isolated** when no energy is transferred into or out of the system. This means the work is zero, giving the **law of conservation of energy:**

$$\Delta K + \Delta U_g + \Delta U_s + \Delta E_{th} + \Delta E_{chem} + \cdots = 0$$

Solving Energy Conservation Problems

PREPARE Choose your system so that it's isolated. Draw a before-and-after visual overview.

SOLVE

- If the system is isolated and there's no friction, then mechanical energy is conserved:

$$K_f + (U_g)_f + (U_s)_f = K_i + (U_g)_i + (U_s)_i$$

- If the system is isolated but there's friction present, then the total energy is conserved:

$$K_f + (U_g)_f + (U_s)_f + \Delta E_{th} = K_i + (U_g)_i + (U_s)_i$$

ASSESS Kinetic energy is always positive, as is the change in thermal energy.

IMPORTANT CONCEPTS

Kinetic energy is an energy of motion:

$$K = \frac{1}{2}mv^2 + \frac{1}{2}I\omega^2$$

Translational ⟶ ⟵ Rotational

Potential energy is energy stored in a system of interacting objects.

- **Gravitational potential energy:** $U_g = mgy$

- **Elastic potential energy:** $U_s = \frac{1}{2}kx^2$

Mechanical energy is the sum of a system's kinetic and potential energies:

$$\text{Mechanical energy} = K + U = K + U_g + U_s$$

Thermal energy is the sum of the microscopic kinetic and potential energies of all the molecules in an object. The hotter an object, the more thermal energy it has. When kinetic (sliding) friction is present, the increase in the thermal energy is $\Delta E_{th} = f_k \Delta x$.

Work is the process by which energy is transferred to or from a system by the application of mechanical forces.

If a particle moves through a displacement $\vec{d}$ while acted upon by a constant force $\vec{F}$, the force does work

$$W = F_\parallel d = Fd\cos\theta$$

Only the component of the force parallel to the displacement does work.

APPLICATIONS

Perfectly elastic collisions
Both mechanical energy and momentum are conserved.

$$(v_{1x})_f = \frac{m_1 - m_2}{m_1 + m_2}(v_{1x})_i$$

$$(v_{2x})_f = \frac{2m_1}{m_1 + m_2}(v_{1x})_i$$

Object 2 initially at rest

Before: ① $(v_{1x})_i$ ② K_i

After: $K_f = K_i$ ① ② $(v_{1x})_f$ $(v_{2x})_f$

Power is the rate at which energy is transformed . . .

$$P = \frac{\Delta E}{\Delta t}$$ ◄····· Amount of energy transformed
◄····· Time required to transform it

. . . or at which work is done.

$$P = \frac{W}{\Delta t}$$ ◄····· Amount of work done
◄····· Time required to do work

™   For homework assigned on MasteringPhysics, go to www.masteringphysics.com

Problem difficulty is labeled as I (straightforward) to IIIII (challenging).

Problems labeled ✎ can be done on a Workbook Energy Work-sheet; INT integrate significant material from earlier chapters; BIO are of biological or medical interest.

QUESTIONS

Conceptual Questions

1. The brake shoes of your car are made of a material that can tolerate very high temperatures without being damaged. Why is this so?
2. When you pound a nail with a hammer, the nail gets quite warm. Describe the energy transformations that lead to the addition of thermal energy in the nail.

For Questions 3 through 10, give a specific example of a system with the energy transformation shown. In these questions, W is the work done on the system, and K, U, and E_{th} are the kinetic, potential, and thermal energies of the system, respectively. Any energy not mentioned in the transformation is assumed to remain constant; if work is not mentioned, it is assumed to be zero.

3. $W \rightarrow K$
4. $W \rightarrow U$
5. $K \rightarrow U$
6. $K \rightarrow W$
7. $U \rightarrow K$
8. $W \rightarrow \Delta E_{th}$
9. $U \rightarrow \Delta E_{th}$
10. $K \rightarrow \Delta E_{th}$

11. A ball of putty is dropped from a height of 2 m onto a hard floor, where it sticks. What object or objects need to be included within the system if the system is to be isolated during this process?
12. A 0.5 kg mass on a 1-m-long string swings in a circle on a horizontal, frictionless table at a steady speed of 2 m/s. How much work does the tension in the string do on the mass during one revolution? Explain.
13. Particle A has less mass than particle B. Both are pushed forward across a frictionless surface by equal forces for 1 s. Both start from rest.
    a. Compare the amount of work done on each particle. That is, is the work done on A greater than, less than, or equal to the work done on B? Explain.
    b. Compare the impulses delivered to particles A and B. Explain.
    c. Compare the final speeds of particles A and B. Explain.
14. The meaning of the word "work" is quite different in physics from its everyday usage. Give an example of an action a person could do that "feels like work" but that does not involve any work as we've defined it in this chapter.
15. To change a tire, you need to use a jack to raise one corner of your car. While doing so, you happen to notice that pushing the jack handle down 20 cm raises the car only 0.2 cm. Use energy concepts to explain why the handle must be moved so far to raise the car by such a small amount.
16. You drop two balls from a tower, one of mass m and the other of mass $2m$. Just before they hit the ground, which ball, if either, has the larger kinetic energy? Explain.

17. A roller coaster car rolls down a frictionless track, reaching speed v at the bottom.
    a. If you want the car to go twice as fast at the bottom, by what factor must you increase the height of the track?
    b. Does your answer to part a depend on whether the track is straight or not? Explain.
18. A spring gun shoots out a plastic ball at speed v. The spring is then compressed twice the distance it was on the first shot.
    a. By what factor is the spring's potential energy increased?
    b. By what factor is the ball's speed increased? Explain.
19. Sandy and Chris stand on the edge of a cliff and throw identical mass rocks at the same speed. Sandy throws her rock horizontally while Chris throws his upward at an angle of 45° to the horizontal. Are the rocks moving at the same speed when they hit the ground, or is one moving faster than the other? If one is moving faster, which one? Explain.
20. A solid cylinder and a cylindrical shell have the same mass, same radius, and turn on frictionless, horizontal axles. (The cylindrical shell has lightweight spokes connecting the shell to the axle.) A rope is wrapped around each cylinder and tied to a block. The blocks have the same mass and are held the same height above the ground as shown in Figure Q10.20. Both blocks are released simultaneously. The ropes do not slip. Which block hits the ground first? Or is it a tie? Explain.

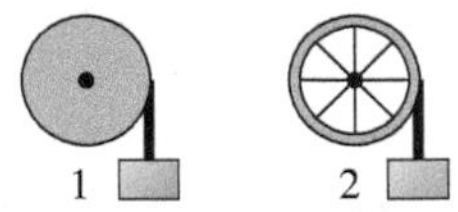

FIGURE Q10.20

21. You are much more likely to be injured if you fall and your head
BIO strikes the ground than if your head strikes a gymnastics pad. Use energy and work concepts to explain why this is so.

Multiple-Choice Questions

22. II If you walk up a flight of stairs at constant speed, gaining vertical height h, the work done on you (the system, of mass m) is
    A. $+mgh$, by the normal force of the stairs.
    B. $-mgh$, by the normal force of the stairs.
    C. $+mgh$, by the gravitational force of the earth.
    D. $-mgh$, by the gravitational force of the earth.
23. I You and a friend each carry a 15 kg suitcase up two flights of stairs, walking at a constant speed. Take each suitcase to be the system. Suppose you carry your suitcase up the stairs in 30 s while your friend takes 60 s. Which of the following is true?
    A. You did more work, but both of you expended the same power.
    B. You did more work and expended more power.
    C. Both of you did equal work, but you expended more power.
    D. Both of you did equal work, but you expended less power.

24. | A woman uses a pulley and a rope to raise a 20 kg weight to a height of 2 m. If it takes 4 s to do this, about how much power is she supplying?
    A. 100 W   B. 200 W   C. 300 W   D. 400 W

25. | A hockey puck sliding along frictionless ice with speed v to the right collides with a horizontal spring and compresses it by 2.0 cm before coming to a momentary stop. What will be the spring's maximum compression if the same puck hits it at a speed of $2v$?
    A. 2.0 cm   B. 2.8 cm   C. 4.0 cm
    D. 5.6 cm   E. 8.0 cm

26. || A block slides down a smooth ramp, starting from rest at a height h. When it reaches the bottom it's moving at speed v. It then continues to slide up a second smooth ramp. At what height is its speed equal to $v/2$?
    A. $h/4$ B. $h/2$ C. $3h/4$ D. $2h$

27. | A wrecking ball is suspended from a 5.0-m-long cable that makes a 30° angle with the vertical. The ball is released and swings down. What is the ball's speed at the lowest point?
    A. 7.7 m/s   B. 4.4 m/s   C. 3.6 m/s   D. 3.1 m/s

PROBLEMS

Section 10.2 Work

1. || During an etiquette class, you walk slowly and steadily at 0.20 m/s for 2.5 m with a 0.75 kg book balanced on top of your head. How much work does your head do on the book?

2. || A 2.0 kg book is lying on a 0.75-m-high table. You pick it up and place it on a bookshelf 2.3 m above the floor.
   a. How much work does gravity do on the book?
   b. How much work does your hand do on the book?

3. || The two ropes seen in Figure P10.3 are used to lower a 255 kg piano exactly 5 m from a second-story window to the ground. How much work is done by each of the three forces?

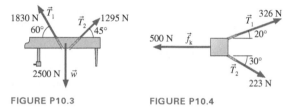

FIGURE P10.3   **FIGURE P10.4**

4. | The two ropes shown in the bird's-eye view of Figure P10.4 are used to drag a crate exactly 3 m across the floor. How much work is done by each of the ropes on the crate?

5. || a. At the airport, you ride a "moving sidewalk" that carries you horizontally for 25 m at 0.70 m/s. Assuming that you were moving at 0.70 m/s before stepping onto the moving sidewalk and continue at 0.70 m/s afterward, how much work does the moving sidewalk do on you? Your mass is 60 kg.
   b. An escalator carries you from one level to the next in the airport terminal. The upper level is 4.5 m above the lower level, and the length of the escalator is 7.0 m. How much work does the up escalator do on you when you ride it from the lower level to the upper level?
   c. How much work does the down escalator do on you when you ride it from the upper level to the lower level?

6. | A boy flies a kite with the string at a 30° angle to the horizontal. The tension in the string is 4.5 N. How much work does the string do on the boy if the boy
   a. Stands still?
   b. Walks a horizontal distance of 11 m away from the kite?
   c. Walks a horizontal distance of 11 m toward the kite?

Section 10.3 Kinetic Energy

7. | Which has the larger kinetic energy, a 10 g bullet fired at 500 m/s or a 10 kg bowling ball sliding at 10 m/s?

8. || At what speed does a 1000 kg compact car have the same kinetic energy as a 20,000 kg truck going 25 km/hr?

9. | A car is traveling at 10 m/s.
   a. How fast would the car need to go to double its kinetic energy?
   b. By what factor does the car's kinetic energy increase if its speed is doubled to 20 m/s?

10. ||| Sam's job at the amusement park is to slow down and bring to a stop the boats in the log ride. If a boat and its riders have a mass of 1200 kg and the boat drifts in at 1.2 m/s, how much work does Sam do to stop it?

11. ||| A 20 g plastic ball is moving to the left at 30 m/s. How much work must be done on the ball to cause it to move to the right at 30 m/s?

12. ||| The turntable in a microwave oven has a moment of inertia of $0.040 \text{ kg} \cdot \text{m}^2$ and is rotating once every 4.0 s. What is its kinetic energy?

13. |||| An energy storage system based on a flywheel (a rotating disk) can store a maximum of 4.0 MJ when the flywheel is rotating at 20,000 revolutions per minute. What is the moment of inertia of the flywheel?

Section 10.4 Potential Energy

14. || The lowest point in Death Valley is 85.0 m below sea level. The summit of nearby Mt. Whitney has an elevation of 4420 m. What is the change in gravitational potential energy of an energetic 65.0 kg hiker who makes it from the floor of Death Valley to the top of Mt. Whitney?

15. | a. What is the kinetic energy of a 1500 kg car traveling at a speed of 30 m/s ($\approx$65 mph)?
    b. From what height should the car be dropped to have this same amount of kinetic energy just before impact?
    c. Does your answer to part b depend on the car's mass?

16. | The world's fastest humans can reach speeds of about 11 m/s. In order to increase his gravitational potential energy by an amount equal to his kinetic energy at full speed, how high would such a sprinter need to climb?

17. | A 72 kg bike racer climbs a 1200-m-long section of road that has a slope of 4.3°. By how much does his gravitational potential energy change during this climb?

18. || A 1000 kg wrecking ball hangs from a 15-m-long cable. The ball is pulled back until the cable makes an angle of 25° with the vertical. By how much has the gravitational potential energy of the ball changed?

19. || How far must you stretch a spring with $k = 1000$ N/m to store 200 J of energy?

20. ‖ How much energy can be stored in a spring with a spring constant of 500 N/m if its maximum possible stretch is 20 cm?

21. ‖‖‖ The elastic energy stored in your tendons can contribute up to 35% of your energy needs when running. Sports scientists have studied the change in length of the knee extensor tendon in sprinters and nonathletes. They find (on average) that the sprinters' tendons stretch 41 mm, while nonathletes' stretch only 33 mm. The spring constant for the tendon is the same for both groups, 33 N/mm. What is the difference in maximum stored energy between the sprinters and the nonathletes?

Section 10.5 Thermal Energy

22. | Marissa drags a 23 kg duffel bag 14 m across the gym floor. If the coefficient of kinetic friction between the floor and bag is 0.15, how much thermal energy does Marissa create?

23. ‖ Mark pushes his broken car 150 m down the block to his friend's house. He has to exert a 110 N horizontal force to push the car at a constant speed. How much thermal energy is created in the tires and road during this short trip?

24. ‖‖ A 900 N crate slides 12 m down a ramp that makes an angle of 35° with the horizontal. If the crate slides at a constant speed, how much thermal energy is created?

25. ‖‖‖ A 25 kg child slides down a playground slide at a *constant speed*. The slide has a height of 3.0 m and is 7.0 m long. Using energy considerations, find the magnitude of the kinetic friction force acting on the child.

Section 10.6 Using the Law of Conservation of Energy

26. ‖ A boy reaches out of a window and tosses a ball straight up with a speed of 10 m/s. The ball is 20 m above the ground as he releases it. Use conservation of energy to find
   a. The ball's maximum height above the ground.
   b. The ball's speed as it passes the window on its way down.
   c. The speed of impact on the ground.

27. ‖ a. With what minimum speed must you toss a 100 g ball straight up to just barely hit the 10-m-high ceiling of the gymnasium if you release the ball 1.5 m above the floor? Solve this problem using energy.
   b. With what speed does the ball hit the floor?

28. ‖‖‖ What minimum speed does a 100 g puck need to make it to the top of a frictionless ramp that is 3.0 m long and inclined at 20°?

29. ‖ A car is parked at the top of a 50-m-high hill. It slips out of gear and rolls down the hill. How fast will it be going at the bottom? (Ignore friction.)

30. ‖‖‖ A 1500 kg car is approaching the hill shown in Figure P10.30 at 10 m/s when it suddenly runs out of gas.
   a. Can the car make it to the top of the hill by coasting?
   b. If your answer to part a is yes, what is the car's speed after coasting down the other side?

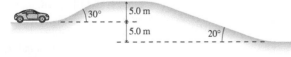

FIGURE P10.30

31. ‖ A 10 kg runaway grocery cart runs into a spring with spring constant 250 N/m and compresses it by 60 cm. What was the speed of the cart just before it hit the spring?

32. ‖ As a 15,000 kg jet lands on an aircraft carrier, its tail hook snags a cable to slow it down. The cable is attached to a spring with spring constant 60,000 N/m. If the spring stretches 30 m to stop the plane, what was the plane's landing speed?

33. ‖ Your friend's Frisbee has become stuck 16 m above the ground in a tree. You want to dislodge the Frisbee by throwing a rock at it. The Frisbee is stuck pretty tight, so you figure the rock needs to be traveling at least 5.0 m/s when it hits the Frisbee. If you release the rock 2.0 m above the ground, with what minimum speed must you throw it?

34. ‖ A fireman of mass 80 kg slides down a pole. When he reaches the bottom, 4.2 m below his starting point, his speed is 2.2 m/s. By how much has thermal energy increased during his slide?

35. ‖ A 20 kg child slides down a 3.0-m-high playground slide. She starts from rest, and her speed at the bottom is 2.0 m/s.
   a. What energy transfers and transformations occur during the slide?
   b. What is the total change in the thermal energy of the slide and the seat of her pants?

36. ‖ A hockey puck is given an initial speed of 5.0 m/s. If the coefficient of kinetic friction between the puck and the ice is 0.05, how far does the puck slide before coming to rest? Solve this problem using conservation of energy.

Section 10.7 Energy in Collisions

37. ‖ A 50 g marble moving at 2.0 m/s strikes a 20 g marble at rest. What is the speed of each marble immediately after the collision? Assume the collision is perfectly elastic and the marbles collide head-on.

38. ‖ Ball 1, with a mass of 100 g and traveling at 10 m/s, collides head-on with ball 2, which has a mass of 300 g and is initially at rest. What are the final velocities of each ball if the collision is (a) perfectly elastic? (b) perfectly inelastic?

39. | An air-track glider undergoes a perfectly inelastic collision with an identical glider that is initially at rest. What fraction of the first glider's initial kinetic energy is transformed into thermal energy in this collision?

40. | Two balls undergo a perfectly elastic head-on collision, with one ball initially at rest. If the incoming ball has a speed of 200 m/s, what are the final speed and direction of each ball if
   a. The incoming ball is *much* more massive than the stationary ball?
   b. The stationary ball is *much* more massive than the incoming ball?

Section 10.8 Power

41. ‖ a. How much work must you do to push a 10 kg block of steel across a steel table at a steady speed of 1.0 m/s for 3.0 s? The coefficient of kinetic friction for steel on steel is 0.60.
   b. What is your power output while doing so?

42. | a. How much work does an elevator motor do to lift a 1000 kg elevator a height of 100 m?
   b. How much power must the motor supply to do this in 50 s at constant speed?

43. ‖‖‖ A 1000 kg sports car accelerates from 0 to 30 m/s in 10 s. What is the average power of the engine?

44. ‖‖‖ In just 0.30 s, you compress a spring (spring constant 5000 N/m), which is initially at its equilibrium length, by 4.0 cm. What is your average power output?

45. ‖‖‖ In the winter sport of curling, players give a 20 kg stone a push across a sheet of ice. A curler accelerates a stone to a speed of 3.0 m/s over a time of 2.0 s.
   a. How much force does the curler exert on the stone?
   b. What average power does the curler use to bring the stone up to speed?

46. ‖ A 710 kg car drives at a constant speed of 23 m/s. It is subject to a drag force of 500 N. What power is required from the car's engine to drive the car
    a. On level ground?
    b. Up a hill with a slope of 2.0°?
47. ‖‖ An elevator weighing 2500 N ascends at a constant speed of 8.0 m/s. How much power must the motor supply to do this?

General Problems

48. ‖ A 2.3 kg box, starting from rest, is pushed up a ramp by a 10 N force parallel to the ramp. The ramp is 2.0 m long and tilted at 17°. The speed of the box at the top of the ramp is 0.80 m/s. Consider the system to be the box + ramp + earth.
    a. How much work W does the force do on the system?
    b. What is the change ΔK in the kinetic energy of the system?
    c. What is the change ΔU_g in the gravitational potential energy of the system?
    d. What is the change ΔE_{th} in the thermal energy of the system?
49. ‖ A 55 kg skateboarder wants to just make it to the upper edge of a "half-pipe" with a radius of 3.0 m, as shown in Figure P10.49. What speed v_i does he need at the bottom if he is to coast all the way up?

FIGURE P10.49

    a. First do the calculation treating the skateboarder and board as a point particle, with the entire mass nearly in contact with the half-pipe.
    b. More realistically, the mass of the skateboarder in a deep crouch might be thought of as concentrated 0.75 m from the half-pipe. Assuming he remains in that position all the way up, what v_i is needed to reach the upper edge?
50. ‖‖ Fleas have remarkable jumping ability. A 0.50 mg flea, jumping straight up, would reach a height of 40 cm if there were no air resistance. In reality, air resistance limits the height to 20 cm.
    a. What is the flea's kinetic energy as it leaves the ground?
    b. At its highest point, what fraction of the initial kinetic energy has been converted to potential energy?
51. ‖‖ A marble slides without friction in a *vertical* plane around the inside of a smooth, 20-cm-diameter horizontal pipe. The marble's speed at the bottom is 3.0 m/s; this is fast enough so that the marble makes a complete loop, never losing contact with the pipe. What is its speed at the top?
52. ‖ A 20 kg child is on a swing that hangs from 3.0-m-long chains, as shown in Figure P10.52. What is her speed v_i at the bottom of the arc if she swings out to a 45° angle before reversing direction?

FIGURE P10.52   FIGURE P10.53

53. ‖ Suppose you lift a 20 kg box by a height of 1.0 m.
    a. How much work do you do in lifting the box?
       Instead of lifting the box straight up, suppose you push it up a 1.0-m-high ramp that makes a 30° degree angle with the horizontal, as shown in Figure P10.53. Being clever, you choose a ramp with no friction.

    b. How much force F is required to push the box straight up the slope at a constant speed?
    c. How long is the ramp?
    d. Use your force and distance results to calculate the work you do in pushing the box up the ramp. How does this compare to your answer to part a?
54. ‖ A cannon tilted up at a 30° angle fires a cannon ball at 80 m/s from atop a 10-m-high fortress wall. What is the ball's impact speed on the ground below? Ignore air resistance.
55. ‖ The sledder shown in Figure P10.55 starts from the top of a frictionless hill and slides down into the valley. What initial speed v_i does the sledder need to just make it over the next hill?

FIGURE P10.55

56. ‖‖‖‖ In a physics lab experiment, a spring clamped to the table shoots a 20 g ball horizontally. When the spring is compressed 20 cm, the ball travels horizontally 5.0 m and lands on the floor 1.5 m below the point at which it left the spring. What is the spring constant?
57. ‖‖‖‖ A 50 g ice cube can slide without friction up and down a 30° slope. The ice cube is pressed against a spring at the bottom of the slope, compressing the spring 10 cm. The spring constant is 25 N/m. When the ice cube is released, what distance will it travel up the slope before reversing direction?
58. ‖‖‖‖ The maximum energy a bone can absorb without breaking is surprisingly small. For a healthy human of mass 60 kg, experimental data show that the leg bones can absorb about 200 J.
    a. From what maximum height could a person jump and land rigidly upright on both feet without breaking his legs? Assume that all the energy is absorbed in the leg bones in a rigid landing.
    b. People jump from much greater heights than this; explain how this is possible.
    Hint: Think about how people land when they jump from greater heights.
59. ‖ In an amusement park water slide, people slide down an essentially frictionless tube. They drop 3.0 m and exit the slide, moving horizontally, 1.2 m above a swimming pool. What horizontal distance do they travel from the exit point before hitting the water? Does the mass of the person make any difference?
60. ‖ The 5.0-m-long rope in Figure P10.60 hangs vertically from a tree right at the edge of a ravine. A woman wants to use the rope to swing to the other side of the ravine. She runs as fast as she can, grabs the rope, and swings out over the ravine.

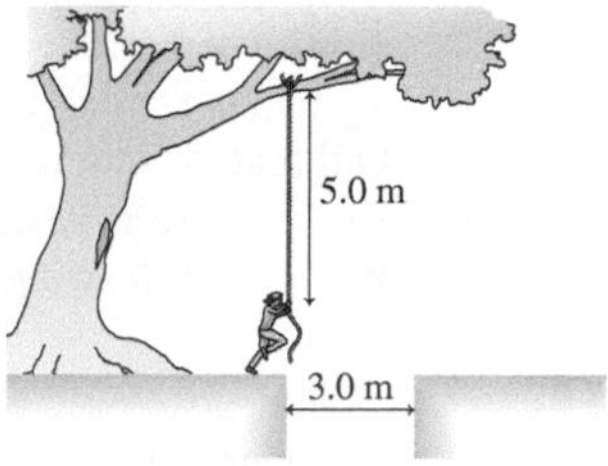

FIGURE P10.60

    a. As she swings, what energy conversion is taking place?
    b. When she's directly over the far edge of the ravine, how much higher is she than when she started?
    c. Given your answers to parts a and b, how fast must she be running when she grabs the rope in order to swing all the way across the ravine?

61. ‖‖ You have been asked to design a "ballistic spring system" to measure the speed of bullets. A bullet of mass m is fired into a block of mass M. The block, with the embedded bullet, then slides across a frictionless table and collides with a horizontal spring whose spring constant is k. The opposite end of the spring is anchored to a wall. The spring's maximum compression d is measured.

    a. Find an expression for the bullet's initial speed v_B in terms of m, M, k, and d.

    Hint: This is a two-part problem. The bullet's collision with the block is an inelastic collision. What quantity is conserved in an inelastic collision? Subsequently the block hits a spring on a frictionless surface. What quantity is conserved in this collision?

    b. What was the speed of a 5.0 g bullet if the block's mass is 2.0 kg and if the spring, with $k = 50$ N/m, was compressed by 10 cm?

    c. What fraction of the bullet's initial kinetic energy is "lost"? Where did it go?

62. ‖‖ A new event, shown in Figure P10.62, has been proposed for the Winter Olympics. An athlete will sprint 100 m, starting from rest, then leap onto a 20 kg bobsled. The person and bobsled will then slide down a 50-m-long ice-covered ramp, sloped at 20°, and into a spring with a carefully calibrated spring constant of 2000 N/m. The athlete who compresses the spring the farthest wins the gold medal. Lisa, whose mass is 40 kg, has been training for this event. She can reach a maximum speed of 12 m/s in the 100 m dash.

    FIGURE P10.62

    a. How far will Lisa compress the spring?

    b. The Olympic committee has very exact specifications about the shape and angle of the ramp. Is this necessary? If the committee asks your opinion, what factors about the ramp will you tell them are important?

63. ‖ Boxes A and B in Figure P10.63 have masses of 12.0 kg and 4.0 kg, respectively. The two boxes are released from rest. Use conservation of energy to find the boxes' speed when box B has fallen a distance of 0.50 m. Assume a frictionless upper surface.

    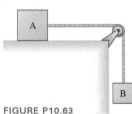
    FIGURE P10.63

64. ‖‖ What would be the speed of the boxes in Problem 63 if the coefficient of kinetic friction between box A and the surface it slides on were 0.20? Use conservation of energy.

65. ‖‖‖ A 20 g ball is fired horizontally with initial speed v_i toward a 100 g ball that is hanging motionless from a 1.0-m-long string. The balls undergo a head-on, perfectly elastic collision, after which the 100 g ball swings out to a maximum angle $\theta_{max} = 50°$. What was v_i?

66. ‖ Two coupled boxcars are rolling along at 2.5 m/s when they collide with and couple to a third, stationary boxcar.

    a. What is the final speed of the three coupled boxcars?

    b. What fraction of the cars' initial kinetic energy is transformed into thermal energy?

67. ‖ A fish scale, consisting of a spring with spring constant $k = 200$ N/m, is hung vertically from the ceiling. A 5.0 kg fish is attached to the end of the unstretched spring and then released. The fish moves downward until the spring is fully stretched, then starts to move back up as the spring begins to contract. What is the maximum distance through which the fish falls?

68. ‖ A 70 kg human sprinter can accelerate from rest to 10 m/s in 3.0 s. During the same interval, a 30 kg greyhound can accelerate from rest to 20 m/s. Compute (a) the change in kinetic energy and (b) the average power output for each.

69. ‖‖ A 50 g ball of clay traveling at speed v_i hits and sticks to a 1.0 kg block sitting at rest on a frictionless surface.

    a. What is the speed of the block after the collision?

    b. Show that the mechanical energy is *not* conserved in this collision. What percentage of the ball's initial kinetic energy is "lost"? Where did this kinetic energy go?

70. ‖ A package of mass m is released from rest at a warehouse loading dock and slides down a 3.0-m-high frictionless chute to a waiting truck. Unfortunately, the truck driver went on a break without having removed the previous package, of mass $2m$, from the bottom of the chute as shown in Figure P10.70.

    a. Suppose the packages stick together. What is their common speed after the collision?

    b. Suppose the collision between the packages is perfectly elastic. To what height does the package of mass m rebound?

    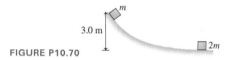
    FIGURE P10.70

71. ‖‖‖ A 50 kg sprinter, starting from rest, runs 50 m in 7.0 s at constant acceleration.

    a. What is the magnitude of the horizontal force acting on the sprinter?

    b. What is the sprinter's average power output during the first 2.0 s of his run?

    c. What is the sprinter's average power output during the final 2.0 s?

72. ‖ Bob can throw a 500 g rock with a speed of 30 m/s. He moves his hand forward 1.0 m while doing so.

    a. How much force, assumed to be constant, does Bob apply to the rock?

    b. How much work does Bob do on the rock?

73. ‖‖ A 2.0 hp electric motor on a water well pumps water from 10 m below the surface. The density of water is 1.0 kg per L. How many liters of water can the motor pump in 1 h?

74. ‖ The human heart has to pump the average adult's 6.0 L of blood through the body every minute. The heart must do work to overcome frictional forces that resist the blood flow. The average blood pressure is 1.3×10^4 N/m^2.

    a. Compute the work done moving the 6.0 L of blood completely through the body, assuming the blood pressure always takes its average value.

    b. What power output must the heart have to do this task once a minute?

    Hint: When the heart contracts, it applies force to the blood. Pressure is just force/area, so we can write work = (pressure) (area)(distance). But (area)(distance) is just the blood volume passing through the heart.

Passage Problems

Tennis Ball Testing

A tennis ball bouncing on a hard surface compresses and then rebounds. The details of the rebound are specified in tennis regulations. Tennis balls, to be acceptable for tournament play, must have a mass of 57.5 g. When dropped from a height of 2.5 m onto a concrete surface, a ball must rebound to a height of 1.4 m. During impact, the ball compresses by approximately 6 mm.

75. | How fast is the ball moving when it hits the concrete surface? (Ignore air resistance.)
    A. 5 m/s   B. 7 m/s   C. 25 m/s   D. 50 m/s

76. | If the ball accelerates uniformly when it hits the floor, what is its approximate acceleration as it comes to rest before rebounding?
    A. 1000 m/s^2 B. 2000 m/s^2 C. 3000 m/s^2 D. 4000 m/s^2

77. | The ball's kinetic energy just after the bounce is less than just before the bounce. In what form does this lost energy end up?
    A. Elastic potential energy
    B. Gravitational potential energy
    C. Thermal energy
    D. Rotational kinetic energy

78. | By approximately what percent does the kinetic energy decrease?
    A. 35%   B. 45%   C. 55%   D. 65%

79. | When a tennis ball bounces from a racket, the ball loses approximately 30% of its kinetic energy to thermal energy. A ball that hits a racket at a speed of 10 m/s will rebound with approximately what speed?
    A. 8.5 m/s   B. 7.0 m/s   C. 4.5 m/s   D. 3.0 m/s

Work and Power in Cycling

When you ride a bicycle at constant speed, almost all of the energy you expend goes into the work you do against the drag force of the air. In this problem, assume that *all* of the energy expended goes into working against drag. As we saw in Section 5.7, the drag force on an object is approximately proportional to the square of its speed with respect to the air. For this problem, assume that $F \propto v^2$ exactly and that the air is motionless with respect to the ground unless noted otherwise. Suppose a cyclist and her bicycle have a combined mass of 60 kg and she is cycling along at a speed of 5 m/s.

80. | If the drag force on the cyclist is 10 N, how much energy does she use in cycling 1 km?
    A. 6 kJ   B. 10 kJ   C. 50 kJ   D. 100 kJ

81. | Under these conditions, how much power does she expend as she cycles?
    A. 10 W   B. 50 W   C. 100 W   D. 200 W

82. | If she doubles her speed to 10 m/s, how much energy does she use in cycling 1 km?
    A. 20 kJ   B. 40 kJ   C. 400 kJ   D. 400 kJ

83. | How much power does she expend when cycling at that speed?
    A. 100 W   B. 200 W   C. 400 W   D. 1000 W

84. | Upon reducing her speed back down to 5 m/s, she hits a headwind of 5 m/s. How much power is she expending now?
    A. 100 W   B. 200 W   C. 500 W   D. 1000 W

STOP TO THINK ANSWERS

Stop to Think 10.1: D. Since the child slides at a constant speed, his kinetic energy doesn't change. But his gravitational potential energy decreases as he descends. It is transformed into thermal energy in the slide and his bottom.

Stop to Think 10.2: C. $W = Fd\cos\theta$. The 10 N force at 90° does no work at all. $\cos 60° = \frac{1}{2}$, so the 8 N force does less work than the 6 N force.

Stop to Think 10.3: B > D > A = C. $K = (1/2)mv^2$. Using the given masses and velocities, we find $K_A = 2.0$ J, $K_B = 4.5$ J, $K_C = 2.0$ J, $K_D = 4.0$ J.

Stop to Think 10.4: $(U_g)_3 > (U_g)_2 = (U_g)_4 > (U_g)_1$. Gravitational potential energy depends only on height, not speed.

Stop to Think 10.5: D. The potential energy of a spring depends on the *square* of the displacement x, so the energy is positive whether the spring is compressed or extended. Furthermore, if the spring is compressed by twice the amount it had been stretched, the energy will increase by a factor of $2^2 = 4$. So the energy will be 4×1 J $= 4$ J.

Stop to Think 10.6: $P_B > P_A = P_C > P_D$. The power here is the rate at which each runner's internal chemical energy is converted into gravitational potential energy. The change in gravitational potential energy is $mg\Delta y$, so the power is $mg\Delta y/\Delta t$. For runner A, the ratio $m\Delta y/\Delta t$ equals (80 kg)(10 m)/(10 s) = 80 kg·m/s. For C, it's the same. For B, it's 100 kg·m/s, while for D the ratio is 64 kg·m/s.

Conservation Laws

In Part II we have discovered that we don't need to know all the details of an interaction to relate the properties of a system "before" the interaction to those "after" the interaction. We also found two important quantities, momentum and energy, that are often conserved. Momentum and energy are characteristics of a system.

Momentum and energy have conditions under which they are conserved. The total momentum $\vec{P}$ and the total energy E are conserved for an *isolated system.* Of course, not all systems are isolated. For both momentum and energy, it was useful to develop a *model* of a system interacting with its environment. Interactions within the system do not change $\vec{P}$ or E. The kinetic, potential, and thermal energies *within* the system can be transformed without changing E. Interactions between the system and the environment *do* change the system's momentum and energy. In particular:

■ Impulse is the transfer of momentum to or from the system: $\Delta\vec{p} = \vec{J}$.

■ Work is the transfer of energy to or from the system in a mechanical interaction: $\Delta E = W$.

■ Heat is the energy transferred to or from the system in a thermal interaction: $\Delta E = Q$.

The laws of conservation of momentum and energy, when coupled with the laws of Newtonian mechanics of Part I, form a powerful set of tools for analyzing motion. But energy is a concept that can be used for much more than the study of motion; it can be used to analyze how your body uses food, how the sun shines, and a host of other problems.

The study of the transformation of energy from one form into another reveals certain limits. Thermal energy is different from other forms of energy. A transformation of energy from another form into thermal energy is *irreversible*. The study of heat and thermal energy thus led us to the discipline of thermodynamics, a subject we will take up further in Part III as we look at properties of matter.

KNOWLEDGE STRUCTURE II Conservation Laws

BASIC GOALS
How is the system "after" an interaction related to the system "before"?
What quantities are conserved, and under what conditions?
Why are some energy changes more efficient than others?

GENERAL PRINCIPLES
Law of conservation of momentum For an isolated system, $\vec{P}_f = \vec{P}_i$.
Law of conservation of energy For an isolated system, there is no change in the system's energy:

$$\Delta K + \Delta U_g + \Delta U_s + \Delta E_{th} + \Delta E_{chem} + \cdots = 0$$

Energy can be exchanged with the environment as work or heat:

$$\Delta K + \Delta U_g + \Delta U_s + \Delta E_{th} + \Delta E_{chem} + \cdots = W + Q$$

Laws of thermodynamics First law: If only thermal energy changes, $\Delta E_{th} = W + Q$.
Second law: The entropy of an isolated system always increases.

BASIC PROBLEM-SOLVING STRATEGY
Draw a visual overview for the system "before" and "after"; then use the conservation of momentum or energy equations to relate the two. If necessary, calculate impulse and/or work.

Momentum and impulse

In a collision, the total momentum

$$\vec{P} = \vec{p}_1 + \vec{p}_2 = m_1\vec{v}_1 + m_2\vec{v}_2$$

is the same before and after.

Before: m_1 ① $(v_{1x})_i$ → ← $(v_{2x})_i$ ② m_2

After: ← $(v_{1x})_f$ ① ② $(v_{2x})_f$ →

A force can change the momentum of an object. The change is the **impulse:** $\Delta p_x = J_x$.

$J_x =$ area under force curve

Basic model of energy

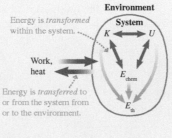

Energy is *transformed* within the system.

Work, heat

Energy is *transferred* to or from the system from or to the environment.

Work $W = F_\parallel d$ is done by the component of a force parallel to a displacement.

$F_\parallel = F\cos\theta$

Limitations on energy transfers and transformations

Thermal energy is random kinetic energy. Changing other forms of energy to thermal energy is **irreversible.** When transforming energy from one form into another, some may be "lost" as thermal energy. This limits efficiency:

$$\text{efficiency: } e = \frac{\text{what you get}}{\text{what you had to pay}}$$

A heat engine can convert thermal energy to useful work. The efficiency must be less than 100%.

Order out of Chaos

The second law of thermodynamics specifies that "the future" is the direction of entropy increase. But, as we have seen, this doesn't mean that systems must invariably become more random. You don't need to look far to find examples of systems that spontaneously evolve to a state of greater order.

A snowflake is a perfect example. As water freezes, the random motion of water molecules is transformed into the orderly arrangement of a crystal. The entropy of the snowflake is less than that of the water vapor from which it formed. Has the second law of thermodynamics been turned on its head?

The entropy of the water molecules in the snowflake certainly decreases, but the water doesn't freeze as an isolated system. For it to freeze, heat energy must be transferred from the water to the surrounding air. The entropy of the air increases by *more* than the entropy of the water decreases. Thus the *total* entropy of the water + air system increases when a snowflake is formed, just as the second law predicts. If the system isn't isolated, its entropy can decrease without violating the second law as long as the entropy increases somewhere else.

Systems that become *more* ordered as time passes, and in which the entropy decreases, are called *self-organizing systems*. These systems can't be isolated. It is common in self-organizing systems to find a substantial flow of energy *through* the system. Your body takes in chemical energy from food, makes use of that energy, and then gives waste heat back to the environment. It is this energy flow that allows systems to develop a high degree of order and a very low entropy. The entropy of the environment undergoes a significant *increase* so as to let selected subsystems decrease their entropy and become more ordered.

Self-organizing systems don't violate the second law of thermodynamics, but this fact doesn't really explain their existence. If you toss a coin, no law of physics says that you can't get heads 100 times in a row—but you don't expect this to happen. Can we show that self-organization isn't just possible, but likely?

Let's look at a simple example. Suppose you heat a shallow dish of oil at the bottom, while holding the temperature of the top constant. When the temperature difference between the top and the bottom of the dish is small, heat is transferred from the bottom to the top by conduction. But convection begins when the temperature difference becomes large enough. The pattern of convection needn't be random, though; it can develop in a stable, highly ordered pattern, as we see in the figure. Convection is a much more efficient means of transferring energy than conduction, so the rate of transfer is *increased* as a result of the development of these ordered *convection cells*.

The development of the convection cells is an example of self-organization. The roughly 10^{23} molecules in the fluid had been moving randomly but now have begun behaving in a very orderly fashion. But there is more to the story. The convection cells transfer energy from the hot lower side of the dish to the cold upper side. This hot-to-cold energy transfer increases the entropy of the surrounding environment, as we have seen. In becoming more organized, the system has become more effective at transferring heat, resulting in a greater rate of entropy increase! Order has arisen out of disorder in the system, but the net result is a more rapid increase of the disorder of the universe.

Convection cells are thus a thermodynamically favorable form of order. We should expect this, because convection cells aren't confined to the laboratory. We see them in the sun, where they transfer energy from lower levels to the surface, and in the atmosphere of the earth, where they give rise to some of our most dramatic weather.

Self-organizing systems are a very active field of research in physical and biological sciences. The 1977 Nobel Prize in chemistry was awarded to the Belgian scientist Ilya Prigogine for his studies of *nonequilibrium thermodynamics*, the basic science underlying self-organizing systems. Prigogine and others have shown how energy flow through a system can, when the conditions are right, "bring order out of chaos." And this spontaneous ordering is not just possible—it can be probable. The existence and evolution of self-organizing systems, from thunderstorms to life on earth, might just be nature's preferred way of increasing entropy in the universe.

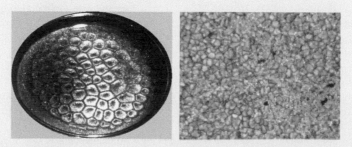

Convection cells in a shallow dish of oil heated from below (left) and in the sun (right). In both, warmer fluid is rising (lighter color) and cooler fluid is sinking (darker color).

PART II PROBLEMS

The following questions are related to the passage "Order Out of Chaos" on the previous page.

1. When water freezes to make a snowflake crystal, the entropy of the water
   A. Decreases.
   B. Increases.
   C. Does not change.
2. When thermal energy is transferred from a hot object to a cold object, the overall entropy
   A. Decreases.
   B. Increases.
   C. Does not change.

3. Do convection cells represent a reversible process?
   A. Yes, because they are orderly.
   B. No, because they transfer thermal energy from hot to cold.
   C. It depends on the type of convection cell.
4. In an isolated system far from thermal equilibrium, as time passes,
   A. The total energy stays the same; the total entropy stays the same.
   B. The total energy decreases; the total entropy increases.
   C. The total energy stays the same; the total entropy increases.
   D. The total energy decreases; the total entropy stays the same.

The following passages and associated questions are based on the material of Part II.

Big Air

A new generation of pogo sticks lets a rider bounce more than 2 meters off the ground by using elastic bands to store energy. When the pogo's plunger hits the ground, the elastic bands stretch as the pogo and rider come to rest. At the low point of the bounce, the stretched bands start to contract, pushing out the plunger and launching the rider into the air. For a total mass of 80 kg (rider plus pogo), a stretch of 0.40 m launches a rider 2.0 m above the starting point.

5. If you were to jump to the ground from a height of 2 meters, you'd likely injure yourself. But a pogo rider can do this repeatedly, bounce after bounce. How does the pogo stick make this possible?
   A. The elastic bands absorb the energy of the bounce, keeping it from hurting the rider.
   B. The elastic bands warm up as the rider bounces, absorbing dangerous thermal energy.
   C. The elastic bands simply convert the rider's kinetic energy to potential energy.
   D. The elastic bands let the rider come to rest over a longer time, meaning less force.
6. Assuming that the elastic bands stretch and store energy like a spring, how high would the 80 kg pogo and rider go for a stretch of 0.20 m?
   A. 2.0 m   B. 1.5 m   C. 1.0 m   D. 0.50 m
7. Suppose a much smaller rider (total mass of rider plus pogo of 40 kg) mechanically stretched the elastic bands of the pogo by 0.40 m, then got on the pogo and released the bands. How high would this unwise rider go?
   A. 8.0 m   B. 6.0 m   C. 4.0 m   D. 3.0 m
8. A pogo and rider of 80 kg total mass at the high point of a 2.0 m jump will drop 1.6 m before the pogo plunger touches the ground, slowing to a stop over an additional 0.40 m as the elastic bands stretch. What approximate average force does the pogo stick exert on the ground during the landing?
   A. 4000 N   B. 3200 N   C. 1600 N   D. 800 N

9. Riders can use fewer elastic bands, reducing the effective spring constant of the pogo. The maximum stretch of the bands is still 0.40 m. Reducing the number of bands will
   A. Reduce the force on the rider and give a lower jump height.
   B. Not change the force on the rider but give a lower jump height.
   C. Reduce the force on the rider but give the same jump height.
   D. Make no difference to the force on the rider or the jump height.

Testing Tennis Balls

Tennis balls are tested by being dropped from a height of 2.5 m onto a concrete floor. The 57 g ball hits the ground, compresses, then rebounds. A ball will be accepted for play if it rebounds to a height of about 1.4 m; it will be rejected if the bounce height is much more or much less than this.

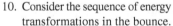

10. Consider the sequence of energy transformations in the bounce. When the dropped ball is motionless on the floor, compressed, and ready to rebound, most of the energy is in the form of
    A. Kinetic energy.
    B. Gravitational potential energy.
    C. Thermal energy.
    D. Elastic potential energy.
11. If a ball is "soft," it will spend more time in contact with the floor and won't rebound as high as it is supposed to. The force on the floor of the "soft" ball is _____ the force on the floor of a "normal" ball.
    A. Greater than
    B. The same as
    C. Less than
12. Suppose a ball is dropped from 2.5 m and rebounds to 1.4 m.
    a. How fast is the ball moving just before it hits the floor?
    b. What is the ball's speed just after leaving the floor?
    c. What happens to the "lost" energy?
    d. If the time of the collision with the floor is 6.0 ms, what is the average force on the ball during the impact?

Squid Propulsion BIO

Squid usually move by using their fins, but they can utilize a form of "jet propulsion," ejecting water at high speed to rocket them backward, as shown in Figure II.1. A 4.0 kg squid can slowly draw in and then quickly eject 0.30 kg of water. The water is ejected in 0.10 s at a speed of 10 m/s. This gives the squid a quick burst of speed to evade predators or catch prey.

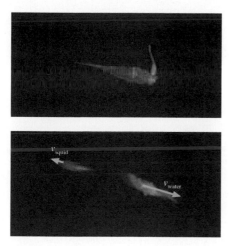

FIGURE II.1

13. What is the speed of the squid immediately after the water is ejected?
    A. 10 m/s
    B. 7.5 m/s
    C. 1.3 m/s
    D. 0.75 m/s
14. What is the squid's approximate acceleration in g?
    A. 10g   B. 7.5g   C. 1.0g   D. 0.75g
15. What is the average force on the water during the jet?
    A. 100 N   B. 30 N   C. 10 N   D. 3.0 N
16. This form of locomotion is speedy, but is it efficient? The energy that the squid expends goes two places: the kinetic energy of the squid and the kinetic energy of the water. Think about how to define "what you get" and "what you had to pay"; then calculate an efficiency for this particular form of locomotion. (You can ignore biomechanical efficiency for this problem.)

Teeing Off

A golf club has a lightweight flexible shaft with a heavy block of wood or metal (called the head of the club) at the end. A golfer making a long shot off the tee uses a driver, a club whose 300 g head is much more massive than the 46 g ball it will hit. The golfer swings the driver so that the club head is moving at 40 m/s just before it collides with the ball. The collision is so rapid that it can be treated as the collision of a moving 300 g mass (the club head) with a stationary 46 g mass (the ball); the shaft of the club and the golfer can be ignored. The collision takes 5.0 ms, and the ball leaves the tee with a speed of 69 m/s.

17. What is the change in momentum of the ball during the collision?
    A. 1.4 kg · m/s   B. 1.8 kg · m/s
    C. 3.2 kg · m/s   D. 5.1 kg · m/s
18. What is the speed of the club head immediately after the collision?
    A. 29 m/s   B. 25 m/s   C. 19 m/s   D. 11 m/s
19. Is this a perfectly elastic collision?
    A. Yes
    B. No
    C. There is insufficient information to make this determination.
20. If we define the kinetic energy of the club head before the collision as "what you paid" and the kinetic energy of the ball immediately after as "what you get," what is the efficiency of this energy transfer?
    A. 0.54   B. 0.46   C. 0.37   D. 0.27

Additional Integrated Problems

21. Football players measure their acceleration by seeing how fast they can sprint 40 yards (37 m). A zippy player can, from a standing start, run 40 yards in 4.1 s, reaching a top speed of about 11 m/s. For an 80 kg player, what is the average power output for this sprint?
    A. 300 W   B. 600 W   C. 900 W   D. 1200 W
22. The unit of horsepower was defined by considering the power output of a typical horse. Working-horse guidelines in the 1900s called for them to pull with a force equal to 10% of their body weight at a speed of 3.0 mph. For a typical working horse of 1200 lb, what power does this represent in W and in hp?
23. A 100 kg football player is moving at 6.0 m/s to the east; a 130 kg player is moving at 5.0 m/s to the west. They meet, each jumping into the air and grabbing the other player. While they are still in the air, which way is the pair moving, and how fast?
24. A swift blow with the hand can break a pine board. As the hand hits the board, the kinetic energy of the hand is transformed into elastic potential energy of the bending board; if the board bends far enough, it breaks. Applying a force to the center of a particular pine board deflects the center of the board by a distance that increases in proportion to the force. Ultimately the board breaks at an applied force of 800 N and a deflection of 1.2 cm.
    a. To break the board with a blow from the hand, how fast must the hand be moving? Use 0.50 kg for the mass of the hand.
    b. If the hand is moving this fast and comes to rest in a distance of 1.2 cm, what is the average force on the hand?
25. A child's sled has rails that slide with little friction across the snow. Logan has an old wooden sled with heavy iron rails that has a mass of 10 kg—quite a bit for a 30 kg child! Logan runs at 4.0 m/s and leaps onto the stationary sled and holds on tight as it slides forward. The impact time with the sled is 0.25 s.
    a. Immediately after Logan jumps on the sled, how fast is it moving?
    b. What was the force on the sled during the impact?
    c. How much energy was "lost" in the impact? Where did this energy go?

359

Solutions

Taken from:
Instructor's Solutions Manual for *College Physics:
A Strategic Approach*, Second Edition

1—Representing Motion
Conceptual Questions

Q1.1. Reason: (a) The basic idea of the particle model is that we will treat an object *as if* all its mass is concentrated into a single point. The size and shape of the object will not be considered. This is a reasonable approximation of reality if: (i) the distance traveled by the object is large in comparison to the size of the object, and (ii) rotations and internal motions are not significant features of the object's motion. The particle model is important in that it allows us to *simplify* a problem. Complete reality—which would have to include the motion of every single atom in the object—is too complicated to analyze. By treating an object as a particle, we can focus on the most important aspects of its motion while neglecting minor and unobservable details.

(b) The particle model is valid for understanding the motion of a satellite or a car traveling a large distance.

(c) The particle model is not valid for understanding how a car engine operates, how a person walks, how a bird flies, or how water flows through a pipe.

Assess: Models are representations of reality—not reality itself. As such they almost all make some simplifying assumptions. The test of a good model is the results it produces. The particle model allows us to model the motion of many objects simply and see common features of the movement of different objects. When used appropriately it is very useful. When used outside the range of its validity, it isn't very helpful.

Q1.3. Reason:

Assess: The dots are equally spaced until the brakes are applied to the car. Equidistant dots indicate constant average speed. On braking, the dots get closer as the average speed decreases.

Q1.5. Reason: Position refers to the location of an object at a given time relative to a coordinate system. Displacement, on the other hand, is the difference between the object's final position at time t_f and the initial position at time t_i. Displacement is a vector, whose direction is from the initial position toward the final position. An airplane at rest relative to a runway lamp, serving as the origin of our coordinate system, will have a position, called the initial position. The location of the airplane as it takes off may be labeled as the final position. The difference between the two positions, final minus initial, is displacement.

Assess: Some physics texts are not as explicit or clear about this terminology, but it pays off to have clear definitions for terms and to use them consistently.

Q1.7. Reason: Both speed and velocity are ratios with a time interval in the denominator, but speed is a scalar because it is the ratio of the scalar distance over the time interval while velocity is a vector because it is the ratio of the vector displacement over the time interval. Speed and velocity have the same SI units, but one must specify the direction when giving a velocity.

An example of speed would be that your hair grows (the end of a strand of hair moves relative to your scalp) at a speed of about 0.75 in/month.

An example of velocity (where direction matters) would be when you spring off a diving board. Your velocity could initially be 2.0 m/s, up, while later it could be 2.0 m/s, down.

Assess: Saying that a velocity has both magnitude and direction does not mean that velocity is somehow "better" and that speeds are never useful. Sometimes the direction is unimportant and the concept of speed is useful. In other cases, the direction is important to the physics, and velocity should be cited. Each shows up in various physics equations.

Q1.9. Reason: Yes, the velocity of an object can be positive during a time interval in which its position is always negative, such as when (in a usual coordinate system with positive to the right) an object is left of the origin, but moving to the right. For example, $x_i = -6.0$ m and $x_f = -2.0$ m. (The magnitude of Δt here is unimportant as long as time goes forward.)

However, the velocity (a vector) is defined to be the displacement (a vector) divided by the time interval (a scalar), and so the velocity *must* have the same sign as the displacement (as long as Δt is positive, which it is when time goes forward). So the answer to the second question is no.

Assess: We see again the importance of defining terms carefully and using them consistently. Students often use physics language incorrectly and then protest, "but you knew what I meant." However, incorrect word usage generally exposes incomplete or incorrect understanding.

Also note that unless stated otherwise, we assume that our coordinate system has positive to the right and that time goes forward (so that Δt is always positive).

Q1.11. Reason:

Assess: The dots get farther apart and the velocity arrows get longer as she speeds up.

Q1.13. Reason: The initial velocity is zero. The velocity increases and the space between position markers increases until the chute is deployed. Once the chute is deployed, the velocity decreases and the spacing between the position markers decreases until a constant velocity is obtained. Once a constant velocity is obtained, the position markers are evenly spaced. See Figure Q.1.13.

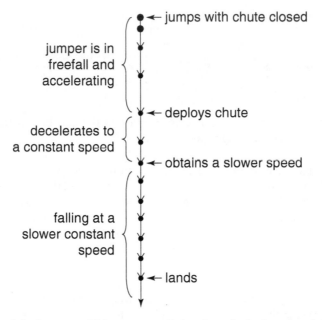

Assess: Knowing the velocity of the jumper will increase until the chute is deployed and then rapidly decrease until a constant decent velocity is obtained allows one to conclude that the figure is correct.

Q1.15. Reason:

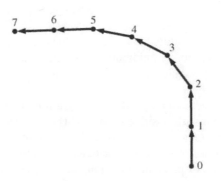

Assess: The car (particle) moves at a constant speed v so the distance between the dots is constant. While turning v remains constant, but the direction of $\vec{v}$ changes.

Q1.17. Reason: As one example, suppose one takes 15 minutes to travel in the car 6.0 miles from home to campus. His average speed would be

$$\frac{6.0 \text{ miles}}{15 \text{ min}}\left(\frac{60 \text{ min}}{1\text{h}}\right) = 24 \text{ mph} = 24 \text{ mph}\left(\frac{0.447 \text{ m/s}}{1 \text{ mph}}\right) = 11 \text{ m/s}$$

In my case, it typically takes me 5 minutes to walk the two blocks from my house to campus. Let's assume a block is 150 yards long. My average speed would be

$$\frac{300 \text{ yards}}{5 \text{ min}}\left(\frac{60 \text{ min}}{1 \text{ h}}\right)\left(\frac{36 \text{ in}}{1 \text{ yard}}\right)\left(\frac{1 \text{ m}}{39.37 \text{ in}}\right)\left(\frac{1 \text{ mile}}{1609 \text{ m}}\right) \approx 2.0 \text{ mph} = 2.0 \text{ mph}\left(\frac{0.447 \text{ m/s}}{1 \text{ mph}}\right) = 0.91 \text{ m/s}$$

which should be reported to one significant figure as 1 m/s Therefore, an order-of-magnitude estimate of my speed is $v \sim 1$ m/s.

  Assess: The second example agrees with the estimate in the book of an approximate walking speed of about 1 m/s.

Q1.19. Reason: Because density is defined to be the ratio of two scalars (mass and volume), it too must be a scalar.

  Assess: This is always true. The ratio of scalars is a scalar. On the other hand, a vector divided by a scalar (as in the definition of velocity) is a vector.

Multiple-Choice Questions

Q1.21. Reason: Because the dots are getting farther apart to the right (and the numbers are increasing to the right) we know that the object is speeding up. The choice that best fits that is a car pulling away (to the right) from a stop sign. So the correct choice is C.

  Assess: An ice skater gliding (choice A) would likely have nearly constant velocity (constant spacing between dots). The motion diagram for a plane braking (choice B) might look like the given diagram with the dots numbered in reverse order. The pool ball reversing direction (choice D) would have dot numbers increasing in one direction at first but then going the other way.

Q1.23. Reason:

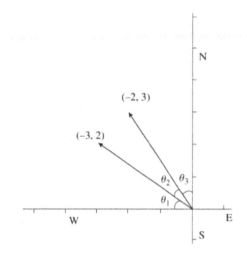

$\theta_1 = \theta_3$ and either of them can be deduced from $\tan^{-1}\left(\dfrac{2}{3}\right) = 33.7°$.

$\theta_2 = 90° - 2(\theta_1) = 90° - 2(33.7°) = 22.6° \approx 23°$

So the correct choice is A.

  Assess: By a quick back-of-the-envelope sketch we can see that choices C and D are much too large.

Q1.25. Reason: The second rule on significant figures says that when adding two numbers the number of decimal places in the answer should match the *smallest* number of decimal places of any number used in the calculation. There are three decimal places in 0.532 m, but only two in 3.24 m, so our answer must have only two decimal places. Therefore the correct choice is B: 3.77 m.

Assess: On contemplation we realize that we don't know the 3.24 m number better than to the nearest cm, and that will also be true of the answer, even though we may know the other number to the nearest millimeter.

Q1.27. Reason: This is a straightforward unit conversion question.

$$4.57 \times 10^9 \text{ years} = 4.57 \times 10^9 \text{ yr} \left(\frac{365.25 \text{d}}{1 \text{yr}} \right) \left(\frac{24 \text{h}}{1 \text{d}} \right) \left(\frac{60 \text{min}}{1 \text{h}} \right) \left(\frac{60 \text{s}}{1 \text{min}} \right) = 1.44 \times 10^{17} \text{s}$$

The correct choice is D.

Assess: Notice that even though we have more significant figures in some of the conversion factors (we accounted for leap year, and the other factors are exact and have as many significant figures as we need) that we obey the significant figure rules and report the answer to the same number of significant figures as the number of significant figures in the least precisely known number in the calculation (the age in years).

Problems

P1.1. Prepare: Frames of the video are taken at equal intervals of time. As a result, we have a record of the position of the car a successive time equal intervals—this information allows us to construct a motion diagram.
  Solve:

Assess: Once the brakes are applied, the car slows down and travels a smaller distance during each successive time interval until it stops. This is what the car in the figure is doing.

P1.3. Prepare: Despite the detail of the problem we must still make some assumptions. For example, does the jogger slow much to get on the bus? Is the bus an express line with no stops until the jogger's home? The simplest case would be to assume the jogger does not slow much before getting on the bus, and yes, the bus is an express line with no stops until the jogger's home.
  Solve:

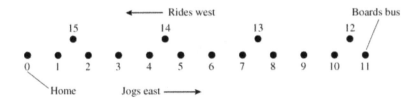

Assess: Without the simplifying assumptions the jogger's dots will get closer together as he slows to board the bus, and while on the bus westbound the dot spacing could change repeatedly as the bus slows down, stops, and then speeds up again from each bus stop.

P1.5. Prepare: Displacement is the difference between a final position x_f and an initial position x_i This can be written as $\Delta x = x_f = x_i$, and we are given that $x_i = 23$ m and that $\Delta x = -45$ m.
  Solve: $\Delta x = x_f - x_i$
Since we want to know the final position we solve this for x_f.

$$x_f = x_i + \Delta x$$
$$= 23 \text{ m} + (-45 \text{ m})$$
$$= -22 \text{ m}$$

Assess: A negative displacement means a movement to the left, and Keira has moved left from $x = 23$ m to $x = -22$ m.

P1.7. Prepare: We have been given three different displacements. The problem is straight forward since all the displacements are along a straight East–West line. All we have to do is add the displacements and see where we end up.

   Solution: The first displacement is $\Delta \vec{x}_1 = 500$ m East, the second is $\Delta \vec{x}_2 = 400$ m West, and the third displacement is $\Delta \vec{x}_3 = 700$ m East. These three displacements are added in the figure below.

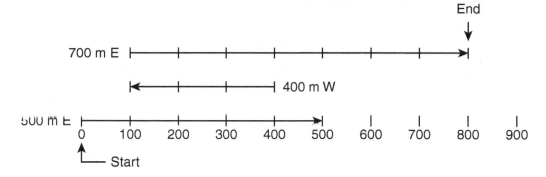

From the figure, note that the result of the sum of the three displacements puts the bee 800 m East of its starting point.

   Assess: Knowing what a displacement is and how to add displacements, we are able to obtain the final position of the bee. Since the bee moved 1200 m to the East and 400 m to the West, it is reasonable that it would end up 800 m to the East of the starting point.

P1.9. Prepare: We are asked to rank order three different speeds, so we simply compute each one according to Equation 1.1:

$$\text{speed} = \frac{\text{distance traveled in a given time interval}}{\text{time interval}}$$

   Solve: (i) Toy

$$\frac{0.15 \text{ m}}{2.5 \text{ s}} = 0.060 \text{ m/s}$$

   (ii) Ball

$$\frac{2.3 \text{ m}}{0.55 \text{ s}} = 4.2 \text{ m/s}$$

   (iii) Bicycle

$$\frac{0.60 \text{ m}}{0.075 \text{ s}} = 8.0 \text{ m/s}$$

   (iv) Cat

$$\frac{8.0 \text{ m}}{2.0 \text{ s}} = 4.0 \text{ m/s}$$

So the order from fastest to slowest is bicycle, ball, cat, and toy.

   Assess: We reported all answers to two significant figures as we should according to the significant figure rules. The result is probably what we would have guessed before solving the problem, although the cat and ball are close. These numbers all seem reasonable for the respective objects.

P1.11. Prepare: Average velocity is defined as the displacement Δx divided by the time interval Δt. We are given $\Delta t = 35$ s, but we will do a preliminary calculation to find the displacement.

$$\Delta x = x_f - x_i = -47 \text{ m} - (-12 \text{ m}) = -35 \text{ m}$$

   Solve:

$$v = \frac{\Delta x}{\Delta t} = \frac{-35 \text{ m}}{35 \text{ s}} = -1.0 \text{ m/s}$$

Assess: The answer is reasonable, and agrees with the approximate walking speed estimated in Example 1.3. The negative sign tells us that Harry is walking to the left.

P1.13. Prepare: In this problem we are given $x_i = 2.1$ m and $x_f = 7.3$ m as well as $v = 0.35$ m/s and asked to solve for Δt.
Solve: We first solve for Δt in $v = \Delta x/\Delta t$ and then apply $\Delta x = x_f - x_i$.

$$\Delta t = \frac{\Delta x}{v} = \frac{x_f - x_i}{v} = \frac{7.3\text{ m} - 2.1\text{ m}}{0.35\text{ m/s}} = \frac{5.2\text{ m}}{0.35\text{ m/s}} = 15\text{ s}$$

Assess: 15 s seems like a long time for a ball to roll, but it is going fairly slowly, so the answer is reasonable.

P1.15. Prepare: We first collect the necessary conversion factors: 1 in = 2.54 cm; 1 cm = 10^{-2} m; 1 ft = 12 in; 39.37 in = 1 m; 1 mi = 1.609 km; 1 km = 10^3 m; 1 h = 3600 s.
Solve:

(a) $8.0\text{ in} = 8.0\text{ (in)}\left(\dfrac{2.54\text{ cm}}{1\text{ in}}\right)\left(\dfrac{10^{-2}\text{ m}}{1\text{ cm}}\right) = 0.20\text{ m}$

(b) $66\text{ ft/s} = 66\left(\dfrac{\text{ft}}{\text{s}}\right)\left(\dfrac{12\text{ in}}{1\text{ ft}}\right)\left(\dfrac{1\text{ m}}{39.37\text{ in}}\right) = 20\text{ m/s}$

(c) $60\text{ mph} = 60\left(\dfrac{\text{mi}}{\text{h}}\right)\left(\dfrac{1.609\text{ km}}{1\text{ mi}}\right)\left(\dfrac{10^3\text{ m}}{1\text{ km}}\right)\left(\dfrac{1\text{ h}}{3600\text{ s}}\right) = 27\text{ m/s}$

P1.17. Prepare: We are to rank order three speeds given in different units. The obvious strategy is to convert units so they are all the same. To make the comparison we could use any set of speed units (such as furlongs per fortnight) including any set of the given units. However, for practice in converting units we will convert them all to m/s.
Solve:

$$1\frac{\text{mm}}{\mu\text{s}} = 1\frac{\text{mm}}{\mu\text{s}}\left(\frac{1\text{ m}}{1\times10^3\text{ mm}}\right)\left(\frac{1\times10^6\,\mu\text{s}}{1\text{ s}}\right) = 1\times10^3\,\frac{\text{m}}{\text{s}}$$

$$1\frac{\text{km}}{\text{ks}} = 1\frac{\text{km}}{\text{ks}}\left(\frac{1\times10^3\text{ m}}{1\text{ km}}\right)\left(\frac{1\text{ ks}}{1\times10^3\text{ s}}\right) = 1\,\frac{\text{m}}{\text{s}}$$

$$1\frac{\text{cm}}{\text{ms}} = 1\frac{\text{cm}}{\text{ms}}\left(\frac{1\text{ m}}{1\times10^2\text{ cm}}\right)\left(\frac{1\times10^3\text{ ms}}{1\text{ s}}\right) = 1\times10^1\,\frac{\text{m}}{\text{s}}$$

The order from smallest to largest, then, is 1 km/ks, 1 cm/ms, and 1 mm/μs.

Assess: This problem helps develop intuition about the relative sizes of the length units, which combined with the time units to give speed units. The fastest speed was obtained by travelling a very small distance (1 mm) in an even smaller time (1 μs).

P1.19. Prepare: Review the rules for significant figures in Section 1.4 of the text, paying particular attention to any zeros and whether or not that they are significant.
Solve:
(a) The number 0.621 has three significant figures.
(b) The number 0.006200 has four significant figures.
(c) The number 1.0621 has five significant figures.
(d) The number 6.21×10^3 has three significant figures.
Assess: In part (b), the initial two zeroes place the decimal point. The last two zeroes do not have to be there, but when they are they are significant.

P1.21. Prepare: Table 1.3 supplies the conversion factor we need: 1 ft = 0.305 m.
   Solve:

$$1250 \text{ ft} = 1250 \text{ ft}\left(\frac{0.305 \text{ m}}{1 \text{ ft}}\right) = 381 \text{ m} = 3.81 \times 10^2 \text{ m}$$

Assess: Field and track fans will quickly recognize that this answer is reasonable. They will note that 1250 ft is a little less than a quarter of a mile and 381 m is a little less than 440 m which is a little more than once around a quarter mile track.

P1.23. Prepare: After making an estimate of the rate at which grass grows (say one inch per week) it's just a matter of unit conversion to get it into m/s.

Solution: $v = \left(\dfrac{1 \text{ in}}{1 \text{ week}}\right)\left(\dfrac{1 \text{ week}}{7 \text{ day}}\right)\left(\dfrac{1 \text{ day}}{24 \text{ hr}}\right)\left(\dfrac{1 \text{ hr}}{3.3 \times 10^3 \text{ s}}\right)\left(\dfrac{2.54 \text{ cm}}{1 \text{ in}}\right)\left(\dfrac{1 \text{ m}}{100 \text{ cm}}\right) = 4.2 \times 10^{-8} \text{ m/s}$

Assess: Since a week is very large compared to a second and a m is about 40 times the size of an inch, we are expecting a very small number. Even professional grass growing watchers don't expect to see much activity in one second.

P1.25. Prepare: Think about how often you cut your fingernails, and how much you cut off each time. Depending on how even and trim you like to keep them you might clip them every 10 days or so; you might clip off about 1 mm every 10 days.
   Solve: The speed $v_x = \Delta x/\Delta t$ of the tip of your fingernails relative to your finger is then about 1 mm/10 d.

$$v_x = \frac{1 \text{ mm}}{10 \text{ d}}\left(\frac{1 \text{ m}}{1000 \text{ mm}}\right)\left(\frac{1 \text{ d}}{24 \text{ h}}\right)\left(\frac{1 \text{ h}}{60 \text{ min}}\right)\left(\frac{1 \text{ min}}{60 \text{ s}}\right) \approx 1 \times 10^{-9} \text{ m/s} \qquad v_x = \frac{1 \text{ mm}}{10 \text{ d}}\left(\frac{1000 \text{ }\mu\text{m}}{1 \text{ mm}}\right)\left(\frac{1 \text{ d}}{24 \text{ h}}\right) \approx 4 \text{ }\mu\text{m/h}$$

Assess: There are various factors that affect the growth rate of fingernails, such as age, sex, and season. Fingernails tend to grow faster than toenails, and not all fingernails grow at the same rate. But our answer seems about right and generally agrees with values found in a Web search. At this rate it takes about 6 months to completely replace a fingernail.

P1.27. Prepare: They went at right angles to each other, so we can use the Pythagorean theorem to compute the distance between them.

Solve: $d = \sqrt{(3.25 \text{ km})^2 + (0.55 \text{ km})^2} = 3.30 \text{ km}$

Assess: It is right that the difference between the two is greater than the distance either of them went; the answer seems about right for a skinny triangle.

P1.29. Prepare: The displacement is the hypotenuse of a right triangle whose legs are 6 m (half the width of the garden) and 8 m, directed from x_i at the top of the tree to x_f at the top of the flower.

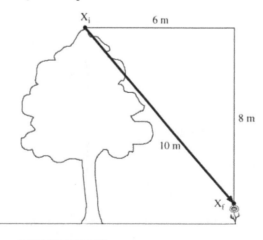

Solve: The length of the hypotenuse is $\sqrt{(6 \text{ m})^2 + (8 \text{ m})^2} = 10 \text{ m}$.

Assess: Displacement is a vector and does have direction (as mentioned in the prepare step), but we were only asked for the magnitude of the displacement.

P1.31. Prepare: Knowing that the total trip consists of two displacements, we can add the two displacements to determine the total displacement and hence the distance of the goose from its original position. A quick sketch will help you visualize the two displacements and the total displacement.

Solution: The distance of the goose from its original position is the magnitude of the total displacement vector. This is determined as follows:

$$d = \sqrt{(32 \text{ km})^2 + (20 \text{ km})^2} = 38 \text{ km}$$

Assess: A quick look at your sketch shows that the total distance should be larger than the largest leg of the trip, and this is the case.

P1.33. Prepare: We know the initial position of the ball (the middle of the field). We know the ball travels 43 yards down field (the first displacement) and 26.5 yards to the side of the field (the second displacement). We can add these two displacements to obtain the net displacement (magnitude and direction). A quick sketch will help you visualize the two displacements and the net displacement.

Solution: The magnitude of the net displacement may be obtained by

$$d = \sqrt{(43 \text{ yd})^2 + (26.5 \text{ yd})^2} = 50 \text{ yd}$$

The direction of the net displacement may be obtained by

$$\theta = \tan^{-1}\left(\frac{26.5 \text{ yd}}{43 \text{ yd}}\right) = 32°$$

Assess: Knowing the two displacements, we can add them to determine the net displacement (magnitude and direction). Looking at your sketch, you should expect the magnitude of the net displacement to be larger than either of the two displacements which contribute to the net displacement, and this is the case. Looking at your sketch, you should also expect the angle of the net displacement to be less than 45°, and this is the case.

P1.35. Prepare: The watermelon, represented as a particle, falls freely and speeds up during its downward motion along the *y*-direction. The average velocity vectors are thus of increasing length, giving an acceleration vector that is pointed in the downward direction. The watermelon's motion diagram including a pictorial representation and a list of values is shown below.

Solve:

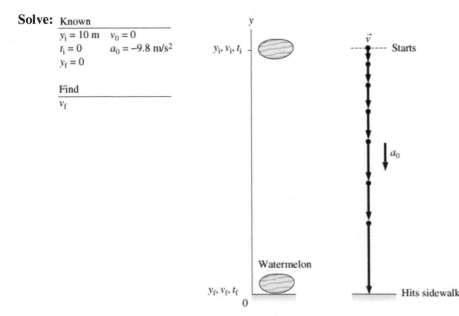

Assess: As a result of the acceleration due to gravity, as the watermelon falls, its velocity and the distance between the position dots increases. This is the case in the figure shown.

P1.37. Prepare: The skater moves along the x-axis. She slows down or has negative acceleration (decreasing velocity vectors) during a patch of rough ice. She has zero acceleration before the rough patch begins and after the rough patch ends—that is, velocity vectors are of the same length. The skater's motion diagram, a pictorial representation, and a list of values are shown in the figure.

Solve:

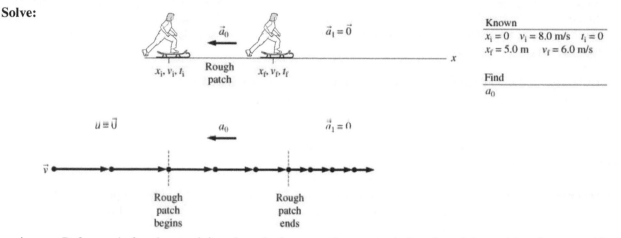

Known
$x_i = 0$	$v_i = 8.0$ m/s	$t_i = 0$
$x_f = 5.0$ m	$v_f = 6.0$ m/s	

Find
a_0

Assess: Before and after the rough ice, the velocity vector is constant in length and the position dots are uniformly spaced. Since the skater is traveling slower after the rough ice than before, the velocity vectors after the rough ice are shorter than they are before the rough ice and the position dots are closer together after the rough ice than they are before the rough ice. During the rough ice section, the velocity vector decreases in length and the dot position gets closer together.

P1.39. Prepare: Represent the ball as a particle which is moving along the ramp defined as the x-axis. As the ball rolls up the ramp it slows down, indicating accelerating down the ramp. The direction of the acceleration vector at the point where the slope changes is due to the fact that the average velocity vector along the ramp is smaller than the vector along the floor.

Solve:

Known
$\theta = 20°$
$x_i = 0$ $v_i = 10$ m/s
$t_i = 0$ $a < 0$
$v_f = 0$

Find
$h = x_f \sin\theta$

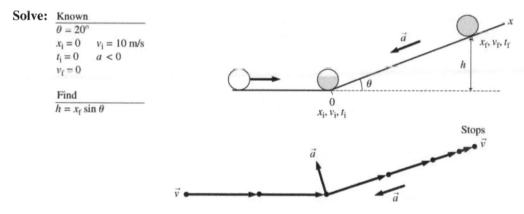

Assess: While the ball is traveling across the horizontal section, the velocity vector and the spacing of the position dots is constant. As the ball makes the transition from the horizontal section to the ramp, there is an acceleration in the direction of the change in velocity. As the ball travels up the ramp the negative acceleration causes the velocity vectors to decrease in length and the position dots to get closer together.

P1.41. Prepare: Knowing the dots represent the position of an object at equal time intervals and the vectors represent the velocity of the object at these times, we can construct a situation to match the motion diagram.

Solve: Rahul was coasting on interstate highway I-44 from Tulsa to Springfield at 70 mph. Seeing an accident at a distance of 200 feet in front of him, he began to brake. What steady deceleration will bring him to a stop at the accident site?

Assess: Since the position dots are initially equally spaced and the first few velocity vectors have the same length, this is consistent with Rahul initially traveling at a constant velocity. The fact that the dots get closer together and the velocity vectors get shorter is consistent with Rahul braking. The fact that there is no velocity vector associated with the last dot is consistent with the fact that he braked to a stop.

P1.43. Prepare: Knowing the dots represent the position of an object at equal time intervals and the vectors represent the velocity of the object at these times, we can construct a situation to match the motion diagram.

Solve: A race car slows down from an initial speed of 100 mph to 50 mph in order to negotiate a tight turn. After making the 90° turn the car accelerates back up to 100 mph in the same time it took to slow down.

Assess: The statement that the car slows down and speeds up in the same time is consistent with the symmetry of the spacing of the position dots and the length of the velocity vectors of the car going into and coming out of the curve. The statement that the car takes the curve at a constant speed is consistent with the fact that all the velocity vectors have the same length as the car negotiates the curve.

P1.45. Prepare: Knowing the dots represent the position of an object at equal time intervals and the vectors represent the velocity of the object at these times, we can construct a situation to match the motion diagram.

Solve: A car drives up a hill, over the top, and down the other side at constant speed.

Assess: The statement that the car drives up the hill, over the top, and down the other side is consistent with the fact that the velocity vectors are changing direction. The statement that the speed of the car is constant is consistent with the fact that all the velocity vectors have the same length (magnitude).

P1.47. Prepare: Given the speed of light $(3.0 = 10^8 \text{ m/s})$ and a time of (1.0 ns), we are asked to compute the distance light can travel in the given time. To solve the problem, two preliminary unit conversions will be helpful: $1.0 \text{ ns} = 1.0 \times 10^{-9}$ s and $1 \text{ m} = 39.37$ in

Solve:

$$\text{speed} = \frac{\text{distance traveled in a given time interval}}{\text{time interval}}$$

Solving for distance, obtain

$$\text{distance} = (\text{speed})(\text{time}) = \left(3.0 \times 10^8 \frac{\text{m}}{\text{s}}\right)(1.0 \text{ ns})\left(1.0 \times 10^{-9} \frac{\text{s}}{\text{ns}}\right)\left(39.37 \frac{\text{in}}{\text{m}}\right) = 12 \text{ in}$$

Assess: Notice that nanoseconds, seconds and meters cancel out neatly, leaving the desired distance (in). Think about the answer: In a billionth of a second light can go 1 foot; this is a useful tidbit to tuck into your brain. Just as we express large astronomical distance in terms of "light years" (a unit of distance—not time; the distance light travels in a year), we can now somewhat whimsically refer to a foot as a "light nanosecond."

P1.49. Prepare: Given a distance (32 mi) and a time (45 min) we are asked to compute the required speed. Since we want the answer in mph, a preliminary unit conversion will be helpful: 45 min = 0.75 h.

Solve:

$$\text{speed} = \frac{\text{distance traveled in a given time interval}}{\text{time interval}} = \frac{32 \text{ mi}}{0.75 \text{ h}} = 43 \text{ mph}$$

Assess: This is, of course, the *slowest* speed Alberta could drive and still arrive in time; any faster speed would simply get her there earlier.

P1.51. Prepare: Knowing that speed is distance divided by time, the distance is the circumference of a circle of radius 93,000,000 miles and the time is one year, we can determine the speed of the earth orbiting the sun. In order to get an answer in m/s, some unit conversion will be required.

Solve: The speed of the earth in its orbit about the sun may be determined by:

$$v = \frac{\text{distance}}{\text{time}} = \frac{2\pi r}{t} = \frac{2\pi \left(9.3 \times 10^7 \text{ mi}\right)}{1 \text{ yr}}\left(\frac{1 \text{ yr}}{3.16 \times 10^7 \text{ s}}\right)\left(\frac{1.61 \times 10^3 \text{ m}}{1 \text{ mi}}\right) = 3.0 \times 10^4 \text{ m/s}$$

Assess: All of the unit conversions are correct. After units are canceled, we obtain the desired units (m/s) and we are expecting a large number.

P1.53. Prepare: Knowing the speed the signal travels (approximately 25 m/s) and estimating distance from your brain to your hand to be about 1.0 m, we can determine the transmission time. Some unit conversion will be required to get the answer in ms.

Solve: The transmission time for the signal may be determined by:

$$t = \frac{\text{distance}}{\text{speed}} = \left(\frac{1 \text{ m}}{25 \text{ m/s}} \right) \left(\frac{10^3 \text{ ms}}{\text{s}} \right) = 40 \text{ ms}$$

Assess: When you touch something very hot, it takes a fraction of a second to remove your hand. Keeping in mind, that in this case the signal must make a round trip, the answer while very small seems reasonable.

P1.55. Prepare: Knowing that a motion diagram consists of dots that represent the position of the object at equal intervals of time and velocity vectors that represent the velocity at each position, we can construct a motion diagram for this situation.

Solve: (a) Figure P1.55 shows the motion diagram for the nerve impulses traveling along fibers A, B, and C. The figure shows the position of each axon and the speed of the nerve impulse as it travels through that axon. In fiber A, the impulses travel slowly (2.0 m/s) through all eight axons. In fiber B, the nerve impulses travel fast (25 m/s) through the first six axons and then slowly (2.0 m/s) through the last two. In fiber C, the impulses travel fast (25 m/s) through all the axons. For case A, the time interval used is the time for the impulse to travel the length of one axon. For case B, some liberties have been taken. Initially, the time interval is the time for the impulse to travel the length of one axon. However, if this was continued to scale, for the last two axons we would need over 10 dots and velocity vectors in the length of each axon. As a result, for the last two axons the dots are closer together and the velocity vectors are shorter, but they are not to scale.

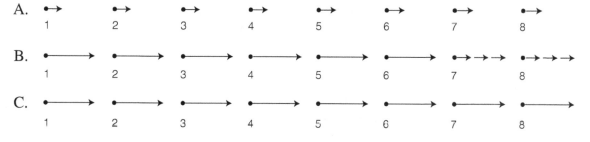

(b) Nerve impulses in the fully myelinated fiber will get to the right end first.

(c) Nerve impulses in the unmyelinated fiber will get to the right end last.

Assess: The impulses travel through fiber A at a slow constant speed. As a result the position dots should be uniformly spaced and the velocity vectors should all be the same length. The impulses travel through fiber C at a fast constant speed. As a result the position dots should be uniformly spaced and the velocity vectors should all be the same length. For fiber B, the impulses travel fast for six axons and then slowly for two axons. As a result the position dots should be uniformly spaced for the first six axons and then uniformly spaced (but close together) for the last two axons. In addition the velocity vectors should be constant in length for the first six axons and constant in length (but shorter) for the last two axons.

P1.57. Prepare: Assume that the bacterium moves along the path to consecutive letters.

Solve: (a) The displacements in segments AB and CD are the same (five right and one up). No other pairs appear to be the same.

(b) The problem explicitly stated that the bacteria move at a constant speed, so the answer is all of the segments.

(c) Since the displacements in segments AB and CD are the same (and the bacterium had the same speed in both segments, i.e., Δt is the same for both segments), then the velocity is the same in those two segments. Since no other pairs of segments have the same direction, they can't have the same velocity.

Assess: Remember that both displacement and velocity are vectors, so the direction matters. Only the length (magnitude) matters with speed since it is a scalar.

P1.59. Prepare: The best way to prepare for this problem is to draw a diagram. In the triangle, the height h of the tree that we want to know is the side opposite to the given angle.

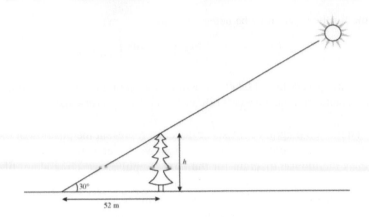

Solve:

$$\tan \theta = \frac{\text{opposite}}{\text{adjacent}}$$

$$\text{opposite} = \text{adjacent} \times \tan \theta$$

$$h = 52 \text{ m} \times \tan 30° = 30 \text{ m}$$

Assess: The shadow is longer than the height of the tree because the sun is low in the sky.

P1.61. Prepare: Draw a right triangle with legs of length 3 and 4. The hypotenuse will have a length of 5. While we are given the time of flight for the legs, we are not actually told what the speed is, so we don't really know the exact distance, but since the speed is constant we know the ratios of the sides of the triangle are as given.

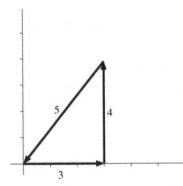

Solve: The bird will fly for 3.0 min + 4.0 min + 5.0 min = 12.0 min.
Assess: The diagram explains everything. The third side of the triangle is less than the sum of the first two sides.

P1.63. Prepare: Assume that the growth is steady, at least for the first three years. We will subtract any two heights and divide by the corresponding time interval.
Solve:

$$v = \frac{30 \text{ ft} - 12 \text{ ft}}{3 \text{ yr} - 1 \text{ yr}} = \frac{18 \text{ ft}}{2 \text{ yr}} = 9 \frac{\text{ft}}{\text{yr}}$$

So the correct answer is B.
   Assess: You should get the same answer by choosing other values, such as year 2 and year 1. Try it.

P1.65. Prepare: Draw a diagram and label the sides and the angle you want to know.

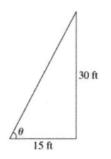

Solve:

$$\tan\theta = \frac{\text{opposite}}{\text{adjacent}}$$

$$\theta = \tan^{-1}\left(\frac{\text{opposite}}{\text{adjacent}}\right) = \tan^{-1}\left(\frac{30 \text{ ft}}{15 \text{ ft}}\right) = 63°$$

The correct answer is A.

   Assess: Imagine holding your protractor to your diagram and convince yourself that 63° is in the right ballpark.

2—Motion in One Dimension
Conceptual Questions

Q2.1. Reason: The elevator must speed up from rest to cruising velocity. In the middle will be a period of constant velocity, and at the end a period of slowing to a rest.

   The graph must match this description. The value of the velocity is zero at the beginning, then it increases, then, during the time interval when the velocity is constant, the graph will be a horizontal line. Near the end, the graph will decrease and end at zero.

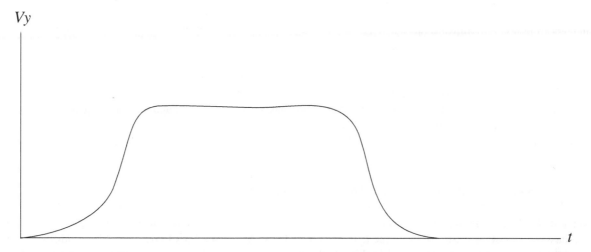

   Assess: After drawing velocity-versus-time graphs (as well as others), stop and think if it matches the physical situation, especially by checking end points, maximum values, places where the slope is zero, etc. This one passes those tests.

Q2.3. Reason: Call "up" the positive direction (this choice is arbitrary, and you could do it the other way, but this is typically easier in cases like this). Also assume that there is no air resistance. This assumption is probably not true (unless the rock is thrown on the moon), but air resistance is a complication that will be addressed later, and for small heavy items like rocks no air resistance is a pretty good assumption if the rock isn't going too fast.

   To be able to draw this graph without help demonstrates a good level of understanding of these concepts. The velocity graph will not go up and down as the rock does—that would be a graph of the position. Think carefully about the velocity of the rock at various points during the flight.

At the instant the rock leaves the hand it has a large positive (up) velocity, so the value on the graph at $t = 0$ needs to be a large positive number. The velocity decreases as the rock rises, but the velocity arrow would still point up. So the graph is still above the t axis, but decreasing. At the tippy-top the velocity is zero; that corresponds to a point on the graph where it crosses the t axis. Then as the rock descends with increasing velocity (in the negative, or down, direction), the graph continues below the t axis. It may not have been totally obvious before, but this graph will be a *straight line* with a negative slope.

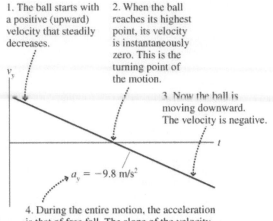

1. The ball starts with a positive (upward) velocity that steadily decreases.

2. When the ball reaches its highest point, its velocity is instantaneously zero. This is the turning point of the motion.

3. Now the ball is moving downward. The velocity is negative.

$a_y = -9.8 \text{ m/s}^2$

4. During the entire motion, the acceleration is that of free fall. The slope of the velocity graph is constant and negative.

Assess: Make sure that the graph touches or crosses the t axis whenever the velocity is zero. In this case, that is only when it reaches the top of its trajectory and the velocity vector is changing direction from up to down.

It is also worth noting that this graph would be more complicated if we were to include the time at the beginning when the rock is being accelerated by the hand. Think about what that would entail.

Q2.5. Reason: Yes. The acceleration vector will point south when the car is slowing down while traveling north.

Assess: The acceleration vector will always point in the direction opposite the velocity vector in straight line motion if the object is slowing down. Feeling good about this concept requires letting go of the common everyday (mis)usage where velocity and acceleration are sometimes treated like synonyms. Physics definitions of these terms are more precise, and when discussing physics we need to use them precisely.

Q2.7. Reason: We will neglect air resistance and thus assume that the ball is in free fall.

(a) $-g$ After leaving your hand the ball is traveling up but slowing; therefore, the acceleration is down (i.e., negative).

(b) $-g$ At the very top the velocity is zero, but it had previously been directed up and will consequently be directed down, so it is changing direction (*i.e.,* accelerating) down.

(c) $-g$ Just before hitting the ground it is going down (velocity is down) and getting faster; this also constitutes an acceleration down.

Assess: As simple as this question is, it is sure to illuminate a student's understanding of the difference between velocity and acceleration. Students would be wise to dwell on this question until it makes complete sense.

Q2.9. Reason: (a) Sirius the dog starts at about 1 m west of a fire hydrant (the hydrant is the $x = 0$ m position) and walks toward the east at a constant speed, passing the hydrant at $t = 1.5$ s. At $t = 4$ s Sirius encounters his faithful friend Fido 2 m east of the hydrant and stops for a 6-second barking hello-and-smell. Remembering some important business, Sirius breaks off the conversation at $t = 10$ s and sprints back to the hydrant, where he stays for 4 s and then leisurely pads back to his starting point.

(b) Sirius is at rest during segments B (while chatting with Fido) and D (while at the hydrant). Notice that the graph is a horizontal line while Sirius is at rest.

(c) Sirius is moving to the right whenever x is increasing. That is only during segment A. Don't confuse something going right on the graph (such as segments C and E) with the object physically moving to the right (as in segment A). Just because t is increasing doesn't mean x is.

(d) The speed is the magnitude of the slope of the graph. Both segments C and E have negative slope, but C's slope is steeper, so Sirius has a greater speed during segment C than during segment E.

Assess: We stated our assumption (that the origin is at the hydrant) explicitly. During segments B and D time continues to increase but the position remains constant; this corresponds to zero velocity.

Q2.11. Reason: (a) A's speed is greater at $t = 1$ s. The slope of the tangent to B's curve at $t = 1$ s is smaller than the slope of A's line.
   (b) A and B have the same speed just before $t = 3$ s. At that time, the slope of the tangent to the curve representing B's motion is equal to the slope of the line representing A's motion.
   Assess: The fact that B's curve is always *above* A's doesn't really matter. The respective *slopes* matter, not how high on the graph the curves are.

Q2.13. Reason: (a) For the velocity to be constant, the velocity-versus-time graph must have zero slope. Looking at the graph, there are three time intervals where the graph has zero slope: Segment A, segment D and segment F.
   (b) For an object to be speeding up, the magnitude of the velocity of the object must be increasing. When the slope of the lines on the graph is nonzero, the object is accelerating and therefore changing speed.
   Consider segment B. The velocity is positive while the slope of the line is negative. Since the velocity and acceleration are in opposite directions, the object is slowing down. At the start of segment B, we can see the velocity is $+2$ m/s, while at the end of segment B, the velocity is 0 m/s.
   During segment E, the slope of the line is positive which indicates positive acceleration, but the velocity is negative. Since the acceleration and velocity are in opposite directions, the object is slowing here also. Looking at the graph, at the beginning of segment E the velocity is -2 m/s, which has a magnitude of 2 m/s. At the end of segment E, the velocity is 0 m/s, so the object has slowed down.
   Consider segment C. Here the slope of the line is negative and the velocity is negative. The velocity and acceleration are in the same direction so the object is speeding up. The object is gaining velocity in the negative direction. At the beginning of that segment the velocity is 0 m/s, and at the end the velocity is -2 m/s, which has a magnitude of 2 m/s.
   (c) In the analysis for part **(b)**, we found that the object is slowing down during segments B and E.
   (d) An object standing still has zero velocity. The only time this is true on the graph is during segment F, where the line has zero slope, and is along $v = 0$ m/s.
   (e) For an object to moving to the right, the convention is that the velocity is positive. In terms of the graph, positive values of velocity are above the time axis. The velocity is positive for segments A and B. The velocity must also be greater than zero. Segment F represents a velocity of 0 m/s.
   Assess: Speed is the magnitude of the velocity vector. Compare to Conceptual Example 2.3 and also Question 2.2.

Multiple-Choice Questions

Q2.15. Reason: This graph shows a curved position-versus-time line. Since the graph is curved the motion is *not* uniform. The instantaneous velocity, or the velocity at any given instant of time is the slope of a line tangent to the graph at that point in time. Consider the graph below, where tangents have been drawn at each labeled time.

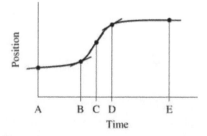

Comparing the slope of the tangents at each time in the figure above, the speed of the car is greatest at time C.
   Assess: Instantaneous velocity is given by the slope of a line tangent to a position-versus-time curve at a given instant of time. This is also demonstrated in Conceptual Example 2.2.

Q2.17. Reason: The velocity of an object is given by the physical slope of the line on the position-versus-time graph. Since the graph has constant slope, the velocity is constant. We can calculate the slope by using Equation 2.1, choosing any two points on the line since the velocity is constant. In particular, at $t_1 = 0$ s the position is $x_1 = 5$ m. At time $t_2 = 3$ s the position is $x_2 = 15$ m. The points on the line can be read to two significant figures.

The velocity is

$$v = \frac{\Delta x}{\Delta t} = \frac{x_2 - x_1}{t_2 - t_1} = \frac{15\text{ m} - 5\text{ m}}{3\text{ s} - 0\text{ s}} = \frac{10\text{ m}}{3\text{ s}} = +3.3\text{ m/s}$$

The correct choice is C.

   Assess: Since the slope is positive, the value of the position is increasing with time, as can be seen from the graph.

Q2.19. Reason: The initial velocity is 20 m/s. Since the car comes to a stop, the final velocity is 0 m/s. We are given the acceleration of the car, and need to find the stopping distance. See the pictorial representation, which includes a list of values below.

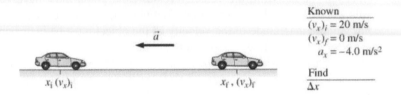

An equation that relates acceleration, initial velocity, final velocity and distance is Equation 2.10.

$$(v_x)_f^2 = (v_x)_i^2 + 2a_x\Delta x$$

Solving for Δx,

$$\Delta x = \frac{(v_x)_f^2 - (v_x)_i^2}{2a_x} = \frac{(0\text{ m/s})^2 - (20\text{ m/s})^2}{2(-4.0\text{ m/s}^2)} = 50\text{ m}$$

The correct choice is D.

   Assess: We are given initial and final velocities and acceleration. We are asked to find a displacement, so Equation 2.10 is an appropriate equation to use.

Q2.21. Reason: The physical slope of the tangent to the velocity-versus-time graph gives the acceleration of each car. At time $t = 0$ s the slope of the tangent to Andy's velocity-versus-time graph is very small. The slope of the tangent to the graph at the same time for Carl is larger. However, the slope of the tangent in Betty's case is the largest of the three. So Betty had the greatest acceleration at $t = 0$ s. See the figure below.

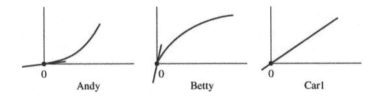

The correct choice is B.

   Assess: Acceleration is given by the physical slope of the tangent to the curve in a velocity-versus-time graph at a given time.

Q2.23. Reason: The dots from time 0 to 9 seconds indicate a direction of motion to the right. The dots are getting closer and closer. This indicates that the object is moving to the right and slowing down. From 9 to 16 seconds, the object remains at the same position, so it has no velocity. From 16 to 23 seconds, the object is moving to the left. Its velocity is constant since the dots are separated by identical distances. The velocity-versus-time graph that matches this motion closest is B.

   Assess: The slope of the line in a velocity-versus-time graph gives an object's acceleration.

Q2.25. Reason: This can be solved with simple ratios. Since $\vec{a} = \frac{\Delta\vec{a}}{\Delta t}$ if $\vec{a}$ is doubled, then the car can change velocity by twice as much in the same amount of time. The answer is A.

   Assess: This result can be checked by actually computing the acceleration, doubling it, and plugging it back into the equation for the second case, but ratios are slicker and quicker.

Problems

P2.1. Prepare: The car is traveling to the left toward the origin, so its position decreases with increase in time.
Solve: (a)

Time t (s)	Position x (m)
0	1200
1	975
2	825
3	750
4	700
5	650
6	600
7	500
8	300
9	0

(b)

Assess: A car's motion traveling down a street can be represented at least three ways: a motion diagram, position-versus-time data presented in a table (part **(a)** above), and a position-versus-time graph (part **(b)** above).

P2.3. Prepare: The graph represents an object's motion along a straight line. The object is in motion for the first 300 s and the last 200 s, and it is not moving from $t = 300$ s to $t = 400$ s.
  Solve: A forgetful physics professor goes for a walk on a straight country road. Walking at a constant speed, he covers a distance of 300 m in 300 s. He then stops and watches the sunset for 100 s. Realizing that it was getting dark, he walks faster back to his house covering the same distance in 200 s.
  Assess: The slope of the graph is positive up to $t = 300$ s, so the velocity is positive and motion is to the right. However, the slope is negative from $t = 400$ s to $t = 600$ s, so the velocity is negative and motion is to the left. Furthermore, because slope for the latter time interval is more than the former, motion to the left is faster than motion to the right.

P2.5. Prepare: The slope of the position graph is the velocity graph. The position graph has a shallow (negative) slope for the first 8 s, and then the slope increases.

Solve:

(a) The change in slope comes at 8 s, so that is how long the dog moved at the slower speed.

(b)

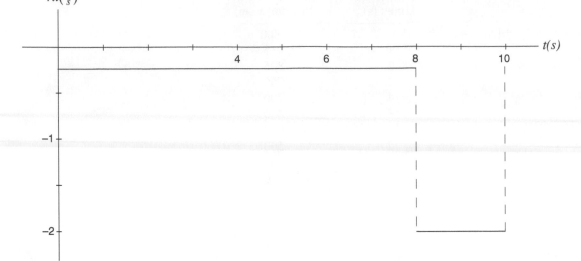

Assess: We expect the sneaking up phase to be longer than the spring phase, so this looks like a realistic situation.

P2.7. Prepare: To get a position from a velocity graph we count the area under the curve.

Solve:

(a)

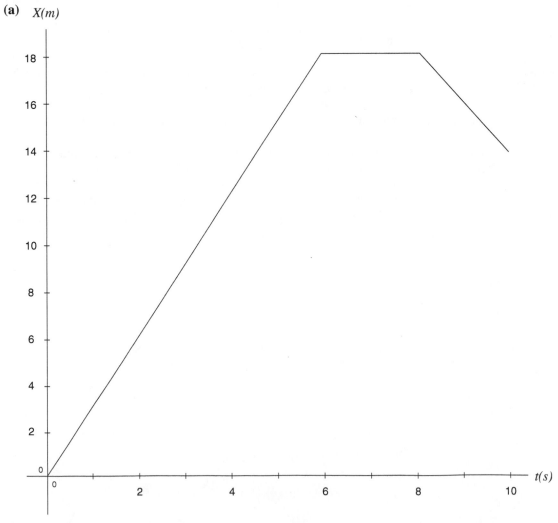

(b) We need to count the area under the velocity graph (are a below the x-axis is subtracted). There are 18 m of area above the axis and 4 m of area below. 18 m − 4 m = 14 m.

Assess: These numbers seem reasonable; a mail carrier could back up 4 m. It is also important that the problem state what the position is at $t = 0$, or we wouldn't know how high to draw the position graph.

P2.9. Prepare: Note that the slope of the position-versus-time graph at every point gives the velocity at that point. Referring to Figure P2.12, the graph has a distinct slope and hence distinct velocity in the time intervals: from $t = 0$ to $t = 20$ s; from 20 s to 30 s; and from 30 s to 40 s.

Solve: The slope at $t = 10$ s is

$$v = \frac{\Delta x}{\Delta t} = \frac{100 \text{ m} - 50 \text{ m}}{20 \text{ s}} = 2.5 \text{ m/s}$$

The slope at $t = 25$ s is

$$v = \frac{100 \text{ m} - 100 \text{ m}}{10 \text{ s}} = 0 \text{ m/s}$$

The slope at $t = 35$ s is

$$v = \frac{0 \text{ m} - 100 \text{ m}}{10 \text{ s}} = -10 \text{ m/s}$$

Assess: As expected a positive slope gives a positive velocity and a negative slope yields a negative velocity.

P2.11. Prepare: A visual overview of Alan's and Beth's motion that includes a pictorial representation, a motion diagram, and a list of values is shown below. Our strategy is to calculate and compare Alan's and Beth's time of travel from Los Angeles to San Francisco.

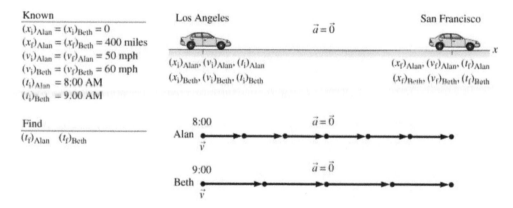

Solve: Beth and Alan are moving at a constant speed, so we can calculate the time of arrival as follows:

$$v = \frac{\Delta x}{\Delta t} = \frac{x_f - x_i}{t_f - t_i} \Rightarrow t_f = t_i + \frac{x_f - x_i}{v}$$

Using the known values identified in the pictorial representation, we find:

$$(t_f)_{\text{Alan}} = (t_i)_{\text{Alan}} + \frac{(x_f)_{\text{Alan}} - (x_i)_{\text{Alan}}}{v} = 8{:}00 \text{ AM} + \frac{400 \text{ mile}}{50 \text{ miles/hour}} = 8{:}00 \text{ AM} + 8 \text{ hr} = 4{:}00 \text{ PM}$$

$$(t_f)_{\text{Beth}} = (t_i)_{\text{Beth}} + \frac{(x_f)_{\text{Beth}} - (x_i)_{\text{Beth}}}{v} = 9{:}00 \text{ AM} + \frac{400 \text{ mile}}{60 \text{ miles/hour}} = 9{:}00 \text{ AM} + 6{:}67 \text{ hr} = 3{:}40 \text{ PM}$$

(a) Beth arrives first.

(b) Beth has to wait 20 minutes for Alan.

Assess: Times of the order of 7 or 8 hours are reasonable in the present problem.

P2.13. Prepare: Since each runner is running at a steady pace, they both are traveling with a constant speed. Each must travel the same distance to finish the race. We assume they are traveling uniformly. We can calculate the time it takes each runner to finish using Equation 2.1.

Solve: The first runner finishes in

$$\Delta t_1 = \frac{\Delta x}{(v_x)_1} = \frac{5.00 \text{ km}}{12.0 \text{ km/hr}} = 0.417 \text{ hr}$$

Converting to minutes, this is $(0.417 \text{ hr})\left(\dfrac{60 \text{ min}}{1 \text{ hr}}\right) = 25.0 \text{ min}$

For the second runner

$$\Delta t_2 = \frac{\Delta x}{(v_x)_2} = \frac{5.00 \text{ km}}{14.5 \text{ km/hr}} = 0.345 \text{ hr}$$

Converting to seconds, this is

$$(0.345 \text{ hr})\left(\frac{60 \text{ min}}{1 \text{ hr}}\right) = 20.7 \text{ min}$$

The time the second runner waits is 25.0 min – 20.7 min = 4.3 min

Assess: For uniform motion, velocity is given by Equation 2.1.

P2.15. Prepare: Assume v_x is constant so the ratio $\dfrac{\Delta x}{\Delta t}$ is also constant.

Solve:

(a)

$$\frac{30 \text{ m}}{3.0 \text{ s}} = \frac{\Delta x}{1.5 \text{ s}} \Rightarrow \Delta x = 1.5 \text{ s}\left(\frac{30 \text{ m}}{3.0 \text{ s}}\right) = 15 \text{ m}$$

(b)

$$\frac{30 \text{ m}}{3.0 \text{ s}} = \frac{\Delta x}{9.0 \text{ s}} \Rightarrow \Delta x = 9.0 \text{ s}\left(\frac{30 \text{ m}}{3.0 \text{ s}}\right) = 90 \text{ m}$$

Assess: Setting up the ratio allows us to easily solve for the distance traveled in any given time.

P2.17. Prepare: The graph in Figure P2.13 shows distinct slopes in the time intervals: 0 – 1s, 1 s – 2 s, and 2 s – 4 s. We can thus obtain the velocity values from this graph using $v = \Delta x/\Delta t$.

Solve: (a)

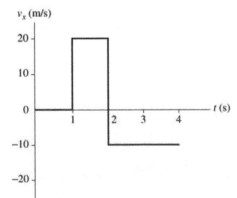

(b) There is only one turning point. At $t = 2$ s the velocity changes from $+20$ m/s to -10 m/s, thus reversing the direction of motion. At $t = 1$ s, there is an abrupt change in motion from rest to $+20$ m/s, but there is no reversal in motion.

Assess: As shown in **(a)**, a positive slope must give a positive velocity and a negative slope must yield a negative velocity.

P2.19. Prepare: Please refer to Figure P2.14. Since displacement is equal to the area under the velocity graph between t_i and t_f, we can find the car's final position from its initial position and the area.

Solve: (a) Using the equation $x_f = x_i +$ area of the velocity graph between t_i and t_f,

$$x_{2s} = 10 \text{ m} + \text{area of trapezoid between 0 s and 2 s}$$

$$= 10 \text{ m} + \frac{1}{2}(12 \text{ m/s} + 4 \text{ m/s})(2 \text{ s}) = 26 \text{ m}$$

$$x_{3s} = 10 \text{ m} + \text{area of triangle between 0 s and 3 s}$$

$$= 10 \text{ m} + \frac{1}{2}(12 \text{ m/s})(3 \text{ s}) = 28 \text{ m}$$

$$x_{4s} = x_{3s} + \text{area between 3 s and 4 s}$$

$$= 28 \text{ m} + \frac{1}{2}(-4 \text{ m/s})(1 \text{ s}) = 26 \text{ m}$$

(b) The car reverses direction at $t = 3$ s, because its velocity becomes negative.

Assess: The car starts at $x_i = 10$ m at $t_i = 0$. Its velocity decreases as time increases, is zero at $t = 3$ s, and then becomes negative. The slope of the velocity-versus-time graph is negative which means the car's acceleration is negative and a constant. From the acceleration thus obtained and given velocities on the graph, we can also use kinematic equations to find the car's position at various times.

P2.21. Prepare: Please refer to Figure P2.15. The graph in Figure P2.15 shows distinct slopes in the time intervals: $0 - 2$ s and 2 s $- 4$ s. We can thus obtain the acceleration values from this graph using $a_x = \Delta v_x / \Delta t$. A linear decrease in velocity from $t = 0$ s to $t = 2$ s implies a constant negative acceleration. On the other hand, a constant velocity between $t = 2$ s and $t = 4$ s means zero acceleration.

Solve:

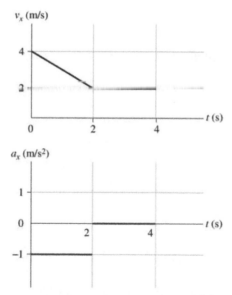

P2.23. Prepare: Acceleration is the rate of change of velocity. The sign conventions for position are in Figure 2.1. Conventions for velocity are in Figure 2.2. Conventions for acceleration are in Figure 2.26.

Solve: (a) Since the displacements are toward the right and the velocity vectors point toward the right, the velocity is always positive. Since the velocity vectors are increasing in length and are pointing toward the right, the acceleration is positive. The position is always negative, but it is only differences in position that are important in calculating velocity.

(b) Since the displacements and the velocity vectors are always downward, the velocity is always negative. Since the velocity vectors are increasing in length and are downward, the acceleration is negative. The position is always negative, but it is only differences in position that are important in calculating velocity.

(c) Since the displacements are downward, and the velocity vectors are always downward, the velocity is always negative. Since the velocity vectors are increasing in length and are downward, the acceleration is negative. The position is always positive, but it is only differences in position that are important in calculating velocity.

Assess: The origin for coordinates can be placed anywhere.

P2.25. Prepare: From a velocity-versus-time graph we find the acceleration by computing the slope. We will compute the slope of each straight-line segment in the graph.

$$a_x = \frac{(v_x)_f - (v_x)_i}{t_f - t_i}$$

The trickiest part is reading the values off the graph.

Solve: (a)

$$a_x = \frac{5.5 \text{ m/s} - 0.0 \text{ m/s}}{0.9 \text{ s} - 0.0 \text{ s}} = 6.1 \text{ m/s}^2$$

(b)

$$a_x = \frac{9.3 \text{ m/s} - 5.5 \text{ m/s}}{2.4 \text{ s} - 0.9 \text{ s}} = 2.5 \text{ m/s}^2$$

(c)

$$a_x = \frac{10.9 \text{ m/s} - 9.3 \text{ m/s}}{3.5 \text{ s} - 2.4 \text{ s}} = 1.5 \text{ m/s}^2$$

Assess: This graph is difficult to read to more than one significant figure. I did my best to read a second significant figure but there is some estimation in the second significant figure.

It takes Carl Lewis almost 10 s to run 100 m, so this graph covers only the first third of the race. Were the graph to continue, the slope would continue to decrease until the slope is zero as he reaches his (fastest) cruising speed. Also, if the graph were continued out to the end of the race, the area under the curve should total 100 m.

P2.27. Prepare: Acceleration is the rate of change of velocity.

$$a_x = \frac{\Delta v_x}{\Delta t}$$

where $\Delta v_x = 4.0$ m/s and $\Delta t = 0.11$ s. We will then use that acceleration in Equation 2.11 (a special case of Equation 2.9) to compute the displacement during the strike:

$$\Delta x = \frac{1}{2} a_x (\Delta t)^2$$

where we are justified in using the special case because $(v_x)_i = 0.0$ m/s.

Solve: (a)

$$a_x = \frac{\Delta v_x}{\Delta t} = \frac{4.0 \text{ m/s}}{0.11 \text{ s}} = 36 \text{ m/s}^2$$

(b)

$$\Delta x = \frac{1}{2} a_x (\Delta t)^2 = \frac{1}{2}(36 \text{ m/s}^2)(0.11 \text{ s})^2 = 0.22 \text{ m}$$

Assess: The answer is remarkable but reasonable. The pike strikes quickly and so is able to move 0.22 m in 0.11 s, even starting from rest. The seconds squared cancel in the last equation.

P2.29. Prepare: We'll do this in parts, first computing the acceleration after the congestion.

Solve:

$$a = \frac{\Delta v}{\Delta t} = \frac{12.0 \text{ m/s} - 5.0 \text{ m/s}}{8.0 \text{ s}} = \frac{7.0 \text{ m/s}}{8.0 \text{ s}}$$

Now use the same acceleration to find the new velocity.

$$v_f = v_i + a\Delta t = 12.0 \text{ m/s} + \left(\frac{7.0}{8.0} \text{ m/s}^2\right)(16 \text{ s}) = 26 \text{ m/s}$$

Access: The answer is a reasonable 58 mph.

P2.31. Prepare: The kinematic equation that relates velocity, acceleration, and distance is $(v_x)_f^2 = (v_x)_i^2 + 2a_x\Delta x$. Solve for Δx.

$$\Delta x = \frac{(v_x)_f^2 - (v_x)_i^2}{2a_x}$$

Note that $(v_x)_i^2 = 0$ for both planes.

  Solve: The accelerations are the same, so they cancel.

$$\frac{\Delta x_{jet}}{\Delta x_{prop}} = \frac{\left(\dfrac{(v_x)_f^2}{2a_x}\right)_{jet}}{\left(\dfrac{(v_x)_f^2}{2a_x}\right)_{prop}} = \frac{((v_x)_f)^2_{jet}}{((v_x)_f)^2_{prop}} = \frac{((2v_x)_f)^2_{prop}}{((v_x)_f)^2_{prop}} = 4 \Rightarrow \Delta x_{jet} = 4\Delta x_{prop} = 4(1/4 \text{ mi}) = 1 \text{ mi}$$

  Access: It seems reasonable to need a mile for a passenger jet to take off.

P2.33. Prepare: A visual overview of the car's motion that includes a pictorial representation, a motion diagram, and a list of values is shown below. We label the car's motion along the x-axis. For the driver's maximum (constant) deceleration, kinematic equations are applicable. This is a two-part problem. We will first find the car's displacement during the driver's reaction time when the car's deceleration is zero. Then we will find the displacement as the car is brought to rest with maximum deceleration.

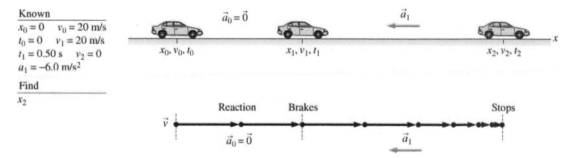

  Solve: During the reaction time when $a_0 = 0$, we can use

$$x_1 = x_0 + v_0(t_1 - t_0) + \frac{1}{2}a_0(t_1 - t_0)^2$$

$$= 0 \text{ m} + (20 \text{ m/s})(0.50 \text{ s} - 0 \text{ s}) + 0 \text{ m} = 10 \text{ m}$$

During deceleration,

$$v_2^2 = v_1^2 + 2a_1(x_2 - x_1) \quad 0 = (20 \text{ m/s})^2 + 2(-6.0 \text{ m/s}^2)(x_2 - 10 \text{ m}) \Rightarrow x_2 = 43 \text{ m}$$

She has 50 m to stop, so she can stop in time.

  Assess: While driving at 20 m/s or 45 mph, a reaction time of 0.5 s corresponds to a distance of 33 feet or only two lengths of a typical car. Keep a safe distance while driving!

P2.35. Prepare: A visual overview of your car's motion that includes a pictorial representation, a motion diagram, and a list of values is shown below. We label the car's motion along the x-axis. For maximum (constant) deceleration of your car, kinematic equations hold. This is a two-part problem. We will first find the car's displacement during your reaction time when the car's deceleration is zero. Then we will find the displacement as you bring the car to rest with maximum deceleration.

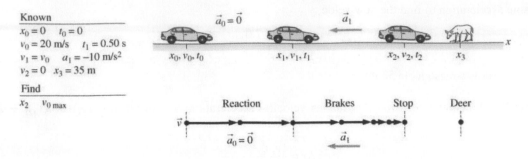

Solve: (a) To find x_2, we first need to determine x_1. Using $x_1 = x_0 + v_0(t_1 - t_0)$, we get $x_1 = 0$ m $+$ (20 m/s) (0.50 s -0 s) $= 10$ m. Now, with $a_1 = 10$ m/s^2, $v_2 = 0$ and $v_1 = 20$ m/s, we can use

$$v_2^2 = v_1^2 + 2a_1(x_2 - x_1) \Rightarrow 0 \text{ m}^2/\text{s}^2 = (20 \text{ m/s})^2 + 2(-10 \text{ m/s}^2)(x_2 - 10 \text{ m}) \Rightarrow x_2 = 30 \text{ m}$$

The distance between you and the deer is ($x_3 - x_2$) or (35 m $-$ 30 m) $= 5$ m.

(b) Let us find $v_{0 \text{ max}}$ such that $v_2 = 0$ m/s at $x_2 = x_3 = 35$ m. Using the following equation,

$$v_2^2 - v_{0 \text{ max}}^2 = 2a_1(x_2 - x_1) \Rightarrow 0 \text{ m}^2/\text{s}^2 - v_{0 \text{ max}}^2 = 2(-10 \text{ m/s}^2)(35 \text{ m} - x_1)$$

Also, $x_1 = x_0 + v_{0 \text{ max}} (t_1 - t_0) = v_{0 \text{ max}} (0.50 \text{ s} - 0 \text{ s}) = (0.50 \text{ s})v_{0 \text{ max}}$. Substituting this expression for x_1 in the above equation yields

$$-v_{0 \text{ max}}^2 = (-20 \text{ m/s}^2)[35 \text{ m} - (0.50 \text{ s})v_{0 \text{ max}}] \Rightarrow v_{0 \text{ max}}^2 + (10 \text{ m/s})v_{0 \text{ max}} - 700 \text{ m}^2/\text{s}^2 = 0$$

The solution of this quadratic equation yields $v_{0 \text{ max}} = 22$ m/s. (The other root is negative and unphysical for the present situation.)

Assess: An increase of speed from 20 m/s to 22 m/s is very reasonable for the car to cover an additional distance of 5 m with a reaction time of 0.50 s and a deceleration of 10 m/s^2.

P2.37. Prepare: We will use the equation for constant acceleration to find out how far the sprinter travels during the acceleration phase. Use Equation 2.8 to find the acceleration.

$$v_x = a_x t_1 \qquad \text{where } v_0 = 0 \text{ and } t_0 = 0$$

$$a_x = \frac{v_x}{t_1} = \frac{11.2 \text{ m/s}}{2.14 \text{ s}} = 5.23 \text{ m/s}^2$$

Solve: The distance traveled during the acceleration phase will be

$$\Delta x = \frac{1}{2}a_x (\Delta t)^2$$

$$= \frac{1}{2}(5.23 \text{ m/s}^2)(2.14 \text{ s})^2$$

$$= 12.0 \text{ m}$$

The distance left to go at constant velocity is 100 m $-$ 12.0 m $= 88.0$. The time this takes at the top speed of 11.2 m/s is

$$\Delta t = \frac{\Delta x}{v_x} = \frac{88.0 \text{ m}}{11.2 \text{ m/s}} = 7.86 \text{ s}$$

The total time is 2.14 s $+$ 7.86 s $= 10.0$ s.

Assess: This is indeed about the time it takes a world-class sprinter to run 100 m (the world record is a bit under 9.8 s). Compare the answer to this problem with the accelerations given in Problem 2.25 for Carl Lewis.

P2.39. Prepare: Review the related "Try It Yourself" in the chapter.

We will assume that, as stated in the chapter, the bill is held at the top, and the other person's fingers are bracketing the bill at the bottom.

Call the initial position of the top of the bill the origin $yo = 0.0$ m, and, for convenience, call the down direction positive. In free fall the acceleration a_y will be 9.8 m/s^2.

The length of the bill will be Δy; the distance the top of the bill can fall from rest in 0.25 s. Use Equation 2.11.

Solve:

$$\Delta y = \frac{1}{2} a_y (\Delta t)^2 = \frac{1}{2} (9.8 \text{ m/s}^2)(0.25 \text{ s})^2 = 0.31 \text{ m}$$

Assess: This is about twice as long as real bills are (they are really 15 cm long), so if a typical reaction time is 0.25 s, then almost no one would catch one in this manner. To catch a bill as small as real bills, one would need a reaction time of 0.13 s.

P2.41. Prepare: If we ignore air resistance, then the only force acting on both balls after they leave the hand (before they land) is gravity; they are therefore in free fall.

Think about ball A's velocity. It decreases until it reaches the top of its trajectory and then increases in the downward direction as it descends. When it gets back to the level of the student's hand it will have the same speed downward that it had initially going upward; it is therefore now just like ball B (only later).

Solve: (a) Because both balls are in free fall they must have the same acceleration, both magnitude and direction, 9.8 m/s^2, down.

(b) Because ball B has the same downward speed when it gets back to the level of the student that ball A had, they will have the same speed when they hit the ground.

Assess: Draw a picture of ball B's trajectory and draw velocity vector arrows at various points of its path. Air resistance would complicate this problem significantly.

P2.43. Prepare: Assume the trajectory is symmetric (i.e., the ball leaves the ground), so half of the total time is the upward portion and half downward. Put the origin at the ground.

Solve:

(a) On the way down $(v_y)_i = 0$ m/s, $y_f = 0$ m, and $\Delta t = 2.6$ s. Solve for y_i.

$$0 = y_i + \frac{1}{2} a_y (\Delta t)^2 \Rightarrow y_i = -\frac{1}{2} a_y (\Delta t)^2 = -\frac{1}{2}(-9.8 \text{ m/s}^2)(2.6 \text{ s})^2 = 33.124 \text{ m} \approx 33 \text{ m}$$

(b) On the way up $(v_y)_f = 0$ m/s.

$$(v_y)_i^2 = -2a_y \Delta y \Rightarrow (v_y)_i = \sqrt{-2a_y \Delta y} = \sqrt{-2(-9.8 \text{ m/s}^2)(33.124 \text{ m})} = 25 \text{ m/s}$$

Assess: When thinking about real football games, this speed seems reasonable.

P2.45. Prepare: There are several steps in this problem, so first draw a picture and, like the examples in the book, list the known quantities and what we need to find. Call the pool of water the origin and call $t = 0$ s when the first stone is released. We will assume both stones are in free fall after they leave the climber's hand, so $a_y = -g$. Let a subscript 1 refer to the first stone and a 2 refer to the second.

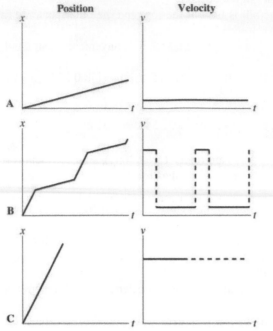

Position	Velocity	Known

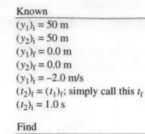

Known
$(y_1)_i = 50$ m
$(y_2)_i = 50$ m
$(y_1)_f = 0.0$ m
$(y_2)_f = 0.0$ m
$(y_1)_i = -2.0$ m/s
$(t_2)_f = (t_1)_f$; simply call this t_f
$(t_2)_i = 1.0$ s

Find
$(t_2)_f$ or t_f
$(v_2)_i$
$(v_1)_f$
$(v_2)_f$

Solve: (a) Using $(t_1)_i = 0$

$$(y_1)_f = (y_1)_i + (v_1)_i \Delta t + \frac{1}{2}a_y \Delta t^2$$

$$0.0 \text{ m} = 50 \text{ m} + (-2 \text{ m/s})t_f + \frac{1}{2}(-g)t_f^2$$

$$0.0 \text{ m} = 50 \text{ m} - (2 \text{ m/s})t_f - (4.9 \text{ m/s}^2)t_f^2$$

Solving this quadratic equation gives two values for t_f: 3.0 s and -3.4 s, the second of which (being negative) is outside the scope of this problem.

Both stones hit the water at the same time, and it is at $t = 3.0$ s, or 3.0 s after the first stone is released.

(b) For the second stone $\Delta t_2 = t_f - (t_2)_i = 3.0 \text{ s} - 1.0 \text{ s} = 2.0$ s. We solve now for $(v_2)_i$.

$$(y_2)_f = (y_2)_i + (v_2)_i \Delta t + \frac{1}{2}a_y \Delta t^2$$

$$0.0 \text{ m} = 50 \text{ m} + (v_2)_i \Delta t_2 + \frac{1}{2}(-g)\Delta t_2^2$$

$$0.0 \text{ m} = 50 \text{ m} + (v_2)_i(2.0 \text{ s}) - (4.9 \text{ m/s}^2)(2.0 \text{ s})^2$$

$$(v_2)_i = \frac{-50 \text{ m} + (4.9 \text{ m/s}^2)(2.0 \text{ s})^2}{2.0 \text{ s}} = -15.2 \text{ m/s}$$

Thus, the second stone is thrown down at a speed of 15.2 m/s.

(c) Equation 2.8 allows us to compute the final speeds for each stone.

$$(v_y)_f = (v_y)_i + a_y \Delta t$$

For the first stone (which was in the air for 3.0 s):

$$(v_1)_f = -2.0 \text{ m/s} + (-9.8 \text{ m/s}^2)(3.0 \text{ s}) = -31.4 \text{ m/s} \approx -31 \text{ m/s}$$

The speed is the magnitude of this velocity, or 31 m/s.

For the second stone (which was in the air for 2.0 s):

$$(v_2)_f = -15.2 \text{ m/s} + (-9.8 \text{ m/s}^2)(2.0 \text{ s}) = -34.8 \text{ m/s} \approx -35 \text{ m/s}$$

The speed is the magnitude of this velocity, or 35 m/s.

Assess: The units check out in each equation above. The answers seem reasonable. A stone dropped from rest takes 3.2 s to fall 50 m; this is comparable to the first stone, which was able to fall the 50 m in only 3.0 s because it started with an initial velocity of −2.0 m/s. So we are in the right ballpark. And the second stone would have to be thrown much faster to catch up (because the first stone is accelerating).

P2.47. Prepare: The position graphs of the nerve impulses will be strictly increasing, since the impulse does, in fact, always travel to the right in this context. The graphs will consist of straight-line segments whose slope depends on the speed (i.e., whether the nerve is myelinated or not).

The velocity graphs will be constant horizontal line segments whose height depends on the speed (i.e., whether the nerve is myelinated or not).

Solve:

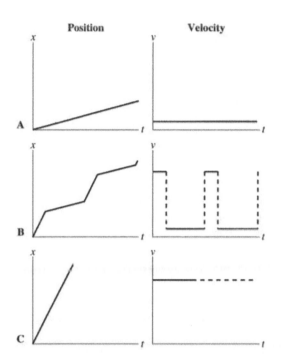

Assess: The velocity graph for fiber C would continue at the same speed if we draw it for a longer fiber than 6 axons.

P2.49. Prepare: Assume the truck driver is traveling with constant velocity during each segment of his trip.
Solve: Since the driver usually takes 8 hours to travel 440 miles, his usual velocity is

$$v_{\text{usual } x} = \frac{\Delta x}{\Delta t_{\text{usual}}} = \frac{440 \text{ mi}}{8 \text{ h}} = 55 \text{ mph}$$

However, during this trip he was driving slower for the first 120 miles. Usually he would be at the 120 mile point in

$$\Delta t_{\text{usual at 120 mi}} = \frac{\Delta x}{v_{\text{usual at 120 mi } x}} = \frac{120 \text{ mi}}{55 \text{ mph}} = 2.18 \text{ h}$$

He is 15 minutes, or 0.25 hr late. So the time he's taken to get 120 mi is 2.18 hr + 0.25 hr = 2.43 hr. He wants to complete the entire trip in the usual 8 hours, so he only has 8 hr − 2.43 hr = 5.57 hr left to complete 440 mi − 120 mi = 320 mi. So he needs to increase his velocity to

$$v_{\text{to catch up } x} = \frac{\Delta x}{\Delta t_{\text{to catch up}}} = \frac{320 \text{ mi}}{5.57 \text{ h}} = 57 \text{ mph}$$

where additional significant figures were kept in the intermediate calculations.

Assess: This result makes sense. He is only 15 minutes late.

P2.51. Prepare: We assume that the track, except for the sticky section, is frictionless and aligned along the x-axis. Because the motion diagram of Figure P2.43 is made at two frames of film per second, the time interval between consecutive ball positions is 0.5 s.

Solve: (a)

Times (s)	Position
0	−4
0.5	−2
1.0	0
1.5	1.75
2.0	3
2.5	4
3.0	5
3.5	6
4.0	7

(b)

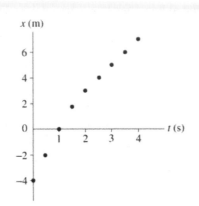

(c) $\Delta x = x$ (at $t = 1$ s) $- x$ (at $t = 0$ s) $= 0$ m $- (-4$ m$) = 4$ m.
(d) $\Delta x = x$ (at $t = 4$ s) $- x$ (at $t = 2$ s) $= 7$ m $- 3$ m $= 4$ m.
(e) From $t = 0$ s to $t = 1$ s, $v_s = \Delta x/\Delta t = 4$ m/s.
(f) From $t = 2$ s to $t = 4$ s, $v_x = \Delta x/\Delta t = 2$ m/s.
(g) The average acceleration is

$$a = \frac{\Delta v}{\Delta t} = \frac{2 \text{ m/s} - 4 \text{ m/s}}{2 \text{ s} - 1 \text{ s}} = -2 \text{ m/s}^2$$

Assess: The sticky section has decreased the ball's speed from 4 m/s, to 2 m/s, which is a reasonable magnitude.

P2.53. Prepare: We will represent the jetliner's motion to be along the x-axis.
Solve: (a) To convert 80 m/s to mph, we calculate 80 m/s $\times$ 1 mi/1609 m $\times$ 3600 s/h = 180 mph.
(b) Using $a_x = \Delta v/\Delta t$, we have,

$$a_x(t = 0 \text{ to } t = 10 \text{ s}) = \frac{23 \text{ m/s} - 0 \text{ m/s}}{10 \text{ s} - 0 \text{ s}} = 2.3 \text{ m/s}^2 \qquad a_x(t = 20 \text{ s to } t = 30 \text{ s}) = \frac{69 \text{ m/s} - 46 \text{ m/s}}{30 \text{ s} - 20 \text{ s}} = 2.3 \text{ m/s}^2$$

For all time intervals a_x is 2.3 m/s².
(c) Because the jetliner's acceleration is constant, we can use kinematics as follows:

$$(v_x)_f = (v_x)_i + a_x(t_f - t_i) \Rightarrow 80 \text{ m/s} = 0 \text{ m/s} + (2.3 \text{ m/s}^2)(t_f - 0 \text{ s}) \Rightarrow t_f = 34.8 \text{ s} = 35 \text{ s}$$

(d) Using the above values, we calculate the takeoff distance as follows:

$$x_f = x_i + (v_x)_i(t_f - t_i) + \frac{1}{2}a_x(t_f - t_i)^2 = 0 \text{ m} + (0 \text{ m/s})(34.8 \text{ s}) + \frac{1}{2}(2.3 \text{ m/s}^2)(34.8 \text{ s})^2 = 1390 \text{ m}$$

For safety, the runway should be 3 $\times$ 1390 m = 4170 m, or 2.6 mi. This is longer than the 2.5 mi-long runway, so the takeoff is not safe.

P2.55. Prepare: We will ignore relativistic effects. After appropriate unit conversions, we'll see how far the spacecraft goes during the acceleration phase and what speed it achieves and then how long it would take to go the remaining distance at that speed.

$$0.50 \ y = 1.578 \times 10^7 \text{ s}$$

Solve: Because $(v_x)_i = 0$ m/s

$$\Delta x = \frac{1}{2} a_x (\Delta t)^2 = \frac{1}{2}(9.8 \text{ m/s}^2)(1.578 \times 10^7 \text{ s})^2 = 1.220 \times 10^{15} \text{ m}$$

which is not a very large fraction of the whole distance. The spacecraft must still go 4.1×10^{16} m $- 1.220 \times 10^{15}$ m $= 3.98 \times 10^{16}$ m at the achieved speed.

The speed is

$$\Delta v_x = a_x \Delta t = (9.8 \text{ m/s}^2)(1.578 \times 10^7 \text{ s}) = 1.55 \times 10^8 \text{ m/s}$$

which is half the speed of light. The time taken to go the remaining distance at that speed is

$$\Delta t = \frac{\Delta x}{v_x} = \frac{3.98 \times 10^{16} \text{ m}}{1.55 \times 10^8 \text{ m/s}} = 2.57 \times 10^8 \text{ s} = 8.15 \text{ y}$$

Now the total time needed is the sum of the time for the acceleration phase and the time for the constant velocity phase.

$$\Delta t = 0.50 \text{ y} + 8.15 \text{ y} = 8.65 \text{ y} \approx 8.7 \text{ y}$$

Access: It is now easy to see why travel to other stars will be so difficult. We even made some overly-generous assumptions and ignored relativistic effects.

P2.57. Prepare: Remember that in estimation problems different people may make slightly different estimates. That is OK as long as they end up with reasonable answers that are the same order-of-magnitude.

By assuming the acceleration to be constant we can use Equation 2.11:

$$\Delta x = \frac{1}{2} a_x (\Delta t)^2$$

Solve: (a) I guessed about 1.0 cm; this was verified with a ruler and mirror.
(b) We are given a closing time of 0.024 s, so we can compute the acceleration from rearranging Equation 2.11:

$$a_x = \frac{2\Delta x}{(\Delta t)^2} = \frac{2(1.0 \text{ cm})}{(0.024 \text{ s})^2}\left(\frac{1 \text{ m}}{100 \text{ cm}}\right) = 35 \text{ m/s}^2$$

(c) Since we know the Δt and the a and $v_i = 0.0$ m/s, we can compute the final speed from Equation 2.8.

$$v_f = a\Delta t = (35 \text{ m/s}^2)(0.024 \text{ s}) = 0.84 \text{ m/s}$$

Assess: The uncertainty in our estimates might or might not barely justify two significant figures. The final speed is reasonable; if we had arrived at an answer 10 times bigger or 10 times smaller we would probably go back and check our work. The lower lid gets smacked at this speed up to 15 times per minute!

P2.59. Prepare: Fleas are amazing jumpers; they can jump several times their body height—something we cannot do.

We assume constant acceleration so we can use the equations in Table 2.4. The last of the three relates the three variables we are concerned with in part **(a)**: speed, distance (which we know), and acceleration (which we want).

$$(v_y)_f^2 = (v_y)_i^2 + 2a_y \Delta y$$

In part **(b)** we use the first equation in Table 2.4 because it relates the initial and final velocities and the acceleration (which we know) with the time interval (which we want).

$$(v_y)_f = (v_y)_i + a_y \Delta t$$

Part **(c)** is about the phase of the jump *after* the flea reaches takeoff speed and leaves the ground. So now it is $(v_y)_i$—that is, 1.0 m/s instead of $(v_y)_f$. And the acceleration is not the same as in part **(a)**—it is now $-g$ (with the positive direction up) since we are ignoring air resistance. We do not know the time it takes the flea to reach maximum height, so we employ the last equation in Table 2.4 again because we know everything in that equation except Δy.

Solve: (a) Use $(v_y)_i = 0.0$ m/s and rearrange the last equation in Table 2.4.

$$a_y = \frac{(v_y)_f^2}{2\Delta y} = \frac{(1.0 \text{ m/s})^2}{2(0.50 \text{ mm})}\left(\frac{1000 \text{ mm}}{1 \text{ m}}\right) = 1000 \text{ m/s}^2$$

(b) Having learned the acceleration from part **(a)** we can now rearrange the first equation in Table 2.4 to find the time it takes to reach takeoff speed. Again use $(v_y)_i = 0.0$ m/s.

$$\Delta t = \frac{(v_y)_f}{a_y} = \frac{1.0 \text{ m/s}}{1000 \text{ m/s}^2} = .0010 \text{ s}$$

(c) This time $(v_y)_f = 0.0$ m/s as the flea reaches the top of its trajectory. Rearrange the last equation in Table 2.4 to get

$$\Delta y = \frac{-(v_y)_i^2}{2a_y} = \frac{-(1.0 \text{ m/s})^2}{2(-9.8 \text{ m/s}^2)} = 0.051 \text{ m} = 5.1 \text{ cm}$$

Assess: Just over 5 cm is pretty good considering the size of a flea. It is about 10–20 times the size of a typical flea. Check carefully to see that each answer ends up in the appropriate units.

The height of the flea at the top will round to 5.2 cm above the ground if you include the 0.050 cm during the initial acceleration phase before the feet actually leave the ground.

P2.61. Prepare: Assume the diver leaves the platform with no initial velocity. There are two parts to the diver's motion. The diver is in free fall after leaving the platform. Gravity accelerates him until he hits the water, and then the water decelerates him. In order for him not to hit the bottom of the pool, his velocity at the bottom of the pool must be zero.

Solve: We can calculate the velocity the diver enters the water with from Equation 2.10. The platform is 10 m above the water. Assuming his initial velocity in leaving the platform is $(v_y)_i = 0$ m/s, the velocity he has before he hits the water is

$$(v_y)_f = \sqrt{2(a_y)_1 \Delta y_1} = \sqrt{2(-9.80 \text{ m/s}^2)(-10 \text{ m})} = 14 \text{ m/s}$$

In order to come to a stop before hitting the bottom of the pool, he must be decelerated to a stop by the water before traveling 3.0 m. His acceleration must be

$$(a_y)_{\text{water}} = \frac{(v_y)_f^2 - (v_y)_i^2}{2\Delta y_2} = \frac{(0 \text{ m/s})^2 - (14 \text{ m/s})^2}{2(-3.0 \text{ m})} = +33 \text{ m/s}^2$$

Assess: This makes sense. In order to lose all the velocity he gained during the jump of 10 m, he must decelerate faster than the acceleration due to gravity. Note the acceleration in the water is positive. His acceleration in the water is upward, as expected.

P2.63. Prepare: A visual overview of the rock's motion that includes a pictorial representation, a motion diagram, and a list of values is shown below. We represent the rock's motion along the y-axis. As soon as the rock is tossed up, it falls freely and thus kinematic equations hold. The rock's acceleration is equal to the acceleration due to gravity that always acts vertically downward toward the center of the earth. The initial position of the rock is at the origin where $y_i = 0$, but the final position is below the origin at $y_f = -10$ m. Recall sign conventions which tell us that v_i is positive and a is negative.

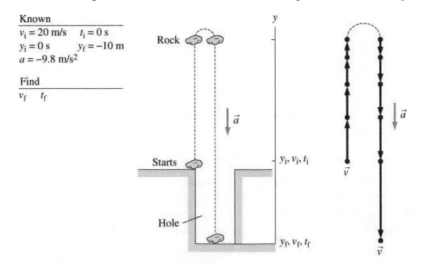

Known	
$v_i = 20$ m/s	$t_i = 0$ s
$y_i = 0$ s	$y_f = -10$ m
$a = -9.8$ m/s^2	

Find
$v_f \quad t_f$

Solve: (a) Substituting the known values into $y_f = y_i + v_i \Delta t + \frac{1}{2} a \Delta t^2$, we get

$$-10 \text{ m} = 0 \text{ m} + 20(\text{m/s})t_f + \frac{1}{2}(-9.8 \text{ m/s}^2)t_f^2$$

One of the roots of this equation is negative and is not physically relevant. The other root is $t_f = 4.53$ s, which is the answer to part **(b)**. Using $v_f = v_i + a\Delta t$, we obtain

$$v_f = 20(\text{m/s}) + (-9.8 \text{ m/s}^2)(4.53 \text{ s}) = -24 \text{ m/s}$$

(b) The time is 4.5 s.

Assess: A time of 4.5 s is a reasonable value. The rock's velocity as it hits the bottom of the hole has a negative sign because of its downward direction. The magnitude of 24 m/s compared to 20 m/s, when the rock was tossed up, is consistent with the fact that the rock travels an additional distance of 10 m into the hole.

P2.65. Prepare: It is clear the second ball must be thrown with a greater initial velocity than the first ball in order to catch up to it at the top. In the Assess step we will verify that this is indeed the case. We are *not* told the second ball has zero velocity when it hits the first ball at the top of the first ball's trajectory (the first ball *would* have zero velocity at this time).

There are several steps in this problem, so first draw a picture and, like the examples in the book, list the known quantities and what we need to find. Call the juggler's hand the origin and call $t = 0$ s when the first ball is released. We will assume both balls are in free fall after they leave the juggler's hand, so $a_y = -g$. Let a subscript 1 refer to the first ball and a 2 refer to the second.

Known
_____

$(y_1)_i = 0.0$ m
$(y_2)_i = 0.0$ m
$(y_2)_f = (y_1)_f$; simply call this y_r
$(v_1)_i = 10$ m/s
$(v_1)_f = 0.0$ m/s
$(t_1)_i = 0.0$ s
$(t_2)_i = 0.50$ s
$(t_2)_f = (t_1)_f$; simply call this t_f

Find
_____

$(v_2)_i$

The strategy will be to find the position and time of the first ball at the top of its trajectory, and then to compute the initial speed needed for the second ball to get to the same place at the same time.

Solve: Use the first equation of Table 2.4 to find t_f (which is equal to $(t_1)_i + \Delta t_1$). Everything is in the y direction so we drop the y subscript.

$$(v_1)_f = (v_1)_i + a\Delta t_1$$

Use the facts that $(v_1)_f = 0.0$ m/s and $a = -g$ to solve for Δt_1.

$$\Delta t_1 = \frac{-(v_1)_i}{-g} = \frac{10 \text{ m/s}}{9.8 \text{ m/s}^2} = 1.02 \text{ s}$$

Then use $(t_1)_i = 0.0$ s to find $t_f = 1.02$ s.

Now use the third equation of Table 2.4 to find the position of the top of the first ball's trajectory.

$$(v_1)_f^2 = (v_1)_i^2 + 2a\Delta y$$

We know that $(v_1)_f = 0.0$ m/s and $a = -g$.

$$\Delta y = \frac{-(v_1)_i^2}{2a} = \frac{-(10.0 \text{ m/s})^2}{2(-g)} = 5.1 \text{ m}$$

Since $(y_1)_i = 0.0$ m we know that $(y_1)_f = y_f = 5.1$ m.

Those were the preliminaries. Now we use $t_f = 1.02$ s and $y_f = 5.1$ m in the second equation of Table 2.4 to solve for $(v_2)_i$. For the second ball, $(t_2)_i = 0.5$ s, so $\Delta t_2 = 1.02$ s $- 0.50$ s $= 0.52$ s.

$$y_f = (y_2)_i + (v_2)_i \Delta t_2 + \frac{1}{2} a (\Delta t_2)^2$$

Solving for $(v_2)_i$:

$$(v_2)_i = \frac{y_f - (y_2)_i - \frac{1}{2}a(\Delta t_2)^2}{\Delta t_2} = \frac{5.1 \text{ m} - 0.0 \text{ m} - \frac{1}{2}(-g)(0.52 \text{ s})^2}{0.52 \text{ s}} = \frac{5.1 \text{ m} + \frac{1}{2}(9.8 \text{ m/s}^2)(0.52 \text{ s})^2}{0.52 \text{ s}} = 12 \text{ m/s}$$

Assess: Our original statement that $(v_2)_i$ had to be greater than $(v_1)_i$ is correct. The answer still seems to be a reasonable throwing speed.

P2.67. Prepare: A visual overview of car's motion that includes a pictorial representation, a motion diagram, and a list of values is shown below. We label the car's motion along the x-axis. This is a three part problem. First the car accelerates, then it moves with a constant speed, and then it decelerates. The total displacement between the stop signs is equal to the sum of the three displacements, that is, $x_3 - x_0 = (x_3 - x_2) + (x_2 - x_1) + (x_1 - x_0)$.

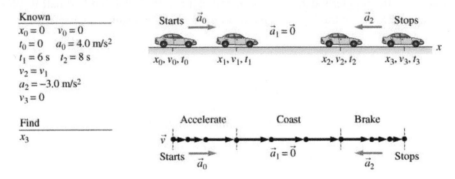

Solve: First, the car accelerates:

$$v_1 = v_0 + a_0(t_1 - t_0) = 0 \text{ m/s} + (2.0 \text{ m/s}^2)(6 \text{ s} - 0 \text{ s}) = 12 \text{ m/s}$$

$$x_1 = x_0 + v_0(t_1 - t_0) + \frac{1}{2}a_0(t_1 - t_0)^2 = 0 \text{ m} + \frac{1}{2}(2.0 \text{ m/s}^2)(6 \text{ s} - 0 \text{ s})^2 = 36 \text{ m}$$

Second, the car moves at v_1:

$$x_2 - x_1 = v_1(t_2 - t_1) + \frac{1}{2}a_1(t_2 - t_1)^2 = (12 \text{ m/s})(8 \text{ s} - 6 \text{ s}) + 0 \text{ m} = 24 \text{ m}$$

Third, the car decelerates:

$$v_3 = v_2 + a_2(t_3 - t_2) \Rightarrow 0 \text{ m/s} = 12 \text{ m/s} + (-1.5 \text{ m/s}^2)(t_3 - t_2) \Rightarrow (t_3 - t_2) = 8 \text{ s}$$

$$x_3 = x_2 + v_2(t_3 - t_2) + \frac{1}{2}a_2(t_3 - t_2)^2 \Rightarrow x_3 - x_2 = (12 \text{ m/s})(8 \text{ s}) + \frac{1}{2}(-1.5 \text{ m/s}^2)(8 \text{ s})^2 = 48 \text{ m}$$

Thus, the total distance between stop signs is:

$$x_3 - x_0 = (x_3 - x_2) + (x_2 - x_1) + (x_1 - x_0) = 48 \text{ m} + 24 \text{ m} + 36 \text{ m} = 108 \text{ m} \approx 110 \text{ m}$$

Assess: A distance of approximately 360 ft in a time of around 16 s with an acceleration/deceleration is reasonable.

P2.69. Prepare: A visual overview of the motion of the two rocks, one thrown down by Heather and the other thrown up at the same time by Jerry, that includes a pictorial representation, a motion diagram, and a list of values is shown below. We represent the motion of the rocks along the y-axis with origin at the surface of the water. As soon as the rocks are thrown, they fall freely and thus kinematics equations are applicable. The initial position for both cases is $y_i = 50$ m, and similarly the final position for both cases is at $y_f = 0$. Recall sign conventions, which tell us that $(v_i)_J$ is positive and $(v_i)_H$ is negative.

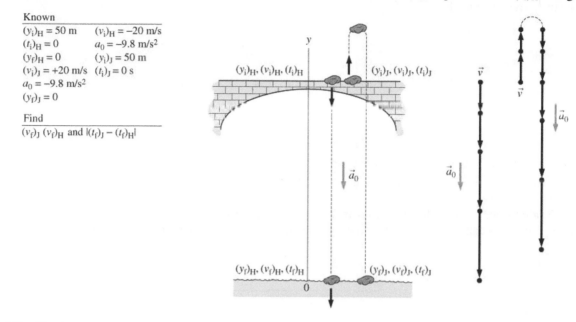

Known

$(y_i)_H = 50$ m	$(v_i)_H = -20$ m/s
$(t_i)_H = 0$	$a_0 = -9.8$ m/s^2
$(y_f)_H = 0$	$(y_i)_J = 50$ m
$(v_i)_J = +20$ m/s	$(t_i)_J = 0$ s
$a_0 = -9.8$ m/s^2	
$(y_f)_J = 0$	

Find

$(v_f)_J$ $(v_f)_H$ and $|(t_f)_J - (t_f)_H|$

Solve: (a) For Heather,

$$(y_f)_H = (y_i)_H + (v_i)_H[(t_f)_H - (t_i)_H] + \frac{1}{2}a_0[(t_f)_H - (t_i)_H)]^2$$

$$\Rightarrow 0 \text{ m} = (50 \text{ m}) + (-20 \text{ m/s})[(t_f)_H - 0 \text{ s}] + \frac{1}{2}(-9.8 \text{ m/s}^2)[(t_f)_H - 0 \text{ s}]^2$$

$$\Rightarrow 4.9 \text{ m/s}^2 \ (t_f)_H^2 + 20 \text{ m/s} \ (t_f)_H - 50 \text{ m} = 0$$

The two mathematical solutions of this equation are -5.83 s and $+1.75$ s. The first value is not physically acceptable since it represents a rock hitting the water before it was thrown, therefore, $(t_f)_H - 1.75$ s.
   For Jerry,

$$(y_f)_J = (y_i)_J + (v_i)_J[(t_f)_J - (t_i)_J] + \frac{1}{2}a_0[(t_f)_J - (t_i)_J)]^2$$

$$\Rightarrow 0 \text{ m} = (50 \text{ m}) + (+20 \text{ m/s})[(t_f)_J - 0 \text{ s}] + \frac{1}{2}(-9.8 \text{ m/s}^2)[(t_f)_J - 0 \text{ s}]^2$$

Solving this quadratic equation will yield $(t_f)_J = -1.75$ s and $+5.83$ s. Again only the positive root is physically meaningful. The elapsed time between the two splashes is $(t_f)_J - (t_f)_H = 5.83$ s $- 1.75$ s $= 4.08$ s $= 4.1$ s.
   (b) Knowing the times, it is easy to find the impact velocities:

$$(v_f)_H = (v_i)_H + a_0[(t_f)_H - (t_i)_H] = (-20 \text{ m/s}) + (-9.8 \text{ m/s})(1.75 \text{ s} - 0 \text{ s}) = -37 \text{ m/s}$$

$$(v_f)_J = (v_i)_J + a_0[(t_f)_J - (t_i)_J] = (+20 \text{ m/s}) + (-9.8 \text{ m/s}^2)(5.83 \text{ s} - 0 \text{ s}) = -37 \text{ m/s}$$

Assess: The two rocks hit water with equal speeds. This is because Jerry's rock has the same downward speed as Heather's rock when it reaches Heather's starting position during its downward motion.

P2.71. Prepare: Before we turn to algebra, carefully examine the velocity-versus-time graph below. We draw the line for car 1 by starting at the origin at time zero and making the slope 2.0 m/s^2. The line for car 2 starts at $v_2 = 0.0$ m/s when $t = 2.0$ s. and has a slope of 8.0 m/s^2. The time where the vertical dotted line should be placed is initially unknown; think of sliding it left and right until the areas of the two triangles (under the graphs of cars 1 and 2) are the same. When that happens then the time where the dotted line ends up is the answer to part **(a)**, and the area under the two lines (*i.e.*, the area of each triangle) will be the answer to part **(b)**.

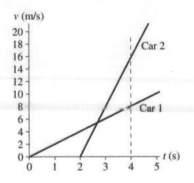

Since the accelerations are constant the equations in Table 2.4 will apply. Assume that each car starts from rest. Call the launch point the origin and call $t = 0$ s when the first car is launched. Let a subscript 1 refer to the first car and a 2 refer to the second.

Known
___

$(x_1)_i = 0.0$ m
$(x_2)_i = 0.0$ m
$(x_2)_f = (x_1)_f$; simply call this x_f
$(v_1)_i = 0.0$ m/s
$(v_2)_i = 0.0$ m/s
$(t_1)_i = 0.0$ s
$(t_2)_i = 2.0$ s
$(t_2)_f = (t_1)_f$; simply call this t_f
$\quad a_1 = 2.0$ m/s^2
$\quad a_2 = 8.0$ m/s^2

Find
___

t_f
x_f

The strategy will be to use equations from Table 2.4 with the twist that no one of them has only one unknown (since both final velocities are unknown). So we will use various instances of the equations to get a system of equations with enough equations to solve for our unknowns.

   Solve: Apply the last equation in Table 2.4 to each car (with the initial velocities both zero) and then divide the equations. Dividing equations to get ratios is an elegant and useful technique.

$$(v_1)_f^2 = 2a_1 \Delta x$$

$$(v_2)_f^2 = 2a_2 \Delta x$$

$$\left(\frac{(v_1)_f}{(v_2)_f} \right)^2 = \frac{a_1}{a_2} = \frac{2.0 \text{ m/s}^2}{8.0 \text{ m/s}^2} = \frac{1}{4}$$

Taking square roots gives

$$\frac{(v_1)_f}{(v_2)_f} = \frac{1}{2}$$

(a) Now turn to the first equation in Table 2.4 and apply it to both cars (again, with both initial velocities zero). Since $(t_1)_i = 0.0$ s, then $\Delta t_1 = t_f$, and since $(t_2)_i = 2.0$ s then $\Delta t_2 = t_f - 2.0$ s

$$(v_1)_f = a_1 t_f \quad (v_2)_f = a_2(t_f - 2.0 \text{ s})$$

Divide the equations and use the previous result.

$$\frac{(v_1)_f}{(v_2)_f} = \frac{a_1}{a_2}\left(\frac{t_f}{t_f - 2.0 \text{ s}}\right)\frac{1}{2} = \frac{1}{4}\left(\frac{t_f}{t_f - 2.0 \text{ s}}\right)$$

Solve for t_f by multiplying both sides by $4(t_f - 2.0)$.

$$2(t_f - 2.0 \text{ s}) = t_f \qquad 2t_f - 4.0 \text{ s} = t_f \qquad 2t_f - t_f = 4.0 \text{ s} \qquad t_f = 4.0 \text{ s}$$

This is the answer to part (a). $t_f = 4.0$ s.

(b) Although we aren't asked for the final velocities, we compute $(v_1)_f$ so can find the distance traveled.

$$(v_1)_f = a_1 t_f = (2.0 \text{ m/s}^2)(4.0 \text{ s}) = 8.0 \text{ m/s}$$

With $(x_1)_i = 0.0$ m then $\Delta x_1 = x_f$. Since $(v_1)_f = 0.0$ m/s, the last equation in Table 2.4 becomes for car 1.

$$(v_1)_f^2 = 2a_1 x_f$$

So

$$x_f = \frac{(v_1)_f^2}{2a_1} = \frac{(8.0 \text{ m/s})^2}{2(2.0 \text{ m/s}^2)} = 16 \text{ m}$$

A similar calculation for car 2 gives the same result; the two cars meet 16 m down the track.

Assess: We have finally answered both parts of the problem. We check that the units are correct. We note the important technique of dividing one equation by another to get dimensionless ratios. Last, we note that the algebra agrees with the graphical approach taken at the beginning.

P2.73. Prepare: A visual overview of the car's motion that includes a pictorial representation, a motion diagram, and a list of values is shown below. We label the car's motion along the x-axis. This is a two-part problem. First, we need to use the information given to determine the acceleration during braking. We will then use this acceleration to find the stopping distance for a different initial velocity.

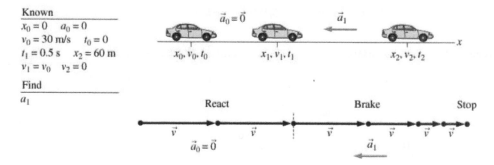

Solve: (a) First, the car coasts at constant speed before braking:

$$x_1 = x_0 + v_0(t_1 - t_0) = v_0 t_1 = (30 \text{ m/s})(0.5 \text{ s}) = 15 \text{ m}$$

Then, the car brakes to a halt. Because we don't know the time interval during braking, we will use

$$v_2^2 = 0 = v_1^2 + 2a_1(x_2 - x_1)$$

$$\Rightarrow a_1 = -\frac{v_1^2}{2(x_2 - x_1)} = -\frac{(30 \text{ m/s})^2}{2(60 \text{ m} - 15 \text{ m})} = -10 \text{ m/s}^2$$

We use $v_1 = v_0 = 30$ m/s. Note the minus sign, because $\vec{a}_1$ points to the left. We can repeat these steps now with $v_0 = 40$ m/s. The coasting distance before braking is

$$x_1 = v_0 t_1 = (40 \text{ m/s})(0.5 \text{ s}) = 20 \text{ m}$$

So the braking distance is

$$v_2^2 = 0 = v_1^2 + 2a_1(x_2 - x_1)$$

$$\Rightarrow x_2 = x_1 - \frac{v_1^2}{2a_1} = 20 \text{ m} - \frac{(40 \text{ m/s})^2}{2(-10 \text{ m/s}^2)} = 100 \text{ m}$$

(b) The car coasts at a constant speed for 0.5 s, traveling 20 m. The graph will be a straight line with a slope of 40 m/s. For $t \geq 0.5$ the graph will be a parabola until the car stops at t_2. We can find t_2 from

$$v_2 = 0 = v_1 + a_1(t_2 - t_1) \Rightarrow t_2 = t_1 - \frac{v_1}{a_1} = 4.5 \text{ s}$$

P2.75. Prepare: We can calculate the initial velocity obtained by the astronaut on the earth and then use that to calculate the maximum height the astronaut can jump on the moon.

Solve: The astronaut can jump a maximum 0.50 m on the earth. The maximum initial velocity his leg muscles can give him can be calculated with Equation 2.10. His velocity at the peak of his jump is zero.

$$(v_y)_i = \sqrt{-2(a_y)\Delta y} = \sqrt{-2(-9.80 \text{ m/s}^2)(0.50 \text{ m})} = 3.1 \text{ m/s}$$

We can also use Equation 2.10 to find the maximum height the astronaut can jump on the moon. The acceleration due to the moon's gravity is $\frac{9.80 \text{ m/s}^2}{6} = 1.63 \text{ m/s}^2$. On the moon, given the initial velocity above, the astronaut can jump

$$\Delta y_{\text{moon}} = \frac{-(v_y)_i^2}{2(a_y)_{\text{moon}}} = \frac{-(3.1 \text{ m/s})^2}{2(-1.63 \text{ m/s}^2)} = 3.0 \text{ m}$$

Assess: The answer, choice B, makes sense. The astronaut can jump much higher on the moon.

P2.77. Prepare: We can calculate the initial velocity with which the astronaut throws the ball on the earth and then use that to calculate the time the ball is in motion after it is thrown and comes back down on the moon.

Solve: The initial velocity with which the ball is thrown on the earth can be calculated from Equation 2.9. Since the ball starts near the ground and lands near the ground, $x_f = x_i$. Solving the equation for $(v_y)_i$,

$$(v_y)_i = -\frac{1}{2}a_y\Delta t = -\frac{1}{2}(-9.80 \text{ m/s}^2)(3.0 \text{ s}) = 15 \text{ m/s}$$

The acceleration due to the moon's gravity is $\frac{9.80 \text{ m/s}^2}{6} = 1.63 \text{ m/s}^2$. We can find the time it takes to return to the lunar surface using the same equation as above, this time solving for Δt. If thrown upward with this initial velocity on the moon,

$$\Delta t = \frac{-2(v_y)_i}{a_y} = \frac{-2(15 \text{ m/s})}{1.63 \text{ m/s}^2} = 18 \text{ s}$$

Assess: The correct choice is B. This makes sense. The ball is in motion for a much longer time on the moon

3—Vectors and Motion in Two Dimensions
Conceptual Questions

Q3.1. Reason: (a) If one component of the vector is zero, then the other component must not be zero (unless the whole vector is zero). Thus the magnitude of the vector will be the value of the other component. For example, if $A_x = 0$ m and $A_y = 5$ m, then the magnitude of the vector is

$$A = \sqrt{(0 \text{ m})^2 + (5 \text{ m})^2} = 5 \text{ m}$$

(b) A zero magnitude says that the length of the vector is zero; thus, each component must be zero.

Assess: It stands to reason that a vector can have a nonzero magnitude with one component zero as long as the other one isn't. It also makes sense that for the magnitude of the vector to be zero *all* the components must be zero.

Q3.3. Reason: Consider two vectors $\vec{A}$ and $\vec{B}$. Their sum can be found using the method of algebraic addition. In Question 3.2 we found that the components of the zero vector are both zero. The components of the resultant of $\vec{A}$ and $\vec{B}$ must then be zero also. So

$$R_x = A_x + B_x = 0$$

$$R_y = A_y + B_y = 0$$

Solving for the components of $\vec{B}$ in terms of $\vec{A}$ gives $B_x = -A_x$ and $B_y = -A_y$. Then the magnitude of $\vec{B}$ is $\sqrt{(B_x)^2 + (B_y)^2} = \sqrt{(-A_x)^2 + (-A_y)^2} = \sqrt{(A_x)^2 + (A_y)^2}$. So then the magnitude of $\vec{B}$ is exactly equal to the magnitude of $\vec{A}$.

Assess: For two vectors to add to zero, the vectors must have exactly the same magnitude and point in opposite directions.

Q3.5. Reason: The ones that are constant are v_x, a_x, and a_y. Furthermore, a_x is not only constant, it is zero.

Assess: There are instants when other quantities can be zero, but not throughout the flight. Remember that $a_y = -g$ throughout the flight and that v_x is constant; that is, projectile motion is nothing more than the combination of two simple kinds of motion: constant horizontal velocity and constant vertical acceleration.

Q3.7. Reason: By extending their legs forward, the runners increase their time in the air. As you will learn in Chapter 7, the "center of mass" of a projectile follows a parabolic path. By raising their feet so that their feet are closer to their center of mass, the runners increase the time it takes for their feet to hit the ground. By increasing their time of flight, they increase their range. Also, having their feet ahead of them means that their feet will land ahead of where they would have landed otherwise.

Assess: By simply moving their feet, runners can change their time of flight and change the spot where their feet land.

Q3.9. Reason: The claim is slightly misleading, since the passenger cannot walk at a speed in excess of 500 mph due to her own efforts relative to the walking surface (the floor of the plane in this case); but she can be walking and moving with such a speed relative to the ground thousands of feet below.

Assess: It is important to specify the coordinate system when reporting velocities.

Q3.11. Reason: The acceleration is due to gravity, so the acceleration will always act to pull the cars back down the ramp. Since the roller coaster is constrained to move along the ramp, the acceleration must be along the ramp. So in all three cases the acceleration is downward along the ramp.

Assess: Gravity always acts, even if motion is constrained by an inclined ramp. See Figure 3.22 in the text.

Q3.13. Reason: The cyclist's speed may be constant, but the direction of her motion is always changing. Since the direction of her velocity vector is constantly changing, she is always accelerating. See Figure 3.39 in the text.

Assess: Acceleration is caused by any change in velocity, either in magnitude or direction. In circular motion, the acceleration is always towards the center of the circle and is called centripetal acceleration.

Q3.15. Reason: Since the plane is moving in a circle and constantly changing direction, the plane is constantly accelerating. At any point along its motion, even directly north, the plane is accelerating. For circular motion, the direction of the acceleration is always toward the center of the circle. When the plane is headed directly north, the plane's acceleration vector points directly east. See the figure below.

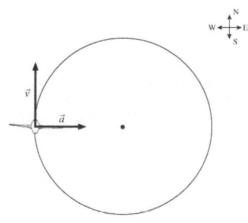

Assess: In circular motion, there is a centripetal acceleration that always points toward the center of the circle.

Multiple Choice Questions

Q3.17. Reason: The longest vector will be obtained by turning $\vec{C}$ around or by turning $\vec{A}$ around so that the two point in the same direction. The choices A, C and D all have $\vec{A}$ and $\vec{C}$ added together. B is the only choice in which the two vectors are subtracted and not added together. Since $\vec{B}$ is perpendicular to $\vec{A}$ and $\vec{C}$, we will get a vector of the same length whether we add or subtract $\vec{B}$ from the other two. See the figure for the lengths of the different vector combinations.

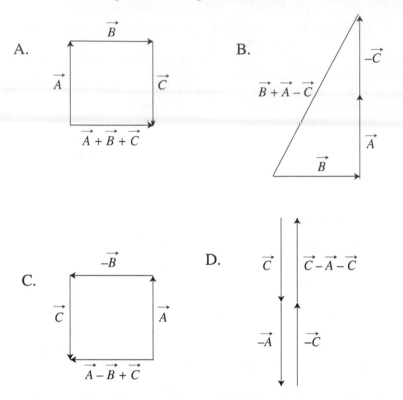

Assess: A longer vector can be created by adding two vectors which point in the same direction.

Q3.19. Reason: The gas pedal can be considered an "accelerator" because it can change the velocity of the car. So can any other controls in the car that change the velocity of the car. The brakes certainly can change the velocity by slowing the car. The steering wheel also can change the velocity by changing the direction of travel. The gear shift can also change the speed (shifting to a lower gear can slow the car).

So the answer is D, all of the above.

Assess: When driving on a straight road at constant speed the gas pedal is not then acting as an "accelerator." You have to keep your foot on the gas pedal just to keep the velocity constant, and so, in that scenario, the gas pedal is a nonaccelerator.

This question certainly highlights the difference in language between everyday usage and the more specific physics usage. It pays to know your audience!

Q3.21. Reason: (a) The ball is going along the trajectory, so the best choice for the velocity at position 2 is D.

(b) The direction of the acceleration is not related to the direction of the velocity—only the direction of the *change* in velocity. The ball is in free fall, and so its acceleration is down, just like the acceleration of all other objects in free fall. The best choice is A. This does, mean, however, that the *change* in velocity vectors ($\Delta \vec{v}$) must also be down.

(c) The ball at position 3 is moving horizontally (the vertical component is zero for an instant), so choice C is best.

(d) The same argument for the acceleration at position 2 applies at position 3; the acceleration is down. So the answer is A.

Assess: Galileo taught us the law of falling bodies: "All bodies in free fall (projectiles) have the same acceleration." The ball is in free fall at both position 2 and position 3 so the accelerations are the same, regardless of the fact that the velocities are in different directions.

Q3.23. Reason: The key to projectile motion problems is to realize that the motion in the x-coordinate is independent of the motion in the y-coordinate. We can solve an equation in one of these directions and use the results in an equation for the other direction. For example, Δt is the same for the horizontal and vertical components of the motion.

(a) First find the horizontal component of the velocity, and, realizing it will be constant, find the time to impact.

$$(v_x)_i = v_i \cos\theta = (89 \text{ m/s})\cos 40° = 68.2 \text{ m/s}$$

$$\text{time} = \frac{\text{distance}}{\text{speed}} = \frac{300 \text{ m}}{68.2 \text{ m/s}} = 4.4 \text{ s}$$

So the correct choice is C.

(b) The vertical component of the initial speed is

$$(v_y)_i - v_i \sin\theta = (89 \text{ m/s})\sin 40° = 57.2 \text{ m/s}$$

Now that we know $\Delta t = 4.4$s and $(v_y)_i = 57.2$ m/s we can solve for h (which is y_f).

$$y_f = y_i + (v_y)_i \Delta t - \frac{1}{2}g(\Delta t)^2 = 0.0 \text{ m} + (57.2 \text{ m/s})(4.4 \text{ s}) - \frac{1}{2}(9.8 \text{ m/s}^2)(4.4 \text{ s})^2 = 157 \text{ m} \approx 160 \text{ m}$$

So the correct choice is D.

Assess: The answers to both parts seem reasonable; in either case if we had been off by a factor of 10 in either direction we would think the result not realistic.

Q3.25. Reason: "To the nearest second" means we don't even need a calculator if we recall that $\sin 30° = \frac{1}{2}$. We can also assume no air resistance. The vertical component of the initial velocity is $(v_y)_i = v_i \sin\theta = (20 \text{ m/s})(\frac{1}{2})$, so we can analyze this as if the projectile had gone *straight up* with an initial velocity of $(v_y)_i = 10$ m/s.

Understanding that $a_y = -g \approx -10$ m/s^2 means that the velocity changes by 10 m/s^2 each second. So after 1 s the ball has lost 10 m/s of vertical speed, which makes its vertical speed zero (and consequently it is at the top of the trajectory). We ignore air resistance and say the motion is symmetric—it will take as long to come down as it did to go up, which is one more second. The total is therefore 2 s and the correct choice is B.

Assess: The value of g is within about 2% of 10 m/s^2, so when we only want one significant figure we can use that value for very easy calculations. Even when you want more significant figures, it is nice to round g to 10 m/s^2 and do a quick mental calculation as an assessment check of your more precise calculator work.

Q3.27. Reason: The magnitude of the centripetal acceleration is

$$a_c = \frac{v^2}{r}$$

where we want to solve for r:

$$r = \frac{v^2}{a_c} = \frac{(4.0 \text{ m/s})^2}{2.0 \text{ m/s}^2} = 8.0 \text{ m}$$

This is r, but the diameter is twice the radius $d = 16$ m, so the correct choice is D.

Assess: Think about Ferris wheels you have been on. One with a radius of 16 m would be reasonable without being overly large.

Problems

P3.1. Prepare: (a) To find $\vec{A} + \vec{B}$ we place the tail of vector $\vec{B}$ on the tip of vector $\vec{A}$ and then connect vector $\vec{A}$'s tail with vector $\vec{B}$'s tip.

(b) To find $\vec{A} - \vec{B}$ we note that $\vec{A} - \vec{B} = \vec{A} + (-\vec{B})$. We place the tail of vector $-\vec{B}$ on the tip of vector $\vec{A}$ and then connect vector $\vec{A}$'s tail with the tip of vector $-\vec{B}$.

Solve:

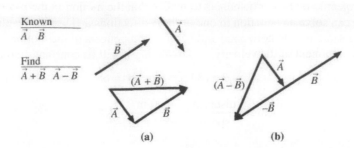

(a)   **(b)**

P3.3. Prepare: We can find the positions and velocity and acceleration vectors using a motion diagram.

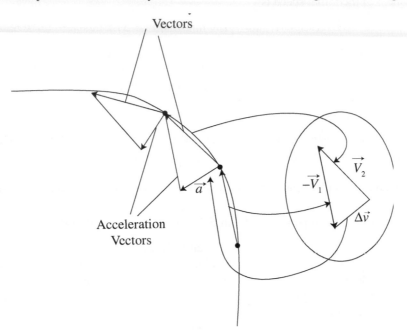

Solve: The figure gives several points along the car's path. The velocity vectors are obtained by connecting successive dots. The acceleration vectors are obtained by subtracting successive velocity vectors. The acceleration vectors point toward the center of the diagram.

Assess: Notice that the acceleration points toward the center of the turn. As you will learn in Chapter 4, whenever your car accelerates, you feel like you are being pushed the opposite way. This is why you feel like you are being pushed away from the center of a turn.

P3.5. Prepare: Acceleration is found by the method of Tactics Box 3.2.

Solve: The acceleration vector at each location points directly toward the center of the Ferris wheel's circular motion.

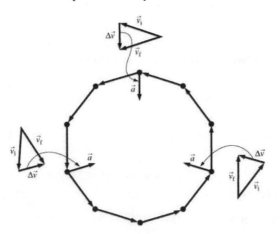

Assess: As we will learn later, this acceleration that is directed toward the center is called centripetal acceleration.

P3.7. Prepare: The figure below shows the components v_x and v_y, and the angle θ. We will use Tactics Box 3.3 to find the sign attached to the components of a vector.

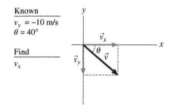

Solve: We have,

$$v_y = -v\sin40°, \quad \text{or} \quad -10 \text{ m/s} = -v\sin40°, \quad \text{or} \quad v = 15.56 \text{ m/s}.$$

Thus the x-component is $v_x = v\cos40° = (15.56 \text{ m/s})\cos40° = 12 \text{ m/s}$.
    Assess: Note that we had to insert the minus sign manually with v_y since the vector is in the fourth quadrant.

P3.9. Prepare: The figure below shows the components $v_\parallel$ and $v_\perp$, and the angle θ. We will use Tactics Box 3.3 to find the sign attached to the components of a vector.

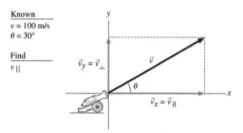

Solve: We have $\vec{v} = \vec{v}_x + \vec{v}_y = \vec{v}_\parallel + \vec{v}_\perp$. Thus, $v_\parallel = v\cos\theta = (100 \text{ m/s})\cos 30° = 87 \text{ m/s}$.
    Assess: For the small angle of 30°, the obtained value of 87 m/s for the horizontal component is reasonable.

P3.11. Prepare: We will follow rules given in the Tactics Box 3.3.

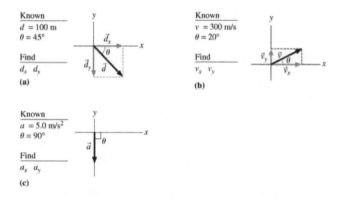

Solve: (a) Vector $\vec{d}$ points to the right and down, so the components d_x and d_y and are positive and negative, respectively:

$$d_x = d\cos\theta = (100 \text{ m})\cos45° = 70.7 \text{ m} \qquad d_y = -d\sin\theta = -(100 \text{ m})\sin45° = -71 \text{ m}$$

(b) Vector $\vec{v}$ points to the right and up, so the components v_x and v_y are both positive:

$$v_x = v\cos\theta = (300 \text{ m/s})\cos20° = 280 \text{ m/s} \qquad v_y = v\sin\theta = (300 \text{ m/s})\sin20° = 100 \text{ m/s}$$

(c) Vector $\vec{a}$ has the following components:

$$a_x = -a\cos\theta = -(5.0 \text{ m/s}^2)\cos90° = 0 \text{ m/s}^2 \qquad a_y = -a\sin\theta = -(5.0 \text{ m/s}^2)\sin90° = -5.0 \text{ m/s}^2$$

Assess: The components have same units as the vectors. Note the minus signs we have manually inserted according to the Tactics Box 3.3.

P3.13. Prepare: We will draw the vectors to scale as best we can and label the angles from the positive *x*-axis (positive angles go CCW). We also use Equations 3.12 and 3.13. Make sure your calculator is in degree mode.
  Solve: (a)

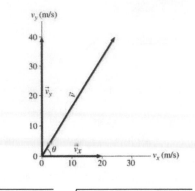

$$v = \sqrt{(v_x)^2 + (v_y)^2} = \sqrt{(20 \text{ m/s})^2 + (40 \text{ m/s})^2} = 45 \text{ m/s}$$

$$\theta = \tan^{-1}\left(\frac{v_y}{v_x}\right) = \tan^{-1}\left(\frac{40 \text{ m/s}}{20 \text{ m/s}}\right) = \tan^{-1}(2) = 63°$$

(b)

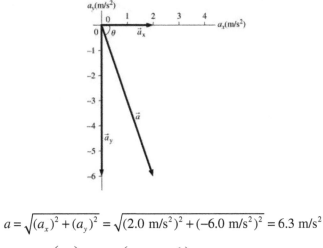

$$a = \sqrt{(a_x)^2 + (a_y)^2} = \sqrt{(2.0 \text{ m/s}^2)^2 + (-6.0 \text{ m/s}^2)^2} = 6.3 \text{ m/s}^2$$

$$\theta = \tan^{-1}\left(\frac{a_y}{a_x}\right) = \tan^{-1}\left(\frac{-6.0 \text{ m/s}^2}{2.0 \text{ m/s}^2}\right) = \tan^{-1}(-3) = -72°$$

Assess: In each case the magnitude is longer than either component, as is required for the hypotenuse of a right triangle. The negative angle in part **(b)** corresponds to a clockwise direction from the positive *x*-axis.

P3.15. Prepare: Assume you start at the spot labeled home and that Strawberry Fields and Penny Lane are perpendicular. We will not assume that the lengths in the figure are to scale.
  We will write each vector in component form for easy addition. We will then need to take the sum and compute the magnitude and direction to report the final answer.
  The Strawberry Fields vector is $\vec{S} = (S_x, S_y) = (2.0 \text{ km}, 0.0 \text{ km})$.
  The Penny Lane vector is $\vec{P} = (P_x, P_y) = (0.0 \text{ km}, -1.0 \text{ km})$.
  The Abbey Road vector is

$$\vec{A} = (A_x, A_y)$$
$$= (A\cos\phi, A\sin\phi)$$
$$= (4.0 \text{ km}\sin(40°), 4.0 \text{ km}\cos(40°))$$
$$= (2.6 \text{ km}, 3.1 \text{ km})$$

(where the cos and sin are interchanged from Equation 3.10 because θ is measured from the *y*-axis).

Solve: Now add the respective components of the three vectors to get the components of the total displacement.

$$\vec{S} = (2.0 \text{ km}, 0.0 \text{ km})$$
$$\vec{P} = (0.0 \text{ km}, -1.0 \text{ km})$$
$$\underline{\vec{A} = (2.6 \text{ km}, 3.1 \text{ km})}$$
$$\vec{D} = (4.6 \text{ km}, 2.1 \text{ km})$$

Now use Equations 3.12 and 3.13.

$$D = \sqrt{(D_x)^2 + (D_y)^2} = \sqrt{(4.6 \text{ km})^2 + (2.1 \text{ km})^2} = 5.1 \text{ km}$$

$$\theta = \tan^{-1}\left(\frac{D_y}{D_x}\right) = \tan^{-1}\left(\frac{2.1 \text{ km}}{4.6 \text{ km}}\right) = 25°$$

where θ is measured ccw from the positive x-axis.

Assess: Even though the figure may not be precisely to scale, it, or one you draw, would convince you that the answers for the magnitude and direction are both reasonable.

P3.17. Prepare: A visual overview of the car's motion that includes a pictorial representation, a motion diagram, and a list of values is shown below. We have labeled the x-axis along the incline. Note that the problem "ends" at a turning point, where the car has an instantaneous speed of 0 m/s before rolling back down. The rolling back motion is *not* part of this problem. If we assume the car rolls without friction, then we have motion on a frictionless inclined plane with acceleration $a = -g \sin \theta = -g \sin \theta = -5.0° = -0.854 \text{ m/s}^2$.

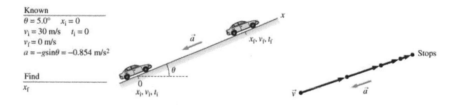

Solve: Constant acceleration kinematics gives

$$v_f^2 = v_i^2 + 2a(x_f - x_i) \Rightarrow 0 = v_i^2 + 2ax_f \Rightarrow x_f = -\frac{v_i^2}{2a} = -\frac{(30 \text{ m/s})^2}{2(-0.854 \text{ m/s}^2)} = 530 \text{ m}$$

Notice how the two negatives canceled to give a positive value for x_f.

Assess: We must include the minus sign because the $\vec{a}$ vector points *down* the slope, which is in the negative x-direction.

P3.19. Prepare: Make a sketch with tilted axes with the x-axis parallel to the ramp and the angle of inclination labeled. We must also make a bold assumption that the piano rolls down as if it were an object sliding down with no friction.

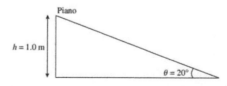

As part of the preparation, compute the length of the ramp in the new tilted x-y coordinates.

$$L = \frac{h}{\sin \theta} = \frac{1.0 \text{ m}}{\sin 20°} = 2.9 \text{ m}$$

The acceleration in the new coordinate system will be $a_x = g\sin\theta = (9.8 \text{ m/s}^2)\sin 20° = 3.4 \text{ m/s}^2$.

Solve: Since this is a case of constant acceleration we can use the second equation from Table 2.4 with $x_i = 0.0$ m and $(v_x)_i = 0.0$ m/s.

$$x_f = \frac{1}{2}a_x(\Delta t)^2$$

Solve for Δt, and use $x_f = 2.9$ m and $a_x = 3.4$ m/s^2, which we obtained previously.

$$\Delta t = \sqrt{\frac{2x_f}{a_x}} = \sqrt{\frac{2(2.9 \text{ m})}{3.4 \text{ m/s}^2}} = 1.3 \text{ s}$$

Assess: They may catch it if they have quick reactions, but the piano will be moving 4.5 m/s when it reaches the bottom.

P3.21. Prepare: For everyday speeds we can use Equation 3.21 to find relative velocities. We will use a subscript A for Anita and a 1 and a 2 for the respective balls; we also use a subscript G for the ground. We will consider all motion in this problem to be along the x-axis (ignore the vertical motion including the fact that the balls also fall under the influence of gravity) and so we drop the x subscript.

It is also worth noting that interchanging the order of the subscripts merely introduces a negative sign. For example, $v_{AG} = 5$ m/s, so $v_{GA} = -5$ m/s.

"According to Anita" means "relative to Anita."

Solve: For ball 1:

$$v_{1A} = v_{1G} + v_{GA} = 10 \text{ m/s} + (-5 \text{ m/s}) = 5 \text{ m/s}$$

For ball 2:

$$v_{2A} = v_{2G} + v_{GA} = -10 \text{ m/s} + (-5 \text{ m/s}) = -15 \text{ m/s}$$

The speed is the magnitude of the velocity, so the speed of ball 2 is 15 m/s.

Assess: You can see that at low speeds velocities simply add or subtract, as the case may be. Mentally put yourself in Anita's place, and you will confirm that she sees ball 1 catching up to her at only 5 m/s while she sees ball 2 speed past her at 15 m/s.

P3.23. Prepare: Assume motion along the x-direction. The velocity of the boat relative to the ground is $(v_x)_{bg}$; the velocity of the boat relative to the water is $(v_x)_{bw}$; and the velocity of the water relative to the ground is $(v_x)_{wg}$. We will use the technique of Equation 3.21: $(\vec{v}_x)_{bg} = (\vec{v}_x)_{bw} + (\vec{v}_x)_{wg}$

Solve: For travel down the river,

$$(v_x)_{bg} = -(v_x)_{bw} + (v_x)_{wg} = \frac{30 \text{ km}}{3.0 \text{ hr}} = 10.0 \text{ km/hr}$$

For travel up the river,

$$(v_x)_{bg} = -(v_x)_{bw} + (v_x)_{wg} = -\left(\frac{30 \text{ km}}{5.0 \text{ hr}}\right) = -6.0 \text{ km/hr}$$

Adding these two equations yields $(v_x)_{wg} = 2.0$ km/hr. That is, the velocity of the flowing river relative to the earth is 2.0 km/hr.

Assess: Note that the speed of the boat relative to the water downstream and upstream are the same.

P3.25. Prepare: First we can find the velocity of the skydiver with respect to the ground using the idea of cancelling subscripts. Then, knowing the components of this vector, we can find the angle of the vector with the vertical.

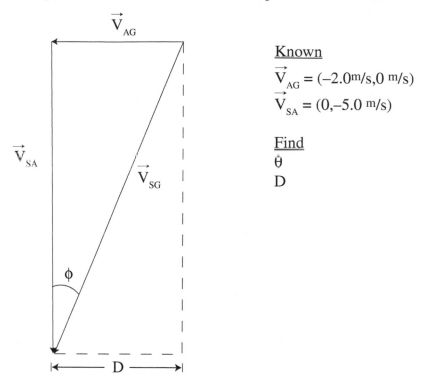

Known

$$\vec{V}_{AG} = (-2.0 \text{m/s}, 0 \text{ m/s})$$

$$\vec{V}_{SA} = (0, -5.0 \text{ m/s})$$

Find

θ

D

Solve: (a) The velocity of the skydiver relative to the ground, $\vec{v}_{SG}$, can be found since we know his velocity relative to the air: $\vec{v}_{SA} = (0, -5.0 \text{ m/s})$ and the velocity of the air relative to the ground, $\vec{v}_{AG} = (-2.0 \text{ m/s}, 0 \text{ m/s})$:

$$\vec{v}_{SG} = \vec{v}_{SA} + \vec{v}_{AG} = (0 \text{ m/s}, -5.0 \text{ m/s}) + (-2.0 \text{ m/s}, 0 \text{ m/s}) = (-2.0 \text{ m/s}, -5.0 \text{ m/s})$$

The figure shows the three velocity vectors. The skydiver's velocity vector relative to the ground forms the angle ϕ with the vertical, where:

$$\phi = \tan^{-1}\left(\frac{|v_x|}{|v_y|}\right) = \tan^{-1}\left(\frac{2.0 \text{ m/s}}{5.0 \text{m/s}}\right) = 22°$$

He falls at an angle of 22° to the vertical.
  (b) The time the skydiver takes to fall is given by:

$$\Delta t = \frac{\Delta y}{v_y} = \frac{-1000 \text{ m}}{-5.0 \text{ m/s}} = 200 \text{ s}$$

The wind causes the skydiver to drift horizontally at a rate of 2.0 m/s and he falls for 200 s. By the time he lands, he has drifted through a distance d, which is a product of drift speed and time:

$$d = (2.0 \text{ m/s})(200 \text{ s}) = 400 \text{ m}$$

He will miss his desired landing spot by 400 m.
  Assess: Notice that the skydiver fell at a constant speed whereas an object in free fall accelerates. This is due to the presence of air resistance. The constant speed at which an object falls when there is air resistance is called "terminal speed."

P3.27. Prepare: We will assume the ball is in free fall (i.e., we neglect air resistance). The trajectory of a projectile is a parabola because it is a combination of constant horizontal velocity ($a_x = 0.0 \text{ m/s}^2$) and constant vertical acceleration ($a_y = -g$). In this case we see only half of the parabola.
  The initial speed given is all in the horizontal direction, that is, $(v_x)_i = 5.0 \text{ m/s}$ and $(v_y)_i = 0.0 \text{ m/s}$.

Solve:

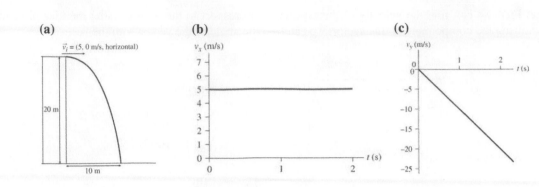

(d) This is a two-step problem. We first use the vertical direction to determine the time it takes, then plug that into the equation for the horizontal direction.

$$\Delta y = \frac{1}{2} a_y (\Delta t)^2$$

$$\Delta t = \sqrt{\frac{2\Delta y}{a_y}} = \sqrt{\frac{2(-20 \text{ m})}{-9.8 \text{ m/s}^2}} = 2.0 \text{ s}$$

We we use the 2.0 s in the equation for the horizontal motion.

$$\Delta x = v_x \Delta t = (5.0 \text{ m/s})(2.0 \text{ s}) = 10 \text{ m}$$

Assess: The answers seem reasonable, and we would get the same answers to two significant figures in a quick mental calculation using $g \approx 10 \text{ m/s}^2$. In fact, I did this before computing the algebra so I would know how to scale the graphs.

P3.29. Prepare: This problem is asking us for a range so we need the horizontal component of velocity, v_x, and the time of flight, Δt. The time of flight, in turn, depends on the initial vertical component of velocity, $(v_y)_i$ and the overall vertical displacement of the rock, Δy.

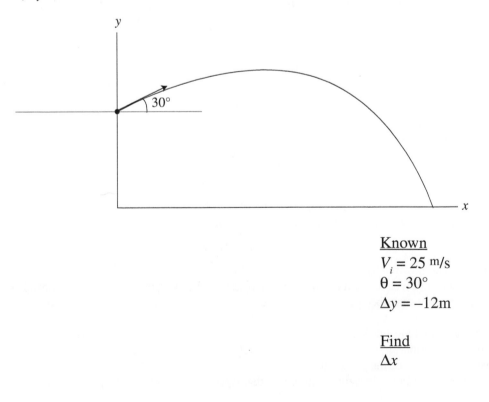

Known
$V_i = 25$ m/s
$\theta = 30°$
$\Delta y = -12$m

Find
Δx

Solve: We first find v_x and $(v_y)_i$ using Equations 3.24:

$$v_x = v_i \cos\theta = (25 \text{ m/s})\cos 30° = 21.7 \text{ m/s}$$

$$(v_y)_i = v_i \sin\theta = (25 \text{ m/s})\sin30° = 12.5 \text{ m/s}$$

Using the equation which relates vertical velocity, acceleration and displacement: $(v_y)_f^2 - (v_y)_i^2 = 2a_y\Delta y$, we can find the final vertical component of velocity:

$$(v_y)_f^2 - (12.5 \text{ m/s})^2 = 2(-9.8 \text{ m/s}^2)(-12 \text{ m})$$

This equation has two solutions: $(v_y)_f = \pm 19.8$ m/s. We choose the negative solution since the rock is descending when it lands. Now we can find the time of flight using $a_y = \Delta v_y/\Delta t$:

$$\Delta t = \Delta v_y / a_y = (-19.8 \text{ m/s} - 12.5 \text{ m/s})/(-9.8 \text{ m/s}^2) = 3.29 \text{ s}$$

Finally, the range of the rock is given by $\Delta x = v_x\Delta t$:

$$\Delta x = v_x \Delta t = (21.7 \text{ m/s})(3.29 \text{ s}) = 71 \text{ m}$$

The rock lands 71 m from the castle wall.

   Assess: Notice that the mass of the rock was not involved. So if this had been a baseball thrown from a tower, it would have gone equally far—about three quarters of a football field.

P3.31. Prepare: We will apply the constant-acceleration kinematic equations to the horizontal and vertical motions as described by Equation 3.24. The effect of air resistance on the motion of the bullet is neglected.

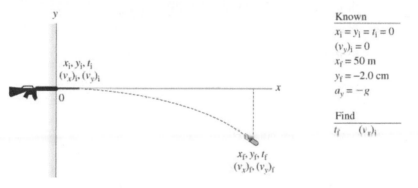

Solve: (a) Using $y_f = y_i + (v_y)_i(t_f - t_i) + \dfrac{1}{2} a_y(t_f - t_i)^2$, we obtain

$$(-2.0 \times 10^{-2} \text{ m}) = 0 \text{ m} + 0 \text{ m} + \frac{1}{2}(-9.8 \text{ m/s}^2)(t_f - 0 \text{ s})^2 \Rightarrow t_f = 0.0639 \text{ s}$$

(b) Using $x_f = x_i + (v_x)_i(t_f - t_i) + \dfrac{1}{2} a_x(t_f - t_i)^2$,

$$(50 \text{ m}) = 0 \text{ m} + (v_x)_i(0.0639 \text{ s} - 0 \text{ s}) + 0 \text{ m} \Rightarrow (v_x)_i = 782 \text{ m/s}$$

   Assess: The bullet falls 2 cm during a horizontal displacement of 50 m. This implies a large initial velocity, and a value of 782 m/s is not surprising.

P3.33. Prepare: The golf ball is a particle following projectile motion. We will apply the constant-acceleration kinematic equations to the horizontal and vertical motions as described by Equation 3.24.

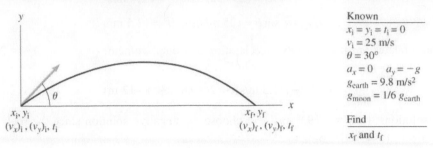

Known
$x_i = y_i = t_i = 0$
$v_i = 25$ m/s
$\theta = 30°$
$a_x = 0 \quad a_y = -g$
$g_{earth} = 9.8$ m/s^2
$g_{moon} = 1/6\ g_{earth}$

Find
x_f and t_f

Solve: (a) The distance traveled is $x_f = (v_i)_x t_f = v_i \cos\theta \times t_f$. The flight time is found from the y-equation, using the fact that the ball starts and ends at $y = 0$:

$$y_f - y_i = 0 = v_i \sin\theta\, t_f - \frac{1}{2}gt_f^2 = (v_i \sin\theta - \frac{1}{2}gt_f)t_f \Rightarrow t_f = \frac{2v_i \sin\theta}{g}$$

Thus the distance traveled is

$$x_f = v_i \cos\theta \times \frac{2v_i \sin\theta}{g} = \frac{2v_i^2 \sin\theta \cos\theta}{g}$$

For $\theta = 30°$, the distances are

$$(x_f)_{earth} = \frac{2v_i^2 \sin\theta \cos\theta}{g_{earth}} = \frac{2(25\text{ m/s})^2 \sin30°\cos30°}{9.80\text{ m/s}^2} = 55.2\text{ m}$$

$$(x_f)_{moon} = \frac{2v_i^2 \sin\theta \cos\theta}{g_{moon}} = \frac{2v_i^2 \sin\theta \cos\theta}{\frac{1}{6}g_{earth}} = 6 \times \frac{2v_i^2 \sin\theta \cos\theta}{g_{earth}} = 6(x_f)_{earth} = 331.2\text{ m}$$

The flight times are

$$(t_f)_{earth} = \frac{2v_i \sin\theta}{g_{earth}} = 2.55\text{ s}$$

$$(t_f)_{moon} = \frac{2v_i \sin\theta}{g_{moon}} = \frac{2v_i \sin\theta}{\frac{1}{6}g_{earth}} = 6(t_f)_{earth} = 15.30\text{ s}$$

The ball spends 15.30 s – 2.55 s = 12.75 s = 13 s longer in flight on the moon.
  (b) From part **(a)**, the distance traveled on the moon is 331 m or 330 m to two significant figures.
  (c) From part **(a)**, the golf ball travels 331.2 m – 55.2 m = 276 m farther on the moon than on earth.

P3.35. Prepare: We need to convert the 5400 rpm to different units and then find the period which is the inverse of frequency.
  Solve: (a) The hard disk's frequency can be converted as follows:

$$5400\frac{rev}{min} = 5400\frac{rev}{min}\left(\frac{1\text{ min}}{60\text{ sec}}\right) = 90\frac{rev}{sec}$$

Its frequency is 90 rev/s.
  (b) Rewriting Equation 3.26, we have:

$$T = \frac{1}{f} = \frac{1}{90\text{ rev/s}} = 11\text{ ms}$$

Its period is 11 ms.
  Assess: This is about the rate that the engine in a car turns if it is straining. So an automobile engine completes a cycle every 10 or 20 ms.

P3.37. Prepare: We are asked to find period, speed and acceleration. Period and frequency are inverses according to Equation 3.26. To find speed we need to know the distance traveled by the speck in one period. Then the acceleration is given by Equation 3.30.

Solve: (a) The disk's frequency can be converted as:

$$10,000 \ \frac{rev}{min} = 10,000 \ \frac{rev}{min} \left(\frac{1 \ min}{60 \ sec}\right) = 167 \ \frac{rev}{sec}$$

The period is the inverse of the frequency:

$$T = \frac{1}{f} = \frac{1}{167 \ rev/s} = 6.00 \ ms$$

(b) The speed of the speck equals the circumference of its orbit divided by the period:

$$v = \frac{2\pi r}{T} = \frac{2\pi(6.0 \ cm)}{6.00 \ ms}\left(\frac{1000 \ ms}{1 \ s}\right)\left(\frac{1 \ m}{100 \ cm}\right) = 62.8 \ m/s,$$

which rounds to 63 m/s.

(c) From Equation 3.30, the acceleration of the speck is given by v^2/r:

$$a = \frac{v^2}{r} = \frac{(62.8 \ m/s)^2}{6.0 \ cm}\left(\frac{100 \ cm}{1 \ m}\right) = 65,700 \ m/s^2,$$

which rounds to 66,000 m/s². In units of g, this is:

$$65,700 \ m/s^2 = 65,700 \ m/s^2\left(\frac{1g}{9.8 \ m/s^2}\right) = 6,700g$$

Assess: The speed and acceleration of the edge of a CD are remarkable. The speed, 63 m/s, is about 140 mi/hr. As you will learn in chapter 4, very large forces are necessary to create large accelerations like 6,700g.

P3.39. Prepare: Examine the formula carefully.

$$a - \frac{v^2}{r}$$

Before plugging in numbers, notice that if the speed is held constant (as in part **(a)**), then a and r are inversely proportional to each other: doubling one halves the other. And if r is held constant (as in part **(b)**), then there is a square relationship between a and v: doubling v quadruples a.

Solve: It is convenient to use ratios to solve this problem, because we never have to know any specific values for r or v. We'll use unprimed variables for the original case ($a = 8.0 \ m/s^2$), and primed variables for the new cases.

(a) With the speed held constant, $v' = v$ but $r' = 2r$.

$$\frac{a'}{a} = \frac{\dfrac{v'^2}{r'}}{\dfrac{v^2}{r}} = \frac{\dfrac{v^2}{2r}}{\dfrac{v^2}{r}} = \frac{1}{2}$$

So $a' = \dfrac{1}{2}a = \dfrac{1}{2}(8.0 \ m/s^2) = 4.0 \ m/s^2$

(b) With the radius held constant, $r'' = r$ but $v'' = 2v$.

$$\frac{a''}{a} = \frac{\dfrac{v''^2}{r''}}{\dfrac{v^2}{r}} = \frac{\dfrac{(2v)^2}{r}}{\dfrac{v^2}{r}} = 2^2 = 4$$

So $a'' = 4a = 4(8.0 \ m/s^2) = 32 \ m/s^2$

Assess: Please familiarize yourself with this ratio technique and look for opportunities to use it. Again, the advantage is not needing to know any specific values of r or v—not only not having to know them, but realizing that the result is independent of them.

The daily life lesson is that driving around a curve with a larger radius produces gentler acceleration. Going around a given curve faster, however, requires a much larger acceleration (produced by the friction between the tires and the road), and the relationship is squared. If your tires are bald or the road slippery there won't be enough friction to keep you on the road if you go too fast. And remember that it is a squared relationship, so going around a curve twice as fast requires four times as much friction.

P3.41. Prepare: The magnitude of centripetal acceleration is given in Equation 3.33.
Solve: The centripetal acceleration is given as 1.5 times the acceleration of gravity, so

$$a = (1.5)(9.80 \text{ m/s}^2) = 15 \text{ m/s}^2$$

Using Equation 3.33, the radius of the turn is given by

$$r = \frac{v^2}{a} = \frac{(20 \text{ m/s})^2}{15 \text{ m/s}^2} = 27 \text{ m}$$

Assess: This seems reasonable.

P3.43. Prepare: The vectors $\vec{A}$, $\vec{B}$, and $\vec{D} = \vec{A} - \vec{B}$ are shown. Because $\vec{A} = \vec{A}_x + \vec{A}_y$ and $\vec{B} = \vec{B}_x + \vec{B}_y$, the components of the resultant vector are $D_x = A_x - B_x$ and $D_y = A_y - B_y$.

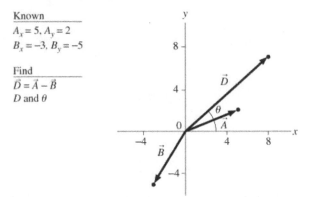

Known
$A_x = 5, A_y = 2$
$B_x = -3, B_y = -5$

Find
$\vec{D} = \vec{A} - \vec{B}$
D and θ

Solve: (a) With $A_x = 5$, $A_y = 2$, $B_x = -3$, and $B_y = -5$, we have $D_x = 8$ and $D_y = 7$.
(b) Vectors $\vec{A}$, $\vec{B}$, and $\vec{D}$ are shown in the above figure.
(c) Since $D_x = 8$ and $D_y = 7$, the magnitude and direction of $\vec{D}$ are

$$D = \sqrt{(8)^2 + (7)^2} = 11 \qquad \theta = \tan^{-1}\left(\frac{D_y}{D_x}\right) = \tan^{-1}\left(\frac{7}{8}\right) = 41°$$

Assess: Since $|D_y| < |D_x|$, the angle θ is less than 45°, as it should be.

P3.45. Prepare: Refer to Figure P3.43 in your textbook. Because $\vec{A} = \vec{A}_x + \vec{A}_y$, $\vec{B} = \vec{B}_x + \vec{B}_y$, and $\vec{C} = \vec{C}_x + \vec{C}_y$, the components of the resultant vector are $D_x = A_x + B_x + C_x$ and $D_y = A_y + B_y + C_y$. D_x and D_y are given, and we will read the components of $\vec{A}$ and $\vec{C}$ off Figure P3.43.

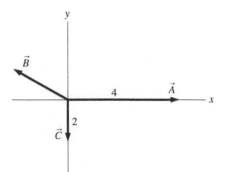

Solve: (a) $A_x = 4$, $C_x = 0$, and $D_x = 2$, so $B_x = A_x - C_x + D_x = -2$. Similarly, $A_y = 0$, $C_y = -2$, and $D_y = 0$, so $B_y = -A_y - C_y + D_y = 2$.
  (b) With the components in (a), $B = \sqrt{(-2)^2 + (2)^2} = 2.8$

$$\theta = \tan^{-1}\frac{B_y}{|B_x|} = \tan^{-1}\frac{2}{2} = 45°$$

Since $\vec{B}$ has a negative x-component and a positive y-component, the angle θ made by $\vec{B}$ is with the $-x$-axis and it is above the $-x$-axis.
  Assess: Since $|B_y| = |B_x|$, $\theta = 45°$, as is obtained above.

P3.47. Prepare: We need to draw a right triangle which represents the staircase. The hypotenuse is given by multiplying speed by distance, and then the other two sides are given from trigonometric ratios.

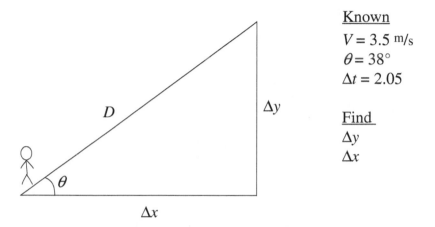

Known
$V = 3.5$ m/s
$\theta = 38°$
$\Delta t = 2.05$

Find
Δy
Δx

Solve: The distance traveled, d, is speed multiplied by time:

This is the hypotenuse of the staircase. The height gained is opposite the 38° angle and so is obtained using the sine function:

$$\Delta y = (7.0 \text{ m})\sin 38° = 4.3 \text{ m}$$

The horizontal distance traveled is adjacent to the 38° angle, so we need to use the cosine function:

$$\Delta x = (7.0 \text{ m/s})\cos 38° = 5.5 \text{ m}$$

Assess: It makes sense that the horizontal distance traveled is greater than the height gained since the angle of the stairs, 38°, is less than 45°. At that angle, the vertical and horizontal distances would have been equal.

P3.49. Prepare: In the coordinate system shown below, the mouse starts from the origin, so his initial position vector is zero. His net displacement is then just the final position vector, which is just the sum of the three vectors $\vec{A}$, $\vec{B}$, and $\vec{C}$.

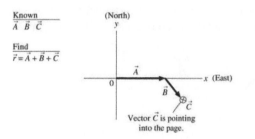

Solve: We are given $\vec{A} = (5 \text{ m, east})$ and $\vec{C} = (1 \text{ m, down})$. Using trigonometry, $\vec{B} = (3\cos 45° \text{ m, east}) + (3\sin 45° \text{ m, south})$. The total displacement is $\vec{r} = \vec{A} + \vec{B} + \vec{C} = (7.12 \text{ m, east}) + (2.12 \text{ m, south}) + (1 \text{ m, down})$.

The magnitude of $\vec{r}$ is

$$r = \sqrt{(7.12)^2 + (2.12)^2 + (1)^2}\,\text{m} = 7.5 \text{ m}$$

Assess: A displacement of 7.5 m is a reasonable displacement.

P3.51. Prepare: We draw a picture of the plane's path. The distance traveled by the plane is given by speed multiplied by time and forms the hypotenuse. The shortest distance to the equator is 100 km and this is the length of the side adjacent to the 30° angle. We can relate these two sides of a triangle using trigonometry.

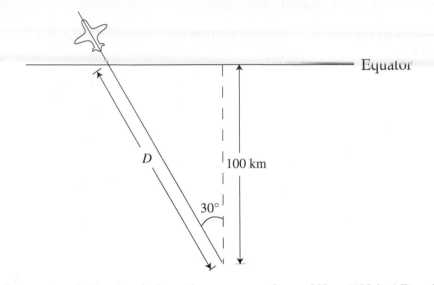

Solve: If D is the distance traveled by the airplane, then we can write cos30° = (100 km)/D and solve for the distance traveled:

$$D = (100 \text{ km})/\cos 30° = 115 \text{ km}$$

The time of flight is equal to the distance traveled divided by speed:

$$\Delta t = (115 \text{ km})/(150 \text{ km/hr}) = 0.767 \text{ hr}$$

Finally, we convert this time to minutes:

$$0.767 \text{ hr} = 0.767 \text{ hr}\left(\frac{60 \text{ min}}{1 \text{ hr}}\right) = 46 \text{ min}$$

It takes the pilot 46 min to reach the equator.

Assess: The pilot's time to reach the equator is greater than it would be if he were flying directly toward the equator. If the flight were direct, the distance would be 100 km instead of 115 km and the time of flight would be 40 min instead of 46 min.

P3.53. Prepare: The skier's motion on the horizontal, frictionless snow is not of any interest to us. The skier's speed increases down the incline due to acceleration parallel to the incline, which is equal to $g \sin 10°$. A visual overview of the skier's motion that includes a pictorial representation, a motion representation, and a list of values is shown below.

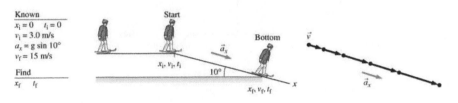

Solve: Using the following constant-acceleration kinematic equations,

$$v_f^2 = v_i^2 + 2a_x(x_f - x_i)$$

$$\Rightarrow (15 \text{ m/s})^2 = (3.0 \text{ m/s})^2 + 2(9.8 \text{ m/s}^2)\sin 10°(x_f - 0 \text{ m}) \Rightarrow x_f = 64 \text{ m}$$

$$v_f = v_i + a_x(t_f - t_i)$$

$$\Rightarrow (15 \text{ m/s}) = (3.0 \text{ m/s}) + (9.8 \text{ m/s}^2)(\sin 10°)t_f \Rightarrow t_f = 7.1 \text{ s}$$

Assess: A time of 7.1 s to cover 64 m is a reasonable value.

P3.55. Prepare: A visual overview of the puck's motion that includes a pictorial representation, a motion diagram, and a list of values is shown below.

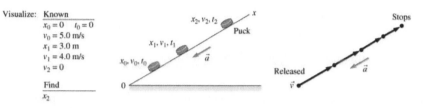

Solve: The acceleration, being the same along the incline, can be found as

$$v_1^2 = v_0^2 + 2a(x_1 - x_0) \Rightarrow (4.0 \text{ m/s})^2 = (5.0 \text{ m/s})^2 + 2a(3.0 \text{ m} - 0 \text{ m}) \Rightarrow a = -1.5 \text{ m/s}^2$$

We can also find the total time the puck takes to come to a halt as

$$v_2 = v_0 + a(t_2 - t_0) \Rightarrow 0 \text{ m/s} = (5.0 \text{ m/s}) + (-1.5 \text{ m/s}^2)t_2 \Rightarrow t_2 = 3.3 \text{ s}$$

Using the above obtained values of a and t_2, we can find x_2 as follows:

$$x_2 = x_0 + v_0(t_2 - t_0) + \frac{1}{2}a(t_2 - t_0)^2 = 0 \text{ m} + (5.0 \text{ m/s})(3.3 \text{ s}) + \frac{1}{2}(-1.5 \text{ m/s}^2)(3.3 \text{ s})^2 = 8.3 \text{ m}$$

That is, the puck goes through a displacement of 8.3 m. Since the end of the ramp is 8.5 m from the starting position x_0 and the puck stops 0.2 m or 20 cm before the ramp ends, you are not a winner.

P3.57. Prepare: Both ships have a common origin at $t = 0$ s.
  Solve: (a) The velocity vectors of the two ships are:

$$\vec{v}_A = (20 \text{ mph} \cos 30°, \text{north}) + (20 \text{ mph} \sin 30°, \text{west}) = (17.32 \text{ mph}, \text{north}) + (10.0 \text{ mph}, \text{west})$$
$$\vec{v}_B = (25 \text{ mph} \cos 20°, \text{north}) + (25 \text{ mph} \sin 20°, \text{east}) = (23.49 \text{ mph}, \text{north}) + (8.55 \text{ mph}, \text{east})$$

Since $\vec{r} = \vec{v}\Delta t$,

$$\vec{r}_A = \vec{v}_A(2 \text{ hr}) = (34.64 \text{ mph}, \text{north}) + (20.0 \text{ mph}, \text{west})$$
$$\vec{r}_B = \vec{v}_B(2 \text{ hr}) = (46.98 \text{ miles}, \text{north}) + (17.10 \text{ miles}, \text{east})$$

So, the displacement between the two ships is

$$\vec{R} = \vec{r}_A - \vec{r}_B = (12.34 \text{ miles}, \text{south}) + (37.10 \text{ miles}, \text{west}) \Rightarrow R = 39.1 \text{ miles}$$

(b) The speed of A as seen by B is: $\vec{V} = \vec{v}_A - \vec{v}_B = (6.17 \text{ mph}, \text{south}) + (18.55 \text{ mph}, \text{west}) \Rightarrow V = 19.5 \text{ mph}$.
Assess: The value of the speed is reasonable.

P3.59. Prepare: A visual overview of the ducks' motion is shown below. The resulting velocity is given by $\vec{v} = \vec{v}_{fly} + \vec{v}_{wind}$, where $\vec{v}_{wind} = 6$ m/s, east) and $\vec{v}_{fly} = (v_{fly} \sin\theta,$ west) + $(v_{fly} \cos\theta,$ south).

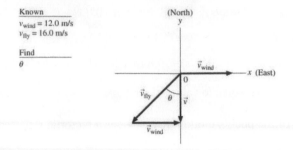

Solve: Substituting the known values we get $\vec{v} = (8$ m/s $\sin\theta,$ west) + $(8$ m/s $\cos\theta,$ south) + $(6$ m/s, east). That is, $\vec{v} = (-8$ m/s $\sin\theta,$ east) + $(8$ m/s $\cos\theta,$ south) + $(6$ m/s, east). We need to have $v_x = 0$. This means $0 = -8$ m/s $\sin\theta + 6$ m/s, so $\sin\theta = \dfrac{6}{8}$ and $\theta = 48.6°$. Thus the ducks should head 48.6° west of south.

P3.61. Prepare: A visual overview of the plane's motion is shown below. The direction the pilot must head the plane can be obtained from $\vec{v}_{pg} = \vec{v}_{pa} + \vec{v}_{ag}$, where $\vec{v}_{pa} = (v_{pa}\sin\theta,$ south) + $(v_{pa}\cos\theta,$ east), $v_{pa} = 200$ mph, $\vec{v}_{ag} = (v_{ag}\sin30°,$ north) + $(v_{ag}\cos30°,$ east), and $\vec{v}_{pg} = (v_{pg},$ east)

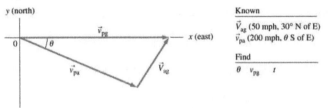

Solve: (a) Writing the equation $\vec{v}_{pg} = \vec{v}_{pa} + \vec{v}_{ag}$ in the form of components:

$(v_{pg},$ east) = [$(200$ mph $\sin\theta,$ south) + $(200$ mph $\cos\theta,$ east)] + [$(50$ mph $\sin30°,$ north) + $(50$ mph $\cos30°,$ east)]

Because $(\vec{v})_{pg}$ should have no component along north,

$$50 \sin30° - 200\sin\theta = 0 \Rightarrow \theta = 7.2°$$

(b) The pilot must head 7.18° south of east. Substituting this value of θ in the above velocity equation gives $(v_{pg},$ east) = $(200$ mph $\cos7.18°,$ east) + $(50$ mph $\cos30°,$ east) = $(240$ mph, east). At a speed of 240 mph, the trip takes $t = 600$ mi/240 mph = 2.5 hours.

P3.63. Prepare: We will apply the velocity and acceleration concepts for projectile motion as shown in Figure 3.30. A visual overview is shown below.

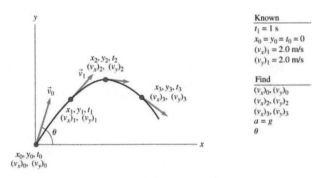

Solve: (a) We know the velocity $\vec{v}_1 = (\vec{v}_x)_1 + (\vec{v}_y)_1$ with $(v_x)_1 = 2.0$ m/s and $(v_y)_1 = 2.0$ m/s at $t = 1$ s. The ball is at its highest point at $t = 2$ s, so $v_y = 0$ m/s. The horizontal velocity is constant in projectile motion, so $v_x = 2.0$ m/s at all times.

Thus, $\vec{v}_2 = (\vec{v}_x)_2 + (\vec{v}_y)_2$, with $(v_x)_2 = 2.0$ m/s and $(v_y)_2 = 0$ m/s at $t = 2$ s. We can see that the y-component of velocity *changed* by $\Delta v_y = -2.0$ m/s between $t = 1$ s and $t = 2$ s. Because a_y is constant, v_y changes by -2.0 m/s in *any* 1-s interval. At $t = 3$ s, v_y is 2.0 m/s less than its value of 0 at $t = 2$ s. At $t = 0$ s, v_y must have been 2.0 m/s more than its value of 2.0 m/s at $t = 1$ s. Consequently, at $t = 0$ s,

$$\vec{v}_0 = (\vec{v}_x)_0 + (\vec{v}_y)_0, \text{ with } (v_x)_0 = 2.0 \text{ m/s and } (v_y)_0 = 4.0 \text{ m/s}$$

At $t = 1$ s,

$$\vec{v}_1 = (\vec{v}_x)_1 + (\vec{v}_y)_1, \text{ with } (v_x)_1 = 2.0 \text{ m/s and } (v_y)_1 = 2.0 \text{ m/s}$$

At $t = 2$ s,

$$\vec{v}_2 = (\vec{v}_x)_2 + (\vec{v}_y)_2, \text{ with } (v_x)_2 = 2.0 \text{ m/s and } (v_y)_2 = 0 \text{ m/s}$$

At $t = 3$ s,

$$\vec{v}_3 = (\vec{v}_x)_3 + (\vec{v}_y)_3, \text{ with } (v_x)_3 = 2.0 \text{ m/s and } (v_y)_3 = -2.0 \text{ m/s}$$

(b) Because v_y is changing at the rate -2.0 m/s per s, the y-component of acceleration is $a_y = -2.0$ m/s². But $a_y = -g$ for projectile motion, so the value of g on Exidor is $g = 2.0$ m/s².

(c) From part **(a)** the components of $\vec{v}_0$ are $(v_x)_0 = 2.0$ m/s and $(v_y)_0 = 4.0$ m/s. This means

$$\theta = \tan^{-1}\left(\frac{(v_y)_0}{(v_x)_0}\right) = \tan^{-1}\left(\frac{4.0 \text{ m/s}}{2.0 \text{ m/s}}\right) = 63° \text{ above} + x$$

Assess: The y-component of the velocity vector decreases from 2.0 m/s at $t = 1$ s to 0 m/s at $t = 2$ s. This gives an acceleration of -2 m/s². All the other values obtained above are also reasonable.

P3.65. Prepare: This problem is somewhat similar to Problem 3.27 with all of the initial velocity in the horizontal direction. We will use the vertical equation for constant acceleration to determine the time of flight and then see how far Captain Brady can go in that time. Of interest is the fact that we will do this two-step problem completely with variables in part **(a)** and only plug in numbers in part **(b)**.

We *could* do part **(b)** in feet (using $g = 32$ ft/s²), but to compare with the world record 100 m dash, let's convert to meters. $L = 22$ ft = 6.71 m and $h = 20$ ft = 6.10 m.

Solve: (a) Given that $(v_y) = 0.0$ ft/s we can use Equation 2.11.

$$\Delta y = \frac{1}{2} a_y (\Delta t)^2$$

With up as the positive direction, Δy is negative and $a_y = -g$; those signs cancel, leaving

$$h = \frac{1}{2} g (\Delta t)^2$$

Solve for Δt.

$$\Delta t = \sqrt{\frac{2h}{g}}$$

Now use that expression for Δt in the equation for constant horizontal velocity.

$$L = \Delta x = v_x \Delta t = v_x \sqrt{\frac{2h}{g}}$$

Finally solve for $v = v_x$ in terms of L and h.

$$v = \frac{L}{\sqrt{\frac{2h}{g}}} = L\sqrt{\frac{g}{2h}}$$

(b) Now plug in the numbers we are given for L and h.

$$v = L\sqrt{\frac{g}{2h}} = (6.71 \text{ m})\sqrt{\frac{9.8 \text{ m/s}^2}{2(6.10 \text{ m})}} = 6.0 \text{ m/s}$$

Compare this result ($v = 6.0$ m/s) with the world-class sprinter ($v = 10$ m/s); a fit person could make this leap.

Assess: The results are reasonable, and not obviously wrong. 6.0 m/s $\approx$ 13 mph, and that would be a fast run, but certainly possible.

By solving the problem first algebraically before plugging in any numbers, we are able to substitute other numbers as well, if we desire, without re-solving the whole problem.

P3.67. Prepare: We will use the initial information (that the marble goes 6.0 m straight up) to find the speed the marble leaves the gun. We also need to know how long it takes something to fall 1.5 m from rest in free fall so we can then use that in the horizontal equation.

Assume that there is no air resistance ($a_y = -g$) and that the marble leaves the gun with the same speed (muzzle speed) each time it is fired.

Solve: To determine the muzzle speed in the straight-up case, use Equation 2.10.

$$(v_y)_f^2 = (v_y)_i^2 + 2a_y \Delta y$$

where at the top of the trajectory $(v_y)_f = 0.0$ m/s and $\Delta y = 6.0$ m.

$$(v_y)_i^2 = 2g\Delta y \Rightarrow (v_y)_i = \sqrt{2g\Delta y} = 10.8 \text{ m/s}$$

We also use Equation 2.11 to find the time for an object to fall 1.5 m from rest: $\Delta y = -15$ m now instead of the 6.0 m used above.

$$\Delta y = \frac{1}{2}a_y(\Delta t)^2$$

$$\Delta t = \sqrt{\frac{2\Delta y}{-g}} = \sqrt{\frac{2(-1.5 \text{ m})}{-9.8 \text{ m/s}^2}} = 0.553 \text{ s}$$

At last we combine this information into the equation for constant horizontal velocity.

$$\Delta x = v_x \Delta t = (10.8 \text{ m/s})(0.553 \text{ s}) = 6.0 \text{ m}$$

Assess: Is it a coincidence that the marble has a horizontal range of 6.0 m when it can reach a height of 6.0 m when fired straight up, or will those numbers always be the same? Well, the 6.0 m horizontal range depends on the height (1.5 m) from which you fire it, so if that were different the range would be different. This leads us to conclude that it *is* a coincidence. You can go back, though, and do the problem algebraically (with no numbers) and find that g cancels and that the horizontal range is 2 times the square root of the product of the vertical height it can reach and the height from which you fire it horizontally.

P3.69. Prepare: We will apply the constant-acceleration kinematics equations to the horizontal and vertical motions of the tennis ball as described by Equation 3.24. A visual overview is shown below. To find whether the ball clears the net, we will determine the vertical fall of the ball as it travels to the net.

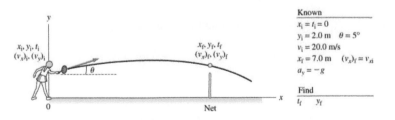

Solve: The initial velocity is

$$(v_x)_i = v_i \cos 5° = (20 \text{ m/s})\cos 5° = 19.92 \text{ m/s}$$
$$(v_y)_i = v_i \sin 5° = (20 \text{ m/s})\cos 5° = 1.743 \text{ m/s}$$

The time it takes for the ball to reach the net is

$$x_f = x_i + (v_x)_i(t_f - t_i) \Rightarrow 7.0 \text{ m} = 0 \text{ m} + (19.92 \text{ m/s})(t_f - 0 \text{ s}) \Rightarrow t_f = 0.351 \text{ s}$$

The vertical position at $t_f = 0.351$ s is

$$y_f = y_i + (v_y)_i(t_f - t_i) + \frac{1}{2}a_y(t_f - t_i)^2$$

$$= (2.0 \text{ m}) + (1.743 \text{ m/s})(0.351 \text{ s} - 0 \text{ s}) + \frac{1}{2}(-9.8 \text{ m/s}^2)(0.351 \text{ s} - 0 \text{ s})^2 = 2.0 \text{ m}$$

Thus the ball clears the net by 1.0 m.

Assess: The vertical free fall of the ball, with zero initial velocity, in 0.351 s is 0.6 m. The ball will clear by approximately 0.4 m if the ball is thrown horizontally. The initial launch angle of 5° provides some initial vertical velocity and the ball clears by a larger distance. The above result is reasonable.

P3.71. Prepare: Projectiles launched at higher angles stay in the air longer. Since objects launched at 30° and at 60° have the same range, we can conclude that their horizontal component of velocity multiplied by time of flight is the same. This fact can be written as an equation: $v_i \cos30°\Delta t_{30°} = v_i \cos60°\Delta t_{60°}$.

Solve: The above equation can be solved to obtain:

$$\Delta t_{60°} = (\cos30°/\cos60°)\Delta t_{30°} = \sqrt{3}(2.0 \text{ s}) = 3.5 \text{ s}$$

The projectile launched at 60° spends 3.5 s in the air.

Assess: The projectile launched at a higher angle stays in the air much longer because it has a higher vertical component of velocity. But the two projectiles have the same range because their launch angles are complementary.

P3.73. Prepare: First draw a picture.

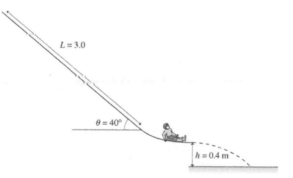

In part **(a)** use tilted axes so the x-axis runs down the slide. The acceleration will be $a_x = g \sin\theta$.
Part **(b)** is a familiar two-step projectile motion problem where we use the vertical direction to determine the time of flight and then plug it into the equation for constant horizontal velocity. Use axes that are *not* tilted for part **(b)**.

Solve: (a) We use Equation 2.10 with $(v_x)_i = 0.0$ m/s.

$$(v_x)_f^2 = 2a_x\Delta x$$

$$(v_x)_f = \sqrt{2(g \sin\theta)\Delta x} = \sqrt{2(9.8 \text{ m/s}^2)(\sin40°)(3.0 \text{ m})} = 6.1 \text{ m/s}$$

(b) We use Equation 2.11 to find the time for an object to fall 0.4 m from rest: $\Delta y = -0.4$ m.

$$\Delta y = \frac{1}{2}a_y(\Delta t)^2$$

$$\Delta t = \sqrt{\frac{2\Delta y}{-g}} = \sqrt{\frac{2(-0.4 \text{ m})}{-9.8 \text{ m/s}^2}} = 0.286 \text{ s}$$

At last we combine this information into the equation for constant horizontal velocity.

$$\Delta x = v_x\Delta t = (6.15 \text{ m/s})(0.286 \text{ s}) = 1.8 \text{ m}$$

Assess: We reported the speed at the bottom of the slide to two significant figures, but kept track of a third to use as a guard digit because this result is also an intermediate result for the final answer. We also kept a third significant figure on the Δt as a guard digit.

The result of landing 1.8 m from the end of the frictionless slide seems just a bit large because this slide was frictionless and real slides aren't, but it doesn't seem to be too far out of expectation, so our result is probably correct.

P3.75. Prepare: We need to convert the radius of the Mini Cooper's turn to meters and convert the final speed of the Mustang to meters per second. The radius of the Mini Cooper's turn is:

$$17 \text{ ft} = 17 \text{ ft}\left(\frac{1 \text{ m}}{3.28 \text{ ft}}\right) = 5.18 \text{ m}$$

And the final speed of the Mustang is:

$$60 \frac{\text{mi}}{\text{hr}} = 60 \frac{\text{mi}}{\text{hr}}\left(\frac{1609 \text{ m}}{1 \text{ mi}}\right)\left(\frac{1 \text{ hr}}{3600 \text{ s}}\right) = 26.8 \text{ m/s}$$

The acceleration of the Mustang is given by $a = \Delta v/\Delta t$:

$$a = (26.8 \text{ m/s})/(5.6 \text{ s}) = 4.79 \text{ m/s}^2$$

Solve: To match the Mustang's acceleration, the Mini Cooper must have a centripetal acceleration of 4.79 m/s². Given the formula for centripetal acceleration, $a = v^2 / r$, we can solve for the necessary radius:

$$v = \sqrt{ar} = \sqrt{(4.79 \text{ m/s}^2)(5.18 \text{ m})} = 4.98 \text{ m/s} = 4.98 \frac{\text{m}}{\text{s}}\left(\frac{1 \text{ mi}}{1609 \text{ m}}\right)\left(\frac{3600 \text{ s}}{1 \text{ hr}}\right) = 11 \text{ mph}$$

The Mini Cooper must travel at 11 mph to have the same acceleration as the Mustang.
   Assess: Even at a fairly low speed, 11 mph, the acceleration is high. This is because the radius of the turn is so small—17 ft.

P3.77. Prepare: We will use Equation 3.30 to relate the acceleration to the speed. But first we need to convert the speed of the car to m/s:

$$40 \frac{\text{mi}}{\text{hr}} = 40 \frac{\text{mi}}{\text{hr}}\left(\frac{1609 \text{ m}}{1 \text{ mi}}\right)\left(\frac{1 \text{ hr}}{3600 \text{ s}}\right) = 17.9 \text{ m/s}$$

Solve: (a) Your acceleration is given from the equation $a = v^2/r$:

$$\frac{(17.9 \text{ m/s})^2}{110 \text{ m}} = 2.91 \text{ m/s}^2$$

which converts as:

$$2.91 \text{ m/s}^2 = (2.91 \text{ m/s}^2)\left(\frac{1g}{9.8 \text{ m/s}^2}\right) = 0.30g$$

The acceleration is 2.9 m/s² or 0.30 g.
   (b) The formula for centripetal acceleration: $a = v^2/r$ can be solved for v as follows: $v = \sqrt{ar}$. In this form we see that if the acceleration is doubled, then the velocity is multiplied by $\sqrt{2}$. So we multiply the 40 mph speed limit by $\sqrt{2}$: $(40 \text{ mph})\sqrt{2} = 57 \text{ mph}$. At 57 mph the acceleration would be twice the acceleration at 40 mph.
   Assess: As noted in the solution to problem 40, a small change in velocity can produce a large change in centripetal acceleration. Here, with an increase in speed of less than 50%, the acceleration doubles and the friction needed for the turn also doubles.

P3.79. Prepare: Equation 3.33 governs circular motion.
   Solve: From Equation 3.33 we can see the centripetal acceleration of a car has a quadratic relationship to velocity and an inverse relationship to the radius of the circular motion. If the velocity of the object is decreased, the acceleration decreases. If the radius of the motion is increased the acceleration of the object *decreases*. We can either decrease the velocity or increase the radius. The choices C and D act to increase the velocity, so the correct answer is B.
   Assess: Centripetal acceleration decreases with increasing radius.

P3.81. Prepare: The riders are in free fall during this part of the motion. We can use Equation 3.24.

Solve: The riders have no initial velocity in the vertical direction after they leave the slide. Their initial velocity in the horizontal direction will be determined by the first and second sections and is unaffected by changing the height of the slide exit above the water, assuming that the first two sections are unchanged.

The time it takes the riders to hit the water after leaving the slide can be calculated with Equation 2.9.

$$y_f = y_i + (v_y)_i \Delta t - \frac{1}{2} g (\Delta t)^2$$

Taking the origin as the exit of the slide and $(v_y)_i = 0$ m/s this equation becomes

$$\Delta t = \sqrt{-\frac{2 y_f}{g}}$$

The initial horizontal velocity of the rider is $(v_x)_i$. The horizontal displacement of the rider once leaving the ramp will be $(v_x)_i \Delta t$. To double the distance the rider travels before hitting the water, we only need to double the time the rider takes to hit the water. From the equation above, to double the time, we must quadruple the vertical distance. So the answer is $(4)(0.6 \text{ m}) = 2.4$ m. The correct choice is C.

Assess: This answer is reasonable, since the distance traveled vertically in free fall has a quadratic relationship to time.

4—Forces and Newton's Laws of Motion
Conceptual Questions

Q4.1. Reason: If friction and air resistance are negligible (as stated) then the net force on the puck is zero (the normal force and gravitational force are equal in magnitude and opposite in direction). If the net force on the puck is zero, then Newton's first law states that it will continue on with constant velocity. So no force is needed to keep the puck moving; it will naturally keep moving unless a force acts on it to change its velocity.

Assess: This question demonstrates the difference between Aristotelian thinking and Newtonian thinking. Objects do not need forces on them to keep them moving; forces are only required when we want to *change* the velocity of the object. The reason one has to normally keep pushing an object to keep it moving is because of friction; to keep it at constant velocity your pushing force must be equal in magnitude to the friction force. But in the case of this question, there is no friction, so there is no force needed to keep it moving.

Q4.3. Reason: Newton's first law does *not* state that there can be no forces acting on an object moving with constant velocity—only that the *sum* of the forces must be zero (sometimes worded as "no unbalanced forces"). There can be forces acting on an object with constant velocity, but the vector sum of those forces must be zero.

Assess: When we say there is no *net* force on an object with constant velocity, we are not saying that there are no forces. Net force means the vector sum of the forces.

Q4.5. Reason: No. If you know all of the forces than you know the direction of the acceleration, not the direction of the motion (velocity). For example, a car moving forward could have on it a net force forward if speeding up or backward if slowing down or no net force at all if moving at constant speed.

Assess: Consider carefully what Newton's second law says, and what it doesn't say. The net force must *always* be in the direction of the acceleration. This is also the direction of the *change* in velocity, although not necessarily in the direction of the velocity itself.

Q4.7. Reason: The picture on the left is more effective at tightening the head because of the greater inertia of the head. Once moving, the head will "want" to continue moving (Newton's first law) after the handle hits the table, thus tightening the head, more so than in the second picture where the light handle has less inertia moving down than the head.

Assess: Newton's first law, the law of inertia, says the greater the mass of an object the more it will tend to continue with its previous velocity. One can assess this by trying it with a real hammer with a loose head.

Q4.9. Reason: Kinetic friction opposes the motion, but static friction is in the direction to prevent motion.

(a) Examples of motion where the frictional force on the object is directed opposite the motion would be a block sliding across a table top or the friction of the road on car tires in a skid.

(b) An example of motion in which the frictional force on the object is in the same direction as the motion would be a crate (not sliding) in the back of a pickup truck that is speeding up. The static frictional force of the truck bed on the crate is in the forward direction (the same direction as the motion) because it *is* the net force on the crate that accelerates it forward.

Assess: It is easy to think that the direction of the frictional force is *always* opposite the direction of motion, but static frictional forces are in the direction to prevent relative motion between the surfaces, and can be in various directions depending on the situation.

Q4.11. Reason: Both objects (Jonathan and his daughter) experience the same acceleration (i.e., the acceleration of the car). However since the objects do not have the same mass, the forces required to accelerate them will be different. The object with the greater mass (Jonathan) will require the greater force.

Assess: This is a straightforward application of Newton's second law.

Q4.13. Reason: The book defines weight as the gravitational pull of the earth on an object, and that doesn't change when the ball is thrown straight up. That is, if the gravitational force of the earth on the ball is 2.0 N while it sits on the scale, then the gravitational force of the earth on the ball is still 2.0 N while it is in flight—even at the very top of its motion. The weight of the ball is 2.0 N all the time the ball is near the surface of the earth, regardless of its motion.

Assess: Hmmm. . . . We previously distinguished between velocity, which *is* zero at the top of the trajectory (if the ball is thrown straight up), and acceleration, which is $-g$ all the while it is in free fall. But how do we explain the fact that the acceleration of the ball is $-g$ at the top of its trajectory but zero while sitting on the scale, if the gravitational force on it is the same in both cases? Doesn't $\vec{F}_{net} = m\vec{a}$? Yes, $\vec{F}_{net} = m\vec{a}$ is true, but in the case of the ball on the scale the net force is zero because the scale is pushing up on the ball with a force of 2.0 N; since the net force is zero the acceleration is zero. While the ball is in flight the scale isn't pushing up on it, so the acceleration is $-g$ because the net force (the weight) is 2.0 N.

It is also worth mentioning that not all physics texts define weight the same way. Some define weight as "what the scale reads," which would be different from the definition in our text because if the scale and ball are thrown up together they would both be in free fall and the scale would read zero. That is, some books would say the ball's weight *is* zero at the top of its motion (because that is what the scale would read). Both definitions have merit, and it is wise to understand the difference and be prepared in future situations if someone defines weight differently than we have in this text. One way to avoid confusion is to always refer to "the gravitational force of the earth on the object" instead of the "weight." Still, the definition in our textbook is very mainstream.

Q4.15. Reason: If the only forces acting on the person are the gravitational force of the earth, the normal force of the hill, and the (static) frictional force of the hill, then the frictional force must *always* point up the hill to prevent sliding down the hill.

However, if there were another agent (say, a second person) pushing or pulling up the hill on the person, then the static frictional force could be preventing a slide *up* the hill; in this case the direction of the static friction force would be down the hill.

Assess: It is a boon to understanding to stop and think about the exceptional cases that we might not have considered in our first encounter with a concept.

Looked at with the second law, if the second person is strongly pushing up the hill, then the static friction force might need to be down the hill to produce a zero net force and the required zero acceleration.

Q4.17. Reason: The force of the road on the tires is what accelerates the car forward, that is, when the acceleration is forward the net force must be forward. An example would be when the car is going forward and speeding up, as in the figure. However, if the car is accelerating backward (while going forward), that is, slowing down, then the force of the tires on the road must be in the direction of the acceleration, or backward.

Assess: Remember to apply Newton's second law. It doesn't answer every question in the universe, but at least it shouldn't be violated in problems like this. The acceleration must be in the same direction as the net force. This gives one a head start in answering this question.

Q4.19. Reason: The force that you exert on the wagon will cause it to move forward if it is greater than all opposing forces *on the wagon*. That is, the wagon will accelerate if the net force *on the wagon* is not zero. This is a proper application of Newton's second law, but you cannot apply Newton's third law in this case. Newton's third law does not apply to the forces on a single object, but only to forces acting on two different objects. A Newton's third law pair of forces can never cancel because they are always acting on different (opposite) objects.

Assess: It is nice to have smart three-year-olds, but in this case she needs even more physics understanding, not less. Both Newton's second law and his third law are true (in classical physics), but they don't address the same forces. Newton's second law addresses all of the forces acting on a single object; Newton's third law addresses pairs of forces that act on opposite objects (these third law forces can't even be added up—let alone cancel—because they aren't on the same object).

Multiple-Choice Questions

Q4.21. Reason: This is a very famous question, and one which many people miss until they understand Newton's laws. Before the string snaps, it provides a tension force toward the center of the circle (centripetal), which keeps the puck going around in a circle; in other words, the net force is toward the center, so the acceleration is toward the center.

However, when the string snaps that centripetal force disappears. There is now no net force acting on the puck, and Newton's first law tells us that its velocity must be constant (both in magnitude and direction) under those conditions. So the puck continues in the direction it was going at the instant the string snapped.

The answer is C.

Assess: Ask some friends, relatives, or roommates this question and then patiently explain to them the right answer.

Q4.23. Reason: We can apply Newton's Second Law twice to solve this problem. First to determine the force and second to determine the mass.

$$F = ma = (5.0 \, kg)(0.20 \text{ m/s}^2) = 1.0 \text{ N}$$

Then

$$m = F / a = 1.0 \text{ N} / 0.10 \text{ m/s}^2 = 10 \text{ kg}$$

The correct answer is A.

Assess: This problem is a straight foreward application of Newton's Second Law.

Q4.25. Reason: The direction of the kinetic friction force will be opposite the motion, so the friction points down while the box goes up, and the friction points up while the box slides down.

The answer is D.

Assess: Drawing a free-body diagram (with tilted axes) and applying Newton's second law will support this conclusion.

Q4.27. Reason: Since the box is moving at a constant velocity the net force on it must be zero. The friction force (which we are told is nonzero) must point in the direction opposite the direction of motion; thus, the friction force is in the same direction as Jon's pushing force. For the net force to be zero, the magnitude of Rachel's force must equal the magnitude of Jon's force plus the magnitude of the friction force, so Rachel's is greater than Jon's.

The correct choice is A.

Assess: A free-body diagram will help demonstrate this answer. If the box is moving to the right (in the direction of Rachel's force) then the arrows representing Jon's force and the friction force both point to the left, and their sum must be the same magnitude as Rachel's.

Q4.29. Reason: Since block A rides without slipping, it, too, must be accelerating to the right. If it is accelerating to the right there must be a net force to the right, according to Newton's second law. The only object that can exert a force to the right is block B. This static friction force is to the right to prevent slippage of block A to the left (relative to block B).

The correct choice is B.

Assess: This is one of those cases in which the static friction force can be in the same direction as the motion, to prevent slippage the other way. Verify with a free-body diagram of block A.

Problems

P4.1. Prepare: First note that time progresses to the right in each sequence of pictures. In one case the head is thrown back, and in the other, forward.

Solve: Using the principle of inertia, the head will tend to continue with the same velocity after the collision that it had before.

In the first series of sketches, the head is lagging behind because the car has been quickly accelerated forward (to the right). This is the result of a rear-end collision.

In the second series of sketches, the head is moving forward relative to the car because the car is slowing down and the head's inertia keeps it moving forward at the same velocity (although external forces do eventually stop the head as well). This is the result of a head-on collision.

Assess: Hopefully you haven't experienced either of these in an injurious way, but you have felt similar milder effects as the car simply speeds up or slows down. It is for this reason that cars are equipped with headrests, to prevent the whiplash shown in the first series of sketches, because rear-end collisions are so common. The laws of physics tell us how wise it is to have the headrests properly positioned for our own height.

Air bags are now employed to prevent injury in the second scenario.

P4.3. Prepare: As background, look at question Q4.8 and problem P4.1. Also think about the design and orientation of the seat and how the child rides in the seat. Finally recall Newton's Second law.

Solve: As the child rides in the seat, his/her head and back rest against the padded back of the seat. If the car is brought to a rapid stop (as in a head-on collision) the child will continue to move forward at the before crash speed until he/she hits something. The object hit is the back of the seat (supporting the entire back and head) which is padded and as a result the force increases to the maximum value over a time interval. Granted this time interval may be small but that is considerable better than instantaneous. Also since the head is supported, there will be no whiplash.

Assess: The fact the force acting on the child is spread over a small time interval is a critical factor. In later chapters you will learn to call this concept impulse.

P4.5. Prepare: Draw the vector sum $\vec{F}_1 + \vec{F}_2$ of the two forces $\vec{F}_1$ and $\vec{F}_2$. Then look for a vector that will "balance" the force vector $\vec{F}_1 + \vec{F}_2$

Solve: The object will be in equilibrium if $\vec{F}_3$ has the same magnitude as $\vec{F}_1 + \vec{F}_2$ but is in the opposite direction so that the sum of all three forces is zero.

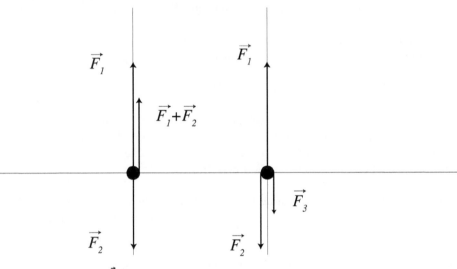

Assess: Adding the new force vector $\vec{F}_3$ with length and direction as shown will cause the object to be at rest.

P4.7. Prepare: Draw a picture of the situation, identify the system, in this case the mountain climber, and draw a closed curve around it. Name and label all relevant contact forces and long-range forces.

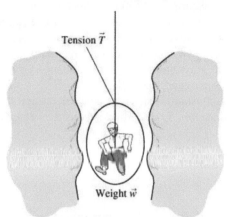

Solve: There are two forces acting on the mountain climber due to her interactions with the two agents earth and rope. One of the forces *on* the climber is the long-range weight force *by* the earth. The other force is the tension force exerted *by* the rope.

Assess: Note that the climber does not touch the sides of the crevasse so there are no forces from the crevasse walls.

P4.9. Prepare: Draw a picture of the situation, identify the system, in this case the baseball player, and draw a closed curve around it. Name and label all relevant contact forces and long-range forces.

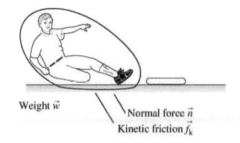

Solve: There are three forces acting *on* the baseball player due to his interactions with the two agents earth and ground. One of the forces *on* the player is the long-range weight force *by* the earth. Another force is the normal force exerted *by* the ground due to the contact between him and the ground. The third force is the kinetic friction force *by* the ground due to his sliding motion on the ground.

Assess: Note that the kinetic friction force would be *absent* if the baseball player were *not* sliding.

P4.11. Prepare: We follow the outline in Tactics Box 4.2. See also Conceptual Example 4.2.

The exact angle of the slope is not critical in this problem; the answers would be very similar for any angle between $0°$ and $90°$.

Solve: The system is the skier.

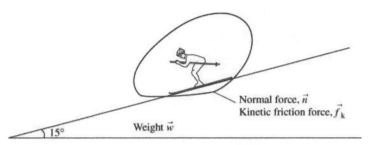

To identify forces, think of objects that are in contact with the object under consideration, as well as any long-range forces that might be acting on it. We are told to not ignore friction, but we will ignore air resistance.

The objects that are in contact with the skier are the snow-covered slope and . . . and that's all (although we will identify two forces exerted by this agent). The long-range force on the skier is the gravitational force of the earth on the skier. One of the forces, then, is the gravitational force of the earth on the skier. This force points straight toward the center of the earth.

The slope, as we mentioned, exerts two forces on the skier: the normal force (directed perpendicularly to the slope) and the frictional force (directed parallel to the slope, backward from the downhill motion).

Assess: Since there are no other objects (agents) in contact with the skier (we are ignoring the air, remember?) and no other long-range forces we can identify (the gravitational force of the moon or the sun on the skier is also too small to be worth mentioning), then we have probably catalogued them all.

We are not told whether the skier has a constant velocity or is accelerating, and that factor would influence the relative lengths of the three arrows representing the forces. If the motion is constant velocity, then the vector sum of the three arrows must be zero.

P4.13. Prepare: Refer to Figure P4.13. From force = mass $\times$ acceleration or mass = force/acceleration or mass = 1/(acceleration/force), mass is

$$m = \frac{1}{\text{slope of the acceleration-versus-force graph}}$$

A larger slope implies a smaller mass.

Solve: We know $m_2 = 0.20$ kg, and we can find the other masses relative to m_2 by comparing their slopes. Thus

$$\frac{m_1}{m_2} = \frac{1/\text{slope } 1}{1/\text{slope } 2} = \frac{\text{slope } 2}{\text{slope } 1} = \frac{1}{5/2} = \frac{2}{5} = 0.40$$

$$\Rightarrow m_1 = 0.40 \; m_2 = 0.40 \times 0.20 \text{ kg} = 0.08 \text{ kg}$$

Similarly,

$$\frac{m_3}{m_2} = \frac{1/\text{slope } 3}{1/\text{slope } 2} = \frac{\text{slope } 2}{\text{slope } 3} = \frac{1}{2/5} = \frac{5}{2} = 2.50$$

$$\Rightarrow m_3 = 2.50 \; m_2 = 2.50 \times 0.20 \text{ kg} = 0.50 \text{ kg}$$

Assess: From the initial analysis of the slopes, we had expected $m_3 > m_2$ and $m_1 > m_2$. This is consistent with our numerical answers.

P4.15. Prepare: Note that an object's acceleration is linearly proportional to the net force.

Solve: (a) One rubber band produces a force F, two rubber bands produce a force $2F$, and so on. Because $F \propto a$ and two rubber bands (force $2F$) produce an acceleration of 1.2 m/s^2, four rubber bands will produce an acceleration of 2.4 m/s^2.

(b) Now, we have two rubber bands (force 2F) pulling two glued objects (mass 2m). Using $F = ma$, $2F = (2m)a \Rightarrow a = F/m = 0.6$ m/s^2.

Assess: Newton's second law predicts that for the same mass, doubling the force doubles the acceleration. It also says that doubling mass alone halves the acceleration. These are consistent with parts **(a)** and **(b)**, respectively.

P4.17. Prepare: The problem may be solved by applying Newton's second law to the present and the new situation.

Solve: (a) We are told that for an unknown force (call it F_o) acting on an unknown mass (call it m_o) the acceleration of the mass is 8 m/s^2. According to Newton's second law,

$$F_o = m_o(8 \text{ m/s}^2) \quad \text{or} \quad F_o/m_o = 8 \text{ m/s}^2$$

For the new situation, the new force is $F_{\text{new}} = 2F_o$, the mass is not changed ($m_{\text{new}} = m_o$) and we may find the acceleration by

$$F_{\text{new}} = m_{\text{new}} a_{\text{new}}$$

or

$$a_{\text{new}} = F_{\text{new}}/m_{\text{new}} = 2F_o/m_o = 2(F_o/m_o) = 2(8 \text{ m/s}^2) = 16 \text{ m/s}^2$$

(b) For the new situation, the force is unchanged $F_{new} = F_o$, the new mass is half the old mass ($m_{new} = m_o / 2$) and we may find the acceleration by

$$F_{new} = m_{new}a_{new}$$

or

$$a_{new} = F_{new} / m_{new} = F_o / 2m_o = (F_o / m_o) / 2 = (8 \text{ m/s}^2) / 2 = 4 \text{ m/s}^2$$

(c) A similar procedure gives $a = 8$ m/s^2.
(d) A similar procedure gives $a = 32$ m/s^2.
Assess: From the algebraic relationship $a = F/m$ we can see that when **(a)** the force is doubled, the acceleration is doubled, **(b)** the mass is doubled, the acceleration is halved, **(c)** both force and mass are doubled, the acceleration doesn't change, and **(d)** force is doubled and mass is halved, the acceleration will be four times larger.

P4.19. Prepare: The principle involved is that "the acceleration is inversely proportional to the mass on which the force acts." We will assume that the same maximum force accelerates the two-car system as was available to the one car alone.
Solve: Doubling the mass halves the acceleration if the force is the same, so the new maximum acceleration would be

$$a' = \frac{a}{2} = \frac{5.0 \text{ m/s}^2}{2} = 2.5 \text{ m/s}^2$$

Assess: Hopefully the second law has had enough time to sink into your psyche so that this just feels right.

P4.21. Prepare: Refer to Figure P4.21.
Solve: Newton's second law is $F = ma$. We can read a force and an acceleration from the graph, and hence find the mass. Choosing the force $F = 1$ N gives us $a = 4$ m/s^2. Newton's second law then yields $m = 0.25$ kg.
Assess: Slope of the acceleration-versus-force graph is 4 m/N·s^2, and therefore, the inverse of the slope will give the mass.

P4.23. Prepare: We can use our knowledge of kinematics and our conceptual understanding of acceleration to determine the acceleration of the car and then Newton's second law to determine the force acting on the car.
Solve: First let's determine the acceleration of the car.

$$a = \Delta v / \Delta t = (v_f - v_i) / \Delta t = \left(21\frac{\text{m}}{\text{s}} - 20\frac{\text{m}}{\text{s}}\right) / 2.0 \text{ s} = 0.50 \text{ m/s}^2$$

Next, let's determine the acceleration of the car.

$$F = ma = (1500 \text{ kg})(0.50 \text{ m/s}^2) = 7.5 \times 10^2 \text{ N}$$

Assess: It should be noted that even though we are in chapter four and dealing primarily with forces, it is critical that we stay up on the content of previous chapters.

P4.25. Prepare: This is a straightforward application of Newton's second law: $\vec{F}_{net} = m\vec{a}$, where $m = 3.0 \times 10^8$ kg, and $\vec{F}_{net} = \vec{F}_{thrust}$ (because we are told the supertanker is subject to no other forces), and $\vec{F}_{thrust} = 5 \times 10^6$ N (as given in Table 4.2).
The vectors $\vec{F}_{net}$ and $\vec{a}$ must point in the same direction (because m is never negative), so we now compute the magnitude.
Solve: Solve the second law for a.

$$a = \frac{F_{net}}{m} = \frac{F_{thrust}}{m} = \frac{5 \times 10^6 \text{ N}}{3.0 \times 10^8 \text{ kg}} = 0.0167 \text{ m/s}^2 \approx 0.02 \text{ m/s}^2$$

Assess: It appears that there is only one significant figure in the data in Table 4.2, hence the rounding to 0.02 m/s^2. If we assume one more significant figure in the table then we can report $a = 0.017$ m/s^2. However, the point of the problem is clear: The rocket motor (the largest force in Table 4.2) was able to give the supertanker only an impressively very small acceleration.

P4.27. Prepare: The free-body diagram shows three forces with a net force (and therefore net acceleration) upward. There is a force labeled $\vec{w}$ directed down, a force $\vec{F}_{thrust}$ directed up, and a force $\vec{D}$ directed down. Now, draw a picture of a real object with three forces to match the given free-body diagram.

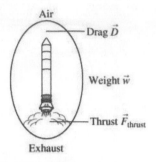

Air

Drag $\vec{D}$

Weight $\vec{w}$

Thrust $\vec{F}_{thrust}$

Exhaust

Solve: A possible description is: "A rocket accelerates upward."

Assess: It is given that the net force is pointing up. Then, $\vec{F}_{net} = \vec{F}_{thrust} - \vec{w} - \vec{D}$ must be greater than zero. In other words, $\vec{F}_{thrust}$ must be larger than $(\vec{w} + \vec{D})$

P4.29. Prepare: Draw a picture of the situation, identify the system, in this case the car, and draw a closed curve around it. Name and label all relevant contact forces and long-range forces.

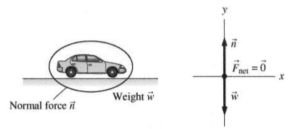

Normal force $\vec{n}$ Weight $\vec{w}$

Solve: There are two forces acting *on* the car due to its interactions with the two agents earth and the ground. One of the forces *on* the car is the long-range weight force *by* the earth. Another force is the normal force exerted *by* the ground due to the contact between the car and the ground. Since the car is sitting in the parking lot, acceleration is zero, and therefore the net force must also be zero. The free-body diagram is shown on the right.

Assess: It is implied that the car is sitting on a level parking lot, and therefore we need to consider only the vertical forces.

P4.31. Prepare: We follow the steps outlined in Tactics Boxes 4.2 and 4.3. We assume the road is level. We do not neglect air resistance, because at a "high speed" it is significant.

Solve: The system is your car.

(a) The objects in contact with your car are the air and the road. The road exerts two forces on the car: the normal force (directed up) and the kinetic friction force (directed horizontally back, parallel to the road). The air exerts a drag force (air resistance) on the car in the same direction as the friction force (i.e., opposite the velocity). The downward pull of the earth's gravitational force is the long-range force.

You could slow to a stop by air resistance alone if you are patient. You could also eventually slow to a stop by the friction of the road on the car (tires), but pressing on the brakes greatly increases the friction force and slows you down more quickly.

(b)

Normal force, $\vec{n}$
Kinetic friction force, $\vec{f}_k$
Air resistance, $\vec{D}$

Weight, $\vec{w}$

scale:
$f_k = 1$ cm
$D = \frac{1}{2}$ cm

$F_{net} = 1\frac{1}{2}$ cm

Assess: $\vec{F}_{net}$ points to the left, as does the $\vec{a}$ for a car that is moving to the right but slowing down.

P4.33. Prepare: Follow the steps outlined in Tactics Boxes 4.2 and 4.3. Draw a picture of the situation, identify the system, in this case the elevator, and draw a closed curve around it. Name and label all relevant contact forces (the tension) and long-range forces (weight).

 Solve:

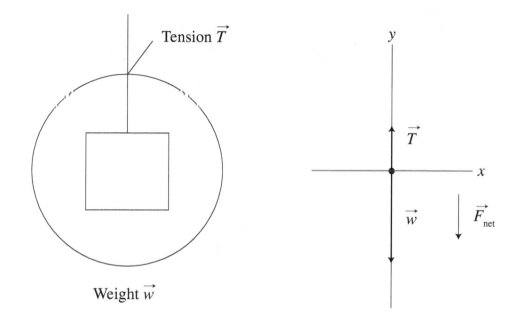

scale $\vec{T}$ = 1 cm
        $\vec{w}$ = 2 cm

There are two forces acting *on* the elevator due to its interactions with the two agents earth and the cable. One of the forces *on* the elevator is the long-range weight force *by* the earth. Another force is the tension force exerted *by* the cable due to the contact between the elevator and the cable. Since the elevator is coming to a stop while ascending, it has a negative acceleration, hence a negative net force. As a result, we know that the length of the vector representing the weight of the elevator must be greater than the length of the vector representing the tension in the cable. The free-body diagram is shown above on the right.

Assess: There are only two forces on the elevator. The weight is directed down and the tension in the cable is directed up. Since the elevator is slowing down (has a negative acceleration) the tension must be less than the weight.

P4.35. Prepare: We follow the steps outlined in Tactics Boxes 4.2 and 4.3.

Solve: The system is the picture.

The objects in contact with the picture are the wall and your hand. The wall exerts a normal force (opposite the pushing force of the hand) and a static friction force, which is directed upward and prevents the picture from falling down.

The important long-range force is the gravitational force of the earth on the picture (i.e., the weight).

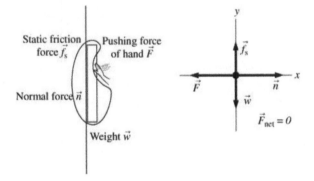

Assess: The net force is zero, as it should be for an object which is motionless (isn't accelerating).

P4.37. Prepare: Knowing that for every action there is an equal and opposite reaction and that these forces are exerted on different objects, we can identify, draw and label all the action-reaction pairs. Knowing all the forces acting on skater 2, we can construct a free-body diagram for skater 2.

Solve:

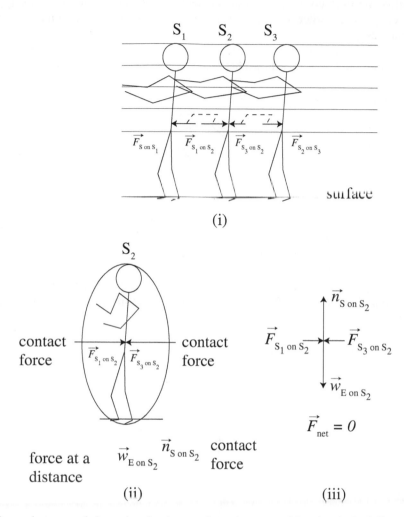

(i)

(ii)   (iii)

Figure (i) shows all three skaters and the pair-wise interactions (connected by the dashed line) between them. Figure (ii) identifies skater 2 as the object of interest, shows the three contact forces that act on her, and the one long-range force that acts on her. Finally Figure (iii) shows a free-body diagram for skater 2.

Assess: We have been informed that there is no friction and that the skaters are standing. If this is the case the net force acting on skater 2 should be zero. Also note that the action reaction pairs act on different objects.

P4.39. Prepare: Redraw the motion diagram as shown below.

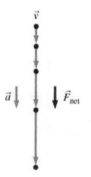

Solve: The above figure shows velocity as downward, so the object is moving down. The length of the vector increases showing that the speed is increasing (like a dropped ball). Thus, the acceleration is directed down. Since $\vec{F} = m\vec{a}$, the force is in the same direction as the acceleration and must be directed down.

Assess: Since the object is speeding up, the acceleration vector must be parallel to the velocity vector and the net force must be parallel to the acceleration. In order to determine the net force, we had to combine our knowledge of motion diagrams, kinematics, and dynamics.

P4.41. Prepare: Redraw the motion diagram as shown below.

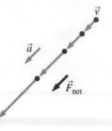

Solve: The velocity vector in the above figure is shown downward and to the left. So movement is downward and to the left. The velocity vectors get successively longer which means the speed is increasing. Therefore the acceleration is downward and to the left. By Newton's second law $\vec{F} = m\vec{a}$, the net force must be in the same direction as the acceleration. Thus, the net force is downward and to the left.

Assess: Since the object is speeding up, the acceleration vector must be parallel to the velocity vector. This means the acceleration vector must be pointing along the direction of velocity. Therefore the net force must also be downward and to the left.

P4.43. Prepare: Redraw the motion diagram as shown below.

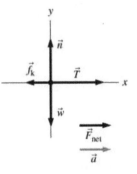

Solve: (a)–(c) Since the net force is to the right, the acceleration will also be to the right.

(d) There is a normal force and a weight, which are equal and opposite, so this is an object on a horizontal surface. The description could be: "A tow truck pulls a stuck car out of the mud."

Assess: Our scenario seems to fit the free body diagram. Check by doing the last part of the problem first: start with the scenario and then draw a free-body diagram. Make sure it matches the original.

P4.45. Prepare: Redraw the motion diagram as shown below.

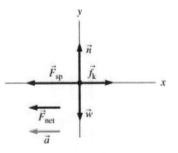

Solve: (a)–(c) The net force is to the left. Therefore acceleration will also be to the left.

(d) This is an object on a surface because $w = n$. It must be moving to the left because the kinetic friction is to the right. The description of the free-body diagram could be: "A compressed spring is shooting a plastic block to the left."

Assess: The scenario fits the free-body diagram. Check by doing the last part of the problem first: start with the scenario and then draw a free-body diagram. Make sure it matches the original.

P4.47. Prepare: Redraw the motion diagram as shown below.

Solve: (a)–(c) There is an object on an inclined surface. The net force is down the plane so the acceleration is down the plane. The net force includes both the frictional force and a component of the weight. Since kinetic friction opposes the motion, the object must be traveling up the incline.

(d) The description could be: "A crate is sliding up a ramp."

Assess: We must look at all the forces and the nature of these forces to accurately determine what will happen to the object.

P4.49. Prepare: Redraw the motion diagram as shown below.

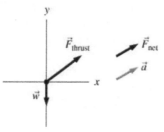

Solve: (a)–(c) There is a thrust at an angle to the horizontal and a weight. There is no normal force so the object is not on a surface. Adding the thrust and the weight we obtain a net force which acts as shown in the figure. The acceleration acts in the direction of the net force.

(d) The description could be: "A rocket is fired at an angle to the horizontal and there is no drag force."

Assess: It is essential that we look at all the forces and the nature of these forces to accurately determine what will happen to the object.

P4.51. Prepare: Review Tactics Box 4.3 about drawing free-body diagrams.

Solve: One error is that there isn't a force along the direction of motion in this case; $\vec{F}_{motion}$ should be erased completely. Another error is that the drag force should be opposite the direction of the velocity, not straight left. A correct free-body diagram would be

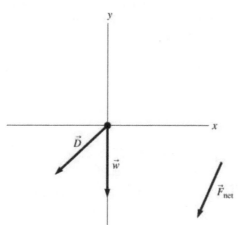

The acceleration (not shown) is in the same direction as $\vec{F}_{net}$. The velocity (not shown) is up to the right, opposite the drag force.

Assess: Motion is not a force. To draw a free-body diagram you must simply consider all of the forces acting *on* the object of interest. Do this by considering which objects are in contact with the object of interest, and which long-range forces act on the object.

P4.53. Prepare: There are three forces acting *on* the rocket due to its interactions with the three agents earth, air, and the hot gases exhausted to the environment. One force on the rocket is the long-range weight force *by* the earth. Second force is the drag force *by* the air. The third is the thrust force exerted on the rocket *by* the hot gas that is being let out to the environment. Since the rocket is being launched upward, it is being accelerated upward. Therefore, the net force on the rocket must also point upward. Draw a picture of the situation, identify the system, in this case the rocket, and draw a motion diagram. Draw a closed curve around the system, and name and label all relevant contact forces and long-range forces.

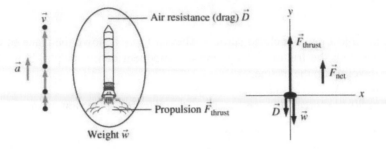

Solve: A force-identification diagram, a motion diagram, and a free-body diagram are shown.

Assess: You now have three important tools in you "Physics Toolbox," motion diagrams, force diagrams and free-body diagrams. Careful use of these tools will give you an excellent conceptual understanding of a situation.

P4.55. Prepare: The normal force is perpendicular to the hill. The frictional force is parallel to the hill.

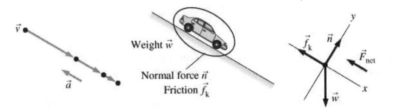

Solve: A force-identification diagram, a motion diagram, and a free-body diagram are shown.

Assess: You now have three important tools in you "Physics Toolbox," motion diagrams, force diagrams, and free-body diagrams. Careful use of these tools will give you an excellent conceptual understanding of a situation.

P4.57. Prepare: There are three forces acting on the bale of hay due to its interactions the the two agents: earth and bed of the truck. The two contact forces between the bale of hay and the bed of the truck are the normal force the force of kinetic friction which is dragging the bale of hay forward (even though it is sliding backward). The force at a distance is the force the earth exerts on the bale of hay (the weight). Since the normal force and the weight are equal in magnitude and opposite in direction, there is no net vertical force. Since the force of kinetic friction provides a net horizontal force, the net force acting on the bale of hay and hence the acceleration of the bale of hay is in the direction of the force of kinetic friction. Now, draw a picture of the situation, identify the system, in this case the bale of hay, and draw a motion diagram. Draw a closed curve around the system, and name and label all relevant contact forces and long-range forces.

Solve:

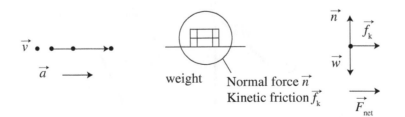

Assess: Since there is a net or unbalanced force acting on the bale of hay, it will experience an acceleration in the direction of this force.

P4.59. Prepare: The ball rests on the floor of the barrel because the weight is equal to the normal force. There is a force of the spring to the right, which causes acceleration. The force of kinetic friction is smaller than the spring force. Now, draw a picture of the situation, identify the system, in this case the plastic ball, and draw a motion diagram. Draw a closed curve around the system, and name and label all relevant contact forces and long-range forces.

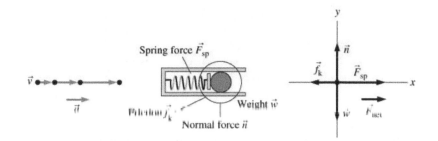

Solve: A force-identification diagram, a motion diagram, and a free-body diagram are shown.

Assess. Since the normal force acting on the ball and the weight of the ball are equal in magnitude and opposite in direction, the ball experiences no vertical motion. Since the spring exerts a greater force on the ball than kinetic friction, the ball accelerates out the barrel of the gun.

P4.61. Prepare: The gymnast experiences the long range force of weight. There is also a contact force from the trampoline, which is the normal force of the trampoline on the gymnast. The gymnast is moving downward and the trampoline is decreasing her speed, so the acceleration is upward and there is a net force upward. Thus the normal force must be larger than the weight. The actual behavior of the normal force will be complicated as it involves the stretching of the trampoline and therefore tensions.

Now, draw a picture of the situation, identify the system, in this case the gymnast, and draw a motion diagram. Draw a closed curve around the system, and name and label all relevant contact forces and long-range forces.

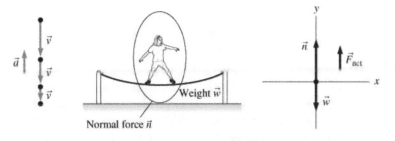

Solve: A force-identification diagram, a motion diagram, and a free-body diagram are shown.

Assess: There are only two forces on the gymnast. The weight force is directed downward and the normal force is directed upward. Since the gymnast is slowing down right after after making contact with the trampoline, upward normal force must be larger than the downward weight force.

P4.63. Prepare: You can see from the motion diagram that the bag accelerates to the left along with the car as the car slows down. According to Newton's second law, $\vec{F} = m\vec{a}$, there must be a force to the *left* acting on the bag. This is friction, but not kinetic friction. The bag is not sliding across the seat. Instead, it is static friction, the force that prevents slipping. Were it not for static friction, the bag would slide off the seat as the car stops. Static friction acts in the direction needed to prevent slipping. In this case, friction must act in the backward (toward the left) direction.

Now, draw a picture of the situation, identify the system, in this case the bag of groceries, and draw a motion diagram. Draw a closed curve around the system, and name and label all relevant contact forces and long-range forces.

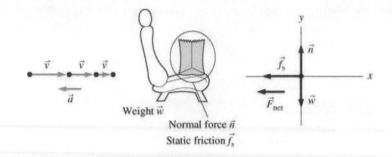

Solve: A force-identification diagram, a motion diagram, and a free-body diagram are shown.

Assess: Since the normal force acting on the bag of groceries and the weight of the groceries are equal in magnitude and opposite in direction, the bag experiences no vertical motion. The only horizontal force acting on the bag of groceries is static friction, and it provides the net force acting on the bag which results in the acceleration of the bag.

P4.65. Prepare: To solve this problem, we will need to think carefully about the forces acting on the object of interest (the passenger in the car). It will also be important to determine what is ment by a *very* slippery bench.

Solve:

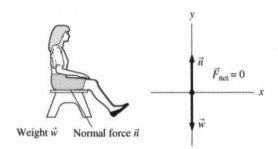

(a) The passenger is sitting on a very slippery bench in a car that is traveling to the right. Both the passenger and the seat are moving with a constant speed. There is a force on the passenger due to her weight, which is directed down. There is a contact force (the normal) between the passenger and the seat, which is directed up. Since the passenger is not accelerating up or down, the net vertical force on her is zero, which means the two vertical forces are equal in magnitude. The statement of the problem gives no indication of any other contact forces. Specifically, we are told that the seat is very slippery. We can take this to mean there is no frictional force. So our force diagram includes only the normal force up, the weight down, but no horizontal force.

(b) The above considerations lead to the free-body diagram shown in the above figure.

(c) The car (and therefore the very slippery seat) begin to slow down. Since the seat cannot exert a force of friction (either static or kinetic) on the passenger, the passenger cannot slow down as fast as the seat which is attached to the car. As a result the passenger continues to move forward with the initial speed of the car. Since the forces acting on the passenger remain the same, the free-body diagram is unchanged but the pictorial representation of the passenger is changed. These are shown below. (Note: The girl has slid forward; the force diagram has NO friction.)

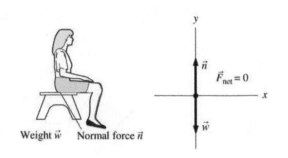

(d) The car slows down because of some new contact force on the car (maybe the brakes lock the wheels and the road exerts a force on the tires). But there is no new contact force on you the passenger. The force diagram for the passenger (you) remains unchanged, there are no horizontal forces on you. You do not slow down, but rather continue at an unchanged velocity until something in the picture changes for you (for example, you slide off the seat or hit the windshield).

(e) The net force on you has remained zero because the net vertical force is zero and there are no horizontal forces. According to Newton's first law, if the net force on you is zero, then you continue to move in a straight line with a constant velocity. That is what happens to you when the car slows down. You continue to move forward with a constant velocity. The statement that you are "thrown forward" is misleading and incorrect. To be "thrown" there would need to be a net force on you and there is none. It might be correct to say that the car has been "thrown backward" leaving you to continue onward (until you part company with the seat).

Assess: Careful thinking and precise language, aided by a good diagram and understanding of Newton's first and second laws are needed to articulate the solution of this problem.

P4.67. Prepare: The jump itself is while the froghopper is still in contact with the ground, but pushing off. During that time the froghopper must be accelerating upward, so the net force is upward.

Solve: (a)

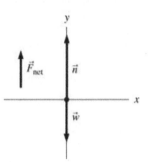

(b) Since the froghopper is accelerating upward the net force is upward; hence, the upward force of the ground on the froghopper is greater than the downward gravitational force (the froghopper's weight).

Assess: Once the froghopper leaves the ground it is accelerating down since it is slowing down; this is due to a net downward force (mainly the gravitational force). But before it leaves the ground it is accelerating upward.

P4.69. Prepare: Think of Newton's first two laws of motion.
Solve: When we assume the vector sum of the forces on an object is zero, it is usually because we know the acceleration of the object is zero.
The correct choice is C.
Assess: The other choices don't really have much to do with whether the vector sum of the forces on an object is zero.

P4.71. Prepare: If the car is not moving then its acceleration is zero.
Solve: If the acceleration on an object is zero then the sum of the forces on the object is zero. In the horizontal direction, the rope is pulling on the car approximately west, and therefore the mud must exert a force on the car approximately east.
The answer is C.
Assess: If there are only two horizontal forces on a stationary object, they must be in opposite directions.

5—Applying Newton's Laws
Conceptual Questions

Q5.1. Reason: For an object to be in equilibrium, the net force (i.e., sum of the forces) must be zero. Assume that the two forces mentioned in the question are the only ones acting on the object.
The question boils down to asking if two forces can sum to zero if they aren't in opposite directions. Mental visualization shows that the answer is no, but so does a careful analysis. Set up a coordinate system with the x-axis along one of the forces. If the other force is not along the negative x-axis then there will be a y (or z) component that cannot be canceled by the first one along the x-axis.
Assess: In summary, two forces not in opposite directions cannot sum to zero. Neither can two forces with different magnitudes. However, three can.

Q5.3. Reason: Assume you are sitting in a chair, and that you are at rest. (Parts of your body may be moving, but if you model your body as a particle, then you generally aren't moving much as you read.) The two forces that act on you are the gravitational force of the earth on you, directed down; and the normal force of the chair pushing up on you. These two forces are equal in magnitude and opposite in direction and so the sum (the net force) is zero.

Assess: When you aren't accelerating Newton's second law says you experience a zero net force. So this analysis would apply equally to the case of you reading this while sitting in a chair on a smoothly moving (constant velocity) train.

Q5.5. Reason: The reading on the moon will be the moon-weight, or the gravitational force of the moon on the astronaut. This would be about 1/6 of the astronaut's earth-weight or the gravitational force of the earth on the astronaut (while standing on the scales on the earth).

Assess: Some physicists and textbooks define weight to be "what the scale reads" in which case it will read the astronaut's weight on the moon—by definition. But it won't read the same weight as on the earth. While not all physicists agree on the best definition of "weight" our textbook uses a very standard and reasonable approach.

The astronaut's *mass* does not change by going to the moon.

Q5.7. Reason: If we ignore air resistance as instructed, then the balls are in free fall.

The net force in free fall is simply the force of gravity, which is the mass times g. Therefore, a ranking of the net forces is the same as a ranking of the masses, since g is constant for all four balls.

$$F_{\text{net }4} > F_{\text{net }2} = F_{\text{net }3} > F_{\text{net }1}$$

Assess: The velocities are irrelevant to the net force.

Note that although all four balls are in free fall (and have the same acceleration), they do not experience the same gravitational force.

Q5.9. Reason: The normal force (by definition) is directed perpendicular to the surface.

(a) If the surface that exerts a force on an object is vertical, then the normal force would be horizontal. An example would be holding a picture on a wall by pushing on it horizontally. The wall would exert a normal force horizontally.

(b) In a similar vein, if the surface that exerts a force on an object is horizontal and above the object, then the normal force would be down. One example would be holding a picture on a ceiling by pushing on it. The ceiling would exert a normal force vertically downward. Another example would be the Newton's third law pair force in the case of you sitting on a chair; the chair exerts a normal force upward on you, so you exert a normal force downward on the chair.

Assess: We see that the normal force can be in any direction; it is always perpendicular to the surface pushing on the object in question.

Q5.11. Reason: Use the simple model in Section 5.6 and assume that

$$D \approx \frac{1}{4}\rho A v^2$$

For object 1: $A = 0.20 \text{ m} \times 0.30 \text{ m} = 0.060 \text{m}^2$; $v^2 = (6 \text{ m/s})^2 = 36 \text{ m}^2/\text{s}^2$;   so $Av^2 = 2.2 \text{ m}^4/\text{s}^2$

For object 2: $A = 0.20 \text{ m} \times 0.20 \text{ m} = 0.040 \text{m}^2$; $v^2 = (6 \text{ m/s})^2 = 36 \text{ m}^2/\text{s}^2$;   so $Av^2 = 1.4 \text{ m}^4/\text{s}^2$

For object 3: $A = 0.30 \text{ m} \times 0.30 \text{ m} = 0.090 \text{m}^2$; $v^2 = (4 \text{ m/s})^2 = 16 \text{ m}^2/\text{s}^2$;   so $Av^2 = 1.4 \text{ m}^4/\text{s}^2$

The density of air ρ is the same for all three objects, so it won't affect the ranking. Therefore, $D_1 > D_2 = D_3$.

Assess: Note that because v is squared, object 3's greater cross-sectional area did not produce the largest drag force.

Q5.13. Reason: Raindrops would all have the same acceleration if they were in free fall, but if some started falling higher or earlier than others they could hit the ground at different speeds. However, raindrops are not in free fall; the air resistance is a significant factor. We can assume that the drops reach terminal speed before hitting the ground.

Bigger drops experience a greater downward gravitational force than small drops, because they have more mass. However, bigger drops also experience a greater upward air resistance drag force because their cross-sectional area is larger. But these two effects do not grow at the same rate; the mass (and hence the downward force) grows with r^3, while the cross-sectional area grows with r^2. Therefore, as the size of drops increases the downward force grows faster than the upward force. So larger, more massive drops fall faster than smaller drops.

Assess: Air resistance makes all the difference. If there weren't any, all drops would have the same acceleration and they would be going *very* fast when they hit the ground. Rain drops generally do reach terminal speed, but not every drop has the same terminal speed. Larger drops have greater terminal speed.

Q5.15. Reason: If you only consider objects dropped from rest and accelerating up to terminal speed you might think that is the maximum speed the object can go through the air. However, terminal speed is merely the condition when the gravitational force and the air resistance force have the same magnitude and sum to zero. That doesn't necessarily mean it is the fastest possible speed.

It would be quite possible to throw or fire an object straight down from a high cliff at greater than terminal speed. The higher speed would mean that the upward drag force is greater than the downward gravitational force, so the net force would be up, the acceleration would be up, and the object would slow down to terminal speed, at which time the forces would cancel and the downward velocity would be constant.

Assess: The direction isn't crucial either; and object can also go up at faster than terminal speed, but the important aspects of the issue are most easily shown in the case above.

It is also possible to start from rest and speed up past terminal speed if there is another force which makes the net force non-zero and so acceleration can continue; an example of this would be a rocket-powered missile.

Q5.17. Reason: The tension is 49 N. It reads the same as it would if the rope were attached to the ceiling. The role of the five kilogram mass on the left is to keep the system in equilibrium, but it doesn't make the tension more than 49 N.

Assess: Apply Newton's second law to the mass on the right; the upward tension in the rope must equal the downward force of gravity. The scale reads the tension in the rope.

Q5.19. Reason: This question is very similar to Question 5.17. The tension is 49 N. It is the same as if the rope were attached to a wall on the left instead of the rope that goes over the left pulley. The role of the five kilogram mass on the left is to keep the system in equilibrium, but it doesn't make the tension more than 49 N.

Assess: Apply Newton's second law to the mass on the right; the upward tension in the rope must equal the downward force of gravity. The pulley (in our simple model) merely changes the direction of the force.

Multiple-Choice Questions

Q5.21. Reason: In this case there is not enough information to tell, because we don't know which way the block would go if the friction were reduced. Think of extreme cases to see this. If block 1 were much, much more massive than block 2 it would slide down the ramp if friction were reduced sufficiently; in that case (if the friction weren't reduced) the static would have to be up the ramp to hold block 1 there. On the other hand, if block 2 were much, much more massive than block 1, then block 1 would slide up the ramp if friction were reduced sufficiently; in that case (if the friction weren't reduced) the static friction would have to be down the ramp to hold block 1 there. Since we don't know the masses we don't know which extreme case is closer to our situation. So the answer is D.

Assess: By examining limiting cases we get a good feel for the situation. It *looks* like block 1 is more massive than block 2, but we aren't told, and there isn't enough information to decide which way it would slide if friction were reduced.

Q5.23. Reason: We will employ Newton's third law in part **(a)** and Newton's second law in part **(b)**.

(a) Newton's third law says that if object A (you) exerts a force on object B (the ceiling), then object B (the ceiling) exerts a force with equal magnitude and opposite direction on object A (you). Therefore the ceiling exerts a force of 100 N on you. The correct choice is B.

(b) This part is trickier; we must use the fact that while standing still, you are in equilibrium (i.e., the net force on you is zero). The individual forces on you are: the downward gravitational force of the earth on you (your weight), the downward force of the ceiling on you (which we just found to be 100 N), and the upward force of the floor on you (which we want to know). These must sum to zero. In other words the magnitude of the upward force of the floor must equal the sum of the magnitudes of the two downward forces, 690 N (your weight) and 100 N. The correct choice is D.

Assess: Especially note that in part **(b)** the magnitude of the force of the floor on you is not the same as the magnitude of the earth's gravitational force on you, as it would have been if you hadn't been pushing on the ceiling.

Q5.25. Reason: We must remember the east-west coordinate is independent of the north-south coordinate. The eastward component of velocity (4.5 m/s) will remain constant.

(a) We treat the northward component of the motion as a constant acceleration problem. First we use $F = ma$ to solve for $a = F/m = (6.0 \text{ N}) (3.0 \text{ kg}) - 2.0 \text{ m/s}^2$. Then we use $\Delta v = a\Delta t$, remembering that $v_i = 0.0$ m/s. So the northward component of the velocity is

$$v_f = a\Delta t = (2.0 \text{ m/s}^2)(1.5 \text{ s}) = 3.0 \text{ m/s}$$

The correct choice is C.

(b) We have a northward component of 3.0 m/s and an eastward component of 4.5 m/s.

$$v = \sqrt{(v_{north})^2 + (v_{east})^2} = \sqrt{(3.0 \text{ m/s})^2 + (4.5 \text{ m/s})^2} = 5.4 \text{ m/s}$$

The correct choice is B.

Assess: This question is reminiscent of projectile motion problems with a constant velocity in one direction and a constant acceleration in a perpendicular direction. A puck with a mass of 3 kg is quite heavy, much more so than a hockey puck.

Q5.27. Reason: This is still a Newton's second law question; the only twist is that the object is not in equilibrium, i.e., the right side of the second law is not zero.

The forces on Eric are the downward gravitational force of the earth on him w, and the upward normal force of the scale on him n (which we want to know). We note that $a = -1.7$ m/s^2 and $w = mg = (60 \text{ kg})(9.8 \text{ m/s}^2) = 5.88$ N.

This is a one-dimensional question in the vertical direction, so the following equations are all in the y-direction.

$$F_{net} = ma$$
$$n - w = ma$$
$$n = ma + w = (60 \text{ kg})(-1.7 \text{ m/s}^2) + 588\text{N} = 486\text{N} \approx 500\text{N}$$

The correct choice is C.

Assess: Because the elevator is accelerating down, we expect the scale to read a bit less than Eric's normal weight. This is the case. It is important that neither the question nor the answer specify whether the elevator is moving up or down. The elevator can be accelerating down in two ways: It can be moving up and slowing (such as the end of a trip from a low floor to a high floor), or it can be moving down and gaining speed (such as the beginning of a trip from a high floor to a low floor). The answer is the same in both cases.

Q5.29. Reason: We will assume a constant direction so that plus the "constant speed" means no acceleration. The sled is in equilibrium and the net force on it must be zero.

In the horizontal direction there are two forces on the sled: the football player pushing on it, and kinetic friction acting in the opposite direction. These two must have the same magnitude.

Equation 5.11 tells us that $f_k = \mu_k n$, but we don't yet know n.

Independently analyzing the vertical direction reveals that the magnitude of $\vec{n}$ is the same as the magnitude of $w = mg = (60 \text{ kg})(9.8 \text{ m/s}^2) = 590$ N. So the kinetic friction force is $f_k = \mu_k n = (0.30)(590 \text{ N}) = 180$ N. And that must also be the magnitude of the football player's pushing force.

The correct answer is C.

Assess: Choices A and B don't seem very strenuous for a football player, but choice D seems like too much. Choice C is in the right range.

Q5.31. Reason: We can find the drag force using Equation 5.14.

Solve: Using Equation 5.15, $D \approx \frac{1}{4}\rho A v^2$ with $\rho = 1.22$ kg/m^3. The area of the car is $A = (1.6 \text{ m})(1.4 \text{ m}) = 2.24$ m^2, where an additional significant figure has been kept in this intermediate calculation.

(a) $D \approx \frac{1}{4}(1.22 \text{ kg/m}^3)(2.24 \text{ m}^2)(10 \text{ m/s})^2 \approx 68\text{N}$

(b) $D \approx \frac{1}{4}(1.22 \text{ kg/m}^3)(2.24 \text{ m}^2)(30 \text{ m/s})^2 \approx 610\text{N}$

Assess: Note that the drag increases with the square of the speed, so that at 30 m/s, the drag force is nine times what it is at 10 m/s.

Problems

P5.1. Prepare: The massless ring is in static equilibrium, so all the forces acting on it must cancel to give a zero net force. The forces acting on the ring are shown on a free-body diagram below.

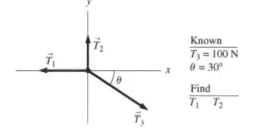

Solve: Written in component form, Newton's first law is

$$(F_{net})_x = \Sigma F_x = T_{1x} + T_{2x} + T_{3x} = 0 \text{ N} \qquad (F_{net})_y = \Sigma F_y = T_{1y} + T_{2y} + T_{3y} = 0 \text{ N}$$

Evaluating the components of the force vectors from the free-body diagram:

$$T_{1x} = -T_1 \qquad T_{2x} = 0 \text{ N} \qquad T_{3x} = T_3\cos30°$$
$$T_{1y} = 0 \text{ N} \qquad T_{2y} = T_2 \qquad T_{3y} = -T_3\sin30°$$

Using Newton's first law:

$$-T_1 + T_3\cos30° = 0 \text{ N} \qquad T_2 - T_3\sin30° = 0 \text{ N}$$

Rearranging:

$$T_1 = T_3\cos30° = (100 \text{ N})(0.8666) = 87 \text{ N} \qquad T_2 = T_3\sin30° = (100 \text{ N})(0.5) = 50 \text{ N}$$

Assess: Since $\vec{T}_3$ acts closer to the x-axis than to the y-axis, it makes sense that $T_1 > T_2$.

P5.3. Prepare: We assume the speaker is a particle in static equilibrium under the influence of three forces: gravity and the tensions in the two cables. So, all the forces acting on it must cancel to give a zero net force. The forces acting on the speaker are shown on a free-body diagram below. Because each cable makes an angle of 30° with the vertical, so $\theta = 60°$.

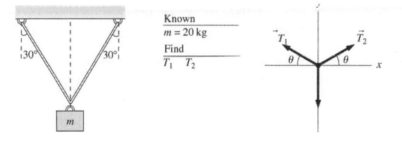

Solve: Newton's first law for this situation is

$$(F_{net})_x = \Sigma F_x = T_{1x} + T_{2x} = 0 \text{ N} \Rightarrow -T_1 \cos\theta + T_2 \cos\theta = 0 \text{ N}$$
$$(F_{net})_y = \Sigma F_y = T_{1y} + T_{2y} + w_y = 0 \text{ N} \Rightarrow T_1 \sin\theta + T_2 \sin\theta - w = 0 \text{ N}$$

The x-component equation means $T_1 = T_2$. From the y-component equation:

$$2T_1 \sin\theta = w \Rightarrow T_1 = \frac{w}{2\sin\theta} = \frac{mg}{2\sin\theta} = \frac{(20 \text{ kg})(9.8 \text{ m/s}^2)}{2\sin60°} = \frac{196 \text{ N}}{1.732} = 113 \text{ N}$$

Assess: It's to be expected that the two tensions are equal, since the speaker is suspended symmetrically from the two cables.

P5.5. Prepare: Draw a free-body diagram showing all three forces on the urn. The net force is zero because the urn is raised at a constant speed.

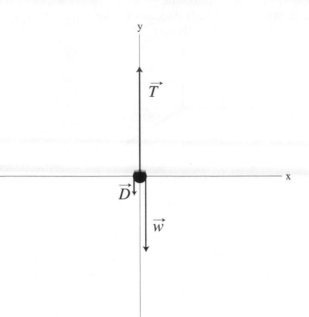

Solve: Use Newton's second law.

$$F_{net} = T - mg - D = 0 \Rightarrow T = mg + D = (25 \text{ kg})(9.8 \text{ m/s}^2) + 25 \text{ N} = 270 \text{ N}$$

Assess: With the drag force we intuitively expect the tension in the rope to be greater than the urn's weight.

P5.7. Prepare: The tension in the more vertical of the two angled ropes (the right one) will have a greater tension, so we apply. Newton's second law and set $T_{right} = 1500$ N and solve for m. T_{left} will be less than 1500 N and will not break.
    Solve:

$$\Sigma F_x = T_{right} \cos 45° - T_{left} \cos 30° = 0$$
$$\Sigma F_y = T_{right} \sin 45° + T_{left} \sin 30° - mg = 0$$

There are various strategies to solve such a system of linear equations. One is to put the two T_{left} terms on the left side and then divide the two equations.

$$T_{left} \sin 30° = mg - T_{right} \sin 45°$$
$$T_{left} \cos 30° = T_{right} \cos 45°$$

Now dividing these two equations cancels T_{left} on the left (since we don't need T_{left}) and leaves $\tan 30°$,

$$\tan 30° = \frac{mg - T_{right} \sin 45°}{T_{right} \cos 45°}$$

Solve for m and set $T_{right} = 1500$ N.

$$m = \frac{T_{right}(\tan 30° \cos 45° + \sin 45°)}{g} = \frac{(1500 \text{ N})(\tan 30° \cos 45° + \sin 45°)}{9.8 \text{ m/s}^2} = 170 \text{ kg}$$

Assess: The answer seems reasonable, since if there were only one vertical rope it could hold $(1500\text{N})/(9.8 \text{ m/s}^2) = 153$ kg and here we have the left rope to help.
    The original set of two linear equations with two unknowns could also be solved with matrices.

$$\begin{bmatrix} \cos 45° & -\cos 30° \\ \sin 45° & \sin 30° \end{bmatrix} \begin{bmatrix} T_{right} \\ T_{left} \end{bmatrix} = \begin{bmatrix} 0 \\ mg \end{bmatrix}$$

P5.9. Prepare: According to Newton's second law $F = ma$, so the acceleration at any time is found simply by dividing the value of the force by the mass of the object.

Solve: We divide each force on the graph in Figure P5.9 by $m = 2.0$ kg and obtain the following acceleration-versus-time graph.

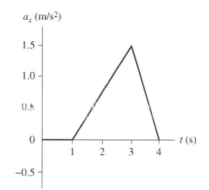

P5.11. Prepare: Please refer to Figure P5.11. The free-body diagram shows three forces acting on an object whose mass is 2.0 kg. The force in the first quadrant has two components: 4 N along the x-axis and 3 N along the y-axis. We will first find the net force along the x- and the y-axes and then divide these forces by the object's mass to obtain the x- and y-components of the object's acceleration.

Solve: Applying Newton's second law to the diagram on the left,

$$a_x = \frac{(F_{net})_x}{m} = \frac{4\text{ N} - 2\text{ N}}{2\text{ kg}} = 1.0\text{ m/s}^2 \qquad a_y = \frac{(F_{net})_y}{m} = \frac{3\text{ N} - 3\text{ N}}{2\text{ kg}} = 0\text{ m/s}^2$$

Assess: The object's motion is only along the x-axis.

P5.13. Prepare: We assume that the box is a particle being pulled in a straight line. Since the ice is frictionless, the tension in the rope is the only horizontal force on the box and is shown below in the free-body diagram. Since we are looking at horizontal motion of the box, we are not interested in the vertical forces in this problem.

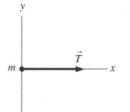

Solve: (a) Since the box is at rest, $a_x = 0$ m/s^2, the net force on the box must be zero or the tension in the rope must be zero.

(b) For this situation again, $a_x = 0$ m/s^2, so $F_{net} = T = 0$ N.

(c) Here, the velocity of the box is irrelevant, since only a *change* in velocity requires a nonzero net force. Since $a_x = 5.0$ m/s^2,

$$F_{net} = T = ma_x = (50\text{ kg})(5.0\text{ m/s}^2) = 250\text{ N}$$

Assess: For parts **(a)** and **(b)**, the zero acceleration immediately implies that the rope is exerting no horizontal force on the box. For part **(c)**, the 250 N force (the equivalent of about half the weight of a small person) seems reasonable to accelerate a box of this mass at 5.0 m/s^2.

P5.15. Prepare: We assume that the seat belt supplies all the force necessary to decelerate the driver (that is, $F_{seatbelt} = F_{net}$), and that the deceleration is constant over the time interval of 0.10 s. Set up a coordinate system with the car traveling to the right along the x-axis.

We use the kinematics equations from Chapter 2 to solve for the constant acceleration, and then $F_{net} = ma$ (with $m = 70$ kg) to solve for the force exerted by the seat belt.

Solve: The definition of acceleration says

$$a_x = \frac{\Delta v_x}{\Delta t} = \frac{0.0 \text{ m/s} - 14 \text{ m/s}}{0.10 \text{ s}} = -140 \text{ m/s}^2$$

where the negative sign indicates that the car (which is traveling to the right) is slowing down.

$$F_{\text{seatbelt}} = F_{\text{net}} = ma_x = (70 \text{ kg})(-140 \text{ m/s}^2) = -9800 \text{ N}$$

where the negative sign shows the force acting in the negative x-direction (the same direction as the acceleration).

Assess: 9800 N is quite a bit of force, but so it is in a head-on collision at a significant speed. You can see from the equations above that if the crash had taken more time the force would not be so severe; save that thought for a future chapter.

P5.17. Solve: (a) The woman's weight on the earth is

$$w_{\text{earth}} = mg_{\text{earth}} = (55 \text{ kg})(9.8 \text{ m/s}^2) = 540 \text{ N}$$

(b) Since mass is a measure of the amount of matter, the woman's mass is the same on the moon as on the earth. Her weight on the moon is

$$w_{\text{moon}} = mg_{\text{moon}} = (55 \text{ kg})(1.62 \text{ m/s}^2) = 89 \text{ N}$$

Assess: The smaller acceleration due to gravity on the moon reveals that objects are less strongly attracted to the moon than to the earth. Thus the woman's smaller weight on the moon makes sense.

P5.19. Prepare: The astronaut and the chair will be denoted by A and C, respectively, and they are separate systems. The launch pad is a part of the environment. The free-body diagrams for both the astronaut and the chair are shown below at rest on the launch pad (top) and while accelerating (bottom).

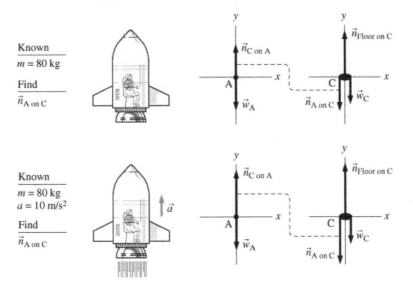

Solve: (a) Newton's second law for the astronaut is

$$\Sigma(F_{\text{on A}})_y = n_{\text{C on A}} - w_A = m_A a_A = 0 \text{ N} \Rightarrow n_{\text{C on A}} = w_A = m_A g$$

By Newton's third law, the astronaut's force on the chair is

$$n_{\text{A on C}} = n_{\text{C on A}} = m_A g = (80 \text{ kg})(9.8 \text{ m/s}^2) = 780 \text{ N}$$

(b) Newton's second law for the astronaut is:

$$\Sigma(F_{\text{on A}})_y = n_{\text{C on A}} - w_A = m_A a_A \Rightarrow n_{\text{C on A}} = w_A + m_A a_A = m_A(g + a_A)$$

By Newton's third law, the astronaut's force on the chair is

$$n_{\text{A on C}} = n_{\text{C on A}} = m_A(g + a_A) = (80 \text{ kg})(9.8 \text{ m/s}^2 + 10 \text{ m/s}^2) = 1600 \text{ N}$$

Assess: This is a reasonable value because the astronaut's acceleration is more than g.

P5.21. Prepare: We'll assume Zach is a particle moving under the effect of two forces acting in a single vertical line: gravity and the supporting force of the elevator. These forces are shown on page 5-18 in a free-body diagram. We will use Equation 5.8 to find the apparent weight.

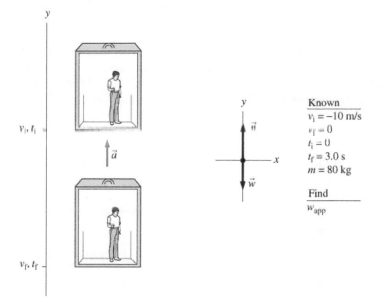

Solve: (a) Before the elevator starts braking, Zach is not accelerating. His apparent weight (see Equation 5.8) is

$$w_{app} = w\left(1+\frac{a}{g}\right) = w\left(1+\frac{0 \text{ m/s}^2}{g}\right) = mg = (80 \text{ kg})(9.8 \text{ m/s}^2) = 784 \text{ N } 780 \text{ N}$$

(b) Using the definition of acceleration,

$$a = \frac{\Delta v}{\Delta t} = \frac{v_f - v_i}{t_f - t_i} = \frac{0-(-10) \text{ m/s}}{3.0 \text{ s}} = 3.33 \text{ m/s}^2$$

$$\Rightarrow w_{app} = w\left(1+\frac{a}{g}\right) = (80 \text{ kg})(9.8 \text{ m/s}^2)\left(1+\frac{3.33 \text{ m/s}^2}{9.8 \text{ m/s}^2}\right) = (784 \text{ N})(1+0.340) = 1100 \text{ N}$$

Assess: While the elevator is braking, it not only must support Zach's weight but must also push upward on him to decelerate him, so the apparent weight is greater than his normal weight.

P5.23. Prepare: In each case the frog is in equilibrium ($\vec{F}_{net} = \vec{0}$).

Solve: (a) The two forces on the frog act in the vertical direction: the weight (gravitational force of the earth down on the frog), and the normal force of the log up on the frog. The two must have equal magnitude; since $w = mg$ (0.60 kg) (9.8 m/s²) = 5.9 N, then the magnitude of the normal force is also 5.9 N.

(b) Draw a free-body diagram for the frog. Use tilted axes with the x-axis running up the log.

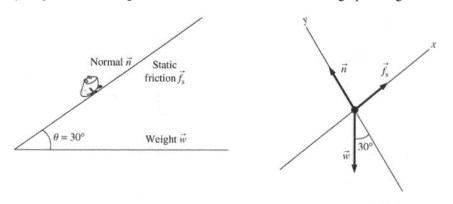

Apply $F_{net} = ma$ in the y-direction.

$$n - w\cos\theta = 0$$
$$n = w\,\cos\theta = mg\cos\theta = (0.60\text{ kg})(9.8\text{ m/s}^2)\cos 30° = 5.1\text{ N}$$

Assess: The answer is less in part (**b**) than in part (**a**), as we would expect. The static friction force is also helping hold up the frog in part (**b**).

Notice that we solved the problem algebraically before putting numbers in. This not only allows us to solve a similar problem for a different frog or log, but it enables us to check our answer in this case for reasonableness. Take the limit as $\theta \to 0$; the slope approaches zero and the conditions revert back to part (**a**) as $\cos\theta \to 1$. Then take the limit as $\theta \to 90°$ and the normal force decreases to zero as the log becomes vertical and there is no normal force on the frog.

P5.25. Prepare: We assume that the safe is a particle moving only in the x-direction. Since it is sliding during the entire problem, the force of kinetic friction opposes the motion by pointing to the left. We give below a pictorial representation and a free-body diagram for the safe. The safe is in dynamic equilibrium, since it's not accelerating.

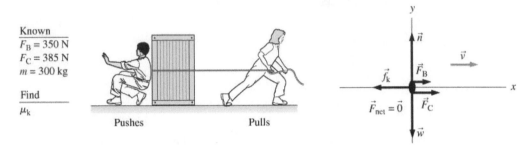

Known
$F_B = 350\text{ N}$
$F_C = 385\text{ N}$
$m = 300\text{ kg}$

Find
μ_k

Pushes Pulls

Solve: We apply Newton's first law in the vertical and horizontal directions:

$$(F_{net})_x = \Sigma F_x = F_B + F_C - f_k = 0\text{ N} \Rightarrow f_k = F_B + F_C = 350\text{ N} + 385\text{ N} = 735\text{ N}$$
$$(F_{net})_y = \Sigma F_y = n - w = 0\text{ N} \Rightarrow n = w = mg = (300\text{ kg})(9.8\text{ m/s}^2) = 2940\text{ N}$$

Then, for kinetic friction:

$$f_k = \mu_k n \Rightarrow \mu_k = \frac{f_k}{n} = \frac{735\text{ N}}{2940\text{ N}} = 0.25$$

Assess: The value of $\mu_k = 0.25$ is hard to evaluate without knowing the material the floor is made of, but it seems reasonable.

P5.27. Prepare: The car is undergoing skidding, so it is decelerating and the force of kinetic friction acts to the left. We give below an overview of the pictorial representation, a motion diagram, a free-body diagram, and a list of values. We will first apply Newton's second law to find the deceleration and then use kinematics to obtain the length of the skid marks.

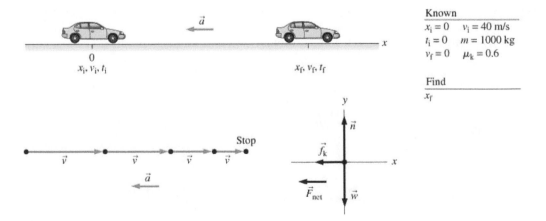

Known
$x_i = 0$ $v_i = 40\text{ m/s}$
$t_i = 0$ $m = 1000\text{ kg}$
$v_f = 0$ $\mu_k = 0.6$

Find
x_f

Solve: We begin with Newton's second law. Although the motion is one-dimensional, we need to consider forces in both the x- and y-directions. However, we know that $a_y = 0$ m/s^2. We have

$$a_x = \frac{(F_{net})_x}{m} = \frac{-f_k}{m} \qquad a_y = 0 \text{ m/s}^2 = \frac{(F_{net})_y}{m} = \frac{n-w}{m} = \frac{n-mg}{m}$$

We used $(f_k)_x = -f_k$ because the free-body diagram tells us that $\vec{f}_k$ points to the left. The force of kinetic friction relates $\vec{f}_k$ to $\vec{n}$ with the equation $f_k = \mu_k n$. The y-equation is solved to give $n = mg$. Thus, the kinetic friction force is $f_k = \mu_k mg$. Substituting this into the x-equation yields:

$$a_x = \frac{-\mu_k mg}{m} = -\mu_k g = -(0.6)(9.8 \text{ m/s}^2) = -5.88 \text{ m/s}^2$$

The acceleration is negative because the acceleration vector points to the left as the car slows. Now we have a constant-acceleration kinematics problem. Δt isn't known, so use

$$v_f^2 = 0 \text{ m}^2/\text{s}^2 = v_i^2 + 2a_x \Delta x \Rightarrow \Delta x = -\frac{(40 \text{ m/s})^2}{2(-5.88 \text{ m/s}^2)} = 140 \text{ m}$$

Assess: The skid marks are 140 m long. This is $\approx$430 feet, reasonable for a car traveling at $\approx$80 mph. It is worth noting that an algebraic solution led to the m canceling out.

P5.29. Prepare: We show below the free-body diagrams of the crate when the conveyer belt runs at constant speed (part **a**) and the belt is speeding up (part **b**).

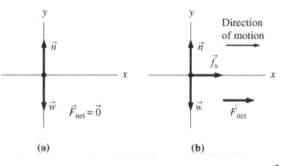

Solve: (a) When the belt runs at constant speed, the crate has an acceleration $\vec{a} = \vec{0}$ m/s^2 and is in dynamic equilibrium. Thus $\vec{F}_{net} = \vec{0}$. It is tempting to think that the belt exerts a friction force on the crate. But if it did, there would be a *net* force because there are no other possible horizontal forces to balance a friction force. Because there is no net force, there cannot be a friction force. The only forces are the upward normal force and the crate's weight. (A friction force would have been needed to get the crate moving initially, but no horizontal force is needed to keep it moving once it is moving with the same constant speed as the belt.)

(b) If the belt accelerates gently, the crate speeds up without slipping on the belt. Because it is accelerating, the crate must have a net horizontal force. So *now* there is a friction force, and the force points in the direction of the crate's motion. Is it static friction or kinetic friction? Although the crate is moving, there is *no* motion of the crate relative to the belt. Thus, it is a *static* friction force that accelerates the crate so that it moves without slipping on the belt.

(c) The static friction force has a maximum possible value $(f_s)_{max} = \mu_s n$. The maximum possible acceleration of the crate is

$$a_{max} = \frac{(f_s)_{max}}{m} = \frac{\mu_s n}{m}$$

If the belt accelerates more rapidly than this, the crate will not be able to keep up and will slip. It is clear from the free-body diagram that $n = w = mg$. Thus,

$$a_{max} = \mu_s g = (0.50)(9.8 \text{ m/s}^2) = 4.9 \text{ m/s}^2$$

(d) The acceleration of the crate will be: $a = \mu_k g = (0.30)(9.8 \text{ m/s}^2) = 2.9 \text{ m/s}^2$.

P5.31. Prepare: We can find the drag force using Equation 5.15.

Solve: Using Equation 5.15, $D \approx \frac{1}{4}\rho A v^2$ with $\rho = 1.29$ kg/m^3. The area of the car is $A = (1.6 \text{ m})(1.4 \text{ m}) = 2.24$ m^2, where an additional significant figure has been kept in this intermediate calculation.

(a) $D \approx \frac{1}{4}(1.29 \text{ kg/m}^3)(2.24 \text{ m}^2)(10 \text{ m/s})^2$, so $D \approx 72$ N

(b) $D \approx \frac{1}{4}(1.29 \text{ kg/m}^3)(2.24 \text{ m}^2)(30 \text{ m/s})^2$, so $D \approx 650$ N

Assess: Note that the drag increases with the square of the speed, so that at 30 m/s, the drag force is nine times what it is at 10 m/s.

P5.33. Prepare: We assume that the skydiver is shaped like a box. A pictorial representation of the skydiver and a free-body diagram at terminal speed are shown below. The skydiver falls straight down toward the earth's surface, that is, the direction of fall is vertical. Since the skydiver falls feet first, the surface perpendicular to the drag has the cross-sectional area $A = 20$ cm $\times$ 40 cm. The physical conditions needed to use Equation 5.15 for the drag force to be satisfied. The terminal speed corresponds to the situation when the net force acting on the skydiver becomes zero.

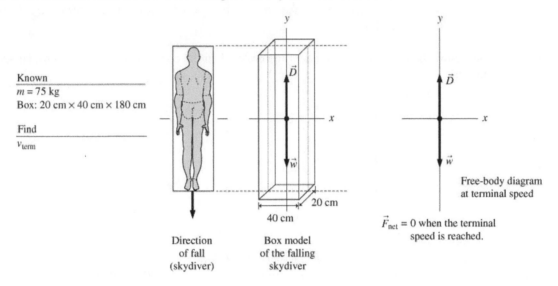

Solve: The expression for the magnitude of the drag with v in m/s is

$$D \approx \frac{1}{4}\rho A v^2 = 0.25(1.22 \text{ kg/m}^3)(0.20 \text{ m} \times 0.40 \text{ m})v^2 \text{ N} = 0.0244 v^2 \text{ N}$$

The skydiver's weight is $w = mg = (75 \text{ kg})(9.8 \text{ m/s}^2) = 735$ N. The mathematical form of the condition defining dynamical equilibrium for the skydiver and the terminal speed is

$$\vec{F}_{net} = \vec{w} + \vec{D} = 0 \text{ N} \Rightarrow 0.0244 v^2_{term} \text{ N} - 735 \text{ N} = 0 \text{ N} \Rightarrow v_{term} = \sqrt{\frac{735}{0.0244}} \approx 170 \text{ m/s}$$

Assess: The result of the above simplified physical modeling approach and subsequent calculation, even if approximate, shows that the terminal velocity is very high. This result implies that the skydiver will be very badly hurt at landing if the parachute does not open in time.

P5.35. Prepare: The blocks are denoted as 1, 2, and 3. The surface is frictionless and along with the earth it is a part of the environment. The three blocks are our three systems of interest. The force applied on block 1 is $F_{A\ on\ 1} = 12$ N. The acceleration for all the blocks is the same and is denoted by a. A visual overview shows a pictorial representation, a list of known and unknown values, and a free-body diagram for the three blocks.

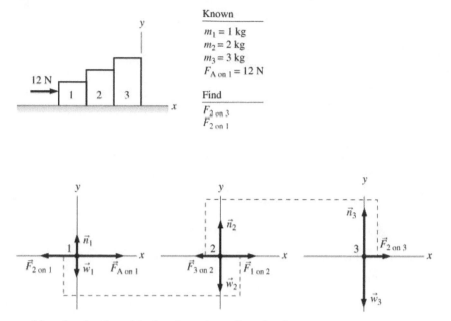

Known
$m_1 = 1$ kg
$m_2 = 2$ kg
$m_3 = 3$ kg
$F_{A\ on\ 1} = 12$ N

Find
$F_{2\ on\ 3}$
$F_{2\ on\ 1}$

Solve: Newton's second law for the three blocks along the x-direction is

$$\Sigma(F_{on\ 1})_x = F_{A\ on\ 1} - F_{2\ on\ 1} = m_1 a \qquad \Sigma(F_{on\ 2})_x = F_{1\ on\ 2} - F_{3\ on\ 2} = m_2 a \qquad \Sigma(F_{on\ 3})_x = F_{2\ on\ 3} = m_3 a$$

Adding these three equations and using Newton's third law ($F_{2\ on\ 1} = F_{1\ on\ 2}$ and $F_{3\ on\ 2} = F_{2\ on\ 3}$), we get

$$F_{A\ on\ 1} = (m_1 + m_2 + m_3)a \Rightarrow (12\ \text{N}) = (1\ \text{kg} + 2\ \text{kg} + 3\ \text{kg})a \Rightarrow a = 2\ \text{m/s}^2$$

Using this value of a, the force equation on block 3 gives

$$F_{2\ on\ 3} = m_3 a = (3\ \text{kg})(2\ \text{m/s}^2) = 6\ \text{N}$$

Substituting into the force equation on block 1,

$$12\ \text{N} - F_{2\ on\ 1} = (1\ \text{kg})(2\ \text{m/s}^2) \Rightarrow F_{2\ on\ 1} = 10\ \text{N}$$

Assess: Because all three blocks are pushed forward by a force of 12 N, the value of 10 N for the force that the 2 kg block exerts on the 1 kg block is reasonable.

P5.37. Prepare: A visual overview shows below a pictorial representation, a list of known and unknown values, and a free-body diagram for both the ice (I) and the rope (R). The force $\vec{F}_{ext}$ acts only on the rope. Since the rope and the ice block move together, they have the same acceleration. Also because the rope has mass, F_{ext} on the front end of the rope is not the same as $F_{I\ on\ R}$ that acts on the rear end of the rope.

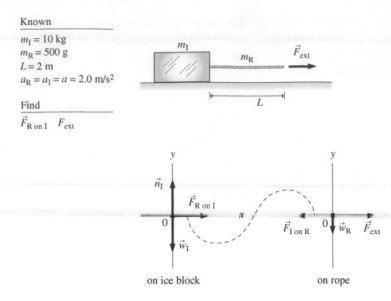

Known

$m_1 = 10$ kg
$m_R = 500$ g
$L = 2$ m
$a_R = a_1 = a = 2.0$ m/s²

Find

$\vec{F}_{\text{R on I}}$ F_{ext}

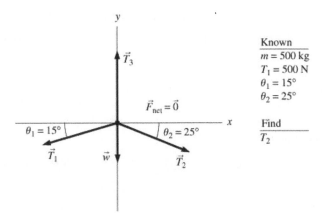

on ice block   on rope

Solve: (a) Newton's second law along the *x*-axis for the ice block is

$$\Sigma(F_{\text{on 1}})_x = F_{\text{R on 1}} = m_1 a = (10 \text{ kg})(2.0 \text{ m/s}^2) = 20 \text{ N}$$

(b) Newton's second law along the *x*-axis for the rope is

$$\Sigma(F_{\text{on R}})_x = F_{\text{ext}} - F_{\text{1 on R}} = m_R a \Rightarrow F_{\text{ext}} - F_{\text{R on 1}} = m_R a \Rightarrow F_{\text{ext}} = F_{\text{R on 1}} + m_R a = 20 \text{ N} + (0.5 \text{ kg})(2.0 \text{ m/s}^2) = 21 \text{ N}$$

P5.39. Prepare: Since each block has the same acceleration as all the others they must each experience the same net force. Each block will have one more newton pulling forward than the force pulling back on it from the blocks behind.
Solve:
(a) 1 N
(b) 50 N
Assess: Since 100 N accelerates 100 blocks, then *n* newtons accelerates *n* blocks.

P5.41. Prepare: Because the piano is to descend at a steady speed, it is in dynamic equilibrium. A free-body diagram of the piano and a list of values are shown below.

Known

$m = 500$ kg
$T_1 = 500$ N
$\theta_1 = 15°$
$\theta_2 = 25°$

Find

T_2

Solve: (a) Based on the free-body diagram, Newton's second law is

$$(F_{\text{net}})_x = 0 \text{ N} = T_{1x} + T_{2x} = T_2 \cos\theta - T_1 \cos\theta_1$$
$$(F_{\text{net}})_y = 0 \text{ N} = T_{1y} + T_{2y} + T_{3y} + w_y = T_3 - T_1 \sin\theta_1 - T_2 \sin\theta_2 - mg$$

Notice how the force components all appear in the second law with *plus* signs because we are *adding* vector forces. The negative signs appear only when we *evaluate* the various components. These are two simultaneous equations in the two unknowns T_2 and T_3. From the *x*-equation we find

$$T_2 = \frac{T_1 \cos\theta_1}{\cos\theta_2} = \frac{(500 \text{ N})\cos 15°}{\cos 25°} = 530 \text{ N}$$

(b) Now we can use the *y*-equation to find

$$T_3 = T_1 \sin\theta_1 + T_2 \sin\theta_2 + mg = 5300 \text{ N}$$

P5.43. Prepare: Please refer to Figure P5.41. To find the net force at a given time, we need the acceleration at that time. Because the times where we are asked to find the net force fall on distinct slopes of the velocity versus time graph, we can use the constant slopes of the three segments of the graph to calculate the three accelerations.
   Solve: For *t* between 0 s and 3 s,

$$a_x = \frac{\Delta v_x}{\Delta t} = \frac{12 \text{ m/s} - 0 \text{ s}}{3 \text{ s}} = 4 \text{ m/s}^2$$

For *t* between 3 s and 6 s, $\Delta v_x = 0$ m/s, so $a_x = 0$ m/s². For *t* between 6 s and 8 s,

$$a_x = \frac{\Delta v_x}{\Delta t} = \frac{0 \text{ m/s} - 12 \text{ m/s}}{2 \text{ s}} = -6 \text{ m/s}$$

From Newton's second law, at *t* = 1 s we have

$$F_{\text{net}} = ma_x = (2.0 \text{ kg})(4 \text{ m/s}^2) = 8 \text{ N}$$

At *t* = 4 s, $a_x = 0$ m/s², so $F_{\text{net}} = 0$ N.
At *t* = 7 s,

$$F_{\text{net}} = ma_x = (2.0 \text{ kg})(-6.0 \text{ m/s}^2) = -12 \text{ N}$$

   Assess: The magnitudes of the forces look reasonable, given the small mass of the object. The positive and negative signs are appropriate for an object first speeding up, then slowing down.

P5.45. Prepare: The box is acted on by two forces: the tension in the rope and the pull of gravity. Both the forces act along the same vertical line which is taken to be the *y*-axis. The free-body diagram for the box is shown below.

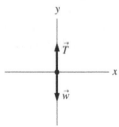

   Solve: (a) Since the box is at rest, $a_y = 0$ m/s² and the net force on it must be zero:

$$F_{\text{net}} = T - w = 0 \text{ N} \Rightarrow T = w = mg = (50 \text{ kg})(9.8 \text{ m/s}^2) = 490 \text{ N}$$

(b) The velocity of the box is irrelevant, since only a *change* in velocity requires a nonzero net force. Since $a_y = 5.0$ m/s²,

$$F_{\text{net}} = T - w = ma_y = (50 \text{ kg})(5.0 \text{ m/s}^2) = 250 \text{ N} \Rightarrow T = 250 \text{ N} + w = 250 \text{ N} + 490 \text{ N} = 740 \text{ N}$$

   Assess: For part **(a)** the zero acceleration immediately implies that the box's weight must be exactly balanced by the upward tension in the rope. For part **(b)** the tension not only has to support the box's weight but must also accelerate it upward, hence, *T* must be greater than *w*.

P5.47. Prepare: We will assume constant acceleration so we can use the equations of Table 2.4. Assume the baseball is initially moving in the positive x-direction. We list the known quantities:

Known
$m = 0.14$ kg
$(v_x)_i = 30$ m/s
$\Delta t = 0.0015$ s

Find
a
F

Solve: (a) With $(v_x)_f = 0$ m/s, we solve for a from $(v_x)_f = (v_x)_i + a_x \Delta t$.

$$a_x = \frac{-(v_x)_i}{\Delta t} = \frac{-(30 \text{ m/s})}{0.0015 \text{ s}} = -20{,}000 \text{ m/s}^2$$

The magnitude of this is 20,000 m/s² or 2.0×10^4 m/s².

(b) Apply Newton's second law: $\Sigma F_x = ma_x$ where the force of the body on the ball is the only force (and is therefore the net force).

$$\Sigma F_x = ma_x = (0.14 \text{ kg})(-20{,}000 \text{ m/s}^2) = -2800 \text{ N}$$

The magnitude of this is 2800 N. This force is exerted by the body the ball hits.

(c) By Newton's third law if the body exerts a force on the ball, then the ball exerts a force equal in magnitude and opposite in direction on the body. Therefore the ball applies a force of 2800 N to the object it hits.

(d) This force of 2.8 kN is less than 6.0 kN, so the forehead is not in danger (although it would still hurt and maybe raise a lump). This force of 2.8 kN is greater than 1.3 kN, so the cheek is in danger of fracture.

Assess: This is a nice real-life problem that employs the definition of acceleration and Newton's second and third laws. The data provided are typical of real baseballs and real pitching speeds, so the conclusion is also true-to-life. Catchers, whose faces are in the line of fire, wear masks for this reason.

P5.49. Prepare: The rock (R) and Bob (B) are two systems of our interest. We give below a pictorial representation, a list of values, and free-body diagrams for Bob and the rock. Motion of the rock is assumed to be along the x-axis. We realize that Bob must accelerate the rock forward until he releases the rock with a speed of 30 m/s. From the given information we can find this acceleration using kinematics. Newton's second law will then yield the force exerted on the rock by Bob. This is also the force that is exerted by the rock on Bob (Newton's third law). We can then calculate Bob's acceleration using his mass in Newton's second law. Kinematics once again can be used to find Bob's recoil speed.

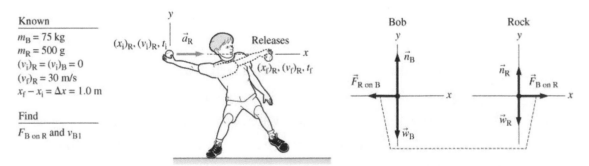

Known
$m_B = 75$ kg
$m_R = 500$ g
$(v_i)_R = (v_i)_B = 0$
$(v_f)_R = 30$ m/s
$x_f - x_i = \Delta x = 1.0$ m

Find
$F_{B \text{ on } R}$ and v_{B1}

Solve: (a) Bob exerts a forward force $\vec{F}_{B \text{ on } R}$ on the rock to accelerate it forward. The rock's acceleration is calculated as follows:

$$(v_f)_R^2 = (v_i)_R^2 + 2a_R \Delta x \Rightarrow a_R = \frac{(v_f)_R^2}{2\Delta x} = \frac{(30 \text{ m/s})^2}{2(1 \text{ m})} = 450 \text{ m/s}^2$$

The force is calculated from Newton's second law:

$$F_{\text{B on R}} = m_R a_R = (0.5 \text{ kg})(450 \text{ m/s}^2) = 225 \text{ N or } 230 \text{ N to two significant figures.}$$

(b) Because Bob pushes on the rock, the rock pushes back on Bob with a force $\vec{F}_{\text{R on B}}$. Forces $\vec{F}_{\text{R on B}}$ and $\vec{F}_{\text{R on B}}$ are an action/reaction pair, so $\vec{F}_{\text{R on B}} = \vec{F}_{\text{B on R}} = 225 \text{ N}$. The force causes Bob to accelerate backward with an acceleration equal to

$$a_B = \frac{(F_{\text{net on B}})_x}{m_B} = -\frac{F_{\text{R on B}}}{m_B} = \frac{225 \text{ N}}{75 \text{ kg}} = -3.0 \text{ m/s}^2$$

This is a rather large acceleration, but it lasts only until Bob releases the rock. We can determine the time interval by returning to the kinematics of the rock:

$$(v_i)_R - (v_i)_R + a_R \Delta t \Rightarrow \Delta t = \frac{(v_f)_R}{a_R} = 0.0667 \text{ s}$$

At the end of this interval, Bob's velocity is

$$(v_f)_B = (v_i)_B + a_B \Delta t = a_B \Delta t = -0.200 \text{ m/s}$$

Thus his recoil speed is 0.200 m/s.

P5.51. Prepare: We assume the rocket is moving in a vertical straight line along the y-axis under the influence of only two forces: gravity and its own thrust. The free-body diagram for the model rocket is shown later.

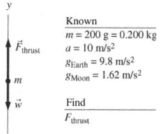

Solve: (a) Using Newton's second law and reading the forces from the free-body diagram,

$$F_{\text{thrust}} - w = ma \Rightarrow F_{\text{thrust}} = ma + mg_{\text{earth}} = (0.200 \text{ kg})(10 \text{ m/s}^2 + 9.8 \text{ m/s}^2) = 4.0 \text{ N}$$

(b) Likewise, the thrust on the moon is $(0.200 \text{ kg})(10 \text{ m/s}^2 + 1.62 \text{ m/s}^2) = 2.3 \text{ N}$.

Assess: The thrust required is smaller on the moon, as it should be, given the moon's weaker gravitational pull. The magnitude of a few newtons seems reasonable for a small model rocket.

P5.53. Prepare: Your body is moving in a straight line along the y-direction under the influence of two forces: gravity and the support force of the scale. The free-body diagrams for you for the following three cases are shown below: no acceleration, upward acceleration, and downward acceleration. The apparent weight (see Equation 5.8) of an object moving in an elevator is $w_{\text{app}} = w\left(1 + \dfrac{a}{g}\right) \Rightarrow a = \left(\dfrac{w_{\text{app}}}{w} - 1\right)g$.

No acceleration: normal weight	Upward acceleration	Downward acceleration (deceleration)	Known
			$w = 150 \text{ lb}$
			$w_{\text{app}} = 170 \text{ lb}$ (upward acceleration)
			$w_{\text{app}} = 120 \text{ lb}$ (deceleration)
			Find
			a for both upward acceleration and deceleration

Solve: (a) When accelerating upward, the acceleration is

$$a = \left(\frac{170 \text{ lb}}{150 \text{ lb}} - 1\right)(9.8 \text{ m/s}^2) = 1.3 \text{ m/s}^2$$

(b) When braking, the acceleration is

$$a = \left(\frac{120 \text{ lb}}{150 \text{ lb}} - 1\right)(9.8 \text{ m/s}^2) = -2.0 \text{ m/s}^2$$

Assess: A 10–20% change in apparent weight seems reasonable for a fast elevator, as the one in the Empire State Building must be. Also note that we did not have to convert the units of the weights from pounds to newtons because the weights appear as a ratio.

P5.55. Prepare: The length of the hill is $\Delta x = h/\sin\theta$. The acceleration is $g\sin\theta$.

Solve: First use the kinematic equation, with $v_1 = 0$ m/s at the top of the hill, to determine the speed at the bottom of the hill.

$$(v_f)_1^2 = (v_i)_1^2 + 2a\Delta x \quad \Rightarrow \quad (v_f)_1^2 = 2(g\sin\theta)(h/\sin\theta) = 2gh$$

Now apply the same kinematic equation to the horizontal patch of snow, only this time we want Δx. To connect the two parts $(v_i)_1 = (v_i)_2$. The final speed is zero: $(v_f)_2 = 0$.

$$(v_f)_2^2 = (v_i)_2^2 + 2a\Delta x = (v_f)_1^2 + 2a\Delta x = 2gh + 2a\Delta x = 0$$

The friction force is the net force, so $a = -f_k/m$. Note $f_k = \mu_k n = \mu_k mg$. Solve for Δx.

$$\Delta x = \frac{-2gh}{2a} = \frac{-gh}{-f_k/m} = \frac{gh}{\mu_k mg/m} = \frac{h}{\mu_k} = \frac{3.0 \text{ m}}{0.05} = 60 \text{ m}$$

Assess: It seems reasonable to glide 60 m with such a low coefficient of friction. It is interesting that we did not need to know the angle of the (frictionless) slope; this will become clear in the chapter on energy. The answer is also independent of Josh's mass.

P5.57. Prepare: The force plate reads the normal force n of the plate on the woman. The other force on the woman is her weight (the gravitational force of the earth down on her). The net force will be the sum of these two and will be different at different times as the normal force of the force plate changes according to the graph. Since the graph is piece-wise constant, the acceleration will be constant during (within) each phase of the jump.

We can do a preliminary calculation to find the woman's mass. During the standing still phases, the force plate reads 500 N. During these equilibrium phases the force plate reads the same magnitude as her weight (so $w = 500$ N); hence her mass must be $m = w/g = (500 \text{ N})/(9.8 \text{ m/s}^2) = 51$ kg.

We will assume air resistance is negligible during all portions of the problem.

Solve: (a) We now know m and the normal force during push-off (1000 N). Apply the second law:

$$\Sigma F_y = n - w = ma_y$$
$$a_y = \frac{n-w}{m} = \frac{1000 \text{ N} - 500 \text{ N}}{51 \text{ kg}} = \frac{500 \text{ N}}{51 \text{ kg}} = 9.8 \text{ m/s}^2$$

This result looks familiar, but it is not the acceleration of an object in free fall for two reasons: (1) she is not in free fall, and (2) this acceleration is up while objects in free fall accelerate down.

(b) After she leaves the force plate she is in free fall, so her acceleration is $a = -g$ or, in other words, 9.8 m/s², down.

(c) During the landing phase the normal force of the plate on her is 1500 N while her weight is still 500 N. Apply the second law:

$$\Sigma F_y = n - w = ma_y$$
$$a_y = \frac{n-w}{m} = \frac{1500 \text{ N} - 500 \text{ N}}{51 \text{ kg}} = \frac{1000 \text{ N}}{51 \text{ kg}} = 20 \text{ m/s}^2$$

This acceleration is positive, or up (opposite the direction of motion, as she is slowing down).

(d) We'll assume she accelerates from rest. We are given that the push-off phase lasts $\Delta t = 0.25$ s. We'll use the answer from part**(a)** for a_y.

$$(v_y)_f = (v_y)_i + a_y\Delta t = 0.0 \text{ m/s} + (9.8 \text{ m/s}^2)(0.25 \text{ s}) = 2.45 \text{ m/s} \approx 2.5 \text{ m/s}$$

(e) After she leaves the force table she is in free fall (see part **(b)**). What was the final velocity in part **(d)** becomes the initial velocity now. Use Equation 2.10 with $(v_y)_f = 0.0$ m/s.

$$(v_y)_f^2 = (v_y)_i^2 + 2a_y \Delta x$$

Solve for Δy:

$$\Delta y = \frac{-(v_y)_i^2}{2a_y} = \frac{-(2.45 \text{ m/s})^2}{2(-9.8 \text{ m/s}^2)} = 0.31 \text{ m}$$

Assess: All of these results appear reasonable. The accelerations are within the expectations of daily life experience. The result of part **(d)** is used in part **(e)**, so we kept a third significant figure to use in the last calculation, but still reported the answers to two significant figures. The last answer is kind of a check on the previous ones, and it is quite reasonable: 31 cm is just over one foot.

Also review each calculation to verify that the units work out.

P5.59. Prepare: Sam is moving along the x-axis under the influence of two forces: the thrust of his jet skis and the resisting force of kinetic friction on the skis. A visual overview of Sam's motion is shown below in a pictorial representation, motion diagram, free-body diagrams in the accelerating and coasting periods, and a list of values. To find Sam's top speed using kinematics, we will first find his acceleration from Newton's second law. Kinematic equations will then allow us to find his displacement during both accelerating and coasting intervals.

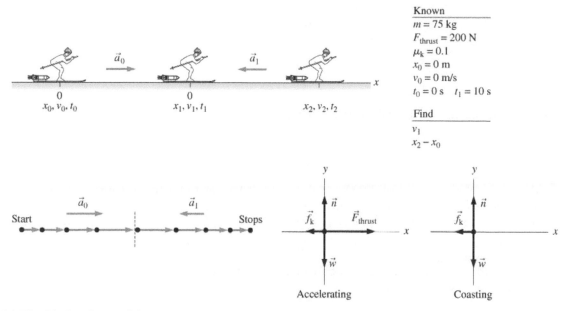

Solve: (a) The friction force of the snow can be found from the free-body diagram and Newton's first law, since there's no acceleration in the vertical direction:

$$n = w = mg = (75 \text{ kg})(9.8 \text{ m/s}^2) = 735 \text{ N} \Rightarrow f_k = \mu_k n = (0.1)(735 \text{ N}) = 73.5 \text{ N}$$

Then, from Newton's second law:

$$(F_{net})_x = F_{thrust} - f_k = ma_0 \Rightarrow a_0 = \frac{F_{thrust} - f_k}{m} = \frac{200 \text{ N} - 73.5 \text{ N}}{75 \text{ kg}} = 1.687 \text{ m/s}^2$$

From kinematics:

$$v_1 = v_0 + a_0 t_1 = 0 \text{ m/s} + (1.687 \text{ m/s}^2)(10 \text{ s}) = 16.87 \text{ m/s or 17 m/s to two significant figures.}$$

(b) During the acceleration, Sam travels to

$$x_1 = x_0 + v_0 t_1 + \frac{1}{2}a_0 t_1^2 = \frac{1}{2}(1.687 \text{ m/s}^2)(10 \text{ s})^2 = 84 \text{ m}$$

After the skis run out of fuel, Sam's acceleration can again be found from Newton's second law:

$$(F_{net})_x = -f_k = -73.5 \text{ N} \Rightarrow a_1 = \frac{F_{net}}{m} = \frac{-73.5 \text{ N}}{75 \text{ kg}} = -0.98 \text{ m/s}^2$$

Since we don't know how much time it takes Sam to stop:

$$v_2^2 = v_1^2 + 2a_1(x_2 - x_1) \Rightarrow x_2 - x_1 = \frac{v_2^2 - v_1^2}{2a_1} = \frac{0 \text{ m}^2/\text{s}^2 - (16.87 \text{ m/s})^2}{2(-0.98 \text{ m/s}^2)} = 145 \text{ m}$$

The total distance traveled is $(x_2 - x_1) + x_1 = 145 \text{ m} + 84 \text{ m} = 229 \text{ m}$ or 230 m to two significant figures.

   Assess: A top speed of 16.9 m/s (roughly 40 mph) seems quite reasonable for this acceleration, and a coasting distance of nearly 150 m also seems possible, starting from a high speed, given that we're neglecting air resistance.

P5.61. Prepare: We show below the free-body diagram of the 1 kg block. The block is initially at rest, so initially the friction force is static friction. If the 12 N pushing force is too strong, the box will begin to move up the wall. If it is too weak, the box will begin to slide down the wall. And if the pushing force is within the proper range, the box will remain stuck in place.

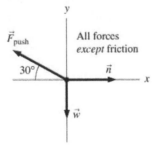

Solve: First, let's evaluate the sum of all the forces *except* friction:

$$\Sigma F_x = n - F_{push} \cos 30° = 0 \text{ N} \Rightarrow n = F_{push} \cos 30°$$

$$\Sigma F_y = F_{push} \sin 30° - w = F_{push} \sin 30° - mg = (12 \text{ N}) \sin 30° - (1 \text{ kg})(9.8 \text{ m/s}^2) = -3.8 \text{ N}$$

In the first equation we have utilized the fact that any motion is parallel to the wall, so $a_x = 0$ m/s^2.

   The two forces in the second y-equation add up to -3.8 N. This means the static friction force will be able to prevent the box from moving if $f_s = +3.8$ N. Using the x-equation we get

$$f_{s \text{ max}} = \mu_s n = \mu_s F_{push} \cos 30° = 5.2 \text{ N}$$

where we used $\mu_s = 0.5$ for wood on wood. The static friction force $\vec{f}_s$ needed to keep the box from moving is *less* than $f_{s \text{ max}}$. Thus the box will stay at rest.

P.5.63 Prepare: We assume that the plane is accelerating in a straight line under the influence of two forces: the thrust of its engines and the rolling friction of the wheels on the runway. We let x-axis run to the right, and show below a visual overview of the situation that includes a pictorial representation, a motion diagram, a free-body diagram and a list of values. We will use one-dimensional kinematics to find acceleration a, and then apply Newton's second law.

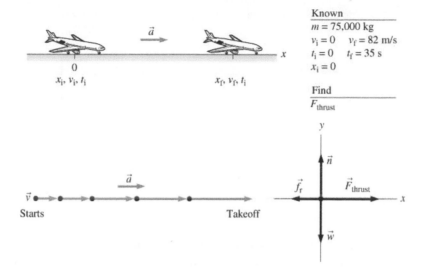

Solve: We obtain:

$$a = \frac{\Delta v}{\Delta t} = \frac{82 \text{ m/s} - 0 \text{ m/s}}{35 \text{ s}} = 2.34 \text{ m/s}^2$$

$$(F_{net}) = \Sigma F_x = F_{thrust} - f_x = ma \Rightarrow F_{thrust} = f_r + ma$$

For rubber rolling on concrete, $\mu_r = 0.02$ (Table 5.1), and since the runway is horizontal, $n = w = mg$. Thus:

$$F_{thrust} = \mu_r w + ma = \mu_r mg + ma = m(\mu_r g + a)$$
$$= (75,000 \text{ kg})[(0.02)(9.8 \text{ m/s}^2) + 2.34 \text{ m/s}^2] = 1.9 \times 10^5 \text{ N}$$

Assess: It's hard to evaluate such an enormous thrust, but comparison with the plane's mass suggests that 190,000 N is enough to produce the required acceleration.

P5.65. Prepare: With no friction, the only forces along the incline are the tension T and a component of the weight, $mg\sin\theta$. Since the blocks aren't accelerating, then $T = mg\sin\theta$.
   Solve: For tension 1:

$$T_1 = (5 \text{ kg})(9.8 \text{ m/s}^2)\sin 20° = 16.76 \text{ N} \approx 17 \text{ N}$$

For tension 2 the mass is the sum of both blocks:

$$T_2 = (5 \text{ kg} + 3 \text{ kg})(9.8 \text{ m/s}^2)\sin 20° = 26.81 \text{ N} \approx 27 \text{ N}$$

Assess: We would expect $T_2 > T_1$.

P5.67. Prepare: Since the block comes to rest for an instant, we use the coefficient of static friction for wood on wood: $\mu_s = 0.50$.
   Solve:

$$\Sigma F_x = mg\sin\theta - \mu_x n = 0$$
$$\Sigma F_y = n - mg\cos\theta = 0$$

Solve the second equation for n and insert into the first.

$$mg\sin\theta - \mu_s mg\cos\theta = 0$$
$$\tan\theta = \mu_s \Rightarrow \theta = \tan^{-1}(\mu_s) = \tan^{-1}(0.50) = 26.57° \approx 27°$$

Assess: From experience, 27° seems like a reasonable tilt for the block to slide back down.

P5.69. Prepare: The ping-pong ball when shot straight up is subject to a net force that is the resultant of the weight and drag force vectors, both acting vertically downward. On the other hand, for the ball's motion straight down, the ball is subject to a net force that is the resultant of the weight and drag force vectors, the former in the downward and the latter in the upward direction. An overview of a pictorial representation and a free-body diagram are shown below. The ping-pong ball experiences a drag force equal to $\frac{1}{2}\rho A v^2$, as modeled in the text with v_{term} as the terminal velocity.

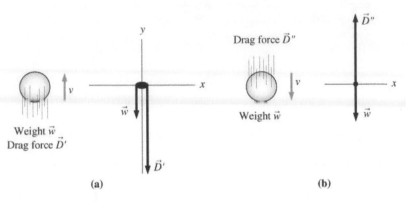

Solve: (a) Imagine the ball falling at its terminal speed. The ball's weight is directed down and the resistive drag force is directed up. The net force is zero because the magnitude of the drag force is equal to the magnitude of the weight, $D = w$. When the ball is shot upward at twice the terminal speed, the drag force is four times the terminal drag force. That is, $D' = 4D = 4w$.

Since all the forces are down, the y-component of Newton's second law is

$$\Sigma F_y = -D' - w = -4w - w = -5mg = ma \Rightarrow a = -5g$$

(b) The ball is initially shot downward. Therefore is upward but w is down. Again and the y-component of Newton's second law is

$$\Sigma F_y = D'' - w = 4w - w = 3mg = ma \Rightarrow a = 3g$$

That is, the ball initially decelerates at $3g$ but as v becomes smaller, the drag force approaches the weight so the deceleration goes to zero and v approaches v_{term}.

Assess: D' is very large and with w yields a large initial deceleration when the ball is shot up. When the ball is shot down w opposes D' so the ball decelerates at a lesser rate.

P5.71. Prepare: Call the 10 kg block m_2 and the 5.0 kg block m_1. Assume the pulley is massless and frictionless.
Solve: On block 2 use tilted axes.

$$\Sigma F_x = T - m_2 g \sin\theta = m_2 a_2$$

Block 1 is also accelerating.

$$\Sigma F_y = T - m_1 g = m_1 a_1$$

The acceleration constraint is $(a_2)_x = -(a_1)_y = a$. Solve for T in the second equation and insert in the first. $T - m_1(g - a)$.

$$m_1(g - a) - m_2 g \sin\theta = m_2 a$$

$$m_1 g - m_2 g \sin\theta = m_2 a + m_1 a$$

$$a = \frac{g(m_1 - m_2 \sin\theta)}{m_1 + m_2} = \frac{(9.8 \text{ m/s}^2)(1.0 \text{ kg} - (2.0 \text{ kg})\sin 40°)}{1.0 \text{ kg} + 2.0 \text{ kg}} = 1.96 \text{ m/s}^2 \approx 2.0 \text{ m/s}^2 = -0.93 \text{ m/s}^2$$

or 0.93 m/s^2, down the ramp.

Assess: The answer depends on θ; for a shallow angle the block accelerates up the ramp, for a steep angle the block accelerates down the ramp. This is expected behavior.

P5.73. Prepare: We assume the dishes have a constant acceleration during the 0.25 s, and we'll use a kinematic equation as well as Newton's second law. The friction force is the net force, $F_{net} = f_k = \mu_k mg$. We also know $a = F_{net}/m$.

Solve: Use the kinematic equation (where $v_1 = 0$):

$$\Delta x = \frac{1}{2}a(\Delta t)^2 = \frac{1}{2}\frac{F_{net}}{m}(\Delta t)^2 = \frac{1}{2}\frac{\mu_k mg}{m}(\Delta t)^2 = \frac{1}{2}\mu_k g(\Delta t)^2 = \frac{1}{2}(0.12)(9.8 \text{ m/s}^2)(0.25 \text{ s})^2 = 3.7 \text{ cm}$$

Assess: This seems to be a reasonable distance the dishes could travel without falling off the edge.

P5.75. Prepare: Please refer to Figure P5.65. The free-body diagram implies accelerating motion along the *x*-direction, as the *y*-forces cancel out.

Solve: (a) A 1 kg block is pulled across a level surface by a string, starting from rest. The string has a tension of 20 N, and the block's coefficient of kinetic friction is 0.50. How long does it take the block to move 1 m?

(b) Newton's second law for the block is

$$a_x = a = \frac{(F_{net})_x}{m} = \frac{T - f_k}{m} = \frac{T - \mu_k n}{m} \qquad a_y = 0 \text{ m/s}^2 = \frac{(F_{net})_y}{m} = \frac{n - w}{m} = \frac{n - mg}{m}$$

where we have incorporated the kinetic friction Equation 5.13 into the first equation. The second equation gives $n = mg$. Substituting this into the first equation gives

$$a = \frac{T - \mu_k mg}{m} = \frac{20 \text{ N} - 4.9 \text{ N}}{1 \text{ kg}} = 15.1 \text{ m/s}^2$$

Finally, constant acceleration kinematics gives

$$x_f = x_i + v_i\Delta t + \frac{1}{2}a(\Delta t)^2 = \frac{1}{2}a(\Delta t)^2 \Rightarrow \Delta t = \sqrt{\frac{2x_f}{a}} = \sqrt{\frac{2(1 \text{ m})}{15.1 \text{ m/s}^2}} = 0.364 \text{ s}$$

P5.77. Solve: (a) A driver traveling at 40 m/s in her 1500 kg auto slams on the brakes and skids to rest. How far does the auto slide before coming to rest?

(b)

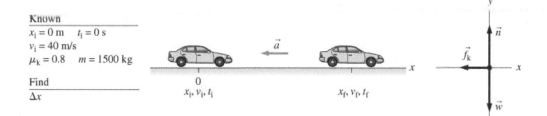

(c) Newton's second law is

$$\Sigma F_y = n_y + w_y = n - mg = ma_y = 0 \text{ N} \qquad \Sigma F_x = -0.8n = ma_x$$

The *y*-component equation gives $n = mg = (1500 \text{ kg})(9.8 \text{ m/s}^2)$. Substituting this into the *x*-component equation yields

$$(1500 \text{ kg})a_x = -0.8(1500 \text{ kg})(9.8 \text{ m/s}^2) \Rightarrow a_x = (-0.8)(9.8 \text{ m/s}^2) = -7.8 \text{ m/s}^2$$

Using the constant-acceleration kinematic equation $v_f^2 = v_i^2 + 2a_x\Delta x$, we find

$$\Delta x = -\frac{v_i^2}{2a_x} = -\frac{(40 \text{ m/s})^2}{2(-7.8 \text{ m/s}^2)} = 100 \text{ m}$$

P5.79. Prepare: The three given equations imply an accelerating object on a flat surface because the third term in the second equation is simply the weight $w = mg$. We also see a force applied to the object at an angle of 30° relative to the horizontal.

Solve: (a) You wish to pull a 20 kg wooden crate across a wood floor ($\mu_k = 0.2$) by pulling on a rope attached to the crate. Your pull is 100 N at an angle of 30° above the horizontal. What will be the acceleration of the crate?

(b)

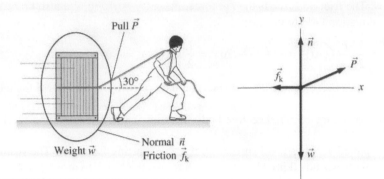

Pull $\vec{P}$

30°

Weight $\vec{w}$

Normal $\vec{n}$
Friction $\vec{f_k}$

(c) Newton's equations and the model of kinetic friction are

$$\Sigma F_x = n_x + P_x + w_x + f_x = 0\ \text{N} + (100\ \text{N})\cos 30° + 0\ \text{N} - f_k = (100\ \text{N})\cos 30° - f_k = ma_x$$
$$\Sigma F_y = n_y + P_y + w_y + f_y = n + (100\ \text{N})\sin 30° - mg - 0\ \text{N} = ma_y = 0\ \text{N}$$
$$f_k = \mu_k n$$

From the y-component equation, $n = 150$ N. From the x-component equation and using the model of kinetic friction with $\mu_k = 0.2$,

$$(100\ \text{N})\cos 30° - (0.2)(150\ \text{N}) = (20\ \text{kg})a_x \Rightarrow a_x = 2.8\ \text{m/s}^2$$

P5.81. Prepare: While the coefficient of friction is low, it is not zero, or the stone would never stop. It is the kinetic friction force that slows the stone.

Solve: Since sweeping can in fact lengthen the travel of the stone it must be that sweeping *decreases* the kinetic friction force (by decreasing the coefficient of kinetic friction).

The correct choice is A.

Assess: Examine the alternate choices. If sweeping increased the coefficient of friction then the stone would stop sooner, not later. As for C and D, sweeping the ice does nothing to change the fact that the stone is in motion. As long as the stone is moving we are talking about kinetic friction, not static friction.

Since sweeping decreases the coefficient of friction, it is probably accomplished by making the ice smoother.

P5.83. Prepare: Let's draw a free-body diagram. Assume the stone is moving in the positive x-direction on level ice.

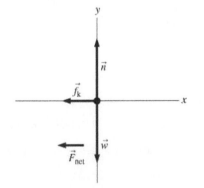

Solve: Newton's second law in the vertical direction tells us that $n = w$ so $n = mg$. Now apply the second law in the horizontal direction.

$$\Sigma F_x = ma_x$$
$$-f_k = ma_x$$
$$-\mu_k n = ma_x$$
$$-\mu_k mg = ma_x \quad \text{cancel } m$$
$$-\mu_k g = a_x$$

Since *m* canceled we see that the deceleration is independent of *m*. Therefore the distance the stone travels will be the same as before if it has the same initial velocity (which it does). This eliminates choices A and B.

The coefficient of friction between two substances only depends on the microscopic makeup of the substances and does not depend on the normal force or the speed (in our simple model) of the two surfaces relative to each other. If it were otherwise, then tables of the coefficient of friction would have to have entries for different normal forces and speeds. This eliminates choice C.

The only choice left (and the correct one) is D; however we actually already knew that when we first wrote $f_k = \mu_k n = \mu_k mg$. The mass appears in the equation and tells us that in this scenario the friction force is proportional to the mass.

Assess: Although the friction force is greater in the 40 kg case, so is the inertia (which tends to keep the stone moving), so the acceleration remains the same.

6—Circular Motion, Orbits, and Gravity
Conceptual Questions

Q6.1. Reason: Looking down from above the player runs around the bases in a counterclockwise direction, hence the angular velocity is positive.

Assess: Note that looking from below (from under the grass) the motion would be clockwise and the angular velocity would be negative. We assumed the bird's eye view because it is standard to do so, and it is difficult to view the game from below the ground. This is akin to setting up a coordinate system with the positive *x*-axis pointing left and the positive *y*-axis pointing down; the real-life physics wouldn't change any, and the calculations of measurable quantities would produce the same results, and it might even be occasionally convenient. But unless there is a clear reason to do otherwise, the usual conventions should be your first thought.

Q6.3. Reason: Acceleration is a change in *velocity*. Since velocity is a vector, it can change by changing direction, even while the magnitude (speed) remains constant. The cyclist's acceleration is *not* zero in uniform circular motion. She has a centripetal (center-seeking) acceleration.

Assess: In everyday usage, acceleration usually means only a change in speed (specifically a speeding up), hence the confusion. But in physics we must use words very carefully to communicate clearly. Everyday usage is fine outside the physics context, but while doing physics we must use the precise physics definitions of the words.

Q6.5. Reason: Because the centripetal acceleration is given by $a = v^2/r$, if the speed is zero then the centripetal acceleration is zero. So the answer is no.

Assess: However, the particle may have a nonzero tangential acceleration at the instant its speed is zero (this would ensure that the particle doesn't stay at rest).

Q6.7. Reason: The discussion in the section on maximum walking speed leads to the equation $v_{max} = \sqrt{gr}$ where *r* is the length of the leg. For a leg as short as a chickadee's this produces a walking speed that is simply too slow to be practical, so they hop or fly.

Assess: The longer the leg the greater the maximum walking speed, and the formula produces reasonable walking speeds for pheasants.

Q6.9. Reason: At the lowest point, the acceleration is upward. Thus, the tension must be greater than the weight for the net force to be upward. The tension in the string not only offsets the weight of the ball, but additionally provides the centripetal force to keep it moving in a circle.

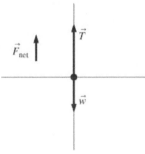

Assess: The string must have a higher strength rating than the weight of the ball in order for the ball to swing in a vertical circle.

Of course at the top of the circle the weight itself points centripetally, so the tension in the string can be less than at the bottom.

Q6.11. Reason: (a) The moon's orbit around the earth is fairly circular, and it is the gravitational force of the earth on the moon that provides the centripetal force to keep the moon in its circular motion.

(b) The riders in the Gravitron carnival ride (Section 6.4) have a centripetal acceleration caused by the normal force of the walls on them.

Another example would be the biological sample in a centrifuge. The test tube walls exert a normal force on the sample toward the center of the circle.

Assess: The point is that centripetal forces are not a new *kind* of force; it is just the name we give to the force (or sum of forces) that points toward the center of the circle and keeps the object from flying off in a straight line.

Q6.13. Reason: The car is traveling along a circle and so it must have centripetal acceleration which points downward. From Newton's second law, if an object is accelerating downward, the total force on the object must be downward. The answer is C because only there is the downward force (the weight of the car) greater than the upward force (the normal force on the car) so that the total force is downward.

Assess: It makes sense that the normal force on the car would be less than the weight of the car because from experience, you know that you feel lighter going over a hill in your car and normal force tells you how heavy you feel. In the same way, the normal force on the car will be less than its weight.

Q6.15. Reason: The radius of the loop decreases as the carts enter and exit the loop. The centripetal acceleration is smaller for larger radius loops and larger for smaller radius loops. This means the centripetal acceleration increases from a minimum at the entry to the loop to a maximum at the top of the loop and then decreases as the cars exit the loop. This prevents a sudden change of acceleration, which can be painful. This also limits the largest accelerations to the top of the loop, so that riders only experience the maximum acceleration for a portion of the trip.

Assess: This is reasonable. If the cars entered a small radius loop directly, the centripetal acceleration would increase suddenly.

Q6.17. Reason: When we walk on the ground we push off with one foot while pivoting on the other; the weight force brings us back down from the push-off for the next step. In an orbiting shuttle, which is in free fall along with the astronaut, after one foot pushes off there isn't a force to bring the astronaut back to the "floor" for the next step; the first push-off sends the astronaut across the cabin.

Assess: If the spacecraft is designed to rotate to provide an artificial gravity then one can walk fairly normally around on the inside; "up" would be toward the center of the circular motion, "down" would be "out"; but that probably isn't the origin of the phrase "down and out."

Q6.19. Reason: An object's weight is defined to be the gravitational force of the earth on the object. And the gravitational force of the earth on an object decreases with distance (as $1/r^2$), where we measure r from center to center. At the top of a mountain the climber's center is farther from the center of the earth, and so the gravitational force (i.e., the weight) is less, even though the climber's mass hasn't changed.

Assess: This is not just a change in *apparent* weight (what the scales read); this is a change in the real weight (the gravitational force). Doubling the height of the mountain would decrease the weight by a factor of 4—but only if you take the height of the mountain to be r (from the center of the earth), *not* the height above sea level.

Multiple Choice Questions

Q6.21. Reason: Originally, the ball is going around once every second. When the ball is sped up so that it goes around once in only half a second, it is moving twice as fast. Consequently its acceleration, which is given by $a = \omega^2 r$ will be four times as great. From Newton's second law, force is directly proportional to acceleration, so if we multiply the acceleration by 4, we must multiply the tension by 4. Thus the tension in the string will be four times as great, or 24 N. The answer is D.

Assess: This accords with our experience that when we swing an object around a circle, as the speed increases, the tension in the string increases.

Q6.23. Reason: There isn't really a centrifugal outward force pushing on you (no agent is pushing outward on you), but instead there is a centripetal inward force holding you in the circular motion. That centripetal force is what we'll compute, since it will have the same magnitude as the apparent outward force you feel. As a preliminary calculation, compute the speed $v = 2\pi r/T = 2\pi(2.0 \text{ m})/6.0 \text{ s} = 2.1 \text{ m/s}$.

$$F_{\text{net}} = ma_c = m\frac{v^2}{r} = (60 \text{ kg})\frac{(2.1 \text{ m/s})^2}{2.0 \text{ m}} = 130 \text{ N}$$

So the correct choice is C.

Assess: The data seem like real-life data. A merry-go-round could easily have a radius of 4.0 m, and two friends could easily have a mass of 60 kg each, and it could easily take 6.0 s to go around (that's neither terribly fast nor terribly slow). A speed of 2.1 m/s seems reasonable. And while we may still be developing an intuitive feel for newtons, 130 N is a reasonable force.

Q6.25. Reason: For a person on the inside of the outer wall to experience the same amount of artificial gravity in the two cases the centripetal acceleration must be the same, $a_1 = a_2$. We are also given that $r_2 = 4r_1$ (if the diameter is four times as large, so is the radius). Remember that for uniform circular motion $v = 2\pi r/T$.

$$a_1 = a_2$$

$$\frac{v_1^2}{r_1} = \frac{v_2^2}{r_2}$$

$$\frac{\left(\dfrac{2\pi r_1}{T_1}\right)^2}{r_1} = \frac{\left(\dfrac{2\pi r_2}{T_2}\right)^2}{r_2}$$

$$\frac{r_1}{T_1^2} = \frac{r_2}{T_2^2}$$

$$T_2^2 = T_1^2\frac{r_2}{r_1}$$

$$T_2 = T_1\sqrt{\frac{r_2}{r_1}} = T_1\sqrt{\frac{4r_1}{r_1}} = 2T_1$$

So the correct choice is B.

Assess: The answer is reasonable in view of the v^2 in the centripetal acceleration; it will take a rotational period twice as long to produce the same artificial gravity if the diameter is four times as large.

Q6.27. Reason: Equation 6.24 gives

$$g_{\text{planet}} = \frac{GM_{\text{planet}}}{R_{\text{planet}}^2}$$

If the mass stays the same while the radius doubles, then the new g will be 1/4 of the old one. Since $g \approx 10 \text{ m/s}^2$ now, then one quarter of that is 2.5 m/s^2.

The correct choice is A.

Assess: Especially note that in part (**b**) the magnitude of the force of the floor on you is not the same as the magnitude of the earth's gravitational force on you, as it would have been if you hadn't been pushing on the ceiling.

Q6.29. Reason: We need to use Equation 6.28 (also known as Kepler's Third Law) because it relates the orbital period T to the orbital radius r. We are given that $r_2 = 4r_1$.

Write Equation 6.28 for each planet (write planet 2 first) and then divide the two equations:

$$T_2^2 = \left(\frac{4\pi^2}{GM}\right) r_2^3$$

$$T_1^2 = \left(\frac{4\pi^2}{GM}\right) r_1^3$$

$$\frac{T_2^2}{T_1^2} = \frac{r_2^3}{r_1^3}$$

$$\frac{T_2^2}{T_1^2} = \frac{(4r_1)^3}{r_1^3}$$

Multiply both sides by T_1^2 and cancel r_1^3:

$$T_2^2 = T_1^2 (4)^3$$

Take square roots:

$$T_2 = T_1 \sqrt{(4)^3} = T_1 \sqrt{64} = 8T_1$$

The correct choice is D.

Assess: When the orbital radius quadruples, the period increases by a factor of eight because planet 2 has not only farther to go, but also moves slower.

It is instructive to test this relationship with real planetary data. Question 21 says $r_{\text{Jupiter}} = 5.2 r_{\text{earth}}$, so using the math above with the new number, $T_{\text{Jupiter}} = T_{\text{earth}} \sqrt{(5.2)^3} = T_{\text{earth}} \sqrt{140.6} = 11.9$ yr. This is correct.

Q6.31. Reason: The skater turns one-and-a-half revolutions in 0.5 s. One-and-a-half revolutions is 3π radians. Her angular velocity is

$$\omega = \frac{\Delta \theta}{\Delta t} = \frac{3\pi \text{ rad}}{0.5 \text{ s}} = 20 \text{ rad/s}$$

The correct choice is D.

Assess: This result is reasonable. She makes 3 revolutions in one second, which is 6π radians per second.

Q6.33. Reason: In Question 6.30 we found that the angular velocity of the skater is 20 rad/s. Estimating the length of her arm to be about 0.75 m from the center of rotation, we can calculate the speed of her hand with Equation 6.6.

$$v = \omega r = (20 \text{ rad/s})(0.75 \text{ m}) = 15 \text{ m/s}$$

The correct choice is D.

Assess: This is actually a high velocity, over 30 mph.

Problems

P6.1. Prepare: The position of the minute hand is determined by the number after the colon. There are sixty minutes in an hour so the number of minutes after the hour, when divided by 60, gives the fraction of a circle which has been covered by the minute hand. Also, the minute hand starts at $\pi/2$ rad and travels clockwise, thus decreasing the angle. If we get a negative angle, we can make it positive by adding 2π rad.

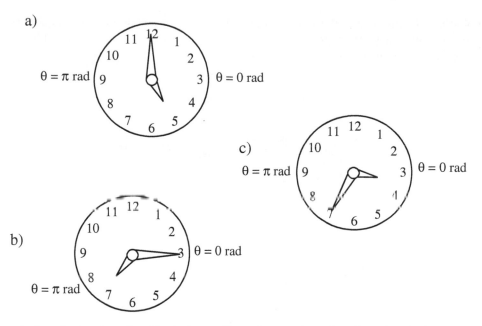

Solve: (a) The angle is calculated as described above. Since the number after the colon is 0, we subtract nothing from $\pi/2$ rad, so $\theta = \pi/2$.

(b) We subtract 15/60 of 2π rad from the starting angle, so we have:

$$\theta = \frac{\pi}{2} - \left(\frac{15}{60}\right)(2\pi) = 0$$

(c) As before, the angle is given by:

$$\theta = \frac{\pi}{2} - \left(\frac{35}{60}\right)(2\pi) = -\frac{2}{3}\pi$$

Since this angle is negative, we can add 2π rad to obtain: $\theta = -2\pi/3 + 2\pi = 4\pi/3$.

Assess: The first two parts make sense from our experience with clocks. In part (a), the minute hand is straight up. In part (b), it points to the right.

P6.3. Prepare: To compute the angular speed ω we use Equation 6.1 and convert to rad/s. The minute hand takes an hour to complete one revolution.

Solve:

$$w = \frac{\Delta\theta}{\Delta t} = \frac{1.0 \text{ rev}}{60 \text{ min}}\left(\frac{2\pi \text{ rad}}{1 \text{ rev}}\right)\left(\frac{1 \text{ min}}{60 \text{ s}}\right) = 0.0017 \text{ rad/s} = 1.7\times10^{-3} \text{ rad/s}$$

Assess: This answer applies not just to the tip, but the whole minute hand. The answer is small, but the minute hand moves quite slowly.

The second hand moves 60 times faster, or 0.10 rad/s. This too seems reasonable.

P6.5. Prepare: The airplane is to be treated as a particle in uniform circular motion on the equator around the center of the earth. We show below a pictorial representation of the problem and a list of values. To convert radians into degrees, we note that 2π rad $= 360°$. We will use Equation 6.2.

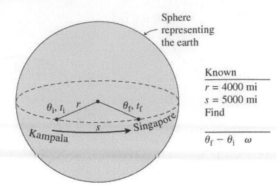

Sphere representing the earth

Known
$r = 4000$ mi
$s = 5000$ mi
Find
$\theta_f - \theta_i \quad \omega$

Solve: (a) The angle you turn through is

$$\theta_f - \theta_i = \frac{s}{r} = \frac{5000 \text{ mi}}{4000 \text{ mi}} = 1.25 \text{ rad} = 1.25 \text{ rad} \times \frac{180°}{\pi \text{ rad}} = 71.6°$$

So, the angle is 1 rad or 70°.
(b) The plane's angular speed is

$$w = \frac{\theta_f - \theta_i}{t_f - t_i} = \frac{1.25 \text{ rad}}{9 \text{ h}} = 0.139 \text{ rad/h} = 0.139 \frac{\text{rad}}{\text{h}} \times \frac{1 \text{ h}}{3600 \text{ s}} = 4 \times 10^{-5} \text{ rad/s}$$

Assess: An angular displacement of approximately one-fifth of a complete rotation is reasonable because the separation between Kampala and Singapore is approximately one-fifth of the earth's circumference.

P6.7. Prepare: We'll use Equation 6.2 to compute the angular displacement. We are given $\theta_i = 5$ 0.45 rad and that $\Delta t = 8.0$ s $- 0$ s $= 8.0$ s.
We'll do a preliminary calculation to convert $\omega = 78$ rpm into rad/s:

$$78 \text{ rpm} = 78 \frac{\text{rev}}{\text{min}} \left(\frac{2\pi \text{ rad}}{1 \text{ rev}} \right) \left(\frac{1 \text{ min}}{60 \text{ s}} \right) = 8.17 \text{ rad/s}$$

Solve: Solve Equation 6.2 for θ_f:

$$\theta_f = \theta_i + \omega \Delta t = 0.45 \text{ rad} + (8.17 \text{ rad/s})(8.0 \text{ s}) = 65.8 \text{ rad} = 10.474 \times 2\pi \text{ rad}$$
$$= 10 \times 2\pi \text{ rad} + 0.474 \times 2\pi \text{ rad} = 10 \times 2\pi \text{ rad} + 2.98 \text{ rad}$$

So the speck completed almost ten and a half revolutions. An observer would say the angular position is 3.0 rad (to two significant figures) at $t = 8.0$ s.
Assess: Ask your grandparents if they remember the old records that turned at 78 rpm. They turned quite fast and so the music didn't last long before it was time to turn the record over. Singles came on smaller records that turned at 45 rpm, and later "long play" (LP) records turned at 33 rpm.
CDs don't have a constant angular velocity; instead they are designed to have constant linear velocity, so the motor has to change speeds. For the old vinyl records the recording had to take into account the changing linear velocity because they had constant angular velocity.

P6.9. Prepare: To find angular displacement we simply subtract the initial value of the angle from the final value of the angle: $\Delta \theta = \theta_F - \theta_I$.
Solve: (a) At $t = 5$ s, the angle is 100 rad and at $t = 15$ s, the angle is 125 rad. Thus

$$\Delta \theta = 125 \text{ rad} - 100 \text{ rad} = 25 \text{ rad}$$

(b) The angular velocity of the wheel at 15 s is the slope of the θ vs t graph at 15 s. We can find this slope by comparing the angle at 10 s and the angle at 20 s:

$$\omega = \frac{\theta_F - \theta_I}{t_F - t_I} = \frac{100 \text{ rad} - 150 \text{ rad}}{20 \text{ s} - 10 \text{ s}} = -5 \text{ rad/s}$$

Assess: The angular velocity is negative at $t = 15$ s because the angle is decreasing, that is, the wheel is rotating clockwise.

P6.11. Prepare: Use Equation 6.6 to find the speed of an object in uniform circular motion. We are given $r = 2.5$ m (half of the diameter). A preliminary calculation will give ω.

$$\omega = 2\pi \text{ rad}/4.0 \text{ s} = 1.57 \text{ rad/s}$$

Solve:

$$v = \omega r = (1.57 \text{ rad/s})(2.5 \text{ m}) = 3.9 \text{ m/s}$$

Assess: A speed of 3.9 m/s seems reasonable for a merry-go-round turning this fast.

P6.13. Prepare: The horse and rider are in uniform circular motion. We are given $r = 4.0$ m.
A preliminary calculation will determine ω in rad/s for part **(b)**:

$$\omega = 0.10 \frac{\text{rev}}{\text{s}} \left(\frac{2\pi \text{ rad}}{1 \text{ rev}} \right) = 0.628 \text{ rad/s}$$

Solve: (a) Solve Equation 6.2 for Δt.

$$\Delta t = \frac{\Delta\theta}{\omega} = \frac{2 \text{ rev}}{0.10 \text{ rev/s}} = 20 \text{ s}$$

(b) Use Equation 6.6:

$$v = \omega r = (0.628 \text{ rad/s})(4.0 \text{ m}) = 2.5 \text{ m/s}$$

Assess: A time for two revolutions of 20 s seems reasonable; a speed of 2.5 m/s also seems reasonable.
Note that for part **(a)** the answer is independent of the radius; it takes 20 s for everything to go around twice, not just the bucking horse.

P6.15. Prepare: The pebble is a particle rotating around the axle in a circular orbit. We will use Equations 6.6 and 6.7. To convert units from rev/s to rad/s, we note that 1 rev = 2π rad.
Solve: The pebble's angular velocity $\omega = (3.0 \text{ rev/s})(2\pi \text{ rad/rev}) = 18.85$ rad/s. The speed of the pebble as it moves around a circle of radius $r = 30$ cm $= 0.30$ m is

$$v = \omega r = (18.85 \text{ rad/s})(0.30 \text{ m}) = 5.65 \text{ m/s} = 5.7 \text{ m/s}$$

The centripetal acceleration is

$$a = \frac{v^2}{r} = \frac{(5.65 \text{ m/s})^2}{0.30 \text{ m}} = 110 \text{ m/s}^2$$

P6.17. Prepare: Equation 6.9 tells us the tension:

$$T = m\frac{v^2}{r}$$

Because all four are moving at the same speed, we need only consider the effect of m and r on T. A small r and a large m would make for a large T, as in case 3.
Solve: $T_3 > T_1 = T_4 > T_2$
Assess: Case 4 is the same as case 1 because both the mass and radius are doubled.

P6.19. Prepare: We are using the particle model for the car in uniform circular motion on a flat circular track. There must be friction between the tires and the road for the car to move in a circle. A pictorial representation of the car, its free-body diagram, and a list of values are shown below.

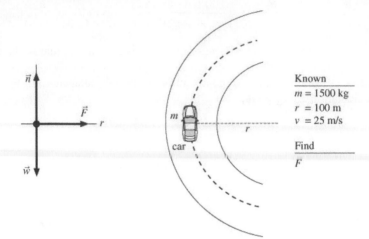

Solve: Equation 6.7 gives the centripetal acceleration

$$a = \frac{v^2}{r} = \frac{(25 \text{ m/s})^2}{100 \text{ m}} = 6.25 \text{ m/s}^2$$

The acceleration points to the center of the circle, so the net force is

$$\vec{F} = m\vec{a} = (1500 \text{ kg})(6.25 \text{ m/s}^2, \text{ toward center}) = (9400 \text{ N, toward center})$$

This force is provided by static friction:

$$f_s = f_r = 9400 \text{ N}$$

P6.21. Prepare: We can calculate the ball's centripetal acceleration using Equation 6.7. The centripetal force is given by Equation 6.8.
Solve: Refer to the figure below.

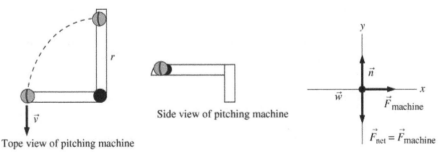

Top view of pitching machine   Side view of pitching machine

(a) Converting the velocity of the ball to meters per second, we have

$$v = (85 \text{ mph})\left(\frac{0.447 \text{ m/s}}{1 \text{ mph}}\right) = 38 \text{ m/s}$$

The centripetal acceleration of the ball is then

$$a = \frac{v^2}{r} = \frac{(38 \text{ m/s})^2}{0.85 \text{ m}} = 1.7 \times 10^3 \text{ m/s}^2$$

(b) From the free-body diagram in the figure above, the net force on the ball is in the centripetal direction and so is equal to the centripetal force on the ball.

$$F_{net} = ma = (0.144 \text{ kg})(1700 \text{ m/s}^2) = 240 \text{ N}$$

Assess: The centripetal acceleration is large. The centripetal force needed during the launch of the ball is about 54 pounds.

P6.23. Prepare: Model the passenger in a roller coaster car as a particle in uniform circular motion. A pictorial representation of the car, its free-body diagram, and a list of values are shown below. Note that the normal force $\vec{n}$ of the seat pushing on the passenger is the passenger's apparent weight.

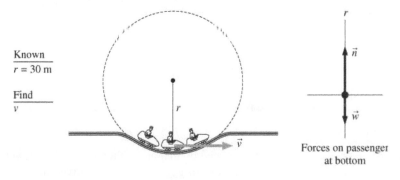

Solve: Since the passengers feel 50% heavier than their true weight, $n = 1.50w$. Thus, from Newton's second law and using Equation 6.10, the net force at the bottom of the dip is:

$$\Sigma F = n - w = 1.50 \ w - w = \frac{mv^2}{r} \Rightarrow 0.50 \ mg = \frac{mv^2}{r} \Rightarrow v = \sqrt{0.50 \ gr} = \sqrt{(0.50)(30 \text{ m})(9.8 \text{ m/s}^2)} = 12 \text{ m/s}$$

Assess: A speed of 12 m/s or 27 mph for the roller coaster is reasonable.

P6.25. Prepare: Model the roller coaster car as a particle undergoing uniform circular motion along a loop. A pictorial representation of the car, its free-body diagram, and a list of values are shown below. Note that the normal force $\vec{n}$ of the seat pushing on the passenger is the passenger's apparent weight, and in this problem the apparent weight is equal to the true weight: $w_{app} = n = mg$.

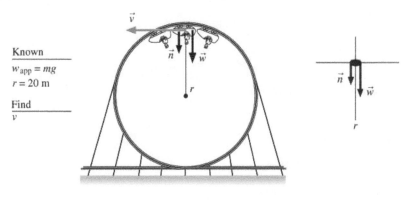

Solve: We have

$$\Sigma F = n + w = \frac{mv^2}{r} = mg + mg \Rightarrow v = \sqrt{2 \ rg} = \sqrt{2(20 \text{ m})(9.8 \text{ m/s}^2)} = 20 \text{ m/s}$$

Assess: A speed of 20 m/s or 44 mph on a roller coaster ride is reasonable.

P6.27. Prepare: Assume the radius of the satellite's orbit is about the same as the radius of the moon itself.

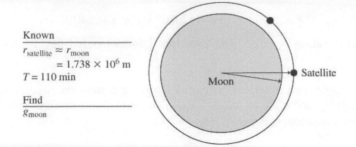

Known

$r_{\text{satellite}} \approx r_{\text{moon}}$
$= 1.738 \times 10^6 \text{ m}$
$T = 110 \text{ min}$

Find
g_{moon}

As a preliminary calculation, compute the angular velocity of the satellite:

$$w = \frac{2\pi}{T} = \left(\frac{2\pi \text{ rad}}{110 \text{ min}}\right)\left(\frac{1 \text{ min}}{60 \text{ s}}\right) = 9.52 \times 10^{-4} \text{ rad/s}$$

Solve: The centripetal acceleration of the satellite is

$$a = \omega^2 r = (9.52 \times 10^{-4} \text{ rad/s})^2 (1.738 \times 10^6 \text{ m}) = 1.58 \text{ m/s}^2$$

Since the acceleration of a body in orbit is the localexperienced by that body, then this is the answer to the problem.
   Assess: Our answer compares very favorably with the value of $g_{\text{Moon}} = 1.62 \text{ m/s}^2$ given in the chapter.

P6.29. Prepare: Call the mass of the star M. Write Newton's law of gravitation for each planet.

$$F_1 = \frac{GMm_1}{r_1^2}$$

$$F_2 = \frac{GMm_2}{r_2^2} = \frac{GM(2m_1)}{(2r_1)^2}$$

Solve: Divide the two equations to get the ratio desired.

$$\frac{F_2}{F_1} = \frac{\dfrac{GM(2m_1)}{(2r_1)^2}}{\dfrac{GMm_1}{r_1^2}} = \frac{1}{2}$$

   Assess: The answer is expected. Even with twice the mass, because the radius in the denominator is squared, we expect the force on planet 2 to be less than the force on planet 1.

P6.31. Prepare: Model the sun (s) and the earth (e) as spherical masses. Due to the large difference between your size and mass and that of either the sun or the earth, a human body can be treated as a particle. Use Equation 6.21.

Solve: $F_{\text{s on you}} = \dfrac{GM_s m_y}{r_{\text{s-e}}^2}$ and $F_{\text{e on you}} = \dfrac{GM_e m_y}{r_e^2}$

Dividing these two equations gives

$$\frac{F_{\text{s on y}}}{F_{\text{e on y}}} = \left(\frac{M_s}{M_e}\right)\left(\frac{r_e}{r_{\text{s-e}}}\right)^2 = \left(\frac{1.99 \times 10^{30} \text{ kg}}{5.98 \times 10^{24} \text{ kg}}\right)\left(\frac{6.37 \times 10^6 \text{ m}}{1.5 \times 10^{11} \text{ m}}\right)^2 = 6.0 \times 10^{-4}$$

   Assess: The result shows the smallness of the sun's gravitational force on you compared to that of the earth.

P6.33. Prepare: Model the sun (s), the earth (e), and the moon (m) as spherical masses and use Equation 6.21.

   Solve: (a) $F_{\text{s on e}} = \dfrac{Gm_s m_e}{r_{\text{s-e}}^2} = \dfrac{(6.67 \times 10^{-11} \text{ N} \cdot \text{m}^2/\text{kg}^2)(1.99 \times 10^{30} \text{ kg})(5.98 \times 10^{24} \text{ kg})}{(1.50 \times 10^{11} \text{ m})^2} = 3.53 \times 10^{22} \text{ N}$

(b) $F_{\text{m on e}} = \dfrac{GM_{\text{m}}M_{\text{e}}}{r_{\text{m-e}}^2} = \dfrac{(6.67 \times 10^{-11} \text{ N} \cdot \text{m}^2/\text{kg}^2)(7.36 \times 10^{22} \text{ kg})(5.98 \times 10^{24} \text{ kg})}{(3.84 \times 10^8 \text{ m})^2} = 1.99 \times 10^{20} \text{ N}$

(c) The moon's force on the earth as a percent of the sun's force on the earth is

$$\left(\frac{1.99 \times 10^{20} \text{ N}}{3.53 \times 10^{22} \text{ N}} \right) \times 100 = 0.56\%$$

P6.35. Prepare: From Equation 6.27 we know that $T^2 \propto r^3$.
 Solve: Thus, at $r_Y = 4r_X$,

$$T_Y^2 \propto (4r_X)^3 = 64r_X^3 \propto (8T_X)^2$$

So $T_t = 8T_A$, and so a year on planet Y is 1600 earth days long.
 Assess: This agrees perfectly with Question 6.29 where we saw that if $r_2 = 4r_1$ then $T_2 = 8T_1$. The constants in Equation 6.27 (including the mass M of the star) cancel out.

P6.37. Prepare: Model the earth (e) as a spherical mass and the shuttle (s) as a point particle. The shuttle with mass m_s and velocity v_s orbits the earth in a circle of radius r_s. We will denote the earth's mass by M_e. As a reminder, the gravitational force between the earth and the shuttle provides the necessary centripetal acceleration for circular motion.
 Solve: Newton's second law is

$$\frac{GM_e m_s}{r_s^2} = \frac{m_s v_s^2}{r_s} \Rightarrow v_s^2 = \frac{GM_e}{r_s} \Rightarrow v_s = \sqrt{\frac{GM_e}{r_s}}$$

Because $r_s = R_e + 250$ miles $= 6.37 \times 10^6$ m $+ 4.023 \times 10^5$ m $= 6.77 \times 10^6$ m,

$$v_s = \sqrt{\frac{(6.67 \times 10^{-11} \text{ N} \cdot \text{m}^2/\text{kg}^2)(5.98 \times 10^{24} \text{ kg})}{(6.77 \times 10^6 \text{ m})}} = 7{,}675 \text{ m/s} = 7{,}700 \text{ m/s}$$

$$T_s = \frac{2\pi r_s}{v_s} = \frac{2\pi (6.77 \times 10^6 \text{ m})}{7.675 \times 10^3 \text{ m/s}} = 5542 \text{ s} = 93 \text{ minutes}$$

 Assess: An orbital period of 92.4 minutes is reasonable for a 250 mile high orbit. As comparison, the orbital period is 1440 minutes for a geostationary orbit at a distance of approximately 25,000 miles.

P6.39. Prepare: Model the earth (e) as a spherical mass and the satellite (s) as a point particle. The satellite has a mass is m_s and orbits the earth with a velocity v_s. The radius of the circular orbit is denoted by r_s and the mass of the earth by M_e. Use Equations 6.25 and 6.5.
 Solve: The satellite experiences a gravitational force that provides the centripetal acceleration required for circular motion:

$$\frac{GM_e m_s}{r_s^2} = \frac{m_s v_s^2}{r_s} \Rightarrow r_s = \frac{GM_e}{v_s^2} = \frac{(6.67 \times 10^{-11} \text{ N} \cdot \text{m}^2/\text{kg}^2)(5.98 \times 10^{24} \text{ kg})}{(5500 \text{ m/s})^2} = 1.32 \times 10^7 \text{ m}$$

$$\Rightarrow T_s = \frac{2\pi R_s}{v_s} = \frac{(2\pi)(1.32 \times 10^7 \text{ m})}{(5500 \text{ m/s})} = 1.51 \times 10^4 \text{s} = 4.2 \text{ h}$$

P6.41. Prepare: Since the speed is constant the acceleration tangent to the path at each point is zero.
 Solve: Since $a = v^2/r$ and v is constant, we see that the radius of curvature of the road at point A is about three times larger than the radius of curvature at point C, so the car's centripetal acceleration at point C is three times larger than at point A.

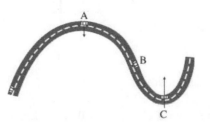

At point B there is no curvature, so there is no centripetal acceleration.

Assess: When you drive on windy roads you know that the tighter the curve the more acceleration you feel, and it is often wise to *not* keep your speed constant. Slowing down for tight curves keeps the centripetal acceleration manageable (it must be produced by the centripetal force of friction of the road on the tires).

P6.43. Prepare: Treat the man as a particle. When at the equator the man undergoes uniform circular motion as the earth rotates.

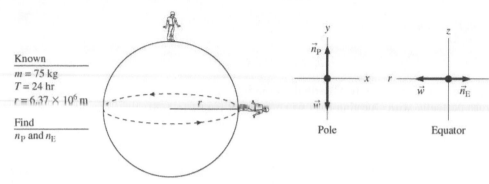

Solve: The scale reads the man's apparent weight $w_{app} = n$, the force of the scale pushing up against his feet. At the North Pole, where the man is in static equilibrium,

$$n_p = (w_{app})_P = mg = 735 \text{ N}$$

At the equator, there must be a net force toward the center of the earth to keep the man moving in a circle. In the radial direction

$$\Sigma F = w - n_E = m\omega^2 r \Rightarrow n_E = (w_{app})_E = mg - m\omega^2 r = (w_{app})_P - m\omega^2 r$$

So the equator scale reads less than the North Pole scale by the amount $m\omega^2 r$.
   The angular velocity of the earth is

$$\omega = \frac{2\pi}{T} = \frac{2\pi \text{rad}}{24 \text{ h} \times (3600 \text{ s/1 h})} = 7.27 \times 10^{-5} \text{ rad/s}$$

Thus the North Pole scale reads more than the equator scale by

$$m\omega^2 r = (75 \text{ kg})(7.27 \times 10^{-5} \text{ rad/s})^2(6.37 \times 10^6 \text{ m}) = 2.5 \text{ N}$$

Assess: The man at the equator appears to have lost approximately 0.25 kg or about 1/2 lb.

P6.45. Prepare: Treat the ball as a particle in circular motion. A visual overview of the ball's circular motion is shown below in a pictorial representation, a free-body diagram, and a list of values. The mass moves in a *horizontal* circle of radius $r = 20$ cm. A component of the tension in the string toward the center of the circle causes the centripetal acceleration needed for circular motion. The acceleration $\vec{a}$ and the net force vector point to the center of the circle, *not* along the string. The other two forces are the string tension $\vec{T}$, which does point along the string, and the weight $\vec{w}$.

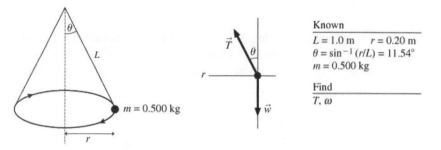

Solve: (a) Newton's second law for circular motion is

$$\Sigma F_y = T\cos\theta - w = T\cos\theta - mg = 0 \text{ N} \qquad \Sigma F_x = T\sin\theta = \frac{mv^2}{r}$$

From the *y*-equation,

$$T = \frac{mg}{\cos\theta} = \frac{(0.5 \text{ kg})(9.8 \text{ m/s}^2)}{\cos 11.54°} = 5.0 \text{ N}$$

(b) We can find the rotation speed from the *x*-equation:

$$v = \sqrt{\frac{rT\sin\theta}{m}} = 0.633 \text{ m/s}$$

The rotation frequency is $\omega = v/r = 3.165$ rad/s. Converting to rpm,

$$\omega = 3.165 \frac{\text{rad}}{\text{sec}} \times \frac{60 \text{ sec}}{1 \text{ min}} \times \frac{1 \text{ rev}}{2\pi\text{rad}} = 30 \text{ rpm}$$

Assess: One revolution in two seconds is reasonable.

P6.47. Prepare: Treat the ball as a particle in uniform circular motion. Rolling friction is ignored. A pictorial representation of the ball and the track is shown below. Work with SI units.

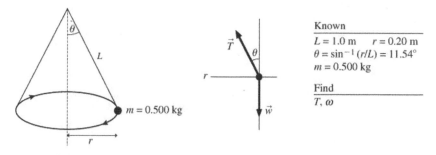

Solve: (a) Two. They are: an upward normal force and an inward normal force.
(b) From Newton's second law,

$$F_{net} = n_2 = mr\omega^2 = (0.030 \text{ kg})(0.20 \text{ m})\left[\frac{60 \text{ rev}}{\text{min}} \times \frac{2\pi \text{ rad}}{1 \text{ rev}} \times \frac{1 \text{ min}}{60 \text{ s}}\right]^2 = 0.24 \text{ N}$$

Assess: Note that the upward normal force cancels with the downward weight.

P6.49. Prepare: Treat the ball as a particle in circular motion. A visual overview of the ball's circular motion is shown below in a pictorial representation, a free-body diagram, and a list of values. The mass moves in a *horizontal* circle of radius $r = 20$ cm. A component of the tension in the string toward the center of the circle causes the centripetal acceleration needed for circular motion. The acceleration $\vec{a}$ and the net force vector point to the center of the circle, *not* along the string. The other two forces are the string tension $\vec{T}$, which does point along the string, and the weight $\vec{w}$.

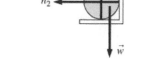

Known
$L = 1.0$ m $r = 0.20$ m
$\theta = \sin^{-1}(r/L) = 11.54°$
$m = 0.500$ kg

Find
T, ω

Solve: (a) Newton's second law for circular motion is

$$\Sigma F_y = T\cos\theta - w = T\cos\theta - mg = 0 \text{ N} \qquad \Sigma F_x = T\sin\theta = \frac{mv^2}{r}$$

From the *y*-equation,

$$T = \frac{mg}{\cos\theta} = \frac{(0.5 \text{ kg})(9.8 \text{ m/s}^2)}{\cos 11.54°} = 5.0 \text{ N}$$

(b) We can find the rotation speed from the *x*-equation:

$$v = \sqrt{\frac{rT\sin\theta}{m}} = 0.633 \text{ m/s}$$

The rotation frequency is $\omega = v/r = 3.165$ rad/s. Converting to rpm,

$$\omega = 3.165\frac{\text{rad}}{\text{sec}} \times \frac{60 \text{ sec}}{1 \text{ min}} \times \frac{1 \text{ rev}}{2\pi\text{rad}} = 30 \text{ rpm}$$

Assess: One revolution in two seconds is reasonable.

P6.51. Prepare: Since the hanging block is at rest, the total force on it is zero. The two forces are the tension in the string, *T*, and the weight of the puck, −*mg*. Since the revolving puck is moving at constant speed in a circle, the total force on the puck is the centripetal force. We must write the equations and solve them.

Solve: The total force on the block is $T - mg$. From Newton's second law, the total force is zero so we write:

$$T = mg = (1.20 \text{ kg})(9.8 \text{ m/s}^2) = 11.8 \text{ N}$$

The centripetal acceleration of the puck is caused by the tension in the string, so $mv^2/r = T$. We solve this to obtain:

$$v = \sqrt{Tr/m} = \sqrt{(11.8 \text{ N})(0.50 \text{ m})/(0.20 \text{ kg})} = 5.4 \text{ m/s}$$

The puck must rotate at a speed of 5.4 m/s.

Assess: It is remarkable that a block can be supported by a puck moving horizontally. But both the puck and the block are able to pull on the string—the block pulls downward on one end and the puck pulls outward on the other end. The relatively small mass of the puck is compensated by its high speed of 5.4 m/s.

P6.53. Prepare: Treat the car as a particle which is undergoing circular motion. The car is in circular motion with the center of the circle below the car. A visual overview of the car's circular motion is shown below in a pictorial representation, a free-body diagram, and a list of values.

Solve: Newton's second law at the top of the hill is

$$F_{net} = \Sigma F_y = w - n = mg - n = ma = \frac{mv^2}{r} \Rightarrow v^2 = r\left(g - \frac{n}{m}\right)$$

This result shows that maximum speed is reached when $n = 0$ and the car is beginning to lose contact with the road. Then,

$$v_{max} = \sqrt{rg} = \sqrt{(50 \text{ m})(9.8 \text{ m/s}^2)} = 22 \text{ m/s}$$

Assess: A speed of 22 m/s is equivalent to 50 mph, which seems like a reasonable value.

P6.55. Prepare: We are given $\omega = 45°/0.5$ s $= 1.57$ rad/s and $r = 0.70$ m. We will need to know the velocity of the drop of blood; it is given by Equation 6.6: $v = \omega r = (1.57 \text{ rad/s})(0.70 \text{ m}) = 1.1$ m/s.

Solve: (a) During the swinging motion, we will consider the drop of blood to be in uniform circular motion and therefore its acceleration will be centripetal

$$a = v^2/r = (1.1 \text{ m/s})^2/0.7 \text{ m} = 1.73 \text{ m/s}^2 \approx 1.7 \text{ m/s}^2$$

The centripetal direction at that instant is up.

(b)

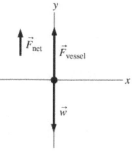

(c) Use Newton's second law $\Sigma \vec{F} = m\vec{a}$ in the y-direction with up positive.

$$F_{vessel} - w = ma$$
$$F_{vessel} = ma + w = ma + mg = m(a + g) = (0.0010 \text{ kg})(1.73 \text{ m/s}^2 + 9.8 \text{ m/s}^2) = 0.012 \text{ N}$$

The force is directed up.

(d) If the arm isn't swinging the drop of blood is in equilibrium and $\Sigma \vec{F} = 0$, so the upward force exerted by the blood vessel must be equal in magnitude to the weight of the drop $w = mg = (0.0010 \text{ kg})(9.8 \text{ m/s}^2) = 0.0098 \text{ N}$. The direction is opposite the weight, or up.

Assess: The acceleration of the drop in the swinging arm was less than 0.2 g, so the force exerted by the blood vessel then is only a bit larger than when the arm isn't swinging.

P6.57. Prepare: We expect the centripetal acceleration to be very large because ω is large. This will produce a significant force even though the mass difference of 10 mg is so small.

A preliminary calculation will convert the mass difference to kg: 10 mg = 1.0×10^{-5} kg. If the two samples are equally balanced then the shaft doesn't feel a net force in the horizontal plane. However, the mass difference of 10 mg is what causes the force.

We'll do another preliminary calculation to convert $\omega = 70,000$ rpm into rad/s.

$$78 \text{ rpm} = 70,000 \frac{\text{rev}}{\text{min}} \left(\frac{2\pi \text{ rad}}{1 \text{ rev}} \right) \left(\frac{1 \text{ min}}{60 \text{ s}} \right) = 7330 \text{ rad/s}$$

Solve: The centripetal acceleration is given by Equation 6.8 and the net force by Newton's second law.

$$F_{net} = (\Delta m)(a) = (\Delta m)(\omega^2 r) = (1.0 \times 10^{-5} \text{ kg})(7330 \text{ rad/s})^2 (0.10 \text{ m}) = 54 \text{ N}$$

Assess: As we expected, the centripetal acceleration is large. The force is not huge (because of the small mass difference) but still enough to worry about. The net force scales with this mass difference, so if the mistake were bigger it could be enough to shear off the shaft.

P6.59. Prepare: Model the earth (e) as a spherical mass. We will take the free-fall acceleration at the sea level to be 9.83 m/s^2 and $R_e = 6.37 \times 10^6$ m. A pictorial representation of the situation is shown below.

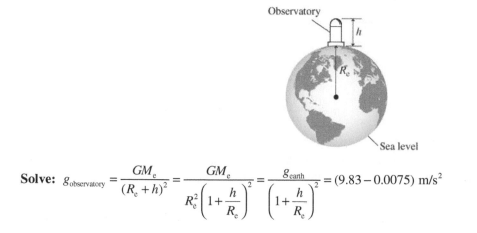

Solve: $g_{observatory} = \dfrac{GM_e}{(R_e + h)^2} = \dfrac{GM_e}{R_e^2 \left(1 + \dfrac{h}{R_e}\right)^2} = \dfrac{g_{earth}}{\left(1 + \dfrac{h}{R_e}\right)^2} = (9.83 - 0.0075) \text{ m/s}^2$

Here $g_{earth} = GM_e/R_e^2$ is the free-fall acceleration on a nonrotating earth, which is why we've used the value 9.83 m/s^2. Solving for h,

$$h = \left(\sqrt{\frac{9.83}{9.8225}} - 1\right) R_e = 2400 \text{ m}$$

Assess: This altitude is relative to the sea level and is at reasonable altitude.

P6.61. Prepare: Model the planet Z as a spherical mass. We will use Equation 6.24.

Solve: (a) $g_{z\,surface} = \dfrac{GM_Z}{R_Z^2} \Rightarrow 8.0 \text{ m/s}^2 = \dfrac{(6.67 \times 10^{-11} \text{ N} \cdot \text{m}^2/\text{kg}^2)M_Z}{(5.0 \times 10^6 \text{ m})^2} \Rightarrow M_Z = 3.0 \times 10^{24} \text{ kg}$

(b) Let h be the height above the north pole. Thus,

$$g_{above\,N\,pole} = \frac{GM_Z}{(R_Z + h)^2} = \frac{GM_Z}{R_Z^2\left(1 + \dfrac{h}{R_Z}\right)^2} = \frac{g_{z\,surface}}{\left(1 + \dfrac{h}{R_Z}\right)^2} = \frac{8.0 \text{ m/s}^2}{\left(1 + \dfrac{10.0 \times 10^6 \text{ m}}{5.0 \times 10^6 \text{ m}}\right)^2} = 0.89 \text{ m/s}^2$$

P6.63. According to the discussion in Section 6.3, the maximum walking speed is $v_{max} = \sqrt{gr}$. The astronaut's leg is about 0.70 m long whether on earth or on Mars, but g will be difficult. Use Equation 6.24 to find g_{Mars}. We look up the required data in the astronomical table: $m_{Mars} = 6.42 \times 10^{23}$ kg, and $R_{Mars} = 3.37 \times 10^6$ m. In part **(b)** we'll make the same assumption as in the text: The length of the leg $r = 0.70$ m.

Solve: (a)

$$g_{Mars} = \frac{GM_{Mars}}{(R_{Mars})^2} = \frac{(6.67 \times 10^{-11} \text{ N} \cdot \text{m}^2/\text{kg}^2)(6.42 \times 10^{23} \text{ kg})}{(3.37 \times 106 \text{ m})^2} = 3.37 \text{ m/s}^2 \approx 3.8 \text{ m/s}^2$$

(b)

$$v_{max} = \sqrt{gr} = \sqrt{(3.77 \text{ m/s}^2)(0.70 \text{ m})} = 1.6 \text{ m/s}$$

Access: The answer is about 3.6 mph, or about 60% of the speed the astronaut could walk on earth. This is reasonable on a smaller celestial body. Astronauts may adopt a hopping gait like some did on the moon.

Carefully analyze the units in the preliminary calculation to see that g ends up in m/s^2 or N/kg.

P6.65. Prepare: We place the origin of the coordinate system on the 20 kg sphere (m_1). The sphere (m_2) with a mass of 10 kg is 20 cm away on the x-axis, as shown below. The point at which the net gravitational force is zero must lie between the masses m_1 and m_2. This is because on such a point, the gravitational forces due to m_1 and m_2 are in opposite directions. As the gravitational force is directly proportional to the two masses and inversely proportional to the square of distance between them, the mass m must be closer to the 10-kg mass. The small mass m, if placed either to the left of m_1 or to the right of m_2, will experience gravitational forces from m_1 and m_2 pointing in the same direction, thus always leading to a nonzero force.

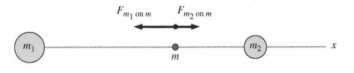

Solve:

$$F_{m_1\,on\,m} = F_{m_2\,on\,m} \Rightarrow G\frac{m_1 m}{x^2} = G\frac{m_2 m}{(0.20 - x)^2} \Rightarrow \frac{20}{x^2} = \frac{10}{(0.20 - x)^2} \Rightarrow 10x^2 - 8x + 0.8 = 0$$
$$\Rightarrow x = 0.683 \text{ m and } 0.117 \text{ m}$$

The value $x = 68.3$ cm is unphysical in the current situation, since this point is not between m_1 and m_2. Thus, the point $(x, y) = (11.7 \text{ cm}, 0 \text{ cm}) = (12 \text{ cm}, 0 \text{ cm})$ is where a small mass is to be placed for a zero gravitational force.

P6.67. Prepare: Model Mars (m) and Phobos as spherical masses. We will use Equation 6.28.
    Solve: The period of a satellite orbiting a planet of mass M_m is

$$T^2 = \left(\frac{4\pi^2}{GM_m}\right) r^3$$

Thus we can use Phobos's orbit to find the mass of Mars:

$$M_m = \frac{4\pi^2 r^3}{GT^2} = \frac{4\pi^2 (9.4 \times 10^6 \text{ m})^3}{(6.67 \times 10^{-11} \text{ N} \cdot \text{m}^2/\text{kg}^2)(2.7540 \times 10^4 \text{ s})^2} = 6.5 \times 10^{23} \text{ kg}$$

    Assess: The mass of Mars is 6.42×10^{23} kg. The slight difference is likely due to Phobos's orbit being somewhat noncircular.

P6.69. Prepare: According to the discussion in Section 6.3 the maximum walking speed is $v_{max} = \sqrt{gr}$. The astronaut's leg is about 0.70 m long whether on earth or on Europa, but g will be different. See Equation 6.24.

$$g_{Europa} = \frac{GM_{Europa}}{(R_{Europa})^2} = \frac{(6.67 \times 10^{-11} \text{ N} \cdot \text{m}^2/\text{kg}^2)(4.8 \times 10^{22} \text{ kg})}{(3.1 \times 10^6 \text{ m})^2} = 0.333 \text{ m/s}^2$$

    Solve:

$$v_{max} = \sqrt{gr} = \sqrt{(0.333 \text{ m/s}^2)(0.70 \text{ m})} = 0.48 \text{ m/s}$$

    Assess: The answer is about 1 mph or about 1/6 of the speed the astronaut could walk on the earth. This is reasonable on a small celestial body. Astronauts may adopt a hopping gait like some did on the moon.
    Carefully analyze the units in the preliminary calculation to see that g ends up in m/s^2 or N/kg.

P6.71. Solve: (a) At what speed does a 1500-kg car going over a hill with a radius of 200 m have an apparent weight of 11,760 N?
    (b) $2940 \text{ N} = \dfrac{1500 \text{ kg } v^2}{200 \text{ m}} \Rightarrow v = 19.8 \text{ m/s}$

P6.73. Solve: (a) A 1000-kg satellite orbits the earth with a speed of 1997 m/s. What is the radius of the orbit?

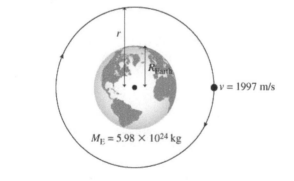

(b) The radius of the orbit is

$$r = \frac{GM_E}{(v_{payload})^2} = \frac{6.67 \times 10^{-11} \text{ N} \cdot \text{m}^2/\text{kg}^2 (5.98 \times 10^{24} \text{ kg})}{(1997 \text{ m/s})^2} = 1.0 \times 10^8 \text{ m}$$

P6.75. Prepare: Equation 6.16 which gives the orbital speed in terms of the free-fall acceleration and orbital radius can be used. The radius is half the diameter, $r_{Moon} = 1.75 \times 10^6$ m.

Solve: Applying Equation 6.16,

$$v_{orbit} = \sqrt{rg} = \sqrt{(1.75 \times 10^6 \text{ m})(1.6 \text{ m/s}^2)} = 1700 \text{ m/s}$$

The correct choice is C.

Assess: Even though the free-fall acceleration on the moon is much less than the free-fall acceleration on earth, the moon's orbital speed is still very high. At 3700 mph, it is still faster than an airplane.

P6.77. Prepare: The centripetal acceleration will be constant if the velocity and radius of the orbit remain the same.

Solve: The gravitational force is stronger on the spacecraft when it is orbiting the near side of the moon. The net centripetal force must remain the same so the spacecraft should compensate for the increased gravitational force towards the center of the moon by firing its rockets so that they exert a force away from the center of the moon. The correct choice is A.

Assess: From Equation 6.26, another way to keep the radius of the orbit the same is to fire the rockets in the direction of motion of the spacecraft. However, if the spacecraft were fired in the direction of motion the velocity of the spacecraft would increase.

7—Rotational Motion
Conceptual Questions

Q7.1. Reason: By convention, clockwise (cw) rotations are negative and counterclockwise (ccw) rotations are positive. As a result, an angular acceleration that decrease/increases a negative angular velocity is positive/negative. In like manner an angular acceleration that decreases/increases a positive angular velocity is negative/positive. Knowing this we can establish the situation for each figure.

Figure (a) the pulley is rotating cw ($\omega = -$), however since the large mass is on the left it is decelerating ($\alpha = +$).
Figure (b) the pulley is rotating ccw ($\omega = +$) and since the large mass is on the left it is accelerating ($\alpha = +$).
Figure (c) the pulley is rotating cw ($\omega = -$) and since the large mass is on the right it is accelerating ($\alpha = -$).
Figure (d) the pulley is rotating ccw ($\omega = +$), however since the large mass is on the right it is decelerating ($\alpha = -$).

Assess: It is important to know the sign convention for all physical quantities that are vectors. This is especially important when working with rotational motion.

Q7.3. Reason: The question properly identified where the torques are computed about (the hinge). Torques that tend to make the door rotate counterclockwise (ccw) in the diagram are positive by convention (general agreement) and torques that tend to make the door rotate clockwise (cw) are negative.

(a) +
(b) −
(c) +
(d) −
(e) 0

Assess: Looking at the diagram we see that $\vec{F}_a$ and $\vec{F}_c$ are parallel and are both creating a negative or ccw torque. But since $\vec{F}_c$ is farther from the hinge, its torque will be greater. A similar argument can be made for $\vec{F}_b$ and $\vec{F}_d$. Note that $\vec{F}_e$ causes no torque since it has no moment arm.

Q7.5. Reason: The reason for large-diameter steering wheels in trucks is that more torque is needed to turn the wheels due to the greater mass of the truck. Making the steering wheel larger means that more torque is exerted on the steering shaft for the same force from the driver's hands.

Assess: Most light cars employ a rack-and-pinion steering system, while larger SUVs and trucks often employ a recirculating-ball steering system; however both systems can be assisted by pressurized hydraulic fluid (power steering), so steering, even in trucks, can be much easier than in the old days.

Q7.7. Reason: The torque you exert on the branch is your weight multiplied by the lever arm, or the distance along the branch from the trunk, so the farther out you are, the greater the torque you exert on the branch.

Assess: It is a good thing that tree branches themselves get thinner away from the trunk, so the weight of the branch itself doesn't break it away from the trunk.

Q7.9. Reason: As suggested by the figure, we will assume that the larger sphere is more massive. Then the center of gravity would be at point 1 because if we suspend the dumbbell from point 1 then the counterclockwise torque due to the large sphere (large weight times small lever arm) will be equal to the clockwise torque due to the small sphere (small weight times large lever arm).

Assess: Look at the figure and mentally balance the dumbbell on your finger; your finger would have to be at point 1.

The sun-earth system is similar to this except that the sun's mass is so much greater than the earth's that the center of mass (called the barycenter for astronomical objects orbiting each other) is only 450 km from the center of the sun.

Q7.11. Reason: Spin them. Because they would have different moments of inertia ($2/5MR^2$ for the solid sphere and $2/3MR^2$ for a thin-walled hollow sphere, with something in between if the wall of the hollow sphere is not particularly thin) their angular accelerations would be different with the same torque acting on them (remember the rotational version of Newton's second law: $\alpha = \tau_{net}/I$). The solid one (with the smaller moment of inertia) would accelerate quicker given the same torque.

Assess: The two balls would have the same linear inertia (having the same mass) so dropping them in free fall, for example, and observing their linear accelerations would not distinguish between them; but the rotational inertia (moment of inertia) is different, and so exerting a net torque on them and measuring the resultant angular acceleration can distinguish between them.

Q7.13. Reason: We will assume that the table has enough friction that the ends of the rods don't slip. We will also ignore air resistance.

The angular acceleration is the quantity of interest in this question. If the two rods have the same angular acceleration then they will hit the table at the same time if released at the same time from the same angle.

However, the angular acceleration is dependent on the torque and the moment of inertia: $\alpha = \tau_{net}/I$. The net torque about the end of the rod on the table is the torque due to the weight of the rod ($w = Mg$) acting at the center of mass ($L/2$ from the end), because the normal and friction forces of the table on the end of the rod will produce a zero torque because the lever arm is zero.

Both the heavy steel rod and the pencil will be modeled as a thin rod so that the moment of inertia (given in Table 7.4) is $I = \frac{1}{3}ML^2$, but of course neither M nor L is the same in the two cases.

Now it is important to watch the mass (as well as one L) cancel out of the calculation for α.

$$\alpha = \frac{\tau_{net}}{I} = \frac{r(F)\sin\phi}{\frac{1}{3}ML^2} = \frac{r(w)\sin\phi}{\frac{1}{3}ML^2} = \frac{(\frac{L}{2})(Mg)\sin\phi}{\frac{1}{3}ML^2} = \frac{(\frac{1}{2})(g)\sin\phi}{\frac{1}{3}L} = \frac{3g\sin\phi}{2L}$$

What do we notice about the result?

1. M canceled, so the mass of the rod does not affect the angular acceleration. This is reminiscent of free fall where the mass also cancels in $a = F_{net}/m = mg/m$.
2. Unlike free fall, since ϕ (the angle the rod makes with the vertical) changes as the rod falls, the acceleration is not constant. In our case ϕ started out at 15° and increases to 90°; $\sin\phi$ also increases over that interval so the acceleration increases as the rod falls.
3. One L canceled, but one is still left in the denominator; the longer the rod the smaller the angular acceleration. This is the point that answers the question. Since the 1.0 m rod is longer than the 0.15 m pencil, it will have less angular acceleration and hence hit the table last.

   The pencil hits first.

Assess: The intuition we've developed about Galileo's law of falling bodies (all bodies in free fall have the same acceleration) doesn't quite apply in this case. Of course the rods aren't in free fall, but it is the way the L didn't cancel in τ_{net}/I that makes the accelerations not the same.

Q7.15. Reason: The bottom of the tire, the point in contact with the road, has (relative to the ground) an instantaneous velocity of zero, but the top of the tire has an instantaneous forward velocity twice as fast as the car's forward velocity. See Figure 7.33.

When the pebble works loose it flies off tangentially forward 60 mph *faster* than the car is going. So it hits the wheel well with a relative speed of about 60 mph.

Assess: Yes, gravity pulls the pebble down and the trajectory is parabolic, but it is going so fast that it hits the wheel well before it falls far.

Multiple Choice Questions

Q7.17. Reason: We are given that $r = 0.15$ m and that $\sin\theta = 1$. Solve Equation 7.4 for F.

$$\tau = rF\sin\theta$$

$$F = \frac{\tau}{r\sin\theta} = \frac{20 \text{ N} \cdot \text{m}}{(0.15 \text{ m})(\sin 90°)} = 133 \text{ N} \approx 130 \text{ N}$$

The correct answer is C.

Assess: This force is not unreasonable; it is like lifting 30 lbs. Notice the units worked out in the equation.

Q7.19. Reason: We look up the formula for the moment of inertia of a disk about its axis of symmetry in Table 7.4. Neglect the small hole in the center. The radius is half the diameter.

$$I = \frac{1}{2}MR^2 = \frac{1}{2}(0.015 \text{ kg})(0.060 \text{ m})^2 = 2.7 \times 10^{-5} \text{ kg} \cdot \text{m}^2$$

The correct answer is A.

Assess: The answer is a small number, but CDs are small and light. An old vinyl LP record would be both larger and more massive so it would have a larger moment of inertia, but modeled as a disk would still be $I = \frac{1}{2}MR^2$.

Q7.21. Reason: Both doors are slabs and the moment of inertia about an edge (the hinge) is given by Table 7.4: $I = \frac{1}{3}Ma^2$ where a is the width of the door. We are told that the width of door 1 is a while the width of door 2 is $2a$:

$$\alpha = \frac{\tau_{\text{net}}}{I} = \frac{r(F)\sin\phi}{I}$$

and since Bob and Barb push "straight against" the door $\phi = 90°$ so $\sin\theta = 1$:

$$\frac{\alpha_2}{\alpha_1} = \frac{(2a)F / \frac{1}{3}M(2a)^2}{a(2F) / \frac{1}{3}Ma^2} = \frac{1}{4}$$

This means that $\alpha_1 = 4\alpha_2$, so the correct choice is A.

Assess: The torque exerted by Bob, $(2a)F$, is the same as the torque exerted by Barb, $a(2F)$, but the moment of inertia of door 2 is four times the moment of inertia of door 1.

Q7.23. Reason: If we consider the motion of a piece of the tread to be a combination of the forward translational motion (which is constant) and the rotational motion, then we will simply compute the acceleration for the rotational part to be $a = v^2/r$, where v is the speed of the center of mass, 30 m/s:

$$a = \frac{v^2}{r} = \frac{(30 \text{ m/s})^2}{0.37 \text{ m}} = 2432 \text{ m/s}^2 \approx 2400 \text{ m/s}^2$$

The correct choice is C.

Assess: The piece of tread moves through the cycloid path shown in Figure 7.34, but the acceleration is due to the change in velocity, and the translational velocity isn't changing, only the rotational velocity is changing.

Problems

P7.1. Prepare: We'll assume a constant acceleration during the one revolution. We'll use the second and third equations for circular motion in Table 7.2, the third to find α and then the second to find ω_f.

Known
_____

$$r = \frac{1}{2}D = .90 \text{ m}$$

$$\Delta t = 1.0 \text{ s}$$

$$\Delta\theta = 1.0 \text{ rev} = 2\pi \text{ rad}$$

Find
_____

$$v_f = r\omega_f$$

Solve: The third equation in Table 7.2 allows us to solve for α. That $\omega_0 = 0$ makes it easier.

$$\Delta\theta = \frac{1}{2}\alpha(\Delta t)^2$$

$$\alpha = \frac{2\Delta\theta}{(\Delta \tau)^2} = \frac{2(2\pi \text{ rad})}{(1.0 \text{ s})^2} 12.6 \text{ rad/s}^2$$

The second equation in Table 7.2 gives ω_f:

$$\omega_f = \omega_0 + \alpha\Delta t = 0 \text{ rad/s} + (12.6 \text{ rad/s}^2)(1.0 \text{ s}) = 12.6 \text{ rad/s}$$

Finally we compute $v_f = r\omega_f = (.90 \text{ m})(12.6 \text{ rad/s}) = 11 \text{ m/s}$.

Assess: This speed seems reasonable, about 1/4 of a baseball fast pitch. The hammer throw is similar to the discus, but the weight is on a wire so the radius of the circular motion is a bit longer than the arm and so the release speed is a bit larger and hence the distance it goes before landing is a few meters more.

P7.3. Prepare: We assume constant angular acceleration; then we can use the equations in Table 7.2.

Known
_____

$$\Delta t = 2.0 \text{ s}$$
$$\omega_0 = 0$$
$$\omega_f = 3000 \text{ rpm}$$

Find
_____

$$\alpha$$
$$\Delta\theta$$

Convert $\Delta\omega$ to rad/s.

$$\Delta\omega = \omega_f - \omega_0 = 3000\frac{\text{rev}}{\text{min}}\left(\frac{2\pi \text{ rad}}{1 \text{ rev}}\right)\left(\frac{1 \text{ min}}{60 \text{ s}}\right) = 314 \text{ rad/s}$$

Solve: (a)

$$\alpha = \frac{\Delta\omega}{\Delta t} = \frac{314 \text{ rad/s}}{2.0 \text{ s}} = 157 \text{ rad/s}^2$$

(b) We'll use the last equation in Table 7.2, using $\omega_0 = 0$.

$$\Delta\theta = \omega_0\Delta t + \frac{1}{2}\alpha(\Delta t)^2 = \frac{1}{2}(157 \text{ rad/s}^2)(2.0 \text{ s})^2 = 314 \text{ rad}$$

Finally, convert to revolutions:

$$314 \text{ rad} = 314 \text{ rad}\left(\frac{1 \text{ rev}}{2\pi \text{ rad}}\right) = 50 \text{ rev}$$

Assess: 50 rev seems like a lot in 2 s, but it is reasonable with the large angular acceleration and the final angular velocity of 3000 rpm.

P7.5. Prepare: The magnitude of the torque in each case is $\tau = rF$ because $\sin\phi = 1$.
   Solve: $\tau_1 = rF$ $\tau_2 = r2F$ $\tau_3 = 2rF$ $\tau_4 = 2r2F$
   Examining the above we see that $\tau_1 < \tau_2 = \tau_3 < \tau_4$. Since for each case $\tau = rF$ (because $\sin\phi = 1$), in order to determine the torque we have just kept track of each force (F), the magnitude of the position vector (r) which locates the point of application of the force and finally the product (rF).
   Assess: As expected, both the force and the lever arm contribute to the torque. Larger forces and larger lever arms make larger torques. Case 4 has both the largest force and the largest lever arm, hence the largest torque.

P7.7. Prepare: Torque by a force is defined as $\tau = Fr\sin\phi$ [Equation 7.5], where ϕ is measured counterclockwise from the $\vec{r}$ vector to the $\vec{F}$ vector. The radial line passing through the axis of rotation is shown below by broken line. We see that the 20 N force makes an angle of $+90°$ relative to the radius vector r_2, but the 30 N force makes an angle of $-90°$ relative to r_1.

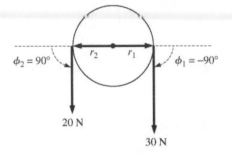

Solve: The net torque on the pulley about the axle is the torque due to the 30 N force plus the torque due to the 20 N force:

$$(30 \text{ N})r_1 \sin\phi_1 + (20 \text{ N})r_2 \sin\phi_2 = (30 \text{ N})(0.02 \text{ m})\sin(-90°) + (20 \text{ N})(0.02 \text{ m})\sin(90°)$$

$$= (-0.60 \text{ N} \cdot \text{m}) + (0.40 \text{ N} \cdot \text{m}) = -0.20 \text{ N} \cdot \text{m}$$

Assess: A negative torque will cause a clockwise rotation of the pulley.

P7.9. Prepare: The height, thickness, and mass of the door are all irrelevant (for this problem, but the mass is important for Problem 7.31). If the door closer exerts a torque of 5.2 N $\cdot$ m, then you need to also apply a torque of 5.2 N $\cdot$ m in the opposite direction. The way to do that with the least force is to make r as big as possible (the entire width of the door), and make sure the angle $\phi = 90°$.
   Solve: From $\tau = rF\sin\phi$ solve for F. Then we see that the needed torque is produced with the smallest force by maximizing r and $\sin\phi$.

$$F = \frac{\tau}{r\sin\phi} = \frac{5.2 \text{ N} \cdot \text{m}}{(0.91 \text{ m})\sin 90°} = 5.7 \text{ N}$$

Assess: It is good to have problems where more than the required information is given. Part of learning to solve real-world problems is knowing (or learning) which quantities are significant, which are irrelevant, and which are negligible. Of course, in this case the mass is used later in Problem 7.31.
   The answer of 5.7 N seems like a reasonable amount of force, which might be supplied, say, by a doorstop. If your doorstop is a simple wedge of wood inserted under the door (as they are at my college), you can see that it should be positioned near the outside edge of the door so the friction force will produce enough torque to keep the door open.

P7.11. Prepare: For both Tom and Jerry $r = 1.5$ m (or half the diameter).
   Compute the magnitude of each torque.

$$\tau_{\text{Tom}} = (1.50 \text{ m})(40.0 \text{ N})\sin 60° = 51.9615 \text{ N} \cdot \text{m}$$

$$\tau_{\text{Jerry}} = (1.50 \text{ m})(35.2 \text{ N})\sin 80° = 51.9978 \text{ N} \cdot \text{m}$$

We keep extra significant figures in the intermediate calculations because we will be subtracting two nearly equal numbers.
   Solve: (a) The torque due to Tom will be positive because it will tend to produce ccw rotation, while the torque due to Jerry will be negative because it will tend to produce cw rotation.

$$\tau = \tau_{\text{Tom}} + \tau_{\text{Jerry}} = 51.9615 \text{ N} \cdot \text{m} + (-51.9978 \text{ N} \cdot \text{m}) = 0.0363 \text{ N} \cdot \text{m}$$

(b) With both Tom's and Jerry's torques tending to produce ccw rotation, they are both positive and so the net torque would be their sum:

$$\tau = \tau_{Tom} + \tau_{Jerry} = 51.9615 \text{ N} \cdot \text{m} + 51.9978 \text{ N} \cdot \text{m} = 104 \text{ N} \cdot \text{m}$$

Assess: As the difference between the two parts of the problem demonstrates, the direction of the forces really matters. But we can produce torques of the same magnitude with forces of different magnitude by adjusting the angles—even with the same r.

Though we used extra significant figures in the intermediate calculations, we still report the answer to three significant figures.

P7.13. Prepare: Knowing that torque may be determined by $\tau = rF_{\perp}$, that counterclockwise torque is positive and clockwise torque negative we can determine the net torque acting on the bar.

Solve:

$$\tau_{cw} = -(0.25 \text{ m})(8.0 \text{ N}) = -2.0 \text{ N} \cdot \text{m}$$
$$\tau_{ccw} = (0.75 \text{ m})(10 \text{ N}) = 7.5 \text{ N} \cdot \text{m}$$
$$\tau_{net} = \tau_{ccw} + \tau_{cw} = 7.5 \text{ N} \cdot \text{m} - 2.0 \text{ N} \cdot \text{m} = 5.5 \text{ N} \cdot \text{m}$$

Since the net torque is $+5.5 \text{N} \cdot \text{m}$, the bar will rotate in the ccw direction around the dot.

Assess: The ccw torque had both the larger r and the larger F, so the net toque was also ccw. The numbers also seem reasonable, and the units work out.

P7.15. Prepare: We'll set up the coordinate system so the barbell lies along the x-axis with the origin at the left end and use Equation 7.7 to determine the x-coordinate of the center of gravity. We'll model each weight (and the barbell itself in part (b)) as a particle, as if the mass were concentrated at each item's own center of gravity.

Solve: (a)

$$x_{cg} = \frac{x_1 m_1 + x_2 m_2}{m_1 + m_2} = \frac{(0.0 \text{ m})(20 \text{ kg}) + (1.7 \text{ m})(35 \text{ kg})}{20 \text{ kg} + 35 \text{ kg}} = 1.08 \text{ m} \approx 1.1 \text{ m}$$

(b) In this part we include the barbell (call it particle 3), whose own center of gravity is at its geometrical center ($x_3 = 1.7 \text{ m}/2 = 0.85 \text{ m}$), since we assume it has uniform density.

$$x_{cg} = \frac{x_1 m_1 + x_2 m_2 + x_3 m_3}{m_1 + m_2 + m_3} = \frac{(0.0 \text{ m})(20 \text{ kg}) + (1.7 \text{ m})(35 \text{ kg}) + (0.85 \text{ m})(8.0 \text{ kg})}{20 \text{ kg} + 35 \text{ kg} + 8.0 \text{ kg}} = 1.25 \text{ m} \approx 1.2 \text{ m}$$

Assess: To two significant figures the answers to both parts are close. Taking the barbell into account didn't move the center of gravity much for two reasons: It wasn't very massive, and its center of mass was already near the center of mass of the system.

P7.17. Prepare: How will you estimate the mass of your arm? Of course different people's arms have different masses, but even different methods of estimating the mass of your specific arm will produce slightly different results. But it is a good exercise, even if we have only one significant figure of precision. One way would be to make some rough measurements. Because the density of your arm is about the density of water, you could fill a garbage can to the brim with water, insert your arm, and weigh the water that overflows. Or you could look at Figure 7.21, which indicates that a guess of $m = 4.0$ kg for a person whose total mass is 80 kg is good.

The gravitational force on a 4.0 kg object is $w = mg$ (4.0 kg)(10 m/s^2) = 40 N.

I know it is about 1 yd from the tip of my outstretched arm to my forward-facing nose, but a meter is a bit bigger than a yard, so I would estimate that from fingertip to shoulder would be about 0.7 m. If I model my arm as a uniform cylinder of uniform density then the center of gravity would be at its center—0.35 m from the shoulder joint (the "hinge"). If I further refine the model of my arm, it is heavier nearer the shoulder and lighter toward the hand, so I will round the location of its center of gravity down to 0.30 m from the shoulder.

Solve: Since the arm is held horizontally $\sin\phi = 1$.

$$\tau = rF\sin\phi = (0.30 \text{ m})(40 \text{ N})(1) = 12 \text{ N} \cdot \text{m}$$

Assess: Your assumptions and estimates (and, indeed, your arm) might be different, but your answer will probably be in the same order of magnitude; you probably won't end up with an answer 10 × bigger or 10 × smaller.

P7.19. Prepare: First let's divide the object into two parts. Let's call part #1 the part to the left of the point of interest and part #2 the part to the right of the point of interest. Next using our sense of center of gravity, we know the cm of part #1 is at 12.5 m and the cm of part #2 is at +37.5 cm. We also know the mass of part #1 is one fourth the total mass of the object and the mass of part #2 is three fourths the total mass of the object. Finally, we can determine the gravitational torque of each part using any of the three expressions for torque as shown below:

Equation (7.3) $\tau = rF_\perp$ is straightforward to use because the forces are perpendicular to the position vectors which locate the point of application of the force.

Equation (7.4) $\tau = r_\perp F$ is straightforward to use because the position vectors which locate the point of application of the forces are also the moment arms for the forces.

Equation (7.4) $\tau = rF\sin\phi$ is straightforward to use because the angles are either 90° or 270°.

Solve: Using equation (7.4) we obtain the following:

$$\tau_{net} = \tau_1 + \tau_2 = m_1 g r_1 \sin(90°) + m_2 g r_2 \sin(-90°)$$
$$= (0.5 \text{ kg})(9.8 \text{ m/s}^2)(-0.125 \text{ m})(1) + (0.75 \text{ kg})(9.8 \text{ m/s}^2)(0.375 \text{ m})(-1) = -2.1 \text{ N} \cdot \text{m}$$

Assess: According to this answer, if released the object should rotate in a clockwise direction. Looking at the figure this is exactly what we would expect to happen.

P7.21. Prepare: Model the arm as a uniform rigid rod. Its mass acts at the center of mass. The force in each case is the weight, $w = mg$.

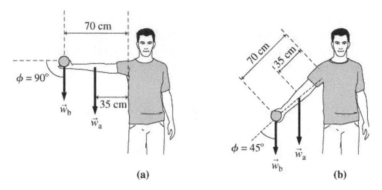

(a)   (b)

Solve: (a) The torque is due both to the weight of the ball and the weight of the arm.

$$\tau = \tau_{ball} + \tau_{arm} = r_b(m_b g)\sin 90° + r_a(m_a g)\sin 90°$$
$$= (0.70 \text{ m})(3.0 \text{ kg})(9.8 \text{ m/s}^2) + (0.35 \text{ m})(4.0 \text{ kg})(9.8 \text{ m/s}^2) = 34 \text{ N} \cdot \text{m}$$

(b) The torque is reduced because the moment arms are reduced. Both forces act at $\phi = 45°$ from the radial line, so

$$\tau = \tau_{ball} + \tau_{arm} = r_b(m_b g)\sin 45° + r_a(m_a g)\sin 45°$$
$$= (0.70 \text{ m})(3.0 \text{ kg})(9.8 \text{ m/s}^2)(0.707) + (0.35 \text{ m})(4.0 \text{ kg})(9.8 \text{ m/s}^2)(0.707) = 24 \text{ N} \cdot \text{m}$$

Assess: This problem could also have been done, as in Problem 7.17, by first finding the center of mass of the arm-ball system and computing the torque due to the combined weight acting at that point. The final answers would be the same.

P7.23. Prepare: Set up a coordinate system along the beams with the origin at the left end. Assume each beam is of uniform density so its own center of gravity is at its geometrical center. Then use Equation 7.7.

Solve: (a)

$$x_{cg} = \frac{x_1 m_1 + x_2 m_2}{m_1 + m_2} = \frac{(0.500 \text{ m})(10.0 \text{ kg}) + (1.00 \text{ m} + 1.00 \text{ m})(40.0 \text{ kg})}{10.0 \text{ kg} + 40.0 \text{ kg}} = 1.70 \text{ m}$$

(b) The gravitational torque on the two-beam system is the total weight acting at the center of gravity of the system: $w = mg = (10.0 \text{ kg} + 40.0 \text{ kg})(9.80 \text{ m/s}^2) = 490 \text{ N}$.

$$\tau = rF\sin\phi = (1.70 \text{ m})(490 \text{ N})\sin 90° = 833 \text{ N} \cdot \text{m}$$

Because this torque is in the cw direction we report it as a negative torque: $\tau = -833 \text{ N} \cdot \text{m}$.

Assess: This problem could also be done by computing the gravitational torque individually on each beam and adding them up. The final answer would be the same. For the beams to remain in equilibrium some other object must supply an equal torque in the opposite direction.

P7.25. Prepare: A table tennis ball is a spherical shell, and we look that up in Table 7.4. The radius is half the diameter.
Solve:

$$I = \frac{2}{3}MR^2 = \frac{2}{3}(0.0027 \text{ kg})(0.020 \text{ m})^2 = 7.2 \times 10^{-7} \text{ kg} \cdot \text{m}^2$$

Assess: The answer is small, but then again, it isn't hard to start a table tennis ball rotating or stop it from doing so.
By the way, this calculation can be done in one's head without a calculator by writing the data in scientific notation and mentally keeping track of the significant figures:

$$I = \frac{2}{3}(2.7 \times 10^{-3} \text{ kg})(2.0 \times 10^{-2} \text{ m})^2 = \frac{2}{3}(27 \times 10^{-4} \text{ kg})(2 \times 10^{-2} \text{ m})^2 = \frac{27}{3} \cdot 2 \cdot 2^2 \times 10^{-4} \times 10^{-4} \text{ kg} \cdot \text{m}^2$$
$$= 9 \cdot 8 \times 10^{-8} \text{ kg} \cdot \text{m}^2 = 72 \times 10^{-8} \text{ kg} \cdot \text{m}^2 = 7.2 \times 10^{-7} \text{ kg} \cdot \text{m}^2$$

P7.27. Prepare: When the problem says the connecting rods are "very light" we know to ignore them (especially since we aren't given their mass).
Since all of the mass (seats plus children) is equally far from the axis of rotation we simply use $I = MR^2$ where M is the total mass.
Solve:

$$I = MR^2 = [4(5.0 \text{ kg}) + 15 \text{ kg} + 20 \text{ kg}](1.5 \text{ m})^2 = 120 \text{ kg} \cdot \text{m}^2$$

Assess: When all of the mass is the same distance R from the axis of rotation, the calculation of I is relatively simple.

P7.29. Prepare: Treat the bicycle rim as a hoop, and use the expression given in Table 7.4 for the moment of inertia of a hoop. Manipulate this expression to obtain the mass.
Solve: The mass of the rim is determined by

$$m = I / R^2 = 0.19 \text{ kg} \cdot \text{m}^2 / (0.65 \text{ m} / 2)^2 = 1.8 \text{ kg}$$

Assess: Note that the units reduce to kg as expected. This amount seems a little heavy, but since we are not told what type of bicycle it is not an unreasonable amount.

P7.31. Prepare: We will assume we are to compute I about an edge (the hinge of the door), so from Table 7.4 we have I = $\frac{1}{3}Ma^2$ where $a = 0.91$ m and $M = 25$ kg.
Solve: (a)

$$I = \frac{1}{3}Ma^2 = \frac{1}{3}(25 \text{ kg})(0.91 \text{ m})^2 = 6.9 \text{ kg} \cdot \text{m}^2$$

(b) After we let go of the door (or remove the doorstop) the net torque is the torque due to the door closer, which Problem 7.9 says is 5.2 N · m.

$$\alpha = \frac{\tau_{net}}{I} = \frac{5.2 \text{ N} \cdot \text{m}}{6.9 \text{ kg} \cdot \text{m}^2} = 0.75 \text{ rad/s}^2$$

Assess: The results seem to be in the reasonable range. As long as the net torque of 0.52 N · m continues to act, the door will continue to accelerate. Usually there are dampeners to exert a slowing torque so the door doesn't slam.

P7.33. Prepare: We will assume that the torque produced by the frictional force of the floor on your foot *is* the net torque (i.e., we will ignore frictional and other torques). We know that $F = 7.0$ N, $r = 0.40$ m, and $\alpha = 1.8$ rad/s^2. We are also indirectly told ("in the direction that causes the greatest angular acceleration") that $\phi = 90°$. We will solve for I from the rotational version of Newton's second law: $\alpha = \tau_{net}/I$.
Solve:

$$I = \frac{\tau_{net}}{\alpha} = \frac{rF\sin\phi}{\alpha} = \frac{(0.40 \text{ m})(7.0 \text{ N})(\sin 90°)}{1.8 \text{ rad/s}^2} = 1.6 \text{ kg} \cdot \text{m}^2$$

Assess: The answer is not particularly large, but your mass is distributed quite close to the axis of rotation, so I is small. Carefully observe the units work out since N = kg · m/s^2.

P7.35. Prepare: A circular plastic disk rotating on an axle through its center is a rigid body. Assume the axis is perpendicular to the disk. Since $\tau = I\alpha$ is the rotational analog of Newton's second law $F = ma$, we can use this relation to find the net torque on the object. To determine the torque (τ) needed to take the plastic disk from $\omega_i = 0$ rad/s to $\omega_f = 1800$ rpm $= (1800)(2\pi)/60$ rad/s $= 60\pi$ rad/s in $t_f - t_i = 4.0$ s, we need to determine the angular acceleration (α) and the disk's moment of inertia (I) about the axle in its center. The radius of the disk is $R = 10.0$ cm.

Solve: We have

$$I = \frac{1}{2}MR^2 = \frac{1}{2}(0.200 \text{ kg})(0.10 \text{ m})^2 = 1.0 \times 10^{-3} \text{ kgm}^2$$

$$\omega_f = \omega_i + \alpha(t_f - t_i) \Rightarrow \alpha = \frac{\omega_f - \omega_i}{t_f - t_i} = \frac{60\pi \text{ rad/s} - 0 \text{ rad/s}}{4.0 \text{ s}} = 15\pi \text{ rad/s}^2$$

Thus, $\tau = I\alpha = (1.0 \times 10^{-3} \text{ kgm}^2)(15\pi \text{ rad/s}^2) = 0.047$ N · m.

Assess: The solution to this problem required a knowledge of torque, moment of inertia, rotational dynamics and rotational kinematics. You should consider it an accomplishment to have mastered these concepts and then combined them to solve a problem.

P7.37. Prepare: What causes angular accelerations? (Net) torques. We'll apply the rotational version of Newton's second law. We'll write the net torque as $\Sigma\tau$ to emphasize that we are summing the two given torques; the 12 N force is producing a positive (ccw) torque, while the 10 N force is producing a negative (cw) torque. For each torque $R = 0.30$ m.

We will assume that the rope comes off tangent to the pulley on each side, so that $\phi = 90°$ and $\sin\phi = 1$.

Looking up the formula for I of a cylinder in Table 7.4, and using $M = 0.80$ kg, gives

$$I = \frac{1}{2}MR^2 = \frac{1}{2}(0.80 \text{ kg})(0.30 \text{ m})^2 = 0.036 \text{ kg} \cdot \text{m}^2$$

Solve:

$$\alpha = \frac{\Sigma\tau}{I} = \frac{(0.30 \text{ m})(12 \text{ N}) - (0.30 \text{ m})(10 \text{ N})}{0.036 \text{ kg} \cdot \text{m}^2} = \frac{(0.30 \text{ m})(12 \text{ N} - 10 \text{ N})}{0.036 \text{ kg} \cdot \text{m}^2} = 17 \text{ rad/s}^2$$

Assess: This result answers the question. The proper units cancel to give α in rad/s². Notice that the specific angles the ropes make with the vertical do not matter, as long as they are exerting torques in opposite directions and coming off of the pulley tangentially.

P7.39. Prepare: With a constant string tension we will have constant angular acceleration, so we can use the equations in Table 7.2, but it is also clear that we will need to do a preliminary calculation to get α. The string will come off tangentially so that $\phi = 90°$. We will also interpret "to get the top spinning" as $\omega_0 = 0$. The radius is half the diameter.

Known

$r = 0.025$ m
$F = 0.30$ N
$\phi = 90°$
$I = 3.0 \times 10^{-5}$ kg · m²
$\Delta\theta = 5.0$ rev $= 31.4$ rad
$\omega_0 = 0$

Find

α (preliminary)
Δt

$$\alpha = \frac{\tau_{net}}{I} = \frac{rF\sin\phi}{I} = \frac{(0.025 \text{ m})(0.30 \text{ N})(1)}{3.0 \times 10^{-5} \text{ kg} \cdot \text{m}^2} = 250 \text{ rad/s}^2$$

Solve: Solve the angular displacement equation for circular motion in Table 7.2 (with for $\omega_0 = 0$) for Δt:

$$\Delta\theta = \frac{1}{2}\alpha(\Delta t)^2$$

$$\Delta t = \sqrt{\frac{2\Delta\theta}{\alpha}} = \sqrt{\frac{2(31.4 \text{ rad})}{250 \text{ rad/s}^2}} = 0.50 \text{ s}$$

Assess: As you may know from personal experience, it doesn't take long for a toy top to complete five revolutions, and this bears that out.

P7.41. Prepare: The rope is a constraint that makes the magnitudes of the accelerations of the blocks the same, and if the rope doesn't slip that further implies that $a_{block} = \alpha_{pulley}R$. See Equation 7.16

We will assume that the pulley is a solid cylinder, so that $I_{pulley} = \frac{1}{2}MR^2$. "Light rope" means we can assume that the mass of the rope is zero. For the torque calculation $r = R = 0.30$ m.

Known
$R = 0.30$ m
$m_1 = 2.5$ kg
$m_2 = 1.5$ kg
$M = 0.75$ kg (pulley)
$\phi = 90°$

Find
a

In order to keep track of directions, draw and label a figure.

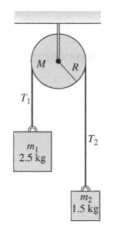

We will need to set up a system of three equations in three unknowns, because we do not know the tensions T_1 and T_2 in the ropes (they are *not* equal to each other nor to the weights of the blocks).

Solve: Use $\Sigma F = ma$ for each block. Call up positive, so block 1 will have a negative (downward) acceleration because it weighs more than block 2.

$$T_1 - m_1g = -m_1a \tag{1}$$

$$T_2 - m_2g = m_2a \tag{2}$$

Also write an equation for the rotational form of Newton's second law for the pulley. The forces producing torques are T_1 and T_2.

$$(T_1 - T_2)R = I\alpha \tag{3}$$

These are the three equations with three unknowns. Now substitute $\alpha = a/R$ and divide both sides by R so that equation (3) becomes

$$T_1 - T_2 = I\frac{a}{R^2}$$
(4)

Solve equations (1) and (2) for T_1 and T_2 and then subtract equation (2) from equation (1).

$$T_1 - T_2 = (m_1 - m_2)g - (m_1 + m_2)a$$
(5)

Now set $T_1 - T_2$ from equations (4) and (5) equal to each other.

$$I\frac{a}{R^2} = (m_1 - m_2)g - (m_1 + m_2)a$$
(6)

All that remains is to solve equation (6) for a.

$$a\left(\frac{I}{R^2} + (m_1 + m_2)\right) = (m_1 - m_2)g$$

$$a = \frac{(m_1 - m_2)g}{\frac{I}{R^2} + (m_1 + m_2)}$$

Substitute $I = \frac{1}{2}MR^2$ for the pulley.

$$a = \frac{(m_1 - m_2)g}{\frac{\frac{1}{2}MR^2}{R^2} + (m_1 + m_2)} = \frac{(m_1 - m_2)g}{\frac{M}{2} + (m_1 + m_2)} = \frac{(2.5 \text{ kg} - 1.5 \text{ kg})(9.8 \text{ m/s}^2)}{\frac{0.75 \text{ kg}}{2} + (2.5 \text{ kg} + 1.5 \text{ kg})} = \frac{(1.0 \text{ kg})(9.8 \text{ m/s}^2)}{0.375 \text{ kg} + 4.0 \text{ kg}} = 2.2 \text{ m/s}^2$$

So block 2 (the lighter one) accelerates up at 2.2 m/s^2.

Assess: Because we had three unknowns, T_1, T_2, and a, we needed three equations.

We are glad to get an answer less than 9.8 m/s^2 since that is the limit that block 1 could accelerate down if m_2 and M were zero. In the other limit, $a \to 0$ as $(m_1 - m_2) \to 0$, as we would expect.

This setup with blocks of unequal masses connected by a light rope over a pulley is called an Atwood Machine.

P7.43. Prepare: The component of the static friction force that keeps the pebble in circular motion is centripetal and the centripetal force is determined by $F_c = mv^2/R$. We must remember that the top of the tire is going twice as fast as the car (see Figure 7.36); therefore, the pebble will be released when it is at the top.

We are given $m = 0.0012$ kg, $r = D/2 = 0.36$ m, and the central frictional force $F = 3.6$ N.

Solve: At the point just before release $F = ma = m\frac{v^2}{r}$. Solve this for v (the speed of the top of the tire).

$$v = \sqrt{Fr/m} = \sqrt{(3.6 \text{ N})(0.38 \text{ m})/0.0012 \text{ kg}} = 33.8 \text{ m/s}$$

The car is going half the speed of the pebble, or 16.9 m/s.

Assess: This is equal to 38 mph, which is a reasonable speed.

P7.45. Prepare: The crankshaft is a rotating rigid body. The crankshaft's angular acceleration is given as $\alpha = \Delta\omega/\Delta t$, or slope of the angular-velocity-versus-time graph.

Solve: The crankshaft at $t = 0$ s has an angular velocity of 250 rad/s. It gradually slows down to 50 rad/s in 2 s, maintains a constant angular velocity for 2 s until $t = 4$ s, and then speeds up to 200 rad/s from $t = 4$ s to $t = 7$ s. The angular acceleration (α) graph is based on the fact that α is the slope of the ω-versus-t graph.

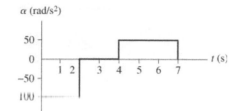

Assess: Knowing that the slope of the angular velocity-versus-time plot is the angular acceleration, we can establish a plot of angular acceleration-versus-time.

P7.47. Prepare: Knowing the kinematic equations and the fact that the distance the car travels is some number of revolutions (or circumferences) of the tire, we can solve this problem.

Solve: The acceleration of the car may be obtained from the expression:

$$v = v_o + at \quad \text{which gives} \quad a = \frac{v - v_o}{t} = \frac{v}{t} \quad \text{since} \quad v_o = 0 \text{ m/s}$$

The distance traveled by the car during the time it is accelerating may be determined by:

$$2a\Delta x = v^2 - v_o^2 \quad \text{which gives} \quad \Delta x = \frac{v^2 - v_o^2}{2a} = \frac{v^2}{2a} = \frac{v^2}{2(v/t)} = \frac{vt}{2}$$

Finally, the number of times the tires rotate (i.e. the number of circumferences of the tires) may be determined by:

$$\Delta x = N(2\pi r) = N\pi d \quad \text{which gives}$$

$$N = \frac{\Delta x}{\pi d} = \frac{(vt/2)}{\pi d} = \frac{vt}{2\pi d} = \frac{(20 \text{ m/s})(10 \text{ s})}{2[\pi(0.58 \text{ m})/\text{rotation}]} - 55 \text{ rotations}$$

Assess: As with many kinematics problems, we can check our work by approaching the problem in a different manner. For example, since the acceleration is constant, the distance the car travels is just the average velocity times the time of travel. This may be expressed as follows:

$$\Delta x = v_{ave} t = \left(\frac{v + v_o}{2}\right)t = \frac{vt}{2}$$

which is the same as the expression obtained above for the distance traveled.

Note also that the final units are in rotations and that 55 is a reasonable number of rotations for a tire in 10 seconds.

P7.49. Prepare: The disk is a rotating rigid body and it rotates on an axle through its center. We will use Equation 7.5 to find the net torque.

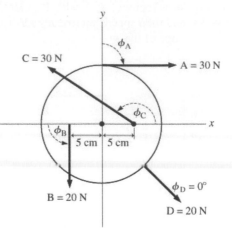

Solve: The net torque on the axle is

$$\tau = F_A r_A \sin\phi_A + F_B r_B \sin\phi_B + F_C r_C \sin\phi_C + F_D r_D \sin\phi_D$$
$$= (30\text{ N})(0.10\text{ m})\sin(-90°) + (20\text{ N})(0.05\text{ m})\sin90° + (30\text{ N})(0.05\text{ m})\sin135° + (20\text{ N})(0.10\text{ m})\sin0°$$
$$= -3\text{ Nm} + 1\text{ Nm} + 1.0607\text{ Nm} = -0.94\text{ Nm}$$

Assess: A negative net torque means a clockwise acceleration of the disk.

P7.51. Prepare: Equation 7.9 tells us the center of gravity of a compound object. If we take all the rest of the body other than the arms as one object (call it the trunk, even though it includes head and legs) then we can write

$$y_{cg} = \frac{y_{trunk}m_{trunk} + 2y_{arm}m_{arm}}{M}$$

where $M = m_{trunk} + m_{arm} = 70$ kg (the mass of the whole body).

The language "by how much does he raise his center of gravity" makes us think of writing Δy_{cg}.

Since we have modeled the arm as a uniform cylinder 0.75 m long, its own center of gravity is at its geometric center, 0.375 m from the pivot point at the shoulder. So raising the arm from hanging down to straight up would change the height of the center of gravity of the arm by twice the distance from the pivot to the center of gravity: $(\Delta y_{cg})_{arm} = 2(0.375\text{ m}) = 0.75$ m.

Solve:

$$\Delta(y_{cg})_{body} = (y_{cg})_{\text{with arms up}} - (y_{cg})_{\text{with arms down}} = \frac{(y_{cg})_{trunk}m_{trunk} + 2(y_{cg})_{arm,\,up}m_{arm}}{M} - \frac{(y_{cg})_{trunk}m_{trunk} + 2(y_{cg})_{arm,down}m_{arm}}{M}$$

$$= \frac{2m_{arm}}{M}((y_{cg})_{arm,\,up} - (y_{cg})_{arm,\,down}) = \frac{2m_{arm}}{M}(\Delta y_{cg})_{arm} = \frac{2(3.5\text{ kg})}{70\text{ kg}}(0.75\text{ m}) = 0.075\text{ m} = 7.5\text{ cm}$$

Assess: 7.5 cm seems like a reasonable amount, not a lot, but not too little. The trunk term subtracted out, which is both expected and good because we didn't know $(y_{cg})_{trunk}$.

P7.53. Prepare: We follow the steps outlined in Tactics Box 7.1. We assume that both blade (b) and handle (h) are of uniform density (so that their respective centers of gravity will be at their geometric centers). The construction of the square is such that the blade extends all the way through the handle (i.e. the left end of the blade is at x = 0).

Solve: (a)

$$x_{cg} = \frac{x_h m_h + x_b m_b}{m_h + m_b} = \frac{(2\text{ cm})(40\text{ g}) + (8\text{ cm})(80\text{ g})}{40\text{ g} + 80\text{ g}} = \frac{80\text{ cm} \cdot \text{g} + 640\text{ cm} \cdot \text{g}}{120\text{ g}} = 6.0\text{ cm}$$

$$y_{cg} = \frac{y_h m_h + y_b m_b}{m_h + m_b} = \frac{(5.5\text{ cm})(4.0\text{ g}) + (9.5\text{ cm})(80\text{ g})}{40\text{ g} + 80\text{ g}} = \frac{220\text{ cm} \cdot \text{g} + 760\text{ cm} \cdot \text{g}}{120\text{ g}} = 8.2\text{ cm}$$

So the center of gravity of the whole carpenter's square is at the point (6.0 cm, 8.2 cm).

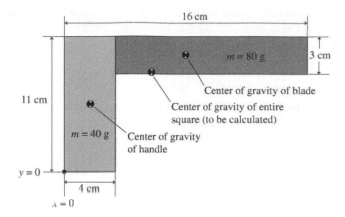

(b) Hanging the tool so that it can freely rotate about the point x = 0, y = 0 we get the result shown in the following figure.

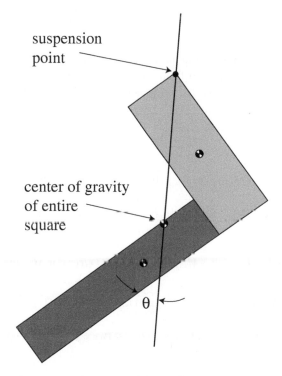

Note that the square will hang such that the center of gravity will be below the point of suspension.

(c) The angle the long side of the blade makes with the vertical is the same as the angle the line from the origin to (6.0 cm, 8.2 cm) makes with the horizontal in the original configuration. Maybe the best way to see this is to look at the original unrotated figure and draw a line from (0,0) to (6.0 cm, 8.2 cm) and remember that in the rotated figure this line becomes the vertical. That angle is

$$\theta = \tan^{-1}\left(\frac{y}{x}\right) = \tan^{-1}\left(\frac{8.2 \text{ cm}}{6.0 \text{ cm}}\right) = 54°$$

Assess: It is easily possible to have the center of gravity of an object lie outside the object's physical boundary (think of a doughnut). However, in this case the center of gravity is inside the boundary of the object (close to the inner edge of the blade); hence we must be able to balance the carpenter's square on our fingertip at the square's center of gravity. The location we found seems like it is about the right place.

P7.55. Prepare: Since the rods are "light" we will neglect their contribution. We will also have to neglect the contribution of the ball through which the axis goes because we do not know the radius of the balls. It is likely that the other two balls contribute vastly more to the total I than the one pierced by the axis does, unless the balls are large compared to the lengths of the rods.

The other two balls will each contribute the same amount, and we will treat them as point particles (both because this is generally safe, and because we do not know their radius). See Equation 7.14. The distance for each of them from the axis is 0.30 m; we also know the mass of each ball is $m = 0.10$ kg.

Solve:

$$I = (2)mr^2 = (2)(0.10 \text{ kg})(0.30 \text{ m})^2 = 0.018 \text{ kg} \cdot \text{m}^2$$

Assess: The balls are not very massive, nor are the rods particularly long, so we are satisfied with an answer that appears smallish. If the balls were 5 times as massive and they were 1 m away from the axis then the answer would be 1 kg · m².

P7.57. Prepare: We can use Equation 7.15, and Table 7.4.
   Solve: Refer to the figure below.

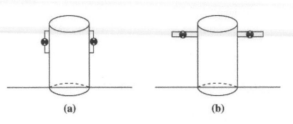

(a)   (b)

(a) The moment of inertia of the skater will be the moment of inertia of her body plus the moment of inertia of her arms. The center of mass of each arm is at her side, 20 cm from the axis of rotation. The mass of each arm is half of one eighth of the mass of her body, which is 4 kg. The mass of her body is 64 kg − 8 kg = 56 kg. With her arms at her sides, her total moment of inertia is

$$I = I_{body} + I_{arm} + I_{arm} = \frac{1}{2} M_{body} (R_{body})^2 + M_{arm} (R_{arm})^2 + M_{arm} (R_{arm})^2$$

$$= \frac{1}{2}(56 \text{ kg})(0.20 \text{ m})^2 + (4 \text{ kg})(0.20 \text{ m})^2 + (4 \text{ kg})(0.20 \text{ m})^2 = 1.4 \text{ kg} \cdot \text{m}^2$$

(b) With her arms outstretched, the center of mass of her arms is now 50 cm from the axis of rotation. Her moment of inertia is now

$$I = I_{body} + I_{arm} + I_{arm} = \frac{1}{2} M_{body} (R_{body})^2 + M_{arm} (R_{arm})^2 + M_{arm} (R_{arm})^2$$

$$= \frac{1}{2}(56 \text{ kg})(0.20 \text{ m})^2 + (4 \text{ kg})(0.50 \text{ m})^2 + (4 \text{ kg})(0.50 \text{ m})^2 = 3.1 \text{ kg} \cdot \text{m}^2$$

Assess: Her moment of inertia with arms outstretched is almost twice as large as with them at her side. This is reasonable, since their distance from the axis of rotation is much larger.

P7.59. Prepare: This problem requires a knowledge of translation ($F_{net} = ma$) and rotational ($\tau_{net} = I\alpha$) dynamics. Notice that the counter clockwise torque is greater than the clockwise torque, hence the system will rotate ccw. Let's agree to call any force that tends to accelerate the system positive and any force that tends to decelerate the system negative. Also let's agree to call the small disk M_1 and the large disk M_2.

Solve:

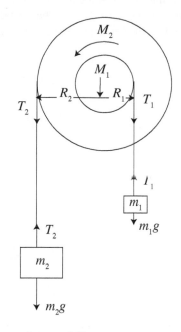

Write Newton's second law equation for m_2 and m_1 as follows:

$$m_2 g - T_2 = m_2 a_2 = m_2 R_2 \alpha \quad \text{or} \quad T_2 = m_2 g - m_2 R_2 \alpha$$

and

$$T_1 - m_1 g = m_1 a_1 = m_1 R_1 \alpha \quad \text{or} \quad T_1 = m_1 g + m_1 R_1 \alpha$$

The net torque acting on the system may be determined by

$$\tau = R_2 T_2 - R_1 T_1 = R_2(m_2 g - m_2 \alpha R_2) - R_1(m_1 g + m_1 \alpha R_1)$$

The moment of inertia of the system is

$$I = I_1 + I_2 = (M_1 R_1^2 / 2) + (M_2 R_2^2 / 2)$$

Knowing

$$\tau = I\alpha$$

we may combine the above to get

$$R_2(m_2 g - m_2 \alpha R_2) - R_1(m_1 g + m_1 \alpha R_1) = [(M_1 R_1^2 / 2) + (M_2 R_2^2 / 2)]\alpha$$

which may be solved for α to obtain

$$\alpha = \frac{(m_2 R_2 - m_1 R_1)g}{R_2^2(m_2 + M_2 / 2) + R_1^2(m_1 + M_1 / 2)} = 3.5 \text{ rad/s}^2$$

Assess: This angular acceleration amounts to speeding up about a half revolution per second every second. That is not an unreasonable amount.

P7.61. Prepare: Two balls connected by a rigid, massless rod are a rigid body rotating about an axis through the center of gravity. Assume that the size of the balls is small compared to 1 m. We have placed the origin of the coordinate system on the 1.0 kg ball. Since $\tau = I_{\text{about cg}}\alpha$, we need the moment of inertia and the angular acceleration to be able to calculate the required torque.

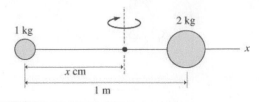

Solve: The center of gravity and the moment of inertia are

$$x_{\text{cm}} = \frac{(1.0 \text{ kg})(0 \text{ m}) + (2.0 \text{ kg})(1.0 \text{ m})}{(1.0 \text{ kg} + 2.0 \text{ kg})} = 0.667 \text{ m and } y_{\text{cm}} = 0 \text{ m}$$

$$I_{\text{about cm}} = \Sigma m_i r_i^2 = (1.0 \text{ kg})(0.667 \text{ m})^2 + (2.0 \text{ kg})(0.333 \text{ m})^2 = 0.667 \text{ kg} \cdot \text{m}^2$$

We have $\omega_f = 0$ rad/s, $t_f - t_i = 5.0$ s, and $\omega_i = 20$ rpm $= 20(2\pi \text{ rad}/60 \text{ s}) = \frac{2}{3}\pi$ rad/s, so $\omega_f = \omega_i + \alpha(t_f - t_i)$ becomes

$$0 \text{ rad/s} = \left(\frac{2\pi}{3} \text{ rad/s}\right) + \alpha(5.0 \text{ s}) \Rightarrow \alpha = -\frac{2\pi}{15} \text{ rad/s}^2$$

Having found I and α, we can now find the torque τ that will bring the balls to a halt in 5.0 s:

$$\tau = I_{\text{about cm}}\alpha = \left(\frac{2}{3} \text{ kg} \cdot \text{m}^2\right)\left(-\frac{2\pi}{15} \text{ rad/s}^2\right) = -\frac{4\pi}{45} \text{ N} \cdot \text{m} = -0.28 \text{ N} \cdot \text{m}$$

The magnitude of the torque is 0.28 N · m.

Assess: The minus sign with the torque indicates that the torque acts clockwise.

P7.63. Prepare: The pulley is a rigid rotating body. We also assume that the pulley has the mass distribution of a disk and that the string does not slip. Because the pulley is not massless and frictionless, tension in the rope on both sides of the pulley is *not* the same. We will have to be careful with the appropriate masses when we write below Newton's second law for the blocks and the pulley. A pictorial diagram of the problem and free-body diagrams for the two blocks are shown below. We have placed the origin of the coordinate system on the ground.

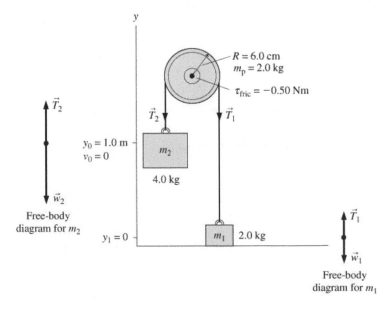

Solve: Applying Newton's second law to m_1, m_2, and the pulley yields the three equations:

$$T_1 - w_1 = m_1 a_1 \qquad -w_2 + T_2 = m_2 a_2 \qquad T_2 R - T_1 R - 0.50 \text{ Nm} = I\alpha$$

Noting that $-a_2 = a_1 = a$, $I = \frac{1}{2} m_p R^2$, and $\alpha = a/R$, the above equations simplify to

$$T_1 - m_1 g = m_1 a \quad m_2 g - T_2 = m_2 a \quad T_2 - T_1 = \left(\frac{1}{2} m_p R^2\right)\left(\frac{a}{R}\right)\frac{1}{R} + \frac{0.50 \text{ Nm}}{R} = \frac{1}{2} m_p a + \frac{0.50 \text{ Nm}}{0.060 \text{ m}}$$

Adding these three equations,

$$(m_2 - m_1)g = a\left(m_1 + m_2 + \frac{1}{2} m_p\right) + 8.333 \text{ N} \Rightarrow a = \frac{(m_2 - m_1)g - 8.333 \text{ N}}{m_1 + m_a + \frac{1}{2} m_p}$$

$$= \frac{(4.0 \text{ kg} - 2.0 \text{ kg})(9.8 \text{ m/s}^2) - 8.333 \text{ N}}{2.0 \text{ kg} + 4.0 \text{ kg} + (2.0 \text{ kg}/2)} = 1.610 \text{ m/s}^2$$

We can now use kinematics to find the time taken by the 4.0 kg block to reach the floor:

$$y_f = y_i + v_i(t_f - t_i) + \frac{1}{2} a_2(t_f - t_i)^2 \Rightarrow 0 = 1.0 \text{ m} + 0 + \frac{1}{2}(-1.610 \text{ m/s}^2)(t_f - 0 \text{ s})^2 \Rightarrow t_f = \sqrt{\frac{2(1.0 \text{ m})}{(1.610 \text{ m/s}^2)}} = 1.1 \text{ s}$$

Assess: Compared to free fall where we would use $a = -9.80 \text{ m/s}^2$, $a = -1.61 \text{ m/s}^2$ and a time of 1.1 s for the block to reach floor are reasonable.

P7.65. Prepare: This is an excellent review problem. In order to work this problem you will need a working knowledge of rotational kinematics ($\omega_f = \omega_0 + \alpha t$), moment of inertia of a cylinder ($I = MR^2 / 2$), rotational dynamics ($\tau = I\alpha$), torque ($\tau = Rf_k \sin\phi$) and kinetic friction ($f_k = \mu_k N$).

Solve: First determine an expression for the angular acceleration.

$$\alpha = (\omega_f - \omega_0) / \Delta t$$

Next obtain an expression for the moment of inertia of the grindstone.

$$I = MR^2 / 2$$

Then obtain an expression for the torque acting on the grindstone.

$$\tau = I\alpha = \left(\frac{MR^2}{2}\right)\left(\frac{\omega_f - \omega_o}{\Delta t}\right)$$

Write a second expression for the torque in terms of the force of friction and then the normal force.

$$\tau = f_k R = \mu_k N R$$

Finally, equate the last two expressions for the torque and solve for N (the force with which the man presses the knife against the grindstone.

$$N = MR(\omega_f - \omega_o)/2\mu_k \Delta t = \frac{(28 \text{ kg})(0.15 \text{ m})(180 \text{ rev/min})(2\pi \text{ rad/rev})(\text{min} / 60 \text{ s})}{2(0.2)(10 \text{ s})} = 9.9 \text{ N}$$

Assess: This is essentially the force equal to the weight of a one kilogram mass. This is a reasonable force (i.e., one that the man could easily exert and yet not grind the knife to a sliver in a matter of minutes).

P7.67. Prepare: The center of gravity must follow a parabolic path, so the answer isn't C.

While it is possible to bend over and get one's center of gravity outside the body (search the web for the Fosbury flop technique in the high jump), in this case the center of gravity of the dancer stays in the body, so the answer isn't D.

Solve: The correct answer is B, with the reasoning being that, as shown in the diagram, the head can stay quite level by bringing up the arms and legs and then lowering them again. This allows the center of gravity to follow the parabola while the head stays about level.

Assess: The whole point of movement is to raise and lower the center of gravity, and this is done by raising and lowering the arms and legs.

P7.69. Prepare: While the dancer is in the air, the gravitational force on her acts as if her mass were concentrated at her center of gravity.

Solve: The correct answer is B; there is no lever arm to create a torque because the gravitational force is directly through the center of gravity. Even if the arms and legs move the center of gravity moves and the gravitational force is still through the center of gravity. So if the axis of rotation is through her center of gravity then there can be no gravitational force.

Assess: Of course computing the gravitational torque about some axis other than through the center of gravity could produce a torque, but we were told to use an axis through the center of gravity.

8—Equilibrium and Elasticity
Conceptual Questions

Q8.1. Reason: Because the definition of equilibrium includes $\Sigma \tau = 0$ as well as $\Sigma \vec{F} = \vec{0}$ an object that experiences exactly two forces that are equal in magnitude and opposite in direction may still not be in equilibrium because the forces could still cause a net torque even though the sum of the forces is zero. See Figure 8.1.

Furthermore, an object could even have $\Sigma \tau = 0$ as well as $\Sigma \vec{F} = \vec{0}$ (and therefore be in equilibrium) but still not be in *static* equilibrium if it is moving at a constant velocity.

Assess: Think carefully about the definition of equilibrium, especially what it *doesn't* say.

Q8.3. Reason: The ladder could *not* be in static equilibrium. Consider the forces in the horizontal direction. There is a normal force exerted by the wall on the top of the ladder, but no other object (in the absence of friction) exerts a counterbalancing force on the ladder in the opposite direction. Examine Figure 8.10.

Assess: This makes sense from a common sense standpoint. If a ladder is about to slip out one tries to increase the friction at the point of contact with the floor, or to produce a horizontal component of a normal force by wedging it.

Q8.5. Reason: For divers to be stable on the board before the dive their center of gravity must be over an area of support, that is, over the board. Extending their arms moves the center of gravity over the board.

Assess: If the arms are not extended, then the center of gravity would be over the edge of the diving board when they stand on their toes with heels extended out. They would not be in static equilibrium and would topple over before getting off a good clean dive. The other option to get the center of gravity over the board (besides extending arms) is to lean forward slightly toward the board.

Q8.7. Reason: Your center of gravity must remain over a region of support (your feet). As you rise your rear end is behind your feet so you must lean forward to compensate.

Assess: This seems to jibe with everyday experience.

Q8.9. Reason: Before Carlos came along the wall also pulled on the spring with a 200 N force when Bob did, that is, there was a 200 N tension force all along the spring. When Carlos arrives he takes the place of the wall but the spring must still stretch 20 cm. The only difference is that now Carlos also moves whereas the wall didn't.

(a) 10 cm. Though the spring stretched 20 cm originally, its center moved by 10 cm and so Bob's end moved 10 cm away from (farther than) the center. In the tug-of-war the center stays still so Bob's end only moves 10 cm.

(b) 10 cm the other direction. The total stretch under a 200 N tension must still be 20 cm.

Assess: These answers fit well with Hooke's law. In either case the 200 N tension produced a total stretch of 20 cm.

Q8.11. Reason: Since both halves of the spring are made of the same material and constructed the same way, the spring constant of each half will be twice the spring constant of the original long spring.

Assess: Hooke's Law does not depend on the length of a spring.

Q8.13. Reason: The force needed to bend a "beam," whether it's a nail or a steel wool fiber, is proportional to the cube of the thickness-to-length ratio (see Equation 8.8). The diameter (thickness) of a steel wool fiber is *much* less, relative to its length, than that of a steel nail, and the cube of this ratio is *much* MUCH less for steel wool than for a steel nail. Thus it takes only a very small force to bend and flex the thin fibers of steel wool, but a very large force to bend a steel nail.

Assess: Fiberglass is also flexible while a thicker glass rod is not, for the same reasons.

The extreme case is carbon nanotubes that are *so* thin that they bend easily, but if made into a solid bulk substance as thick as nails would be more resistant to bending.

Multiple-Choice Questions

Q8.15. Reason: Use equilibrium calculations $\Sigma r = 0$ around the suspended end. The weight of the rod acts at its center ($L/2$ away from the right end) and the normal force acts at L from the right end. For $\Sigma r = 0$ the normal force must be half the force at twice the distance, so the answer is A.

Assess: for $\Sigma F = 0$ the tension in the suspension string must also be 7.0 N. This also makes sense when computing the torques around the center of the rod.

Q8.17. Reason: The fact that the board is "very light" means we will neglect its mass (which we weren't given anyway). We know that the student weighs 165 lbs because the downward force of gravity on the student must equal the upward sum of the two scale readings for the student to be in equilibrium.

Also required for equilibrium is $\Sigma \tau = 0$ and we are free to choose the axis around which we compute the torques anywhere we want. It would be most convenient to select a point above one of the scales so that the upward normal force due to that scale will not produce a torque. Furthermore, since we want to know the distance from the right hand scale, choose it as the pivot.

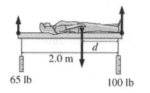

$$\Sigma \tau = d(165 \text{ lb}) - (2.0 \text{ m})(65 \text{ lb}) = 0$$

Where the ccw torque is positive and the cw torque is negative:

$$d = \frac{(2.0 \text{ m})(65 \text{ lb})}{165 \text{ lb}} = 0.79 \text{ m} \approx 0.8 \text{ m}$$

So the correct choice is B.

Assess: Not only *could* we have chosen the pivot point at the left scale and produced the same answer (using $L - d$ as the lever arm), but we *should* do so as a check.

$$\Sigma \tau = (2.0 \text{ m})(100 \text{ lb}) - (L - d)(165 \text{ lb}) = 0$$

$$L - d = \frac{(2.0 \text{ m})(100 \text{ lb})}{165 \text{ lb}}$$

$$d = 2.0 \text{ m} - \frac{(2.0 \text{ m})(100 \text{ lb})}{165 \text{ lb}} = 0.79 \text{ m} \approx 0.8 \text{ m}$$

Q8.19. Reason: As is quite clear from the figure, the force of the tendon on the lower leg is up. However, if we compute torques around a pivot point where the tendon attaches to the lower leg we see that there is a counterclockwise torque produced by the weight of the lower leg acting at the center of gravity 25 cm from the knee joint. There must be a clockwise torque to counterbalance it if the lower leg is to be in equilibrium. That clockwise torque is provided by the force of the upper leg *down* on the lower leg at the knee joint.

The correct answer is B.

Assess: This may be surprising at first. It may help to visualize it as a lever with an upside down fulcrum (suspension point) where the tendon attaches to the lower leg.

Q8.21. Reason: Because $\Delta L = FL/AY$ if L is doubled then A must be doubled too to keep ΔL the same. To double A requires an increase in the diameter by a factor of $\sqrt{2}$. So the answer is B.

Assess: Doubling the diameter (an incorrect answer) would actually make the twice-as-long wire stretch less.

Q8.23. Reason: The tension in the rope is the same as if there were no pulley and one 20 kg block were suspended, that is, $T = mg = (20 \text{ kg})(9.8 \text{ m/s}^2) = 196 \text{ N}$. Use this tension as the F in the equation below.

$$\Delta L = \frac{FL}{YA} = \frac{(196 \text{ N})(2.0 \text{ m})}{(1.5 \times 10^9 \text{ N/m}^2) \pi (0.0025 \text{ m})^2} = 1.3 \text{ cm}$$

The answer is then D.

Assess: A 1.3 cm stretch of a 2.0 m of rope seems reasonable.

Problems

P8.1. Prepare: Because the board is "very light" we will assume that it is massless and does not contribute to the scale reading, nor does it contribute any torques. The sum of the two scale readings must equal the woman's weight: $w = mg = (64 \text{ kg})(9.8 \text{ m/s}^2) = 627 \text{ N} \approx 630 \text{ N}$.

Solve: Compute the torques around the point the board rests on the left scale. The woman's weight creates a clockwise (negative) torque; and the normal force n_{right} of the right scale creates a counterclockwise (positive) torque.

$$\Sigma \tau = (2.0 \text{ m})(n_{\text{right}}) - (1.5 \text{ m})(627 \text{ N}) = 0 \text{ N} \cdot \text{m}$$

The right scale reads n_{right}:

$$n_{\text{right}} = \frac{(1.5 \text{ m})(627 \text{ N})}{2.0 \text{ m}} = 470 \text{ N}$$

By simple subtraction the left scale reads

$$n_{\text{left}} = 627 \text{ N} - 470 \text{ N} = 160 \text{ N}$$

Assess: The answer is reasonable. Since the woman is three times farther from the left scale than the right one, it (the left one) reads three times less. And the two scale readings sum to the woman's weight, as required.

Not only *could* we have chosen the pivot point at the right scale and produced the same answer, but we *should* do so as a check.

$$\Sigma \tau = (0.5 \text{ m})(627 \text{ N}) - (2.0 \text{ m})(n_{\text{left}}) = 0 \text{ N} \cdot \text{m}$$

$$n_{\text{left}} = \frac{(0.5 \text{ m})(627 \text{ N})}{2.0 \text{ m}} = 160 \text{ N}$$

And so

$$n_{\text{right}} = 627 \text{ N} - 157 \text{ N} = 470 \text{ N}$$

It is true that $\Sigma \tau = 0$ around *any* point (for equilibrium), but we picked the two we did (the second as a check) because then the resulting torque equations each had only one unknown in them.

P8.3. Prepare: Compute the torques around the bottom of the right leg of the table. The horizontal distance from there to the center of gravity of the table is $\frac{2.10 \text{ m}}{2} = 0.55 \text{ m} = 0.50 \text{ m}$.

Solve: Call the horizontal distance from the bottom of the right leg to the center of gravity of the man x.

$$\Sigma \tau = (56 \text{ kg})(9.8 \text{ m/s}^2)(0.50 \text{ m}) - (70 \text{ kg})(9.8 \text{ m/s}^2)x = 0 \qquad \Rightarrow \qquad x = 0.40 \text{ m}$$

The distance from the right edge of the table is now $0.55 \text{ m} - 0.40 \text{ m} = 0.15 \text{ m} = 15 \text{ cm}$.

Assess: It seems likely that the table would tip if the man were closer than 15 cm to the edge.

P8.5. Prepare: Assume the pole is uniform in diameter and density. We will use the equilibrium equation $\Sigma \tau = 0$. The weight of the pole is $w = mg = (25 \text{ kg})(9.8 \text{ m/s}^2) = 245 \text{ N}$.

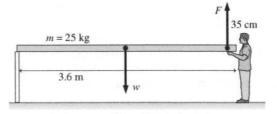

Solve: Compute the torques around the left end, where the pole rests on the fence. The weight of the pole (acting at its center of gravity) will produce a clockwise (negative) torque, and your force near the right end of the pole will produce a counterclockwise (positive) torque.

$$\Sigma\tau = (3.6\ \text{m} - 0.35\ \text{m})F - (1.8\ \text{m})(245\ \text{N})$$
$$= (3.25\ \text{m})F - (1.8\ \text{m})(245\ \text{N})$$
$$= 0\ \text{N}\cdot\text{m}$$

Now solve for F:

$$F = \frac{(1.8\ \text{m})(245\ \text{N})}{3.25\ \text{m}} = 140\ \text{N}$$

Assess: This really is a rest because you only have to exert a force of just over half the pole's weight, instead of the whole weight when you were carrying it. The fence is helping hold up the pole.

Think carefully about the figure and imagine moving your hands toward the fence. The upward force you would have to exert to keep $\Sigma\tau = 0$ would increase, and when you support the pole at its center of gravity the torque equation says your force is equal to the weight of the pole. At that point the fence is no longer helping (and you aren't resting) as it exerts no upward force. If you tried moving even farther toward the fence, past the center of gravity, there would be no way to keep the pole in equilibrium and it would rotate, fall, and hit the ground.

P8.7. Prepare: The massless rod is a rigid body. To be in equilibrium, the object must be in both translational equilibrium $(\vec{F}_{\text{net}} = 0\ \text{N})$ and rotational equilibrium $(\tau_{\text{net}} = 0)$. We have $(F_{\text{net}})_y = (40\ \text{N}) - (100\ \text{N}) + (60\ \text{N}) = 0\ \text{N}$, so the object is in translational equilibrium. Our task now is to calculate the net torque.

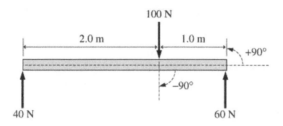

Solve: Measuring τ_{net} about the left end,

$$\tau_{\text{net}} = (60\ \text{N})(3.0\ \text{m})\sin(+90°) + (100\ \text{N})(2.0\ \text{m})\sin(-90°) = -20\ \text{N m}$$

The object is not in equilibrium.

P8.9. Prepare: In this problem we are given the mass of the board, but because of the symmetry of the distances (the fulcrum, or right support, is right in the center) we don't need it. We'll compute the torques around the right support, which is under the center of gravity of the board, so the weight of the board won't produce a torque.

The weight of the diver is $w = mg = (60\ \text{kg})(9.8\ \text{m/s}^2) = 590\ \text{N}$.

Solve: Because of the symmetry of the situation (the two lever arms are equal in length), we can examine the torque equation in our heads and realize that the force exerted by the hinge must have the same magnitude as the weight of the diver. Therefore, the force the hinge exerts on the board is 590 N.

Assess: We computed the torques around the right support because of the symmetry, but also because had we computed them around the hinge on the left, we would be eliminating from the equation the very torque we need to answer the problem.

Since both the weight of the diver and the force of the hinge act in the downward direction, it is also clear that the right support must exert a force of twice the diver's weight in the upward direction.

P8.11. Prepare: The pole is in equilibrium, which means $\Sigma\tau = 0$; it is convenient to compute the torques around the bottom of the pole (as suggested by the hinge there). It is definitely worth noting that the triangles made by the wires, the ground, and the pole are congruent (rotate one triangle 90° around corner at the bottom of the pole to see this).

Solve: For $\Sigma\tau = 0$ we want the magnitude of the clockwise torque to equal the magnitude of the counterclockwise torque. The magnitude of each torque is the force (the tension in the guy wire) multiplied by the lever arm (the perpendicular distance from the line in the direction of the force to the pivot, see Equation 7.5). Examination of the figure, and realization that the triangles are congruent, leads to the realization that the lever arms are equal for the two wires.

Since the magnitudes of the torques must be equal, and the lever arms are equal, then the magnitudes of the forces must be equal. Hence the ratio of the tension in the left wire to the tension in the right wire is 1. $T_2/T_1 = 1$.

Assess: Theoretically, the pole could be at rest in equilibrium if there were no wires, but any slight perturbation would make it fall over (an example of unstable equilibrium), and so guy wires are used which can keep the pole in equilibrium even if perturbed. Whether it is preferable to use guy wires like the one on the left or like the one on the right may depend on how much room around the base of the pole is available, and where one would rather attach the wires to the pole.

P8.13. Prepare: The center of gravity of the magazine rack must be over the base of support to be stable. In this case the rule of thumb given in the text that "a wider base of support and/or a lower center of gravity improve stability" indicates that we expect the tipping angle to be small. The center of gravity need only move 2.5 cm horizontally for the rack to be on the verge of tipping.

On the diagram construct a right triangle by first dropping a vertical from the center of gravity to the middle of the base and drawing the hypotenuse from the center of gravity to the edge of the base. Now we have a right triangle with legs of 16 cm and 2.5 cm. The angle we desire is the small angle at the top of the triangle.

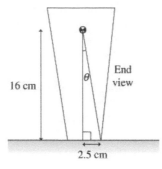

If this is not yet clear, draw a second diagram with the rack tipped just so the center of gravity is over the edge of the base of support and see that the tipping angle is the same θ that we labeled in the triangle.

Solve: The angle will be given by the arctangent of the opposite side over the adjacent side.

$$\theta = \tan^{-1}\left(\frac{2.5 \text{ cm}}{16 \text{ cm}}\right) = 8.9°$$

Assess: The angle of 8.9° is fairly small, as expected.

The precise shape of the cross section of the rack is unimportant as long as the base of support and the center of gravity are where they are.

P8.15. Prepare: Review Conceptual Example 8.1, as this problem is very similar. We must find where the box will be when the combined center of gravity of the box and board is exactly over the edge of the table. We'll use the edge of the table as the pivot point to calculate the torques. We will assume the board is uniform so that its center of gravity is at its geometrical center, which is 5.00 cm (which is 0.0500 m) left of the table edge. We will also assume that the box is uniform and that its center of gravity is at its geometrical center.

The ccw torque due to the board will be

$$\tau_{ccw} = (r_{board})(w_{board}) = (r_{board})(m_{board}g) = (0.0500 \text{ m})(6.00 \text{ kg})(9.80 \text{ m/s}^2) = 2.94 \text{ N} \cdot \text{m}$$

Solve: In equilibrium $\tau_{net} = 0$:

$$\tau_{net} = \tau_{ccw} - \tau_{cw} = (2.94 \text{ N} \cdot \text{m}) - (r_{box})w_{box} = (2.94 \text{ N} \cdot \text{m}) - (r_{box})m_{box}g = 0.00 \text{ N} \cdot \text{m}$$

Solve for r_{box}, which is where the center of the box will be to just balance. This is the answer to the problem.

$$r_{box} = \frac{2.94 \text{ N} \cdot \text{m}}{m_{box}g} = \frac{2.94 \text{ N} \cdot \text{m}}{(2.00 \text{ kg})(9.80 \text{ m/s}^2)} = 0.150 \text{ m} = 15 \text{ cm}$$

Assess: The answer of 15.0 cm is the position of the center of the box, to the right of the edge of the table. It is still on the board (not off the edge), and three times farther from the pivot then the center of gravity of the board because the box is three times less massive than the board.

P8.17. Prepare: Hooke's law is given in Equation 8.3, $(F_{sp})_x = -k\Delta x$. It relates the force on a spring to the stretch; the constant of proportionality is k, the spring constant that we are asked to find.

Solve: The minus sign in Equation 8.3 simply indicates that the force and the stretch are in opposite directions (that the force is a *restoring* force); k is always positive, so we'll drop the minus sign and just use magnitudes of $(F_{sp})_x$ and Δx since we would otherwise have to set up a more explicit coordinate system. See Equation 8.1.

$$k = \frac{(F_{sp})_x}{\Delta x} = \frac{25\ \text{N}}{0.030\ \text{m}} = 830\ \text{N/m}$$

Assess: This result indicates a fairly stiff spring, but certainly within reason.

P8.19. Prepare: A visual overview below shows the details, including a free-body diagram, of the problem. We will assume an ideal spring that obeys Hooke's law.

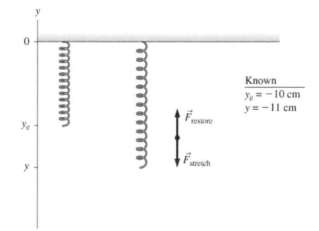

Solve: (a) The spring force or the restoring force is $F_{sp} = -k\Delta y$. For $\Delta y = -1.0$ cm and the force in Newtons,

$$F_{sp} = F = -k\Delta y \Rightarrow k = -F/\Delta y = -F/(-0.01\ \text{m}) = 100F\ \text{N/m}$$

Notice that Δy is negative, so F_{sp} is positive.

We can now calculate the new length for a restoring force of 3F:

$$F_{sp} = 3F = -k\Delta y = (-100\ F)\Delta y \Rightarrow \Delta y = -0.03\ \text{m}$$

From $\Delta y = y - y_e = -0.03$ m, or $y = -0.03$ m $+ y_e$, or $y = -0.03$ m $+ (-0.10$ m$) = -0.13$ m, the length of the spring is 0.13 m.

(b) The new compressed length for a restoring force of 2F can be calculated as:

$$F_{sp} = 2F = -k\Delta y = (-100\ F)\Delta y \Rightarrow \Delta y = -0.02\ \text{m}$$

Using $\Delta y = y_e - y = -0.02$ m, or $y = 0.02$ m $+ y_e$, or $y = 0.02$ m $+ (-0.10$ m$) = -0.08$ m, the length of the compressed spring is 0.08 m.

Assess: The stretch Δx is proportional to the applied force, as both parts of this problem demonstrate. Of course, this bet is off if the spring is stretched or compressed far enough to take it out of the linear region.

P8.21. Prepare: We do not know the original unstretched length of the spring, but that's okay, since what Hooke's law tells us is the *stretch*, or Δx, and that *is* given. We will assume that this problem is in the linear region of the spring. We'll use the initial data to find and then compute the new stretch. The restoring force is equal in magnitude to the weight of the hanging mass; in the initial data this is $w = wg = (0.20\ \text{kg})(9.8\ \text{m/s}^2) = 1.96\ \text{N}$.

Solve: Solve Equation 8.1 for k.

$$k = \frac{F_{sp}}{\Delta x} = \frac{1.96\ \text{N}}{0.050\ \text{m}} = 39.2\ \text{N/m}$$

If the 0.20 kg block is replaced with a 0.70 kg block, the new stretch (measured from the unstretched length) is

$$\Delta x = \frac{F_{sp}}{k} = \frac{mg}{k} = \frac{(0.70 \text{ kg})(9.8 \text{ m/s}^2)}{39.2 \text{ N/m}} = 0.175 \text{ m} = 17.5 \text{ cm} \approx 18 \text{ cm}$$

Assess: The above method is actually the long way. The short way is to realize that since we are in the linear region of the spring the stretch is directly proportional to the force, so the new stretch must be 7/2 (that is, 0.70 kg/ 0.20 kg) of the old one.

$$\frac{7}{2}(5.0 \text{ cm}) = 17.5 \text{ cm} \approx 18 \text{ cm}$$

P8.23. Prepare: Assume that the spring is ideal and obeys Hooke's law. Also we will model the sled as a particle. The only horizontal force acting on the sled is $\vec{F}_{sp}$. A pictorial representation and a free-body diagram are shown below.

Solve: Applying Newton's second law to the sled gives

$$\Sigma(F_{\text{on sled}})_x = F_{sp} = ma_x \Rightarrow k\Delta x = ma_x \Rightarrow a_x = k\Delta x/m = (150 \text{ N/m})(0.20 \text{ m})/20 \text{ kg} = 1.5 \text{ m/s}^2$$

P8.25. Prepare: Rearrange Equation 8.6 to see that the stretch is proportional to the length (for part **(a)**) and inversely proportional to the area (for part **(b)**).

$$\Delta L = \frac{LF}{AY}$$

Solve: (a) In this part everything on the right side of the equation stays constant except the length L. Since the length of the second wire is twice the length of the first wire, then the second wire will stretch twice as much by the same force. So the answer is 2 mm.

(b) In this part everything on the right side of the equation stays constant except the cross-sectional area A. The cross-sectional area of the third wire is four times the area of the first wire, since $A = \pi r^2 = \pi (D/2)^2$ and the diameter of the third wire is twice the diameter of the first wire, so the third wire will stretch one-quarter as much by the same force. So the answer is 0.25 mm.

Assess: This problem is worth mentally reviewing to make sure the explanation given makes sense, and to tuck the results away as tidbits of practical knowledge.

P8.27. Prepare: Equation 8.6 relates the quantities in question.

Look up Young's modulus for steel in Table 8.1: $Y_{\text{steel}} = 20 \times 10^{10} \text{ N/m}^2$. Convert all length data to meters: $D = 1.0 \text{ cm} = 0.010 \text{ m}$, $\Delta L = 5.0 \text{ mm} = 0.0050 \text{ m}$.

Assume a circular cross section: $A = \pi r^2 = \pi\left(\dfrac{D}{2}\right)^2 = \pi(0.0050 \text{ m})^2 = 7.85 \times 10^{-5} \text{ m}^2$.

Solve:

$$F = \frac{YA}{L}\Delta L = \frac{(20 \times 10^{10} \text{ N/m}^2)(7.85 \times 10^{-5} \text{ m}^2)}{10 \text{ m}} 0.0050 \text{ m} = 7900 \text{ N}$$

This is the force required to stretch a steel cable of the given length and diameter by 5.0 mm.

Assess: A 1-cm-diameter cable is fairly substantial, so it ought to take a few thousand newtons to stretch it 5.0 mm. Notice the m^2 cancel in the numerator and so do the other m, leaving only N.

P8.29. Prepare: Equation 8.6 relates the quantities in question. Since we know neither the material (and therefore Y) nor the length nor the cross-sectional area, the best way to proceed is by ratios.

Known
_____

$F_1 = 2000$ N
$\Delta L_1 = 0.001$ m
$L_2 = 2L_1$
$D_2 = 2D_1; A_2 = 4A_1$ A scales as the squre of r or D
$\Delta L_2 = 0.001$ m $= \Delta L$
$L_3 = 2L_1$
$D_3 = D_1 A_3$ A_1
$F_3 = 4000$ N $= 2F_1$

Find
_____

F_2
ΔL_3

Solve: (a)

$$\frac{F_2}{F_1} = \frac{(YA_2 / L_2)\Delta L_2}{(YA_1 / L_1)\Delta L_1} = \frac{Y(4A_1)/(2L_1)\Delta L_1}{(YA_1 / L_1)AL_1\Delta L_1} = \frac{4}{2} = 2$$

So $F_2 = 2F_1 = 2(2000$ N$) = 4000$ N.
   (b) Assume the third wire is made of the same material as the first and second wires. Solve Equation 8.6 for ΔL.

$$\frac{\Delta L_3}{\Delta L_1} = \frac{L_3 F_3 / A_3 Y}{L_1 F_1 / A_1 Y} = \frac{(2L_1)(2F_1) / A_1 Y}{L_1 F_1 / A_1 Y} = 4$$

So $\Delta L_3 = 4\Delta L_1 = 4(1$ mm$) = 4$ mm.
   Assess: This ratio technique is very powerful, especially when unknown quantities cancel out.

P8.31. Prepare: Equation 8.6 relates the quantities in question; solve it for which is what we want to know.
   Look up Young's modulus for steel in Table 8.1: $Y_{steel} = 20 \times 10^{10}$ N/m^2. Assume a circular cross section: $A = \pi r^2 = \pi(D/2)^2 = \pi(0.0125$ m$)^2 = 4.91 \times 10^{-4}$ m^2.
   We are also given that $L = 500$ m. Compute $F = w = mg = (3000$ kg$)(9.8$ m/s$^2) = 29,400$ N.
   Solve:

$$\Delta L = \frac{LF}{AY} = \frac{(500 \text{ m})(29,400 \text{ N})}{(4.91 \times 10^{-4} \text{ m}^2)(20 \times 10^{10} \text{ N/m}^2)} = 0.15 \text{ m} = 15 \text{ cm}$$

   Assess: 15 cm is quite a stretch, but 3000 kg (times g) is quite a bit of weight, and 500 m is quite a long cable, so the answer is reasonable. The design of the shaft would have to take this 15 cm stretch into account.
   Also check to see that the units work out.

P8.33. Prepare: Equation 8.6 relates the quantities in question; the fractional decrease in length will be so rearrange the equation so $\Delta L/L$ is isolated.
   Look up Young's modulus for Douglas fir in Table 8.1: $Y_{Doublas \, fir} = 1 \times 10^{10}$ N/m^2. The total cross section will be three times the area of one leg:

$$A_{tot} = 3(\pi r^2) = 3\left(\pi\left(\frac{D}{2}\right)^2\right) = 3\pi(0.010 \text{ m})^2 = 9.42 \times 10^{-4} \text{ m}^2$$

Compute $F = w = mg = (75$ kg$)(9.8$ m/s$^2) = 735$ N.

Solve:

$$\frac{\Delta L}{L} = \frac{F}{AY} = \frac{735 \text{ N}}{(9.42 \times 10^{-4} \text{ m}^2)(1 \times 10^{10} \text{ N/m}^2)} = 7.8 \times 10^{-5}$$

This is a 0.0078% change in length.

Assess: We were not given the original length of the stool legs, but regardless of the original length, they decrease in length by only a small percentage—0.0078%—because F isn't large but A is.

P8.35. Prepare: The beam is a rigid body of length 3.0 m and the student is a particle. $\vec{F}_1$ and $\vec{F}_2$ are the normal forces on the beam due to the supports, $\vec{w}_{\text{beam}}$ is the weight of the beam acting at the center of gravity, and $\vec{w}_{\text{student}}$ is the student's weight. The student is 1 m away from support 2.

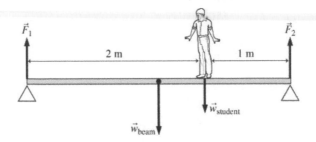

Solve: To stay in place, the beam must be in both translational equilibrium ($\vec{F}_{\text{net}} = \vec{0}$ N) and rotational equilibrium ($\tau_{\text{net}} = 0$ Nm). The first condition is

$$\Sigma F_y = -w_{\text{beam}} - w_{\text{student}} + F_1 + F_2 = 0 \text{ N} \Rightarrow \text{F1} + \text{F2} = w_{\text{beam}} + w_{\text{student}} = (100 \text{ kg} + 80 \text{ kg})(9.80 \text{ m/s}^2) = 1764 \text{ N}$$

Taking the torques about the left end of the beam, the second condition is

$$-w_{\text{beam}}(1.5 \text{ m}) - w_{\text{student}}(2.0 \text{ m}) + F_2(3.0 \text{ m}) = 0 \text{ N m}$$

$$-(100 \text{ kg})(9.8 \text{ m/s}^2)(1.5 \text{ m}) - (80 \text{ kg})(9.8 \text{ m/s}^2)(2.0 \text{ m}) + F_2(3.0 \text{ m}) = 0 \text{ Nm} \Rightarrow F_2 = 1013 \text{ N}$$

From $F_1 + F_2 = 1764$ N, we get $F_1 = 1764$ N $- 1013$ N $= 750$ N.

Assess: To establish rotational equilibrium, the choice for the pivot is arbitrary. We can take torques about any point on the body of interest.

P8.37. Prepare: Neglect the weight of the arm. The arm is 45° below horizontal, which introduces sin 45° in each term, but it will cancel out.

Solve:

$$\Sigma \tau = T(14 \text{ cm})\sin 45° - (10 \text{ kg})(9.8 \text{ m/s}^2)(35 \text{ cm})\sin 45° = 0 \quad \Rightarrow \quad T = 860 \text{ N}$$

Assess: This answer is in the general range of the results in the example.

P8.39. Prepare: Assume equilibrium and compute the torques around the point labeled pivot. The angle between the lever arm and the force is 60° for the weight of the torso and the head and arms.

Solve: (a)

$$\Sigma \tau = T\left(\frac{2}{3}L\right)\sin 12° - 320 \text{ N}\left(\frac{1}{2}L\right)\sin 60° - 160 \text{ N}(L)\sin 60° = 0$$

$$T = \frac{320 \text{ N}(L)\sin 60°}{\frac{2}{3}L\sin 12°} = 480 \text{ N}\frac{\sin 60°}{\sin 12°} = 2000 \text{ N}$$

(b) Align the x-axis with the spine to find the force from the pelvic girdle.

$$\Sigma F_x = F_{\text{p.g.}} - (320 \text{ N})\cos 60° - (160 \text{ N})\cos 60° - (2000 \text{ N})\cos 12° = 0$$

$$F_{\text{p.g.}} = 2196 \text{ N} \approx 2200 \text{ N}$$

Assess: These are large forces, which is why they can cause back injuries. Squat when you lift.

P8.41. Prepare: Assume that the flagpole has a uniform diameter so that its center of mass is at the center, 7.5 m/2 = 3.75 m from either end. Since the pole is motionless, it is in equilibrium, so $\tau_{net} = 0$. The magnitude of the ccw torque due to the tension in the rope must equal the magnitude of the cw torque due to the weight of the flagpole.

Use Equation 7.4 for the torques: $\tau = rF\sin\phi$.

Solve: The clockwise torque is due to the weight of the flagpole. Draw a quick right triangle to see that the angle between r and F (that is, w) is 60°.

$$\tau_{cw} = rF\sin\phi = rw\sin\phi = r(mg)\sin\phi = (3.75 \text{ m})(28 \text{ kg})(9.8 \text{ m/s}^2)\sin60° = 891 \text{ N} \cdot \text{m}$$

In the counterclockwise direction we want to know the force (tension in the rope), so solve the torque equation for F and put in the previous result for the torque. This time r is the distance from the pivot at the bottom of the pole to where the rope is attached at the top of the pole, or 7.5 m.

$$F_{rope} = \frac{\tau}{r\sin\phi} = \frac{891 \text{ N} \cdot \text{m}}{(7.5 \text{ m})(\sin20°)} = 350 \text{ N}$$

Assess: The man must exert 350 N of force because the angle 20° is so small. One way to increase the angle (and the sine of the angle) is to use a longer rope and stand farther back. This will slightly decrease the needed force. By doing this r is not changed; it is still the length of the pole if the rope is attached to the top of the pole.

P8.43. Prepare: Model the beam as a rigid body. For the beam not to fall over, it must be both in translational equilibrium ($\vec{F}_{net} = \vec{0}$ N) and rotational equilibrium ($\vec{\tau}_{net} = 0$ N m). The boy walks along the beam a distance x, measured from the left end of the beam. There are four forces acting on the beam. $\vec{F}_1$ and $\vec{F}_2$ are from the two supports, $\vec{w}_b$ is the weight of the beam, and $\vec{w}_B$ is the weight of the boy.

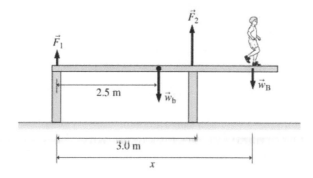

Solve: We pick our pivot point on the left end through the first support. The equation for rotational equilibrium is

$$-w_b (2.5 \text{ m}) + F_2 (3.0 \text{ m}) - w_B x = 0 \text{ N m}$$
$$-(40 \text{ kg})(9.80 \text{ m/s}^2)(2.5 \text{ m}) + F_2 (3.0 \text{ m}) - (20 \text{ kg})(9.80 \text{ m/s}^2)x = 0 \text{ N m}$$

The equation for translation equilibrium is

$$\Sigma F_y = 0 \text{ N} = F_1 + F_2 - w_b - w_B \Rightarrow F_1 + F_2 = w_b + w_B = (40 \text{ kg} + 20 \text{ kg})(9.8 \text{ m/s}^2) = 588 \text{ N}$$

Just when the boy is at the point where the beam tips, $F_1 = 0$ N. Thus $F_2 = 588$ N. With this value of F_2, we can simplify the torque equation to

$$-(40 \text{ kg})(9.80 \text{ m/s}^2)(2.5 \text{ m}) + (588 \text{ N})(3.0 \text{ m}) - (20 \text{ kg})(9.80 \text{ m/s}^2)x = 0 \text{ N m} \Rightarrow x = 4.0 \text{ m}$$

Thus, the distance from the right end is 5.0 m − 4.0 m = 1.0 m.

P8.45. Prepare: Assume that the spring is ideal and it obeys Hooke's law. We also model the 5.0 kg mass as a particle. We will use the subscript s for the scale and sp for the spring. With the *y*-axis representing vertical positions, pictorial representations and free-body diagrams are shown for parts (a) through (c).

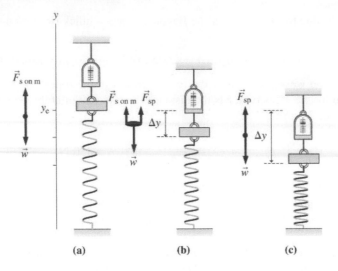

(a)   (b)   (c)

Solve: (a) The scale reads the upward force $F_{\text{s on m}}$ that it applies to the mass. Newton's second law gives

$$\Sigma(F_{\text{on m}})_y = F_{\text{s on m}} - w = 0 \Rightarrow F_{\text{s on m}} = w = mg = (5.0 \text{ kg})(9.8 \text{ m/s}^2) = 49 \text{ N}$$

(b) In this case, the force is

$$\Sigma(F_{\text{on m}})_y = F_{\text{s on m}} + F_{\text{sp}} - w = 0 \Rightarrow 20 \text{ N} + k\Delta y - mg = 0 \Rightarrow k = (mg - 20 \text{ N})/\Delta y$$
$$= (49 \text{ N} - 20 \text{ N})/0.02 \text{ m} = 1450 \text{ N/m}$$

(c) In this case, the force is

$$\Sigma(F_{\text{on m}})_y = F_{\text{sp}} - w = 0 \Rightarrow k\Delta y - mg = 0 \Rightarrow \Delta y = mg/k = (49 \text{ N})/(1450 \text{ N/m}) = 0.0338 \text{ m} = 3.4 \text{ cm}$$

P8.47. Prepare: Both springs are compressed by the same amount: $\Delta x = 1.00$ cm. Each spring obeys Hooke's law (we assume we are in the linear region of the springs) and so exerts a force back on the block with a magnitude of $F_{\text{sp}} = k\Delta x$. The net spring force will simply be the sum of the two individual spring forces.
Solve:

$$(F_{\text{sp}})_1 = k_1 \Delta x = (12.0 \text{ N/cm})(1.00 \text{ cm}) = 12.0 \text{ N}$$
$$(F_{\text{sp}})_2 = k_2 \Delta x = (5.4 \text{ N/cm})(1.00 \text{ cm}) = 5.4 \text{ N}$$
$$(F_{\text{sp}})_{\text{tot}} = (F_{\text{sp}})_1 + (F_{\text{sp}})_2 = 12.0 \text{ N} + 5.4 \text{ N} = 17.4 \text{ N}$$

Assess: We have purposefully omitted the negative sign in Hooke's law since it only reflects the fact that the force and the stretch are in opposite directions—something we had kept in mind, but did not worry about since we only needed the magnitude of the forces.

These two springs are said to be in parallel, and they are equivalent to one spring whose spring constant is the sum of the spring constants of the two parallel springs.

P8.49. Prepare: When the block is in its equilibrium position, $\Sigma\vec{F} = \vec{0}$. So the force exerted to the right by the left spring must be balanced by a force exerted to the left by the right spring. The force exerted by the left spring is

$$(F_{\text{sp}})_1 = (10 \text{ N/m})(0.020 \text{ m}) = 0.20 \text{ N}.$$

In part **(b)** the left spring will exert a force to the left (because it will be stretched to the right); the right force will also exert a force to the left since it will be quite compressed. Remember, the block is no longer in equilibrium, and so we do not expect $\Sigma\vec{F} = \vec{0}$.
Solve: (a) The force exerted by the right spring must be 0.20 N. This will be produced if

$$\Delta x_2 = \frac{F_{\text{sp}}}{k_2} = \frac{0.20 \text{ N}}{20 \text{ N/m}} = 0.010 \text{ m} = 1.0 \text{ cm}$$

(b) The spring on the left will be stretched 15 cm − 2.0 cm = 13 cm beyond its unstretched length. The force will be toward the left.

$$(F_{sp})_1 = k_1 \Delta x_1 = (10 \text{ N/m})(0.13 \text{ m}) = 1.3 \text{ N}$$

The spring on the right will be compressed 15 cm + 1.0 cm = 16 cm from its uncompressed length. This force will also be toward the left.

$$(F_{sp})_2 = k_2 \Delta x_2 = (20 \text{ N/m})(0.16 \text{ m}) = 3.2 \text{ N}$$

Both forces are to the left so we simply add them up.

$$F_{net} = (F_{sp})_1 + (F_{sp})_2 = 1.3 \text{ N} + 3.2 \text{ N} = 4.5 \text{ N}$$

to the left.

Assess: In part **(b)** the right spring exerted a greater force because its k is greater and its length is farther from its unstretched/uncompressed length.

P8.51. Prepare: We will model the student (S) as a particle and the spring as obeying Hooke's law. The only two forces acting on the student are his weight and the force due to the spring.

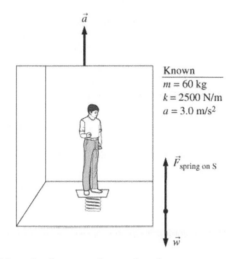

Solve: According to Newton's second law the force on the student is

$$\Sigma(F_{on S})_y = F_{spring \text{ on } S} - w = ma_y \Rightarrow F_{spring \text{ on } S} = w + ma_y = mg + ma_y = (60 \text{ kg})(9.8 \text{ m/s}^2 + 3.0 \text{ m/s}^2) = 768 \text{ N}$$

since $F_{spring \text{ on } S} = F_{S \text{ on spring}} = k\Delta y$, $k\Delta y = 768$ N. This means $\Delta y = (768 \text{ N})/(2500 \text{ N/m}) = 0.307$ m = 0.31 m.

P8.53. Prepare: There seem to be a lot of pieces to this puzzle; where does one start? Since the only horizontal force on the right block is due to the spring, let's start there: $F_{sp} = k\Delta x = (1000 \text{ N/m})(0.015 \text{ m}) = 15$ N.

We apply Newton's second law to find the acceleration of the right block. $F_{net} = F_{sp} = ma$:

$$a = F_{sp}/m = 15 \text{ N}/3.0 \text{ kg} = 5.0 \text{ m/s}^2$$

For part **(b)** we note that since the spring's compression is constant over the time interval the two blocks must move together; i.e., they must have the same acceleration, so the left block's acceleration is also 5.0 m/s². Also note that while the spring pushes to the right on the right block, it pushes to the left on the left block.

Solve: (a) We now apply Equation 2.8 (since the acceleration is constant) to find the final velocity of the right block at $t = 1.0$ s.

$$(v_x)_f = (v_x)_i + a_x \Delta t = 3.2 \text{ m/s} + (5.0 \text{ m/s}^2)(1.0 \text{ s}) = 8.2 \text{ m/s}$$

(b) Think about a simple free-body diagram for the left block and apply Newton's second law, noting that F_{sp} is subtracted because it is to the left.

$$F_{net} = F - F_{sp} = ma$$
$$F = F_{sp} + ma = 15 \text{ N} + (3.0 \text{ kg})(5.0 \text{ m/s}^2) = 30 \text{ N}$$

Assess: This is an interesting situation to analyze from a slightly different perspective. Think about both blocks making up a system (the parts of which are connected by the spring). It will take a certain amount of force to accelerate that system at 5.0 m/s². Now isolate the right block and call it a new system. It has half the mass of the old system and so will need only half the force to accelerate it at the same rate. That is, F must accelerate twice as much mass as F_{sp} does on the right block.

P8.55. Prepare: Call the distance from the pivot to the machinery at maximum distance x. Compute the torques around the pivot at the left end of the plank. The plank's center of gravity is at $\dfrac{3.5 \text{ m}}{2}$. The cross-section area of the rope is

$A = \pi\left(\dfrac{7.0 \text{ mm}}{2}\right)^2 = 3.848 \times 10^{-5} \text{ m}^2$ The maximum tension the rope can support is $T = (6.0 \times 10^7 \text{ N/m}^2)(3.848 \times 10^{-5} \text{ m}^2) = 2309$ N.

Solve:

$$\Sigma\tau = T(3.5 \text{ m}) - (100 \text{ kg})(9.8 \text{ m/s}^2)\left(\dfrac{3.5 \text{ m}}{2}\right) - (800 \text{ kg})(9.8 \text{ m/s}^2)x = 0$$

$$x = \dfrac{(2309 \text{ N})(3.5 \text{ m}) - (100 \text{ kg})(9.8 \text{ m/s}^2)\left(\dfrac{3.5 \text{ mm}}{2}\right)}{(800 \text{ kg})(9.8 \text{ m/s}^2)} = 81 \text{ cm}$$

Access: 81 cm isn't very far along the plank, but the machinery is heavy. We could have moved the machinery farther out if the rope had been thicker.

P8.57. Prepare: Model the disk as a short wide rod. We are asked for the strain—the fractional change in length of the disk. We can solve for $\Delta L/L$ from Equation 8.7.

Assume that the disk is circular so that the area is $A = \pi R^2 = \pi(D/2)^2 = \pi(0.020 \text{ m})^2 = 0.00126 \text{ m}^2$.

The force is half the weight of the person: $F = \dfrac{1}{2}mg = \dfrac{1}{2}(65 \text{ kg})(9.8 \text{ m/s}^2) = 319$ N.

Young's modulus for cartilage is not given in the chapter, but is in the problem: $Y = 1.0 \times 10^6 \text{ N/m}^2$.

Solve: Solve Equation 8.6 for $\Delta L/L$.

$$\dfrac{\Delta L}{L} = \dfrac{F}{YA} = \dfrac{319 \text{ N}}{(1.0 \times 10^{10} \text{ N/m}^2)(0.00126 \text{ m}^2)} = 0.000025 = 0.0025\%$$

Assess: This means the disk compresses by only a tiny amount. This seems reasonable. Notice that the actual thickness of the disk, given as 0.50 cm, is not needed in the calculation of the fractional compression.

P8.59. Prepare: We'll use the data from Example 8.11: $m_{original} = 70$ kg and $A_{original} = 4.8 \times 10^{-4} \text{ m}^2$.

The femur is not solid cortical bone material; we model it as a tube with an inner diameter and an outer diameter. Look up Young's modulus for cortical bone in Table 8.1.

Solve: (a) Both the inner and outer diameters are increased by a factor of 10; however, the cross-sectional area of the bone material does not increase by a factor of 10. Instead, because $A = \pi R^2$ the outer cross-sectional area and the inner cross-sectional area (the "hollow" of the tube) both increase by a factor of 100. But this means that the cross-sectional area of the bone material (the difference of the outer and inner areas) also increases by a factor of 100. So the new area is $A_{new} = 100(4.8 \times 10^{-4} \text{ m}^2) = 4.8 \times 10^{-2} \text{ m}^2$.

(b) Since volume is a three-dimensional concept, if we increase each linear dimension by a factor of 10 then the volume increases by a factor of $10^3 = 1000$. We assume the density of the man is the same as before, so his mass increases by the same factor as the volume: $m_{new} = 1000(70 \text{ kg}) = 70{,}000$ kg.

(c) We follow the strategy of Example 8.11. The force compressing the femur is the man's weight, $F = mg = (70{,}000 \text{ kg})(9.8 \text{ m/s}^2) = 690{,}000$ N. The resulting stress on the femur is

$$\dfrac{F}{A} = \dfrac{690{,}000 \text{ N}}{4.8 \times 10^{-2} \text{ m}^2} = 1.4 \times 10^7 \text{ N/m}^2$$

A stress of $1.4 \times 10^7 \text{ N/m}^2$ is 14% of the tensile strength of cortical bone given in Table 8.4.

Assess: This scaling problem illustrates clearly why animals of different sizes have different proportions. Because the volume scales with the cube of the linear dimensions and the area scales with the square of the linear dimensions then the force in F/A grows more quickly than the cross sectional area does.

P8.61. Prepare: For equilibrium, the sum of the forces must be zero.
  Solve: For one foot:

$$\Sigma F_y = n - \frac{mg}{2} = 0 \quad \Rightarrow \quad n = \frac{mg}{2} = \frac{(60 \text{ kg})(9.8 \text{ m/s}^2)}{2} = 294 \text{ N}$$

So the correct choice is B.
  Assess: This is half the weight of a typical person.

P8.63. Prepare: Use Equation 8.7 and solve for ΔL.
  Solve:

$$\Delta L = \frac{FL}{AY} = \frac{(882 \text{ N})(0.15 \text{ m})}{(110 \text{ mm}^2)(0.15 \times 10^{10} \text{ N/m}^2)} = 8.0 \times 10^{-4} \text{ m} = 0.8 \text{ mm}$$

The correct choice is B.
  Assess: We expect the tendon to stretch a tiny bit, but not much.

Part I—Force and Motion

Ppt I.1. Reason: The orbital speed depends on the mass of the central body. If there were no dark matter then the stars would orbit around the Milky Way slower so the period would be longer. The answer is A.
  Assess: If the sun's mass were smaller then the earth would take more than 365 days to orbit.

Ppt I.3. Reason: If the orbital speeds are the same, then we simply compare the centripetal accelerations.

$$\frac{a_S}{a_e} = \frac{\dfrac{v_S^2}{R_S}}{\dfrac{v_e^2}{R_e}} = \frac{\dfrac{v_e^2}{10R_e}}{\dfrac{v_e^2}{R_e}} = \frac{1}{10}$$

The answer is A.
  Assess: The acceleration is greater with the dark matter than without.

Ppt I.5. Reason: Solve $\vec{a} = \Delta\vec{v}/\Delta t$ for Δt.

$$\Delta t = \frac{\Delta\vec{v}}{\vec{a}} = \frac{20 \text{ m/s}}{6.0 \text{ m/s}^2} = 3.2 \text{ s}$$

The correct answer is C.
  Assess: It would take a greyhound less time to reach top speed, but 3.2 s seems reasonable for a horse.

Ppt I.7. Reason: Solve $a_c = v^2/r$ for r.

$$r = \frac{v^2}{a_c} = \frac{(1.5 \text{ m/s})^2}{7.1 \text{ m/s}^2} = 31.7 \text{ m}$$

The correct answer is B.
  Assess: From the photograph it appears 32 m is in the ballpark for the radius of the turn.

Ppt I.9. Reason: Because $\vec{F}_{net} = m\vec{a}$, the net force on the dog must be in the same direction as the dog's acceleration. In uniform circular motion the acceleration is toward the center of the circle, so the answer is D.
  Assess: The force is provided by friction of the ground acting on the dog's paws.

Ppt I.11. Reason: Solve $v_f^2 = v_i^2 + 2a\Delta x$ for Δx. The equation is simple because $v_f = 0$.

$$\Delta x = \frac{-v_i^2}{2a} = \frac{-(0.25 \text{ mm/s})^2}{2(-1.812 \text{ m/s}^2)} = 1.72 \times 10^{-8} \text{ m} \approx 0.02 \ \mu\text{m}$$

The answer is A.

Assess: The paramecium comes to rest in a distance much less than its own length.

Ppt I.13. Reason: At terminal speed the acceleration is zero, so the net force is also zero. The answer is B.

Assess: At terminal speed the magnitude of the drag force is the same as the magnitude of the gravitational force.

Ppt I.15. Reason: The mass of the falcon is $(8.0 \text{ N})/g = 0.816 \text{ kg}$.

$$F_{\text{net}} = F_{\text{lift}} - mg = ma \Rightarrow F_{\text{lift}} = m(a + g) = (0.816 \text{ kg})(15 \text{ m/s}^2 + 9.8 \text{ m/s}^2) = 20 \text{ N}$$

Assess: The gravitational force cannot be neglected in this problem.

Ppt I.17. Reason: F and d are directly proportional, so if the force (due to the weight of the person) is only half, then the deflection will also be only half. The answer is B.

Assess: This makes intuitive sense since the variables are proportional.

Ppt I.19. Reason: With all other variables held constant, the defection is proportional to L^3.

$$d = F\left[\frac{4}{Ywt^3}\right]L^3$$

If the length is decreased to half, then the deflection will only be $(1/2)^3 = 1/8$ as much.

$$d^f = \frac{1}{8}(4.0 \text{ cm}) = 0.50 \text{ cm}$$

The correct choice is A.

Assess:

Ppt I.21. Reason:
  (a)

  (b) The new reading is n, and the amount the reading is reduced is $mg - n$. The radius of the earth is 6.37×10^6 m. The mass of the person is $(800 \text{ N})/(9.8 \text{ m/s}^2) = 81.6 \text{ kg}$. $1d = 86,400 \text{ s}$.

$$mg - n = \Sigma F = ma = m\left(\frac{v^2}{r}\right) = m\frac{\left(\frac{2\pi r}{\Delta t}\right)^2}{r} = m\left(\frac{2\pi}{\Delta t}\right)^2 r =$$

$$(81.6 \text{ kg})\left(\frac{2\pi}{86,400 \text{ s}}\right)^2 (6.37 \times 10^6 \text{ m}) = 3.369 \text{ N} \approx 3.4 \text{ N}$$

Assess: The reading is only 3.4 N less than 800 N.

9—Momentum
Conceptual Questions

Q9.1. Reason: The velocities and masses vary from object to object, so there is no choice but to compute $p_x = mv_x$ for each one and then compare.

$$p_{1x} = (20\ \text{g})(1\ \text{m/s}) = 20\ \text{g} \cdot \text{m/s}$$
$$p_{2x} = (20\ \text{g})(2\ \text{m/s}) = 40\ \text{g} \cdot \text{m/s}$$
$$p_{3x} = (10\ \text{g})(2\ \text{m/s}) = 20\ \text{g} \cdot \text{m/s}$$
$$p_{4x} = (10\ \text{g})(1\ \text{m/s}) = 10\ \text{g} \cdot \text{m/s}$$
$$p_{5x} = (200\ \text{g})(0.1\ \text{m/s}) = 20\ \text{g} \cdot \text{m/s}$$

So the answer is $p_{2x} > p_{1x} = p_{3x} = p_{5x} > p_{4x}$.

Assess: The largest, most massive object did not have the greatest momentum because it was moving slower than the rest.

Q9.3. Reason: When the question talks about forces, times, and momenta, we immediately think of the impulse-momentum theorem, which tells us that to change the momentum of an object we must exert a net external force on it over a time interval: $\vec{F}_{avg}\Delta t = \Delta \vec{p}$.

Because equal forces are exerted over equal times, the impulses are equal and the changes in momentum are equal. Because both carts start from rest, their changes in momentum are the same as the final momentum for each, so their final momenta are equal.

Assess: Notice that we did not need to know the mass of either cart, or even the specific time interval (as long as it was the same for both carts) to answer the question.

Q9.5. Reason: The sum of the momenta of the three pieces must be the zero vector. Since the first piece is traveling east, its momentum will have the form: $(p_1, 0)$, where p_1 is a positive number. Since the second piece is traveling north, its momentum will have the form: $(0, p_2)$, where p_2 is a positive number. If a third momentum is to be added to these and the result is to be $(0,0)$, then the third momentum must be: $(-p_1, -p_2)$. Since its east-west and north-south components are both negative, the momentum of the third piece must point south west and so the velocity must be southwest. The answer is D.

Assess: It makes sense that the third piece would need to travel southwest. It needs a western component of momentum to cancel the eastern component of the first piece and it needs a southern component to cancel the northern component of the second piece.

Q9.7. Reason: (a) Both particles cannot be at rest immediately after the collision. If they were both at rest, then the sum of the momenta after the collision would be zero, and since momentum is conserved in collisions, it would have had to be zero before as well (and it wasn't).

(b) If the masses are equal and the collision elastic, the moving particle will stop and give all of its momentum to the previously resting particle. A good example of this appears when a billiard ball rolls directly into another resting billiard ball.

Assess: We say momentum is conserved in all collisions because we assume that both colliding objects are part of the system and we assume the "impulse approximation" that other forces can be neglected during the short time interval of the collision.

In part **(a)** if the system contained a third particle that participated in the collision, then it is possible for the first two particles to end up at rest if the momentum is carried off by the third.

Q9.9. Reason: The ball must change speed from its original speed to zero whether you wear the glove or not. So $\Delta \vec{p}$ is the same in either case. The impulse-momentum theorem also tells us $\vec{F}_{avg}\Delta t = \Delta \vec{p}$.

Given that the right side is the same in either case, the left side must also be the same in either case. But if we can increase Δt then F will be decreased correspondingly. The padding of the glove increases the collision time, thereby decreasing the force.

Assess: This is also how air bags work in car collisions.

Q9.11. Reason: See Example 9.5. The two skaters interact with each other, but they form an isolated system because, for each skater, the upward normal force of the ice balances their downward weight force to make $\vec{F}_{net} = \vec{0}$. Thus the total momentum of the system of the two skaters will be conserved. Assume that both skaters are at rest before the push so that the total momentum before they push off is $\vec{P}_i = \vec{0}$. Consequently, the total momentum will still be $\vec{0}$ after they push off.

(a) Because the total momentum of the two-skater system is $\vec{0}$ after the push off, Megan and Jason each have momentum of the same magnitude but in the opposite direction as the other. Therefore the magnitude Δp is the same for each: $\vec{F}_{avg}\Delta t = \Delta \vec{p}$. From the impulse-momentum theorem each experiences the same amount of impulse.

(b) They each experience the same amount of impulse because they experience the same magnitude force over the same time interval. However, over that time interval they do not experience the same acceleration. $\vec{F}_{net} = m\vec{a}$ says that since Megan and Jason experience the same force but Megan's mass is half of Jason's, then Megan's acceleration during push off will be twice Jason's. So she will have the greater speed at the end of the push off Δt.

Assess: It is important to think about both results until you are comfortable with them.

Q9.13. Reason: If you do not move backward when passing the basketball it is because the ball-you system is not isolated: There is a net external force on the system to keep you from moving backward that changes the momentum of the system. If the ball-you system *is* isolated (say you are on frictionless ice), then you *do* move backward when you pass the ball.

Assess: If the friction force of the floor on you keeps you from moving backward (relative to the floor), then the law of conservation of momentum doesn't apply because the system isn't isolated. But you could then include the floor, building, and earth in the system so it (the system) is isolated; then momentum of the system is conserved—and that means the earth does recoil ever so slightly when you pass the basketball.

Q9.15. Reason: Assume that each angular momentum is to be calculated about the axis of symmetry.

It will be useful to derive a general formula for the angular momentum of a particle in uniform circular motion of radius r, calculated around the axis of symmetry. Equation 7.15 reminds us that I for such a situation is mr^2, and Equation 6.6 tells us that $\omega = v/r$. Putting this all together gives the angular momentum for a particle in uniform circular motion: $L = I\omega = (mr^2)(v/r) = rmv$. So we compute $L = rmv$ for each of the five situations.

$$L_1 = (2 \text{ m})(2 \text{ kg})(2 \text{ m/s}) = 8 \text{ kg} \cdot \text{m}^2/\text{s}$$

$$L_2 = (2 \text{ m})(3 \text{ kg})(1 \text{ m/s}) = 6 \text{ kg} \cdot \text{m}^2/\text{s}$$

$$L_3 = (2 \text{ m})(1 \text{ kg})(3 \text{ m/s}) = 6 \text{ kg} \cdot \text{m}^2/\text{s}$$

$$L_4 = (4 \text{ m})(2 \text{ kg})(1 \text{ m/s}) = 8 \text{ kg} \cdot \text{m}^2/\text{s}$$

$$L_5 = (4 \text{ m})(2 \text{ kg})(2 \text{ m/s}) = 16 \text{ kg} \cdot \text{m}^2/\text{s}$$

Finally, comparison gives $L_5 > L_1 = L_4 > L_2 = L_3$.

Assess: Since $p = mv$ the angular momentum for a particle in uniform circular motion can also be written $L = rp$, or, more generally, $L = rp_\perp$ (compare with Equation 7.3).

Q9.17. Reason: Since there is no net torque on the earth, the angular momentum of the earth is conserved. As water from the polar ice caps moves farther from the earth's rotation axis, the moment of inertia of the earth with increase from consideration of Equation 7.15. In order to keep the angular momentum of the earth constant, the angular velocity of the earth must decrease. If the angular velocity of the earth decreases, the period of rotation will increase, so the length of the day will increase.

Assess: Since the mass of the polar ice caps is very small compared to the mass of the entire earth, the effect on the length of the day will probably be small.

Multiple-Choice Questions

Q9.19. Reason: From Equations 9.5, 9.2, and 9.8, Newton's second law can be profitably rewritten as

$$\vec{F}_{avg} = \frac{\Delta \vec{p}}{\Delta t}$$

In fact, this is much closer to what Newton actually wrote than $\vec{F} = m\vec{a}$. This allows us to directly solve the question.

$$\vec{F}_{avg} = \frac{\Delta \vec{p}}{\Delta t} = \frac{m\vec{v}_f - m\vec{v}_i}{\Delta t} = \frac{m(\vec{v}_f - \vec{v}_i)}{\Delta t} = \frac{(20 \text{ kg})(0 \text{ m/s} - 1 \text{ m/s})}{0.002 \text{ s}} = -10,000 \text{ N}$$

Since we only need the magnitude, the correct answer is D.

Assess: This is a large force but the speeds aren't very large. However, the time interval is so short that a large force is needed to change the momentum that much in so short a time.

Q9.21. Reason: The system consisting of both blocks is isolated and so the momentum of the system is conserved.

$$\vec{P}_i = \vec{P}_f$$
$$(m)(2v_i) + (3m)(v_i) = (m + 3m)(v_f)$$

where the two blocks stick together to make one compound object after the collision. We want to know v_f:

$$v_f = \frac{(m)(2v_i) + (3m)(v_i)}{m + 3m} = \frac{5mv_i}{4m} = \frac{5v_i}{4}$$

The correct answer is D.

Assess: One could mentally confirm that the answer is reasonable by thinking of the larger block on the right. It gets a little kick from the other block and so will go a bit faster than the v_i it had before. Only answer D fits that.

Q9.23. Reason: The initial momentum of the first block is $(p_1)_i = (2.5 \text{ kg})(12.0 \text{ m/s}) = 30 \text{ kg} \cdot \text{m/s}$ and the initial momentum of the second block is $(p_2)_i = (14 \text{ kg})(-3.4 \text{ m/s}) = -47.6 \text{ kg} \cdot \text{m/s}$. The sum of these, $-17.6 \text{ kg} \cdot \text{m/s}$, gives the total momentum, before and after the collision. After the collision, the final velocity of the two is obtained by dividing the total momentum by the total mass:

$$v_f = p_{total} / (m_1 + m_2) = (-17.6 \text{ kg} \cdot \text{m/s}) / (16.5 \text{ kg}) = -1.07 \text{ m/s}.$$

Now the final momentum of block 2 is the product of its mass and final velocity: $(p_2)_f = (14 \text{ kg})(-1.07 \text{ m/s}) = -15.0 \text{ kg} \cdot \text{m/s}$. The impulse of block 1 on block 2 equals the change in momentum of block 2:

$$J_{1 \text{ on } 2} = \Delta p_2 = -15.0 \text{ kg} \cdot \text{m/s} - -47.6 \text{ kg} \cdot \text{m/s} = 32.6 \text{ kg} \cdot \text{m/s}.$$

Now impulse equals the area under a force versus time graph. So we need to choose the graph whose area is about 32.6 kg · m/s. The graphs are approximately triangular so their areas are about half the base times the height. Choice D looks the best because the height is 3000 N and the base is about 25 ms for an area of about:

$$A = \frac{1}{2}(25 \times 10^{-3} \text{ s})(3000 \text{ N}) = 37.5 \text{ N} \cdot \text{s} = 37.5 \text{ kg} \cdot \text{m/s}.$$

The other graphs differ from this by a factor of 10 or more.

Assess: Even though we can't determine the value of the force on block 2 at each time, we can find the area under the force curve which is just the impulse.

Q9.25. Reason: Momentum is conserved in this process. Consider the figure below.

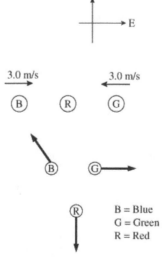

The total momentum of the system before the collision is

$$(p_x)_i = m_B(v_{Bx})_i + m_G(v_{Gx})_i = m(3.0 \text{ m/s}) + m(-3.0 \text{ m/s}) = 0 \text{ kg} \cdot \text{m/s}$$
$$(p_y)_i = 0 \text{ kg} \cdot \text{m/s}$$

since the blue ball is initially at rest. The total initial momentum is zero.

The final momentum of the system must be zero also. This gives

$$(p_x)_f = m_R(v_{Rx})_f + m_B(v_{Bx})_f + m_G(v_{Gx})_f = m(v_{Bx})_f + m(v_{Gx})_f = 0 \text{ kg} \cdot \text{m/s}$$
$$(p_y)_f = m_R(v_{Ry})_f + m_B(v_{By})_f + m_G(v_{Gy})_f = m(v_{By})_f + m(v_{Ry})_f = 0 \text{ kg} \cdot \text{m/s}$$

Solving for the momentum of the blue ball,

$$(v_{Bx})_f = -(v_{Gx})_f$$
$$(v_{By})_f = -(v_{Ry})_f$$

Since the red ball is moving south and the green ball is moving east, the blue ball must be moving west and north. The correct choice is C.

Assess: The final direction of the blue ball could be inferred from the fact that the total initial momentum is zero and the velocities of the red and green balls on the vector diagram above.

Q9.27. Reason: Not all of the information given in this question is needed to find the change in angular momentum. In fact, Equation 9.22, $\tau_{net}\Delta t = \Delta L$, tells us that to find the change in angular momentum of the disk, all we need is the net torque and the time the torque is applied. The change in L is given by:

$$\Delta L = \tau \cdot \Delta t = (0.040 \text{ N} \cdot \text{m})(5.0 \text{ s}) = 0.20 \text{ kg} \cdot \text{m}^2/\text{s}.$$

The answer is B.

Assess: We do not need to know anything about the disk itself to find its change in angular momentum; we only need the torque and the time interval. Similarly, from the equation $\Delta p = F\Delta t$, to find the change in momentum of an object, we do not need any information about the object, but only the force and the time interval.

Problems

P9.1. Prepare: Model the bicycle and its rider as a particle. Also model the car as a particle. We will use Equation 9.7 for momentum.

Solve: From the definition of momentum,

$$P_{car} = P_{bicycle} \Rightarrow m_{car} v_{car} = m_{bicycle} v_{bicycle} \Rightarrow v_{bicycle} = \frac{m_{car}}{m_{bicycle}} v_{car} = \left(\frac{1500 \text{ kg}}{100 \text{ kg}} \right)(5.0 \text{ m/s}) = 7.5 \text{ m/s}$$

Assess: This is a very high speed (≈ 168 mph). This problem shows the importance of mass in comparing two momenta.

P9.3. Prepare: From Equations 9.5, 9.2, and 9.8, Newton's second law can be profitably rewritten as

$$\vec{F}_{avg} = \frac{\Delta \vec{p}}{\Delta t}$$

In fact, this is much closer to what Newton actually wrote than $\vec{F} = m\vec{a}$.

Solve: This allows us to find the force on the snowball. By Newton's third law we know that the snowball exerts a force of equal magnitude on the wall.

$$\vec{F}_{avg} = \frac{\Delta \vec{p}}{\Delta t} = \frac{m\vec{v}_f - m\vec{v}_i}{\Delta t} = \frac{m(\vec{v}_f - \vec{v}_i)}{\Delta t} = \frac{(0.12 \text{ kg})(0 \text{ m/s} - 7.5 \text{ m/s})}{0.15 \text{ s}} = -6.0 \text{ N}$$

where the negative sign indicates that the force on the snowball is opposite its original momentum. So the force on the wall is also 6.0 N.

Assess: This is not a large force, but the snowball has low mass, a moderate speed, and the collision time is fairly long.

P9.5. Prepare: We use the equation: $J = \Delta p$.

Solve: The initial momentum of sled and rider is $p_i = mv_i = (80 \text{ kg})(4.0 \text{ m/s}) = 320 \text{ kg} \cdot \text{m/s}$ and the final momentum of sled and rider is $p_f = mv_f = (80 \text{ kg})(3.0 \text{ m/s}) = 240 \text{ kg} \cdot \text{m/s}$. So the impulse is given by:

$$J = p_f - p_i = 320 \text{ kg} \cdot \text{m/s} - 240 \text{ kg} \cdot \text{m/s} = 80 \text{ kg} \cdot \text{m/s} = 80 \text{ N} \cdot \text{s}$$

Assess: This is a reasonable impulse. It could result, for example, from a force of around nine pounds for two seconds.

P9.7. Prepare: Please refer to Figure P9.7. Model the object as a particle and its interaction with the force as a collision. We will use Equations 9.1 and 9.9. Because $p = mv$, so $v = p/m$.
Solve: (a) Using the equations

$$(p_x)_f = (p_x)_i + J_x$$

$$J_x = \text{ area under the force curve} \Rightarrow (v_x)_f = (1.0 \text{ m/s}) + \frac{1}{2.0 \text{ kg}} \text{ (area under the force curve)}$$

$$= (1.0 \text{ m/s}) + \frac{1}{2.0 \text{ kg}}(1.0 \text{ N s}) = 1.5 \text{ m/s}$$

(b) Likewise,

$$(v_x)_f = (1.0 \text{ m/s}) + \left(\frac{1}{2.0 \text{ kg}}\right) \text{ (area under the force curve)} = (1.0 \text{ m/s}) + \left(\frac{1}{2.0 \text{ kg}}\right)(-1.0 \text{ N s}) = 0.5 \text{ m/s}$$

Assess: For an object with positive velocity, a negative impulse slows down an object and a positive impulse increases speed. The opposite is true for an object with negative velocity.

P9.9. Prepare: From Equations 9.5, 9.2, and 9.8, Newton's second law can be profitably rewritten as

$$\vec{F}_{avg} = \frac{\Delta \vec{p}}{\Delta t}$$

In fact, this is much closer to what Newton actually wrote than $\vec{F} = m\vec{a}$.
Solve: This allows us to find the force on the child and sled.

$$\vec{F}_{avg} = \frac{\Delta \vec{p}}{\Delta t} = \frac{m\vec{v}_f - m\vec{v}_i}{\Delta t} = \frac{m(\vec{v}_f - \vec{v}_i)}{\Delta t} = \frac{(35 \text{ kg})(0 \text{ m/s} - 1.5 \text{ m/s})}{0.50 \text{ s}} = -105 \text{ N} \approx -110 \text{ N}$$

where the negative sign indicates that the force is in the direction opposite the original motion, as stated in the problem. So the *amount* (magnitude) of the average force you need to exert is 105 N.
Assess: This result is neither too large nor too small. In some collision problems Δt is quite a bit shorter and so the force is correspondingly larger.

P9.11. Prepare: From Equations 9.5, 9.2, and 9.8, Newton's second law can be profitably rewritten as

$$\vec{F}_{avg} = \frac{\Delta \vec{p}}{\Delta t}$$

In fact, this is much closer to what Newton actually wrote than $\vec{F} = m\vec{a}$.
Solve: This allows us to find the average force on the cars.
(a) Water barrels $\vec{F}_{avg} = \frac{\Delta \vec{p}}{\Delta t} = \frac{m\vec{v}_f - m\vec{v}_i}{\Delta t} = \frac{m(\vec{v}_f - \vec{v}_i)}{\Delta t} = \frac{(1400 \text{ kg})(0 \text{ m/s} - 20 \text{ m/s})}{1.5 \text{ s}} = -19,000 \text{ N}$

(b) Concrete barrier $\vec{F}_{avg} = \frac{\Delta \vec{p}}{\Delta t} = \frac{m\vec{v}_f - m\vec{v}_i}{\Delta t} = \frac{m(\vec{v}_f - \vec{v}_i)}{\Delta t} = \frac{(1400 \text{ kg})(0 \text{ m/s} - 20 \text{ m/s})}{0.1 \text{ s}} = -280,000 \text{ N}$

where the negative sign indicates that the force is in the direction opposite the original motion.
Assess: We clearly see that a shorter collision time dramatically affects the magnitude of the average force. From a practical standpoint, find something like water barrels or a haystack if you have to crash your car.

P9.13. Prepare: We'll call the system the two carts and consider it an isolated system so we can apply the law of conservation of momentum. The action all takes place in one dimension, so we don't need y-components. Let the subscript 1 stand for the small cart and 2 for the large.
Solve:

$$(P_x)_i = (P_x)_f$$
$$(p_{1x})_i + (p_{2x})_i = (p_{1x})_f + (p_{2x})_f$$
$$m_1(v_{1x})_i + m_2(v_{2x})_i = (m_1(v_{1x})_f + m_2(v_{2x})_f$$

We want to know $(v_{2x})_f$ so we solve for it. Also recall that $(v_{2x})_i = 0$ m/s, so the middle term in the following numerator drops out. The small cart recoils, which means its velocity after the collision is negative.

$$(v_{2x})_f = \frac{m_1(v_{1x})_i + m_2(v_{2x})_i - m_i(v_{1x})_f}{m_2} = \frac{(0.100 \text{ kg})(1.20 \text{ m/s}) - (0.100 \text{ kg})(-0.850 \text{ m/s})}{1.00 \text{ kg}} = 0.205 \text{ m/s}$$

Assess: The large cart does not move quickly, but the answer is reasonable because of the greater mass of the large cart. We have followed the significant figure-rules and kept three significant figures.

P9.15. Prepare: This is a problem with no external forces so we can use the law of conservation of momentum.
  Solve: The total momentum before the bullet hits the block equals the total momentum after the bullet passes through the block so we can write:

$$m_b(v_b)_i + m_{bl}(v_{bl})_i - m_b(v_b)_f \mathrel{I} m_{bl}(v_{bl})_t \rightarrow$$
$$(3.0 \times 10^{-3} \text{ kg})(500 \text{ m/s}) + (2.7 \text{ kg})(0 \text{ m/s}) = (3.0 \times 10^{-3} \text{ kg})(220 \text{ m/s}) + (2.7 \text{ kg})(v_{bl})_f.$$

We can solve for the final velocity of the block: $(v_{bl})_f = 0.31$ m/s.

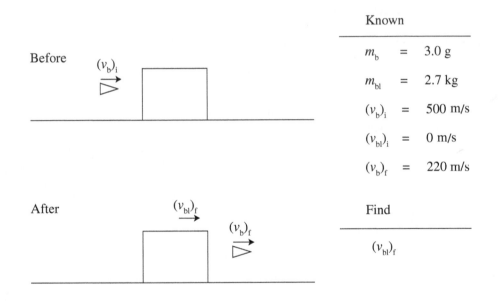

Known		
m_b	=	3.0 g
m_{bl}	=	2.7 kg
$(v_b)_i$	=	500 m/s
$(v_{bl})_i$	=	0 m/s
$(v_b)_f$	=	220 m/s

Find
_____

$(v_{bl})_f$

Assess: This is reasonable since the block is about one thousand times more massive than the bullet and its change in speed is about one thousand times less.

P9.17. Prepare: We will choose car + gravel to be our system. The initial x-velocity of the car is 2 m/s and that of the gravel is 0 m/s. To find the final x-velocity of the system, we will apply the momentum conservation Equation 9.13.

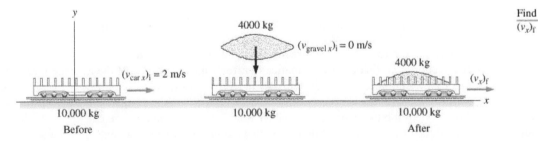

Solve: There are no *external* forces on the car + gravel system, so the horizontal momentum is conserved. This means $(p_x)_f + (p_x)_i$. Hence,

$$(10{,}000 \text{ kg} + 4{,}000 \text{ kg})(v_x)_f = (10{,}000 \text{ kg})(2.0 \text{ m/s}) + (4{,}000 \text{ kg})(0.0 \text{ m/s}) \Rightarrow (v_x)_f = 1.4 \text{ m/s}$$

Assess: The motion of railroad has to be on a level track for conservation of linear momentum to hold. As we would have expected, the final speed is smaller than the initial speed.

P9.19. Prepare: We will define our system to be archer + arrow. The force of the archer (A) on the arrow (a) is equal to the force of the arrow on the archer. These are internal forces within the system. The archer is standing on frictionless ice, and the normal force by ice on the system balances the weight force. Thus $\vec{F}_{ext} = \vec{0}$ on the system, and momentum is conserved. The initial momentum p_{ix} of the system is zero, because the archer and the arrow are at rest. The final moment p_{fx} must also be zero.

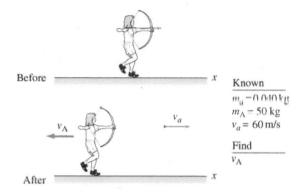

Before ———————————————— x

Known
$m_a = 0.010$ kg
$m_A = 50$ kg
$v_a = 60$ m/s

Find
v_A

v_A ⟵ v_a →

After ———————————————— x

Solve: We have $M_A v_A + m_a v_a = 0$ kg m/s. Therefore,

$$v_A = \frac{-m_a v_a}{m_A} = \frac{-(0.04 \text{ kg})(60 \text{ m/s})}{50 \text{ kg}} = -0.48 \text{ m/s}$$

The archer's recoil *speed* is 0.48 m/s.

   Assess: It is the total final momentum that is zero, although the individual momenta are nonzero. Since the arrow has forward momentum, the archer will have backward momentum.

P9.21. Prepare: We will define our system to be bird + bug. This is the case of an inelastic collision because the bird and bug move together after the collision. Horizontal momentum is conserved because there are no external forces acting on the system during the collision.

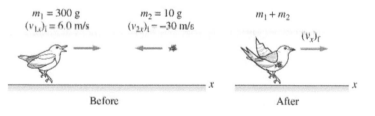

$m_1 = 300$ g $m_2 = 10$ g $m_1 + m_2$
$(v_{1x})_i = 6.0$ m/s $(v_{2x})_i = -30$ m/s $(v_x)_f$

Before   After

Solve: The conservation of momentum equation $p_{fx} = p_{ix}$ is

$$(m_1 + m_2)(v_x)_f = m_1(v_{1x})_i + m_2(v_{2x})_f$$
$$\Rightarrow (300 \text{ g} + 10 \text{ g})(v_x)_f = (300 \text{ g})(6.0 \text{ m/s}) + (10 \text{ g})(-30 \text{ m/s}) \Rightarrow (v_x)_f = 4.8 \text{ m/s}$$

   Assess: We left masses in grams, rather than convert to kilograms, because the mass units cancel out from both sides of the equation. Note that $(v_{2x})_i$ is negative. As would have been expected, the final speed is a little lower than the initial speed because (1) the bug has finite mass and (2) the bug has relatively large speed compared to the bird.

P9.23. Prepare: Even though this is an inelastic collision, momentum is still conserved during the short collision if we choose the system to be spitball plus carton. Let SB stand for the spitball, CTN the carton, and BOTH be the combined object after impact (we assume the spitball sticks to the carton). We are given $m_{SB} = 0.0030$ kg, $m_{CTN} = 0.020$ kg, and $(v_{BOTHx})_f = 0.30$ m/s.
   Solve:

$$(P_x)_i = (P_x)_f$$
$$(p_{SBx})_i + (p_{CTNx})_i = (p_{BOTHx})_f$$
$$m_{SB}(v_{SBx})_i + m_{CTN}(v_{CTNx})_i = (m_{SB} + m_{CTN})(v_{BOTHx})_f$$

We want to know $(v_{SBx})_i$ so we solve for it. Also recall that $(v_{CTNx})_i = 0$ m/s so the last term in the following numerator drops out.

$$(v_{SBx})_i = \frac{(m_{SB} + m_{CTN})(v_{BOTHx})_f - m_{CTN}(v_{CTNx})_i}{m_{SB}} = \frac{(0.0030 \text{ kg} + 0.020 \text{ kg})(0.30 \text{ m/s})}{0.0030 \text{ kg}} = 2.3 \text{ m/s}$$

Assess: The answer of 2.3 m/s is certainly within the capability of an expert spitballer.

P9.25. Prepare: Since there are no external forces, we can use the law of conservation of momentum.
   Solve: The sum of the momenta of the two blocks before the collision equals the momentum of the coupled blocks after the collision so we write:

$$m_1(v_1)_i + m_2(v_2)_i = (m_1 + m_2)v_f \Rightarrow$$
$$(2.0 \text{ kg})(1.0 \text{ m/s}) + m_2(4.0 \text{ m/s}) = (2.0 \text{ kg} + m_2)(2.0 \text{ m/s}).$$

We can solve this last equation for the second mass and obtain: $m_2 = 1.0$ kg.
   Assess: It is reasonable that the second mass is less than the first because the final speed, 2.0 m/s, is closer to the initial speed of the first block, 1.0 m/s, that it is to the initial speed of the second block, 4.0 m/s.

P9.27. Prepare: We assume that the momentum is conserved in the collision. Please refer to Figure P9.27.
   Solve: The conservation of momentum Equation 9.16 yields

$$(p_{1x})_f + (p_{2x})_f = (p_{1x})_i + (p_{2x})_i \Rightarrow (p_{1x})_f + 0 \text{ kg m/s} = 2 \text{ kg m/s} - 4 \text{ kg m/s} \Rightarrow (p_{1x})_f = -2 \text{ kg m/s}$$
$$(p_{1y})_f + (p_{2y})_f = (p_{1y})_i + (p_{2y})_i \Rightarrow (p_{1y})_f - 1 \text{ kg m/s} = 2 \text{ kg m/s} + 1 \text{ kg m/s} \Rightarrow (p_{1y})_f = 4 \text{ kg m/s}$$

The final momentum vector of particle 1 that has the above components is shown below.

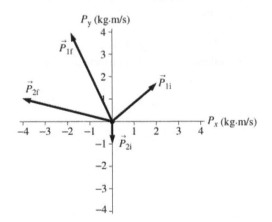

P9.29. Prepare: This problem deals with a case that is the opposite of a collision. Our system is comprised of three coconut pieces that are modeled as particles. During the blow up or "explosion," the total momentum of the system is conserved in the x-direction and the y-direction. We can thus apply Equation 9.16.

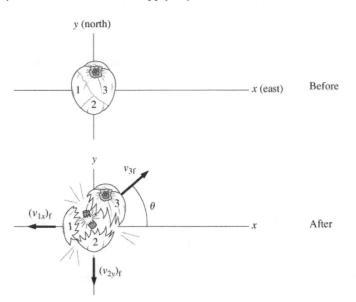

Solve: The initial momentum is zero. From $(p_x)_f = (p_x)_i$ we get

$$+m_1(v_{1x})_f + m_3(v_{3f})\cos\theta = 0 \text{ kg m/s} \Rightarrow (v_{3f})\cos\theta = \frac{-m_1(v_{fx})_1}{m_3} = \frac{-m(-20 \text{ m/s})}{2m} = 10 \text{ m/s}$$

From $(p_y)_f = (p_y)_i$, we get

$$+m_2(v_{2y})_f + m_3(v_{3f})\sin\theta = 0 \text{ kg m/s} \Rightarrow (v_{3f})\sin\theta = \frac{-m_2(v_{fy})_2}{m_3} = \frac{-m(-20 \text{ m/s})}{2m} = 10 \text{ m/s}$$

$$\Rightarrow (v_{3f}) = \sqrt{(10 \text{ m/s})^2 + (10 \text{ m/s})^2} = 14 \text{ m/s} \quad \theta = \tan^{-1}(1) = 45°$$

Assess: The obtained speed of the third piece is of similar order of magnitude as the other two pieces, which is physically reasonable.

P9.31. Prepare: We will model the mother as a particle with $m = 47$ kg, $v = 4.2$ m/s, and $r = 2.6$ m.

It will be useful to derive a general formula for the angular momentum of a particle in uniform circular motion of radius calculated around the axis of symmetry. Equation 7.15 reminds us that I for such a situation is mr^2, and Equation 6.6 tells us that $(-55 \text{ m/s})\cos(25) = -23.2$ m/s. Putting this all together gives the angular momentum for a particle in uniform circular motion:

$$L = I\omega = (mr^2)(v/r) = rmv$$

Solve:

$$L = rmv = (2.6 \text{ m})(47 \text{ kg})(4.2 \text{ m/s}) = 510 \text{ kg} \cdot \text{m}^2/\text{s}$$

to two significant figures.

Assess: Until one gets a feel for how much angular momentum objects have it is difficult to know if our answer is reasonable, but the derivation of $L = rmv$ is straightforward and we checked our multiplication twice, so it is probably correct.

P9.33. Prepare: The disk is a rotating rigid body. Please refer to Figure P9.33. The angular velocity ω is 600 rpm = $600 \times 2\pi/60$ rad/s = 20π rad/s. From Table 7.4, the moment of inertial of the disk about its center is (1/2) MR^2, which can be used with $L = I\omega$ to find the angular momentum.

Solve:

$$I = \frac{1}{2}MR^2 = \frac{1}{2}(2.0 \text{ kg})(0.020 \text{ m})^2 = 4.0 \times 10^{-4} \text{ kg m}^2$$

Thus, $L = I\omega = (4.0 \times 10^{-4}\ \text{kg m}^2)(20\pi\ \text{rad/s}) = 0.025\ \text{kg m}^2/\text{s}$. If we wrap our right fingers in the direction of the disk's rotation, our thumb will point in the $-x$ direction. Consequently,

$$\vec{L} = (0.025\ \text{kg m}^2/\text{s, into page})$$

Assess: Don't forget the direction of the angular momentum because it is a vector quantity.

P9.35. Prepare: We neglect any small frictional torque the ice may exert on the skater and apply the law of conservation of angular momentum.

$$L_i = L_f$$
$$I_i\omega_i = I_f\omega_f$$

Even though the data for $\omega_i = 5.0$ rev/s is not in SI units, it's okay because we are asked for the answer in the same units. We are also given $I_i = 0.80\ \text{kg} \cdot \text{m}^2$ and $I_f = 3.2\ \text{kg} \cdot \text{m}^2$.

Solve:

$$\omega_f = \frac{I_i\omega_i}{I_f} = \frac{(0.80\ \text{kg} \cdot \text{m}^2)(5.0\ \text{rev/s})}{3.2\ \text{kg} \cdot \text{m}^2} = 1.25\ \text{rev/s} \approx 1.3\ \text{rev/s}$$

Assess: I increased by a factor of 4, so we expect ω to decrease by a factor of 4.

P9.37. Prepare: Please refer to Figure P9.37. Model the glider cart as a particle, and its interaction with the spring as a collision. The initial and final speeds of the glider are shown on the velocity graph and the mass of the glider is known. We can thus find the momentum change of the glider, which is equal to the impulse. Impulse is also given by the area under the force graph, which we will find from the force graph in terms of Δt.

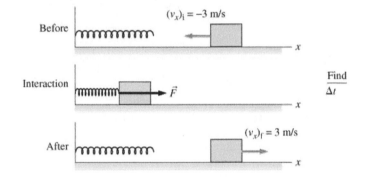

Solve: Using the impulse-momentum theorem $(p_x)_f - (p_x)_i = J_x$,

$$(0.6\ \text{kg})(3\ \text{m/s}) - (0.6\ \text{kg})(-3\ \text{m/s}) = \text{area under force curve} = \frac{1}{2}(36\ \text{N})(\Delta t) \Rightarrow \Delta t = 0.20\ \text{s}$$

Assess: You can solve this problem using kinematics to check your answer. From the graph you have the average force during compression to be 18 N, and therefore the average acceleration to be 30 m/s^2. Now calculate the time taken for the velocity to go from 3 m/s to 0 m/s, and twice this time should match the 0.20 s found above.

P9.39. Prepare: Model the ball as a particle that is subjected to an impulse when it is in contact with the floor. We will also use constant-acceleration kinematic equations.

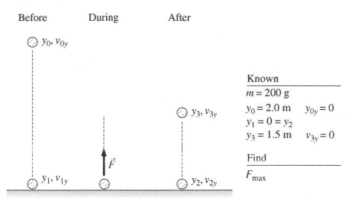

Before   During   After

Known
$m = 200$ g
$y_0 = 2.0$ m $v_{0y} = 0$
$y_1 = 0 = y_2$
$y_3 = 1.5$ m $v_{3y} = 0$

Find
F_{max}

Solve: To find the ball's velocity just before and after it hits the floor:

$$v_{1y}^2 = v_{0y}^2 + 2a_y(y_1 - y_0) = 0 \text{ m}^2/\text{s}^2 + 2(-9.8 \text{ m/s}^2)(0 - 2.0 \text{ m}) \Rightarrow v_{1y} = -6.261 \text{ m/s}$$

$$v_{3y}^2 = v_{2y}^2 + 2a_y(y_3 - y_2) \Rightarrow 0 \text{ m}^2/\text{s}^2 = v_{2y}^2 + 2(-9.8 \text{ m/s}^2)(1.5 \text{ m} - 0 \text{ m}) \Rightarrow v_{2y} = 5.422 \text{ m/s}$$

The force exerted by the floor on the ball can be found from the impulse-momentum theorem:

$$mv_{2y} = mv_{1y} + \text{ area under the force curve} \Rightarrow (0.2 \text{ kg})(5.422 \text{ m/s})$$

$$= -(0.2 \text{ kg})(6.261 \text{ m/s}) + \frac{1}{2}F_{max}(5 \times 10^{-3} \text{ s}) \Rightarrow F_{max} = 940 \text{ N}$$

Assess: A force of 940 N exerted by the floor is typical of such collisions.

P9.41. Prepare: We combine Equation 9.1 $J = F_{avg} \Delta t$ with the impulse-momentum theorem in the y-direction $J_y = \Delta p_y$. See Example 9.1. This tells us that Δp_y is the area under the curve of the net force in the vertical direction vs. time. And if we know the change in the woman's vertical momentum we can figure out the speed with which she leaves the ground; to do this last step, however, we'll need her mass.

Look at the first part of the graph while the force exerted by the floor is constant. During that time she isn't accelerating, so the force the floor exerts must be equal in magnitude to her weight; so she weighs 600 N and her mass is 600 N/(9.8 m/s²) = 61 kg. It should also be clear from the graph that she leaves the floor at $t = 0.5$ s when the force of the floor on her is zero.

The graph we are given is not the graph of the net force. The hint warns us that the upward force of the floor is not the only force on the woman. We have just concluded that the earth is exerting a downward gravitational force of 600 N (her weight) on her. Therefore a graph of the *net* vertical force on her vs. time would simply be the same graph only 600 N lower on the force axis.

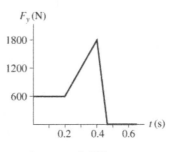

Note carefully that the graph now crosses the t-axis at $t = 0.475$ s.

Solve: What is the area under the new graph? We'll take the area of the triangle above the *t*-axis to be positive and then subtract the area of the smaller triangle below the *t*-axis. The general formula for the area of a triangle is

$$A = \frac{1}{2} \times \text{height} \times \text{base}$$

$$A_{\text{big}} = \frac{1}{2}(1800 \text{ N})(0.275 \text{ s}) = 248 \text{ N} \cdot \text{s}$$

$$A_{\text{small}} = \frac{1}{2}(600 \text{ N})(0.025 \text{ s}) = 15 \text{ N} \cdot \text{s}$$

The total area (with the triangle above the axis positive and the triangle below the axis negative) is 248 N · s 15 N · s = 233 N · s; this is the vertical impulse on the woman, and is also equal to her change in vertical momentum. Since $\Delta p_y = m\Delta v_y$, we simply divide by her mass to find her change in velocity:

$$\Delta v_y = \Delta p_y / m = (233 \text{ N} \cdot \text{s})/(61 \text{ kg}) = 3.8 \text{ m/s}$$

Because she started from rest this value is also her final speed, just as she leaves the ground.

Assess: We assumed the ability to read the data from the graph to two significant figures. If we were not confident in this we would report the result to just one significant figure: $(v_y)_f \approx 4$ m/s. The answer of ≈ 4 m/s does seem to be in the reasonable range.

It is worth following the units in the last equation to see the answer end up in m/s.

P9.43. Prepare: To find the impulse delivered by the bat to the ball, we need to know the change in the ball's momentum and use $J = \Delta p$. Since the direction of the ball changes, we need to use vector notation. The *x*-component of the ball's final velocity is

$(-55 \text{ m/s})\cos(25) = -49.8$ m/s and the *y*-component is $(-55 \text{ m/s})\cos(25) = -23.2$ m/s

Solve: The initial velocity of the ball is $\vec{v}_i = (35 \text{ m/s}, 0)$ and its initial momentum is obtained by multiplying by the mass of the ball:

$$\vec{p}_i = (0.140 \text{ kg})(35 \text{ m/s}, 0 \text{ m/s}) = (4.90 \text{ kg} \cdot \text{m/s}, 0 \text{ kg} \cdot \text{m/s})$$

The initial final momentum is the final velocity of the ball times its mass:

$$\vec{p}_f = (0.140 \text{ kg})(-49.8 \text{ m/s}, 23.2 \text{ m/s}) = (-6.97 \text{ kg} \cdot \text{m/s}, 3.25 \text{ kg} \cdot \text{m/s})$$

Finally, the impulse on the ball equals the change in the ball's momentum:

$$J = \vec{p}_f - \vec{p}_i = (-11.9 \text{ kg} \cdot \text{m/s}, 3.25 \text{ kg} \cdot \text{m/s})$$

The magnitude of the impulse can be obtained from the Pythagorean theorem: $J = 12$ N · s and we can find the angle, θ, above the horizontal using inverse tangent: $\theta = \tan^{-1}(3.36 / 12.30 = 15°)$. The direction is to the left and 15° above the horizontal.

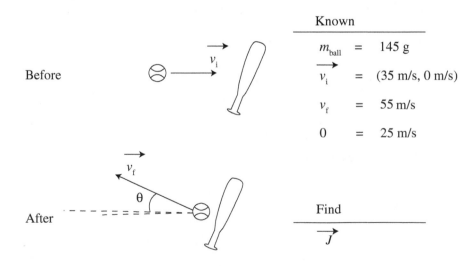

Known	
m_{ball} =	145 g
$\vec{v}_i$ =	(35 m/s, 0 m/s)
v_f =	55 m/s
0 =	25 m/s

Before

After

Find
$\vec{J}$

Assess: The angle 15° makes sense because the ball comes in at 0° with the horizontal and leaves the bat at 25° above the horizontal. We expect the force, and therefore the impulse, exerted by the bat to have an angle intermediate to these two.

P9.45. Prepare: We are asked for the impulse given to the pollen grain; impulse is defined in Equation 9.1: $J = F_{avg}\Delta t$. We are given that $\Delta t = 3.0 \times 10^{-4}$ s, but we note that since we are not given any velocities, we will not use momentum or the impulse-momentum theorem. With that approach eliminated, how will we find F_{avg}? Given $m = 1.0 \times 10^{-10}$ kg and $a = 2.5 \times 10^4$ m/s² guides us to use Newton's second law to find F_{avg} (assuming a is constant over Δt). The F_{avg} in the impulse equation is the same as the F_{net} in Newton's law because we are ignoring any other forces on the grain.

$$F_{avg} = F_{net} = ma = (1.0 \times 10^{-10} \text{ kg})(2.5 \times 10^4 \text{ m/s}^2) = 2.5 \times 10^{-6} \text{ N}$$

Solve:

$$J = F_{avg}\Delta t = (2.5 \times 10^{-6} \text{ N})(3.0 \times 10^{-4} \text{ s}) = 7.5 \times 10^{-10} \text{ N} \cdot \text{s} = 7.5 \times 10^{-10} \text{ kg} \cdot \text{m/s}$$

Assess: This is certainly a small impulse, but the pollen grains have such small mass that the impulse is sufficient to give them the stated acceleration. Note that $\text{N} \cdot \text{s} = \text{kg} \cdot \text{m/s}$.

P9.47. Prepare: Let the system be ball + racket. During the collision of the ball and the racket, momentum is conserved because all external interactions are insignificantly small. We will also use the momentum-impulse theorem.

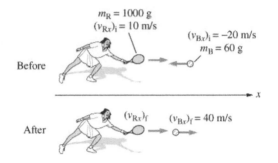

Solve: (a) The conservation of momentum equation $(p_x)_f = (p_x)_i$ is

$$m_R(v_{Rx})_f + m_B(v_{Bx})_f = m_R(v_{Rx})_i + m_B(v_{Bx})_i$$
$$(1.0 \text{ kg})(v_{Rx})_f + (0.06 \text{ kg})(40 \text{ m/s}) = (1.0 \text{ kg})(10 \text{ m/s}) + (0.06 \text{ kg})(-20 \text{ m/s}) \Rightarrow (v_{Rx})_f = 6.4 \text{ m/s}$$

(b) The impulse on the ball is calculated from $(p_{Bx})_f = (p_{Bx})_i + J_x$ as follows:

$$(0.06 \text{ kg})(40 \text{ m/s}) = (0.06 \text{ kg})(-20 \text{ m/s}) + J_x \Rightarrow J_x = 3.6 \text{ N s} = F_{avg}\Delta t$$

$$\Rightarrow F_{avg} = \frac{3.6 \text{ Ns}}{10 \text{ ms}} = 360 \text{ N}$$

Assess: Let us now compare this force with the ball's weight $w_B = m_B g = (0.06 \text{ kg})(9.8 \text{ m/s}^2) = 0.588$ N. Thus, $F_{avg} = 610 w_B$. This is a significant force and is reasonable because the impulse due to this force changes the direction as well as the speed of the ball from approximately 45 mph to 90 mph.

P9.49. Prepare: We will define our system to be Dan + skateboard. The system has nonzero initial momentum p_{ix}. As Dan (D) jumps backward off the gliding skateboard (S), the skateboard will move forward in such a way that the final total momentum of the system is equal to the initial momentum$_x$. This conservation of momentum occurs because $\vec{F}_{ext} = \vec{0}$ on the system.

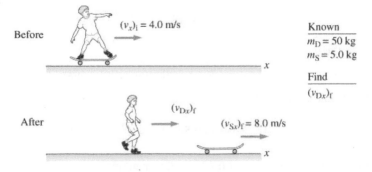

Solve: We have $m_s(v_{Sx})_f + m_D(v_{Dx})_f = (m_S + m_D)(v_x)_i$. Hence,

$$(5.0 \text{ kg})(8.0 \text{ m/s}) + (50 \text{ kg})(v_{Dx})_f = (5.0 \text{ kg} + 50 \text{ kg})(4.0 \text{ m/s}) \Rightarrow (v_{Dx})_f = 3.6 \text{ m/s}$$

Assess: A speed of 3.6 m/s or 8 mph is reasonable.

P9.51. Prepare: We can find the speed of the cart using the law of conservation of momentum. What makes this tricky is that Ethan's speed is given relative to the cart but we need to find the speed of the cart relative to the ground. When using the conservation of momentum, all the velocities must be relative to the same observer. Ethan's velocity relative to the ground is the sum of his velocity relative to the cart and the velocity of the cart relative to the ground. When he has reached his top speed, we have: $(v_{Eg})_f = 8.0 \text{ m/s} + (v_{cg})_f$.

Solve: Initially, Ethan and the cart are at rest, so their total momentum is zero. We can now write down the equation for the conservation of momentum relative to the ground:

$$0 \text{ kg} \cdot \text{m/s} = m_E(v_{Eg})_f + m_c(v_{cg})_f \Rightarrow$$
$$0 \text{ kg} \cdot \text{m/s} = (80 \text{ kg})(8.0 \text{ m/s} + (v_{cg})_f) + (500 \text{ kg})(v_{cg})_f.$$

The equation can be solved for the velocity of the cart: $(v_{cg})_f = -1.1 \text{ m/s}$. The speed of the cart when Ethan has reached his top speed is 1.1 m/s.

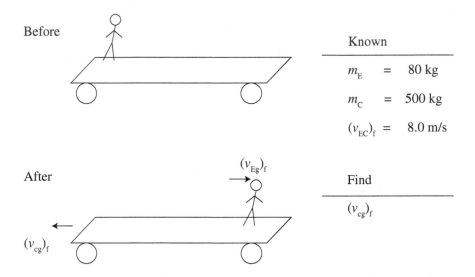

Known		
m_E	=	80 kg
m_C	=	500 kg
$(v_{EC})_f$	=	8.0 m/s

Find

$(v_{cg})_f$

Assess: Relative to the ground, Ethan's speed is 6.9 m/s. It is reasonable that Ethan is moving about six times as fast as the cart because the cart is about six times as massive as Ethan.

P9.53. Prepare: Model the train cars as particles. Since the train cars stick together, we are dealing with perfectly inelastic collisions. Momentum is conserved in the collisions of this problem.

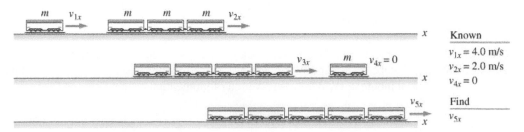

Known

$v_{1x} = 4.0$ m/s
$v_{2x} = 2.0$ m/s
$v_{4x} = 0$

Find

v_{5x}

Solve: In the collision between the three-car train and the single car:

$$mv_{1x} + (3m)v_{2x} = 4mv_{3x} \Rightarrow v_{1x} + 3v_{2x} = 4v_{3x} \Rightarrow (4.0 \text{ m/s}) + 3(2.0 \text{ m/s}) = 4v_{3x} \Rightarrow v_{3x} = 2.5 \text{ m/s}$$

In the collision between the four-car train and the stationary car:

$$(4m)v_{3x} + mv_{4x} = (5m)v_{5x} \Rightarrow 4v_{3x} + 0 \text{ m/s} = 5v_{5x} \Rightarrow v_{5x} = \frac{4v_{3x}}{5} = (0.8)(2.5 \text{ m/s}) = 2.0 \text{ m/s}$$

Assess: The motion of railroad has to be on a level track for linear momentum to be constant. The speed of the five-car train, as expected, is of the same order of magnitude as the other speeds.

P9.55. Prepare: Model the earth (E) and the asteroid (A) as particles. Earth + asteroid is our system. Since the two stick together during the collision, this is a case of a perfectly inelastic collision. Momentum is conserved in the collision since no significant external force acts on the system.

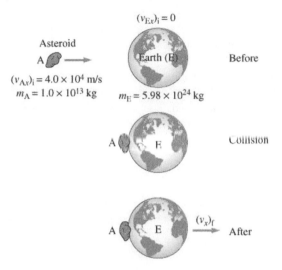

Solve: (a) The conservation of momentum equation $(p_x)_f = (p_x)_i$ is

$$m_A(v_{Ax})_i + m_E(v_{Ex})_i = (m_A + m_E)(v_x)_f$$

$$\Rightarrow (1.0 \times 10^{13} \text{ kg})(4 \times 10^4 \text{ m/s}) + 0 \text{ kg m/s} = (1.0 \times 10^{13} \text{ kg} + 5.98 \times 10^{24} \text{ kg})(v_x)_f \Rightarrow (v_x)_f = 6.7 \times 10^{-8} \text{ m/s}$$

(b) The speed of the earth going around the sun is

$$v_E = \frac{2\pi r}{T} = \frac{2\pi(1.50 \times 10^{11} \text{ m})}{3.15 \times 10^7 \text{ s}} = 3.0 \times 10^4 \text{ m/s}$$

Hence, $(v_x)_f / v_E = 2 \times 10^{-12} = 2 \times 10^{-10}\%$.

Assess: The earth's recoil speed is insignificant compared to its orbital speed because of its large mass.

P9.57. Prepare: This problem deals with a case that is the opposite of a collision. The two ice skaters, heavier and lighter, will be modeled as particles. The skaters (or particles) move apart after pushing off against each other. During the "explosion," the total momentum of the system is conserved.

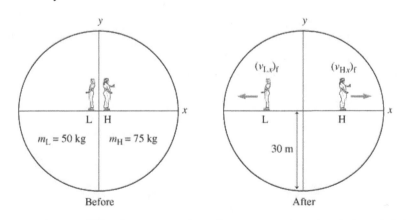

Solve: The initial momentum is zero. Thus the conservation of momentum equation $(p_x)_f = (p_x)_i$ is

$$m_H(v_{Hx})_f + m_L(v_{Lx})_f = 0 \text{ kg m/s} \Rightarrow (75 \text{ kg})(v_{Hx})_f + (50 \text{ kg})(v_{Lx})_f = 0 \text{ kg m/s}$$

Using the observation that the heavier skater takes 20 s to cover a distance of 30 m, we find $(v_{Hx})_f = 30 \text{ m}/20 \text{ s} = 1.5 \text{ m/s}$. Thus,

$$(75 \text{ kg})(1.5 \text{ m/s}) + (50 \text{ kg})(v_{Lx})_f = 0 \text{ kg m/s} \Rightarrow (v_{Lx})_f = -2.25 \text{ m/s}$$

Thus, the time for the lighter skater to reach the edge is

$$\frac{30 \text{ m}}{(v_{Lx})_f} = \frac{30 \text{ m}}{2.25 \text{ m/s}} = 13 \text{ s}$$

Assess: Conservation of momentum leads to a higher speed for the lighter skater, and hence a shorter time to reach the edge of the ice rink. A time of 13 s at the speed of 2.3 m/s is reasonable.

P9.59. Prepare: This is a two-part problem. First, we have an inelastic collision between the wood block and the bullet. The bullet and the wood block are an isolated system. Since any external force acting during the collision is not going to be significant, the momentum of the system will be conserved. The second part involves the dynamics of the block + bullet sliding on the wood table. We treat the block and the bullet as particles.

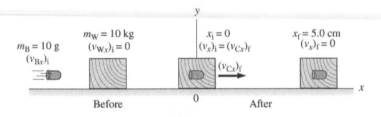

Solve: The equation $(p_x)_f = (p_x)_i$ gives

$$(m_B + m_W)(v_{Cx})_f = m_B(v_{Bx})_i + m_W(v_{Wx})_i$$

$$\Rightarrow (0.01 \text{ kg} + 10 \text{ kg})(v_{Cx})_f = (0.01 \text{ kg})(v_{Bx})_i + (10.0 \text{ kg})(0 \text{ m/s}) \Rightarrow (v_{Cx})_f = \frac{1}{1001}(v_{Bx})_i$$

using $-f_k = -\mu_k n = -\mu_k(m_B + m_W)g = (m_B + m_W)a_x \Rightarrow a_x = -\mu_k g$. Note that the negative sign appears in front of f_k because the force of friction points in the $-x$ direction.

Using the kinematics equation $(v_x)_f^2 = (v_x)_i^2 + 2a_x(x_f - x_i)$,

$$0 = (v_{Cx})_f^2 - 2\mu_k g(x_f - x_i) \Rightarrow 0 \text{ m}^2/\text{s}^2 = \left(\frac{1}{1001}\right)^2 (v_{Bx})_i^2 - 2\mu_k g x_f \Rightarrow 0 \text{ m}^2/\text{s}^2 = \left(\frac{1}{1001}\right)^2 (v_{Bx})_i^2 - 2\mu_k g x_f$$

$$\Rightarrow (v_{Bx})_i = 1001\sqrt{2\mu_k g x_f} = 1001\sqrt{2(0.2)(9.8 \text{ m/s}^2)(0.05 \text{ m})} = 440 \text{ m/s}$$

Assess: The bullet's speed is reasonable (≈ 1000 mph).

P9.61. Prepare: We will model the two fragments of the rocket after the explosion as particles. We assume the explosion separates the two parts in a vertical manner. This is a three-part problem. In the first part, we will use kinematics equations to find the vertical position where the rocket breaks into two pieces. In the second part, we will apply conservation of momentum along the y direction to the system (that is, the two fragments) in the explosion. The momentum conservation "applies" because the forces involved during the explosion are much larger than the external force due to gravity during the small period that the explosion lasts. In the third part, we will again use kinematics equations to find the velocity of the heavier fragment just after the explosion.

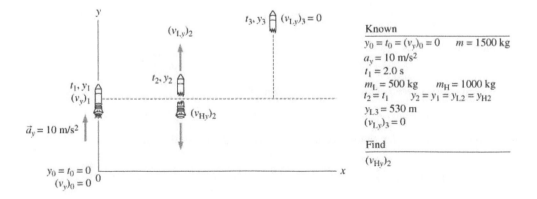

Solve: The rocket accelerates for 2.0 s from rest, so

$$(v_y)_1 = (v_y)_0 + a_y(t_1 - t_0) = 0 \text{ m/s} + (10 \text{ m/s}^2)(2 \text{ s} - 0 \text{ s}) = 20 \text{ m/s}$$

$$y_1 = y_0 + (v_y)_0(t_1 - t_0) + \frac{1}{2}a_y(t_1 - t_0)^2 = 0 \text{ m} + 0 \text{ m} + \frac{1}{2}(10 \text{ m/s}^2)(2 \text{ s})^2 = 20 \text{ m}$$

At the explosion the equation $(p_y)_f = (p_y)_i$ is

$$m_L(v_{Ly})_2 + m_H(v_{Hy})_2 = (m_L + m_H)(v_y)_1 \Rightarrow (500 \text{ kg})(v_{Ly})_2 + (1000 \text{ kg})(v_{Hy})_2 = (1500 \text{ kg})(20 \text{ m/s})$$

To find $(v_{Hy})_2$ we must first find $(v_{Ly})_2$, the velocity after the explosion of the upper section. Using kinematics,

$$(v_{Ly})_3^2 = (v_{Ly})_2^2 + 2(-9.8 \text{ m/s}^2)((y_1)_3 - (y_1)_2) \Rightarrow (v_{Ly})_2 = \sqrt{2(9.8 \text{ m/s}^2)(530 \text{ m} - 20 \text{ m})} = 99.98 \text{ m/s}$$

Now, going back to the momentum conservation equation we get

$$(500 \text{ kg})(99.8 \text{ m/s}) + (1000 \text{ kg})(v_{Hy})_2 = (1500 \text{ kg})(20 \text{ m/s}) \Rightarrow (v_{Hy})_2 = -20 \text{ m/s}$$

The negative sign indicates downward motion.

P9.63. Prepare: Choose the system to be cannon + ball. There are no significant external horizontal forces during the brief interval in which the cannon fires, so within the impulse approximation the horizontal momentum is conserved. We'll ignore the very small mass loss of the exploding gunpowder. The statement that the ball travels at 200 m/s relative to the cannon can be written $(v_{Bx})_f = (v_{Cx})_f + 200 \text{ m/s}$. That is, the ball's speed is 200 m/s more than the cannon's speed.

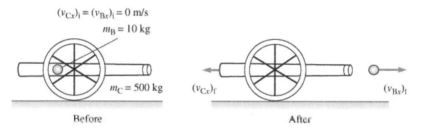

Solve: The initial momentum is zero, so the conservation of momentum equation $(p_x)_f = (p_x)_i$ is

$$(p_x)_f = m_C(v_{Cx})_f + m_B(v_{Bx})_f = m_C(v_{Cx})_f + m_B((v_{Cx})_f + 200 \text{ m/s}) = 0 \text{ kg m/s}$$

$$\Rightarrow (v_{Cx})_f = \frac{m_B}{m_C + m_B}(200 \text{ m/s}) = -\frac{10 \text{ kg}}{510 \text{ kg}}(200 \text{ m/s}) = -3.9 \text{ m/s}$$

That is, the cannon recoils to the left (negative sign) at 3.9 m/s. Thus the cannonball's speed relative to the ground is $(v_{Bx})_f = -3.9 \text{ m/s} + 200 \text{ m/s} = 196 \text{ m/s}$.

Assess: An expected relatively small recoil speed is essentially due to the large mass of the cannon.

P9.65. Prepare: This is an isolated system, so momentum is conserved in the explosion. Momentum is a *vector* quantity, so the direction of the initial velocity vector $\vec{v}_1$ establishes the direction of the momentum vector. The final momentum vector, after the explosion, must still point in the +x-direction. The two known pieces continue to move along this line and have no y-components of momentum. The missing third piece cannot have a y-component of momentum if momentum is to be conserved, so it must move along the x-axis–either straight forward or straight backward. From the conservation of mass, the mass of piece 3 is $m_3 = m_{total} - m_1 - m_2 = 7.0 \times 10^5 \text{ kg}$.

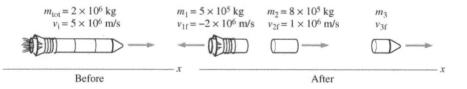

Solve: To conserve momentum along the x-axis, we require

$$[p_i = m_{total}v_i] = [p_f = p_{1f} + p_{2f} + p_{3f} = m_1v_{1f} + m_2v_{2f} + p_{3f}] \Rightarrow p_{3f} = m_{total}v_i - m_1v_{1f} - m_2v_{2f} = +1.02 \times 10^{13} \text{ kg m/s}$$

Because $p_{3f} > 0$, the third piece moves in the $+x$-direction, that is, straight forward. Because we know the mass m_3, we can find the velocity of the third piece as follows:

$$v_{3f} = \frac{p_{3f}}{m_3} = \frac{1.02 \times 10^{13} \text{ kg m/s}}{7.0 \times 10^5 \text{ kg}} = 1.5 \times 10^7 \text{ m/s}$$

Assess: Since this event is taking place in outer space, we don't have to worry about any external forces, and naturally the total momentum has to be constant regardless of the direction.

P9.67. Prepare: Model the three balls of clay as particle 1 (moving north), particle 2 (moving west), and particle 3 (moving southeast). The three stick together during their collision, which is perfectly inelastic. The momentum of the system is conserved. All the three masses and the three velocities before the collision are known; it is thus easy to find the speed and the direction of the resulting blob using momentum conservation equations in two dimensions.

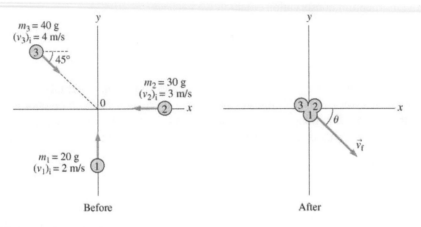

Before   After

Solve: The three initial momenta are

$$(\vec{p}_1)_i = m_1(\vec{v}_1)_i = (0.02 \text{ kg})(2 \text{ m/s}) \text{ along} + x = (0.04 \text{ kg m/s, along} + x)$$
$$(\vec{p}_2)_i = m_2(\vec{v}_2)_i = (0.03 \text{ kg})(3 \text{ m/s}) \text{ along} - x = (0.09 \text{ kg m/s, along} - x)$$
$$(\vec{p}_3)_i = m_3(\vec{v}_3)_i = [(0.04 \text{ kg})(4 \text{ m/s})\cos45°, \text{ along} + x] + [(0.04 \text{ kg})(4 \text{ m/s})\sin45°, \text{ along} - x]$$
$$= (0.113 \text{ kg m/s, along} + x) + (0.113 \text{ kg m/s, along} - x)$$

Since $\vec{p}_f = \vec{p}_i = (\vec{p}_1)_i + (\vec{p}_2)_i + (\vec{p}_3)_i$, we have

$$(m_1 + m_2 + m_3)\vec{v}_f = (0.023 \text{ kg m/s, along} + x) + (0.073 \text{ kg m/s, along} - x)$$
$$\Rightarrow \vec{v}_f = (0.256 \text{ m/s, along} + x) + (-0.811 \text{ m/s, along} + x)$$
$$\Rightarrow v_f = \sqrt{(0.256 \text{ m/s})^2 + (-0.811 \text{ m/s})^2} = 0.85 \text{ m/s}$$
$$\theta = \tan^{-1}\frac{|v_{fy}|}{v_{fx}} = \tan^{-1}\frac{0.811}{0.256} = 73° \text{ below} + x$$

Assess: The final speed is of the same order of magnitude as the initial speeds, as one would expect.

P9.69. Prepare: Because there's no friction or other tangential forces, the angular momentum of the block + rod system is conserved. The rod is massless, so the angular momentum is entirely that of a mass in circular motion.

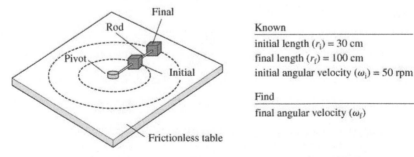

Known	
initial length (r_i) = 30 cm	
final length (r_f) = 100 cm	
initial angular velocity (ω_i) = 50 rpm	

Find	
final angular velocity (ω_f)	

Solve: The conservation of angular momentum equation $L_f = L_i$ is

$$mv_f r_f = mv_i r_i \Rightarrow (r_f \omega_f) r_f = (r_i \omega_i) r_i \Rightarrow \omega_f = \left(\frac{r_i}{r_f}\right)^2 \omega_i = \left(\frac{30 \text{ cm}}{100 \text{ cm}}\right)^2 (50 \text{ rpm}) = 4.5 \text{ rpm}$$

Assess: An angular speed of 4.5 rpm is reasonable, since the angular speed varies inversely as the square of the object's distance from the rotation axis.

P9.71. Prepare: Model the puck and the 200 g weights as particles. The puck is in circular motion and the forces acting on the puck are its weight downward, the radial tension in the string, and a normal force upward. There is no tangential force acting on the puck, and thus the angular momentum of the puck is conserved. For the puck to move in a circle, the force causing the centripetal acceleration is provided by the two 200 g weights.

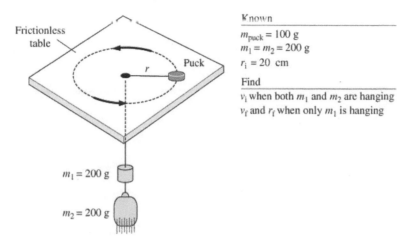

Frictionless table

Puck

Known
$m_{puck} = 100$ g
$m_1 = m_2 = 200$ g
$r_i = 20$ cm

Find
v_i when both m_1 and m_2 are hanging
v_f and r_f when only m_1 is hanging

$m_1 = 200$ g

$m_2 = 200$ g

Solve: (a) Equating the two weights with the centripetal force

$$(0.40 \text{ kg})(9.8 \text{ m/s}^2) = m_{puck} \frac{v_i^2}{r_i} = (0.010 \text{ kg}) \frac{v_i^2}{(0.020 \text{ m})} \Rightarrow v_i = 2.8 \text{ m/s}$$

(b) The conservation of angular momentum equation $L_f = L_i$ implies

$$m_{puck} v_f r_f = m_{puck} v_i r_i \Rightarrow v_f r_f = v_i r_i = (2.8 \text{ m/s})(0.20 \text{ m}) = 0.56 \text{ m}^2/\text{s}$$

Now for the new weight to cause circular motion

$$\frac{m_{puck} v_f^2}{r_f} = (0.20 \text{ kg})(9.8 \text{ m/s}^2) \Rightarrow r_f = \frac{m_{puck} v_f^2}{1.96 \text{ kg m/s}^2} = \frac{v_f^2}{19.6 \text{ m/s}^2}$$

Substituting this expression into the conservation of angular momentum equation, we have

$$v_f \left(\frac{v_f^2}{19.6 \text{ m/s}^2}\right) = 0.56 \text{ m}^2/\text{s} \Rightarrow v_f^3 = 10.976 \text{ m}^3/\text{s}^3 \Rightarrow v_f = 2.22 \text{ m/s} = 2.2 \text{ m/s}$$

Now we can obtain r_f from the previous equation as

$$r_f = \frac{v_f^2}{19.6 \text{ m/s}^2} = \frac{(2.22 \text{ m/s})^2}{19.6 \text{ m/s}^2} = 0.252 \text{ m} = 25 \text{ cm}$$

Assess: As expected, reduced weight decreases tension in the string, which implies a little lower speed and a little larger radius of trajectory.

P9.73. Prepare: Since there are no external torques, we can use the conservation of angular momentum to solve this problem. We need to use the moment of inertia of a rotating disk: $I_{disk} = \frac{1}{2} MR^2$ in order to write the final angular momentum of the merry-go-round: $(L_m)_f = I_{disk} \omega_f$. The final angular momentum of Joey is given by $(L_J)_f = m(v_J)_f R$.

Solve: Before Joey begins running, both he and the merry-go-round are at rest, so the total angular momentum is 0. Let us say that he runs counterclockwise so that his final angular momentum is positive. Then the merry-go-round must rotate clockwise so that its final angular momentum is negative. In this way the angular momenta of Joey and the merry-go-round will still add to 0. The equation for conservation of angular momentum is:

$$0 \text{ kg} \cdot \text{m}^2/\text{s} = m(v_{\text{J}})_{\text{f}} R + \left(\frac{1}{2} MR^2 \right) \omega_{\text{f}} \Rightarrow$$

$$0 \text{ kg} \cdot \text{m}^2/\text{s} = (36 \text{ kg})(5.0 \text{ m/s})(2.0 \text{ m}) + \left(\frac{1}{2} \right)(200 \text{ kg})(2.0 \text{ m})^2 \omega_{\text{f}}.$$

This equation can be solved for the angular velocity: $\omega_{\text{f}} = -0.90$ rad/s.

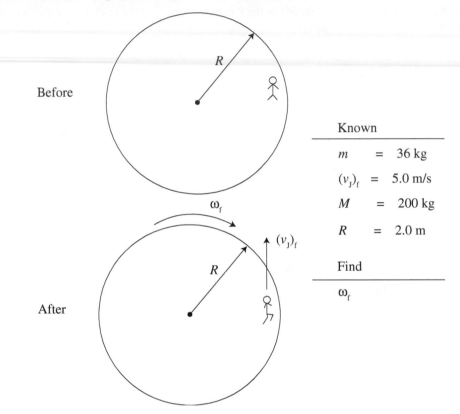

Known		
m	=	36 kg
$(v_{\text{J}})_{\text{f}}$	=	5.0 m/s
M	=	200 kg
R	=	2.0 m

Find

ω_{f}

Assess: The negative sign is as expected considering that the total angular momentum is zero. For this to be true, the two bodies, the merry-go-round and Joey, must move in opposite directions around the axis.

P9.75. Prepare: Define the system to be Disk A plus Disk B so that during the time of the collision there are no net torques on this isolated system. This allows us to use the law of conservation of angular momentum. After the collision the combined object will have a moment of inertia equal to the sum of the moments of inertia of Disk A and Disk B and it will have one common angular speed ω_{f} (which we seek).

We must remember to call counterclockwise angular speeds positive and clockwise angular speeds negative.

Known

$M_{\text{A}} = 2.0$ kg
$R_{\text{A}} = 0.40$ m
$(\omega_{\text{A}})_{\text{i}} = -30$ rev/s
$M_{\text{B}} = 2.0$ kg
$R_{\text{B}} = 0.20$ m
$(\omega_{\text{B}})_{\text{i}} = 30$ rev/s

Find

ω_{f}

Preliminarily compute the moments of inertia of the disks:

$$I_A = \frac{1}{2}M_A R_A^2 = \frac{1}{2}(2.0 \text{ kg})(0.40 \text{ m})^2 = 0.16 \text{ kg} \cdot \text{m}^2$$

$$I_B = \frac{1}{2}M_B R_B^2 = \frac{1}{2}(2.0 \text{ kg})(0.20 \text{ m})^2 = 0.040 \text{ kg} \cdot \text{m}^2$$

Solve:

$$\Sigma L_i = \Sigma L_f$$
$$(L_A)_i + (L_B)_i = (L_{A+B})_f$$
$$I_A(\omega_A)_i + I_B(\omega_B)_i = (I_A + I_B)\omega_f$$

Solving for ω_f gives

$$\omega_f = \frac{I_A(\omega_A)_i + I_B(\omega_B)_i}{I_A + I_B} = \frac{(0.16 \text{ kg} \cdot \text{m}^2)(-30 \text{ rev/s}) + (0.040 \text{ kg} \cdot \text{m}^2)(30 \text{ rev/s})}{0.16 \text{ kg} \cdot \text{m}^2 + 0.040 \text{ kg} \cdot \text{m}^2} = -18 \text{ rev/s}$$

That is, the angular speed is 18 rev/s and the direction is clockwise.

Assess: Since the two disks were rotating in opposite directions at the same speed we expect the angular speed afterwards to be less than the original speeds, and indeed it is.

P9.77. Prepare: In this problem we make all the usual assumptions: that the collision happens quickly enough that we can ignore any net external forces and consider the system (club plus ball) to be isolated.

Solve: Since the system is isolated the momentum of the system is conserved.

The correct choice is B.

Assess: Momentum is conserved in *all* collisions if we make the usual assumptions.

P9.79. Prepare: Because the system is isolated we can use the law of conservation of momentum. We are asked to find $(v_{Cx})_f - (v_{Cx})_i$.

Solve:

$$(P_x)_i = (P_x)_f$$
$$(p_{Cx})_i + (p_{Dx})_i = (p_{Cx})_f + (p_{Bx})_f$$
$$m_C(v_{Cx})_i + m_B(v_{Bx})_i = m_C(v_{Cx})_f + m_B(v_{Bx})_f$$

Rearranging terms allows us to solve for $(v_{Cx})_f - (v_{Cx})_i$:

$$(v_{Cx})_f - (v_{Cx})_i = \frac{m_B[(v_{Bx})_i - (v_{Bx})_f]}{m_C} = \frac{0.0460 \text{ kg}(0.0 \text{ m/s} - 60.0 \text{ m/s})}{0.200 \text{ kg}} = -14 \text{ m/s}$$

The correct choice is C. The negative sign indicates that the club slowed down.

Assess: Examining our equation for $(v_{Cx})_f - (v_{Cx})_i$ confirms that we had a different (and maybe easier) approach from the very beginning. If the momentum is conserved for a two-body system, then the change in momentum of the club must be equal in magnitude (and opposite in direction) to the change in momentum of the ball. The numerator above is the change in momentum of the ball, so simply dividing by the mass of the club gives the difference in the club's velocity.

10—Energy and Work
Conceptual Questions

Q10.1. Reason: The brakes in a car slow down the car by converting the car's kinetic energy to thermal energy in the brake shoes through friction. Cars have large kinetic energies, and all of that energy is converted to thermal energy in the brake shoes, which causes their temperature to increase greatly. Therefore they must be made of material that can tolerate very high temperatures without being damaged.

Assess: This is an example of an energy conversion. All of the car's kinetic energy is converted to thermal energy through friction. To get an appreciation of how much kinetic energy is absorbed by the brake shoes, consider instead the energy explicit in stopping the car by hitting a stationary object instead!

Q10.3. Reason: We must think of a process that increases an object's kinetic energy without increasing any potential energy. Consider pulling an object across a level floor with a constant force. The force does work on the object, which will increase the object's kinetic energy. Since the floor is level the gravitational potential energy does not change. The other form of potential energy possible is that stored in a spring, which is also zero here.

Assess: For there to be no potential energy change, the object in question must remain at the same height.

Q10.5. Reason: The system must convert kinetic energy directly to potential energy with no external force doing work. For gravitational potential energy we must change the height of the object. One simple example would be rolling a ball up a hill. The initial kinetic energy is converted to gravitational potential energy as the ball increases its height. The ball loses kinetic energy while it gains potential energy. Another example is rolling a ball into an uncompressed spring on level ground. As the ball compresses the spring, the system gains potential energy, while losing kinetic energy. Since there are no forces external to the systems in these examples, no work is done on the systems by the environment.

Assess: As long as no forces external to the system are applied, work done on a system is zero.

Q10.7. Reason: Here we need to convert potential energy to kinetic energy without any work done on the system. Consider dropping a ball from a height. The ball's gravitational energy is converted to the kinetic energy of the ball as it falls. Another example would be releasing a ball at the end of a compressed spring. The potential energy stored in the compressed spring is converted to the kinetic energy of the ball as the spring stretches to its equilibrium length. Since no external forces act on a system, the work on the system is zero.

Assess: Many examples in the problem section will involve just this type of conversion of potential energy to kinetic energy. If no forces from the environment act on a system, the work done on the system is zero.

Q10.9 Reason: We need a process that converts potential energy totally into thermal energy without changing the kinetic energy. Consider a wood block sliding down a rough inclined surface at a constant speed. The gravitational potential energy is decreasing and the kinetic energy is constant. All the decrease in gravitational potential energy becomes an increase in thermal energy.

Assess: Gravitational potential energy decreases because there is a change in height of the block. The kinetic energy does not change because the speed of the block is constant.

Q10.11. Reason: The energies involved here are kinetic energy, gravitational potential energy, elastic potential energy and thermal energy. For the system to be isolated, we must not have any work being done on the system and no heat being transferred into or out of the system. The ball's kinetic and elastic energy is changing, so we should consider it part of the system. Since its gravitational potential energy is changing, we need to also consider the earth as part of the system. Thermal energy will be generated in the ball and floor when the ball hits the floor, so we must consider both to be part of the system. In as much as the earth itself is not an isolated system (heat can leave the earth) we really should consider the universe the system to consider the system completely isolated.

Assess: In order to have an isolated system no heat can leave or enter the system and all forces must be internal.

Q10.13. Reason: (a) The work done is $W = Fd$. Both particles experience the same force, so the greater work is done on the particle that undergoes the greater displacement. Particle A, which is less massive than B, will have the greater acceleration and thus travel further during the 1 s interval. Thus more work is done on particle A.

(b) Impulse is $F\Delta t$. Both particles experience the same force F for the same time interval $\Delta t = 1$ s. Thus the same impulse is delivered to both particles.

(c) Both particles receive the same impulse, so the change in their momenta is the same, that is, $m_A(v_f)_A = m_B(v_f)_B$. But because $m_A < m_B$, it must be that $(v_f)_A > (v_f)_B$. This result can also be found from kinematics, as in part (a).

Assess: Work is the product of the force and the displacement, while impulse is the product of the force and the time during which the force acts.

Q10.15. Reason: Neglecting frictional losses, the work you do on the jack is converted into gravitational potential energy of the car as it is raised. The work you do is Fd, where F is the force you apply to the jack handle and d is the 20 cm distance you move the handle. This work goes into increasing the potential energy by an amount $mgh = wh$, where w is the car's weight and $h = 0.2$ cm is the change in the car's height. So $Fd = wh$ so that $F / w = h / d$.

Assess: Because the force F you can apply is so much less than the weight w of the car, h must be much less than d.

Q10.17. Reason: (a) If the car is to go twice as fast at the bottom, its kinetic energy, proportional to v^2, will be *four times* as great. You thus need to give it four times as much gravitational potential energy at the top. Since gravitational potential energy is linearly proportional to the height h, you'll need to increase the height of the track by a factor of four.

(b) Using considerations of conservation of energy, as in part (a), we see that the speed of the car at the bottom depends only on the height of the track, not its shape.

Assess: Kinetic energy is proportional to the *square* of the velocity.

Q10.19. Reason: Because both rocks are thrown from the same height, they have the same potential energy. And since they are thrown with the same speed, they have the same kinetic energy. Thus both rocks have the same total energy. When they reach the ground, they will have this same total energy. Because they're both at the same height at ground level, their potential energy there is the same. Thus they must have the same kinetic energy, and hence the same speed.

Assess: Although Chris's rock was thrown angled upward, so that it slows as it first rises, it then speeds up as it begins to fall, attaining the same speed as Sandy's as it passes the initial height. Sandy's rock will hit the ground *first*, but its speed will be no greater than Chris's.

Q10.21. Reason: As you land, the force of the ground or pad does negative work on your body, transferring out the kinetic energy you have just before impact. This work is $-Fd$, where d is the distance over which your body stops. With the short stopping distance involved upon hitting the ground, the force F will be much greater than it is with the long stopping distance upon hitting the pad.

Assess: For a given amount of work, the force is large when the displacement is small.

Multiple-Choice Questions

Q10.23. Reason: Work is defined by $W = Fd$ when the force is parallel to the displacement, as it is in this case. Since you and your friend each carry suitcases of the same mass up the same flights of stairs, you both exert the same force on the suitcases over the same vertical distance and therefore do the same amount of work. Your friend takes longer than you to get up the flight of stairs, so you expend a greater amount of power since $P = W/\Delta t$. The correct choice is C.

Assess: For a given amount of work differing amounts of power are expended depending on how quickly the work is done.

Q10.25. Reason: Since kinetic energy is proportional to the square of the velocity of an object, an object with twice the velocity will have four times the amount of kinetic energy. In this question, all the kinetic energy is converted to elastic potential energy in the spring. The potential energy stored in a spring is proportional to the square of the compression from its equilibrium position. Since we start with four times the kinetic energy, four times as much energy is stored in the spring. But since the energy stored in the spring is proportional to the *square* of the compression, the compression is only twice the compression previously, or 2(2.0 cm) = 4.0 cm. The correct choice is C.

Assess: Kinetic energy is proportional to the *square* of the velocity of an object and the potential energy of a spring is proportional to the *square* of the displacement from the equilibrium position.

Q10.27. Reason: As the ball falls, energy is conserved since the only force doing work is the force of gravity. Since gravity is conserved we may write

$$\Delta E = 0$$

or

$$\Delta K + \Delta U_g = 0$$

As the ball falls we have

$$\Delta K = mv^2 / 2 \text{ and } \Delta U_g = -mgh = -mg(L - L\cos30°) = -mgL(1 - \cos30°)$$

Combining these, obtain

$$mv^2 / 2 = mgL(1 - \cos30°)$$

or

$$v = \sqrt{2gL(1-\cos 30°)} = 3.6 \text{ m/s}$$

The correct response is C.

Assess: The key to the problem is to realize that energy is conserved and then find the change in kinetic and potential energy. A speed of 3.6 m/s is reasonable.

Problems

P10.1. Prepare: Since this is an etiquette class and you are walking slowly and steadily, assume the book remains level. We will use the definition of work, Equation 10.9, to explicitly calculate the work done. Since no component of the force is along the displacement of the book, we expect the work done by your head will be zero.

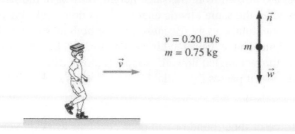

Solve: Refer to the diagram above. There is no force in the horizontal direction since your velocity is constant. Your head exerts a normal force on the book, which counteracts the weight of the book. Since you are walking steadily there is no acceleration in the vertical direction, so the normal force is equal to the weight of the book. The force your head exerts on the book is then

$$n = w = (0.75 \text{ kg})(9.80 \text{ m/s}^2) = 7.4 \text{ N}$$

The work done on the book by your head is

$$W = Fd\cos\theta = (7.4 \text{ N})(2.5 \text{ m})\cos(90°) = (7.4 \text{ N})(2.5 \text{ m})(0) = 0 \text{ J}$$

The work done by your head on the book is exactly 0 Joules.
Assess: As expected, no work is done since the force and the displacement are at right angles. Note that your speed, which is given in the problem statement, is irrelevant.

P10.3. Prepare: Note that not all the forces in this problem are parallel to the displacement. Equation 10.6 gives the work done by a constant force which is not parallel to the displacement: $W = Fd\cos(\theta)$, where W is the work done by the force F at an angle θ to the displacement d. Here the displacement is exactly downwards in the same direction as $\vec{w}$. We will take all forces as having four significant figures (as implied by $T_2 = 1295 \text{ N}$).

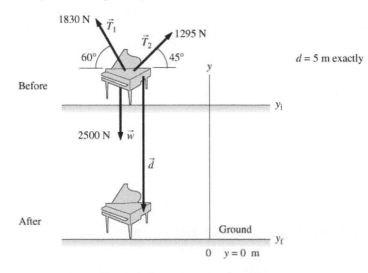

Solve: Refer to the diagram above. The angle between the force $\vec{w}$ and the displacement is 0°, so

$$W_{\vec{w}} = wd\cos\theta = (2500 \text{ N})(5 \text{ m})\cos(0°) = 12.50 \text{ kJ}.$$

The angle between the force $\vec{T}_1$ and the displacement is $90° + 60° = 150°$.

$$W_{\vec{T}_1} = T_1 d\cos\theta = (1830 \text{ N})(5 \text{ m})\cos(150°) = -7.924 \text{ kJ}$$

The angle between the tension $\vec{T}_2$ and the displacement is $90° + 45° = 135°$.

$$W_{\vec{T}_2} = T_2 d\cos\theta = (1295 \text{ N})(5 \text{ m})\cos(135°) = -4.579 \text{ kJ}$$

Assess: Note that the displacement d in all the above cases is directed downwards and that it is always the angle between the force and displacement used in the work equation. For example, the angle between $\vec{T}_1$ and $\vec{d}$ is 150°, not 60°.

P10.5. Prepare: We will use the definition of work, Equation 10.6 to calculate the work done. The sidewalk and escalators exert a normal force on you, and may exert a force to propel you forward. We will assume that the escalator propels you at constant velocity, as the sidewalk does.

  Solve: (a) Since you get on the sidewalk moving at 0.70 m/s, and you continue at 0.70 m/s afterwards, there is no acceleration and therefore no force on you in the horizontal direction. See the diagram below.

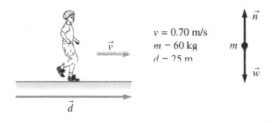

The work is then $W = Fd\cos\theta = (F)(d)\cos(90°) = (F)(d)(0) = 0$ J. The work done by the sidewalk is exactly zero Joules.

  (b) The escalator moves you across some distance like the sidewalk, but it also moves you upwards. See the diagram below.

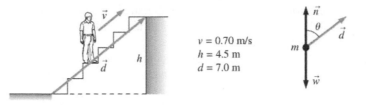

The force exerted on you by the escalator is the normal force, which is equal to your weight.

$$n = w = mg = (60 \text{ kg})(9.80 \text{ m/s}^2) = 588 \text{ N}$$

which should be reported as 590 N to two significant figures.

  Unlike the sidewalk case, there is a component of the displacement parallel to the normal force. The angle between the force and displacement is $\cos^{-1}(4.5/7) = 50°$, so $d\cos(\theta) = 4.5$ m. Then

$$W = Fd\cos\theta = (588 \text{ N})(4.5 \text{ m}) = 2.6 \text{ kJ}$$

  (c) Refer to the figure below.

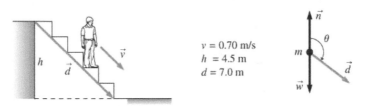

Here, the displacement is in the opposite direction compared to part **(b)**, so the angle between the force and the displacement is now $180° - 50° = 130°$. So

$$W = Fd\cos\theta = (588 \text{ N})(7.0 \text{ m})\cos(130°) = -2.6 \text{ kJ}$$

  Assess: In part (a), since the force has no component in the direction of your displacement, the force does no work. In part (b), there is a component of the force along and in the same direction as the displacement, so the force does positive work. In part (c), the component of the force along the displacement is in the opposite direction to the displacement, so the force does negative work.

P10.7. Prepare: The kinetic energy for any object moving of mass m with velocity v is given in Equation 10.8: $K = \frac{1}{2}mv^2$.

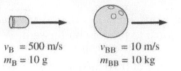

$v_B = 500$ m/s
$m_B = 10$ g

$v_{BB} = 10$ m/s
$m_{BB} = 10$ kg

Solve: For the bullet,

$$K_B = \frac{1}{2}m_B v_B^2 = \frac{1}{2}(0.010 \text{ kg})(500 \text{ m/s})^2 = 1.3 \text{ kJ}$$

For the bowling ball,

$$K_{BB} = \frac{1}{2}m_{BB}v_{BB}^2 = \frac{1}{2}(10 \text{ kg})(10 \text{ m/s})^2 = 0.50 \text{ kJ}$$

Thus, the bullet has the larger kinetic energy.

Assess: Kinetic energy depends not only on mass but also on the square of the velocity. The above calculation shows this dependence. Although the mass of the bullet is 1000 times smaller than the mass of the bowling ball, its speed is 50 times larger, which leads to the bullet having over twice the kinetic energy of the bowling ball.

P10.9. Prepare: In order to work this problem, we need to know that the kinetic energy of an object is given by $K = mv^2 / 2$.

Solve: The problem may be solved in a qualitative manner or in a quantitative manner. Since some students think one way and some the other, we will use both methods.

(a) First, in a qualitative manner. Since the kinetic energy depends on the square of the speed, The kinetic energy will be doubled if the speed is increases by a factor of $\sqrt{2}$. This is true because $(\sqrt{2})^2 = 2$. Then the new speed is $\sqrt{2}$ (10 m/s) = 14 m/s.

Second, in a more quantitive manner. Use a subscript 1 for the present case where the speed is 10 m/s and a subscript 2 for the new case where the speed is such that the kinetic energy is doubled.

$$K_1 = mv_1^2 / 2 \quad \text{and} \quad K_2 = mv_2^2 / 2$$

We want

$$K_2 = 2K_1$$

Inserting expressions for K_1 and K_2, obtain

$$\frac{mv_2^2}{2} = 2\frac{mv_1^2}{2} \quad \text{or} \quad v_2 = \sqrt{2}v_1 = 14 \text{ m/s}$$

(b) First, in a qualitative manner. If the speed is doubled and the kinetic energy depends on the square of the speed, the kinetic energy will increase by a factor of 4.

Second, in a more quantitative manner. Use a subscript 1 for the present case and a subscript 2 for the new case where the speed is doubled.

$$K_1 = mv_1^2 / 2 \quad \text{and} \quad K_2 = mv_2^2 / 2$$

We want $v_2 = 2v_1$. Inserting v_2 into K_2, we obtain

$$K_2 = \frac{mv_2^2}{2} = \frac{m(2v_1)^2}{2} = 4\left(\frac{mv_1^2}{2}\right) = 4K_1$$

The above expression clearly shows that the kinetic energy is increased by a factor of four when the speed is doubled.

Assess: The key to the problem is to know that the kinetic energy depends on the speed squared. After that, we can approach the problem in a qualitative or a quantitative manner. You may prefer one method over the other, but you should be able to work in either mode.

P10.11. Prepare: Use the law of conservation of energy, Equation 10.4, to find the work done on the particle. We will assume there is no change in thermal energy of the ball.

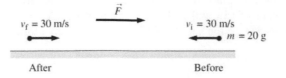

After   Before

Solve: Consider the system to be the plastic ball. Since there is no change in potential, thermal or chemical energy of the ball and there is no heat leaving or entering the system, the conservation of energy equation becomes

$$W = \Delta K = \frac{1}{2}mv_f^2 - \frac{1}{2}mv_i^2 = \frac{1}{2}m(v_f^2 - v_i^2) = \frac{1}{2}(0.020 \text{ kg})[(30 \text{ m/s})^2 - (-30 \text{ m/s})^2] = 0 \text{ J}$$

Assess: Note that no work is done on the ball in reversing its velocity. This is because negative work is done in slowing the ball down to rest, and an equal amount of positive work is done in bringing the ball to the original speed but in the opposite direction.

P10.13. Prepare: Energy is stored in the flywheel by virtue of the motion of the particles and is given by Equation 10.9. In this equation, units for rotational velocity must be rad/s.
   Solve: Using Equation 10.92,

$$K_{rot} = \frac{1}{2}I\omega^2, \text{ so } I = \frac{2K_{rot}}{\omega^2}$$

We need to convert $\dot{\omega}$ to proper units, radians/second. Since $\omega = 20{,}000$ revolutions/minute and there are 2π radians/revolution and 60 seconds in a minute,

$$\omega = \left(20{,}000 \frac{\text{rev}}{\text{min}}\right)\left(\frac{1 \text{ min}}{60 \text{ s}}\right)\left(\frac{2\pi \text{ rad}}{\text{rev}}\right)$$

So

$$I = \frac{(2)(4.0 \times 10^6 \text{ J})}{\left[\left(20{,}000 \frac{\text{rev}}{\text{min}}\right)\left(\frac{1 \text{ min}}{60 \text{ s}}\right)\left(\frac{2\pi \text{ rad}}{\text{rev}}\right)\right]^2} = 1.8 \text{ kg m}^2$$

   Assess: The flywheel can store this large amount of energy even though it has a low moment of inertia because of its high rate of rotation.

P10.15. Prepare: In part **(a)** we can simply use the definition of kinetic energy in Equation 10.8. We then use this result in part **(b)** to find the height the car must be dropped from to obtain the same kinetic energy. The car is falling under the influence of gravity. We can use conservation of energy to calculate its kinetic energy as a result of the fall. The sum of kinetic and potential energy does not change as the car falls.
   Solve: (a) The kinetic energy of the car is

$$K_C = \frac{1}{2}m_C v_C^2 = \frac{1}{2}(1500 \text{ kg})(30 \text{ m/s})^2 = 6.75 \times 10^5 \text{ J}$$

We keep one additional significant figure here for use in part **(b)**.
   (b) Refer to the diagram below.

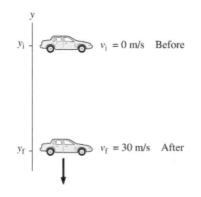

Here we set K_f equal to K_C in part **(a)** and place our coordinate system on the ground at $y_f = 0$ m. At this point, the car's potential energy $(U_g)_f$ is zero, its velocity is v_f, and its kinetic energy is K_f. At position y_i, $v_i = 0$ m/s, so $K_i = 0$ J, and the only energy the car has is $(U_g)_i = mgy_i$. Since the sum $K_f + U_g$ is unchanged by motion, $K_f + (U_g)_f = K_i + (U_g)_i$. This means

$$K_f + mgy_f = K_i + mgy_i \Rightarrow K_f + 0 = K_i + mgy_i$$

$$\Rightarrow y_i = \frac{(K_f - K_i)}{mg} = \frac{(6.75 \times 10^5 \text{ J} - 0 \text{ J})}{(1500 \text{ kg})(9.80 \text{ m/s}^2)} = 46 \text{ m}$$

To check if this result depends on the car's mass, rewrite the result of part **(b)** leaving m as a variable, and check if it cancels out.

$$y_i = \frac{(K_f - K_i)}{mg} = \frac{\frac{1}{2}mv_f^2 - \frac{1}{2}mv_i^2}{mg} - \frac{(v_f^2 - v_i^2)}{2g}$$

Since m cancels out, the distance does *not* depend upon the mass.

Assess: A car traveling at 30 m/s is traveling at 108 km/hr or 67 mi/hr. At that speed, it has the same amount of energy as from being dropped 46 m, which is 151 ft, or from the top of an approximately 19-story building!

P10.17. Prepare: In this case the bike racer will increase his gravitational potential energy by an amount $\Delta U_g = mgh$, where h is the change in his vertical position.

Solve: The change in the bike racers gravitation potential energy as he executes the climb is

$$\Delta U_g = mgh = mgd \sin 4.3° = 63 \text{ kJ}$$

Assess: The bike racer would increase his gravitational potential energy this same about by climbing up a flight of stairs that increased his vertical position by 90 m. This allows one to conclude that stair climbing is excellent exercise.

P10 19. Prepare: Assume an ideal spring that obeys Hooke's law. Equation 10.15 gives the energy stored in a spring. The elastic potential energy of a spring is defined as $U_s = \frac{1}{2}kx^2$, where x is the magnitude of the stretching or compression relative to the unstretched or uncompressed length. $\Delta U_s = 0$ when the spring is at its equilibrium length and $x = 0$.

Solve: We have $U_s = 200$ J and $k = 1000$ N/m. Solving for x:

$$x = \sqrt{2U_s / k} = \sqrt{2(200 \text{ J}) / (100 \text{ N/m})} = 0.632 \text{ m}$$

Assess: In the equation for the elastic potential energy stored in a spring, it is always the distance of the stretching of compression relative to the *unstretched* or *equilibrium* length.

P10.21. Prepare: We will assume the knee extensor tendon behaves according to Hooke's law and stretches in a straight line. The elastic energy stored in a spring is given by Equation 10.15, $U_s = \frac{1}{2}kx^2$.

Solve: For athletes,

$$U_{s,\text{athlete}} = \frac{1}{2}kx^2 = \frac{1}{2}(33,000 \text{ N/m})(0.041 \text{ m})^2 = 27.7 \text{ J}$$

For non-athletes,

$$U_{s,\text{non-athlete}} = \frac{1}{2}kx^2 = \frac{1}{2}(33,000 \text{ N/m})(0.033 \text{ m})^2 = 18.0 \text{ J}$$

The difference in energy stored between athletes and non-athletes is therefore 9.7 J.

Assess: Notice the energy stored by athletes is over 1.5 times the energy stored by non-athletes.

P10.23. Prepare: Since the gravitational potential energy and the kinetic energy of the car do not change, all the work Mark does on the car goes into thermal energy.

Solve: The thermal energy created in the tires and the road may be determined by:

$$\Delta E_{th} = W_{Mark} = F_{Mark}d\cos 0° = (110 \text{ N})(150 \text{ } m)\cos 0° = 473 \text{ J}$$

Assess: All the work Mark does in pushing the car, becomes thermal energy of the tires and road. Since Mark is pushing in the direction the car is moving, the angle between the direction of F and d is 50°.

P10.25. Reason: The force of gravity and the force of friction are doing work on the child. Since the child slides at a constant speed, the net work (which is the change in kinetic energy) is zero. This allows us to write:

$$W_g + W_f = \Delta K = 0 \quad \text{or} \quad W_f = -W_g$$

Knowing how the work done by gravity is related to the change in gravitational potential energy and how the work done by friction is related to the force of friction, we can determine the force of friction.

Solve: Writing expressions for the work done by friction, obtain

$$W_f = -W_g = -(-\Delta U_g) = \Delta U_g = Mgh \quad \text{and} \quad W_f = F_f L\cos 180° = -F_f L$$

Combining these and solving for the force of friction, obtain

$$F_f = -Mgh / L = -(25 \text{ kg})(9.8 \text{ m/s}^2)(3.0 \text{ m}) / (7.0 \text{ m}) = -1.0 \times 10^2 \text{ N}$$

The minus reminds us that the force of friction opposes the motion of the object.

Assess: A100 N force of friction for a child sliding down a playground slide is a reasonable number.

P10.27. Prepare: The only force acting on the ball during its trip is gravity. The sum of the kinetic and gravitational potential energy for the ball, considered as a particle, does not change during its motion. Use Equation 10.4. Note that at the top of its trajectory when the ball turns around, the velocity of the ball is zero. Assume there is no friction.

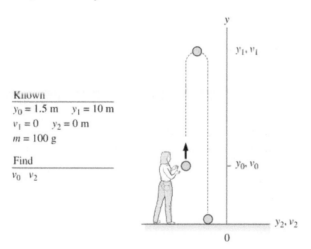

Known
$y_0 = 1.5$ m $y_1 = 10$ m
$v_1 = 0$ $y_2 = 0$ m
$m = 100$ g

Find

v_0 v_2

The figure shows the ball's before-and-after pictorial representation for the two situations described in parts (a) and (b).

Solve: Since energy is conserved, the quantity $K + U_g$ is the same during the entire trip. Thus, $K_f + U_{gf} = K_i + U_{gi}$.

(a) $\frac{1}{2}mv_1^2 + mgy_1 = \frac{1}{2}mv_0^2 + mgy_0 \Rightarrow v_0^2 = v_1^2 + 2g(y_1 - y_0)$

$\Rightarrow v_0^2 = (0 \text{ m/s})^2 + 2(9.80 \text{ m/s}^2)(10 \text{ m} - 1.5 \text{ m}) = 167 \text{ m}^2/\text{s}^2 \Rightarrow v_0 = 13 \text{ m/s}$

(b) $\frac{1}{2}mv_2^2 + mgy_2 = \frac{1}{2}mv_0^2 + mgy_0 \Rightarrow v_2^2 = v_0^2 + 2g(y_0 - y_2)$

$\Rightarrow v_2^2 = 167 \text{ m}^2/\text{s}^2 + 2(9.80 \text{ m/s}^2)(1.5 \text{ m} - 0 \text{ m}) \Rightarrow v_2 = 14 \text{ m/s}$

Assess: An increase in speed from 13 m/s to 14 m/s as the ball falls through a distance of 1.5 m is reasonable. Also, note that mass does not appear in the calculations that involve free fall since both gravitational potential energy and kinetic energy are proportional to mass. The mass cancels out in the equations.

P10.29. Prepare: The figure below shows a before-and-after pictorial representation of the rolling car. The car starts at rest from the top of the hill since it slips out of gear. Since we are ignoring friction, energy is conserved. The total energy of the car at the top of the hill is equal to total energy of the car at any other point.

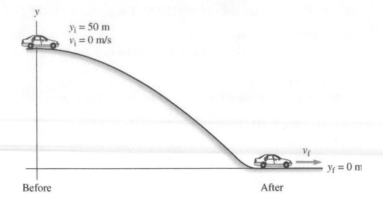

Solve: The energy conservation equation then becomes

$$K_i + (U_g)_i = K_f + (U_g)_f$$

or

$$\frac{1}{2}mv_i^2 + mgy_i = \frac{1}{2}mv_f^2 + mgy_f$$

Since the car starts from rest, so $v_i = 0$ m/s, which gives $K_i = 0$ J. Taking the bottom of the hill as the reference point for gravitational potential, $y_f = 0$ m, and so $U_f = 0$ J. The energy conservation equation becomes

$$\frac{1}{2}mv_f^2 = mgy_i$$

Canceling m and solving for v_f,

$$v_f = \sqrt{2gy_i} = \sqrt{(2)(9.80 \text{ m/s}^2)(50 \text{ m})} = 31 \text{ m/s}$$

Assess: Note that the problem does not give the shape of the hill, so the acceleration of the car is not necessarily constant. Constant acceleration kinematics can't be used to find the car's final speed. However, energy is conserved no matter what the shape of the hill. Note that the mass of the car is not needed. Since kinetic energy and gravitational potential energy are both proportional to mass, the mass cancels out in the equation. The final speed of the car, after traveling to the bottom of the 50 m hill is 31 m/s which is nearly 70 mi/hr!

P10.31. Prepare: Consider the spring as an ideal spring that obeys Hooke's law. We will also assume zero rolling friction during the compression of the spring, so that mechanical energy is conserved. At the maximum compression of the spring, 60 cm, the velocity of the cart will be zero.

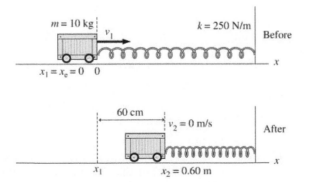

The figure shows a before-and-after pictorial representation. The "before" situation is when the cart hits the spring in its equilibrium position. We put the origin of our coordinate system at this equilibrium position of the free end of the spring. This give $x_1 = x_e = 0$ and $x_2 = 60$ cm.

Solve: The conservation of energy equation $K_2 + U_{s2} = K_1 + U_{s1}$ is

$$\frac{1}{2}mv_2^2 + \frac{1}{2}kx_2^2 = \frac{1}{2}mv_1^2 + \frac{1}{2}kx_1^2$$

Using $v_2 = 0$ m/s, $x_2 = 0.60$ m, and $x_1 = 0$ m gives:

$$\frac{1}{2}kx_2^2 = \frac{1}{2}mv_1^2 \Rightarrow v_1 = \left(\sqrt{\frac{k}{m}}\right)x_2 = \left(\sqrt{\frac{250 \text{ N/m}}{10 \text{ kg}}}\right)(0.60 \text{ m}) = 3.0 \text{ m/s}$$

Assess: Elastic potential energy is always measured from the unstretched or uncompressed length of the spring.

P10.33. Prepare: This is a case of free fall, so the sum of the kinetic and gravitational potential energy does not change as the rock is thrown. Assume there is no friction. The direction the rock is thrown is not known.

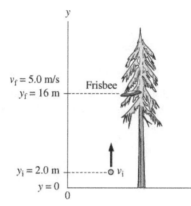

The coordinate system is put on the ground for this system, so that $y_f = 16$ m. The rock's final velocity v_f must be at least 5.0 m/s to dislodge the Frisbee.

Solve: (a) The energy conservation equation for the rock $K_f + U_{gf} + K_i + U_{gi}$ is

$$\frac{1}{2}mv_f^2 + mgy_f = \frac{1}{2}mv_i^2 + mgy_i$$

This equation involves only the velocity magnitudes and not the angle at which the rock is to be thrown to dislodge the Frisbee. This equation is true for all angles that will take the rock to the Frisbee 16 m above the ground and moving with a speed of 5.0 m/s.

(b) Using the above equation we get

$$v_f^2 + 2gy_f = v_i^2 + 2gy_i \quad v_i = \sqrt{v_f^2 + 2g(y_f - y_i)} = \sqrt{(5.0 \text{ m/s})^2 + 2(9.80 \text{ m/s}^2)(16 \text{ m} - 2.0 \text{ m})} = 17 \text{ m/s}$$

Assess: Kinetic energy is defined as $K = \frac{1}{2}mv^2$ and is a scalar quantity. Scalar quantities do not have directional properties. Note also that the mass of the rock is not needed.

P10.35. Prepare: The thermal energy of the slide and the child's pants changes during the slide. If we consider the system to be the child and slide, total energy is conserved during the slide. The energy transformations during the slide are governed by the conservation of energy equation, Equation 10.4.

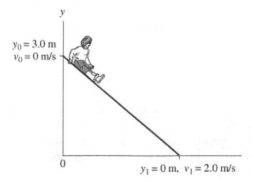

Solve: (a) The child's kinetic and gravitational potential energy will be changing during the slide. There is no heat entering or leaving the system, and no external work done on the child. There is a possible change in the thermal energy of the slide and seat of the child's pants. Use the ground as reference for calculating gravitational potential energy.

$$K_i = K_0 = \frac{1}{2}mv_0^2 = 0 \text{ J} \quad U_i = U_{g0} = mgy_0 = (20 \text{ kg})(9.80 \text{ m/s}^2)(3.0 \text{ m}) = 590 \text{ J}$$

$$W = 0 \text{ J} \quad K_f = K_1 = \frac{1}{2}mv_1^2 = \frac{1}{2}(20 \text{ kg})(2.0 \text{ m/s})^2 = 40 \text{ J} \quad U_f = U_{g1} = mgy_1 = 0 \text{ J}$$

At the top of the slide, the child has gravitational potential energy of 590 J. This energy is transformed partly into the kinetic energy of the child at the bottom of the slide. Note that the final kinetic energy of the child is only 40 J, much less than the initial gravitational potential energy of 590 J. The remainder is the change in thermal energy of the child's pants and the slide.

(b) The energy conservation equation becomes $\Delta K + \Delta U_g + \Delta E_{th} = 0$. With $\Delta U_g = -590$ J and $\Delta K = 40$ J, the change in the thermal energy of the slide and of the child's pants is then 590 J − 40 J = 550 J.

Assess: Note that most of the gravitational potential energy is converted to thermal energy, and only a small amount is available to be converted to kinetic energy.

P10.37. Prepare: This is a one-dimensional collision that obeys the conservation laws of momentum. Since the collision is perfectly elastic, mechanical energy is also conserved. Equation 10.20 applies to perfectly elastic collisions.

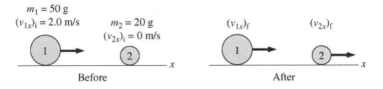

Solve: Using Equation 10.20,

$$(v_{1x})_f = \frac{m_1 - m_2}{m_1 + m_2}(v_{1x})_i = \frac{50 \text{ g} - 20 \text{ g}}{50 \text{ g} + 20 \text{ g}}(2.0 \text{ m/s}) = 0.86 \text{ m/s}$$

$$(v_{1x})_f = \frac{2m_1}{m_1 + m_2}(v_{1x})_i = \frac{2(50 \text{ g})}{50 \text{ g} + 20 \text{ g}}(2.0 \text{ m/s}) = 2.9 \text{ m/s}$$

Assess: These velocities are of a reasonable magnitude. Since both these velocities are positive, both balls move along the positive x direction. This makes sense since ball 1 is more massive than ball 2 and ball 2 is initially at rest.

P10.39. Reason: For a perfectly inelastic collision, the two collision objects stick together after the collision and energy is not conserved. Since we are given no information about outside forces acting during the collision, we will assume there are none and that momentum is conserved. Knowing these two pieces of information we can solve the problem.

Solve: Conserving momentum we obtain the velocity of the compound object: $mv = 2mV$ or $V = v / 2$. The initial kinetic energy (the kinetic energy of the incident glider) is

$$K_i = mv^2 / 2$$

The final kinetic energy (the kinetic energy of the combined two gliders) is

$$K_f = (2m)V^2 / 2 = (2m)(v / 2)^2 / 2 = mv^2 / 4$$

The final kinetic energy is some fraction of the initial kinetic energy, or $K_f = fK_i$.
Solving for the fraction f, obtain

$$f = \frac{K_f}{K_i} = \frac{(mv^2 / 4)}{(mv^2 / 2)} = \frac{1}{2}$$

Knowing that the final kinetic energy is one-half the initial kinetic energy, we may conclude that one-half the first gliders kinetic energy is transformed into thermal energy during the collision.

Assess: After a quick first glance at this problem, one might conclude that nothing is given and that the problem can not be solved. After thinking about the concepts involved, the problem can be solved and a numerical value obtained even though no values are given.

P10.41. Prepare: We can use the definition of work, Equation 10.5 to calculate the work you do in pushing the block. The displacement is parallel to the force, so we can use $W = Fd$. Since the block is moving at a steady speed, the force you exert must be exactly equal and opposite to the force of friction.

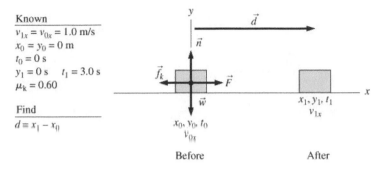

Solve: (a) The work done on the block is $W = Fd$ where d is the displacement. We will find the displacement using kinematic equations. The displacement in the x-direction is

$$d = (1.0 \text{ m/s})(3.0 \text{ s}) = 3.0 \text{ m}$$

We will find the force using Newton's second law of motion. Consider the diagram above. The equations for Newton's second law along the x and y components are

$$(F)_y = n - w = 0 \text{ N} \Rightarrow n = w = mg = (10 \text{ kg})(9.80 \text{ m/s}^2) = 98.0 \text{ N}$$
$$(F)_x = \vec{F} - \vec{f}_k = 0 \text{ N} \Rightarrow F = f_k = \mu_k n = (0.60)(98 \text{ N}) = 58.8 \text{ N}$$
$$\Rightarrow W = Fd = (58.8 \text{ N})(3.0 \text{ m}) = 176 \text{ J, which should be reported as } 1.8 \times 10^2 \text{ J to two significant figures.}$$

An extra significant figure has been kept in intermediate calculations.
 (b) The power required to do this much work in 3.0 s is

$$P = \frac{W}{t} = \frac{176 \text{ J}}{3.0 \text{ s}} = 59 \text{ W}$$

Assess: This seems like a reasonable amount of power to push a 10 kg block at 1.0 m/s. Note that this power is almost what a standard 60 W lightbulb requires!

P10.43. Prepare: The work done on the car while it is accelerating from rest to the final speed is the change in kinetic energy. Knowing the work done and the time to do this work we can determine the power associated with this work.
 Solve: The change in kinetic energy of the car is

$$W = \Delta K = K_f - K_i = \frac{1}{2}mv_f^2 = \frac{1}{2}(1000 \text{ kg})(30 \text{ m/s})^2 = 4.5 \times 10^5 \text{ J}$$

since the initial kinetic energy is zero.
 The power associated with this work is

$$P = \frac{W}{\Delta t} = \frac{4.5 \times 10^5 \text{ J}}{10 \text{ s}} = 45 \text{ kW}$$

Assess: This is reasonable. In most cars only a small fraction of the work done by the engine goes into propelling the car.

P10.45. Prepare: Neglecting friction, the only horizontal force on the stone is the force exerted by the curler. The work done by this force will be transferred entirely into the stone's kinetic energy. We can use the conservation of energy equation to calculate this work. We will assume the ice is frictionless, that the acceleration of the stone is constant, and that the stone starts from rest.

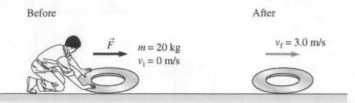

Solve: (a) Refer to the diagram above. We can find the force exerted on the stone by the curler from the acceleration of the stone. Since $v_i = 0$ m/s,

$$a = \frac{v_f - v_i}{\Delta t} = \frac{3.0 \text{ m/s}}{2.0 \text{ s}} = 1.5 \text{ m/s}^2$$

The force on the stone is given by

$$F = ma = (20 \text{ kg})(1.5 \text{ m/s}) = 30 \text{ N}$$

(b) Since , $\Delta E_{th} = \Delta E_{chem} = \Delta U_g = \Delta U_s = 0$ J, in this case, the law of conservation of energy (10.3) reads

$$W = K_f - K_i = \frac{1}{2}mv_f^2 - \frac{1}{2}mv_i^2$$

Since $v_i = 0$ m/s

$$W = \frac{1}{2}mv_f^2 = \left(\frac{1}{2}\right)(20 \text{ kg})(3.0 \text{ m/s})^2 = 90 \text{ J}$$

The average power is given by Equation 10.22,

$$P = \frac{W}{\Delta t} = \frac{90 \text{ J}}{2.0 \text{ s}} = 45 \text{ W}$$

Assess: Note that the amount of muscle power needed to quickly accelerate this relatively heavy stone would not even fully light a 60 W lightbulb.

P10.47. Prepare: The two forces acting on the elevator are its weight and the force $\vec{F}$ due to the motor. Since the elevator is moving with constant velocity, the net force on the elevator is zero.
  Solve: Since the net force on the elevator is zero, $\vec{F} + \vec{w} = \vec{0}$ N. So

$$\vec{F} = -\vec{w} = 2500 \text{ N}$$

The power due to this force acting on the elevator moving with constant velocity can be calculated using Equation 10.23.

$$P = Fv = (2500 \text{ N})(8.0 \text{ m/s}) = 2.0 \times 10^4 \text{ W}$$

Assess: One horsepower (hp) is 746 W, so the power of the motor is 26.8 hp. This is a reasonable amount of power to lift an elevator.

P10.49. Prepare: Assuming that the track offers no rolling friction, the sum of the skateboarder's kinetic and gravitational potential energy does not change during his rolling motion.

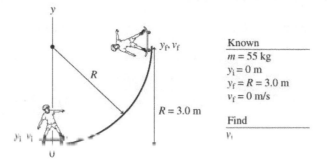

The vertical displacement of the skateboarder is equal to the radius of the track.

Solve: (a) The quantity $K + U_g$ is the same at the upper edge of the quarter-pipe track as it was at the bottom. The energy conservation equation $K_f + U_{gf} = K_i + U_{gi}$ is

$$\frac{1}{2}mv_f^2 + mgy_f = \frac{1}{2}mv_i^2 + mgy_i \Rightarrow v_i^2 = v_f^2 + 2g(y_f - y_i)$$

$$v_i^2 = (0 \text{ m/s})^2 + 2(9.80 \text{ m/s}^2)(3.0 \text{ m} - 0 \text{ m}) = 58.8 \text{ m/s} \Rightarrow v_i = 7.7 \text{ m/s}$$

(b) If the skateboarder is in a low crouch, his height above ground at the beginning of the trip changes to 0.75 m. His height above ground at the top of the pipe remains the same since he is horizontal at that point. Following the same procedure as for part (a),

$$\frac{1}{2}mv_f^2 + mgy_f = \frac{1}{2}mv_i^2 + mgy_i \Rightarrow v_i^2 = v_f^2 + 2g(y_f - y_i)$$

$$v_i^2 = (0 \text{ m/s})^2 + 2(9.80 \text{ m/s}^2)(3.0 \text{ m} - 0.75 \text{ m}) = 44.1 \text{ m/s} \Rightarrow v_i = 6.6 \text{ m/s}$$

Assess: Note that we did not need to know the skateboarder's mass, as is the case with free-fall motion. Note that the shape of the track is irrelevant.

P10.51. Prepare: For the marble sliding around the inside of a smooth pipe, the sum of the kinetic and gravitational potential energy does not change.

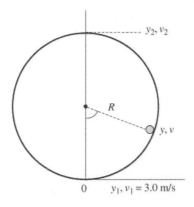

We use a coordinate system with the origin at the bottom of the pipe, that is, $y_1 = 0$. The diameter of the pipe is 20 cm, and therefore $y_{top} = y_2 = 0.20$ m.

Solve: (a) The energy conservation equation $K_2 + U_{g2} = K_1 + U_{g1}$ is

$$\Rightarrow \frac{1}{2}mv_2^2 + mgy_2 = \frac{1}{2}mv_1^2 + mgy_1$$

$$\Rightarrow v_2 = \sqrt{v_1^2 + 2g(y_1 - y_2)} = \sqrt{(3.0 \text{ m/s})^2 + 2(9.8 \text{ m/s}^2)(0 \text{ m} - 0.20 \text{ m}} = 2.3 \text{ m/s}$$

Assess: Beginning with a speed of 3.0 m/s at the bottom, the marble's potential energy increases and kinetic energy decreases as it gets toward the top of the circle. At the top, its speed is 2.3 m/s. This is reasonable since some of the kinetic energy has been transformed into the marble's potential energy.

P10.53. Prepare: We will need to use Newton's laws here along with the definition of work (Equation 10.5). Assume you lift the box with constant speed.

Solve: (a) You lift the box with constant speed so the force you exert must equal the weight of the box. So $F = mg = (20 \text{ kg})(9.80 \text{ m/s}^2) = 196 \text{ N}$. The work done by this force is then

$$W = Fd = (196 \text{ N})(1.0 \text{ m}) = 196 \text{ J},$$ which should be reported as 0.20 kJ to two significant figures.

(b)

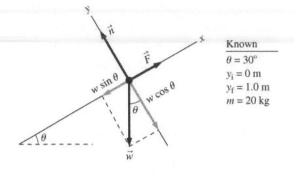

Known
$\theta = 30°$
$y_i = 0 \text{ m}$
$y_f = 1.0 \text{ m}$
$m = 20 \text{ kg}$

Refer to the diagram above. Since the box moves at constant speed, the force that is required to push the box up the ramp must exactly equal the component of the gravitational force along the slope.

$$F = mg \sin(\theta) = (20 \text{ kg})(9.80 \text{ m/s}^2)\sin(30°) = 98 \text{ N}$$

(c) Since the height of the ramp is 1.0 m and the angle of the ramp is 30°, the length of the ramp is the length of the hypotenuse in the diagram above, which is

$$y = L \sin \theta \Rightarrow L = \frac{y}{\sin \theta} = \frac{1.0 \text{ m}}{\sin 30°} = 2.0 \text{ m}$$

(d) We will use the result of parts (b) and (c) here. The force is parallel to the displacement of the block, so we can use Equation 10.5 again. The work done by the force to push the block up the ramp is $W = Fd = (98 \text{ N})(2.0 \text{ m}) = 196 \text{ J}$, which should be reported as 0.20 kJ to two significant figures. This is exactly the same result as part (a), where the block is lifted straight up.

Assess: We could have expected that the answers to parts (d) and (a) would be the same. In both cases, the force we exert opposes gravity. We know that gravitational potential energy depends only on the change in height of an object, and not the exact path the object follows to change its height. Note that the answer doesn't even depend on the shape of the ramp.

P10.55. Prepare: Since the hill is frictionless, mechanical energy will be conserved during the sledder's trip. To make it over the next hill, the sledder's velocity must be greater than or equal to zero at the top of the hill. The minimum velocity the sledder can have at the top of the second hill is 0 m/s to just make it over. The corresponding velocity at the top of the initial hill will be the minimum the sledder needs to just make it over the next hill.

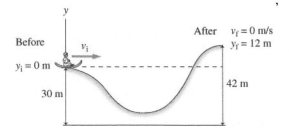

Solve: Consider the before and after pictorial representation above. We will use the sledder's initial height as the reference for gravitational potential energy. Since there is no friction, the conservation of energy equation, Equation 10.4 reads

$$\frac{1}{2}mv_i^2 + mgy_i = \frac{1}{2}mv_f^2 + mgy_f \Rightarrow v_i^2 = 2gy_f$$

$$v_i = \sqrt{2gy_f} = \sqrt{2(9.80 \text{ m/s}^2)(12 \text{ m})} = 15 \text{ m/s}$$

where we have used $y_i = 0$ m, and $v_f = 0$ m/s for the sledder to just make it over the second hill. Note that since we are using the top of the first hill as the reference of gravitational potential energy, we must use the height of the top of the second hill above the first for y_f, $y_f = 42 \text{ m} - 30 \text{ m} = 12 \text{ m}$.

Assess: Note the shape of the hill doesn't matter, only the difference in height between the first and second hill is needed, as expected for gravitational potential energy. Since the second hill is higher than the first, we expect that the sledder needs the additional kinetic energy at the initial hill to make up for the additional potential energy needed at the top of the second hill.

P10.57. Prepare: Assume an ideal spring that obeys Hooke's law. There is no friction, and therefore the mechanical energy $K + U_s + U_g$ is conserved. At the top of the slope, as the ice cube is reversing direction, the velocity of the ice cube is 0 m/s.

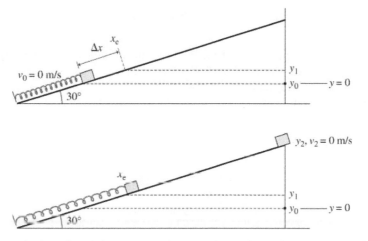

The figure shows a before-and-after pictorial representation. We have chosen to place the origin of the coordinate system at the position where the ice cube has compressed the spring 10.0 cm. That is, $y_0 = 0$.

Solve: The energy conservation equation $K_2 + U_{s2} + U_{g2} = K_0 + U_{s0} + U_{g0}$ is

$$\frac{1}{2}mv_2^2 + \frac{1}{2}k(x_e - x_e)^2 + mgy_2 = \frac{1}{2}mv_0^2 + \frac{1}{2}k(x - x_e)^2 + mgy_0$$

Using $v_2 = 0$ m/s, $y_0 = 0$ m, and $v_0 = 0$ m/s,

$$mgy_2 = \frac{1}{2}k(x - x_e)^2 \Rightarrow y_2 = \frac{k(x - x_e)^2}{2 mg} = \frac{(25 \text{ N/m})(0.10 \text{ m})^2}{2(0.050 \text{ kg})(9.80 \text{ m/s}^2)} = 26 \text{ cm}$$

The distance traveled along the incline is $y_2/\sin 30° = 51$ cm.

Assess: The net effect of the launch is to transform the potential energy stored in the spring into gravitational potential energy. The block has kinetic energy as it comes off the spring, but we did not need to know this energy to solve the problem since energy is conserved during the whole process.

P10.59. Prepare: This is a two-part problem. The slide is frictionless, so mechanical energy is conserved. We will calculate the final velocity of the people as they exit the slide and then use that result to calculate how far they travel from the exit before they hit the water.

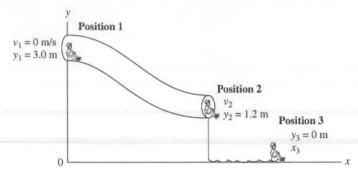

Solve: Refer to the diagram above. Setting the reference for gravitational potential energy to be zero at the bottom of the slide, the energy conservation equation becomes

$$mgy_1 = \frac{1}{2}mv_1^2 \Rightarrow v_1 = \sqrt{2gy_1} = \sqrt{2(9.80 \text{ m/s}^2)(3.0 \text{ m})} = 7.67 \text{ m/s}$$

Note that this result does not depend on the person's mass. We keep an additional significant figure here for the second part of the calculation.

After they leave the slide, they are falling under the influence of gravity. Their initial velocity in the y direction is zero. The time it takes for them to fall to the water can be calculated with ordinary kinematics.

$$\Delta y = v_{0y}\Delta t - \frac{1}{2}a\Delta t^2, \text{ with } v_{0y} = 0 \text{ m/s, gives}$$

$$\Delta y = -1.2 \text{ m} = \frac{1}{2}(9.80 \text{ m/s}^2)\Delta t^2 \text{ or}$$

$$\Delta t = \sqrt{\frac{(2)(1.2 \text{ m})}{9.80 \text{ m/s}^2}} = 0.50 \text{ s}$$

Using $v_i = 7.67$ s from the first part of the problem, we find

$$\Delta x = v_i\Delta t = (7.67 \text{ m/s})(0.50 \text{ s}) = 3.8 \text{ m}$$

The mass of the person was not necessary for this part of the calculation either.

Assess: Though this is a two-part problem mechanical energy is conserved throughout the whole process. However we could not use conservation of energy to solve the problem since we are not given the final velocity of the person before they hit the water, which is necessary for the conservation of energy equation. Note that it does not matter what the mass of the person is, they will always travel 3.8 m from the exit of the tube before hitting the water.

P10.61. Prepare: Assume an ideal spring that obeys Hooke's law. This is a two-part problem. The first part, when the bullet embeds itself in the block, is a perfectly inelastic collision. In a perfectly inelastic collision, the momentum is conserved while energy is not conserved. In the second part of the problem, when the bullet and block hit the spring, there is no friction. Since there is no friction after the bullet enters the block, the mechanical energy of the system (bullet ? block ? spring) is conserved during that part of the motion.

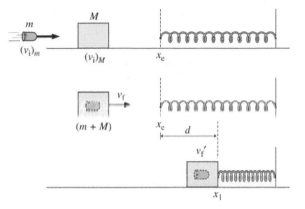

We place the origin of our coordinate system at the end of the spring that is not anchored to the wall.

Solve: (a) Momentum conservation for perfectly inelastic collision states $p_f = p_i$. This means

$$(m+M)v_f = m(v_i)_m + M(v_i)_M \Rightarrow (m+M)v_f = mv_B + 0 \text{ kg m/s} \Rightarrow v_f = \left(\frac{m}{m+M}\right)v_B$$

where we have used v_B for the initial speed of the bullet. This is velocity of the bullet and block after the bullet embeds itself in the block. Now, when the bullet and block hit the spring and compress it, mechanical energy is conserved. The mechanical energy conservation equation $K_1 + U_{s1} = K_e + U_{se}$ as the bullet-embedded block compresses the spring is:

$$\frac{1}{2}m(v_f')^2 + \frac{1}{2}k(x_1 - x_e)^2 = \frac{1}{2}(m+M)(v_f)^2 + \frac{1}{2}k(x_e - x_e)^2$$

$$0 \text{ J} + \frac{1}{2}kd^2 = \frac{1}{2}(m + M)\left(\frac{m}{m+M}\right)^2 v_B^2 + 0 \text{ J} \Rightarrow v_B = \sqrt{\frac{(m+M)kd^2}{m^2}}$$

(b) Using the above formula with $m = 5.0$ g, $M = 2.0$ kg, $k = 50$ N/m, and $d = 10$ cm,

$$v_B = \sqrt{\frac{(0.0050 \text{ kg} + 2.0 \text{ kg})(50 \text{ N/m})(0.10 \text{ m})^2}{(0.0050 \text{ kg})^2}} = 200 \text{ m/s}$$

which should be reported as 2.0×10^2 m/s to two significant figures.

(c) The fraction of energy lost is (initial energy − final energy)/(initial energy), which is

$$\frac{\frac{1}{2}mv_B^2 - \frac{1}{2}(m+M)v_f^2}{\frac{1}{2}mv_B^2} = 1 - \frac{m+M}{m}\left(\frac{v_f}{v_B}\right)^2 = 1 - \frac{m+M}{m}\left(\frac{m}{m+M}\right)^2$$

$$= 1 - \frac{m}{m+M} = 1 - \frac{0.0050 \text{ kg}}{(0.0050 \text{ kg} + 2.0 \text{ kg})} = 99.8\%$$

where we have kept an additional significant figure.

Assess: During the perfectly inelastic collision 99.8% of the bullet's energy is lost. The energy is transformed into the energy needed to deform the block and bullet and to the thermal energy of the bullet and block combination.

P10.63. Reason: If we consider the system of interest to be the two masses and the pulley, the only outside force doing work on the system is gravity. Since gravity is a conservative force, energy is conserved and we may write

$$\Delta K + \Delta U_g = \Delta E = 0 \quad \text{or} \quad \Delta K = -\Delta U_g.$$

Solve: Knowing $\Delta K = -\Delta U_g$, we may write

$$(M_A + M_B)v^2 / 2 = -(-M_B g h)$$

or

$$v = [2M_B g h / (M_A + M_B)]^{1/2} = 1.6 \text{ m/s}$$

Assess: This is a reasonable speed for this situation.

P10.65. Prepare: We can divide this problem into two parts. First, we have an elastic collision between the 20 g ball (m) and the 100 g ball (M). Second, the 100 g ball swings up as a pendulum.

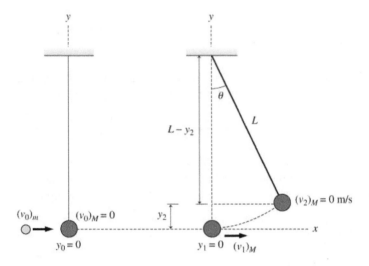

The figure shows three distinct moments of time: the time before the collision, the time after the collision but before the two balls move, and the time the 100 g ball reaches its highest point. We place the origin of our coordinate system on the 100 g ball when it is hanging motionless.

Solve: For a perfectly elastic collision, the ball moves forward with speed

$$(v_1)_M = \frac{2m_m}{m_m + m_M}(v_0)_m = \frac{1}{3.0}(v_0)_m$$

In the second part, the sum of the kinetic and gravitational potential energy is conserved as the 100 g ball swings up after the collision. That is, $K_2 + U_{g2} = K_1 + U_{g1}$. We have

$$\frac{1}{2}M(v_2)_M^2 + mgy_2 = \frac{1}{2}M(v_1)_M^2 + Mgy_1$$

Using $(v_2)_M = 0$ m/s, $(v_1)_M = \dfrac{(v_0)_m}{3.0}$, $y_1 = 0$ m, and $y_2 = L - L\cos\theta$, the energy equation simplifies to

$$g(L - L\cos\theta) = \frac{1}{2}\frac{(v_0)_m^2}{9.0}$$

$$\Rightarrow (v_0)_m = \sqrt{18\,g\,L(1 - \cos\theta)} = \sqrt{18(9.80 \text{ m/s}^2)(1.0 \text{ m})(1 - \cos 50°)} = 8.0 \text{ m/s}$$

Assess: Since the collision is elastic, mechanical energy is conserved during the whole process. We could apply conservation of mechanical energy alone to solve this problem. However, solving this particular problem in two parts using momentum conservation for the first part leads to a simpler calculation.

P10.67. Prepare: Initially the spring is hanging at its equilibrium position and you hang the fish on the spring, but don't release it. Let's agree to call this position 1 and to make this the point for zero gravitational and elastic potential energy. For the case where the fish is at position 1, we can write the following:

The position of the fish is $y_1 = 0$
The speed of the fish $v_1 = 0$
The kinetic energy of the fish $K_1 = 0$
The gravitational potential energy $U_{g_1} = 0$
The elastic potential energy of the spring $U_{S_1} = 0$
Total energy at this point is $E_1 = K_1 + U_{g_1} + U_{S_1}$

When the fish is released it falls to position 2, stretching the spring a maximum amount. For the case where the fish is at position 2, we can write the following:

The position of the fish is $y_2 = -h$
The speed of the fish $v_2 = 0$
The kinetic energy of the fish $K_2 = 0$
The gravitational potential energy $U_{g_2} = -mgh$
The elastic potential energy of the spring $U_{S_1} = kh^2 / 2$
Total energy at this point is $E_2 = K_2 + U_{g_2} + U_{S_2}$
Knowing that energy is conserved ($E_1 = E_2$), we can determine the maximum distance the fish falls.

Solve: Inserting values for the kinetic energy, gravitational potential energy and the elastic potential energy into

$$E_1 = E_2$$

obtain

$$0 = -mgh - kh^2 / 2$$

or

$$h = 2mg / k = 2(5.0 \text{ kg})(9.8 \text{ m/s}^2) / 200 \text{ N} / \text{m} = 0.49 \text{ m}$$

Assess: This is a reasonable amount for the maximum stretch of the spring.

P10.69. Prepare: This is the case of a perfectly inelastic collision. Momentum is conserved because no external force acts on the system (clay block). Mechanical energy is not conserved during perfectly inelastic collisions.

Solve: (a) The conservation of momentum equation $p_{fx} = p_{ix}$ is

$$(m_1 = m_2)v_{fx} = m_1(v_{ix})_1 + m_2(v_{ix})_2$$

Using $(v_{ix})_1 = v_0$ and $(v_{ix})_2 = 0$, we get

$$v_{Fx} = \frac{m_1}{m_1 + m_2}(v_{ix})_1 = \frac{0.050 \text{ kg}}{(1.0 \text{ kg} + 0.050 \text{ kg})}(v_{ix})_1 = 0.048(v_{ix})_1 = 0.048 \, v_0$$

(b) The initial and final kinetic energies are given by

$$K_i = \frac{1}{2}m_1(v_{ix})_1^2 + \frac{1}{2}m_2(v_{ix})_2^2 = \frac{1}{2}(0.050 \text{ kg})v_0^2 + \frac{1}{2}(1 \text{ kg})(0 \text{ m/s})^2 = (0.025 \text{ kg})v_0^2$$

$$K_f = \frac{1}{2}(m_1 + m_2)v_{fx}^2 = \frac{1}{2}(1 \text{ kg} + 0.050 \text{ kg})(0.0476)^2 v_0^2 = 0.0012 \, v_0^2$$

The percent of energy lost $= \left(\dfrac{K_i - K_f}{K_i}\right) \times 100\% = \left(1 - \dfrac{0.0012}{0.025}\right) \times 100\% = 95\%$

The energy goes into the permanent deformation of the ball of clay and into thermal energy.
    Assess: Mechanical energy is never conserved during inelastic collisions.

P10.71. Note: The Physics is fine—changed the equation reference and minor editing in the first equation. However, the Figure has a problem—the sprinter accelerates for the entire trip (i.e. from x_0 to x_2). The figure implies that the acceleration in only from x_0 to x_1.

Prepare: We will use the constant-acceleration kinematic equations and the definition of power in terms of work, Equation 10.22.

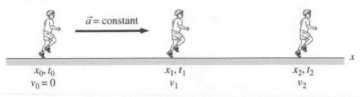

Solve: Refer to the the diagram above.

(a) We can find the acceleration from the kinematic equations and the horizontal force from Newton's second law. We have

$$x_2 = x_0 + v_0(t_2 - t_0) + \frac{1}{2}a(t_2 - t_0)^2 \Rightarrow 50 \text{ m} = 0 \text{ m} + 0 \text{ m} + \frac{1}{2}a(7.0 \text{ s} - 0 \text{ s})^2 \Rightarrow a = 2.0 \text{ m/s}^2$$

$$\Rightarrow F = ma = (50 \text{ kg})(2.0 \text{ m/s}^2) = 100 \text{ N}$$

Which should be reported as 1.0×10^2 N to two significant figures.

(b) We obtain the sprinter's power output by using $P = \dfrac{W}{\Delta t}$ where W is the work done by the sprinter. After $t = 2.0$ s, the sprinter has moved a distance of $d = \frac{1}{2}(2.0 \text{ m/s}^2)(2.0\text{ s})^2 = 4.0$ m. The work done by the sprinter is then $W = Fd = (100 \text{ N})$ (4.0 m) = 0.40 kJ. His power output is then $P = \dfrac{W}{\Delta t} = \dfrac{0.40 \text{ kJ}}{2.0 \text{ s}} = 0.20$ kW.

(c) During the final two seconds of his run, the distance he has moved is given by

$$d = x_2 - x_1 = v_1(t_2 - t_1) + \frac{1}{2}a(t_2 - t_1)^2 = v_1(2.0 \text{ s}) + \frac{1}{2}(2.0 \text{ m/s}^2)(2.0 \text{ s})^2$$

We need his velocity at 5.0 s after he starts running, which is given by

$$v_1 = v_0 + a\Delta t = 0 \text{ m/s} + (2.0 \text{ m/s}^2)(5.0 \text{ s}) = 10 \text{ m/s}$$

So then

$$d = (10 \text{ m/s})(2.0 \text{ s}) + \frac{1}{2}(2.0 \text{ m/s}^2)(2.0 \text{ s})^2 = 24 \text{ m}$$

The work done by the sprinter is then $W = Fd = (100 \text{ N})(24 \text{ m}) = 2.4$ kJ. His power output is then

$$P = \frac{W}{\Delta t} = \frac{2.4 \text{ kJ}}{2.0 \text{ s}} = 1.2 \text{ kW}$$

Assess: Note the power output required for the last two seconds of the sprint is much larger than during the first two seconds. This is because the sprinter travels a much larger distance during the last two seconds of his trip since he has accelerated to a high velocity by that time. The force is the same during both time intervals.

P10.73. Prepare: The motor must pump water to a higher level, and therefore raises the gravitational potential energy of the water. We will calculate the total energy the motor can deliver in one hour, and then use this to calculate the mass of water that can be lifted with this energy.

Solve: Using the conversion 746 W = 1 hp, the motor can put our a power of 1.5 kJ/s. This means $W = Pt = (1.5 \text{ kJ/s})(3600 \text{ s}) = 5.4 \times 10^6$ J is the total work that can be done by the electric motor in one hour. Since all this work goes into giving the water gravitational potential energy,

$$W_{motor} = U_{gf} - U_{gi} = mg(y_f - y_i) = mg\Delta y$$

$$m = \frac{W_{motor}}{g\Delta y} = \frac{5.4 \times 10^6 \text{ J}}{(9.80 \text{ m/s}^2)(10 \text{ m})} = 5.5 \times 10^4 \text{ kg}$$

Converting to liters,

$$5.5 \times 10^4 \text{ kg} \times \frac{1 \text{ liter}}{1 \text{ kg}} = 5.5 \times 10^4 \text{ liters}$$

Assess: This seems like a reasonable amount of water for an input power of 2.0 hp.

P10.75. Prepare: Energy is conserved during the fall of the ball since we are ignoring air resistance. We assume the ball is dropped from rest.

Solve: Apply conservation of energy. The ball's initial kinetic energy is 0 J since it's dropped from rest. Taking the reference for gravitational potential energy to be the ground, the ball's final potential energy is 0 J. The conservation of energy equation,

$$K_f + (U_g)_f = K_i + (U_g)_i$$

becomes

$$\frac{1}{2}mv_f^2 = mgy_i \Rightarrow v_f = \sqrt{2gy_i} = \sqrt{2(9.80 \text{ m/s}^2)(2.5 \text{ m})} = 7.0 \text{ m/s}$$

The answer is choice B.

Assess: All the ball's initial potential energy is converted to kinetic energy here.

P10.77. Prepare: The collision is not elastic. We assume the ball recovers its exact shape from before the collision after the rebound. Since the ball is dropped, we assume it is not rotating right after release.

Solve: As the ball compresses, its kinetic energy is converted to elastic potential energy. However, when the ball decompresses this elastic potential energy is recovered since the ball regains its initial shape. During the compression the ball's gravitational energy also changes by a slight amount, but this is also recovered as the ball regains its initial shape. If the ball is dropped straight down, there is no torque available to change the rotational state of the ball when it hits the ground, so its rotational kinetic energy also remains the same. However, during the collision with the floor, the thermal energy of the ball (and the floor) increase. This energy is lost from the system as heat.

The answer is C.

Assess: In inelastic collisions, these are generally the type of energy transformations that may occur. In all cases some energy is converted to thermal energy which is eventually lost to the environment.

P10.79. Prepare: Since we know that 30% of the initial kinetic energy is lost, we can calculate the final kinetic energy and then the final velocity of the ball after being hit by a racket.

Solve: We have that 30% of the initial kinetic energy is converted to thermal energy. In equation form this is

$$K_f = K_i - (0.30)K_i = (0.70)K_i$$

$$\frac{1}{2}mv_f^2 = (0.70)\frac{1}{2}mv_i^2 \Rightarrow v_f = \left(\sqrt{0.70}\right)v_i = (0.84)(10 \text{ m/s}) = 8.4 \text{ m/s}$$

The closest choice is A.

Assess: Note that this situation is a bounce from a stationary racket. Normally the ball collides with a moving racket and therefore gains kinetic energy.

P10.81. Prepare: We can use the definition of power in the form of Equation 10.23.

Solve: The drag force on the cyclist is 10 N, and her velocity is 5 m/s. The power she is using to overcome drag is $P = Fv = (10 \text{ N})(5 \text{ m/s}) = 50 \text{ W}$.

The correct choice is B.

Assess: This amount of power would just light a 60 W bulb and could be supplied by a 1/15 hp motor. This helps one appreciate the efficiency of a bicycle.

P10.83. Prepare: We can calculate the power using the result of Problem 10.82 and the definition of power given by Equation 10.23.

Solve: She is cycling at 10 m/s, with a drag force of 40 N. The power expended is then

$$P = Fv = (40 \text{ N})(10 \text{ m/s}) = 400 \text{ W}$$

The correct choice is C.

Assess: Comparing this to Problem 10.81, we see that when she the speed increases by a factor or two, the force increases by a factor of four and the power (which is the product of the speed and force) increases by a factor of eight.

Part II Conservation Laws

PptII.1. Reason: The water molecules that become the snowflake become more ordered, so the entropy of the water decreases. The answer is B.

    Assess: But the entropy of the entire universe increases. The entropy of the air increases by more than the entropy of the water decreases.

PptII.3. Reason: When energy is transferred between hot and cold (as in convection cells) the entropy increases, so the process is not reversible. The answer is B.

    Assess: The entropy of the universe never decreases.

PptII.5. Reason: The rubber bands slow down the rider over a longer period of time so the force is reduced. $F_{net}\Delta t = \Delta p$ shows this. The answer is D.

    Assess: This is the same reason it doesn't hurt to land on a trampoline from a large height.

PptII.7. Reason: Solve $\frac{1}{2}kx^2 = mgh$ for h, so the height the rider will go is inversely proportional to the mass (given that the spring energy in the numerator is the same). $h = \frac{1}{2}kx^2 / mg$ so the rider will go twice as high with half the mass. The answer is C.

    Assess: Four meters is dangerously high.

PptII.9. Reason: Since $F = kx$, reducing the spring constant will reduce the force on the rider. And since $\frac{1}{2}kx^2 = mgh$, reducing the spring constant will also reduce the final height (all else remaining equal). So the answer is A.

    Assess: It makes sense that a smaller force would produce a lower jump height.

PptII.11. Reason: The force is what makes the ball change momentum and bounce back up, so if it doesn't bounce as high it must be because the force wasn't as great. So the answer is C.

    Assess: The force must also be less to slow the ball down over a longer time.

PptII.13. Reason: Use conservation of momentum, with the initial momentum of the system zero.

$$m_s v_s = -m_w v_w \Rightarrow v_s = \frac{-m_w v_0}{m_s} = \frac{-(0.30 \text{ kg})(10 \text{ m/s})}{4.0 \text{ kg}} = -0.75 \text{ m/s}$$

So the answer is D.

    Assess: Because the water's mass is less than the squid's, we expect the squid's speed to be less than the water's.

PptII.15. Reason: Compute the average force from

$$F_{net} = \frac{\Delta p}{\Delta t} = \frac{m \Delta v}{\Delta t} = \frac{(0.30 \text{ kg})(10 \text{ m/s})}{0.10 \text{ s}} = 30 \text{ N}$$

    Assess: This force is not very big.

PptII.17. Reason:

$$\Delta p = m \Delta v = (0.046 \text{ kg})(70 \text{ m/s}) = 3.2 \text{ kg} \cdot \text{m/s}$$

The answer is C.

    Assess: Momentum is conserved for the club-ball system.

PptII.19. Reason: See if the kinetic energy is the same before and after.

$$K_i = \frac{1}{2}m_c(v_c)_i^2 = \frac{1}{2}(0.30 \text{ kg})(40 \text{ m/s})^2 = 240 \text{ J}$$

$$K_f = \frac{1}{2}m_c(v_c)_f^2 + \frac{1}{2}m_b(v_b)_f^2 = \frac{1}{2}(0.30 \text{ kg})(29 \text{ m/s})^2 + \frac{1}{2}(0.046 \text{ kg})(70 \text{ m/s})^2 = 240 \text{ J}$$

Kinetic energy is conserved, so the answer is A.
Assess: We would be worried if $K_f > K_i$.

PptII.21. Reason:

$$P = \frac{\Delta E}{\Delta t} = \frac{\frac{1}{2}mv^2}{\Delta t} = \frac{\frac{1}{2}(80 \text{ kg})(11 \text{ m/s})^2}{4.1 \text{ s}} = 1180 \text{ W} \approx 1200 \text{ W}$$

The answer is D.

PptII.23. Reason: Momentum is conserved in this inelastic collision.

$$m_1(v_1)_i + m_2(v_2)_i = (m_1 + m_2)v_f$$

$$v_f = \frac{m_1(v_1)_i + m_2(v_2)_i}{m_1 + m_2} = \frac{(100 \text{ kg})(6.0 \text{ m/s,E}) + (130 \text{ kg})(5.0 \text{ m/s,W})}{230 \text{ Kg}} = (0.22 \text{ m/s,W})$$

Assess: Since they are about equal in momentum, the final speed is small.

PptII.25. Reason:
(a) Use conservation of momentum.

$$m_L(v_L)_i = (m_L + m_s)v_f \Rightarrow v_f = \frac{m_L(v_L)_i}{m_L + m_s} = \frac{(30 \text{ kg})(4.0 \text{ m/s})}{40 \text{ kg}} = 3.0 \text{ m/s}$$

(b)

$$F = \frac{\Delta p}{\Delta t} = \frac{(30 \text{ kg})(4.0 \text{ m/s})}{0.25 \text{ s}} = 480 \text{ N}$$

(c) Use $K = \frac{1}{2}mv^2$.

$$K_i = \frac{1}{2}(30 \text{ kg})(4.0 \text{ m/s})^2 = 240 \text{ J} \qquad K_f = \frac{1}{2}(40 \text{ kg})(3.0 \text{ m/s})^2 = 180 \text{ J}$$

$$\Delta K = K_f - K_i = 180 \text{ K} - 240 \text{ J} = -60 \text{ J}$$

This energy was dissipated as thermal energy.
Assess: In part (c) it seems reasonable to "lose" a quarter of the energy.

Credits

Index

Astronomical Data

Planetary body	Mean distance from sun (m)	Period (years)	Mass (kg)	Mean radius (m)
Sun	—	—	1.99×10^{30}	6.96×10^{8}
Moon	3.84×10^{8}*	27.3 days	7.36×10^{22}	1.74×10^{6}
Mercury	5.79×10^{10}	0.241	3.18×10^{23}	2.43×10^{6}
Venus	1.08×10^{11}	0.615	4.88×10^{24}	6.06×10^{6}
Earth	1.50×10^{11}	1.00	5.98×10^{24}	6.37×10^{6}
Mars	2.28×10^{11}	1.88	6.42×10^{23}	3.37×10^{6}
Jupiter	7.78×10^{11}	11.9	1.90×10^{27}	6.99×10^{7}
Saturn	1.43×10^{12}	29.5	5.68×10^{26}	5.85×10^{7}
Uranus	2.87×10^{12}	84.0	8.68×10^{25}	2.33×10^{7}
Neptune	4.50×10^{12}	165	1.03×10^{26}	2.21×10^{7}

*Distance from earth

Typical Coefficients of Friction

Material	Static μ_s	Kinetic μ_k	Rolling μ_r
Rubber on concrete	1.00	0.80	0.02
Steel on steel (dry)	0.80	0.60	0.002
Steel on steel (lubricated)	0.10	0.05	
Wood on wood	0.50	0.20	
Wood on snow	0.12	0.06	
Ice on ice	0.10	0.03	

Melting/Boiling Temperatures, Heats of Transformation

Substance	T_m (°C)	L_f (J/kg)	T_b (°C)	L_v (J/kg)
Water	0	3.33×10^{5}	100	22.6×10^{5}
Nitrogen (N_2)	−210	0.26×10^{5}	−196	1.99×10^{5}
Ethyl alcohol	−114	1.09×10^{5}	78	8.79×10^{5}
Mercury	−39	0.11×10^{5}	357	2.96×10^{5}
Lead	328	0.25×10^{5}	1750	8.58×10^{5}

Properties of Materials

Substance	ρ (kg/m³)	c (J/kg·K)	v_{sound} (m/s)
Helium gas (1 atm, 20°C)	0.166		1010
Air (1 atm, 0°C)	1.28		331
Air (1 atm, 20°C)	1.20		343
Ethyl alcohol	790	2400	1170
Gasoline	680		
Glycerin	1260		
Mercury	13,600	140	1450
Oil (typical)	900		
Water ice	920	2090	3500
Liquid water	1000	4190	1480
Seawater	1030		1500
Blood	1060		
Muscle	1040	3600	
Fat	920	3000	
Mammalian body	1005	3400	1540
Granite	2750	790	6000
Aluminum	2700	900	5100
Copper	8920	385	
Gold	19,300	129	
Iron	7870	449	
Lead	11,300	128	1200
Diamond	3520	510	12,000
Osmium	22,610		